✻ **HAESE & HARRIS PUBLICATIONS**

Specialists in mathema

Mathematics

for the international student
Mathematics HL (Core)

Paul Urban

John Owen

David Martin

Robert Haese

Sandra Haese

Mark Bruce

International
Baccalaureate
Diploma
Programme

MATHEMATICS FOR THE INTERNATIONAL STUDENT
International Baccalaureate Mathematics HL Course

Paul Urban	B.Sc.(Hons.), B.Ec.
John Owen	B.Sc., Dip.T.
David Martin	B.A., B.Sc., M.A., M.Ed.Admin.
Robert Haese	B.Sc.
Sandra Haese	B.Sc.
Mark Bruce	B.Ed.

Haese & Harris Publications
3 Frank Collopy Court, Adelaide Airport, SA 5950, AUSTRALIA
Telephone: +61 8 8355 9444, Fax: + 61 8 8355 9471
Email: info@haeseandharris.com.au
Web: www.haeseandharris.com.au

National Library of Australia Card Number & ISBN 1 876543 09 4

© Haese & Harris Publications 2004

Published by Raksar Nominees Pty Ltd
3 Frank Collopy Court, Adelaide Airport, SA 5950, AUSTRALIA

First Edition	2004
Reprinted	2005 three times *(with minor corrections)*, 2006 twice, 2007

Cartoon artwork by John Martin. Artwork by Piotr Poturaj and David Purton
Cover design by Piotr Poturaj
Computer software by David Purton

Typeset in Australia by Susan Haese (Raksar Nominees). Typeset in Times Roman $10\frac{1}{2}/11\frac{1}{2}$

The textbook and its accompanying CD have been developed independently of the International Baccalaureate Organization (IBO). The textbook and CD are in no way connected with, or endorsed by, the IBO.

Acknowledgements: The publishers acknowledge the cooperation of Oxford University Press, Australia, for the reproduction of material originally published in textbooks produced in association with Haese & Harris Publications.

While every attempt has been made to trace and acknowledge copyright, the authors and publishers apologise for any accidental infringement where copyright has proved untraceable. They would be pleased to come to a suitable agreement with the rightful owner.

Disclaimer: All the internet addresses (URL's) given in this book were valid at the time of printing. While the authors and publisher regret any inconvenience that changes of address may cause readers, no responsibility for any such changes can be accepted by either the authors or the publisher.

FOREWORD

Mathematics for the International Student: Mathematics HL has been written to embrace the syllabus for the new two-year Mathematics HL Course, which is one of the courses of study in the International Baccalaureate Diploma Programme. It is not our intention to define the course. Teachers are encouraged to use other resources. We have developed the book independently of the International Baccalaureate Organization (IBO) in consultation with many experienced teachers of IB Mathematics. The text is not endorsed by the IBO.

This package is language rich and technology rich. The combination of textbook and interactive Student CD will foster the mathematical development of students in a stimulating way. Frequent use of the interactive features on the CD is certain to nurture a much deeper understanding and appreciation of mathematical concepts.

The book contains many problems from the basic to the advanced, to cater for a wide range of student abilities and interests. While some of the exercises are simply designed to build skills, every effort has been made to contextualise problems, so that students can see everyday uses and practical applications of the mathematics they are studying, and appreciate the universality of mathematics.

Emphasis is placed on the gradual development of concepts with appropriate worked examples, but we have also provided extension material for those who wish to go beyond the scope of the syllabus. Some proofs have been included for completeness and interest although they will not be examined.

For students who may not have a good understanding of the necessary background knowledge for this course, we have provided printable pages of information, examples, exercises and answers on the Student CD. To access these pages, simply click on the 'Background knowledge' icon when running the CD.

It is not our intention that each chapter be worked through in full. Time constraints will not allow for this. Teachers must select exercises carefully, according to the abilities and prior knowledge of their students, to make the most efficient use of time and give as thorough coverage of work as possible.

Investigations throughout the book will add to the discovery aspect of the course and enhance student understanding and learning. Many Investigations could be developed into portfolio assignments. Teachers should follow the guidelines for portfolio assignments to ensure they set acceptable portfolio pieces for their students that meet the requirement criteria for the portfolios.

Review sets appear at the end of each chapter and a suggested order for teaching the two-year course is given at the end of this Foreword.

The extensive use of graphics calculators and computer packages throughout the book enables students to realise the importance, application and appropriate use of technology. No single aspect of technology has been favoured. It is as important that students work with a pen and paper as it is that they use their calculator or graphics calculator, or use a spreadsheet or graphing package on computer.

The interactive features of the CD allow immediate access to our own specially designed geometry packages, graphing packages and more. Teachers are provided with a quick and easy way to demonstrate concepts, and students can discover for themselves and re-visit when necessary.

...ructions appropriate to each graphic calculator problem are on the CD and can be printed ...r students. These instructions are written for Texas Instruments and Casio calculators.

In this changing world of mathematics education, we believe that the contextual approach shown in this book, with the associated use of technology, will enhance the students' understanding, knowledge and appreciation of mathematics, and its universal application.

We welcome your feedback.

Email: info@haeseandharris.com.au
Web: www.haeseandharris.com.au

PMU JTO DCM
RCH SHH MFB

Thank you

The authors and publishers would like to thank all those teachers who offered advice and encouragement. Many of them read the page proofs and offered constructive comments and suggestions. These teachers include: Marjut Mäenpää, Cameron Hall, Fran O'Connor, Glenn Smith, Anne Walker, Malcolm Coad, Ian Hilditch, Phil Moore, Julie Wilson, Kerrie Clements, Margie Karbassioun, Brian Johnson, Carolyn Farr, Rupert de Smidt, Terry Swain, Marie-Therese Filippi, Nigel Wheeler, Sarah Locke, Rema George.

TEACHING THE TWO-YEAR COURSE – A SUGGESTED ORDER

Teachers are encouraged to carefully check the BACKGROUND KNOWLEDGE sections supplied on the accompanying CD to ensure that basics have been mastered relatively early in the two-year HL course. Some of these topics naturally occur at the beginning of a specific chapter, as indicated in the table of contents. Click on the BACKGROUND KNOWLEDGE active icon to access the printable pages on the CD.

For the first year, it is suggested that students work progressively from Chapter 1 through to Chapter 21, but not necessarily including chapters 8, 16, 17. Chapter 10 'Mathematical Induction' could also be attempted later, perhaps early in Year 12. Traditionally, the topics of Polynomials, Complex Numbers, 3-D Vector Geometry and Calculus are not covered until the final year of school.

However, it is acknowledged that there is no single best way for all teachers to work through the syllabus. Individual teachers have to consider particular needs of their students and other requirements and preferences that they may have.

We invite teachers to email their preferred order or suggestions to us so that we can put these suggestions on our website to be shared with other teachers.

USING THE INTERACTIVE STUDENT CD

The CD is ideal for independent study. Frequent use will nurture a deeper understanding of Mathematics. Students can revisit concepts taught in class and undertake their own revision and practice. The CD also has the text of the book, allowing students to leave the textbook at school and keep the CD at home.

The icon denotes an active link on the CD. Simply 'click' the icon to access a range of interactive features:

- spreadsheets
- video clips
- graphing and geometry software
- graphics calculator instructions
- computer demonstrations and simulations
- background knowledge

For those who want to make sure they have the prerequisite levels of understanding for this new course, printable pages of background information, examples, exercises and answers are provided on the CD. Click the 'Background knowledge' icon.

Graphics calculators: Instructions for using graphics calculators are also given on the CD and can be printed. Instructions are given for Texas Instruments and Casio calculators. Click on the relevant icon (TI or C) to access printable instructions.

Examples in the textbook are not always given for both types of calculator. Where that occurs, click on the relevant icon to access the instructions for the other type of calculator.

NOTE ON ACCURACY

Students are reminded that in assessment tasks, including examination papers, unless otherwise stated in the question, all numerical answers must be given exactly or to three significant figures.

HL & SL COMBINED CLASSES

Refer to our website www.haeseandharris.com.au for guidance in using this textbook in HL and SL combined classes.

HL OPTIONS

We intend to cover the HL Options either as a separate Options Book or as printable pages on a separate Options CD. To register your interest, please email info@haeseandharris.com.au

LE OF CONTENTS

SYMBOLS AND NOTATION USED IN THIS BOOK

This notation is based on that indicated by the International Organisation for Standardisation.

N	the set of positive integers and zero, $\{0, 1, 2, 3, \ldots\}$
Z	the set of integers, $\{0, \pm1, \pm2, \pm3, \ldots\}$
Z^+	the set of positive integers, $\{1, 2, 3, \ldots\}$
Q	the set of rational numbers
Q^+	the set of positive rational numbers, $\{x \mid x \in Q, \ x > 0\}$
$\mathcal{R}$	the set of real numbers
$\mathcal{R}^+$	the set of positive real numbers, $\{x \mid x \in \mathcal{R}, \ x > 0\}$
C	the set of complex numbers, $\{a + bi \mid a, b \in \mathcal{R}\}$
i	$\sqrt{-1}$
z	a complex number
z^*	the complex conjugate of z
$\lvert z \rvert$	the modulus of z
$\arg z$	the argument of z
$\operatorname{Re} z$	the real part of z
$\operatorname{Im} z$	the imaginary part of z
$\{x_1, x_2, \ldots\}$	the set with elements $x_1, x_2, \ldots$
$n(A)$	the number of elements in the finite set A
$\{x \mid \ldots$ or $\{x : \ldots$	the set of all x such that
$\in$	is an element of
$\notin$	is not an element of
$\varnothing$	the empty (null) set
U	the universal set
$\cup$	union
$\cap$	intersection
A'	the complement of the set A
$a^{\frac{1}{n}}, \sqrt[n]{a}$	a to the power of $\frac{1}{n}$, nth root of a (if $a \geqslant 0$ then $\sqrt[n]{a} \geqslant 0$)
$a^{\frac{1}{2}}, \sqrt{a}$	a to the power $\frac{1}{2}$, square root of a (if $a \geqslant 0$ then $\sqrt{a} \geqslant 0$)
$\lvert x \rvert$	the modulus or absolute value of x, that is $\begin{cases} x \text{ for } x \geqslant 0 & x \in \mathcal{R} \\ -x \text{ for } x < 0 & x \in \mathcal{R} \end{cases}$
$\equiv$	identity or is equivalent to
$\approx$ or $\doteqdot$	is approximately equal to
$>$	is greater than
$\geq$ or $\geqslant$	is greater than or equal to
$<$	is less than
$\leq$ or $\leqslant$	is less than or equal to
$\ngtr$	is not greater than
$\nless$	is not less than
$[a, b]$	the closed interval $a \leqslant x \leqslant b$
$]a, b[$	the open interval $a < x < b$
u_n	the nth term of a sequence or series
d	the common difference of an arithmetic sequence
r	the common ratio of a geometric sequence
S_n	the sum of the first n terms of a sequence, $u_1 + u_2 + \ldots + u_n$
S_∞	the sum to infinity of a sequence, $u_1 + u_2 + \ldots$
$\displaystyle\sum_{i=1}^{n} u_i$	$u_1 + u_2 + \ldots + u_n$
$\dbinom{n}{r}$	$\dfrac{n!}{r!(n-r)!}$
$f : A \to B$	f is a function under which each element of set A has an image in set B
$f : x \mapsto y$	f is a function under which x is mapped to y
$f(x)$	the image of x under the function f
f^{-1}	the inverse function of the function f
$f \circ g$	the composite function of f and g
$\displaystyle\lim_{x \to a} f(x)$	the limit of $f(x)$ as x tends to a
$\dfrac{dy}{dx}$	the derivative of y with respect to x
$f'(x)$	the derivative of $f(x)$ with respect to x
$\dfrac{d^2y}{dx^2}$	the second derivative of y with respect to x
$f''(x)$	the second derivative of $f(x)$ with respect to x
$\dfrac{d^ny}{dx^n}$	the nth derivative of y with respect to x
$f^{(n)}(x)$	the nth deriviative of $f(x)$ with respect to x
$\displaystyle\int y \, dx$	the indefinite integral of y with respect to x
$\displaystyle\int_a^b y \, dx$	the definite integral of y with respect to x between the limits $x = a$ and $x = b$
e^x	exponential function of x
$\log_a x$	logarithm to the base a of x
$\ln x$	the natural logarithm of x, $\log_e x$

continued next page

sin, cos, tan	the circular functions
arcsin, arccos, arctan	the inverse circular functions
csc, sec, cot	the reciprocal circular functions
$A(x, y)$	the point A in the plane with Cartesian coordinates x and y
[AB]	the line segment with end points A and B
AB	the length of [AB]
(AB)	the line containing points A and B
$\widehat{A}$	the angle at A
$\widehat{CAB}$ or $\angle CAB$	the angle between [CA] and [AB]
$\triangle ABC$	the triangle whose vertices are A, B and C
v	the vector **v**
$\overrightarrow{AB}$	the vector represented in magnitude and direction by the directed line segment from A to B
a	the position vector $\overrightarrow{OA}$
i, j, k	unit vectors in the directions of the Cartesian coordinate axes
$|\mathbf{a}|$	the magnitude of **a**
$|\overrightarrow{AB}|$	the magnitude of $\overrightarrow{AB}$
$\mathbf{v} \bullet \mathbf{w}$	the scalar product of **v** and **w**
$\mathbf{v} \times \mathbf{w}$	the vector product of **v** and **w**
$\mathbf{A}^{-1}$	the inverse of the non-simular matrix **A**
det**A** or $|\mathbf{A}|$	the determinant of the square matrix **A**
I	the identity matrix
P(A)	probability of event A
P'(A)	probability of the event "not A"
P(A|B)	probability of the event A given B
$x_1, x_2, ...$	observations of a variable
$f_1, f_2, ...$	frequencies with which the observations $x_1, x_2, x_3, ...$ occur
p_x	probability distribution function $P(X = x)$ of the discrete random variable X

$f(x)$	probability density function of the continuous random variable X
$E(X)$	the expected value of the random variable X
$Var\,(X)$	the variance of the random variable X
μ	population mean
σ	population standard deviation
σ^2	population variance, $\sigma^2 = \dfrac{\sum\limits_{i=1}^{k} f_i(x_i - \mu)^2}{n}$, where $n = \sum\limits_{i=1}^{k} f_i$
$\overline{x}$	sample mean
s_n^2	sample variance, $s_n^2 = \dfrac{\sum\limits_{i=1}^{k} f_i(x_i - \overline{x})^2}{n}$, where $n = \sum\limits_{i=1}^{k} f_i$
s_n	standard deviation of the sample
s_{n-1}^2	unbiased estimate of the population variance, $s_{n-1}^2 = \dfrac{n}{n-1} s_n^2 = \dfrac{\sum\limits_{i=1}^{k} f_i(x_i - \overline{x})^2}{n-1}$, where $n = \sum\limits_{i=1}^{k} f_i$
$B(n, p)$	binomial distribution with parameters n and p
$Po(m)$	Poisson distribution with mean m
$N(\mu, \sigma^2)$	normal distribution with mean μ and variance σ^2
$X \sim B(n, p)$	the random variable X has a binomial distribution with parameters n and p
$X \sim Po(m)$	the random variable X has a Poisson distribution with mean m
$X \sim N(\mu, \sigma^2)$	the random variable X has a normal distribution with mean μ and variance σ^2

BACKGROUND KNOWLEDGE

Before starting this course you can make sure that you have a good understanding of the necessary background knowledge. Click on the icon alongside to obtain a printable set of exercises and answers on this background knowledge.

BACKGROUND KNOWLEDGE

Click on the icon to access printable facts about number sets

NUMBER SETS

SUMMARY OF CIRCLE PROPERTIES

- A **circle** is a set of points which are equidistant from a fixed point, which is called its **centre**.

- The **circumference** is the distance around the entire circle boundary.

- An **arc** of a circle is any continuous part of the circle.

- A **chord** of a circle is a line segment joining any two points of a circle.

- A **semi-circle** is a half of a circle.

- A **diameter** of a circle is any chord passing through its centre.

- A **radius** of a circle is any line segment joining its centre to any point on the circle.

- A **tangent** to a circle is any line which touches the circle in exactly one point.

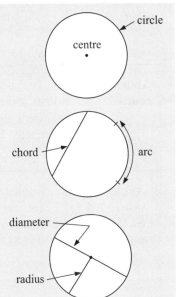

Click on the appropriate icon to revisit these well known theorems.

Name of theorem	Statement	Diagram
Angle in a semi-circle	The angle in a semi-circle is a right angle.	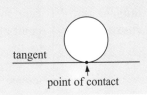

Name of theorem	Statement	Diagram
Chords of a circle	The perpendicular from the centre of a circle to a chord bisects the chord.	If ... then $AM = BM$. GEOMETRY PACKAGE
Radius-tangent	The tangent to a circle is perpendicular to the radius at the point of contact.	If ... then $\angle OAT = 90°$. GEOMETRY PACKAGE
Tangents from an external point	Tangents from an external point are equal in length.	If ... then $AP = BP$. GEOMETRY PACKAGE
Angle at the centre	The angle at the centre of a circle is twice the angle on the circle subtended by the same arc.	If ... then $\angle AOB = 2\angle ACB$. GEOMETRY PACKAGE
Angles subtended by the same arc	Angles subtended by an arc on the circle are equal in size.	If ... then $\angle ADB = \angle ACB$. GEOMETRY PACKAGE
Angle between a tangent and a chord	The angle between a tangent and a chord at the point of contact is equal to the angle subtended by the chord in the alternate segment.	If ... then $\angle BAS = \angle BCA$. GEOMETRY PACKAGE

SUMMARY OF MEASUREMENT FACTS

PERIMETER FORMULAE

The distance around a closed figure is its **perimeter**.

For some shapes we can derive a formula for perimeter. The formulae for the most common shapes are given below:

 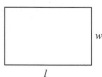

square	rectangle	triangle	circle	arc
$P = 4l$	$P = 2(l + w)$	$P = a + b + c$	$C = 2\pi r$ or $C = \pi d$	$l = \left(\frac{\theta}{360}\right)2\pi r$

> The length of an arc is a fraction of the circumference of a circle.

AREA FORMULAE

Shape	Figure	Formula
Rectangle	width / length	**Area = length × width**
Triangle	height / base / base	**Area = $\frac{1}{2}$base × height**
Parallelogram	height / base	**Area = base × height**
Trapezium or **Trapezoid**	a / h / b	**Area = $\left(\dfrac{a+b}{2}\right) \times h$**
Circle	r	**Area = πr^2**
Sector	θ / r	**Area = $\left(\dfrac{\theta}{360}\right) \times \pi r^2$**

SURFACE AREA FORMULAE

RECTANGULAR PRISM

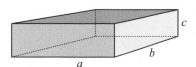

$$A = 2(ab + bc + ac)$$

CYLINDER

Object	Outer surface area
Hollow cylinder	$A = 2\pi rh$ (no ends)
Open can	$A = 2\pi rh + \pi r^2$ (one end)
Solid cylinder	$A = 2\pi rh + 2\pi r^2$ (two ends)

CONE

Object	Outer surface area
Open cone	$A = \pi rs$ (no base)
Solid cone	$A = \pi rs + \pi r^2$ (solid)

SPHERE

Area,
$A = 4\pi r^2$

VOLUME FORMULAE

Object	Figure	Volume
Solids of uniform cross-section	height / end / height / end	Volume of uniform solid = **area of end × length**
Pyramids and cones	height / height / h / base / base	Volume of a pyramid or cone $= \frac{1}{3}(\text{area of base} \times \text{height})$
Spheres	r	Volume of a sphere $= \frac{4}{3}\pi r^3$

Chapter 1

Functions

Contents:

A   RELATIONS AND FUNCTIONS

The charges for parking a car in a short-term car park at an Airport are given in the table shown alongside.

Car park charges	
Period (h)	Charge
0 - 1 hours	$5.00
1 - 2 hours	$9.00
2 - 3 hours	$11.00
3 - 6 hours	$13.00
6 - 9 hours	$18.00
9 - 12 hours	$22.00
12 - 24 hours	$28.00

There is an obvious relationship between time spent and the cost. The cost is dependent on the length of time the car is parked.

Looking at this table we might ask: How much would be charged for exactly one hour? Would it be $5 or $9?

To make the situation clear, and to avoid confusion, we could adjust the table and draw a graph. We need to indicate that 2-3 hours really means for time over 2 hours up to and including 3 hours   i.e., $2 < t \leqslant 3$.

So, we now have

Car park charges	
Period	Charge
$0 < t \leqslant 1$ hours	$5.00
$1 < t \leqslant 2$ hours	$9.00
$2 < t \leqslant 3$ hours	$11.00
$3 < t \leqslant 6$ hours	$13.00
$6 < t \leqslant 9$ hours	$18.00
$9 < t \leqslant 12$ hours	$22.00
$12 < t \leqslant 24$ hours	$28.00

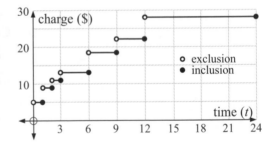

In mathematical terms, because we have a relationship between two variables, time and cost, the schedule of charges is an example of a **relation**.

A relation may consist of a finite number of ordered pairs, such as {(1, 5), (−2, 3), (4, 3), (1, 6)} or an infinite number of ordered pairs.

The parking charges example is clearly the latter as any real value of time (t hours) in the interval $0 < t \leqslant 24$ is represented.

The set of possible values of the variable on the horizontal axis is called the **domain** of the relation.

For example:
- {t: $0 < t \leqslant 24$}   is the domain for the car park relation
- {−2, 1, 4}   is the domain of   {(1, 5), (−2, 3), (4, 3), (1, 6)}.

The set which describes the possible y-values is called the **range** of the relation.

For example:
- the range of the car park relation is   {5, 9, 11, 13, 18, 22, 28}
- the range of   {(1, 5), (−2, 3), (4, 3), (1, 6)}   is   {3, 5, 6}.

We will now look at relations and functions more formally.

RELATIONS

> A **relation** is any set of points on the Cartesian plane.

A relation is often expressed in the form of an **equation** connecting the **variables** x and y.
For example $y = x + 3$ and $x = y^2$ are the equations of two relations.
These equations generate sets of ordered pairs.

Their graphs are:

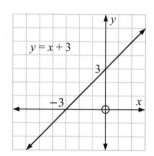
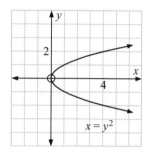

However, a relation may not be able to be defined by an equation. Below are two examples which show this:

(1)
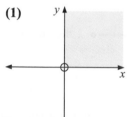
All points in the first quadrant are a relation.
$x > 0, y > 0$

(2)
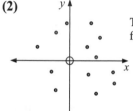
These 13 points form a relation.

FUNCTIONS

> A **function**, sometimes called a **mapping**, is a relation in which no two different ordered pairs have the same x-coordinate (first member).

We can see from the above definition that a function is a special type of relation.

TESTING FOR FUNCTIONS

Algebraic Test:

> If a relation is given as an equation, and the substitution of any value for x results in one and only one value of y, we have a function.

For example: • $y = 3x - 1$ is a function, as for any value of x there is only one value of y
  • $x = y^2$ is not a function since if $x = 4$, say, then $y = \pm 2$.

Geometric Test   ("Vertical Line Test"):

> If we draw all possible vertical lines on the graph of a relation, the relation:
> • is a function if each line cuts the graph no more than once
> • is not a function if one line cuts the graph more than once.

DEMO

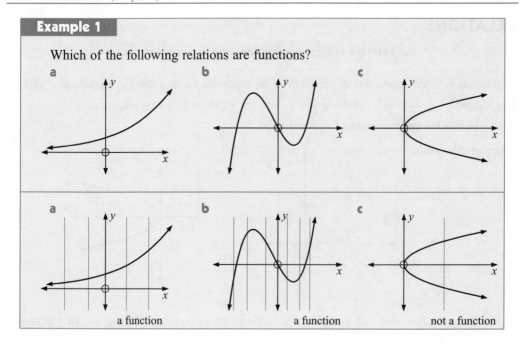

Example 1

Which of the following relations are functions?

a

b

c

a

b

c

a function   a function   not a function

GRAPHICAL NOTE

- If a graph contains a small **open circle** end point such as ———o , the end point is **not included**.

- If a graph contains a small **filled-in circle** end point such as ———• , the end point **is included**.

- If a graph contains an **arrow head** at an end such as ———▸ then the graph continues indefinitely in that general direction, or the shape may repeat as it has done previously.

EXERCISE 1A

1 Which of the following sets of ordered pairs are functions? Give reasons.

   a (1, 3), (2, 4), (3, 5), (4, 6)
   b (1, 3), (3, 2), (1, 7), (−1, 4)
   c (2, −1), (2, 0), (2, 3), (2, 11)
   d (7, 6), (5, 6), (3, 6), (−4, 6)
   e (0, 0), (1, 0), (3, 0), (5, 0)
   f (0, 0), (0, −2), (0, 2), (0, 4)

2 Use the vertical line test to determine which of the following relations are functions:

   a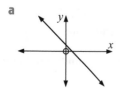
   b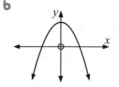
   c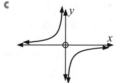
   d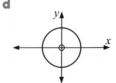

   e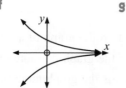
   f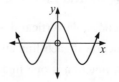
   g
   h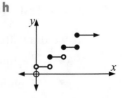

3 Will the graph of a straight line always be a function? Give evidence.

4 Give algebraic evidence to show that the relation $x^2 + y^2 = 9$ is not a function.

B ▎ INTERVAL NOTATION, DOMAIN AND RANGE

DOMAIN AND RANGE

> The **domain** of a relation is the set of permissible values that x may have.
>
> The **range** of a relation is the set of permissible values that y may have.

For example:

(1)

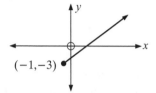

All values of $x \geqslant -1$ are permissible.

So, the domain is $\{x:\ x \geqslant -1\}$ or $x \in [-1, \infty[$.

All values of $y \geqslant -3$ are permissible.

So, the range is $\{y:\ y \geqslant -3\}$ or $y \in [-3, \infty[$.

(2)

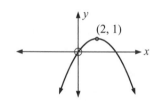

x can take any value.

So, the domain is $\{x:\ x$ is in $\mathcal{R}\}$ or $x \in \mathcal{R}$.

y cannot be > 1

$\therefore$ range is $\{y:\ y \leqslant 1\}$ or $y \in\ ]-\infty, 1]$.

(3)

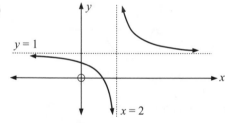

x can take all values except $x = 2$.

So, the domain is $\{x:\ x \neq 2\}$.

Likewise, the range is $\{y:\ y \neq 1\}$.

The domain and range of a relation are best described where appropriate using **interval notation**.

For example:

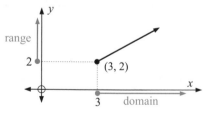

The domain consists of all real x such that $x \geqslant 3$ and we write this as

$$\{x:\ x \geqslant 3\} \quad \text{or} \quad x \in [3, \infty[.$$

the set of all x such that

Likewise the range would be
$\{y:\ y \geqslant 2\}$ or $y \in [2, \infty[$.

For this profit function:

- the domain is $\{x:\ x \geqslant 0\}$
  or $x \in [0, \infty[$
- the range is $\{y:\ y \leqslant 100\}$
  or $y \in\ ]-\infty, 100]$.

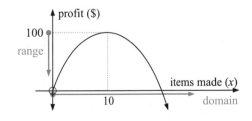

Intervals have corresponding graphs.   For example:

$\{x: x \geqslant 3\}$ or $x \in [3, \infty[$ is read "the set of all x such that x is greater than or equal to 3" and has number line graph

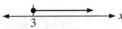

$\{x: x < 2\}$ or $x \in]-\infty, 2[$ has number line graph

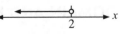

$\{x: -2 < x \leqslant 1\}$ or $x \in]-2, 1]$ has number line graph

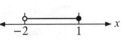

$\{x: x \leqslant 0$ or $x > 4\}$ has number line graph
i.e., $x \in]-\infty, 0]$ or $]4, \infty[$

Note: for numbers *between* a and b we write $a < x < b$ or $x \in]a, b[$.

for numbers '*outside*' a and b we write $x < a$ or $x > b$
i.e., $x \in]-\infty, a[$ or $]b, \infty[.$

Example 2

For each of the following graphs state the domain and range:

a
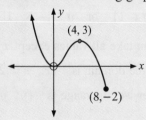

b
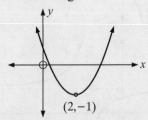

a   Domain is $\{x: x \leqslant 8\}$
      or $x \in]-\infty, 8]$

  Range is $\{y: y \geqslant -2\}$
      or $y \in [-2, \infty[$

b   Domain is $\{x: x$ is in $\mathcal{R}\}$
      or $x \in \mathcal{R}$

  Range is $\{y: y \geqslant -1\}$
      or $y \in [-1, \infty[$

EXERCISE 1B

1 For each of the following graphs find the domain and range:

a

$(-1, 1)$ $(5, 3)$

b

$y = -1$
$x = 2$

c

$(0, 2)$

d

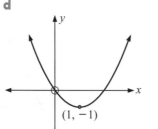

e

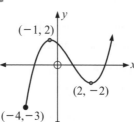

f

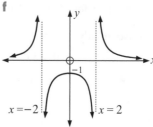

2 Use a graphics calculator to help sketch carefully the graphs of the following functions and find the domain and range of each:

a $f(x) = \sqrt{x}$

b $f(x) = \dfrac{1}{x^2}$

c $f(x) = \sqrt{4 - x}$

d $y = x^2 - 7x + 10$

e $y = 5x - 3x^2$

f $y = x + \dfrac{1}{x}$

g $y = \dfrac{x + 4}{x - 2}$

h $y = x^3 - 3x^2 - 9x + 10$

i $y = \dfrac{3x - 9}{x^2 - x - 2}$

j $y = x^2 + x^{-2}$

k $y = x^3 + \dfrac{1}{x^3}$

l $y = x^4 + 4x^3 - 16x + 3$

C   FUNCTION NOTATION

Function machines are sometimes used to illustrate how functions behave.

For example:

So, if 4 is fed into the machine,
$2(4) + 3 = 11$ comes out.

The above 'machine' has been programmed to perform a particular function.
If f is used to represent that particular function we can write:

f is the function that will convert x into $2x + 3$.

So, f would convert 2 into $2(2) + 3 = 7$ and
-4 into $2(-4) + 3 = -5$.

This function can be written as:

$$f : \; x \longmapsto \; 2x + 3$$

function f such that x is converted into $2x + 3$

Two other equivalent forms we use are: $f(x) = 2x + 3$ or $y = 2x + 3$

So, $f(x)$ is the value of y for a given value of x,   i.e., $y = f(x)$.

Notice that for $f(x) = 2x + 3$, $f(2) = 2(2) + 3 = 7$ and $f(-4) = 2(-4) + 3 = -5$.

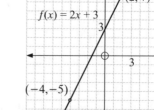

Consequently, $f(2) = 7$ indicates that the point $(2, 7)$ lies on the graph of the function.

Likewise $f(-4) = -5$ indicates that the point $(-4, -5)$ also lies on the graph.

Note: • $f(x)$ is read as "f of x" and is the value of the function (or y) at any value of x.

• If (x, y) is any point on the graph then $y = f(x)$, x belongs to the domain and y belongs to the range.

• f is the function which converts x into $f(x)$,   i.e., $f : x \longmapsto f(x)$.

• $y = f(x)$ is sometimes called the **image** of x.

Example 3

If $f : x \longmapsto 2x^2 - 3x$,   find the value of: **a** $f(5)$ **b** $f(-4)$

$f(x) = 2x^2 - 3x$

a $f(5) = 2(5)^2 - 3(5)$ {replacing x by (5)}
$\quad\quad = 2 \times 25 - 15$
$\quad\quad = 35$

b $f(-4) = 2(-4)^2 - 3(-4)$ {replacing x by (-4)}
$\quad\quad\quad = 2(16) + 12$
$\quad\quad\quad = 44$

EXERCISE 1C

1 If $f : x \longmapsto 3x + 2$,   find the value of:

   a $f(0)$ **b** $f(2)$ **c** $f(-1)$ **d** $f(-5)$ **e** $f(-\frac{1}{3})$

2 If $f : x \longmapsto 3x - x^2 + 2$,   find the value of:

   a $f(0)$ **b** $f(3)$ **c** $f(-3)$ **d** $f(-7)$ **e** $f(\frac{3}{2})$

Example 4

If $f(x) = 5 - x - x^2$,   find in simplest form: **a** $f(-x)$ **b** $f(x + 2)$

a $f(-x) = 5 - (-x) - (-x)^2$ {replacing x by $(-x)$}
$\quad\quad\quad = 5 + x - x^2$

b $f(x + 2) = 5 - (x + 2) - (x + 2)^2$ {replacing x by $(x + 2)$}
$\quad\quad\quad\quad = 5 - x - 2 - [x^2 + 4x + 4]$
$\quad\quad\quad\quad = 3 - x - x^2 - 4x - 4$
$\quad\quad\quad\quad = -x^2 - 5x - 1$

3 If $f(x) = 7 - 3x$,   find in simplest form:

    a $f(a)$ **b** $f(-a)$ **c** $f(a+3)$ **d** $f(b-1)$ **e** $f(x+2)$

4 If $F(x) = 2x^2 + 3x - 1$,   find in simplest form:

    a $F(x+4)$ **b** $F(2-x)$ **c** $F(-x)$ **d** $F(x^2)$ **e** $F(x^2 - 1)$

5 If $G(x) = \dfrac{2x+3}{x-4}$:   **a** evaluate   **i** $G(2)$ **ii** $G(0)$ **iii** $G(-\frac{1}{2})$

                      b find a value of x where $G(x)$ does not exist

                      c find $G(x+2)$ in simplest form

                      d find x if $G(x) = -3$.

6 f represents a function. What is the difference in meaning between f and $f(x)$?

7 If the value of a photocopier t years after purchase is given by $V(t) = 9650 - 860t$ Yen:

    a find $V(4)$ and state what $V(4)$ means

    b find t when $V(t) = 5780$ and explain what this represents

    c find the original purchase price of the photocopier.

8 On the same set of axes draw the graphs of three different functions $f(x)$ such that $f(2) = 1$ and $f(5) = 3$.

9 Find $f(x) = ax + b$, a linear function, in which $f(2) = 1$ and $f(-3) = 11$.

10 Given $T(x) = ax^2 + bx + c$, find a, b and c if $T(0) = -4$, $T(1) = -2$ and $T(2) = 6$.

INVESTIGATION   **FLUID FILLING FUNCTIONS**

When water is added at a **constant rate** to a cylindrical container the depth of water in the container is a function of time.

This is because the volume of water added is directly proportional to the time taken to add it. If water was not added at a constant rate the direct proportionality would not exist.

The depth-time graph for the case of a cylinder would be as shown alongside:

The question arises: 'What changes in appearance of the graph occur for different shaped containers?' Consider a vase of conical shape.

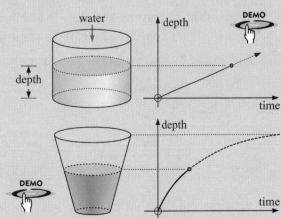

What to do:

1 For each of the following containers, draw a 'depth v time' graph as water is added:

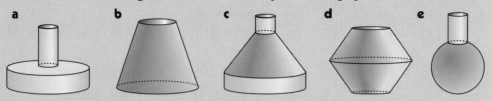

a   **b**   **c**   **d**   **e**

2 Use the water filling demonstration to check your answers to question **1**.

3 Write a brief report on the connection between the shape of a vessel and the corresponding shape of its depth-time graph. You may wish to discuss this in parts. For example, first examine cylindrical containers, then conical, then other shapes. Gradients of curves must be included in your report.

4 Draw possible containers as in question **1** which have the following 'depth v time' graphs:

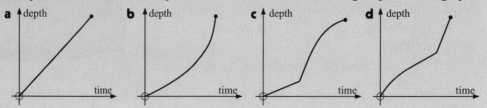

a depth time **b** depth time **c** depth time **d** depth time

D COMPOSITE FUNCTIONS, f ∘ g

Given $f : x \longmapsto f(x)$ and $g : x \longmapsto g(x)$, then the **composite function** of f and g will convert x into $f(g(x))$.

$f \circ g$ is used to represent the composite function of f and g.

$f \circ g$ means f following g and $(f \circ g)(x) = f(g(x))$ i.e., $f \circ g : x \longmapsto f(g(x))$.

Consider $f : x \longmapsto x^4$ and $g : x \longmapsto 2x + 3$.

$f \circ g$ means that g converts x to $2x + 3$ and then
$\qquad\qquad\quad f$ converts $(2x + 3)$ to $(2x + 3)^4$.

DEMO

This is illustrated by the two function machines below.

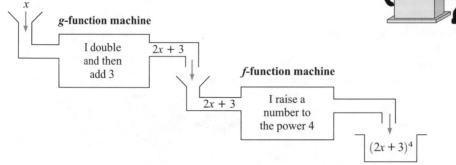
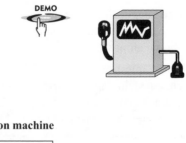

x

g-function machine

I double
and then
add 3

$2x + 3$

f-function machine

$2x + 3$

I raise a
number to
the power 4

$(2x + 3)^4$

Algebraically, if $f(x) = x^4$ and $g(x) = 2x + 3$, then

$(f \circ g)(x) = f(g(x))$ and $(g \circ f)(x) = g(f(x))$

$\qquad = f(2x + 3)$ {g operates on x first} $= g(x^4)$

$\qquad = (2x + 3)^4$ {f operates on $g(x)$ next} $= 2(x^4) + 3$

$\qquad\qquad\qquad\qquad\qquad\qquad\qquad\qquad\qquad\qquad\qquad\qquad = 2x^4 + 3$

So, in general, $f(g(x)) \neq g(f(x))$.

The ability to break down functions into composite functions is useful in **differential calculus**.

Example 5

Given $f : x \longmapsto 2x + 1$ and $g : x \longmapsto 3 - 4x$ find in simplest form:

a $(f \circ g)(x)$ **b** $(g \circ f)(x)$

$f(x) = 2x + 1$ and $g(x) = 3 - 4x$

a $\therefore$ $(f \circ g)(x) = f(g(x))$ **b** $(g \circ f)(x) = g(f(x))$

$\qquad\qquad\quad = f(3 - 4x)$ $\qquad\qquad = g(2x + 1)$

$\qquad\qquad\quad = 2(3 - 4x) + 1$ $\qquad\qquad = 3 - 4(2x + 1)$

$\qquad\qquad\quad = 6 - 8x + 1$ $\qquad\qquad = 3 - 8x - 4$

$\qquad\qquad\quad = 7 - 8x$ $\qquad\qquad = -8x - 1$

Note: If $f(x) = 2x + 1$ then $f(\Delta) = 2(\Delta) + 1,$

$\qquad\qquad\qquad\qquad\qquad\qquad\qquad f(*) = 2(*) + 1,$

$\qquad\qquad\qquad\qquad\qquad\qquad f(3x - 4) = 2(3x - 4) + 1.$

EXERCISE 1D

1 Given $f : x \longmapsto 2x + 3$ and $g : x \longmapsto 1 - x$, find in simplest form:

    a $(f \circ g)(x)$ **b** $(g \circ f)(x)$ **c** $(f \circ g)(-3)$

2 Given $f : x \longmapsto x^2$ and $g : x \longmapsto 2 - x$ find $(f \circ g)(x)$ and $(g \circ f)(x)$.

    Find also the domain and range of $f \circ g$ and $g \circ f$.

3 Given $f : x \longmapsto x^2 + 1$ and $g : x \longmapsto 3 - x$, find in simplest form:

    a $(f \circ g)(x)$ **b** $(g \circ f)(x)$ **c** x if $(g \circ f)(x) = f(x)$

4 **a** If $ax + b = cx + d$ for all values of x, show that $a = c$ and $b = d$.

      (**Hint:** If it is true for all x, it is true for $x = 0$ and $x = 1$.)

    b Given $f(x) = 2x + 3$ and $g(x) = ax + b$ and that $(f \circ g)(x) = x$ for all values of x, deduce that $a = \frac{1}{2}$ and $b = -\frac{3}{2}$.

    c Is the result in **b** true if $(g \circ f)(x) = x$ for all x?

E   THE RECIPROCAL FUNCTION $x \mapsto \frac{1}{x}$

$x \longmapsto \frac{1}{x}$,   i.e., $f(x) = \frac{1}{x}$ is defined as the **reciprocal function**.

It has graph:

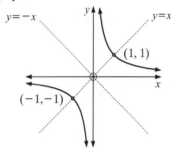

Notice that:

- $f(x) = \frac{1}{x}$ is meaningless when $x = 0$

- The graph of $f(x) = \frac{1}{x}$ exists in the first and third quadrants only.

- $f(x) = \frac{1}{x}$ is symmetric about $y = x$ and $y = -x$

- $f(x) = \frac{1}{x}$ is **asymptotic** to the x-axis and to the y-axis.

  [The graph gets closer to the axes as it gets further from the origin.]

- as $x \to \infty$, $f(x) \to 0$ (from above)
  as $x \to -\infty$, $f(x) \to 0$ (from below)
  as $x \to 0$ (from right), $y \to \infty$
  as $x \to 0$ (from left), $y \to -\infty$
  $\to$ reads *approaches*   or   *tends to*

EXERCISE 1E

1   Sketch the graph of $f(x) = \frac{1}{x}$, $g(x) = \frac{2}{x}$, $h(x) = \frac{4}{x}$ on the same set of axes.
    Comment on any similarities and differences.

2   Sketch the graphs of $f(x) = -\frac{1}{x}$, $g(x) = -\frac{2}{x}$, $h(x) = -\frac{4}{x}$ on the same set of axes.
    Comment on any similarities and differences.

F   INVERSE FUNCTIONS

The operations of $+$ and $-$, $\times$ and $\div$, squaring and finding the square root are inverse operations as one undoes what the other does.

For example, $x + 3 - 3 = x$, $x \times 3 \div 3 = x$ and $\sqrt{8^2} = 8$.

A function $y = f(x)$ *may or may not* have an inverse function.

If $y = f(x)$ has an **inverse function**, this new function
- must indeed be a function, i.e., satisfy the vertical line test
- must be the reflection of $y = f(x)$ in the line $y = x$
- must satisfy the condition that $f^{-1}: f(x) \to x$ (i.e.,   the inverse).

The function $y = x$,   defined as $e: x \longmapsto x$,   i.e., $e(x) = x$ is the **identity function**.

This means that, for any function f that has an inverse function f^{-1}, $f \circ f^{-1}$ and $f^{-1} \circ f$ must always equal the identity function e, i.e., $(f \circ f^{-1})(x) = (f^{-1} \circ f)(x) = x$, i.e., the inverse function undoes the effect of the function on x.

The inverse function of $y = f(x)$ is denoted by $y = f^{-1}(x)$.

If (x, y) lies on f, then (y, x) lies on f^{-1}. So reflecting the function in $y = x$ has the algebraic effect of interchanging x and y,

e.g., $f : y = 5x + 2$ becomes $f^{-1} : x = 5y + 2$.

For example,

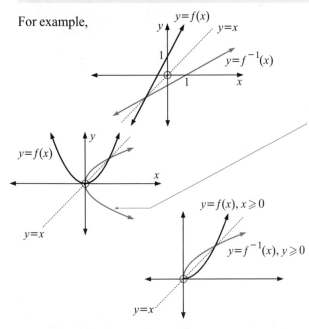

$y = f^{-1}(x)$ is the inverse of $y = f(x)$ as

- it is also a function
- it is the reflection of $y = f(x)$ in the oblique line $y = x$.

This is the reflection of $y = f(x)$ in $y = x$, but it is not the inverse function of $y = f(x)$ as it fails the vertical line test.

We say that the function $y = f(x)$ does not have an inverse.

Note: $y = f(x)$ subject to $x \geqslant 0$ does have an inverse function, drawn alongside. Also, although not drawn here, $y = f(x)$ subject to $x \leqslant 0$ does have an inverse function.

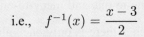

Example 6

Consider $f : x \longmapsto 2x + 3$.

a   On the same axes, graph f and its inverse function f^{-1}.

b   Find $f^{-1}(x)$ using   **i**   coordinate geometry and the slope of $f^{-1}(x)$ from **a**
                                   ii   variable interchange.

c   Check that $(f \circ f^{-1})(x) = (f^{-1} \circ f)(x) = x$

---

a $f(x) = 2x + 3$ passes through $(0, 3)$ and $(2, 7)$.

   ∴ $f^{-1}(x)$ passes through $(3, 0)$ and $(7, 2)$.

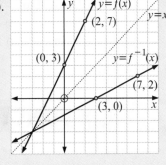

b   **i**   This line has slope $\dfrac{2 - 0}{7 - 3} = \dfrac{1}{2}$.

      So, its equation is $\dfrac{y - 0}{x - 3} = \dfrac{1}{2}$

      i.e., $y = \dfrac{x - 3}{2}$

     i.e., $f^{-1}(x) = \dfrac{x - 3}{2}$

  ii f is $y = 2x + 3$, so f^{-1} is $\quad x = 2y + 3$

        ∴ $\quad x - 3 = 2y$

        ∴ $\quad \dfrac{x - 3}{2} = y$ i.e., $f^{-1}(x) = \dfrac{x - 3}{2}$

c $(f \circ f^{-1})(x)$ and $(f^{-1} \circ f)(x)$

$= f(f^{-1}(x))$ $= f^{-1}(f(x))$

$= f\left(\dfrac{x-3}{2}\right)$ $= f^{-1}(2x+3)$

$= 2\left(\dfrac{x-3}{2}\right) + 3$ $= \dfrac{(2x+3)-3}{2}$

$= x$ $= \dfrac{2x}{2}$

                                  $= x$

Note:
If f includes point $(a,\,b)$ then f^{-1} includes point $(b,\,a)$, i.e., the point obtained by interchanging the coordinates.

EXERCISE 1F

1   For each of the following functions f

    i   on the same axes graph $y = x$, f and f^{-1}

    ii find $f^{-1}(x)$ using coordinate geometry and i

    iii find $f^{-1}(x)$ using variable interchange:

    a $f : x \longmapsto 3x + 1$

    b $f : x \longmapsto \dfrac{x+2}{4}$.

2   For each of the following functions f

    i find $f^{-1}(x)$ ii sketch $y = f(x)$, $y = f^{-1}(x)$ and $y = x$ on the same axes

    iii show that $f^{-1} \circ f = f \circ f^{-1} = e$, the identity function:

    a $f : x \longmapsto 2x + 5$ b $f : x \longmapsto \dfrac{3 - 2x}{4}$ c $f : x \longmapsto x + 3$

3   Copy the graphs of the following functions and in each case include the graphs of $y = x$ and $y = f^{-1}(x)$.

a 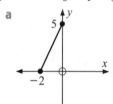   b 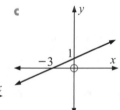   c 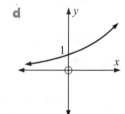   d

4   a   Sketch the graph of $f : x \longmapsto x^2 - 4$ and reflect it in the line $y = x$.

    b   Does f have an inverse function?

    c   Does f where $x \geqslant 0$ have an inverse function?

5   Sketch the graph of $f : x \longmapsto x^3$ and its inverse function $f^{-1}(x)$.

G   FUNCTIONS WHICH HAVE INVERSES

It is important to understand the distinction between one-to-one and many-to-one functions.

A **one-to-one** function is any function where • for each x there is only one value of y and
                                                  • for each y there is only one value of x.

Functions that are **one-to-one** satisfy both the '**vertical line test**' and the '**horizontal line test**'. This means that: • no vertical line can meet the graph more than once and
                    • no horizontal line can meet the graph more than once.

Functions that are not one-to-one are called **many-to-one** and whilst these functions must satisfy the '**vertical line test**' they *do not satisfy* the '**horizontal line test**',   i.e.,   at least one y-value has more than one corresponding x-value.

Note:
- If the function $y = f(x)$ is **one-to-one**, it will have an inverse function $y = f^{-1}(x)$.
- If a function $y = f(x)$ is **many-to-one**, it *will not* have an inverse function.
- Many-to-one functions can have inverse functions for a restricted part of the domain (see **Example 7**).

Example 7

Consider $f : x \longmapsto x^2$.

a   Explain why the function defined above does not have an inverse function.

b   Does $f : x \longmapsto x^2$ where $x \geqslant 0$ have an inverse function?

c   Find $f^{-1}(x)$ for $f : x \longmapsto x^2$, $x \geqslant 0$.

d   Sketch $y = f(x)$, $y = x$ and $y = f^{-1}(x)$ for f in **b** and f^{-1} in **c**.

---

a $f : x \longmapsto x^2$ has domain $x \in \mathcal{R}$ and is many-to-one.

It does not pass the 'horizontal line test'.

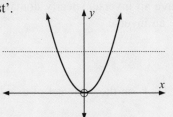

b   If we restrict the domain to $x \geqslant 0$ or $x \in [0, \infty[$, or in fact any domain which makes f one-to-one, it satisfies the 'horizontal line test' and so has an inverse function.

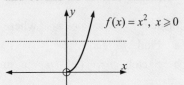

c f is defined by $y = x^2$, $x \geqslant 0$

$\therefore$ f^{-1} is defined by $x = y^2$, $y \geqslant 0$

$\therefore$ $y = \pm\sqrt{x}$, $y \geqslant 0$

i.e., $y = \sqrt{x}$

$\{$as $-\sqrt{x}$ is $\leqslant 0\}$

So, $f^{-1}(x) = \sqrt{x}$

d

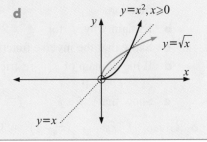

Note: The function $f(x) = \dfrac{1}{x}$, $x \neq 0$,   called the **reciprocal function**, is said to be a **self-inverse function** as $f = f^{-1}$.

This is because the graph of $y = \dfrac{1}{x}$ is symmetrical about the line $y = x$.

Any function with a graph which is symmetrical about the line $y = x$ must be a **self-inverse function**.

EXERCISE 1G

Note: If the domain of a function is the set of all real numbers, then the statement $x \in \mathcal{R}$ will be omitted.

1   **a**   Show that $f : x \longmapsto \dfrac{1}{x}$ has an inverse function for all $x \neq 0$.

   b   Find f^{-1} algebraically and show that f is a self-inverse function.

2   Show that $f : x \longmapsto \dfrac{3x - 8}{x - 3}$, $x \neq 3$ is a self-inverse function by:

   a   reference to its graph   **b**   using algebra.

3   The '**horizontal line test**' says that:

   for a function to have an inverse function, no horizontal line can cut it more than once.

   a   Explain why this is a valid test for the existence of an inverse function.

   b   Which of the following functions have an inverse function?

   i 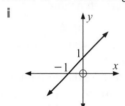   **ii** 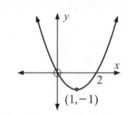   **iii**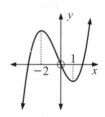

   c   For the functions in **b** which do not have an inverse, specify domains as wide as possible where each function does have an inverse.

4   Consider $f : x \longmapsto x^2$ where $x \leqslant 0$.

   a   Find $f^{-1}(x)$.

   b   Sketch $y = f(x)$, $y = x$ and $y = f^{-1}(x)$ on the same set of axes.

5   **a**   Explain why $f : x \longmapsto x^2 - 4x + 3$ is a function but does not have an inverse function.

   b   Explain why f for $x \geqslant 2$ has an inverse function.

   c   Show that the inverse function of the function in **b** is $f^{-1}(x) = 2 + \sqrt{1 + x}$.

   d   If the domain of f is restricted to $x \geqslant 2$,   state the domain and range of

   i f **ii** f^{-1}.

   e   Show that $f \circ f^{-1} = f^{-1} \circ f = e$,   the identity function.

6   Given $f : x \longmapsto (x + 1)^2 + 3$ where $x \geqslant -1$,

   a   find the defining equation of f^{-1}

   b   sketch, using technology, the graphs of $y = f(x)$, $y = x$ and $y = f^{-1}(x)$

   c   state the domain and range of   **i** f **ii** f^{-1}.

7   Consider the functions $f : x \longmapsto 2x + 5$ and $g : x \longmapsto \dfrac{8 - x}{2}$.

   a   Find $g^{-1}(-1)$.   **b**   Solve for x the equation $(f \circ g^{-1})(x) = 9$.

8   Given $f : x \longmapsto 5^x$ and $g : x \longmapsto \sqrt{x}$,

   a   find   **i** $f(2)$ **ii** $g^{-1}(4)$ **b**   solve the equation $(g^{-1} \circ f)(x) = 25$.

9   Given $f : x \longmapsto 2x$ and $g : x \longmapsto 4x - 3$ show that $(f^{-1} \circ g^{-1})(x) = (g \circ f)^{-1}(x)$.

10   Which of these functions is a self inverse function, that is $f^{-1}(x) = f(x)$?

   a $f(x) = 2x$ **b** $f(x) = x$ **c** $f(x) = -x$ **d** $f(x) = \dfrac{2}{x}$ **e** $f(x) = -\dfrac{6}{x}$

11   Show that $(f \circ f^{-1})(x) = (f^{-1} \circ f)(x) = x$ for:

   a $f(x) = 3x + 1$ **b** $f(x) = \dfrac{x + 3}{4}$ **c** $f(x) = \sqrt{x}$

12

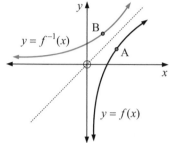

   a   B is the image of A under a reflection in the line $y = x$.
   If A is $(x, f(x))$, what are the coordinates of B under the reflection?

   b   Substitute your result from **a** into $y = f^{-1}(x)$. What result do you obtain?

   c   Explain how to establish that $f(f^{-1}(x)) = x$ also.

REVIEW SET 1A

1   If $f(x) = 2x - x^2$ find: **a** $f(2)$ **b** $f(-3)$ **c** $f(-\frac{1}{2})$

2   For the following graphs determine:

   i   the range and domain   **ii**   the x and y-intercepts   **iii**   whether it is a function
   iv   if they have an inverse function

   a

   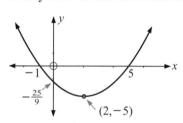

   b

   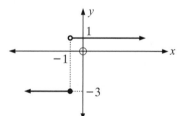

3   For each of the following graphs find the domain and range:

   a

   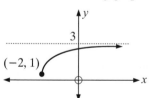

   b

   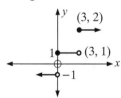

4   If $h(x) = 7 - 3x$:

   a   find in simplest form $h(2x - 1)$ **b**   find x if $h(2x - 1) = -2$

5   Find a, b and c if $f(0) = 5$, $f(-2) = 21$ and $f(3) = -4$ and $f(x) = ax^2 + bx + c$.

6   Consider $f(x) = \dfrac{1}{x^2}$.   **a**   For what value of x is $f(x)$ meaningless?
   b   Sketch the graph of this function using technology.
   c   State the domain and range of the function.

7 If $f(x) = 2x - 3$ and $g(x) = x^2 + 2$, find: **a** $f(g(x))$ **b** $g(f(x))$

8 If $f(x) = 1 - 2x$ and $g(x) = \sqrt{x}$:
  a find in simplest form   **i** $(f \circ g)(x)$ **ii** $(g \circ f)(x)$
  b What is the domain and range of $f \circ g$ and $g \circ f$?

9 Find an f and a g function given that:

  a $f(g(x)) = \sqrt{1 - x^2}$ **b** $g(f(x)) = \left(\dfrac{x - 2}{x + 1}\right)^2$

REVIEW SET 1B

1 If $g(x) = x^2 - 3x$, find in simplest form   **a** $g(x + 1)$ **b** $g(x^2 - 2)$

2 For each of the following functions $f(x)$ find $f^{-1}(x)$:

  a $f(x) = 7 - 4x$ **b** $f(x) = \dfrac{3 + 2x}{5}$

3 For each of the following graphs, find the domain and range.

  a 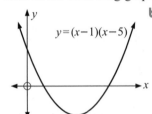   **b**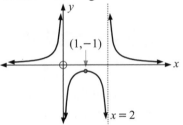

4 Copy the following graphs and draw the graph of each inverse function:

  a 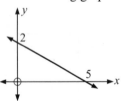   **b**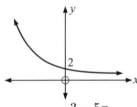

5 Find $f^{-1}(x)$ given that $f(x)$ is: **a** $4x + 2$ **b** $\dfrac{3 - 5x}{4}$

6 Consider $x \longmapsto 2x - 7$.
  a On the same set of axes graph $y = x$, f and f^{-1}.
  b Find $f^{-1}(x)$ using variable interchange.
  c Show that $f \circ f^{-1} = f^{-1} \circ f = e$, the identity function.

7 **a** Sketch the graph of $g : x \longmapsto x^2 + 6x + 7$.
  b Explain why g for $x \in \,]-\infty, -3]$ has an inverse function g^{-1}.
  c Find algebraically, the equation of g^{-1}.   **d** Sketch the graph of g^{-1}.
  e Find the range of g and hence the domain and range of g^{-1}.

8 Given $h : x \longmapsto (x - 4)^2 + 3$, $x \in [4, \infty[$
  a find the defining equation of h^{-1}.   **b** Show that $h \circ h^{-1} = h^{-1} \circ h = x$

9 Given $f : x \longmapsto 3x + 6$ and $h : x \longmapsto \dfrac{x}{3}$, show that $(f^{-1} \circ h^{-1})(x) = (h \circ f)^{-1}(x)$.

Chapter 2

Sequences and series

Contents:

A   NUMBER PATTERNS

An important skill in mathematics is to be able to
- **recognise** patterns in sets of numbers,
- **describe** the patterns in words, and
- **continue** the patterns.

A list of numbers where there is a pattern is called a **number sequence**.
The members (numbers) of a sequence are said to be its **terms**.

For example,   3, 7, 11, 15, ... form a number sequence.

The first term is 3,   the second term is 7,   the third term is 11, etc.

We describe this pattern in words:

"The sequence starts at 3 and each term is 4 more than the previous one."

Thus, the fifth term is 19, and the sixth term is 23, etc.

Example 1

Describe the sequence: 14, 17, 20, 23, ... and write down the next two terms.

The sequence starts at 14 and each term is 3 more than the previous term.
The next two terms are 26 and 29.

EXERCISE 2A

1 Write down the first four terms of the sequence if you start with:
  a 4 and add 9 each time
  b 45 and subtract 6 each time
  c 2 and multiply by 3 each time
  d 96 and divide by 2 each time.

2 For each of the following write a description of the sequence and find the next 2 terms:
  a 8, 16, 24, 32, ...
  b 2, 5, 8, 11, ...
  c 36, 31, 26, 21, ...
  d 96, 89, 82, 75, ...
  e 1, 4, 16, 64, ...
  f 2, 6, 18, 54, ...
  g 480, 240, 120, 60, ...
  h 243, 81, 27, 9, ...
  i 50 000, 10 000, 2000, 400, ...

3 Describe the following number patterns and write down the next 3 terms:
  a 1, 4, 9, 16, ...
  b 1, 8, 27, 64, ...
  c 2, 6, 12, 20, ...
  [Hint: In **c** $2 = 1 \times 2$ and $6 = 2 \times 3$.]

B   SEQUENCES OF NUMBERS

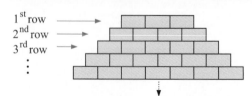

1st row
2nd row
3rd row
⋮

Consider the illustrated tower of bricks. The top row, or first row, has three bricks. The second row has four bricks. The third row has five, etc.

If u_n represents the number of bricks in row n (from the top)
then $u_1 = 3$, $u_2 = 4$, $u_3 = 5$, $u_4 = 6$, ...

The number pattern: 3, 4, 5, 6, ... is called a **sequence** of numbers.

This sequence can be specified by:

- **Using words**

  The top row has three bricks and each successive row under it has one more brick.

- **Using an explicit formula**

  $u_n = n + 2$ is the **general term** (or **nth term**) formula for $n = 1, 2, 3, 4, 5, ...$ etc.

  Check: $u_1 = 1 + 2 = 3$ ✓ $u_2 = 2 + 2 = 4$ ✓

  $u_3 = 3 + 2 = 5$ ✓   etc.

Early members of a sequence can be graphed. Each term is represented by a dot.

The dots *must not* be joined. Why?

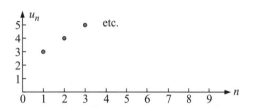

OPENING PROBLEM

A circular stadium consists of sections as illustrated, with aisles in between. The diagram shows the tiers of concrete steps for the final section, **Section K**. Seats are to be placed along every step, with each seat being 0.45 m wide. AB, the arc at the front of the first row is 14.4 m long, while CD, the arc at the back of the back row is 20.25 m long.

For you to consider:

1 How wide is each concrete step?

2 What is the length of the arc of the back of Row 2, Row 3, etc?

3 How many seats are there in Row 1, Row 2, Row 3, ... Row 13?

4 How many sections are there in the stadium?

5 What is the total seating capacity of the stadium?

6 What is the radius of the 'playing surface'?

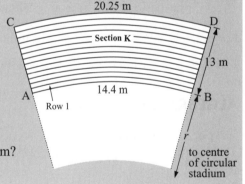

To solve problems like the **Opening Problem** and many others, a detailed study of **sequences** and their sums (called **series**) is required.

NUMBER SEQUENCES

A **number sequence** is a set of numbers defined by a rule for positive integers.

A number sequence can be thought as a function whose domain is the positive integers.

Sequences may be defined in one of the following ways:

- by using a formula which represents the **general term** (called the **nth term**)
- by giving a description in words
- by listing the first few terms and assuming that the pattern represented continues indefinitely.

THE GENERAL TERM

u_n, T_n, t_n, A_n, etc. can all be used to represent the **general term** (or nth **term**) of a sequence and are defined for $n = 1, 2, 3, 4, 5, 6, ...$

$\{u_n\}$ represents the sequence that can be generated by using u_n as the nth **term**.

$\{u_n\}$ is a function, i.e., $n \longmapsto u_n$, $n \in Z^+$

For example, $\{2n + 1\}$ generates the sequence $3, 5, 7, 9, 11, ...$

EXERCISE 2B

1 List the first *five* terms of the sequence:

    a $\{2n\}$ **b** $\{2n + 2\}$ **c** $\{2n - 1\}$ **d** $\{2n - 3\}$

    e $\{2n + 3\}$ **f** $\{2n + 11\}$ **g** $\{3n + 1\}$ **h** $\{4n - 3\}$

2 List the first *five* terms of the sequence:

    a $\{2^n\}$ **b** $\{3 \times 2^n\}$ **c** $\{6 \times (\frac{1}{2})^n\}$ **d** $\{(-2)^n\}$

3 List the first *five* terms of the sequence $\{15 - (-2)^n\}$.

C   ARITHMETIC SEQUENCES

> An **arithmetic sequence** is a sequence in which each term differs from the previous one by the same fixed number.

For example: $2, 5, 8, 11, 14, ...$ is arithmetic as $5 - 2 = 8 - 5 = 11 - 8 = 14 - 11$, etc.

Likewise, $31, 27, 23, 19, ...$ is arithmetic as $27 - 31 = 23 - 27 = 19 - 23$, etc.

ALGEBRAIC DEFINITION

> $\{u_n\}$ is **arithmetic** $\Leftrightarrow$ $u_{n+1} - u_n = d$ for all positive integers n where d is a constant (the **common difference**).

Note:
- $\Leftrightarrow$ is read as 'if and only if'
- If $\{u_n\}$ is arithmetic then $u_{n+1} - u_n$ is a constant *and* if $u_{n+1} - u_n$ is a constant then $\{u_n\}$ is arithmetic.

THE 'ARITHMETIC' NAME

If a, b and c are any consecutive terms of an arithmetic sequence then

$$b - a = c - b \quad \text{\{equating common differences\}}$$
$$\therefore \quad 2b = a + c$$
$$\therefore \quad b = \frac{a + c}{2}$$

    i.e., middle term = arithmetic mean (average) of terms on each side of it.

      Hence the name *arithmetic sequence*.

THE GENERAL TERM FORMULA

Suppose the first term of an arithmetic sequence is u_1 and the common difference is d.

Then $u_2 = u_1 + d$ $\therefore$ $u_3 = u_1 + 2d$ $\therefore$ $u_4 = u_1 + 3d$ etc.

then, $u_n = u_1 + \underbrace{(n-1)}d$

The coefficient of d is one less than the subscript.

So,   for an **arithmetic sequence** with **first term u_1** and **common difference d** the **general term** (or nth **term**) is $u_n = u_1 + (n-1)d$.

Example 2

Consider the sequence   2, 9, 16, 23, 30, ...

a   Show that the sequence is arithmetic.

b   Find the formula for the general term u_n.

c   Find the 100th term of the sequence.

d   Is   **i**   828   **ii**   2341   a member of the sequence?

---

a $9 - 2 = 7$ So, assuming that the pattern continues,
          $16 - 9 = 7$ consecutive terms differ by 7
          $23 - 16 = 7$ $\therefore$ the sequence is arithmetic with $u_1 = 2$, $d = 7$.
          $30 - 23 = 7$

b $u_n = u_1 + (n-1)d$ $\therefore$ $u_n = 2 + 7(n-1)$ i.e., $u_n = 7n - 5$

c   If $n = 100$, $u_{100} = 7(100) - 5 = 695$.

d   **i**   Let $u_n = 828$ **ii**   Let $u_n = 2341$
          $\therefore$ $7n - 5 = 828$ $\therefore$ $7n - 5 = 2341$
          $\therefore$ $7n = 833$ $\therefore$ $7n = 2346$
          $\therefore$ $n = 119$ $\therefore$ $n = 335\frac{1}{7}$

$\therefore$ 828 is a term of the sequence.   which is not possible as n is an
In fact it is the 119th term.   integer. $\therefore$ 2341 cannot be a term.

EXERCISE 2C

1   Consider the sequence   6, 17, 28, 39, 50, ...

    a   Show that the sequence is arithmetic.   **b**   Find the formula for its general term.

    c   Find its 50th term.   **d**   Is 325 a member?

    e   Is 761 a member?

2   Consider the sequence 87, 83, 79, 75, ...

    a   Show that the sequence is arithmetic.   **b**   Find the formula for the general term.

    c   Find the 40th term.   **d**   Is -143 a member?

3 A sequence is defined by $u_n = 3n - 2$.

    a Prove that the sequence is arithmetic. (**Hint:** Find $u_{n+1} - u_n$.)

    b Find u_1 and d.   **c** Find the 57th term.

    d What is the least term of the sequence which is greater than 450?

4 A sequence is defined by $u_n = \dfrac{71 - 7n}{2}$.

    a Prove that the sequence is arithmetic. **b** Find u_1 and d. **c** Find u_{75}.

    d For what values of n are the terms of the sequence less than -200?

Example 3

Find k given that $3k + 1$, k and -3 are consecutive terms of an arithmetic sequence.

Since the terms are consecutive, $k - (3k + 1) = -3 - k$ {equating differences}

$$\therefore \quad k - 3k - 1 = -3 - k$$
$$\therefore \quad -2k - 1 = -3 - k$$
$$\therefore \quad -1 + 3 = -k + 2k$$
$$\therefore \quad k = 2$$

---

5 Find k given the consecutive arithmetic terms:

    a $32, k, 3$ **b** $k + 1, 2k + 1, 13$ **c** $5, k, k^2 - 8$

Example 4

Find the general term u_n for an arithmetic sequence with $u_3 = 8$ and $u_8 = -17$.

$u_3 = 8$ $\therefore \quad u_1 + 2d = 8$ ....(1) $\{u_n = u_1 + (n - 1)d\}$

$u_8 = -17$ $\therefore \quad u_1 + 7d = -17$ ....(2)

We now solve (1) and (2) simultaneously

$$-u_1 - 2d = -8$$
$$\underline{u_1 + 7d = -17}$$
$$\therefore \quad 5d = -25 \qquad \text{\{adding the equations\}}$$
$$\therefore \quad d = -5$$

So in (1) $u_1 + 2(-5) = 8$ *Check:*

$$\therefore \quad u_1 - 10 = 8 \qquad\qquad u_3 = 23 - 5(3)$$
$$\therefore \quad u_1 = 18 \qquad\qquad\qquad = 23 - 15$$
$$= 8 \ \checkmark$$

Now $u_n = u_1 + (n - 1)d$

$$\therefore \quad u_n = 18 - 5(n - 1) \qquad u_8 = 23 - 5(8)$$
$$\therefore \quad u_n = 18 - 5n + 5 \qquad\quad = 23 - 40$$
$$\therefore \quad u_n = 23 - 5n \qquad\qquad = -17 \ \checkmark$$

6 Find the general term u_n for an arithmetic sequence given that:

    a $u_7 = 41$ and $u_{13} = 77$ **b** $u_5 = -2$ and $u_{12} = -12\frac{1}{2}$

    c   the seventh term is 1 and the fifteenth term is -39

    d   the eleventh and eighth terms are -16 and $-11\frac{1}{2}$ respectively.

Example 5

Insert four numbers between 3 and 12 so that all six numbers are in arithmetic sequence.

If the numbers are 3, $3 + d$, $3 + 2d$, $3 + 3d$, $3 + 4d$, 12

$$\text{then} \quad 3 + 5d = 12$$
$$\therefore \quad 5d = 9$$
$$\therefore \quad d = \tfrac{9}{5} = 1.8$$

So we have   3, 4.8, 6.6, 8.4, 10.2, 12.

---

7   **a**   Insert three numbers between 5 and 10 so that all five numbers are in arithmetic sequence.

    b   Insert six numbers between -1 and 32 so that all eight numbers are in arithmetic sequence.

8 Consider the finite arithmetic sequence   36, $35\frac{1}{3}$, $34\frac{2}{3}$, ..., -30.

    a   Find u_1 and d.   **b**   How many terms does the sequence have?

9 An arithmetic sequence starts   23, 36, 49, 62, ...   What is the first term of the sequence to exceed 100 000?

D   GEOMETRIC SEQUENCES

A sequence is **geometric** if each term can be obtained from the previous one by multiplying by the same non-zero constant.

For example: 2, 10, 50, 250, ...   is a geometric sequence as
$$2 \times 5 = 10 \quad \text{and} \quad 10 \times 5 = 50 \quad \text{and} \quad 50 \times 5 = 250.$$

Notice that $\frac{10}{2} = \frac{50}{10} = \frac{250}{50} = 5$,   i.e.,   each term divided by the previous one is constant.

Algebraic definition:

$\{u_n\}$ is **geometric** $\quad\Leftrightarrow\quad \dfrac{u_{n+1}}{u_n} = r \quad$ for all positive integers n

where r is a **constant** (the **common ratio**).

Notice: •   2, 10, 50, 250, ...   is geometric with $r = 5$.

        •   2, -10, 50, -250, ...   is geometric with $r = -5$.

THE 'GEOMETRIC' NAME

If a, b and c are any consecutive terms of a geometric sequence then

$$\frac{b}{a} = \frac{c}{b} \qquad \text{\{equating common ratios\}}$$

$\therefore \quad b^2 = ac$ and so $b = \pm\sqrt{ac}$ where $\sqrt{ac}$ is the **geometric mean** of a and c.

THE GENERAL TERM

Suppose the first term of a geometric sequence is u_1 and the common ratio is r.

Then $u_2 = u_1 r \qquad \therefore \quad u_3 = u_1 r^2 \qquad \therefore \quad u_4 = u_1 r^3$ etc.

then $u_n = u_1 r^{n-1}$

The power of r is one less than the subscript.

So,   for a **geometric sequence** with **first term u_1** and **common ratio r**,

the **general term** (or nth **term**) is $u_n = u_1 r^{n-1}$.

Example 6

For the sequence $8, 4, 2, 1, \frac{1}{2}, \dots$

a   Show that the sequence is geometric.   b   Find the general term u_n.

c   Hence, find the 12th term as a fraction.

---

a $\dfrac{4}{8} = \dfrac{1}{2} \qquad \dfrac{2}{4} = \dfrac{1}{2} \qquad \dfrac{1}{2} = \dfrac{1}{2} \qquad \dfrac{\frac{1}{2}}{1} = \dfrac{1}{2}$

So, assuming the pattern continues, consecutive terms have a common ratio of $\frac{1}{2}$

$\therefore$ the sequence is geometric with $u_1 = 8$ and $r = \frac{1}{2}$.

b $u_n = u_1 r^{n-1} \qquad \therefore \quad u_n = 8 \left(\frac{1}{2}\right)^{n-1}$ or $u_n = 2^3 \times (2^{-1})^{n-1}$

$$= 2^3 \times 2^{-n+1}$$
$$= 2^{3+(-n+1)}$$
$$= 2^{4-n}$$

c $u_{12} = 8 \times \left(\frac{1}{2}\right)^{11}$

$\qquad = \frac{1}{256}$

(See Chapter 3 for exponent simplification)

EXERCISE 2D

1   For the geometric sequence with first two terms given, find b and c:

    a $2, 6, b, c, \dots$ b $10, 5, b, c, \dots$ c $12, -6, b, c, \dots$

2   a   Show that the sequence $5, 10, 20, 40, \dots$ is geometric.

    b   Find u_n and hence find the 15th term.

3   a   Show that the sequence $12, -6, 3, -1.5, \dots$ is geometric.

    b   Find u_n and hence find the 13th term (as a fraction).

4 Show that the sequence $8, -6, 4.5, -3.375, ...$ is geometric and hence find the 10th term as a decimal.

5 Show that the sequence $8, 4\sqrt{2}, 4, 2\sqrt{2}, ...$ is geometric and hence find, in simplest form, the general term u_n.

Example 7

$k - 1$, $2k$ and $21 - k$ are consecutive terms of a geometric sequence. Find k.

Since the terms are geometric, $\dfrac{2k}{k-1} = \dfrac{21-k}{2k}$ {equating r's}

$$\therefore \quad 4k^2 = (21-k)(k-1)$$
$$\therefore \quad 4k^2 = 21k - 21 - k^2 + k$$
$$\therefore \quad 5k^2 - 22k + 21 = 0$$
$$\therefore \quad (5k-7)(k-3) = 0 \quad \text{and so} \quad k = \tfrac{7}{5} \text{ or } 3$$

Check: If $k = \tfrac{7}{5}$ terms are: $\tfrac{2}{5}, \tfrac{14}{5}, \tfrac{98}{5}$. ✓ $\{r = 7\}$

If $k = 3$ terms are: $2, 6, 18$. ✓ $\{r = 3\}$

---

6 Find k given that the following are consecutive terms of a geometric sequence:

    a $7, k, 28$ **b** $k, 3k, 20 - k$ **c** $k, k + 8, 9k$

Example 8

A geometric sequence has $u_2 = -6$ and $u_5 = 162$. Find its general term.

$$u_2 = u_1 r = -6 \quad .... \ (1)$$
$$\text{and} \quad u_5 = u_1 r^4 = 162 \quad .... \ (2)$$

So, $\dfrac{u_1 r^4}{u_1 r} = \dfrac{162}{-6}$ $\{(2) \div (1)\}$

$$\therefore \quad r^3 = -27$$
$$\therefore \quad r = \sqrt[3]{-27}$$
$$\therefore \quad r = -3$$

Note:
$(-3)^{n-1} \neq -3^{n-1}$
as we do not know the value of n.
If n is odd, then $(-3)^{n-1} = 3^{n-1}$
If n is even, then $(-3)^{n-1} = -3^{n-1}$

and so in (1) $u_1(-3) = -6$
$$\therefore \quad u_1 = 2$$

Thus $u_n = 2 \times (-3)^{n-1}$.

---

7 Find the general term u_n, of the geometric sequence which has:

    a $u_4 = 24$ and $u_7 = 192$ **b** $u_3 = 8$ and $u_6 = -1$

    c $u_7 = 24$ and $u_{15} = 384$ **d** $u_3 = 5$ and $u_7 = \tfrac{5}{4}$

Example 9

Find the first term of the geometric sequence $6, 6\sqrt{2}, 12, 12\sqrt{2}, \ldots$ which exceeds 1400.

First we find u_n :   Now $u_1 = 6$ and $r = \sqrt{2}$

so as $u_n = u_1 r^{n-1}$ then $u_n = 6 \times (\sqrt{2})^{n-1}$.

Next we need to find n such that $u_n > 1400$.

Using a graphics calculator with $Y_1 = 6 \times (\sqrt{2})\char`\^(n-1)$,   we view a *table of values:*

X	Y₁
15	768
16	1086.1
17	1536
18	2172.2
19	3072
20	4344.5
21	6144
X=15	

So, the first term to exceed 1400 is u_{17} where $u_{17} = 1536$.

Note: Later we can solve problems like this one using logarithms.

---

8 **a** Find the first term of the sequence $2, 6, 18, 54, \ldots$ which exceeds $10\,000$.

   b Find the first term of the sequence $4, 4\sqrt{3}, 12, 12\sqrt{3}, \ldots$ which exceeds 4800.

   c Find the first term of the sequence $12, 6, 3, 1.5, \ldots$ which is less than 0.0001.

COMPOUND INTEREST

Consider the following: You invest $1000 in the bank. You leave the money in the bank for 3 years. You are paid an interest rate of 10% p.a. The interest is added to your investment each year.

An interest rate of 10% p.a. is paid, *increasing the value* of your investment yearly.

Your percentage increase each year is 10%,   i.e., $100\% + 10\% = 110\%$ of the value at the start of the year, which corresponds to a *multiplier* of 1.1 .

After one year your investment is worth $\$1000 \times 1.1 = \$1100$

After two years it is worth
$\$1100 \times 1.1$
$= \$1000 \times 1.1 \times 1.1$
$= \$1000 \times (1.1)^2 = \$1210$

After three years it is worth
$\$1210 \times 1.1$
$= \$1000 \times (1.1)^2 \times 1.1$
$= \$1000 \times (1.1)^3$

This suggests that if the money is left in your account for n years it would amount to $\$1000 \times (1.1)^n$.

Note: $u_1 = \$1000$ = initial investment

$u_2 = u_1 \times 1.1$ = amount after 1 year

$u_3 = u_1 \times (1.1)^2$ = amount after 2 years

$u_4 = u_1 \times (1.1)^3$ = amount after 3 years

$\vdots$

$u_{n+1} = u_1 \times (1.1)^n$ = amount after n years

In general, $u_{n+1} = u_1 \times r^n$ is used for compound growth, u_1 = initial investment
r = growth multiplier
n = number of years
u_{n+1} = amount after n years

Example 10

$5000 is invested for 4 years at 7% p.a. compound interest, compounded anually. What will it amount to at the end of this period?

$u_5 = u_1 \times r^4$ is the amount after 4 years

$\quad = 5000 \times (1.07)^4$ {for a 7% increase 100% becomes 107%}

$\quad \doteqdot 6553.98$ {5000 ☒ 1.07 ⌃ 4 ▣ }

So, it amounts to 6553.98.

---

9   **a**   What will an investment of $3000 at 10% p.a. compound interest amount to after 3 years?

   b   What part of this is interest?

10   How much compound interest is earned by investing 20 000 Euro at 12% p.a. if the investment is over a 4 year period?

11   **a**   What will an investment of 30 000 Yen at 10% p.a. compound interest amount to after 4 years?

   b   What part of this is interest?

12   How much compound interest is earned by investing $80 000 at 9% p.a., if the investment is over a 3 year period?

13   What will an investment of 100 000 Yen amount to after 5 years if it earns 8% p.a. compounded semi-annually?

14   What will an investment of £45 000 amount to after 21 months if it earns 7.5% p.a. compounded quarterly?

Example 11

How much should I invest now if I want the maturing value to be $10 000 in 4 years' time, if I am able to invest at 8.5% p.a. compounded annually?

$u_1 = ?, \quad u_5 = 10\,000, \quad r = 1.085$

$\qquad u_5 = u_1 \times r^4 \qquad$ {using $u_{n+1} = u_1 \times r^n$}

$\therefore \quad 10\,000 = u_1 \times (1.085)^4$

$\therefore \quad u_1 = \dfrac{10\,000}{(1.085)^4}$

$\therefore \quad u_1 \doteqdot 7215.74 \qquad$ {10 000 ➗ 1.085 ⌃ 4 ▣ }

So, you should invest $7215.74 now.

15 How much money must be invested now if you require $20 000 for a holiday in 4 years' time and the money can be invested at a fixed rate of 7.5% p.a. compounded annually?

16 What initial investment is required to produce a maturing amount of £15 000 in 60 months' time given that a fixed rate of 5.5% p.a. compounded annually is guaranteed?

17 How much should I invest now if I want a maturing amount of 25 000 Euro in 3 years' time and the money can be invested at a fixed rate of 8% p.a. compounded quarterly?

18 What initial investment is required to produce a maturing amount of 40 000 Yen in 8 years' time if your money can be invested at 9% p.a., compounded monthly?

Example 12

The initial population of rabbits on a farm was 50.
The population increased by 7% each week.

a   How many rabbits were present after:

  i   15 weeks   **ii**   30 weeks?

b   How long would it take for the population to reach 500?

We notice that $u_1 = 50$ and $r = 1.07$

$u_2 = 50 \times 1.07 =$ the population after 1 week

a   **i** $u_{n+1} = u_1 \times r^n$ **ii**   and

$$\therefore \quad u_{16} = 50 \times (1.07)^{15} \qquad\qquad u_{31} = 50 \times (1.07)^{30}$$

$$\doteqdot 137.95.... \qquad\qquad\qquad \doteqdot 380.61....$$

i.e.,   138 rabbits   i.e.,   381 rabbits

b $u_{n+1} = u_1 \times (1.07)^n$ after n weeks

So, we need to find when $50 \times (1.07)^n = 500$.

Trial and error on your calculator gives $n \doteqdot 34$ weeks

or   using the **Equation Solver** gives $n \doteqdot 34.03$

or   by finding the **point of intersection**
of $Y_1 = 50 \times 1.07^{\wedge}X$ and $Y_2 = 500$
on a graphics calculator, the solution is
$\doteqdot 34.03$ weeks.

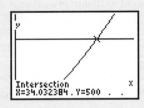

Intersection
X=34.032384 Y=500

---

19 A nest of ants initially consists of 500 ants.
The population is increasing by 12% each week.

a   How many ants will there be after

  i   10 weeks   **ii**   20 weeks?

b   Use technology to find how many weeks it will take for the ant population to reach 2000.

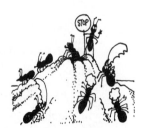

20   The animal *Eraticus* is endangered. Since 1985 there has only been one colony remaining and in 1985 the population of the colony was 555. Since then the population has been steadily decreasing at 4.5% per year. Find:

   a   the population in the year 2000

   b   the year in which we would expect the population to have declined to 50.

E   SERIES

A **series** is the addition of the terms of a sequence,

i.e., $u_1 + u_2 + u_3 + ... + u_n$ is a series.

The **sum** of a series is the result when all terms of the series are added.

Notation: $S_n = u_1 + u_2 + u_3 + ... + u_n$ is the sum of the first n terms.

Example 13

For the sequence   1, 4, 9, 16, 25, ...

   a   Write down an expression for S_n.   **b**   Find S_n for $n = 1, 2, 3, 4$ and 5.

   a $S_n = 1^2 + 2^2 + 3^2 + 4^2 + ... + n^2$ **b** $S_1 = 1$
      {all terms are perfect squares} $S_2 = 1 + 4 = 5$
                                             $S_3 = 1 + 4 + 9 = 14$
                                             $S_4 = 1 + 4 + 9 + 16 = 30$
                                             $S_5 = 1 + 4 + 9 + 16 + 25 = 55$

EXERCISE 2E.1

1   For the following sequences:

      i   write down an expression for S_n **ii**   find S_5.

   a   3, 11, 19, 27, ...   **b**   42, 37, 32, 27, ...   **c**   12, 6, 3, $1\frac{1}{2}$, ...

   d   2, 3, $4\frac{1}{2}$, $6\frac{3}{4}$, ...   **e**   1, $\frac{1}{2}$, $\frac{1}{4}$, $\frac{1}{8}$, ...   **f**   1, 8, 27, 64, ...

ARITHMETIC SERIES

An **arithmetic series** is the addition of successive terms of an arithmetic sequence.

For example: 21, 23, 25, 27, ..., 49   is an arithmetic sequence.

              So, $21 + 23 + 25 + 27 + ... + 49$ is an arithmetic series.

SUM OF AN ARITHMETIC SERIES

Recall that if the first term is u_1 and the common difference is d, then the terms are:
$u_1, u_1 + d, u_1 + 2d, u_1 + 3d$, etc.

Suppose that u_n is the last or final term of an arithmetic series.

Then, $S_n = u_1 + (u_1 + d) + (u_1 + 2d) + \dots + (u_n - 2d) + (u_n - d) + u_n$

but, $S_n = u_n + (u_n - d) + (u_n - 2d) + \dots + (u_1 + 2d) + (u_1 + d) + u_1$ {reversing them}

Adding these two expressions vertically we get

$$2S_n = \underbrace{(u_1 + u_n) + (u_1 + u_n) + (u_1 + u_n) + \dots + (u_1 + u_n) + (u_1 + u_n) + (u_1 + u_n)}_{n \text{ of these}}$$

$\therefore$ $2S_n = n(u_1 + u_n)$

i.e., $S_n = \dfrac{n}{2}(u_1 + u_n)$ where $u_n = u_1 + (n - 1)d$

so $\boxed{S_n = \dfrac{n}{2}(u_1 + u_n)}$ or $\boxed{S_n = \dfrac{n}{2}(2u_1 + (n - 1)d)}$

Example 14

Find the sum of $4 + 7 + 10 + 13 + \dots$ to 50 terms.

The series is arithmetic with $u_1 = 4$, $d = 3$ and $n = 50$.

So, $S_{50} = \dfrac{50}{2}(2 \times 4 + 49 \times 3)$ {Using $S_n = \dfrac{n}{2}(2u_1 + (n - 1)d)$}

$= 3875$

EXERCISE 2E.2

1   Find the sum of:

   a $3 + 7 + 11 + 15 + \dots$ to 20 terms   **b** $\frac{1}{2} + 3 + 5\frac{1}{2} + 8 + \dots$ to 50 terms
   c $100 + 93 + 86 + 79 + \dots$ to 40 terms   **d** $50 + 48\frac{1}{2} + 47 + 45\frac{1}{2} + \dots$ to 80 terms

Example 15

Find the sum of $-6 + 1 + 8 + 15 + \dots + 141$.

The series is arithmetic with $u_1 = -6$, $d = 7$ and $u_n = 141$.

First we need to find n.

Now $u_n = u_1 + (n - 1)d = 141$

$\therefore$ $-6 + 7(n - 1) = 141$

$\therefore$ $7(n - 1) = 147$

$\therefore$ $n - 1 = 21$

$\therefore$ $n = 22$

Using $S_n = \dfrac{n}{2}(u_1 + u_n)$

$\therefore$ $S_{22} = \dfrac{22}{2}(-6 + 141)$

$= 11 \times 135$

$= 1485$

2   Find the sum of:

   a $5 + 8 + 11 + 14 + \dots + 101$ **b** $50 + 49\frac{1}{2} + 49 + 48\frac{1}{2} + \dots + (-20)$
   c $8 + 10\frac{1}{2} + 13 + 15\frac{1}{2} + \dots + 83$

3 An arithmetic series has seven terms. The first term is 5 and the last term is 53. Find the sum of the series.

4 An arithmetic series has eleven terms. The first term is 6 and the last term is -27. Find the sum of the series.

5 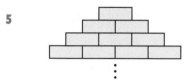 A bricklayer builds a triangular wall with layers of bricks as shown. If the bricklayer uses 171 bricks, how many layers are placed?

6 Each section of a soccer stadium has 44 rows with 22 seats in the first row, 23 in the second row, 24 in the third row, and so on. How many seats are there

    a in row 44   **b** in a section   **c** at a stadium which has 25 sections?

7 Find the sum of:

    a the first 50 multiples of 11   **b** the multiples of 7 between 0 and 1000

    c the integers between 1 and 100 which are not divisible by 3.

8 Prove that the sum of the first n positive integers is $\dfrac{n(n+1)}{2}$.

9 Consider the series of odd numbers $1 + 3 + 5 + 7 + ...$

    a What is the nth odd number, that is, u_n?

    b Prove that "the sum of the first n odd numbers is n^2 ".

    c Check your answer to **b** by finding S_1, S_2, S_3 and S_4.

10 Find the first two terms of an arithmetic sequence where the sixth term is 21 and the sum of the first seventeen terms is 0.

11 Three consecutive terms of an arithmetic sequence have a sum of 12 and a product of -80. Find the terms. **(Hint:** Let the terms be $x - d$, x and $x + d$.**)**

12 Five consecutive terms of an arithmetic sequence have a sum of 40. The product of the middle and the two end terms is 224. Find the terms of the sequence.

GEOMETRIC SERIES

> A **geometric series** is the addition of successive terms of a geometric sequence.

For example, 1, 2, 4, 8, 16, ..., 1024 is a geometric sequence.

So, $1 + 2 + 4 + 8 + 16 + ... + 1024$ is a geometric series.

SUM OF A GEOMETRIC SERIES

Recall that if the first term is u_1 and the common ratio is r, then the terms are:

$$u_1, \ u_1 r, \ u_1 r^2, \ u_1 r^3, \ .... \ \text{etc.}$$

So, $\qquad S_n = \underset{\uparrow}{u_1} + \underset{\underset{u_2}{\uparrow}}{u_1 r} + \underset{\underset{u_3}{\uparrow}}{u_1 r^2} + \underset{\underset{u_4}{\uparrow}}{u_1 r^3} + \ .... \ + \underset{\underset{u_{n-1}}{\uparrow}}{u_1 r^{n-2}} + \underset{\underset{u_n}{\uparrow}}{u_1 r^{n-1}}$

and $\quad$ for $\; r \neq 1, \quad S_n = \dfrac{u_1(r^n - 1)}{r - 1} \quad$ *or* $\quad S_n = \dfrac{u_1(1 - r^n)}{1 - r}.$

Proof: $\qquad$ If $\; S_n = u_1 + u_1 r + u_1 r^2 + u_1 r^3 + ... + u_1 r^{n-2} + u_1 r^{n-1} \quad$ .... (1)

$\qquad$ then $\; r S_n = (u_1 r + u_1 r^2 + u_1 r^3 + u_1 r^4 + ... + u_1 r^{n-1}) + u_1 r^n$

$\qquad\; \therefore \quad r S_n = (S_n - u_1) + u_1 r^n \qquad \{\text{from } (1)\}$

$\therefore \quad r S_n - S_n = u_1 r^n - u_1$

$\therefore \quad S_n(r - 1) = u_1(r^n - 1)$

$\qquad\quad \therefore \quad S_n = \dfrac{u_1(r^n - 1)}{r - 1} \quad$ or $\quad \dfrac{u_1(1 - r^n)}{1 - r} \quad$ p.v. $\; r \neq 1.$

Example 16

Find the sum of $\; 2 + 6 + 18 + 54 + ...$ to 12 terms.

The series is geometric with $\; u_1 = 2, \; r = 3 \;$ and $\; n = 12.$

So, $\; S_{12} = \dfrac{2(3^{12} - 1)}{3 - 1} \qquad \left\{\text{Using} \; S_n = \dfrac{u_1(r^n - 1)}{r - 1}\right\}$

$\qquad\quad = 531\,440$

EXERCISE 2E.3

1 Find the sum of the following series:

$\quad$ **a** $\; 12 + 6 + 3 + 1.5 + ... \;$ to 10 terms

$\quad$ **b** $\; \sqrt{7} + 7 + 7\sqrt{7} + 49 + ... \;$ to 12 terms

$\quad$ **c** $\; 6 - 3 + 1\frac{1}{2} - \frac{3}{4} + ... \;$ to 15 terms

$\quad$ **d** $\; 1 - \frac{1}{\sqrt{2}} + \frac{1}{2} - \frac{1}{2\sqrt{2}} + ... \;$ to 20 terms

> **Note:**
> This answer cannot be simplified as we do not know if n is odd or even.

Example 17

Find a formula for $\; S_n \;$ for $\; 9 - 3 + 1 - \frac{1}{3} + ... \;$ to n terms.

The series is geometric with $\; u_1 = 9, \; r = -\frac{1}{3}, \; \text{“}n\text{”} = n.$

So, $\; S_n = \dfrac{u_1(1 - r^n)}{1 - r} = \dfrac{9(1 - (-\frac{1}{3})^n)}{\frac{4}{3}}$

$\quad \therefore \quad S_n = \frac{27}{4}\left(1 - (-\frac{1}{3})^n\right)$

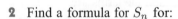

---

2 Find a formula for S_n for:

$\quad$ **a** $\; \sqrt{3} + 3 + 3\sqrt{3} + 9 + ... \;$ to n terms $\qquad$ **b** $\; 12 + 6 + 3 + 1\frac{1}{2} + ... \;$ to n terms

$\quad$ **c** $\; 0.9 + 0.09 + 0.009 + 0.0009 + ... \;$ to n terms

$\quad$ **d** $\; 20 - 10 + 5 - 2\frac{1}{2} + ... \;$ to n terms

3 Each year a sales-person is paid a bonus of $2000 which is banked into the same account which earns a fixed rate of interest of 6% p.a. with interest being paid annually. The amount at the end of each year in the account is calculated as follows:

$$A_0 = 2000$$
$$A_1 = A_0 \times 1.06 + 2000$$
$$A_2 = A_1 \times 1.06 + 2000 \quad \text{etc.}$$

a Show that $A_2 = 2000 + 2000 \times 1.06 + 2000 \times (1.06)^2$.

b Show that $A_3 = 2000[1 + 1.06 + (1.06)^2 + (1.06)^3]$.

c Hence find the total bank balance after 10 years.   (Assume no fees and charges.)

4 Consider $S_n = \frac{1}{2} + \frac{1}{4} + \frac{1}{8} + \frac{1}{16} + ... + \frac{1}{2^n}$.

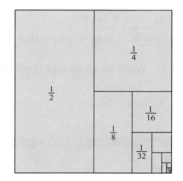

a Find S_1, S_2, S_3, S_4 and S_5 in fractional form.

b From **a** guess the formula for S_n.

c Find S_n using $S_n = \dfrac{u_1(1 - r^n)}{1 - r}$.

d Comment on S_n as n gets very large.

e What is the relationship between the given diagram and **d**?

5

A ball takes 1 second to hit the ground when dropped. It then takes 90% of this time to rebound to its new height and this continues until the ball comes to rest.

a Show that the total time of motion is given by $1 + 2(0.9) + 2(0.9)^2 + 2(0.9)^3 + ...$

b Find S_n for the series in **a**.

ground   **c** How long does it take for the ball to come to rest?

Note: This diagram is inaccurate as the motion is really up and down on the same spot. It has been separated out to help us visualise what is happening.

SUM TO INFINITY OF GEOMETRIC SERIES

Sometimes it is necessary to consider $S_n = \dfrac{u_1(1 - r^n)}{1 - r}$ when n gets very large.

What happens to S_n in this situation?

If $-1 < r < 1$, i.e., $|r| < 1$, then r^n approaches 0 for very large n.

This means that S_n will get closer and closer to $\dfrac{u_1}{1 - r}$.

We say that the series **converges** and has a sum to infinity of $\dfrac{u_1}{1 - r}$.

We write
$$\boxed{S_\infty = \frac{u_1}{1 - r} \quad \text{for } |r| < 1.}$$

The **sum to infinity** is sometimes called the **limiting sum**.

This result can be used to find the value of recurring decimals.

Example 18

Write $0.\bar{7}$ as a rational number.

$0.\bar{7} = \frac{7}{10} + \frac{7}{100} + \frac{7}{1000} + \frac{7}{10\,000} + ...$

which is a geometric series with infinitely many terms

$\therefore \quad S_\infty = \frac{u_1}{1 - r} = \frac{\frac{7}{10}}{1 - \frac{1}{10}}$ which simplifies to $\frac{7}{9}$

so, $0.\bar{7} = \frac{7}{9}$

6 Consider $0.\bar{3} = \frac{3}{10} + \frac{3}{100} + \frac{3}{1000} + ...$ which is an infinite geometric series.

    a What are   **i** u_1 and   **ii** r?

    b Using **a**, show that $0.\bar{3} = \frac{1}{3}$.

7 Write as a rational number: **a** $0.\bar{4}$ **b** $0.\overline{16}$ **c** $0.\overline{312}$

8 Use $S_\infty = \dfrac{u_1}{1 - r}$ to check your answers to **4d** and **5c**.

F   SIGMA NOTATION

$u_1 + u_2 + u_3 + u_4 + ... + u_n$ can be written more compactly using **sigma notation**.

$\sum$, which is called **sigma**, is the equivalent of capital S in the Greek alphabet.

We write $u_1 + u_2 + u_3 + u_4 + ... + u_n$ as $\displaystyle\sum_{r=1}^{n} u_r$.

So, $\displaystyle\sum_{r=1}^{n} u_r$ reads "the **sum of all numbers** of the form u_r where $r = 1, 2, 3, ...$, up to n".

Example 19

Expand and find the sum of: **a** $\displaystyle\sum_{r=1}^{7}(r+1)$ **b** $\displaystyle\sum_{r=1}^{5}\frac{1}{2^r}$

a $\displaystyle\sum_{r=1}^{7}(r+1)$

$= 2 + 3 + 4 + 5 + 6 + 7 + 8$

which has a sum of 35

b $\displaystyle\sum_{r=1}^{5}\frac{1}{2^r}$

$= \frac{1}{2} + \frac{1}{4} + \frac{1}{8} + \frac{1}{16} + \frac{1}{32}$

which has a sum of $\frac{31}{32}$

EXERCISE 2F

1 Expand and find the sum of:

    a $\displaystyle\sum_{r=1}^{4}(3r-5)$ **b** $\displaystyle\sum_{r=1}^{5}(11-2r)$ **c** $\displaystyle\sum_{r=1}^{7}r(r+1)$ **d** $\displaystyle\sum_{i=1}^{5}10 \times 2^{i-1}$

2 For $u_n = 3n - 1$, list $u_1 + u_2 + u_3 + ... + u_{20}$ and find its sum.

3 Find the sum of these arithmetic series:

a $\displaystyle\sum_{r=1}^{10}(2r+5)$ **b** $\displaystyle\sum_{r=1}^{15}(r-50)$ **c** $\displaystyle\sum_{r=1}^{20}\left(\frac{r+3}{2}\right)$

Hint: List the first 3 terms and the last term.

4 Find the sum of these geometric series:

a $\displaystyle\sum_{r=1}^{10}3\times 2^{r-1}$ **b** $\displaystyle\sum_{r=1}^{12}(\tfrac{1}{2})^{r-2}$ **c** $\displaystyle\sum_{r=1}^{25}6\times(-2)^r$

Hint: List the first 3 terms and the last term.

5 Find the sum of: **a** $\displaystyle\sum_{k=1}^{5}k(k+1)(k+2)$ **b** $\displaystyle\sum_{k=6}^{12}100\times(1.2)^{k-3}$

6 Find n given that: **a** $\displaystyle\sum_{r=1}^{n}(2r+3)=1517$ **b** $\displaystyle\sum_{r=1}^{n}2\times 3^{r-1}=177\,146$

G   MISCELLANEOUS PROBLEMS

EXERCISE 2G

1 Henk starts a new job selling TV sets. He hopes to sell 11 sets in the first week, 14 in the next, 17 in the next, etc., in arithmetic sequence. In what week will Henk hope to sell his 2000th TV set?

2 A computer is bought for \$2795 and depreciates at a rate of 2% per month. After how many months will its value reduce to \$500?

3 A geometric series has a second term of 6 and the sum of its first three terms is -14. Find its fourth term.

4 When a ball falls vertically off a table it rebounds 75% of its height after each bounce. If it travels a total distance of 490 cm, how high was the table top above the floor?

5 An arithmetic and a geometric sequence both have a first term of 1 and their second terms are equal. The 14th term of the arithmetic sequence is three times the third term of the geometric sequence. Find the twentieth term of each sequence.

6 Find x if $\displaystyle\sum_{r=1}^{\infty}\left(\frac{3x}{2}\right)^{r-1}=4$.

7 The sum of the first n terms of an arithmetic sequence is $\dfrac{n(3n+11)}{2}$.

 a Find its first two terms. **b** Find the twentieth term of the sequence.

8 **Mortgage repayments:**

 \$8000 is borrowed over a 2-year period at a rate of 12% p.a. Quarterly repayments are made and the interest is adjusted each quarter, which means that the amount repaid in the period is deducted and the interest is charged on the new amount owed.

 There are $2\times 4=8$ repayments and the interest per quarter is $\frac{12\%}{4}=3\%$.

 At the end of the first quarter the amount owed, A_1, is given by   \$8000 $\times 1.03 - R$, where R is the amount of each repayment.

At the end of the second quarter the amount owed, A_2, is given by

$$A_2 = A_1 \times 1.03 - R$$
$$= (\$8000 \times 1.03 - R) \times 1.03 - R$$
$$= \$8000 \times (1.03)^2 - 1.03R - R$$

a Find a similar expression for the amount owed at the end of the third quarter, A_3.

b Write down an expression for the amount owed at the end of the 8th quarter, A_8, and hence deduce the value of R.   [**Hint:** What value do we want A_8 to have?]

c If the amount borrowed is $\$P$ at adjusted interest conditions, the interest rate is $r\%$ per repayment interval and there are m repayments, show that the amount of each repayment is

$$R = \frac{P(1 + \frac{r}{100})^m \times \frac{r}{100}}{(1 + \frac{r}{100})^m - 1}.$$

INVESTIGATION   VON KOCH'S SNOWFLAKE CURVE

  , ,  , 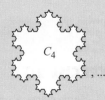 , ...

To draw **Von Koch's Snowflake curve** we

- start with an equilateral triangle, C_1
- then divide each side into 3 equal parts _____
- then on each middle part draw an equilateral triangle _____
- then delete the side of the smaller triangle which lies on C_1. _____

The resulting curve is C_2, and C_3, C_4, C_5, ... are found by 'pushing out' equilateral triangles on each edge of the previous curve as we did with C_1 to get C_2.

We get a sequence of special curves C_1, C_2, C_3, C_4, ... and Von Koch's curve is the limiting case, i.e., when n is infinitely large for this sequence.

Your task is to investigate the perimeter and area of Von Koch's curve.

What to do:

1 Suppose C_1 has a perimeter of 3 units. Find the perimeter of C_2, C_3, C_4 and C_5.

(**Hint:** _____ becomes _____ i.e.,   3 parts become 4 parts.)

Remembering that Von Koch's curve is C_n, where n is infinitely large, find the perimeter of Von Koch's curve.

2 Suppose the area of C_1 is 1 unit^2. Explain why the areas of C_2, C_3, C_4 and C_5 are

$$A_2 = 1 + \tfrac{1}{3} \text{ units}^2 \qquad\qquad A_3 = 1 + \tfrac{1}{3}[1 + \tfrac{4}{9}] \text{ units}^2$$

$$A_4 = 1 + \tfrac{1}{3}[1 + \tfrac{4}{9} + (\tfrac{4}{9})^2] \text{ units}^2 \qquad A_5 = 1 + \tfrac{1}{3}[1 + \tfrac{4}{9} + (\tfrac{4}{9})^2 + (\tfrac{4}{9})^3] \text{ units}^2.$$

Use your calculator to find A_n where $n = 1, 2, 3, 4, 5, 6, 7$, etc., giving answers which are as accurate as your calculator permits.

What do you think will be the area within Von Koch's snowflake curve?

3 Similarly, investigate the sequence of curves obtained by *pushing out* squares on successive curves from the middle third of each side,

i.e., the curves C_1, C_2, C_3, C_4, etc.

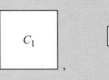 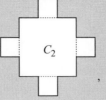 

Region contains 8 holes.

REVIEW SET 2A

1 List the first four members of the following sequences defined by:

   a $u_n = 3^{n-2}$ **b** $u_n = \dfrac{3n+2}{n+3}$ **c** $u_n = 2^n - (-3)^n$

2 A sequence is defined by $u_n = 68 - 5n$.

   a Prove that the sequence is arithmetic.   **b** Find u_1 and d.   **c** Find the 37th term.

   d What is the first term of the sequence less than -200?

3   **a** Show that the sequence 3, 12, 48, 192, ... is geometric.

   b Find u_n and hence find u_9.

4 Find k if $3k$, $k-2$ and $k+7$ are consecutive terms of an arithmetic sequence.

5 Find the general term of an arithmetic sequence given that $u_7 = 31$ and $u_{15} = -17$. Hence, find the value of u_{34}.

6 A sequence is defined by $u_n = 6(\frac{1}{2})^{n-1}$.

   a Prove that the sequence is geometric.   **b** Find u_1 and r.

   c Find the 16th term to 3 significant figures.

7 Show that 28, 23, 18, 13, ... is arithmetic and hence find u_n and the sum S_n of the first n terms in simplest form.

8 Find k given that 4, k and $k^2 - 1$ are consecutive geometric terms.

9 Determine the general term of a geometric sequence given that its sixth term is $\frac{16}{3}$ and its tenth term is $\frac{256}{3}$.

REVIEW SET 2B

1   **a** Determine the number of terms in the sequence 24, $23\frac{1}{4}$, $22\frac{1}{2}$, ..., -36.

   b Find the value of u_{35} for the sequence in **a**.

   c Find the sum of the terms of the sequence in **a**.

2 Insert six numbers between 23 and 9 so that all eight numbers are in arithmetic sequence.

3 Find the formula for u_n, the general term of:

   a 86, 83, 80, 77, ...   **b** $\frac{3}{4}$, 1, $\frac{7}{6}$, $\frac{9}{7}$, ...   **c** 100, 90, 81, 72.9, ...

[**Note:** One of these sequences is neither arithmetic nor geometric.]

4 Write down the expansion of: **a** $\sum\limits_{r=1}^{7} r^2$ **b** $\sum\limits_{r=1}^{8} \dfrac{r+3}{r+2}$

5 Write in the form $\sum\limits_{r=1}^{n} (.....)$:

    a $4 + 11 + 18 + 25 + ...$ for n terms   **b** $\frac{1}{4} + \frac{1}{8} + \frac{1}{16} + \frac{1}{32} + ...$ for n terms.

6 Find the sum of:

    a $3 + 9 + 15 + 21 + ...$ to 23 terms   **b** $24 + 12 + 6 + 3 + ...$ to 12 terms.

7 Find the sum of   **a** $\sum\limits_{r=1}^{8} \left(\dfrac{31 - 3r}{2} \right)$ **b** $\sum\limits_{r=1}^{15} 50(0.8)^{r-1}$

8 Find the first term of the sequence 5, 10, 20, 40, ... which exceeds 10 000.

9 What will an investment of 6000 Euro at 7% p.a. compound interest amount to after 5 years if the interest is compounded:

    a annually   **b** quarterly   **c** monthly?

REVIEW SET 2C

1 A geometric sequence has $u_6 = 24$ and $u_{11} = 768$.   Determine the general term of the sequence and hence find:

    a u_{17} **b** the sum of the first 15 terms.

2 How many terms of the series $11 + 16 + 21 + 26 + ...$ are needed to exceed a sum of 450?

3 Find the first term of the sequence 24, 8, $\frac{8}{3}$, $\frac{8}{9}$, ... which is less than 0.001 .

4 **a** Determine the number of terms in the sequence 128, 64, 32, 16, ..., $\frac{1}{512}$.
    b Find the sum of these terms.

5 \$12 500 is invested in an account which pays 8.25% p.a. compounded. Find the value of the investment after 5 years if the interest is compounded:

    a half-yearly   **b** monthly.

6 How much should be invested at a fixed rate of 9% p.a. compounded interest if you wish it to amount to \$20 000 after 4 years with interest paid monthly?

7 In 1998 there were 3000 koalas on Koala Island. Since then, the population of koalas on the island has increased by 5% each year.

    a How many koalas were on the island in 2001?
    b In what year will the population first exceed 5000?

8 A ball bounces from a height of 2 metres and returns to 80% of its previous height on each bounce. Find the total distance travelled by the ball until it stops bouncing.

9 **a** Under what conditions will the series $\sum\limits_{r=1}^{\infty} 50(2x - 1)^{r-1}$ converge?   Explain!

    b Find $\sum\limits_{r=1}^{\infty} 50(2x - 1)^{r-1}$ if $x = 0.3$.

Chapter 3

Exponents

Contents:

We often deal with numbers that are repeatedly multiplied together. Mathematicians use **indices** or **exponents** to easily represent such expressions. For example, $5 \times 5 \times 5 = 5^3$.

Indices have many applications in areas such as finance, engineering, physics, biology, electronics and computer science.

Problems encountered in these areas may involve situations where quantities increase or decrease over time. Such problems are often examples of **exponential growth** or **decay**.

OPENING PROBLEM

In 1995, a research establishment started testing the rabbit calicivirus on an island in an attempt to eradicate rabbits. The island was relatively isolated and overrun by rabbits and it thus provided an excellent test site.

The disease was found to be highly contagious and the introduction of the virus had a dramatic impact on the island's rabbit population.

Scientists monitored rabbit numbers over a series of weeks and found that the number of rabbits R, could be predicted by the formula

$R = 8000 \times (0.837)^t$ where t is the number of weeks after the calicivirus was released.

Consider the following questions:

1 If we let $t = 0$ weeks, how many rabbits were on the island?

2 If we let $t = 3\frac{1}{2}$ weeks, we get $R = 8000 \times (0.837)^{3.5}$.
    Discuss 'to the power of 3.5'.

3 How long would it take to reduce the rabbit numbers to 80?

4 Will all rabbits ever be eradicated?

5 What would the graph of rabbit numbers plotted against the time after the release of the virus look like?

After studying the concepts of this chapter, you should be able to investigate the questions above.

A   INDEX NOTATION

Rather than write $2 \times 2 \times 2 \times 2 \times 2$, we write such a product as 2^5.

2^5 reads "two to the power of five" or "two with index five".

Thus $5^3 = 5 \times 5 \times 5$ and $3^6 = 3 \times 3 \times 3 \times 3 \times 3 \times 3$.

2^5 power, index or exponent   base

If n is a positive integer, then a^n is the product of n factors of a

i.e., $a^n = \underbrace{a \times a \times a \times a \times .... \times a}_{n \text{ factors}}$

EXERCISE 3A

1 Copy and complete the values of these common powers.

    a $2^1 = ...,$ $2^2 = ...,$ $2^3 = ...,$ $2^4 = ...,$ $2^5 = ...,$ $2^6 = ...$

    b $3^1 = ...,$ $3^2 = ...,$ $3^3 = ...,$ $3^4 = ...$

    c $5^1 = ...,$ $5^2 = ...,$ $5^3 = ...,$ $5^4 = ...$

    d $7^1 = ...,$ $7^2 = ...,$ $7^3 = ...$

HISTORICAL NOTE

Nicomachus discovered an interesting number pattern involving cubes and sums of odd numbers.

$$1 = 1^3$$
$$3 + 5 = 8 = 2^3$$
$$7 + 9 + 11 = 27 = 3^3 \quad \text{etc.}$$

Nicomachus was born in Roman Syria (now Jerash, Jordan), around 100 AD. He wrote in Greek and was a Pythagorean.

B   NEGATIVE BASES

So far we have only considered **positive** bases raised to a power.

We will now briefly look at **negative** bases. Consider the statements below:

$$(-1)^1 = -1 \qquad\qquad (-2)^1 = -2$$
$$(-1)^2 = -1 \times -1 = 1 \qquad\qquad (-2)^2 = -2 \times -2 = 4$$
$$(-1)^3 = -1 \times -1 \times -1 = -1 \qquad\qquad (-2)^3 = -2 \times -2 \times -2 = -8$$
$$(-1)^4 = -1 \times -1 \times -1 \times -1 = 1 \qquad\qquad (-2)^4 = -2 \times -2 \times -2 \times -2 = 16$$

In the pattern above it can be seen that:

> A **negative** base raised to an **odd** power is **negative**; whereas a **negative** base raised to an **even** power is **positive**.

Example 1

Evaluate:

  a $(-2)^4$ **b** -2^4 **c** $(-2)^5$ **d** $-(-2)^5$

Notice the effect of the brackets in these examples.

a $(-2)^4$	**b** -2^4	**c** $(-2)^5$	**d** $-(-2)^5$
$= 16$	$= -1 \times 2^4$	$= -32$	$= -1 \times (-2)^5$
	$= -16$		$= -1 \times -32$
			$= 32$

EXERCISE 3B

1 Simplify: (check on a calculator)

    a $(-1)^3$ **b** $(-1)^4$ **c** $(-1)^{12}$ **d** $(-1)^{17}$

    e $(-1)^6$ **f** -1^6 **g** $-(-1)^6$ **h** $(-2)^3$

    i -2^3 **j** $-(-2)^3$ **k** $-(-5)^2$ **l** $-(-5)^3$

CALCULATOR USE

Although different calculators vary in the appearance of keys, they all perform operations of raising to powers in a similar manner.

Power keys $\boxed{x^2}$ squares the number in the display.

$\boxed{\wedge}$ 3   raises the number in the display to the power 3.

$\boxed{\wedge}$ 5   raises the number in the display to the power 5.

$\boxed{\wedge}$ $\boxed{(-)}$ 4   raises the number in the display to the power -4.

Example 2	
Find, using your calculator: **a** 6^5 **b** $(-5)^4$ **c** -7^4	
	Answer
a Press: 6 $\boxed{\wedge}$ 5 $\boxed{\textbf{ENTER}}$	7776
b Press: $\boxed{(}$ $\boxed{(-)}$ 5 $\boxed{)}$ $\boxed{\wedge}$ 4 $\boxed{\textbf{ENTER}}$	625
c Press: $\boxed{(-)}$ 7 $\boxed{\wedge}$ 4 $\boxed{\textbf{ENTER}}$	-2401

Note: You will need to check if your calculator uses the same key sequence as in the examples. If not, work out the sequence which gives you the correct answers.

2 Use your calculator to find the value of the following, recording the entire display:

a 2^9 **b** $(-5)^5$ **c** -3^5 **d** 7^5 **e** 8^3

f $(-9)^4$ **g** -9^4 **h** 1.16^{11} **i** -0.981^{14} **j** $(-1.14)^{23}$

Example 3	
Find using your calculator, and comment on: **a** 5^{-2} **b** $\dfrac{1}{5^2}$	
	Answer
a Press: 5 $\boxed{\wedge}$ $\boxed{(-)}$ 2 $\boxed{\textbf{ENTER}}$	0.04
b Press: 1 $\boxed{\div}$ 5 $\boxed{\wedge}$ 2 $\boxed{\textbf{ENTER}}$	0.04
The answers indicate that $5^{-2} = \dfrac{1}{5^2}$.	

3 Use your calculator to find the values of the following:

a 7^{-1} **b** $\dfrac{1}{7^1}$ **c** 3^{-2} **d** $\dfrac{1}{3^2}$

e 4^{-3} **f** $\dfrac{1}{4^3}$ **g** 13^0 **h** 172^0

What do you notice?

4 By considering 3^1, 3^2, 3^3, 3^4, 3^5 .... and looking for a pattern, find the last digit of 3^{33}.

5 What is the last digit of 7^{77}?

C   INDEX LAWS

Recall the following **index laws** where the bases a and b are both positive and the indices m and n are integers.

$a^m \times a^n = a^{m+n}$	To **multiply** numbers with the **same base**, keep the base and **add** the indices.
$\dfrac{a^m}{a^n} = a^{m-n}$	To **divide** numbers with the **same base**, keep the base and **subtract** the indices.
$(a^m)^n = a^{m \times n}$	When **raising** a **power** to a **power**, keep the base and **multiply** the indices.
$(ab)^n = a^n b^n$	The power of a product is the product of the powers.
$\left(\dfrac{a}{b}\right)^n = \dfrac{a^n}{b^n}$	The power of a quotient is the quotient of the powers.
$a^o = 1, \quad a \neq 0$	Any non-zero number raised to the power of zero is **1**.

$$a^{-n} = \frac{1}{a^n}, \quad a \neq 0 \quad \text{and} \quad \frac{1}{a^{-n}} = a^n, \quad a \neq 0 \quad \text{and in particular} \quad a^{-1} = \frac{1}{a}.$$

Example 4

Simplify using $a^m \times a^n = a^{m+n}$:

  a $11^5 \times 11^3$ **b** $a^4 \times a^5$ **c** $x^4 \times x^a$

a $11^5 \times 11^3$	**b** $a^4 \times a^5$	**c** $x^4 \times x^a$
$= 11^{5+3}$	$= a^{4+5}$	$= x^{4+a}$
$= 11^8$	$= a^9$	$(= x^{a+4})$

EXERCISE 3C

1 Simplify using $a^m \times a^n = a^{m+n}$:

  a $7^3 \times 7^2$ **b** $5^4 \times 5^3$ **c** $a^7 \times a^2$ **d** $a^4 \times a$

  e $b^8 \times b^5$ **f** $a^3 \times a^n$ **g** $b^7 \times b^m$ **h** $m^4 \times m^2 \times m^3$

Example 5

Simplify using $\dfrac{a^m}{a^n} = a^{m-n}$:

  a $\dfrac{7^8}{7^5}$ **b** $\dfrac{b^6}{b^m}$

a $\dfrac{7^8}{7^5}$	**b** $\dfrac{b^6}{b^m}$
$= 7^{8-5}$	$= b^{6-m}$
$= 7^3$	

2 Simplify using $\dfrac{a^m}{a^n} = a^{m-n}$:

a $\dfrac{5^9}{5^2}$

b $\dfrac{11^{13}}{11^9}$

c $7^7 \div 7^4$

d $\dfrac{a^6}{a^2}$

e $\dfrac{b^{10}}{b^7}$

f $\dfrac{p^5}{p^m}$

g $\dfrac{y^a}{y^5}$

h $b^{2x} \div b$

Example 6

Simplify using $(a^m)^n = a^{m \times n}$:

a $(2^4)^3$

b $(x^3)^5$

c $(b^7)^m$

a $(2^4)^3$	**b** $(x^3)^5$	**c** $(b^7)^m$
$= 2^{4 \times 3}$	$= x^{3 \times 5}$	$= b^{7 \times m}$
$= 2^{12}$	$= x^{15}$	$= b^{7m}$

---

3 Simplify using $(a^m)^n = a^{m \times n}$:

a $(3^2)^4$

b $(5^3)^5$

c $(2^4)^7$

d $(a^5)^2$

e $(p^4)^5$

f $(b^5)^n$

g $(x^y)^3$

h $(a^{2x})^5$

Example 7

Express in simplest form with a prime number base:

a 9^4

b 4×2^p

c $\dfrac{3^x}{9^y}$

d 25^{x-1}

a 9^4
$= (3^2)^4$
$= 3^{2 \times 4}$
$= 3^8$

b 4×2^p
$= 2^2 \times 2^p$
$= 2^{2+p}$

c $\dfrac{3^x}{9^y}$
$= \dfrac{3^x}{(3^2)^y}$
$= \dfrac{3^x}{3^{2y}}$
$= 3^{x-2y}$

d 25^{x-1}
$= (5^2)^{x-1}$
$= 5^{2(x-1)}$
$= 5^{2x-2}$

---

4 Express in simplest form with a prime number base:

a 8

b 25

c 27

d 4^3

e 9^2

f $3^a \times 9$

g $5^t \div 5$

h $3^n \times 9^n$

i $\dfrac{16}{2^x}$

j $\dfrac{3^{x+1}}{3^{x-1}}$

k $(5^4)^{x-1}$

l $2^x \times 2^{2-x}$

m $\dfrac{2^y}{4^x}$

n $\dfrac{4^y}{8^x}$

o $\dfrac{3^{x+1}}{3^{1-x}}$

p $\dfrac{2^t \times 4^t}{8^{t-1}}$

Example 8

Remove the brackets of:

a $(2x)^3$ b $\left(\dfrac{3c}{b}\right)^4$

a $(2x)^3$
$= 2^3 \times x^3$
$= 8x^3$

b $\left(\dfrac{3c}{b}\right)^4$
$= \dfrac{3^4 \times c^4}{b^4}$
$= \dfrac{81c^4}{b^4}$

Remember that each factor within the brackets has to be raised to the power outside them.

5 Remove the brackets of:

a $(ab)^3$ b $(ac)^4$ c $(bc)^5$ d $(abc)^3$

e $(2a)^4$ f $(5b)^2$ g $(3n)^4$ h $(2bc)^3$

i $(4ab)^3$ j $\left(\dfrac{a}{b}\right)^3$ k $\left(\dfrac{m}{n}\right)^4$ l $\left(\dfrac{2c}{d}\right)^5$

6 Express the following in simplest form, without brackets:

a $(2b^4)^3$ b $\left(\dfrac{3}{x^2y}\right)^2$ c $(5a^4b)^2$ d $\left(\dfrac{m^3}{2n^2}\right)^4$

e $\left(\dfrac{3a^3}{b^5}\right)^3$ f $(2m^3n^2)^5$ g $\left(\dfrac{4a^4}{b^2}\right)^2$ h $(5x^2y^3)^3$

i $(-2a)^2$ j $(-6b^2)^2$ k $(-2a)^3$ l $(-3m^2n^2)^3$

m $(-2ab^4)^4$ n $\left(\dfrac{-2a^2}{b^2}\right)^3$ o $\left(\dfrac{-4a^3}{b}\right)^2$ p $\left(\dfrac{-3p^2}{q^3}\right)^2$

Example 9

Simplify using the index laws:

a $3x^2 \times 5x^5$ b $\dfrac{20a^9}{4a^6}$ c $\dfrac{b^3 \times b^7}{(b^2)^4}$

a $\quad 3x^2 \times 5x^5$
$= 3 \times 5 \times x^2 \times x^5$
$= 15 \times x^{2+5}$
$= 15x^7$

b $\quad \dfrac{20a^9}{4a^6}$
$= \dfrac{20}{4} \times a^{9-6}$
$= 5a^3$

c $\quad \dfrac{b^3 \times b^7}{(b^2)^4}$
$= \dfrac{b^{10}}{b^8}$
$= b^{10-8}$
$= b^2$

7 Simplify the following expressions using one or more of the index laws:

a $\dfrac{a^3}{a}$ b $4b^2 \times 2b^3$ c $\dfrac{m^5n^4}{m^2n^3}$

d $\dfrac{14a^7}{2a^2}$ e $\dfrac{12a^2b^3}{3ab}$ f $\dfrac{18m^7a^3}{4m^4a^3}$

g $10hk^3 \times 4h^4$ **h** $\dfrac{m^{11}}{(m^2)^8}$ **i** $\dfrac{p^2 \times p^7}{(p^3)^2}$

Notice that

$$\left(\dfrac{a}{b}\right)^{-2} = \left(\dfrac{b}{a}\right)^{2}$$

Example 10

Simplify, giving answers in simplest rational form:

a 7^0 **b** 3^{-2} **c** $3^0 - 3^{-1}$ **d** $\left(\tfrac{5}{3}\right)^{-2}$

a 7^0	**b** 3^{-2}	**c** $3^0 - 3^{-1}$	**d** $\left(\tfrac{5}{3}\right)^{-2}$
$= 1$	$= \dfrac{1}{3^2}$	$= 1 - \tfrac{1}{3}$	$= \left(\tfrac{3}{5}\right)^{2}$
	$= \tfrac{1}{9}$	$= \tfrac{2}{3}$	$= \tfrac{9}{25}$

8   Simplify, giving answers in simplest rational form:

a 5^0 **b** 3^{-1} **c** 6^{-1} **d** 8^0

e 2^2 **f** 2^{-2} **g** 2^3 **h** 2^{-3}

i 5^2 **j** 5^{-2} **k** 10^2 **l** 10^{-2}

9   Simplify, giving answers in simplest rational form:

a $\left(\tfrac{2}{3}\right)^0$ **b** $\dfrac{4^3}{4^3}$ **c** $3y^0$ **d** $(3y)^0$

e 2×3^0 **f** 6^0 **g** $\dfrac{5^2}{5^4}$ **h** $\dfrac{2^{10}}{2^{15}}$

i $\left(\tfrac{1}{3}\right)^{-1}$ **j** $\left(\tfrac{2}{5}\right)^{-1}$ **k** $\left(\tfrac{4}{3}\right)^{-1}$ **l** $\left(\tfrac{1}{12}\right)^{-1}$

m $\left(\tfrac{2}{3}\right)^{-2}$ **n** $5^0 - 5^{-1}$ **o** $7^{-1} + 7^0$ **p** $2^0 + 2^1 + 2^{-1}$

Example 11

Write the following without brackets or negative indices:

a $(5x)^{-1}$

b $5x^{-1}$

c $(3b^2)^{-2}$

a $(5x)^{-1}$	**b** $5x^{-1}$	**c** $(3b^2)^{-2}$
$= \dfrac{1}{5x}$	$= \dfrac{5}{x}$	$= \dfrac{1}{(3b^2)^2}$
		$= \dfrac{1}{3^2 b^4}$
		$= \dfrac{1}{9b^4}$

In $5x^{-1}$ the index -1 refers to the x only.

10   Write the following without brackets or negative indices:

a $(2a)^{-1}$ **b** $2a^{-1}$ **c** $3b^{-1}$ **d** $(3b)^{-1}$

e $\left(\tfrac{2}{b}\right)^{-2}$ **f** $(2b)^{-2}$ **g** $(3n)^{-2}$ **h** $(3n^{-2})^{-1}$

i ab^{-1} **j** $(ab)^{-1}$ **k** ab^{-2} **l** $(ab)^{-2}$

m $(2ab)^{-1}$ **n** $2(ab)^{-1}$ **o** $2ab^{-1}$ **p** $\dfrac{(ab)^2}{b^{-1}}$

11 Write the following as powers of 2, 3 and/or 5:

a $\dfrac{1}{3}$ **b** $\dfrac{1}{2}$ **c** $\dfrac{1}{5}$ **d** $\dfrac{1}{4}$

e $\dfrac{1}{27}$ **f** $\dfrac{1}{25}$ **g** $\dfrac{1}{8^x}$ **h** $\dfrac{1}{16^y}$

i $\dfrac{1}{81^a}$ **j** $\dfrac{9}{3^4}$ **k** 25×5^{-4} **l** $\dfrac{5^{-1}}{5^2}$

m $2 \div 2^{-3}$ **n** 1 **o** 6^{-3} **p** 4×10^2

12 The water lily *Growerosa Veryfasterosa* doubles its size every day. From the time it was planted until it completely covered the pond took 26 days.

How many days did it take to cover half the pond?

13 Read about Nicomachus' pattern on page **59** and find the sequence of odd numbers for:

a 5^3 **b** 7^3 **c** 12^3

14 Find the smaller of 2^{175} and 5^{75} without a calculator.

D   RATIONAL INDICES

Since $a^{\frac{1}{2}} \times a^{\frac{1}{2}} = a^{\frac{1}{2}+\frac{1}{2}} = a^1 = a,$ {for index laws to be obeyed}

and $\sqrt{a} \times \sqrt{a} = a$ also, then

$$a^{\frac{1}{2}} = \sqrt{a} \qquad \text{\{by direct comparison\}}$$

Likewise $a^{\frac{1}{3}} \times a^{\frac{1}{3}} \times a^{\frac{1}{3}} = a^1 = a,$

compared with $\sqrt[3]{a} \times \sqrt[3]{a} \times \sqrt[3]{a} = a$

suggests $a^{\frac{1}{3}} = \sqrt[3]{a}$

Thus in general, $a^{\frac{1}{n}} = \sqrt[n]{a}$ { $\sqrt[n]{a}$ reads "the nth root of a"}

Notice also that $a^{\frac{2}{3}} \times a^{\frac{2}{3}} \times a^{\frac{2}{3}} = a^2$

i.e., $\left(a^{\frac{2}{3}}\right)^3 = a^2$ {if $(a^m)^n = a^{mn}$ is to be used}

$\therefore \quad a^{\frac{2}{3}} = \sqrt[3]{a^2}.$

In general, $a^{\frac{m}{n}} = \sqrt[n]{a^m}$ or $\left(\sqrt[n]{a}\right)^m$

Example 12

Write as a single power of 2:
 	
a $\sqrt[3]{2}$ b $\dfrac{1}{\sqrt{2}}$
 	
c $\sqrt[5]{4}$
	a $\quad \sqrt[3]{2}$ b $\quad \dfrac{1}{\sqrt{2}}$ c $\quad \sqrt[5]{4}$
	 $= 2^{\frac{1}{3}}$ $= \dfrac{1}{2^{\frac{1}{2}}}$ $= (2^2)^{\frac{1}{5}}$
	             $= 2^{-\frac{1}{2}}$ $= 2^{2 \times \frac{1}{5}}$
	                      $= 2^{\frac{2}{5}}$

EXERCISE 3D

1 Write as a single power of 2:

   a $\sqrt[5]{2}$ **b** $\dfrac{1}{\sqrt[5]{2}}$ **c** $2\sqrt{2}$ **d** $4\sqrt{2}$ **e** $\dfrac{1}{\sqrt[3]{2}}$

   f $2 \times \sqrt[3]{2}$ **g** $\dfrac{4}{\sqrt{2}}$ **h** $(\sqrt{2})^3$ **i** $\dfrac{1}{\sqrt[3]{16}}$ **j** $\dfrac{1}{\sqrt{8}}$

2 Write as a single power of 3:

   a $\sqrt[3]{3}$ **b** $\dfrac{1}{\sqrt[3]{3}}$ **c** $\sqrt[4]{3}$ **d** $3\sqrt{3}$ **e** $\dfrac{1}{9\sqrt{3}}$

3 Write the following in the form a^x where a is a prime number and x is rational:

   a $\sqrt[3]{7}$ **b** $\sqrt[4]{27}$ **c** $\sqrt[5]{16}$ **d** $\sqrt[3]{32}$ **e** $\sqrt[7]{49}$

   f $\dfrac{1}{\sqrt[3]{7}}$ **g** $\dfrac{1}{\sqrt[4]{27}}$ **h** $\dfrac{1}{\sqrt[5]{16}}$ **i** $\dfrac{1}{\sqrt[3]{32}}$ **j** $\dfrac{1}{\sqrt[7]{49}}$

Example 13

Use your calculator to evaluate to 3 decimal places   **a** $2^{\frac{7}{5}}$ **b** $9^{-\frac{3}{4}}$

a $\quad 2^{\frac{7}{5}} \doteqdot 2.639$ 2 $\boxed{\wedge}$ $\boxed{(}$ 7 $\boxed{\div}$ 5 $\boxed{)}$ $\boxed{\textbf{ENTER}}$

b $\quad 9^{-\frac{3}{4}} \doteqdot 0.192$ 9 $\boxed{\wedge}$ $\boxed{(}$ $\boxed{(-)}$ 3 $\boxed{\div}$ 4 $\boxed{)}$ $\boxed{\textbf{ENTER}}$

4 Use your calculator to evaluate to 3 decimal places:

   a $3^{\frac{3}{4}}$ **b** $2^{\frac{7}{8}}$ **c** $2^{-\frac{1}{3}}$ **d** $4^{-\frac{3}{5}}$

Example 14

Use your calculator to evaluate to 3 decimal places: **a** $\sqrt[5]{4}$ **b** $\dfrac{1}{\sqrt[6]{11}}$

a $\quad \sqrt[5]{4} = 4^{\frac{1}{5}} \doteqdot 1.320$ 4 $\boxed{\wedge}$ $\boxed{(}$ 1 $\boxed{\div}$ 5 $\boxed{)}$ $\boxed{\textbf{ENTER}}$

b $\quad \dfrac{1}{\sqrt[6]{11}} = 11^{-\frac{1}{6}} \doteqdot 0.671$ 11 $\boxed{\wedge}$ $\boxed{(}$ $\boxed{(-)}$ 1 $\boxed{\div}$ 6 $\boxed{)}$ $\boxed{\textbf{ENTER}}$

5 Use your calculator to find to 3 decimal places:

a $\sqrt{9}$ b $\sqrt[4]{8}$ c $\sqrt[5]{27}$ d $\dfrac{1}{\sqrt[3]{7}}$

Example 15

Without using a calculator, write in simplest rational form: a $8^{\frac{4}{3}}$ b $27^{-\frac{2}{3}}$	a $8^{\frac{4}{3}}$ $= (2^3)^{\frac{4}{3}}$ $= 2^{3 \times \frac{4}{3}}$ $= 2^4$ $= 16$	b $27^{-\frac{2}{3}}$ $= (3^3)^{-\frac{2}{3}}$ $= 3^{3 \times -\frac{2}{3}}$ $= 3^{-2}$ $= \frac{1}{9}$

---

6 Without using a calculator, write in simplest rational form:

a $4^{\frac{3}{2}}$ b $8^{\frac{5}{3}}$ c $16^{\frac{3}{4}}$ d $25^{\frac{3}{2}}$ e $32^{\frac{2}{5}}$

f $4^{-\frac{1}{2}}$ g $9^{-\frac{3}{2}}$ h $8^{-\frac{4}{3}}$ i $27^{-\frac{4}{3}}$ j $125^{-\frac{2}{3}}$

E ALGEBRAIC EXPANSION

Recall the expansion laws:

$$(a+b)(c+d) = ac+ad+bc+bd \qquad \text{\{sometimes called 'FOIL'\}}$$
$$(a+b)(a-b) = a^2 - b^2 \qquad \text{\{difference of squares\}}$$
$$(a+b)^2 = a^2 + 2ab + b^2 \qquad \text{\{perfect squares\}}$$
$$(a-b)^2 = a^2 - 2ab + b^2$$

Example 16

Expand and simplify: $x^{-\frac{1}{2}}(x^{\frac{3}{2}} + 2x^{\frac{1}{2}} - 3x^{-\frac{1}{2}})$

$x^{-\frac{1}{2}}(x^{\frac{3}{2}} + 2x^{\frac{1}{2}} - 3x^{-\frac{1}{2}})$

$= x^{-\frac{1}{2}} \times x^{\frac{3}{2}} + x^{-\frac{1}{2}} \times 2x^{\frac{1}{2}} - x^{-\frac{1}{2}} \times 3x^{-\frac{1}{2}}$ {each term is $\times$ by $x^{-\frac{1}{2}}$}

$= x^1 + 2x^0 - 3x^{-1}$ {adding indices}

$= x + 2 - \dfrac{3}{x}$

EXERCISE 3E

1 Expand and simplify:

a $x^2(x^3 + 2x^2 + 1)$ b $2^x(2^x + 1)$ c $x^{\frac{1}{2}}(x^{\frac{1}{2}} + x^{-\frac{1}{2}})$

d $e^x(e^x + 2)$ e $3^x(2 - 3^{-x})$ f $x^{\frac{1}{2}}(x^{\frac{3}{2}} + 2x^{\frac{1}{2}} + 3x^{-\frac{1}{2}})$

g $2^{-x}(2^x + 5)$ h $5^{-x}(5^{2x} + 5^x)$ i $x^{-\frac{1}{2}}(x^2 + x + x^{\frac{1}{2}})$

Example 17

Expand and simplify: **a** $(2^x + 3)(2^x + 1)$ **b** $(e^x + e^{-x})^2$

a $(2^x + 3)(2^x + 1)$
$= 2^x \times 2^x + 2^x + 3 \times 2^x + 3$
$= 2^{2x} + 4 \times 2^x + 3$
$= 4^x + 2^{2+x} + 3$

b $(e^x + e^{-x})^2$
$= (e^x)^2 + 2e^x \times e^{-x} + (e^{-x})^2$
$= e^{2x} + 2e^0 + e^{-2x}$
$= e^{2x} + 2 + e^{-2x}$

2 Expand and simplify:

a $(2^x + 1)(2^x + 3)$ **b** $(3^x + 2)(3^x + 5)$ **c** $(5^x - 2)(5^x - 4)$

d $(2^x + 3)^2$ **e** $(3^x - 1)^2$ **f** $(4^x + 7)^2$

g $(x^{\frac{1}{2}} + 2)(x^{\frac{1}{2}} - 2)$ **h** $(2^x + 3)(2^x - 3)$ **i** $(x^{\frac{1}{2}} + x^{-\frac{1}{2}})(x^{\frac{1}{2}} - x^{-\frac{1}{2}})$

j $(x + \dfrac{2}{x})^2$ **k** $(e^x - e^{-x})^2$ **l** $(5 - 2^{-x})^2$

F   EXPONENTIAL EQUATIONS

An **exponential equation** is an equation in which the unknown occurs as part of the index or exponent. For example: $2^x = 8$ and $30 \times 3^x = 7$ are both exponential equations.

If $2^x = 8$, then $2^x = 2^3$.   Thus $x = 3$, and this is the only solution.

Hence:

> If $a^x = a^k$, then $x = k$,
>
> i.e., if the base numbers are the same, we can **equate indices**.

Example 18

Solve for x: **a** $2^x = 16$ **b** $3^{x+2} = \frac{1}{27}$

> Once we have the same base we then equate the indices.

a $2^x = 16$
$\therefore$ $2^x = 2^4$
$\therefore$ $x = 4$

b $3^{x+2} = \frac{1}{27}$
$\therefore$ $3^{x+2} = 3^{-3}$
$\therefore$ $x + 2 = -3$
$\therefore$ $x = -5$

EXERCISE 3F

1 Solve for x:

a $2^x = 2$ **b** $2^x = 4$ **c** $3^x = 27$ **d** $2^x = 1$

e $2^x = \frac{1}{2}$ **f** $3^x = \frac{1}{3}$ **g** $2^x = \frac{1}{8}$ **h** $2^{x+1} = 8$

i $2^{x-2} = \frac{1}{4}$ **j** $3^{x+1} = \frac{1}{27}$ **k** $2^{x+1} = 64$ **l** $2^{1-2x} = \frac{1}{2}$

Example 19

Solve for x:

a $4^x = 8$

b $9^{x-2} = \frac{1}{3}$

a $4^x = 8$

$\therefore (2^2)^x = 2^3$

$\therefore 2^{2x} = 2^3$

$\therefore 2x = 3$

$\therefore x = \frac{3}{2}$

b $9^{x-2} = \frac{1}{3}$

$\therefore (3^2)^{x-2} = 3^{-1}$

$\therefore 3^{2(x-2)} = 3^{-1}$

$\therefore 2x - 4 = -1$

$\therefore 2x = 3$

$\therefore x = \frac{3}{2}$

Remember to use the index laws correctly!

2   Solve for x:

a $4^x = 32$ b $8^x = \frac{1}{4}$ c $9^x = \frac{1}{3}$ d $49^x = \frac{1}{7}$

e $4^x = \frac{1}{8}$ f $25^x = \frac{1}{5}$ g $8^{x+2} = 32$ h $81^{-x} = \frac{1}{4}$

i $4^{2x-1} = \frac{1}{2}$ j $9^{x-3} = 3$ k $(\frac{1}{2})^{x+1} = 2$ l $(\frac{1}{3})^{x+2} = 9$

m $4^x = 8^{-x}$ n $(\frac{1}{4})^{1-x} = 8$ o $(\frac{1}{7})^x = 49$ p $(\frac{1}{2})^{x+1} = 32$

3   Solve for x:

a $4^{2x+1} = 8^{1-x}$ b $9^{2-x} = (\frac{1}{3})^{2x+1}$ c $2^x \times 8^{1-x} = \frac{1}{4}$

4   Solve for x:

a $3 \times 2^x = 24$ b $7 \times 2^x = 56$ c $3 \times 2^{x+1} = 24$

d $12 \times 3^{-x} = \frac{4}{3}$ e $4 \times (\frac{1}{3})^x = 36$ f $5 \times (\frac{1}{2})^x = 20$

G   GRAPHS OF EXPONENTIAL FUNCTIONS

The general **exponential function** has form $y = a^x$
where $a > 0$, $a \neq 1$.

For example, $y = 2^x$ is an exponential function.

Table of values:

x	-3	-2	-1	0	1	2	3
y	$\frac{1}{8}$	$\frac{1}{4}$	$\frac{1}{2}$	1	2	4	8

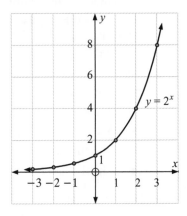

We notice that for $x = -10$,   say, $y = 2^{-10} \doteqdot 0.001$

Also when $x = -50$, $y = 2^{-50} \doteqdot 8.88 \times 10^{-16}$

So, it appears that as x becomes large and negative, the graph of $y = 2^x$ approaches the x-axis from above it.

We say that $y = 2^x$ is '**asymptotic** to the x-axis', or '$y = 0$ is a **horizontal asymptote**'.

INVESTIGATION   EXPONENTIAL GRAPHS

 We will investigate families
of exponential functions.

GRAPHING
PACKAGE

What to do:

1 **a** On the same set of axes, use a **graphing package** or **graphics calculator** to
graph the following functions: $y = 2^x$, $y = 3^x$, $y = 10^x$, $y = (1.3)^x$.

   b The functions in **a** are all members of the family $y = b^x$.
   i   What effect does changing b values have on the shape of the graph?
   ii   What is the y-intercept of each graph?
   iii   What is the horizontal asymptote of each graph?

2 **a** On the same set of axes, use a **graphing package** or **graphics calculator** to
graph the following functions: $y = 2^x$, $y = 2^x + 1$, $y = 2^x - 2$.

   b The functions in **a** are all members of the family $y = 2^x + d$, d is a constant.
   i   What effect does changing d values have on the position of the graph?
   ii   What effect does changing d values have on the shape of the graph?
   iii   What is the horizontal asymptote of each graph?
   iv   What is the horizontal asymptote of $y = 2^x + d$?

   c To graph $y = 2^x + d$ from $y = 2^x$ what transformation is used?

3 **a** On the same set of axes, use a **graphing package** or **graphics calculator** to
graph the following functions: $y = 2^x$, $y = 2^{x-1}$, $y = 2^{x+2}$, $y = 2^{x-3}$

   b The functions in **a** are all members of the family $y = 2^{x-c}$.
   i   What effect does changing c values have on the position of the graph?
   ii   What effect does changing c values have on the shape of the graph?
   iii   What is the horizontal asymptote of each graph?

   c To graph $y = 2^{x-c}$ from $y = 2^x$, what transformation is used?

4 **a** On the same set of axes, use a **graphing package** or **graphics calculator** to
graph the functions $y = 2^x$ and $y = 2^{-x}$.

   b **i**   What is the y-intercept of each graph?
   ii   What is the horizontal asymptote of each graph?
   iii   What transformation moves $y = 2^x$ to $y = 2^{-x}$?

5 **a** On the same set of axes, use a **graphing package** or **graphics calculator** to
graph the following functions:
   i $y = 2^x$, $y = 3 \times 2^x$, $y = \frac{1}{2} \times 2^x$ **ii** $y = -2^x$, $y = -3 \times 2^x$, $y = -\frac{1}{2} \times 2^x$

   b The functions in **a** are all members of the family $y = a \times 2^x$ where a is a
constant. Comment on the effect on the graph when **i** $a > 0$ **ii** $a < 0$.

   c What is the horizontal asymptote of each graph?

From your investigation you should have discovered that:

For the general exponential function $y = a \times b^{x-c} + d$
   ▶ b controls how steeply the graph increases or decreases
   ▶ c controls horizontal translation
   ▶ d controls vertical translation and $y = d$ is the equation of the horizontal asymptote.

- • if $a > 0$, $b > 1$
  i.e., increasing

- • if $a > 0$, $0 < b < 1$
  i.e., decreasing

- • if $a < 0$, $b > 1$
  i.e., decreasing

- • If $a < 0$, $0 < b < 1$
  i.e., increasing

EXERCISE 3G

1 Given the graph of $y = 2^x$ we can find approximate values of 2^x for various x values.

For example:

▶ $2^{1.8} \doteqdot 3.5$ (see point A)

▶ $2^{2.3} \doteqdot 5$ (see point B)

Use the graph to determine approximate

values of:

a $2^{\frac{1}{2}}$ (i.e., $\sqrt{2}$)   **b** $2^{0.8}$

c $2^{1.5}$ **d** $2^{-1.6}$

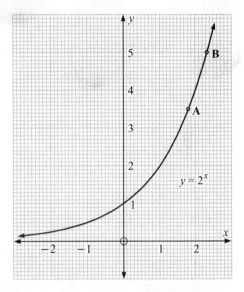

2 Draw freehand sketches of the following pairs of graphs based on your observations from the previous investigation.

a $y = 2^x$ and $y = 2^x - 2$ **b** $y = 2^x$ and $y = 2^{-x}$

c $y = 2^x$ and $y = 2^{x-2}$ **d** $y = 2^x$ and $y = 2 \times 2^x$

3 Check your answers to 2 using technology.

4 Draw freehand sketches of the following pairs of graphs:

a $y = 3^x$ and $y = 3^{-x}$ **b** $y = 3^x$ and $y = 3^x + 1$

c $y = 3^x$ and $y = -3^x$ **d** $y = 3^x$ and $y = 3^{x-1}$

HORIZONTAL ASYMPTOTES

From the previous investigation we noted that for the general exponential function $y = a \times b^{x-c} + d$, $y = d$ is the **horizontal asymptote**.

We can actually obtain reasonably accurate sketch graphs of exponential functions using

- • the horizontal asymptote
- • the y-intercept
- • two other points, say when $x = 2$, $x = -2$

All exponential graphs are similar in shape and have a horizontal asymptote.

Example 20

Sketch the graph of $y = 2^{-x} - 3$.

For $y = 2^{-x} - 3$
the horizontal asymptote is $y = -3$

when $x = 0$, $\begin{aligned} y &= 2^0 - 3 \\ &= 1 - 3 \\ &= -2 \end{aligned}$

$\therefore$ the y-intercept is -2

when $x = 2$, $\begin{aligned} y &= 2^{-2} - 3 \\ &= \frac{1}{4} - 3 \\ &= -2\frac{3}{4} \end{aligned}$

when $x = -2$, $y = 2^2 - 3 = 1$

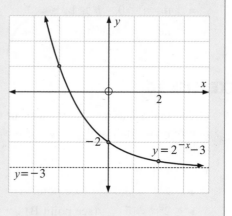

5 Sketch the graphs of:

    a $y = 2^x + 1$ **b** $y = 2 - 2^x$ **c** $y = 2^{-x} + 3$ **d** $y = 3 - 2^{-x}$

H GROWTH

In this exercise we will examine situations where quantities are increasing exponentially (i.e., growth).

Populations of animals, people, bacteria, etc usually grow in an exponential way whereas radioactive substances and items that depreciate usually decay exponentially.

BIOLOGICAL GROWTH

Consider a population of 100 mice which under favourable conditions is increasing by 20% each week. To increase a quantity by 20%, we multiply it by 120% or 1.2.

So, if P_n is the population after n weeks, then

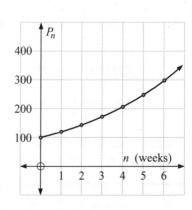

$P_0 = 100$ {the *original* population}
$P_1 = P_0 \times 1.2 = 100 \times 1.2$
$P_2 = P_1 \times 1.2 = 100 \times (1.2)^2$
$P_3 = P_2 \times 1.2 = 100 \times (1.2)^3$, etc

and from this pattern we see that $P_n = 100 \times (1.2)^n$.

Alternatively:

This is an example of a *geometric sequence* and we could have found the rule to generate it. Clearly $r = 1.2$ and so as $P_n = P_0 r^n$, then $P_n = 100 \times (1.2)^n$ for $n = 0, 1, 2, 3, \ldots$

Example 21

An entomologist, monitoring a grasshopper plague, notices that the area affected by the grasshoppers is given by $A_n = 1000 \times 2^{0.2n}$ hectares, where n is the number of weeks after the initial observation.

a Find the original affected area.
b Find the affected area after **i** 5 weeks   **ii** 10 weeks.
c Find the affected area after 12 weeks.
d Draw the graph of A_n against n.

a $A_0 = 1000 \times 2^0$
$\quad\quad = 1000 \times 1$
$\quad\quad = 1000$ $\therefore$ original area was 1000 ha.

b **i** $A_5 = 1000 \times 2^1$ **ii** $A_{10} = 1000 \times 2^2$
$\quad\quad\quad = 2000$ $\quad\quad\quad\quad = 4000$
$\quad$ i.e., area is 2000 ha. $\quad$ i.e., area is 4000 ha.

c $A_{12} = 1000 \times 2^{0.2 \times 12}$

$\quad\quad = 1000 \times 2^{2.4}$ {Press: $1000 \boxed{\times} 2 \boxed{\wedge} 2.4 \boxed{=}$ }

$\quad\quad \doteqdot 5278$

$\quad \therefore$ after 12 weeks, area affected is about 5300 ha.

d

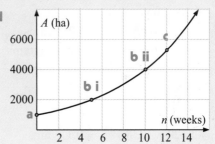

EXERCISE 3H

1 The weight W_t grams, of bacteria in a culture t hours after establishment is given by $W_t = 100 \times 2^{0.1t}$ grams. Find:
   a the initial weight
   b the weight after **i** 4 hours   **ii** 10 hours   **iii** 24 hours.
   c Sketch the graph of W_t against t using only **a** and **b** results.
   d Use technology to graph $Y_1 = 100 \times 2^{0.1X}$ and check your answers to **a**, **b** and **c**.

2 A breeding program to ensure the survival of pygmy possums was established with an initial population of 50 (25 pairs). From a previous program the expected population P_n in n years time is given by $P_n = P_0 \times 2^{0.3n}$.
   a What is the value of P_0?
   b What is the expected population after: **i** 2 years   **ii** 5 years   **iii** 10 years?
   c Sketch the graph of P_n against n using only **a** and **b**.
   d Use technology to graph $Y_1 = 50 \times 2^{0.3X}$ and use it to check your answers in **b**.

3 The speed V_t of a chemical reaction is given by $V_t = V_0 \times 2^{0.05t}$ where t is the temperature in $°C$. Find:

    a the speed at $0°C$ **b** the speed at $20°C$

    c the percentage increase in speed at $20°C$ compared with the speed at $0°C$.

    d Find $\left(\dfrac{V_{50} - V_{20}}{V_{20}} \right) \times 100\%$. What does this calculation represent?

4 A species of bear is introduced to a large island off Alaska where previously there were no bears. 6 pairs of bears were introduced in 1998. It is expected that the population will increase according to $B_t = B_0 \times 2^{0.18t}$ where t is the time since the introduction.

    a Find B_0.   **b** Find the expected bear population in 2018.

    c Find the percentage increase from year 2008 to 2018.

I   DECAY

Now consider a radioactive substance of original weight 20 grams which decays (reduces) by 5% each year. The multiplier is now 95% or 0.95.

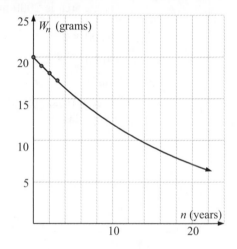

So, if W_n is the weight after n years, then:

$W_0 = 20$ grams
$W_1 = W_0 \times 0.95 = 20 \times 0.95$ grams
$W_2 = W_1 \times 0.95 = 20 \times (0.95)^2$ grams
$W_3 = W_2 \times 0.95 = 20 \times (0.95)^3$ grams
$\vdots$ etc.
$W_{20} = 20 \times (0.95)^{20} \doteqdot 7.2$ grams
$\vdots$
$W_{100} = 20 \times (0.95)^{100} \doteqdot 0.1$ grams

and from this we see that $W_n = 20 \times (0.95)^n$

and so $W_n = W_0 \times (0.95)^n$ if the original weight W_0 is unknown.

Alternatively:

Once again we have an example of a *geometric sequence* with $W_0 = 20$ and $r = 0.95$, and consequently $W_n = 20 \times (0.95)^n$ for $n = 0, 1, 2, 3, ...$

Example 22

When a CD player is switched off, the current dies away according to the formula $I(t) = 24 \times (0.25)^t$ amps, where t is the time in seconds.

    a Find $I(t)$ when $t = 0, 1, 2$ and 3.

    b What current flowed in the CD player at the instant when it was switched off?

    c Plot the graph of $I(t)$ against t $(t \geqslant 0)$ using the information above.

    d Use your graph and/or technology to find how long it takes for the current to reach 4 amps.

a $I(t) = 24 \times (0.25)^t$ amps

$I(0)$	$I(1)$	$I(2)$	$I(3)$
$= 24 \times (0.25)^0$	$= 24 \times (0.25)^1$	$= 24 \times (0.25)^2$	$= 24 \times (0.25)^3$
$= 24$ amps	$= 6$ amps	$= 1.5$ amps	$= 0.375$ amps

b   When $t = 0$, $I(0) = 24$ $\therefore$ 24 amps of current flowed.

c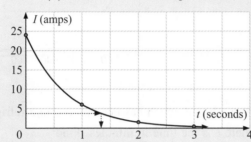

d   From the graph above, the approximate time to reach 4 amps is 1.3 seconds.
(This solution can be refined by trial and   *or*
error.)
By finding the **point of intersection** of
$Y_1 = 24 \times (0.25)^\wedge X$ and $Y_2 = 4$
on a graphics calculator.
The solution is $\doteqdot 1.29$ seconds.

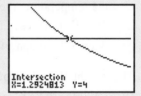

EXERCISE 31

1   The weight of a radioactive substance t years after being set aside is given by
$W(t) = 250 \times (0.998)^t$ grams.
    a   How much radioactive substance was put aside?
    b   Determine the weight of the substance after:
        i   400 years   ii   800 years   iii   1200 years.
    c   Sketch the graph of W against t for $t \geqslant 0$, using the above information.
    d   Use your graph or **graphics calculator** to find how long it takes for the substance
to decay to 125 grams.

2   Revisit the **Opening Problem** on page **58** and answer the questions posed.

Example 23

The weight of radioactive material remaining after t years is given by
$W_t = 11.7 \times 2^{-0.0067t}$ grams.
    a   Find the original weight.
    b   Find the weight after i   10 years ii   100 years iii   1000 years.
    c   Graph W_t against t using **a** and **b** only.

$W_t = 11.7 \times 2^{-0.0067t}$
a   When $t = 0$, $W_0 = 11.7 \times 2^0 = 11.7$ grams

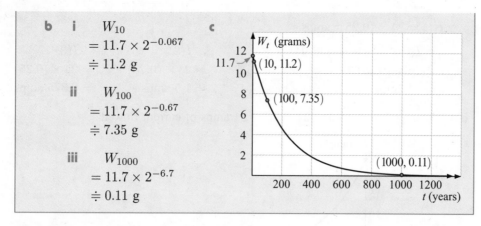

b i W_{10}
$= 11.7 \times 2^{-0.067}$
$\doteqdot 11.2$ g

ii W_{100}
$= 11.7 \times 2^{-0.67}$
$\doteqdot 7.35$ g

iii W_{1000}
$= 11.7 \times 2^{-6.7}$
$\doteqdot 0.11$ g

3 The temperature $T_t(^oC)$ of a liquid which has been placed in a refrigerator is given by $T_t = 100 \times 2^{-0.02t}$ where t is the time in minutes. Find:
  a the initial temperature
  b the temperature after:
    i 15 minutes   **ii** 20 minutes   **iii** 78 minutes.
  c Sketch the graph of T_t against t using **a** and **b** only.

4 The weight W_t grams of radioactive substance remaining after t years is given by $W_t = 1000 \times 2^{-0.03t}$ grams. Find:
  a the initial weight
  b the weight after:
    i 10 years   **ii** 100 years   **iii** 1000 years.
  c Graph W_t against t using **a** and **b** only.

Example 24

The weight of radioactive material remaining after t years is given by $W_t = W_0 \times 2^{-0.001t}$ grams.
a Find the original weight.
b Find the percentage remaining after 200 years.

a When $t = 0$, $W_0 = W_0 \times 2^0 = W_0$
$\therefore$ W_0 is the original weight.

b When $t = 200$, $W_{200} = W_0 \times 2^{-0.001 \times 200}$
$= W_0 \times 2^{-0.2}$
$\doteqdot W_0 \times 0.8706$
$\doteqdot 87.06\%$ of W_0 $\therefore$ 87.1% remains.

---

5 The weight W_t of radioactive uranium remaining after t years is given by the formula $W_t = W_0 \times 2^{-0.0002t}$ grams, $t \geqslant 0$. Find:
  a the original weight   **b** the percentage weight loss after 1000 years.

6 The current I_t amps, flowing in a transistor radio, t seconds after it is switched off is given by $I_t = I_0 \times 2^{-0.02t}$ amps. Find:

    a the initial current   **b** the current after 1 second

    c the percentage change in current after 1 second

    d I_{50} and I_{100} and hence sketch the graph of I_t against t.

REVIEW SET 3A

1 Simplify: **a** $-(-1)^{10}$ **b** $-(-3)^3$ **c** $3^0 - 3^{-1}$

2 Simplify using the index laws:

    a $a^4 b^5 \times a^2 b^2$ **b** $6xy^5 \div 9x^2 y^5$ **c** $\dfrac{5(x^2 y)^2}{(5x^2)^2}$

3 Write the following as a power of 2:

    a 2×2^{-4} **b** $16 \div 2^{-3}$ **c** 8^4

4 Write without brackets or negative indices:

    a b^{-3} **b** $(ab)^{-1}$ **c** ab^{-1}

5 Find the value of x, without using your calculator: **a** $2^{x-3} = \frac{1}{32}$ **b** $9^x = 27^{2-2x}$

6 Evaluate without using a calculator: **a** $8^{\frac{2}{3}}$ **b** $27^{-\frac{2}{3}}$

7 Evaluate, correct to 3 significant figures, using your calculator:

    a $3^{\frac{3}{4}}$ **b** $27^{-\frac{1}{5}}$ **c** $\sqrt[4]{100}$

8 If $f(x) = 3 \times 2^x$, find the value of: **a** $f(0)$ **b** $f(3)$ **c** $f(-2)$

9 On the same set of axes draw the graphs of   **a** $y = 2^x$ **b** $y = 2^x - 4$, stating the y-intercept and the equation of the horizontal asymptote.

10 The temperature of a liquid t minutes after it was heated is given by $T = 80 \times (0.913)^t$ °C. Find:

    a the initial temperature of the liquid

    b the temperature after **i** $t = 12$ **ii** $t = 24$ **ii** $t = 36$ minutes.

    c Draw the graph of T against t, $t \geqslant 0$, using the above or technology.

    d Hence, find the time taken for the temperature to reach 25°C.

REVIEW SET 3B

1 Simplify: **a** $-(-2)^3$ **b** $5^{-1} - 5^0$

2 Simplify using the index laws:

    a $(a^7)^3$ **b** $pq^2 \times p^3 q^4$ **c** $\dfrac{8ab^5}{2a^4 b^4}$

3 Write as powers of 2:   **a** $\frac{1}{16}$ **b** $2^x \times 4$ **c** $4^x \div 8$

4 Write without brackets or negative indices:

  a $x^{-2} \times x^{-3}$ **b** $2(ab)^{-2}$ **c** $2ab^{-2}$

5 Solve for x without using a calculator: **a** $2^{x+1} = 32$ **b** $4^{x+1} = \left(\frac{1}{8}\right)^x$

6 Write as powers of 3:   **a** 81   **b** 1   **c** $\frac{1}{27}$ **d** $\frac{1}{243}$

7 Write as a single power of 3:   **a** $\dfrac{27}{9^a}$ **b** $(\sqrt{3})^{1-x} \times 9^{1-2x}$

8 For $y = 3^x - 5$:

  a find y when $x = 0, \pm 1, \pm 2$ **b** discuss y as $x \to \infty$ and as $x \to -\infty$

  c sketch the graph of $y = 3^x - 5$ **d** state the equation of any asymptote.

9 Without using a calculator, solve for x: **a** $27^x = 3$ **b** $9^{1-x} = 27^{x+2}$

10 Solve simultaneously for x and y: $4^x \times 2^y = 16$ and $8^x = 2^{\frac{y}{2}}$.

REVIEW SET 3C

1 **a** Write 4×2^n as a power of 2.   **b** Evaluate $7^{-1} - 7^0$.

  c Write $\left(\frac{2}{3}\right)^{-3}$ in simplest fractional form.

  d Simplify $\left(\dfrac{2a^{-1}}{b^2}\right)^2$. Do not have negative indices or brackets in your answer.

2 **a** Write 288 as a product of prime numbers in index form.   **b** Simplify $\dfrac{2^{x+1}}{2^{1-x}}$.

3 Write as powers of 5 in simplest form:

  a 1   **b** $5\sqrt{5}$ **c** $\dfrac{1}{\sqrt[4]{5}}$ **d** 25^{a+3}

4 Simplify:

  a $-(-2)^2$ **b** $\left(-\frac{1}{2}a^{-3}\right)^2$ **c** $(-3b^{-1})^{-3}$

5 Expand and simplify:

  a $e^x(e^{-x} + e^x)$ **b** $(2^x + 5)^2$ **c** $(x^{\frac{1}{2}} - 7)(x^{\frac{1}{2}} + 7)$

6 Expand and simplify:

  a $(3 - 2^a)^2$ **b** $(\sqrt{x} + 2)(\sqrt{x} - 2)$ **c** $2^{-x}(2^{2x} + 2^x)$

7 Solve for x: **a** $6 \times 2^x = 192$ **b** $4 \times \left(\frac{1}{3}\right)^x = 324$.

8 The weight of a radioactive substance after t years is given by $W = 1500 \times (0.993)^t$ grams.

  a Find the original amount of radioactive material.

  b Find the amount of radioactive material remaining after:

    i 400 years   **ii** 800 years.

  c Sketch the graph of W against t, $t \geqslant 0$, using the above or technology.

  d Hence, find the time taken for the weight to reduce to 100 grams.

Chapter 4

Logarithms

Contents:

A   INTRODUCTION

Consider the function $f : x \longmapsto 10^x$.

The defining equation of f is $f(x) = 10^x$
or $y = 10^x$.

Now consider the graph of f and its inverse
function f^{-1}.

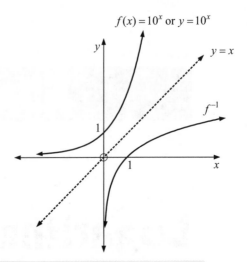

$f(x) = 10^x$ or $y = 10^x$

$y = x$

f^{-1}

The question arises:

How can we write f^{-1} in functional form,
i.e., what is the defining function of f^{-1}?

As f is defined by $y = 10^x$,

f^{-1} is defined by $x = 10^y$.

{interchanging x and y}

So, y is the exponent to which 10 (the base) is raised in order to get x,

and we write this as $y = \log_{10} x$

and say that "y is the logarithm of x in base 10."

So,   • if $f(x) = 10^x$,   then $f^{-1}(x) = \log_{10} x$

• if $f(x) = 2^x$,   then $f^{-1}(x) = \log_2 x$

• if $f(x) = b^x$,   then $f^{-1}(x) = \log_b x$

LOGARITHMS IN BASE b

In general,   if $A = b^n$ $b \neq 1, b > 0$ we say that n is the logarithm of A, in base b
and that $A = b^n \Leftrightarrow n = \log_b A$, $A > 0$.

$A = b^n \Leftrightarrow n = \log_b A$ is a short way of writing
if $A = b^n$ then $n = \log_b A$,   and if $n = \log_b A$ then $A = b^n$.

We say that $A = b^n$ and $n = \log_b A$ are equivalent or interchangeable.

For example: • If $8 = 2^3$ we can immediately say that $3 = \log_2 8$ and vice versa.

• If $\log_5 25 = 2$ we can deduce that $5^2 = 25$ or $25 = 5^2$.

Example 1

a   Write an equivalent exponential statement for $\log_{10} 1000 = 3$.
b   Write an equivalent logarithmic statement for $3^4 = 81$.

a   From $\log_{10} 1000 = 3$ we deduce that $10^3 = 1000$.

b   From $3^4 = 81$ we deduce that $\log_3 81 = 4$.

EXERCISE 4A

1   Write an equivalent exponential statement for:

    a $\log_{10} 10\,000 = 4$ **b** $\log_{10}(0.1) = -1$ **c** $\log_{10} \sqrt{10} = \frac{1}{2}$

    d $\log_2 8 = 3$ **e** $\log_2(\frac{1}{4}) = -2$ **f** $\log_3 \sqrt{27} = 1.5$

2   Write an equivalent logarithmic statement for:

    a $2^2 = 4$ **b** $2^{-3} = \frac{1}{8}$ **c** $10^{-2} = 0.01$

    d $7^2 = 49$ **e** $2^6 = 64$ **f** $3^{-3} = \frac{1}{27}$

Example 2

Find: **a** $\log_{10} 100$ **b** $\log_2 32$ **c** $\log_5(0.2)$

    a   To find $\log_{10} 100$ we ask "What power must 10 be raised to, to get 100?"
        As $10^2 = 100$,   then $\log_{10} 100 = 2$.

    b   As $2^5 = 32$,   then $\log_2 32 = 5$.

    c   As $5^{-1} = \frac{1}{5} = 0.2$,   then $\log_5(0.2) = -1$.

---

3   Find:

    a $\log_{10} 100\,000$ **b** $\log_{10}(0.01)$ **c** $\log_3 \sqrt{3}$ **d** $\log_2 8$

    e $\log_2 64$ **f** $\log_2 128$ **g** $\log_5 25$ **h** $\log_5 125$

    i $\log_2(0.125)$ **j** $\log_9 3$ **k** $\log_4 16$ **l** $\log_{36} 6$

    m $\log_3 243$ **n** $\log_2 \sqrt[3]{2}$ **o** $\log_a a^n$ **p** $\log_8 2$

    q $\log_t \left(\frac{1}{t}\right)$ **r** $\log_6 6\sqrt{6}$ **s** $\log_4 1$ **t** $\log_9 9$

4   Use your calculator to find:

    a $\log_{10} 152$ **b** $\log_{10} 25$ **c** $\log_{10} 74$ **d** $\log_{10} 0.8$

5   Solve for x:

    a $\log_2 x = 3$ **b** $\log_4 x = \frac{1}{2}$ **c** $\log_x 81 = 4$ **d** $\log_2(x - 6) = 3$

Example 3

In question **3o** of this exercise we observed that $\log_a a^n = n$.   Discuss.

Use this result to find: **a** $\log_2 16$ **b** $\log_{10} \sqrt[5]{100}$ **c** $\log_2 \left(\frac{1}{\sqrt{2}}\right)$

    a $\log_2 16$
       $= \log_2 2^4$
       $\{\text{as } 16 = 2^4\}$
       $= 4$

    b $\log_{10} \sqrt[5]{100}$
       $= \log_{10}(10^2)^{\frac{1}{5}}$
       $= \log_{10} 10^{\frac{2}{5}}$
       $= \frac{2}{5}$

    c $\log_2 \left(\frac{1}{\sqrt{2}}\right)$
       $= \log_2 2^{-\frac{1}{2}}$
       $= -\frac{1}{2}$

6 Use $\log_a a^n = n$ to find:

    a $\log_2 4$ **b** $\log_3 \left(\frac{1}{3}\right)$ **c** $\log_5(25\sqrt{5})$ **d** $\log_3 \left(\frac{1}{\sqrt{3}}\right)$

B   LOGARITHMS IN BASE 10

Many positive numbers can be easily written in the form 10^x.   For example,

$$10\,000 = 10^4$$
$$1000 = 10^3$$
$$100 = 10^2$$
$$10 = 10^1$$
$$1 = 10^0$$
$$0.1 = 10^{-1}$$
$$0.01 = 10^{-2}$$
$$0.001 = 10^{-3} \quad \text{etc.}$$

Also, numbers like $\sqrt{10}$, $10\sqrt{10}$ and $\dfrac{1}{\sqrt[5]{10}}$ can be written in the form 10^x.

$$\sqrt{10} = 10^{\frac{1}{2}} = 10^{0.5} \qquad 10\sqrt{10} = 10^1 \times 10^{0.5} = 10^{1.5} \qquad \frac{1}{\sqrt[5]{10}} = 10^{-\frac{1}{5}} = 10^{-0.2}$$

In fact, all positive numbers can be written in the form 10^x by introducing the concept of **logarithms**.

Definition: The **logarithm** of a positive number, in base 10, is its power of 10.

For example:

- Since $1000 = 10^3$,   we write $\log_{10} 1000 = 3$ or $\log 1000 = 3$.
- Since $0.01 = 10^{-2}$,   we write $\log_{10}(0.01) = -2$ or $\log(0.01) = -2$.

In algebraic form, $\mathbf{a = 10^{\log a}}$ for any $a > 0$.   Why is $a > 0$?

> If no base is indicated we assume that it is base 10.

Notice also that $\log 1000 = \log 10^3 = 3$ and $\log 0.01 = \log 10^{-2} = -2$

give us the useful alternative $\mathbf{\log 10^x = x}$

Example 4

  a Without using a calculator, find: **i** $\log 100$ **ii** $\log(\sqrt[4]{10})$.
  b Check your answers using technology.

  a **i** $\log 100 = \log 10^2$ **ii** $\log(\sqrt[4]{10}) = \log(10^{\frac{1}{4}})$
             $= 2$ $= \frac{1}{4}$ $\{\log 10^x = x\}$

  b **i** press  *Answer:* 2

     ii press log 10 ^ 0.25) ENTER   *Answer:* 0.25

EXERCISE 4B

1   Without using a calculator, find:

    a $\log 10\,000$ **b** $\log 0.001$ **c** $\log 10$ **d** $\log 1$

    e $\log \sqrt{10}$ **f** $\log(\sqrt[3]{10})$ **g** $\log\left(\frac{1}{\sqrt[4]{10}}\right)$ **h** $\log 10\sqrt{10}$

    i $\log \sqrt[3]{100}$ **j** $\log\left(\frac{100}{\sqrt{10}}\right)$ **k** $\log(10 \times \sqrt[3]{10})$ **l** $\log 1000\sqrt{10}$

    m $\log 10^n$ **n** $\log(10^a \times 100)$ **o** $\log\left(\frac{10}{10^m}\right)$ **p** $\log\left(\frac{10^a}{10^b}\right)$

2   Find using a calculator:

    a $\log 10\,000$ **b** $\log 0.001$ **c** $\log \sqrt{10}$ **d** $\log \sqrt[3]{10}$

    e $\log \sqrt[3]{100}$ **f** $\log 10\sqrt{10}$ **g** $\log\left(\frac{1}{\sqrt{10}}\right)$ **h** $\log\left(\frac{1}{\sqrt[4]{10}}\right)$

Example 5

Use your calculator to write the following in the form 10^x where x is correct to 4 decimal places: **a** 8   **b** 800   **c** 0.08

a 8	**b** 800	**c** 0.08
$= 10^{\log 8}$	$= 10^{\log 800}$	$= 10^{\log 0.08}$
$\doteqdot 10^{0.9031}$	$\doteqdot 10^{2.9031}$	$\doteqdot 10^{-1.0969}$

---

3   Use your calculator to write these in the form 10^x where x is correct to 4 decimal places:

    a   6   **b**   60   **c**   6000   **d**   0.6   **e**   0.006

    f   15   **g**   1500   **h**   1.5   **i**   0.15   **j**   0.000 15

Example 6

    a   Use your calculator to find: **i** $\log 2$ **ii** $\log 20$

    b   Explain why $\log 20 = \log 2 + 1$.

a **i** $\log 2 \doteqdot 0.3010$	**b** $\log 20 = \log(2 \times 10)$
ii $\log 20 = 1.3010$	$\doteqdot \log(10^{0.3010} \times 10^1)$
{calculator}	$\doteqdot \log 10^{1.3010}$ {adding indices}
	$\doteqdot 1.3010$
	$\doteqdot \log 2 + 1$

---

4   **a**   Use your calculator to find: **i** $\log 3$ **ii** $\log 300$

    b   Explain why $\log 300 = \log 3 + 2$.

5   **a**   Use your calculator to find: **i** $\log 5$ **ii** $\log 0.05$

    b   Explain why $\log 0.05 = \log 5 - 2$.

Example 7

Find x if:

a $\log x = 3$

b $\log x \doteqdot -0.271$

a As $x = 10^{\log x}$
$\therefore \quad x = 10^3$
$\therefore \quad x = 1000$

b As $x = 10^{\log x}$
$\therefore \quad x \doteqdot 10^{-0.271}$
$\therefore \quad x \doteqdot 0.536$

---

6 Find x if:

a $\log x = 2$ b $\log x = 1$ c $\log x = 0$ d $\log x = -1$

e $\log x = \frac{1}{2}$ f $\log x = -\frac{1}{2}$ g $\log x \doteqdot 0.8351$ h $\log x \doteqdot -3.1997$

INVESTIGATION   DISCOVERING THE LAWS OF LOGARITHMS

What to do:

1 Use your calculator to find

a $\log 2 + \log 3$ b $\log 3 + \log 7$ c $\log 4 + \log 20$

d $\log 6$ e $\log 21$ f $\log 80$

From your answers, suggest a possible simplification for $\log a + \log b$.

2 Use your calculator to find

a $\log 6 - \log 2$ b $\log 12 - \log 3$ c $\log 3 - \log 5$

d $\log 3$ e $\log 4$ f $\log(0.6)$

From your answers, suggest a possible simplification for $\log a - \log b$.

3 Use your calculator to find

a $3 \log 2$ b $2 \log 5$ c $-4 \log 3$

d $\log(2^3)$ e $\log(5^2)$ f $\log(3^{-4})$

From your answers, suggest a possible simplification for $n \log a$.

C   LAWS OF LOGARITHMS

There are 3 important
laws of logarithms.

$$\log A + \log B = \log(AB)$$

$$\log A - \log B = \log\left(\frac{A}{B}\right), \quad B \neq 0$$

$$n \log A = \log(A^n)$$

These laws are easily established using index laws; they correspond to the first 3 index laws.

Since $A = 10^{\log A}$ and $B = 10^{\log B}$

- $AB = 10^{\log A} \times 10^{\log B} = 10^{\log A + \log B}$.
  But, $AB = 10^{\log(AB)}$
  $\therefore \quad \log A + \log B = \log(AB)$.

- $\dfrac{A}{B} = \dfrac{10^{\log A}}{10^{\log B}} = 10^{\log A - \log B}$.
  But, $\dfrac{A}{B} = 10^{\log(\frac{A}{B})}$
  $\therefore \quad \log A - \log B = \log\left(\dfrac{A}{B}\right)$.

- $A^n = (10^{\log A})^n = 10^{n \log A}$.
  But, $A^n = 10^{\log(A^n)}$
  $\therefore \quad n \log A = \log(A^n)$.

Example 8

Use the laws of logarithms to write the following as a single logarithm:

a $\log 5 + \log 3$ **b** $\log 24 - \log 8$ **c** $\log 5 - 1$

a $\log 5 + \log 3$
  $= \log(5 \times 3)$
  $= \log 15$

b $\log 24 - \log 8$
  $= \log\left(\frac{24}{8}\right)$
  $= \log 3$

c $\log 5 - 1$
  $= \log 5 - \log 10^1$
  $= \log\left(\frac{5}{10}\right)$
  $= \log\left(\frac{1}{2}\right)$

EXERCISE 4C

1 Write as a single logarithm:

a $\log 8 + \log 2$ **b** $\log 8 - \log 2$ **c** $\log 40 - \log 5$

d $\log 4 + \log 5$ **e** $\log 5 + \log(0.4)$ **f** $\log 2 + \log 3 + \log 4$

g $1 + \log 3$ **h** $\log 4 - 1$ **i** $\log 5 + \log 4 - \log 2$

j $2 + \log 2$ **k** $\log 40 - 2$ **l** $\log 6 - \log 2 - \log 3$

m $\log 50 - 4$ **n** $3 - \log 50$ **o** $\log\left(\frac{4}{3}\right) + \log 3 + \log 7$

Example 9

Write as a single logarithm, i.e., in the form $\log a$, $a \in Q$.

a $2\log 7 - 3\log 2$
b $2\log 3 - 1$

a $2\log 7 - 3\log 2$
  $= \log(7^2) - \log(2^3)$
  $= \log 49 - \log 8$
  $= \log\left(\frac{49}{8}\right)$

b $2\log 3 - 1$
  $= \log(3^2) - \log 10^1$
  $= \log 9 - \log 10$
  $= \log(0.9)$

2 Write as a single logarithm or integer:

a $5\log 2 + \log 3$ **b** $2\log 3 + 3\log 2$ **c** $3\log 4 - \log 8$

d $2\log 5 - 3\log 2$ **e** $\frac{1}{2}\log 4 + \log 3$ **f** $\frac{1}{3}\log\left(\frac{1}{8}\right)$

g $3 - \log 2 - 2\log 5$ **h** $1 - 3\log 2 + \log 20$ **i** $2 - \frac{1}{2}\log 4 - \log 5$

Example 10

Simplify, without using a calculator: $\dfrac{\log 8}{\log 4}$

$\dfrac{\log 8}{\log 4} = \dfrac{\log 2^3}{\log 2^2} = \dfrac{3\log 2}{2\log 2} = \dfrac{3}{2}$

3 Simplify without using a calculator:

a $\dfrac{\log 4}{\log 2}$ **b** $\dfrac{\log 27}{\log 9}$ **c** $\dfrac{\log 8}{\log 2}$ **d** $\dfrac{\log 3}{\log 9}$ **e** $\dfrac{\log 25}{\log(0.2)}$ **f** $\dfrac{\log 8}{\log(0.25)}$

Check your answers using a calculator.

Example 11

Show that:

a $\log\left(\frac{1}{9}\right) = -2\log 3$

b $\log 500 = 3 - \log 2$

a $\log\left(\frac{1}{9}\right)$
$= \log(3^{-2})$
$= -2\log 3$

b $\log 500 = \log\left(\frac{1000}{2}\right)$
$= \log 1000 - \log 2$
$= \log 10^3 - \log 2$
$= 3 - \log 2$

---

4   Show that:

   a $\log 9 = 2\log 3$ **b** $\log\sqrt{2} = \frac{1}{2}\log 2$ **c** $\log\left(\frac{1}{8}\right) = -3\log 2$

   d $\log\left(\frac{1}{5}\right) = -\log 5$ **e** $\log 5 = 1 - \log 2$ **f** $\log 5000 = 4 - \log 2$

Example 12

Write the following as logarithmic equations (in base 10):

a $y = a^2 b$ **b** $y = \dfrac{a}{b^3}$ **c** $P = \dfrac{20}{\sqrt{n}}$

a $y = a^2 b$
$\therefore \ \log y = \log(a^2 b)$
$\therefore \ \log y = \log a^2 + \log b$
$\therefore \ \log y = 2\log a + \log b$

b $y = \dfrac{a}{b^3}$
$\therefore \ \log y = \log\left(\dfrac{a}{b^3}\right)$
$\therefore \ \log y = \log a - \log b^3$
$\therefore \ \log y = \log a - 3\log b$

c $P = \left(\dfrac{20}{\sqrt{n}}\right)$

$\therefore \ \log P = \log\left(\dfrac{20}{n^{\frac{1}{2}}}\right)$ and so $\log P = \log 20 - \frac{1}{2}\log n$

---

5   Write the following as logarithmic equations (in base 10):

   a $y = 2^x$ **b** $y = 20b^3$ **c** $M = ad^4$ **d** $T = 5\sqrt{d}$

   e $R = b\sqrt{l}$ **f** $Q = \dfrac{a}{b^n}$ **g** $y = ab^x$ **h** $F = \dfrac{20}{\sqrt{n}}$

   i $L = \dfrac{ab}{c}$ **j** $N = \sqrt{\dfrac{a}{b}}$ **k** $S = 200 \times 2^t$ **l** $y = \dfrac{a^m}{b^n}$

Example 13

Write the following equations without logarithms:

a $\log A = \log b + 2\log c$

b $\log M = 3\log a - 1$

a $\log A = \log b + 2\log c$
$\therefore \ \log A = \log b + \log c^2$
$\therefore \ \log A = \log(bc^2)$
$\therefore \quad A = bc^2$

b $\log M = 3\log a - 1$
$\therefore \ \log M = \log a^3 - \log 10^1$
$\therefore \ \log M = \log\left(\dfrac{a^3}{10}\right)$
$\therefore \quad M = \dfrac{a^3}{10}$

6 Write the following equations without logarithms:

   a $\log D = \log e + \log 2$ **b** $\log F = \log 5 - \log t$

   c $\log P = \frac{1}{2}\log x$ **d** $\log M = 2\log b + \log c$

   e $\log B = 3\log m - 2\log n$ **f** $\log N = -\frac{1}{3}\log p$

   g $\log P = 3\log x + 1$ **h** $\log Q = 2 - \log x$

7 If $p = \log_b 2$, $q = \log_b 3$ and $r = \log_b 5$, write the following in terms of p and/or q and/or r:

   a $\log_b 6$ **b** $\log_b 108$ **c** $\log_b 45$

   d $\log_b\left(\frac{5\sqrt{3}}{2}\right)$ **e** $\log_b\left(\frac{5}{32}\right)$ **f** $\log_b(0.\overline{2})$

8 If $\log_2 P = x$, $\log_2 Q = y$ and $\log_2 R = z$, write the following in terms of x and/or y and/or z:

   a $\log_2(PR)$ **b** $\log_2(RQ^2)$ **c** $\log_2\left(\dfrac{PR}{Q}\right)$

   d $\log_2(P^2\sqrt{Q})$ **e** $\log_2\left(\dfrac{Q^3}{\sqrt{R}}\right)$ **f** $\log_2\left(\dfrac{R^2\sqrt{Q}}{P^3}\right)$

9 If $\log_t M = 1.29$ and $\log_t N^2 = 1.72$ find:

   a $\log_t N$ **b** $\log_t(MN)$ **c** $\log_t\left(\dfrac{N^2}{\sqrt{M}}\right)$

10 Solve for x:

   a $\log_3 27 + \log_3(\frac{1}{3}) = \log_3 x$ **b** $\log_5 x = \log_5 8 - \log_5(6 - x)$

   c $\log_5 125 - \log_5 \sqrt{5} = \log_5 x$ **d** $\log_{20} x = 1 + \log_{20} 10$

   e $\log x + \log(x + 1) = \log 30$ **f** $\log(x + 2) - \log(x - 2) = \log 5$

D   EXPONENTIAL EQUATIONS (USING LOGARITHMS)

In earlier exercises we found solutions to simple exponental equations by equating indices after creating equal bases. However, when the bases cannot easily be made the same we find solutions using logarithms.

Example 14

Solve for x: $2^x = 30$, giving your answer to 3 significant figures.

$$2^x = 30$$
$$\therefore \quad \log 2^x = \log 30 \qquad \text{\{find the logarithm of each side\}}$$
$$\therefore \quad x \log 2 = \log 30 \qquad \text{\{} \log a^n = n\log a \text{\}}$$
$$\therefore \quad x = \frac{\log 30}{\log 2}$$
$$\therefore \quad x \doteqdot 4.91 \quad \text{(3 s.f.)}$$

EXERCISE 4D

1 Solve for x, giving your answer correct to 3 significant figures:

    a $2^x = 10$ **b** $3^x = 20$ **c** $4^x = 100$

    d $(1.2)^x = 1000$ **e** $2^x = 0.08$ **f** $3^x = 0.00025$

    g $(\frac{1}{2})^x = 0.005$ **h** $(\frac{3}{4})^x = 10^{-4}$ **i** $(0.99)^x = 0.00001$

Example 15

Solve for t (to 3 s.f.)   given that $200 \times 2^{0.04t} = 6$.

$$200 \times 2^{0.04t} = 6$$
$$\therefore \quad 2^{0.04t} = \frac{6}{200} \qquad \text{\{dividing both sides by 200\}}$$
$$\therefore \quad 2^{0.04t} = 0.03$$
$$\therefore \quad \log 2^{0.04t} = \log 0.03 \qquad \text{\{find the logarithm of each side\}}$$
$$\therefore \quad 0.04t \times \log 2 = \log 0.03$$
$$\therefore \quad t = \frac{\log 0.03}{0.04 \times \log 2} \doteqdot -126 \quad \text{(3 s.f.)}$$
$$\text{\{using a calculator\}}$$

---

2 Find, correct to 4 s.f., the solution to:

    a $200 \times 2^{0.25t} = 600$ **b** $20 \times 2^{0.06t} = 450$ **c** $30 \times 3^{-0.25t} = 3$

    d $12 \times 2^{-0.05t} = 0.12$ **e** $50 \times 5^{-0.02t} = 1$ **f** $300 \times 2^{0.005t} = 1000$

E   GROWTH AND DECAY REVISITED

Earlier we considered growth and decay problems in which we were required to find the value of the dependent variable for a given value of the independent variable.

For example:

The grasshopper problem where the area of infestation was given by $A_n = 1000 \times 2^{0.2n}$ hectares   (n is the number of weeks after initial observation).

We found A when $n = 0, 5, 10$ and 12 and drew a graph of the growth in area.

In this section we will consider the **reverse problem** of finding n (the independent variable) given values of A_n (the dependent variable).

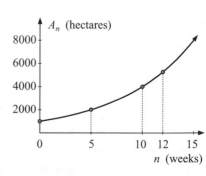

We can do this by:

* reading from an accurate **graph** to get approximate solutions
* using **logarithms** to solve the appropriate equation
* using **technology** in the form of a graphics calculator or computer graphing package.

Example 16

An entomologist, monitoring a grasshopper plague, notices that the area affected by the grasshoppers is given by $A_n = 1000 \times 2^{0.7n}$ hectares, where n is the number of weeks after the initial observation.

a Draw an accurate graph of A_n against n and use your graph to estimate the time taken for the infested area to reach 5000 ha.

b Find the answer to **a** using logarithms.

c Check your answer to **b** using suitable technology.

a

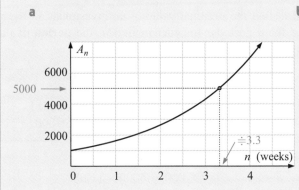

b When $A_n = 5000$,

$$1000 \times 2^{0.7n} = 5000$$

$$\therefore \quad 2^{0.7n} = 5$$

$$\therefore \quad \log 2^{0.7n} = \log 5$$

$$\therefore \quad 0.7n \log 2 = \log 5$$

$$\therefore \quad n = \frac{\log 5}{(0.7 \times \log 2)}$$

$$\therefore \quad n \doteqdot 3.32$$

i.e.,   it takes about 3 weeks and 2 more days.

c Go to the graphing package or graphics calculator icon to find the intersection of $y = 1000 \times 2^{0.7x}$ and $y = 5000$. $(n \doteqdot 3.32)$

As graphing by hand is rather tedious we will use logarithms and/or technology to solve problems of this kind.

GRAPHING
PACKAGE

EXERCISE 4E

1 The weight W_t grams, of bacteria in a culture t hours after establishment is given by $W_t = 20 \times 2^{0.15t}$.   Find the time for the weight of the culture to reach:

    a   30 grams   **b**   100 grams.

2 The temperature $T(^\circ C)$, of a liquid which has been placed in a refrigerator is given by $T = 100 \times 2^{-0.03t}$ where t is the time in minutes.   Find the time required for the temperature to reach: **a** $25^\circ C$ **b** $1^\circ C$.

3 The weight W_t grams, of radioactive substance remaining after t years is given by $W_t = 1000 \times 2^{-0.04t}$ grams.   Find the time taken for the weight to:

    a   halve   **b**   reach 20 grams   **c**   reach 1% of its original value.

4 The weight W grams, of radioactive uranium remaining after t years is given by the formula $W = W_0 \times 2^{-0.0002t}$ grams, $t \geqslant 0$.   Find the time taken for the original weight to fall to:

    a   25% of its original value   **b**   0.1% of its original value.

5 The speed V, of a chemical reaction is given by $V = V_0 \times 2^{0.1t}$ where t is the temperature in $^\circ C$. Find the temperature at which the speed is three times as fast as it was at $0^\circ C$.

6 The current I amps, flowing in a transistor radio, t seconds after it is switched off is given by $I = I_0 \times 2^{-0.02t}$ amps. Find the time taken for the current to drop to 10% of its original value.

7 A man jumps from the basket of a stationary balloon and his speed of descent is given by $V = 50(1 - 2^{-0.2t})$ m/s where t is the time in seconds. Find the time taken for his speed to reach 40 m/s.

F   COMPOUND INTEREST REVISITED

Recall that $u_{n+1} = u_1 \times r^n$ is used to find the eventual value of an investment of u_1 at a rate of $r\%$ each compounding period for n periods. In order to find n, the **period** of the investment, we need to use **logarithms**.

Example 17

Iryna has \$5000 to invest in an account that pays 5.2% p.a. interest compounded annually. How long will it take for the value of her investment to reach \$20 000?

$u_{n+1} = 20\,000$ after n years   Now $u_{n+1} = u_1 \times r^n$

$\quad u_1 = 5000$ $\therefore \quad 20\,000 = 5000 \times (1.052)^n$

$\quad\; r = 105.2\% = 1.052$ $\therefore \quad (1.052)^n = 4$

$\qquad\qquad\qquad\qquad\qquad \therefore \quad \log(1.052)^n = \log 4$

$\qquad\qquad\qquad\qquad\qquad \therefore \quad n \times \log 1.052 = \log 4$

i.e., it will take at least 28 years. $\therefore \quad n = \dfrac{\log 4}{\log 1.052} \doteq 27.3$ years

EXERCISE 4F

1 A house is expected to increase in value at an average rate of 7.5% p.a. How long will it take for a \$160 000 house to be worth \$250 000?

2 Thabo has \$10 000 to invest in an account that pays 4.8% p.a. compounded annually. How long will it take for his investment to grow to \$15 000?

3 Dien invests \$15 000 at 8.4% p.a. compounded *monthly*. He will withdraw his money when it reaches \$25 000, at which time he plans to travel. The formula $u_{n+1} = u_1 \times r^n$ can be used to calculate the time needed. $u_{n+1} = 25\,000$ after n months.

   a Explain why $r = 1.007$. **b** After how many months can he withdraw the money?

G   THE CHANGE OF BASE RULE

Let $\log_b A = x$,   then $b^x = A$

$\qquad\qquad\qquad \therefore \quad \log_c b^x = \log_c A$ {taking logarithms in base c}

$\qquad\qquad\qquad \therefore \quad x \log_c b = \log_c A$ {power law of logarithms}

$\qquad\qquad\qquad \therefore \quad x = \dfrac{\log_c A}{\log_c b}$ So, $\log_b A = \dfrac{\log_c A}{\log_c b}$

Example 18

Find $\log_2 9$ by: **a**   letting $\log_2 9 = x$

              b   using the rule $\log_b A = \dfrac{\log_c A}{\log_c b}$ with $c = 10$.

---

a   Let $\log_2 9 = x$

$\therefore \quad 9 = 2^x$

$\therefore \quad \log 2^x = \log 9$

$\therefore \quad x \log 2 = \log 9$

$\therefore \quad x = \dfrac{\log 9}{\log 2} \doteqdot 3.17$

b $\log_2 9 = \dfrac{\log_{10} 9}{\log_{10} 2}$

$\doteqdot 3.17$

EXERCISE 4G

1   Use the rule $\log_b A = \dfrac{\log_{10} A}{\log_{10} b}$ to find correct to 3 significant figures:

   a $\log_3 12$ **b** $\log_{\frac{1}{2}} 1250$ **c** $\log_3(0.067)$ **d** $\log_{0.4}(0.006\,984)$

2   Use the rule $\log_b A = \dfrac{\log_{10} A}{\log_{10} b}$ to solve, correct to 3 significant figures:

   a $2^x = 0.051$ **b** $4^x = 213.8$ **c** $3^{2x+1} = 4.069$

Hint: In   **a** $2^x = 0.051$ implies that $x = \log_2(0.051)$.

Example 19

Solve for x: $8^x - 5 \times 4^x = 0$

$8^x - 5 \times 4^x = 0$

$\therefore \quad 2^{3x} - 5 \times 2^{2x} = 0$

$\therefore \quad 2^{2x}(2^x - 5) = 0$

$\therefore \quad 2^x = 5 \qquad \{\text{as} \quad 2^{2x} > 0 \quad \text{for all } x\}$

$\therefore \quad x = \log_2 5$

$\therefore \quad x = \dfrac{\log 5}{\log 2} \doteqdot 2.32 \quad \{\text{check this using technology}\}$

3   Solve for x:

   a $25^x - 3 \times 5^x = 0$ **b** $8 \times 9^x - 3^x = 0$

4   Solve for x:

   a $\log_4 x^3 + \log_2 \sqrt{x} = 8$ **b** $\log_{16} x^5 = \log_{64} 125 - \log_4 \sqrt{x}$

5   Find the exact value of x for which $4^x \times 5^{4x+3} = 10^{2x+3}$

H ■ GRAPHS OF LOGARITHMIC FUNCTIONS

Consider the general exponential function $f: x \longmapsto a^x,\ a > 0,\ a \neq 1.$

The defining equation of f is $f(x) = a^x$ (or $y = a^x$). The graph of $y = a^x$ is:

for $0 < a < 1$ or   for $a > 1$

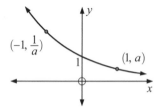
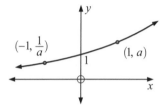

These functions have a **horizontal asymptote** $y = 0$ (the x-axis)   and have
domain $\mathcal{R}$ (all real numbers)   and   range, $\{y:\ y > 0\}$ or $y \in \,]0, \infty[\,$.

Obviously the function $y = a^x$ is one-to-one and has an inverse function f^{-1}.

Now as f is $y = a^x$,   then f^{-1} is $x = a^y$ i.e., $y = \log_a x$.

So,   if $f(x) = a^x$,   then $f^{-1}(x) = \log_a x$

Note: •   The domain of f^{-1} is $\{x:\ x > 0\}$ or $x \in \,]0, \infty[\,$.
                The range of f^{-1} is $y \in \mathcal{R}$.

           •   The domain of $f =$ the range of f^{-1}.
                The range of $f =$ the domain of f^{-1}.

LOGARITHMIC GRAPHS

The graphs of $y = \log_a x$ are:

for $0 < a < 1$ or   for $a > 1$

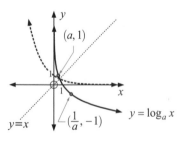
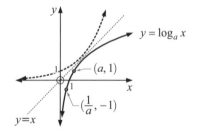

Note: •   both graphs are reflections of $y = a^x$ in the line $y = x$
           •   both functions have domain $\{x:\ x > 0\}$ or $x \in \,]0, \infty[$
           •   we can only find **logarithms of positive numbers**
           •   both graphs have a vertical asymptote of $x = 0$ (the y-axis)
           •   for $0 < a < 1$, as $x \to \infty,\ y \to -\infty$ and as $x \to 0$ (from right), $y \to \infty$
                for $a > 1$,   as $x \to \infty,\ y \to \infty$ and as $x \to 0$ (from right), $y \to -\infty$
           •   to find the **domain** of $\log_a g(x)$, find the solutions of $g(x) > 0$.

Example 20

Consider the function $f : x \longmapsto \log_2(x - 1) + 1$.

a   Find the domain and range of f.

b   Find any asymptotes and axis intercepts.

c   Sketch the graph of f showing all important features.

d   Find f^{-1} and explain how to verify your answer.

a $x - 1 > 0 \quad \therefore \quad x > 1 \qquad$ So,   the domain is $x \in \,]1, \, \infty[$

the range is $y \in \mathcal{R}$

b   As $x \to 1$ (from right), $y \to -\infty$. So, $x = 1$ is the vertical asymptote.

Note: as $x \to \infty, \; y \to \infty$

When $x = 0$, y is undefined $\therefore$ no y-intercept

When $y = 0$, $\log_2(x - 1) = -1 \qquad \therefore \quad x - 1 = 2^{-1} \quad \therefore \quad x = 1\frac{1}{2}$

So, the x-intercept is $1\frac{1}{2}$

c   To graph using your calculator
we need to change the base.

So, we graph $\quad y = \dfrac{\log(x - 1)}{\log 2} + 1$

$y = \log_2(x-1)+1$

$(5, 3)$

$x = 1$

d $\qquad f$ is defined by $\quad y = \log_2(x - 1) + 1$

$\therefore \; f^{-1}$ is defined by $\quad x = \log_2(y - 1) + 1$

$\therefore \quad x - 1 = \log_2(y - 1)$

$\therefore \quad y - 1 = 2^{x-1}$

$\therefore \quad y = 2^{x-1} + 1$

i.e., $\quad f^{-1}(x) = 2^{x-1} + 1 \quad$ which has a H.A. of $y = 1$ ✓

Its domain is $x \in \mathcal{R}$, range is $y \in \,]1, \, \infty[$.

Graphics calculator tip:

When graphing f, f^{-1} and $y = x$ on the same axes it is best to view $y = x$ as
making 45° with both axes. Why?

EXERCISE 4H

1   For the following functions f:

    i   Find the domain and range.

    ii   Find any asymptotes and axis intercepts.

    iii   Sketch the graph of $y = f(x)$ showing all important features.

    iv   Solve algebraically, $f(x) = -1$ and check the solution on your graph.

    v   Find f^{-1} and explain how to verify your answer.

a $f : x \longmapsto \log_3(x + 1)$ b $f : x \longmapsto 1 - \log_3(x + 1)$

c $f : x \longmapsto \log_5(x - 2) - 2$ d $f : x \longmapsto 1 - \log_5(x - 2)$

e $f : x \longmapsto 1 - \log_2 x^2$ f $f : x \longmapsto \log_2(x^2 - 3x - 4)$

REVIEW SET 4A

1 Find the following *without* using a calculator. Show all working.

    a $\log_4 64$ **b** $\log_2 256$ **c** $\log_2(0.25)$ **d** $\log_{25} 5$ **e** $\log_8 1$

    f $\log_6 6$ **g** $\log_{81} 3$ **h** $\log_9(0.\overline{1})$ **i** $\log_{27} 3$ **j** $\log_k \sqrt{k}$

2 Without using a calculator, find: **a** $\log \sqrt{10}$ **b** $\log \dfrac{1}{\sqrt[3]{10}}$ **c** $\log 10^a \times 10^{b+1}$

3 Find x if: **a** $\log_2 x = -3$ **b** $\log_5 x \doteqdot 2.743$ **c** $\log_3 x \doteqdot -3.145$

4 Write as logarithmic equations: **a** $P = 3 \times b^x$ **b** $m = \dfrac{n^3}{p^2}$

5 Write the following equations without logarithms:

    a $\log_2 k \doteqdot 1.699 + x$ **b** $\log_a Q = 3 \log_a P + \log_a R$ **c** $\log A \doteqdot 5 \log B - 2.602$

6 Solve for x, giving your answer correct to 4 significant figures:

    a $5^x = 7$ **b** $20 \times 2^{2x+1} = 500$

7 The weight of radioactive substance after t years is $W_t = 2500 \times 3^{-\frac{t}{3000}}$ grams.

    a Find the initial weight.

    b Find the time taken for the weight to reduce to 30% of its original value.

    c Find the percentage weight loss after 1500 years.

    d Sketch the graph of W_t against t.

8 Solve for x: $16^x - 5 \times 8^x = 0$

REVIEW SET 4B

1 Without using a calculator, find the base 10 logarithms of: **a** $\sqrt{1000}$ **b** $\dfrac{10}{\sqrt[3]{10}}$ **c** $\dfrac{10^a}{10^{-b}}$

2 Solve for x:

    a $\log x = 3$ **b** $\log_3(x+2) = 1.732$ **c** $\log_2\left(\dfrac{x}{10}\right) = -0.671$

3 Write as a single logarithm:

    a $\log 16 + 2 \log 3$ **b** $\log_2 16 - 2 \log_2 3$ **c** $2 + \log_4 5$

4 Write the following equations without logarithms:

    a $\log T = 2 \log x - \log y$ **b** $\log_2 K = \log_2 n + \frac{1}{2} \log_2 t$

5 Solve for x: **a** $3^x = 300$ **b** $30 \times 5^{1-x} = 0.15$ **c** $3^{x+2} = 2^{1-x}$

6 If $A = \log_2 2$ and $B = \log_2 3$,   write the following in terms of A and B:

    a $\log_2 36$ **b** $\log_2 54$ **c** $\log_2(8\sqrt{3})$ **d** $\log_2(20.25)$ **e** $\log_2(0.\dot{8})$

7 For the function $g : x \longmapsto \log_3(x+2) - 2$:

    a Find the domain and range.

    b Find any asymptotes and axes intercepts for the graph of the function.

    c Sketch the graph of $y = g(x)$.

    d Find g^{-1}. Explain how to verify your answer for g^{-1}.

    e Sketch the graphs of g, g^{-1} and $y = x$ on the same axes.

8 Solve exactly for a, the equation $\log_4 a^5 + \log_2 a^{\frac{3}{2}} = \log_8 625$.

Chapter 5

Natural logarithms

Contents:

A

INTRODUCTION

The simplest exponential functions are of the form $f(x) = a^x$ where a is any positive number, $a \neq 1$.

Below are some examples of the graphs of simple exponential functions.

Note: All members of the family $f(x) = a^x$ ($a > 0$, $a \neq 1$) have graphs which

- pass through the point $(0, 1)$
- are above the x-axis for all values of x
- are asymptotic to the x-axis.

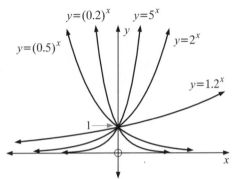

This means that as x gets large (positively or negatively) the graph gets closer and closer to the x-axis.

We can see from the graphs that a^x is positive for all x.

So, there are a vast number of possible choices for the base number.

However, in all branches of science, engineering, sociology, etc. where exponential data is being examined, the base e where $e \doteqdot 2.7183$ is commonly used.

We will examine the function $f(x) = e^x$ where $e \doteqdot 2.7183$ in detail.

The inverse function of $f(x) = e^x$ is $f^{-1}(x) = \log_e x$ also written $\ln x$.

"Where does e come from?" is a reasonable question to ask.

INVESTIGATION 1 e OCCURS NATURALLY

Suppose $\$u_1$ is invested at a fixed rate of 10% p.a. for 10 years.

If *one* interest payment is made each year, then using $u_{n+1} = u_1 r^n$ where r is the rate per period and n is the number of periods, the investment will be worth $\$u_{11}$ after 10 years and $u_{11} = u_1(1.1)^{10} \doteqdot u_1 \times 2.593\,742$ {we are multiplying by 1.1 which equals 110%}

If 10 interest payments are made each year, then $u_{11} = u_1(1.01)^{100} \doteqdot u_1 \times 2.704\,814$

What to do:

1 Calculate u_{11} for
   a 100 interest payments per year $\{r = 1.001\}$
   b 1000 interest payments per year
   c 10 000 interest payments per year
   d 100 000 interest payments per year
   e 1 000 000 interest payments per year

2 If 1 000 000 interest payments are made each year, how frequently does this occur?

3 Comment on your results to **1** above

A more difficult but worthwhile investigation on 'where e comes from' follows:

INVESTIGATION 2   CONTINUOUS COMPOUND INTEREST

 A formula for calculating the amount to which an investment grows is given by
$u_n = u_0(1 + i)^n$ where

     u_n is the **final amount** u_0 is the **initial amount**

     i is the **interest rate per compounding period**

     n is the **number of periods** (i.e., the number of times the interest is compounded).

We are to investigate the final value of an investment for various values of n, and allow n to get extremely large.

What to do:

1 Suppose \$1000 is invested for 4 years at a fixed rate of 6% p.a. Use your calculator to find the final amount (sometimes called the *maturing value*) if the interest is paid:

    a   annually   (once a year and so $n = 4$, $i = 6\% = 0.06$)

    b   quarterly   (four times a year and so $n = 4 \times 4 = 16$ and $i = \frac{6\%}{4} = 0.015$)

    c   monthly   **d**   daily   **e**   by the second   **f**   by the millisecond.

2 Comment on your answers obtained in **1**.

3 If r is the percentage rate per year, t is the number of years,

     N is the number of interest payments per year,   then $i = \dfrac{r}{N}$ and $n = Nt$.

This means that the growth formula becomes $u_n = u_0 \left(1 + \dfrac{r}{N}\right)^{Nt}$

    a   Show that $u_n = u_0 \left(1 + \dfrac{1}{\frac{N}{r}}\right)^{\frac{N}{r} \times rt}$.

    b   Now let $\dfrac{N}{r} = a$.   Show that $u_n = u_0 \left[\left(1 + \dfrac{1}{a}\right)^a\right]^{rt}$.

4 For continuous compound growth, the number of interest payments per year, N, gets very large.

    a   Explain why a gets very large as N gets very large.

    b   Copy and complete the table:

Give answers as accurately as technology permits.

a	$\left(1 + \dfrac{1}{a}\right)^a$
10	
100	
1000	
10 000	
100 000	
⋮	

5 You should have discovered that for very large a values,

$$\left(1 + \frac{1}{a}\right)^a \doteqdot 2.718\,281\,828\,235......$$

6 Now use the $\boxed{e^x}$ key of your calculator to find the value of e^1,

i.e., press   1 $\boxed{e^x}$ $\boxed{=}$ or $\boxed{e^x}$ 1 $\boxed{=}$.   What do you notice?

7 For continuous growth, $u_n = u_0 e^{rt}$ where u_0 is the initial amount
we have shown that: r is the annual percentage rate
                                           t is the number of years

Use this formula to find the amount which an investment of \$1000 for 4 years at a fixed rate of 6% p.a., will reach if the interest is calculated continuously (instantaneously).

From **Investigation 2** we observed that:

"If interest is paid continuously (instantaneously) then the formula for calculating a compounding amount $u_n = u_0(1 + i)^n$ can be replaced by $u_n = u_0 e^{rt}$, where r is the percentage rate p.a. and t is the number of years."

RESEARCH   RESEARCHING e

What to do:

1 The 'bell curve' which models statistical distributions is shown alongside. Research the equation of this curve.

2 $e^{i\pi} + 1 = 0$ is called **Euler's equation** where $i = \sqrt{-1}$. Research the significance of this equation.

3 The series $f(x) = 1 + x + \frac{1}{2}x^2 + \frac{1}{2\times 3}x^3 + \frac{1}{2\times 3\times 4}x^4 + \ldots$ has infinitely many terms.

It has been shown that $f(x) = e^x$.

Check this statement by finding an approximation for $f(1)$ using its first 20 terms.

EXERCISE 5A

1 Use the $\boxed{e^x}$ key of your calculator to find the approximate value of e to as many digits as are possible.

GRAPHING PACKAGE

2 Sketch, on the same set of axes, the graphs of $y = 2^x$, $y = e^x$ and $y = 3^x$. Comment on any observations.

3 Sketch, on the same set of axes, the graphs of $y = e^x$ and $y = e^{-x}$. What is the geometric connection between these two graphs?

4 For the general exponential function $y = ae^{kx}$, what is the y-intercept?

5 Consider $y = 2e^x$.
    a Explain why y can never be < 0.   **b** Find y if: **i** $x = -20$ **ii** $x = 20$.

6 Find to 3 significant figures, the value of:
    a e^2 **b** e^3 **c** $e^{0.7}$ **d** $\sqrt{e}$ **e** e^{-1}

7 Write the following as powers of e:
    a $\sqrt{e}$ **b** $e\sqrt{e}$ **c** $\dfrac{1}{\sqrt{e}}$ **d** $\dfrac{1}{e^2}$

8 Simplify, but retain base e:
    a $\left(e^{0.36}\right)^{\frac{1}{2}}$ **b** $\left(e^{0.064}\right)^{\frac{t}{16}}$ **c** $\left(e^{-0.04}\right)^{\frac{t}{8}}$ **d** $\left(e^{-0.836}\right)^{\frac{t}{5}}$

9 Find, to five significant figures, the values of:
    a $e^{2.31}$ **b** $e^{-2.31}$ **c** $e^{4.829}$ **d** $e^{-4.829}$
    e $50e^{-0.1764}$ **f** $80e^{-0.6342}$ **g** $1000e^{1.2642}$ **h** $0.25e^{-3.6742}$

10 On the same set of axes, sketch and clearly label the graphs of:

$$f : x \longmapsto e^x, \qquad g : x \longmapsto e^{x-2}, \qquad h : x \longmapsto e^x + 3$$

State the domain and range of each function.

11 On the same set of axes, sketch and clearly label the graphs of:

$$f : x \longmapsto e^x, \qquad g : x \longmapsto -e^x, \qquad h : x \longmapsto 10 - e^x$$

State the domain and range of each function.

12 The weight of bacteria in a culture is given by $W(t) = 2e^{\frac{t}{2}}$ grams where t is the time in hours after the culture was set to grow.

    a What is the weight of the culture at:

        i $t = 0$ **ii** $t = 30$ min   **iii** $t = 1\frac{1}{2}$ hours   **iv** $t = 6$ hours?

    b Use **a** to sketch the graph of $W(t) = 2e^{\frac{t}{2}}$.

13 The current flowing in an electrical circuit t seconds after it is switched off is given by $I(t) = 75e^{-0.15t}$ amps.

    a What current is still flowing in the circuit after: **i** $t = 1$ sec **ii** $t = 10$ sec?

    b Use your graphics calculator to sketch $I(t) = 75e^{-0.15t}$ and $I = 1$.

    c Find how long it would take for the current to fall to 1 amp.

14 Given $f : x \longmapsto e^x$

    a find the defining equation of f^{-1}.

    b Sketch the graphs of $y = e^x$, $y = x$ and $y = f^{-1}(x)$ on the same set of axes.

B   NATURAL LOGARITHMS

If f is the exponential function $x \longmapsto e^x$ (i.e., $f(x) = e^x$ or $y = e^x$) then its inverse function, f^{-1} is $x = e^y$ or $y = \log_e x$.

So, $y = \log_e x$ is the reflection of $y = e^x$ in the mirror line $y = x$.

Notation: $\ln x$ is used to represent $\log_e x$. $\ln x$ is called the natural logarithm of x.

    Note: $\ln 1 = 0$ $\{$as $1 = e^0\}$

                $\ln e = 1$ $\{$as $e = e^1\}$

                $\ln e^2 = 2\ln e = 2$

                $\ln \sqrt{e} = \frac{1}{2}$ $\{$as $\sqrt{e} = e^{\frac{1}{2}}\}$

                $\ln\left(\dfrac{1}{e}\right) = -1$ $\{$as $\dfrac{1}{e} = e^{-1}\}$

          In general, $\boldsymbol{\ln e^x = x.}$

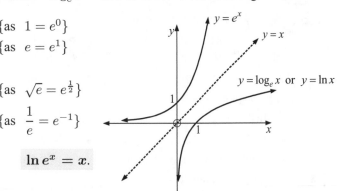

EXERCISE 5B

1 Without using a calculator find:

    a $\ln e^3$ **b** $\ln 1$ **c** $\ln \sqrt[3]{e}$ **d** $\ln\left(\dfrac{1}{e^2}\right)$

2 Check your answers to question **1** using a calculator.

3 Explain why $\ln(-2)$ and $\ln 0$ cannot be found. Conclusion?

4 Simplify:

    a $\ln e^a$ **b** $\ln(e \times e^a)$ **c** $\ln(e^a \times e^b)$ **d** $\ln(e^a)^b$ **e** $\ln\left(\dfrac{e^a}{e^b}\right)$

Example 1

Use your calculator to write the following in the form e^k where k is correct to 4 decimal places: **a** 50   **b** 0.005

a 50	**b** 0.005
$= e^{\ln 50}$ $\{$using $a = e^{\ln a}\}$	$= e^{\ln 0.005}$
$\doteqdot e^{3.9120}$	$\doteqdot e^{-5.2983}$

---

5 Use your calculator to write these in the form e^x where x is correct to 4 dec. places:

    a 6   **b** 60   **c** 6000   **d** 0.6   **e** 0.006

    f 15   **g** 1500   **h** 1.5   **i** 0.15   **j** 0.000 15

Example 2

If $\ln x = a$ then $x = e^a$.

Find x if:	
a $\ln x = 2.17$	**a** $\ln x = 2.17$ **b** $\ln x = -0.384$
b $\ln x = -0.384$	$\therefore\ \ x = e^{2.17}$ $\therefore\ \ x = e^{-0.384}$
	$\therefore\ \ \ \ x \doteqdot 8.76$ $\therefore\ \ \ \ x \doteqdot 0.681$

---

6 Find x if:

    a $\ln x = 3$ **b** $\ln x = 1$ **c** $\ln x = 0$ **d** $\ln x = -1$

    e $\ln x = -5$ **f** $\ln x \doteqdot 0.835$ **g** $\ln x \doteqdot 2.145$ **h** $\ln x \doteqdot -3.2971$

INVESTIGATION 3   THE LAWS OF NATURAL LOGARITHMS

What to do:

1 Use your calculator to find:

    a $\ln 2 + \ln 3$ **b** $\ln 3 + \ln 7$ **c** $\ln 4 + \ln 20$

    d $\ln 6$ **e** $\ln 21$ **f** $\ln 80$

  From your answers, suggest a possible simplification for $\ln a + \ln b$.

2 Use your calculator to find:

    a $\ln 6 - \ln 2$ **b** $\ln 12 - \ln 3$ **c** $\ln 3 - \ln 5$

    d $\ln 3$ **e** $\ln 4$ **f** $\ln(0.6)$

  From your answers, suggest a possible simplification for $\ln a - \ln b$.

3 Use your calculator to find:

    a $3 \ln 2$ **b** $2 \ln 5$ **c** $-4 \ln 3$

    d $\ln(2^3)$ **e** $\ln(5^2)$ **f** $\ln(3^{-4})$

  From your answers, suggest a possible simplification for $n \ln a$.

C   LAWS OF NATURAL LOGARITHMS

There are 3 important **laws of logarithms** for any base including base e.

These are:
- $\ln A + \ln B = \ln(AB)$
- $\ln A - \ln B = \ln\left(\dfrac{A}{B}\right)$
- $n \ln A = \ln(A^n)$

These laws are easily established using index laws:

Since $A = e^{\ln A}$ and $B = e^{\ln B}$

- $AB = e^{\ln A} \times e^{\ln B} = e^{\ln A + \ln B}$.

  But, $AB = e^{\ln(AB)}$ $\therefore$ $\ln A + \ln B = \ln(AB)$.

- $\dfrac{A}{B} = \dfrac{e^{\ln A}}{e^{\ln B}} = e^{\ln A - \ln B}$.

  But, $\dfrac{A}{B} = e^{\ln\left(\frac{A}{B}\right)}$ $\therefore$ $\ln A - \ln B = \ln\left(\dfrac{A}{B}\right)$.

- $A^n = (e^{\ln A})^n = e^{n \ln A}$.   But, $A^n = e^{\ln(A^n)}$ $\therefore$ $n \ln A = \ln(A^n)$.

Example 3

Use the laws of logarithms to write the following as a single logarithm:

   a $\ln 5 + \ln 3$ **b** $\ln 24 - \ln 8$ **c** $\ln 5 - 1$

a	**b**	**c**
$\ln 5 + \ln 3$	$\ln 24 - \ln 8$	$\ln 5 - 1$
$= \ln(5 \times 3)$	$= \ln\left(\frac{24}{8}\right)$	$= \ln 5 - \ln e^1$
$= \ln 15$	$= \ln 3$	$= \ln\left(\frac{5}{e}\right)$

EXERCISE 5C

1   Write as a single logarithm:

   a $\ln 8 + \ln 2$ **b** $\ln 8 - \ln 2$ **c** $\ln 40 - \ln 5$

   d $\ln 4 + \ln 5$ **e** $\ln 5 + \ln(0.4)$ **f** $\ln 2 + \ln 3 + \ln 4$

   g $1 + \ln 3$ **h** $\ln 4 - 1$ **i** $\ln 5 + \ln 4 - \ln 2$

   j $2 + \ln 2$ **k** $\ln 40 - 2$ **l** $\ln 6 - \ln 2 - \ln 3$

Example 4

Write as a single logarithm:

   a $2\ln 7 - 3\ln 2$

   b $2\ln 3 - 1$

a $2\ln 7 - 3\ln 2$	**b** $2\ln 3 - 1$
$= \ln(7^2) - \ln(2^3)$	$= \ln(3^2) - \ln e$
$= \ln 49 - \ln 8$	$= \ln 9 - \ln e$
$= \ln\left(\frac{49}{8}\right)$	$= \ln\left(\dfrac{9}{e}\right)$

2 Write in the form $\ln a, \quad a \in Q$:

a $5\ln 2 + \ln 3$	**b** $2\ln 3 + 3\ln 2$	**c** $3\ln 4 - \ln 8$
d $2\ln 5 - 3\ln 2$	**e** $\frac{1}{2}\ln 4 + \ln 3$	**f** $\frac{1}{3}\ln\left(\frac{1}{8}\right)$
g $-\ln 2$	**h** $-\ln\left(\frac{1}{3}\right)$	**i** $-2\ln\left(\frac{1}{4}\right)$

Example 5

Show that:

a $\ln\left(\frac{1}{9}\right) = -2\ln 3$

b $\ln 500 \doteqdot 6.9078 - \ln 2$

a $\ln\left(\frac{1}{9}\right)$
$= \ln(3^{-2})$
$= -2\ln 3$

b $\ln 500 = \ln\left(\dfrac{1000}{2}\right)$
$= \ln 1000 - \ln 2$
$\doteqdot 6.9078 - \ln 2$

---

3 Show that:

a $\ln 9 = 2\ln 3$	**b** $\ln \sqrt{2} = \frac{1}{2}\ln 2$	**c** $\ln\left(\frac{1}{8}\right) = -3\ln 2$
d $\ln\left(\frac{1}{5}\right) = -\ln 5$	**e** $\ln\left(\frac{1}{\sqrt{2}}\right) = -\frac{1}{2}\ln 2$	**f** $\ln\left(\frac{e}{5}\right) = 1 - \ln 5$
g $\ln \sqrt[3]{5} = \frac{1}{3}\ln 5$	**h** $\ln\left(\frac{1}{32}\right) = -5\ln 2$	**i** $\ln\left(\frac{1}{\sqrt[5]{2}}\right) = -\frac{1}{5}\ln 2$

Example 6

Write the following equations without logarithms:
a $\ln A = 2\ln c + 3$ **b** $\ln M = 3\ln a - 2$

a $\ln A = 2\ln c + 3$
$\therefore \quad \ln A - 2\ln c = 3$
$\therefore \ln A - \ln c^2 = 3$
$\therefore \quad \ln\left(\dfrac{A}{c^2}\right) = 3$
$\therefore \quad \dfrac{A}{c^2} = e^3$
$\therefore \quad A = e^3 c^2$

b $\ln M = 3\ln a - 2$
$\therefore \quad \ln M - 3\ln a = -2$
$\therefore \quad \ln M - \ln a^3 = -2$
$\therefore \quad \ln\left(\dfrac{M}{a^3}\right) = -2$
$\therefore \quad \dfrac{M}{a^3} = e^{-2}$
$\therefore \quad M = e^{-2}a^3 \quad \text{or} \quad M = \dfrac{a^3}{e^2}$

---

4 Write the following equations without logarithms:

a $\ln D = \ln x + 1$	**b** $\ln F = -\ln p + 2$	**c** $\ln P = \frac{1}{2}\ln x$
d $\ln M = 2\ln y + 3$	**e** $\ln B = 3\ln t - 1$	**f** $\ln N = -\frac{1}{3}\ln g$
g $\ln Q \doteqdot 3\ln x + 2.159$	**h** $\ln D \doteqdot 0.4\ln n - 0.6582$	

D EXPONENTIAL EQUATIONS INVOLVING e

To solve exponential equations of the form $e^x = a$ we simply use the property:

If $e^x = a$ then $x = \ln a$.

This rule is clearly true as if $e^x = a$

then $\ln e^x = \ln a$ {finding ln of both sides}

and $x = \ln a$ {$\ln e^x = x$}

Example 7

Find x to 4 sig. figs. if: **a** $e^x = 30$ **b** $e^{\frac{x}{3}} = 21.879$ **c** $20e^{4x} = 0.0382$

a $\quad e^x = 30$

$\therefore \quad x = \ln 30$

$\therefore \quad x \doteqdot 3.401$

b $\quad e^{\frac{x}{3}} = 21.879$

$\therefore \quad \dfrac{x}{3} = \ln 21.879$

$\therefore \quad x \doteqdot 9.257$

c $\quad 20e^{4x} = 0.0382$

$\therefore \quad e^{4x} = 0.00191$

$\therefore \quad 4x = \ln 0.00191$

$\therefore \quad 4x \doteqdot -6.2607....$

$\therefore \quad x \doteqdot -1.565$

EXERCISE 5D

1 Solve for x, giving answers correct to 4 significant figures:

a $e^x = 10$

b $e^x = 1000$

c $e^x = 0.00862$

d $e^{\frac{x}{2}} = 5$

e $e^{\frac{x}{3}} = 157.8$

f $e^{\frac{x}{10}} = 0.01682$

g $20 \times e^{0.06x} = 8.312$

h $50 \times e^{-0.03x} = 0.816$

i $41.83e^{0.652x} = 1000$

E	**GROWTH AND DECAY REVISITED**

Earlier, in **Chapter 3**, we considered growth and decay problems in which we were required to find the value of the dependent variable for a given value of the independent variable.

For example:

Consider a locust plague for which the area of infestation is given by $A_n = 1000 \times e^{0.2n}$ hectares (n is the number of weeks after initial observation).

If we find A when $n = 0$, 5, 10 and 12 we can draw a graph of the growth in area of the infestation.

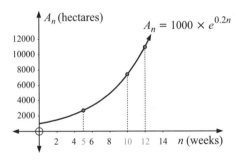

In this section we will consider the **reverse problem** of finding n (the independent variable) given values of A_n (the dependent variable). We can do this by:

- reading from an accurate **graph** to get approximate solutions
- using **logarithms** to solve the appropriate equation
- using **technology** (graphics calculator or computer graphing package).

Example 8

A biologist, monitoring a fire ant infestation, notices that the area affected by the ants is given by $A_n = 1000 \times e^{0.7n}$ hectares, where n is the number of weeks after the initial observation.

a Draw an accurate graph of A_n against n and use your graph to estimate the time taken for the infested area to reach 5000 ha.

b Find the answer to **a** using logarithms.

c Check your answer to **b** using suitable technology.

a

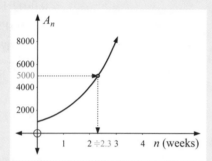

b   When $A_n = 5000$,

$$1000 \times e^{0.7n} = 5000$$

$$\therefore \quad e^{0.7n} = 5$$

$$\therefore \quad 0.7n = \ln 5$$

$$\therefore \quad n = \frac{\ln 5}{0.7} \doteqdot 2.30$$

i.e.,   it takes about 2 weeks and 2 more days.

c   Go to the graphing package or graphics calculator icon to find the intersection of $y = 1000 \times e^{0.7x}$ and $y = 5000$. $(x \doteqdot 2.30)$

As graphing by hand is rather tedious we will use logarithms and/or technology to solve problems of this kind.

GRAPHING PACKAGE

EXERCISE 5E

1 The mass M_t grams, of bacteria in a culture t hours after establishment is given by $M_t = 20 \times e^{0.15t}$.   Find the time for the mass of the culture to reach:

  a   25 grams   **b**   100 grams.

2 The mass M_t grams, of radioactive substance remaining after t years is given by $M_t = 1000 \times e^{-0.04t}$ grams.   Find the time taken for the mass to:

  a   halve   **b**   reach 25 grams   **c**   reach 1% of its original value.

3 A man jumps from an aeroplane and his speed of descent is given by $V = 50(1 - e^{-0.2t})$ m/s where t is the time in seconds. Find the time taken for his speed to reach 40 m/s.

4 Hot cooking oil is placed in a refrigerator and its temperature after m minutes is given by $T_m = (225 \times e^{-0.17m} - 6)$ °C. Find the time taken for the temperature to fall to 0°C.

F   INVERSE FUNCTIONS REVISITED

Recall that   • inverse functions are formed by interchanging x and y

   • $y = f^{-1}(x)$ is the reflection of $y = f(x)$ in the line $y = x$.

 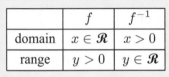

Given $f : x \longmapsto e^{x-3}$
a   find the defining equation of f^{-1}
b   sketch the graphs of f and f^{-1} on the same set of axes
c   state the domain and range of f and f^{-1}.

a
$$f(x) = e^{x-3}$$
i.e., $y = e^{x-3}$
$\therefore$ f^{-1} is $x = e^{y-3}$
i.e., $y - 3 = \ln x$
or $y = 3 + \ln x$

b
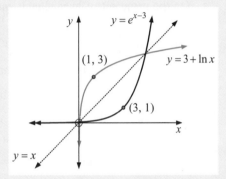

c

	f	f^{-1}
domain	$x \in \mathcal{R}$	$x > 0$
range	$y > 0$	$y \in \mathcal{R}$

Note: $y = e^{x-3}$ is the translation of $y = e^x$ under $\begin{bmatrix} 3 \\ 0 \end{bmatrix}$.   (See **Chapter 6**)

EXERCISE 5F

1   For the following functions
   i   find the defining equation of f^{-1}
   ii   sketch the graphs of f and f^{-1} on the same set of axes
   iii   state the domain and range of f and f^{-1}.

   a $f : x \longmapsto e^x + 5$ **b** $f : x \longmapsto e^{x+1} - 3$

   c $f : x \longmapsto \ln x - 4$ where $x > 0$ **d** $f : x \longmapsto \ln(x - 1) + 2$ where $x > 1$

2   Given $f : x \longmapsto e^{2x}$ and $g : x \longmapsto 2x - 1$,   find the defining equations of:
   a $(f^{-1} \circ g)(x)$ **b** $(g \circ f)^{-1}(x)$

3   Consider the graphs A and B. One of them is the graph of $y = \ln x$ and the other is the graph of $y = \ln(x - 2)$.

   a   Identify which is which. Give evidence for your answer.

   b   Redraw the graphs on a new set of axes and add to them the graph of $y = \ln(x + 2)$.

   c   Name the vertical asymptotes for each graph.

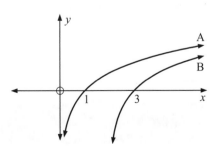

4   Kelly said that in order to graph $y = \ln(x^2)$,
    first graph $y = \ln x$ and double the distances
    away from the x-axis. Connecting these points
    will give the graph of $y = \ln x^2$.

    Is she correct? Give evidence.

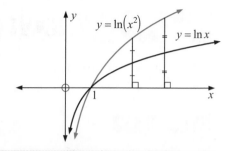

REVIEW SET 5A

1   Find, to 3 significant figures, the value of:

     a e^4 **b** $3e^2$ **c** $\dfrac{1}{6e}$ **d** $\dfrac{10}{\sqrt{e}}$

2   **a** On the same set of axes sketch and clearly label graphs of

       $f : x \longmapsto e^x$, $g : x \longmapsto e^{-x}$ and $h : x \longmapsto -e^{-x}$.

     b What is the geometric connection between: **i** f and g **ii** g and h?

3   Sketch on the same set of axes the graphs of $y = e^x$ and $y = 3e^x$.

4   A particle moves in a straight line such that its displacement from the origin O is given

    by $s(t) = 120t - 40e^{-\frac{t}{5}}$ metres, where t is the time in seconds, $t \geqslant 0$.

     a Find the position of the particle at   **i** $t = 0$ **ii** $t = 5$ **iii** $t = 20$.

     b Hence sketch the graph of $s(t) = 120t - 40e^{-\frac{t}{5}}$ for $t \geqslant 0$.

5   Without using a calculator, find:

     a $\ln(e^5)$ **b** $\ln(\sqrt{e})$ **c** $\ln\left(\dfrac{1}{e}\right)$

6   Simplify:

     a $\ln(e^{2x})$ **b** $\ln(e^2 e^x)$ **c** $\ln\left(\dfrac{e}{e^x}\right)$

7   Solve for x, giving your answers to 3 significant figures:

     a $\ln x = 5$ **b** $3\ln x + 2 = 0$

8   Write as a single logarithm:

     a $\ln 6 + \ln 4$ **b** $\ln 60 - \ln 20$

     c $\ln 4 + \ln 1$ **d** $\ln 200 - \ln 8 + \ln 5$

9   Write in the form $a \ln k$ where a and k are positive whole numbers and k is prime:

     a $\ln 32$ **b** $\ln 125$ **c** $\ln 729$

10 Solve for x, giving answers correct to 3 significant figures:

     a $e^x = 400$ **b** $e^{2x+1} = 11$ **c** $25e^{\frac{x}{2}} = 750$ **d** $e^{2x} = 7e^x - 12$

REVIEW SET 5B

Click on the icon to obtain printable review sets and answers

REVIEW SET 5B

Chapter 6

Graphing and transforming functions

FAMILIES OF FUNCTIONS

In this section we will consider these functions:

Name	General form	
Linear	$f(x) = ax + b, \quad a \neq 0$	$f : x \longmapsto ax + b, \quad a \neq 0$
Quadratic	$f(x) = ax^2 + bx + c, \quad a \neq 0$	$f : x \longmapsto ax^2 + bx + c, \quad a \neq 0$
Cubic	$f(x) = ax^3 + bx^2 + cx + d, \, a \neq 0$	$f : x \longmapsto ax^3 + bx^2 + cx + d, \, a \neq 0$
Absolute value	$f(x) = |x|$	$f : x \longmapsto |x|$
Exponential	$f(x) = a^x, \quad a > 0, \quad a \neq 1$	$f : x \longmapsto a^x, \quad a > 0, \quad a \neq 1$
Logarithmic	$f(x) = \log_e x \quad$ or $\quad f(x) = \ln x$	$f : x \longmapsto \ln x$
Reciprocal	$f(x) = \dfrac{k}{x}, \quad x \neq 0$	$f : x \longmapsto \dfrac{k}{x}, \quad x \neq 0$

Although the above functions have different graphs, they do have some similar features.

The main features we are interested in are:

- the axis intercepts   (where the graph cuts the x and y-axes)
- slopes
- turning points   (maxima and minima)
- values of x where the function does not exist
- the presence of asymptotes   (lines or curves that the graph approaches).

INVESTIGATION   FUNCTION FAMILIES

In this investigation you are encouraged to use the graphing package supplied. Click on the icon to access this package.

GRAPHING
PACKAGE

What to do:

1 From the menu, graph on the same set of axes:
$y = 2x + 1, \quad y = 2x + 3, \quad y = 2x - 1$
Comment on all lines of the form $y = 2x + b$.

2 From the menu, graph on the same set of axes:
$y = x + 2, \quad y = 2x + 2, \quad y = 4x + 2, \quad y = -x + 2, \quad y = -\tfrac{1}{2}x + 2$
Comment on all lines of the form $y = ax + 2$.

3 On the same set of axes graph:
$y = x^2, \quad y = 2x^2, \quad y = \tfrac{1}{2}x^2, \quad y = -x^2, \quad y = -3x^2, \quad y = -\tfrac{1}{5}x^2$
Comment on all functions of the form $y = ax^2, \quad a \neq 0$.

4 On the same set of axes graph:
$y = x^2, \quad y = (x - 1)^2 + 2, \quad y = (x + 1)^2 - 3, \quad y = (x - 2)^2 - 1$
and other functions of the form $y = (x - h)^2 + k$ of your choice.
Comment on the functions of this form.

5 On the same set of axes, graph these absolute value functions:

    a $y = |x|$, $y = 2|x|$, $y = |2x|$

    b $y = |x|$, $y = |x| + 2$, $y = |x| - 3$

    c $y = |x|$, $y = |x - 2|$, $y = |x + 3|$, $y = |x - 1| + 2$

Write a brief report on your discoveries.

6 On the same set of axes, graph these functions:

    a $y = \dfrac{1}{x}$, $y = \dfrac{3}{x}$, $y = \dfrac{10}{x}$
        b $y = \dfrac{-1}{x}$, $y = \dfrac{-2}{x}$, $y = \dfrac{-5}{x}$

    c $y = \dfrac{1}{x}$, $y = \dfrac{1}{x - 2}$, $y = \dfrac{1}{x + 3}$
        d $y = \dfrac{1}{x}$, $y = \dfrac{1}{x} + 2$, $y = \dfrac{1}{x} - 2$

    e $y = \dfrac{2}{x}$, $y = \dfrac{2}{x - 1} + 2$, $y = \dfrac{2}{x + 2} - 1$

Write a brief report on your discoveries.

Example 1

If $f(x) = x^2$, find in simplest form:

    a $f(2x)$ **b** $f\left(\dfrac{x}{3}\right)$ **c** $2f(x) + 1$ **d** $f(x + 3) - 4$

---

  a $f(2x)$ **b** $f\left(\dfrac{x}{3}\right)$ **c** $2f(x) + 1$ **d** $f(x + 3) - 4$

      $= (2x)^2$ $= 2x^2 + 1$ $= (x + 3)^2 - 4$

      $= 4x^2$ $= \left(\dfrac{x}{3}\right)^2$ $= x^2 + 6x + 9 - 4$

                      $= \dfrac{x^2}{9}$ $= x^2 + 6x + 5$

EXERCISE 6A

1 If $f(x) = x$, find in simplest form:

    a $f(2x)$ **b** $f(x) + 2$ **c** $\frac{1}{2}f(x)$ **d** $2f(x) + 3$

2 If $f(x) = x^3$, find in simplest form:

    a $f(4x)$ **b** $\frac{1}{2}f(2x)$ **c** $f(x + 1)$ **d** $2f(x + 1) - 3$

[**Note:** $(x + 1)^3 = x^3 + 3x^2 + 3x + 1$. See the binomial theorem, **Chapter 9**]

3 If $f(x) = 2^x$, find in simplest form:

    a $f(2x)$ **b** $f(-x) + 1$ **c** $f(x - 2) + 3$ **d** $2f(x) + 3$

4 If $f(x) = \dfrac{1}{x}$, find in simplest form:

    a $f(-x)$ **b** $f(\frac{1}{2}x)$ **c** $2f(x) + 3$ **d** $3f(x - 1) + 2$

B   KEY FEATURES OF FUNCTIONS

In this exercise you should use your **graphics calculator** to graph and find the key features.

EXERCISE 6B

1 Consider $f : x \longmapsto 2x + 3$ or $y = 2x + 3$.

   a Graph this function using a graphics calculator.

   b Find algebraically, the: **i** x-axis intercept **ii** y-axis intercept **iii** slope.

   c Use your graphics calculator to check that:

     i the x-axis intercept is $-1\frac{1}{2}$ **ii** the y-axis intercept is 3.

2 Consider $f : x \longmapsto (x - 2)^2 - 9$.

   a Graph the function using a graphics calculator.

   b Find algebraically the x and y-axis intercepts.

   c Use your graphics calculator to check that:

     i the x-axis intercepts are -1 and 5   **ii** the y-intercept is -5

     iii the vertex is $(2, -9)$.

3 Consider $f : x \longmapsto 2x^3 - 9x^2 + 12x - 5$.

   a Graph the function using your graphics calculator.

   b Sketch the graph of the function.

   c Check that: **i** the x-intercepts are 1 and $2\frac{1}{2}$ **ii** the y-intercept is -5

            iii the minimum turning point is at $(2, -1)$

            iv the maximum turning point is at $(1, 0)$.

4 Use your graphics calculator to sketch the graph of $y = |x|$.

   Note: $|x| = x$ if $x \geqslant 0$ and $|x| = -x$ if $x < 0$.

5 Consider $f : x \longmapsto 2^x$. After graphing on a calculator, check these key features:

   a as $x \to \infty$, $2^x \to \infty$ ($\to$ reads 'approaches')

   b as $x \to -\infty$, $2^x \to 0$ (from above) i.e., the x-axis, $y = 0$, is a horiz. asymptote

   c the y-intercept is 1   **d** 2^x is > 0 for all x.

6 Consider $f : x \longmapsto \log_e x$.

   Graph on a graphics calculator and then check that:

   a as $x \to \infty$, $\ln x \to \infty$ **b** as $x \to 0$ (from the right), $\ln x \to -\infty$

   c $\ln x$ only exists if $x > 0$ **d** the x-intercept is 1   **e** the y-axis is an asymptote.

C   TRANSFORMATIONS OF GRAPHS

In the next exercise you should discover the graphical connection between $y = f(x)$ and the functions of the form:

- $y = f(x) + b$, b is a constant
- $y = p\, f(x)$, p is a constant
- $y = -f(x)$
- $y = f(x - a)$, a is a constant
- $y = f(kx)$, k is a constant
- $y = f(-x)$

Types $y = f(x) + b$ **and** $y = f(x - a)$

EXERCISE 6C.1

1   **a**   Sketch the graph of $f(x) = x^2$.

  b   On the same set of axes sketch the graphs of:

   i $y = f(x) + 2$,   i.e., $y = x^2 + 2$ **ii** $y = f(x) - 3$,   i.e., $y = x^2 - 3$

  c   What is the connection between the graphs of $y = f(x)$ and $y = f(x) + b$ if:

   i $b > 0$ **ii** $b < 0$?

2   For each of the following functions f, sketch on the same set of axes $y = f(x)$, $y = f(x) + 1$ and $y = f(x) - 2$.

  a $f(x) = |x|$ **b** $f(x) = 2^x$ **c** $f(x) = x^3$ **d** $f(x) = \dfrac{1}{x}$

  Summarise your observations by describing the graphical transformation of $y = f(x)$ as it becomes $y = f(x) + b$.

3   **a**   On the same set of axes, graphs: $f(x) = x^2$, $y = f(x - 3)$ and $y = f(x + 2)$.

  b   What is the connection between the graphs of $y = f(x)$ and $y = f(x - a)$ if:

   i $a > 0$ **ii** $a < 0$?

4   For each of the following functions f, sketch on the same set of axes the graphs of $y = f(x)$, $y = f(x - 1)$ and $y = f(x + 2)$.

  a $f(x) = |x|$ **b** $f(x) = x^3$ **c** $f(x) = \ln x$ **d** $f(x) = \dfrac{1}{x}$

  Summarise your observations by describing the geometrical transformation of $y = f(x)$ as it becomes $y = f(x - a)$.

5   For each of the following functions sketch:

  $y = f(x)$, $y = f(x - 2) + 3$ and $y = f(x + 1) - 4$ on the same set of axes.

  a $f(x) = x^2$ **b** $f(x) = e^x$ **c** $f(x) = \dfrac{1}{x}$

6   Copy these functions and then draw the graph of $y = f(x - 2) - 3$.

  a   **b**

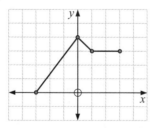   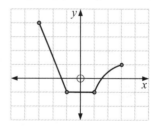

Types $y = p\,f(x)$, $p > 0$ **and** $y = f(kx)$, $k > 0$

EXERCISE 6C.2

1   Sketch on the same set of axes, the graphs of $y = f(x)$, $y = 2\,f(x)$ and $y = 3\,f(x)$ for each of:

  a $f(x) = x^2$ **b** $f(x) = |x|$ **c** $f(x) = x^3$

  d $f(x) = e^x$ **e** $f(x) = \ln x$ **f** $f(x) = \dfrac{1}{x}$

2 Sketch on the same set of axes, the graphs of $y = f(x)$, $y = \frac{1}{2}f(x)$ and $y = \frac{1}{4}f(x)$ for each of:

    a $f(x) = x^2$ **b** $f(x) = x^3$ **c** $f(x) = e^x$

3 Using **1** and **2**, summarise your observations by describing the graphical transformation of $y = f(x)$ to $y = p\,f(x)$ for $p > 0$.

4 Sketch on the same set of axes, the graphs of $y = f(x)$ and $y = f(2x)$ for each of:

    a $y = x^2$ **b** $y = (x-1)^2$ **c** $y = (x+3)^2$

5 Sketch on the same set of axes, the graphs of $y = f(x)$ and $y = f(3x)$ for each of:

    a $y = x$ **b** $y = x^2$ **c** $y = e^x$

6 Sketch on the same set of axes, the graphs of $y = f(x)$ and $y = f\left(\frac{x}{2}\right)$ for each of:

    a $y = x^2$ **b** $y = 2x$ **c** $y = (x+2)^2$

7 Using **4**, **5** and **6**, summarise your observations by describing the graphical transformation of $y = f(x)$ to $y = f(kx)$ for $k > 0$.

8 Consider the function $f : x \longmapsto x^2$.

On the same set of axes sketch the graphs of:

    a $y = f(x)$, $y = 3\,f(x-2)+1$ and $y = 2\,f(x+1)-3$

    b $y = f(x)$, $y = f(x-3)$, $y = f\left(\frac{x}{2}-3\right)$, $y = 2\,f\left(\frac{x}{2}-3\right)$ and
$y = 2\,f\left(\frac{x}{2}-3\right)+4$

    c $y = f(x)$ and $y = \frac{1}{4}\,f(2x+5)+1$.

Types $y = -f(x)$ and $y = f(-x)$

EXERCISE 6C.3

1 On the same set of axes, sketch the graphs of:

    a $y = 3x$ and $y = -3x$ **b** $y = e^x$ and $y = -e^x$

    c $y = x^2$ and $y = -x^2$ **d** $y = \ln x$ and $y = -\ln x$

    e $y = x^3 - 2$ and $y = -x^3 + 2$ **f** $y = 2(x+1)^2$ and $y = -2(x+1)^2$

2 Based on question **1**, what transformation moves $y = f(x)$ to $y = -f(x)$?

3   **a** Find $f(-x)$ for:

      i $f(x) = 2x + 1$ **ii** $f(x) = x^2 + 2x + 1$ **iii** $f(x) = |x - 3|$

  b Graph $y = f(x)$ and $y = f(-x)$ for:

      i $f(x) = 2x + 1$ **ii** $f(x) = x^2 + 2x + 1$ **iii** $f(x) = |x - 3|$

4 Based on question **3**, what transformation moves $y = f(x)$ to $y = f(-x)$?

Summary of graphical transformations on $y = f(x)$

▶   For $y = f(x) + b$, the effect of changes in b is to **translate** the graph of
$y = f(x)$ **vertically** through b units.
   • If $b > 0$ it moves **upwards**.   • If $b < 0$ it moves **downwards**.

▶   For $y = f(x - a)$, the effect of changes in a is to **translate** the graph of
$y = f(x)$ **horizontally** through a units.
   • If $a > 0$ it moves to the **right**.   • If $a < 0$ it moves to the **left**.

▶   For $y = f(x - a) + b$, the graph of $y = f(x)$ has been translated horizontally
a units and vertically b units. We say it has been translated by the vector $\begin{bmatrix} a \\ b \end{bmatrix}$.

▶   For $y = p\,f(x)$, $p > 0$, the effect of changes in p is to **vertically stretch or
compress** the graph of $y = f(x)$ by a factor of p.
   • If $p > 1$ it moves points of $y = f(x)$ **further away** from the x-axis.
   • If $0 < p < 1$ it moves points of $y = f(x)$ **closer** to the x-axis.

▶   For $y = f(kx)$, $k > 0$, the effect of changes in k is to **horizontally stretch
or compress** the graph of $y = f(x)$ by a factor of $\frac{1}{k}$.
   • If $k > 1$ it moves points of $y = f(x)$ **closer** to the y-axis.
   • If $0 < k < 1$ it moves points of $y = f(x)$ **further away** from the y-axis.

▶   For $y = -f(x)$, the effect on the graph of $y = f(x)$ is to **reflect it in the x-axis**.

▶   For $y = f(-x)$, the effect on the graph of $y = f(x)$ is to **reflect it in the y-axis**.

D | FUNCTIONAL TRANSFORMATIONS

EXERCISE 6D

1   Copy the following sketch graphs for $y = f(x)$ and hence sketch the graph of
$y = -f(x)$ on the same axes.

   a 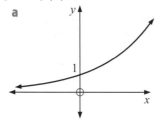   **b** 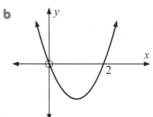   **c**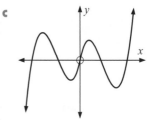

2   Given the following graphs of $y = f(x)$, sketch graphs of $y = f(-x)$:

   a 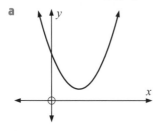   **b** 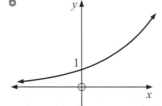   **c**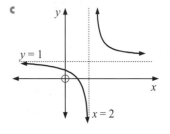

3 Match each equation to its graph drawn below:

   A $y = x^4$ **B** $y = 2x^4$ **C** $y = \frac{1}{2}x^4$ **D** $y = 6x^4$

  a   **b**   **c**   **d**

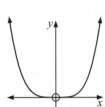 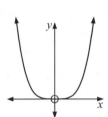 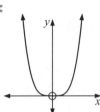 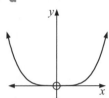

4 For the graph of $y = f(x)$ given, draw sketches of:

  a $y = 2f(x)$ **b** $y = \frac{1}{2}f(x)$

  c $y = f(x + 2)$ **d** $y = f(2x)$

  e $y = f(\frac{1}{2}x)$

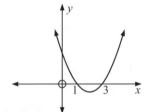

5

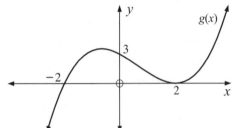

For the graph of $y = g(x)$ given, draw sketches of:

  a $y = g(x) + 2$ **b** $y = -g(x)$

  c $y = g(-x)$ **d** $y = g(x + 1)$

6 For the graph of $y = h(x)$ given, draw sketches of:

  a $y = h(x) + 1$ **b** $y = \frac{1}{2}h(x)$

  c $y = h(-x)$ **d** $y = h\left(\dfrac{x}{2}\right)$

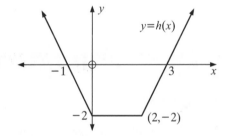

E   SIMPLE RATIONAL FUNCTIONS

Any function $\quad x \longmapsto \dfrac{ax + b}{cx + d}, \quad x \neq -\dfrac{d}{c} \quad$ (a, b, c and d are constants) is called a **simple rational function**.

These functions are characterised by the presence of both a **horizontal asymptote** (HA) and a **vertical asymptote** (VA).

Any graph of a simple rational function can be obtained from the reciprocal function $\quad x \longmapsto \dfrac{1}{x}$ by a combination of some or all of these transformations:

-   a **translation**   (vertical and/or horizontal)
-   **stretches**   (vertical and/or horizontal)

Example 2

a Find the function $y = g(x)$ that results when transforming the reciprocal

function, $x \longmapsto \dfrac{1}{x}$ by: a vertical stretch, factor 2

then a horizontal stretch, factor $\frac{1}{3}$ then a translation of $\begin{bmatrix} 3 \\ -2 \end{bmatrix}$.

b Find the asymptotes of each function found in **a**.

c Is the function found in **a** a self inverse function? Explain.

---

a Under a vertical stretch, factor 2, $\quad \dfrac{1}{x}$ becomes $2\left(\dfrac{1}{x}\right) \qquad \{2f(x)\}$

Under a horizontal stretch, factor $\frac{1}{3}$, $\quad \dfrac{2}{x}$ becomes $\dfrac{2}{(3x)} \qquad \{f(3x)\}$

Under a translation of $\begin{bmatrix} 3 \\ -2 \end{bmatrix}$, $\quad \dfrac{2}{3x}$ becomes $\dfrac{2}{3(x-3)} - 2 \quad \{f(x-3) - 2\}$

$$\therefore \quad f(x) = \dfrac{2}{3x - 9} - 2 = \dfrac{2}{3x - 9} - \dfrac{2(3x - 9)}{3x - 9} = \dfrac{-6x + 20}{3x - 9}$$

b The asymptotes of $y = \dfrac{1}{x}$ are: VA $x = 0$,   HA $y = 0$

$\therefore$ for the new function VA is $x = 3$,   HA is $y = -2$ $\{$as translated $\begin{bmatrix} 3 \\ -2 \end{bmatrix}\}$

c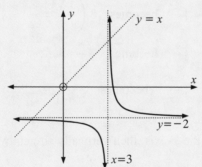

From a graphics calculator the graph is found as shown.

It is not symmetrical about $y = x$

Hence, it is *not* a self inverse function.

Note: $f(x) = \dfrac{k}{x}$, $x \neq 0$ is a vertical stretch, of factor k, of $x \longmapsto \dfrac{1}{x}$, $x \neq 0$.

EXERCISE 6E

1 **a** Find, in the form $y = \dfrac{ax + b}{cx + d}$, the function that results when $x \longmapsto \dfrac{1}{x}$ is transformed by:

    i a vertical stretch of factor $\frac{1}{2}$ **ii** a horizontal stretch of factor 3

    iii a horizontal translation of -3 **iv** a vertical translation of 4

    v all of **a**, **b**, **c** and **d**.

b Find the domain and range of $y = \dfrac{ax + b}{cx + d}$ as found in **a v**.

Example 3

For the function $f : x \longmapsto \dfrac{2x - 6}{x + 1}$, find:

a the asymptotes   **b** how to transform the function to give $x \longmapsto \dfrac{1}{x}$

a $f(x) = \dfrac{2x - 6}{x + 1}$

$= \dfrac{2(x + 1) - 8}{x + 1}$

$= 2 - \dfrac{8}{x + 1}$

$= \dfrac{-8}{x + 1} + 2$

This represents a transformation of $\begin{bmatrix} -1 \\ 2 \end{bmatrix}$

from $f(x) = \dfrac{-8}{x}$ which has   VA $x = 0$
                                          HA $y = 0$

So, $f(x) = \dfrac{2x - 6}{x + 1}$ has a

VA of $x = -1$ and a   HA of $y = 2$

Note: • $\dfrac{2x - 6}{x + 1}$ is undefined when $x = -1$ • as $|x| \to \infty,\ f(x) \to 2$

• the domain of $f(x) = \dfrac{2x - 6}{x + 1}$ is $\{x:\ x \neq -1\}$

the range of $f(x) = \dfrac{2x - 6}{x + 1}$ is $\{y:\ y \neq 2\}$

b To get $f(x) = \dfrac{2x - 6}{x + 1}$ from $f(x) = \dfrac{1}{x}$ we

vertically stretch by a factor of 8 $\{\dfrac{1}{x}$ becomes $8\left(\dfrac{1}{x}\right) = \dfrac{8}{x}\}$

then reflect in the x-axis $\{\dfrac{8}{x}$ becomes $-\dfrac{8}{x}\}$

then translate by $\begin{bmatrix} -1 \\ 2 \end{bmatrix}$ $\{\dfrac{-8}{x}$ becomes $\dfrac{-8}{x + 1} + 2\}$

So, to do the **opposite** we

translate by $\begin{bmatrix} 1 \\ -2 \end{bmatrix}$, then reflect in the x-axis, then vertically stretch by factor $\frac{1}{8}$.

Check: $y = \dfrac{2x - 6}{x + 1}$ becomes $y = \dfrac{2(x - 1) - 6}{(x - 1) + 1} - 2 = \dfrac{2x - 8}{x} - 2 = -\dfrac{8}{x}$

then $-\dfrac{8}{x}$ becomes $\dfrac{8}{x}$ and $\dfrac{8}{x}$ becomes $\dfrac{8}{(8x)} = \dfrac{1}{x}$.

2 For the function $f : x \longmapsto \dfrac{2x + 4}{x - 1}$ find:

a the asymptotes

b how to transform $f(x)$ to give the function $x \longmapsto \dfrac{1}{x}$.

Example 4

Consider $f(x) = \dfrac{4x + 3}{x - 2}$.

a Find the asymptotes of $y = f(x)$. **b** Find the axes intercepts.

c Discuss the behaviour of f near its **i** VA **ii** HA.

d Sketch the graph of the function.

e Describe the transformations which move $x \longmapsto \dfrac{1}{x}$ to $x \longmapsto \dfrac{4x + 3}{x - 2}$.

---

a $y = \dfrac{4x + 3}{x - 2} = \dfrac{4(x - 2) + 11}{x - 2} = 4 + \dfrac{11}{x - 2}$

So, the function has VA $x = 2$ {where y is undefined}

and has HA $y = 4$ {as $|x| \to \infty$, $y \to 4$}

b When $x = 0$, $y = \dfrac{3}{-2}$ $\therefore$ x-intercept is $-1\frac{1}{2}$

when $y = 0$, $4x + 3 = 0$

$x = -\frac{3}{4}$ $\therefore$ y-intercept is $-\frac{3}{4}$

c **i** as $x \to 2$ (from the left), $y \to -\infty$ **ii** as $x \to -\infty$, $y \to 4$ (from below)

as $x \to 2$ (from the right), $y \to \infty$ as $x \to \infty$, $y \to 4$ (from above)

d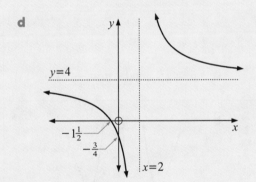

e $\dfrac{1}{x}$ becomes $\dfrac{11}{x}$ under a vertical stretch, factor 11, and $\dfrac{11}{x}$ becomes $\dfrac{4x + 3}{x - 2}$ under a translation of $\begin{bmatrix} 2 \\ 4 \end{bmatrix}$

i.e., a vertical stretch, factor 11 followed by a translation of $\begin{bmatrix} 2 \\ 4 \end{bmatrix}$

---

3 For the following functions:

i find the asymptotes **ii** find the axes intercepts

iii discuss the graph's behaviour near its VA and its HA

iv sketch the graph.

v Describe the transformations which move $x \longmapsto \dfrac{1}{x}$ to the given function.

a $y = \dfrac{2x + 3}{x + 1}$ **b** $y = \dfrac{3}{x - 2}$ **c** $y = \dfrac{2x - 1}{3 - x}$ **d** $y = \dfrac{5x - 1}{2x + 1}$

4 In order to remove noxious weeds from her property Helga sprays with a weedicide. The chemical is slow acting and the number of weeds per hectare remaining after t days is modelled by $N = 20 + \dfrac{100}{t + 2}$ weeds/ha.

a How many weeds per ha were alive before the spraying?

b How many weeds were alive after 8 days?

c How long would it take for the number of weeds still alive to be 40/ha?

d Sketch the graph of N against t

e Is the spraying going to eradicate all weeds according to the model?

Some graphics calculator tips

- To find **zeros** of functions simply **graph** the function and find its x-**intercepts**. This also finds **roots** (or **solutions**) of the equation $f(x) = 0$.

  Note: The **zeros** of $y = f(x)$ are the same as the **roots** of $f(x) = 0$, and are the same as the x-**intercepts** of $y = f(x)$.

- To check that you have found the correct asymptotes (VA and HA):
  - ▶ Try to find y for the x-asymptote value. It should be undefined.
  - ▶ Try to find y for large x values, e.g., $\pm 10^9$. It should give a value close to the y-asymptote value.

F FURTHER GRAPHICAL TRANSFORMATIONS

In this exercise you should discover the graphical connection between $y = f(x)$ and functions of the form $y = \dfrac{1}{f(x)}$, $y = |f(x)|$ and $y = f(|x|)$.

Example 5

Graph on the same set of axes:

a $y = x - 2$ and $y = \dfrac{1}{x-2}$ **b** $y = x^2$ and $y = \dfrac{1}{x^2}$

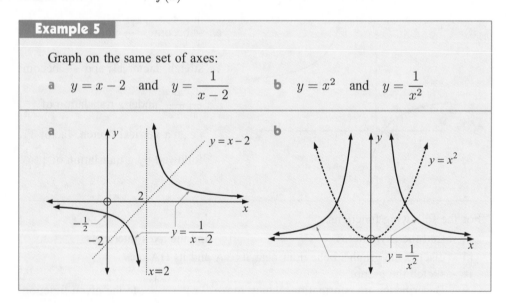

EXERCISE 6F

1 On the same set of axes graph:

a $y = -x^2$ and $y = \dfrac{-1}{x^2}$ **b** $y = (x-1)(x-3)$ and $y = \dfrac{1}{(x-1)(x-3)}$

2 **Invariant points** are points which do not move under a transformation.

Show that if $y = f(x)$ is transformed to $y = \dfrac{1}{f(x)}$, invariant points occur at $y = \pm 1$.

Check your results of question **1** for invariant points.

DISCUSSION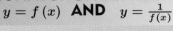

THE GRAPHICAL CONNECTION BETWEEN $y = f(x)$ **AND** $y = \frac{1}{f(x)}$

True or false!   Discuss:

- the zeros of $f(x)$ become VA values of $\frac{1}{f(x)}$

  VA values of $f(x)$ become the zeros of $\frac{1}{f(x)}$

- maximum values of $f(x)$ become minimum values of $\frac{1}{f(x)}$

  minimum values of $f(x)$ become minimum values of $\frac{1}{f(x)}$

- when $f(x) > 0$, $\frac{1}{f(x)} > 0$ also and when $f(x) < 0$, $\frac{1}{f(x)} < 0$ also

- when $f(x) \to 0$, $\frac{1}{f(x)} \to \pm\infty$ and when $\frac{1}{f(x)} \to 0$, $f(x) \to \pm\infty$.

Example 6

Draw the graph of $f(x) = 3x(x - 2)$ and on the same axes draw the graphs of:

a $y = |f(x)|$ **b** $y = f(|x|)$

a $y = |f(x)| = \begin{cases} f(x) & \text{if } f(x) \geqslant 0 \\ -f(x) & \text{if } f(x) < 0 \end{cases}$ **b** $y = f(|x|) = \begin{cases} f(x) & \text{if } x \geqslant 0 \\ f(-x) & \text{if } x < 0 \end{cases}$

This means the graph is
unchanged for $f(x) \geqslant 0$,
reflected in the x-axis for $f(x) < 0$.

This means the graph is
unchanged if $x \geqslant 0$,
reflected in the y-axis if $x < 0$.

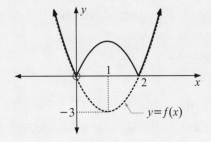 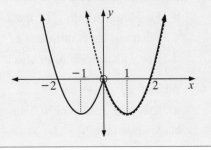

3 Draw $y = x(x+2)$ and on the same set of axes graph: **a** $y = |f(x)|$ **b** $y = f(|x|)$

4 For the following graphs re-sketch $y = f(x)$ and on the same axes graph $y = \frac{1}{f(x)}$:

a 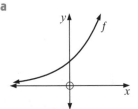 **b** 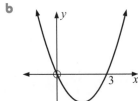 **c**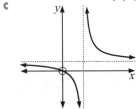

5 For the following graphs re-sketch $y = f(x)$ and on the same axes graph $y = |f(x)|$.

a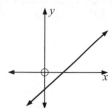

b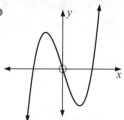

c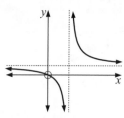

6 Repeat question **5**, but this time graph $y = f(|x|)$ instead of $y = |f(x)|$.

REVIEW SET 6A

1 If $f(x) = x^2 - 2x$, find in simplest form:

    a $f(3)$ **b** $f(-2)$ **c** $f(2x)$ **d** $f(-x)$ **e** $3f(x) - 2$

2 If $f(x) = 5 - x - x^2$, find in simplest form:

    a $f(4)$ **b** $f(-1)$ **c** $f(x - 1)$ **d** $f\left(\dfrac{x}{2}\right)$ **e** $2f(x) - f(-x)$

3 If $f(x) = \dfrac{4}{x}$, find in simplest form:

    a $f(-4)$ **b** $f(2x)$ **c** $f\left(\dfrac{x}{2}\right)$ **d** $4f(x + 2) - 3$

4 Consider $f(x) : x \longmapsto 3x - 2$.

    a Sketch the function f.

    b Find algebraically the **i** x-intercept   **ii** y-intercept   **iii** slope.

    c **i** Find y when $x = 0.3$ **ii** Find x when $y = 0.7$

5 Consider $f(x) = (x + 1)^2 - 4$.

    a Use your calculator to help graph the function.

    b Find algebraically **i** the x-intercepts   **ii** the y-intercept

    c What are the coordinates of the vertex of the function?

    d Use your calculator to check your answers to **b** and **c**.

6 Consider $f : x \longmapsto 2^{-x}$.

    a Use your calculator to help graph the function.

    b True or false?   **i** as $x \to \infty$, $2^{-x} \to 0$ **ii** as $x \to -\infty$, $2^{-x} \to 0$

        iii the y-intercept is $\frac{1}{2}$ **iv** $2^{-x} > 0$ for all x.

7 Sketch the graph of $f(x) = -x^2$, and on the same set of axes sketch the graph of:

    a $y = f(-x)$ **b** $y = -f(x)$ **c** $y = f(2x)$ **d** $y = f(x - 2)$

8 Consider the function $f : x \longmapsto x^2$. On the same set of axes graph:

    a $y = f(x)$ **b** $y = f(x + 2)$ **c** $y = 2f(x + 2)$ **d** $y = 2f(x + 2) - 3$

REVIEW SET 6B

REVIEW SET 6B
Click on the icon to obtain printable review sets and answers

Chapter 7

Quadratic equations and functions

Contents:

INTRODUCTION

Consider the functions:

$$f : x \longmapsto ax + b, \quad a \neq 0 \qquad \textbf{Linear}$$
$$f : x \longmapsto ax^2 + bx + c, \quad a \neq 0 \qquad \textbf{Quadratic}$$
$$f : x \longmapsto ax^3 + bx^2 + cx + d, \quad a \neq 0 \qquad \textbf{Cubic}$$
$$f : x \longmapsto ax^4 + bx^3 + cx^2 + dx + e, \quad a \neq 0 \qquad \textbf{Quartic}$$

These functions are the simplest members of the family of polynomials.

In this chapter we will examine quadratic functions in detail.

Quadratic functions arise in many situations.

> You may need to review algebraic expansion and factorisation. To do this click on the 'Background Knowledge' icon on page 13.

HISTORICAL NOTE

Over 400 years ago, **Galileo** (born in Pisa, Italy) conducted a series of experiments on the paths of projectiles, attempting to find a mathematical description of falling bodies.

Two of Galileo's experiments consisted of rolling a ball down a grooved ramp that was placed at a fixed height above the floor and inclined at a fixed angle to the horizontal. In one experiment the ball left the end of the ramp and descended to the floor.

In a related experiment a horizontal shelf was placed at the end of the ramp, and the ball would travel along this shelf before descending to the floor.

In each experiment Galileo altered the release height (h) of the ball and measured the distance (d) the ball travelled before landing.

The units of measurement were called 'punti'.

Galileo

THE SIMPLEST QUADRATIC FUNCTION

The simplest quadratic function is $y = x^2$ and its graph can be drawn from a table of values.

x	-3	-2	-1	0	1	2	3
y	9	4	1	0	1	4	9

Note:

- The curve is a **parabola** and it opens upwards.

- There are no negative y values, i.e., the curve does not go below the x-axis.

- The curve is **symmetrical** about the y-axis because, for example, when $x = -3$, $y = (-3)^2$ and when $x = 3$, $y = 3^2$ have the same value.

- The curve has a **minimum turning point** or **vertex** at (0, 0).

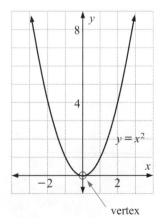

Special note: It is essential that you can draw the graph of $y = x^2$ without having to refer to a table of values.

OPENING PROBLEM

A tennis ball is thrown vertically upwards and its height H, in m, above the ground is given at one second intervals as:

t	0	1	2	3	4	5
H	6.2	25.2	34.2	33.2	20.2	1.2

VIDEO CLIP

For you to consider:

• When the ball was released, was the thrower likely to be standing at ground level, standing on the roof of a single storey building or standing on the roof of a two storey building?

• What would the flight of the ball look like from a distance of 50 m away or from directly above the thrower?

• What is the function equation which gives the height H in terms of time t and what would its graph look like when H is plotted against t?   SIMULATION

• What is the maximum height reached and when does this occur?

• When is the ball 30 m above the ground?

A   FUNCTION NOTATION $f : x \mapsto ax^2 + bx + c$

The function $f : x \mapsto ax^2 + bx + c$ can be represented by $f(x) = ax^2 + bx + c$.

As with linear functions, for any value of x a corresponding value of y can be found by substituting into the function equation.

For example,   if $y = 2x^2 - 3x + 5$, and $x = 3$, then $y = 2 \times 3^2 - 3 \times 3 + 5 = 14$
Hence, the ordered pair (3, 14) satisfies the function $y = 2x^2 - 3x + 5$.

Similarly, using function notation we could write,
if $f(x) = 2x^2 - 3x + 5$ and $x = 3$, then $f(3) = 2 \times 3^2 - 3 \times 3 + 5 = 14$

EXERCISE 7A

1   Which of the following are quadratic functions?

    a $y = 3x^2 - 4x + 1$ **b** $y = 5x - 7$ **c** $y = -x^2$

    d $y = \frac{2}{3}x^2 + 4$ **e** $2y + 3x^2 - 5 = 0$ **f** $y = 5x^3 + x - 6$

2   For each of the following functions, find the value of y for the given value of x:

    a $y = x^2 + 5x - 4$ $\{x = 3\}$ **b** $y = 2x^2 + 9$ $\{x = -3\}$

    c $y = -2x^2 + 3x - 5$ $\{x = 1\}$ **d** $y = 4x^2 - 7x + 1$ $\{x = 4\}$

3 For each of the following functions find the value of $f(x)$ given in brackets:

    a $f(x) = x^2 - 2x + 3$ $\{f(2)\}$ **b** $f(x) = 4 - x^2$ $\{f(-3)\}$

    c $f(x) = -\frac{1}{4}x^2 + 3x - 4$ $\{f(0)\}$ **d** $f(x) = \frac{1}{2}x^2 + 3x$ $\{f(2)\}$

Example 1

State whether the following functions are satisfied by the given ordered pairs:

    a $y = 3x^2 + 2x$ $(2, 16)$ **b** $f(x) = -x^2 - 2x + 1$ $(-3, 1)$

---

    a $y = 3(2)^2 + 2(2)$ **b** $f(-3) = -(-3)^2 - 2(-3) + 1$

           $= 12 + 4$ $= -9 + 6 + 1$

           $= 16$ $= -2$

       i.e., when $x = 2$, $y = 16$ i.e., $f(-3) \neq 1$

       $\therefore$ $(2, 16)$ does satisfy $\therefore$ $(-3, 1)$ does not satisfy

           $y = 3x^2 + 2x$ $f(x) = -x^2 - 2x + 1$

---

4 State whether the following quadratic functions are satisfied by the given ordered pairs:

    a $f(x) = 5x^2 - 10$ $(0, 5)$ **b** $y = 2x^2 + 5x - 3$ $(4, 9)$

    c $y = -2x^2 + 3x$ $(-\frac{1}{2}, 1)$ **d** $y = -7x^2 + 8x + 15$ $(-1, 16)$

B   GRAPHS OF QUADRATIC FUNCTIONS

The graphs of all quadratic functions are **parabolas**. The parabola is one of the conic sections.

Conic sections are curves which can be obtained by cutting a cone with a plane. The Ancient Greek mathematicians were fascinated by conic sections.

You may like to find the conic sections for yourself by cutting an icecream cone. Cutting parallel to the side produces a parabola,   i.e.,

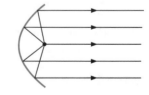

There are many examples of parabolas in every day life. The name parabola comes from the Greek word for **thrown** because when an object is thrown its path makes a parabolic shape.

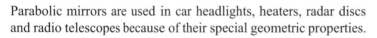

Parabolic mirrors are used in car headlights, heaters, radar discs and radio telescopes because of their special geometric properties.

Alongside is a single span parabolic bridge.

Some archways also have parabolic shape.

INVESTIGATION 1   GRAPHING $y = a(x-\alpha)(x-\beta)$

This investigation is best done using a **graphing package** or **graphics calculator**.

What to do:

1 **a** Use technology to assist you to draw sketch graphs of:
$$y = (x-1)(x-3), \quad y = 2(x-1)(x-3), \quad y = -(x-1)(x-3),$$
$$y = -3(x-1)(x-3) \quad \text{and} \quad y = -\tfrac{1}{2}(x-1)(x-3)$$

   b Find the x-intercepts for each function in **a**.

   c What is the geometrical significance of a in $y = a(x-1)(x-3)$?

2 **a** Use technology to assist you to draw sketch graphs of:
$$y = 2(x-1)(x-4), \quad y = 2(x-3)(x-5), \quad y = 2(x+1)(x-2),$$
$$y = 2x(x+5) \quad \text{and} \quad y = 2(x+2)(x+4)$$

   b Find the x-intercepts for each function in **a**.

   c What is the geometrical significance of α and β in $y = 2(x-\alpha)(x-\beta)$?

3 **a** Use technology to assist you to draw sketch graphs of:
$$y = 2(x-1)^2, \quad y = 2(x-3)^2, \quad y = 2(x+2)^2, \quad y = 2x^2$$

   b Find the x-intercepts for each function in **a**.

   c What is the geometrical significance of α in $y = 2(x-\alpha)^2$?

4 Copy and complete:
   - If a quadratic has factorisation $y = a(x-\alpha)(x-\beta)$ it ...... the x-axis at ......
   - If a quadratic has factorisation $y = a(x-\alpha)^2$ it ...... the x-axis at ......

INVESTIGATION 2   GRAPHING $y = a(x-h)^2 + k$

This investigation is also best done using technology.

What to do:

1 **a** Use technology to assist you to draw sketch graphs of:
$$y = (x-3)^2 + 2, \quad y = 2(x-3)^2 + 2, \quad y = -2(x-3)^2 + 2,$$
$$y = -(x-3)^2 + 2 \quad \text{and} \quad y = -\tfrac{1}{3}(x-3)^2 + 2$$

   b Find the coordinates of the vertex for each function in **a**.

   c What is the geometrical significance of a in $y = a(x-3)^2 + 2$?

2 **a** Use technology to assist you to to draw sketch graphs of:
$$y = 2(x-1)^2 + 3, \quad y = 2(x-2)^2 + 4, \quad y = 2(x-3)^2 + 1,$$
$$y = 2(x+1)^2 + 4, \quad y = 2(x+2)^2 - 5 \quad \text{and} \quad y = 2(x+3)^2 - 2$$

   b Find the coordinates of the vertex for each function in **a**.

   c What is the geometrical significance of h and k in $y = 2(x-h)^2 + k$?

3 Copy and complete:
   If a quadratic is in the form $y = a(x-h)^2 + k$ then its vertex has coordinates ....

From **Investigations 1** and **2** you should have discovered that:

- The coefficient of x^2 (which is a) controls the degree of width of the graph and whether it opens upwards or downwards.

  ▶ $a > 0$ ⌣ (concave up) whereas $a < 0$ produces ⌢ (concave down)

  ▶ If $-1 < a < 1$, $a \neq 0$ the graph is wider than $y = x^2$.
  If $a < -1$ or $a > 1$ the graph is narrower than $y = x^2$.

- In the form $y = a(x - \alpha)(x - \beta)$ the graph **cuts** the x-axis at α and β.

- In the form $y = a(x - \alpha)^2$ the graph **touches** the x-axis at α.

- In the form $y = a(x - h)^2 + k$ the graph has vertex (h, k) and axis of symmetry $x = h$.

THE FORM $y = a(x - \alpha)(x - \beta)$

If we are given an equation of the form $y = a(x - \alpha)(x - \beta)$ we can easily graph it using

- the x-intercepts (α and β)
- the axis of symmetry $\left(x = \frac{\alpha + \beta}{2}\right)$
- the coordinates of its vertex $\left(\frac{\alpha + \beta}{2}, f\left(\frac{\alpha + \beta}{2}\right)\right)$
- the y-intercept (let $x = 0$).

Example 2

Using axis intercepts only, sketch the graph of $y = 2(x + 1)(x - 3)$.

$y = 2(x + 1)(x - 3)$
has x-intercepts -1 and 3, $\therefore$ the axis
of symmetry is midway between
the x-intercepts i.e., $x = 1$

when $x = 1$, $y = 2(2)(-2) = -8$
$\therefore$ the vertex is $(1, -8)$

when $x = 0$, $y = 2(1)(-3) = -6$
$\therefore$ the y-intercept is -6

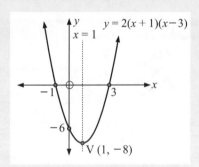

EXERCISE 7B.1

1 For each of the following functions:

    i state the x-intercepts   **ii** state the equation of the axis of symmetry
    iii find the coordinates of the vertex   **iv** find the y-intercept
    v sketch the graph of the function   **vi** use technology to check your answers.

    a $y = (x + 2)(x - 2)$ **b** $y = 2(x - 1)(x - 3)$ **c** $y = 3(x - 1)(x - 2)$

    d $y = \frac{1}{2}x(x - 4)$ **e** $y = -2x(x + 3)$ **f** $y = -\frac{1}{2}(x + 2)(x + 3)$

2 Match each function with its corresponding graph:

    a $y = x(x - 2)$ **b** $y = 3x(x - 2)$ **c** $y = -x(x - 2)$

    d $y = (x + 2)(x - 1)$ **e** $y = 2(x + 2)(x - 1)$ **f** $y = -2(x + 2)(x - 1)$

A 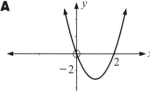   **B** 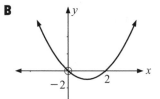   **C**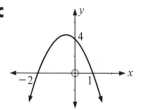

D 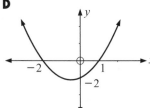   **E** 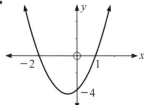   **F**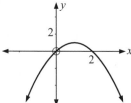

THE FORM $y = a(x - h)^2 + k$

If we are given an equation of the form $\;y = a(x - h)^2 + k\;$ we can easily graph it using:

- the axis of symmetry $(x = h)$
- the coordinates of the vertex (h, k)
- the y-intercept.   (let $x = 0$)

> In this form the axis of symmetry and the coordinates of the vertex are easy to read off.

Example 3

Use the vertex, axis of symmetry and y-intercept to sketch the graph of:

    a $y = -2(x - 2)^2 - 1$ **b** $y = \frac{1}{2}(x + 3)^2$

---

a $y = -2(x - 2)^2 - 1$

has axis of symmetry $\;x = 2$ and vertex $(2, -1)$

when $x = 0$, $\;y = -2(-2)^2 - 1 = -9$

$\therefore$ y-intercept is -9

$a < 0$, $\therefore$ the shape is $\cap$

b $y = \frac{1}{2}(x + 3)^2$

has axis of symmetry $\;x = -3$ and vertex $(-3, 0)$

when $\;x = 0$, $\;y = \frac{1}{2}(3)^2 = 4\frac{1}{2}$

$\therefore$ y-intercept is $4\frac{1}{2}$

$a > 0$, $\therefore$ the shape is $\cup$

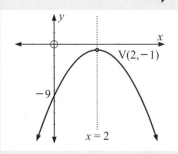

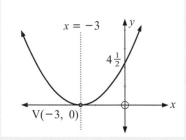

EXERCISE 7B.2

1 For each of the following functions:

    i   state the equation of the axis of symmetry   **ii**   find the coordinates of the vertex

    iii find the y-intercept   **iv**   sketch the graph of the function

    v   use technology to check your answers.

    a $y = (x - 4)^2 + 3$ **b** $y = 2(x + 1)^2$ **c** $y = -(x + 3)^2 + 2$

    d $y = 3(x + 2)^2 - 4$ **e** $y = \frac{1}{2}(x - 2)^2$ **f** $y = -\frac{3}{2}(x + 2)^2 - 4$

2 Match each quadratic function with its corresponding graph:

    a $y = -(x + 1)^2 + 3$ **b** $y = -2(x - 3)^2 + 2$ **c** $y = x^2 + 2$

    d $y = -(x - 1)^2 + 1$ **e** $y = (x - 2)^2 - 2$ **f** $y = \frac{1}{3}(x + 3)^2 - 3$

    g $y = -x^2$ **h** $y = -\frac{1}{2}(x - 1)^2 + 1$ **i** $y = 2(x + 2)^2 - 1$

A 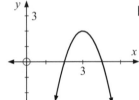   **B** 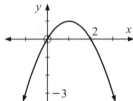   **C**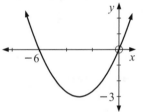

D 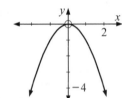   **E** 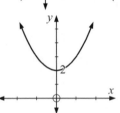   **F**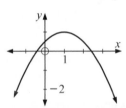

G 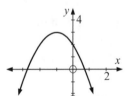   **H** 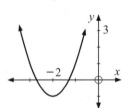   **I**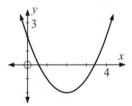

3 For each of the following find the equation of the axis of symmetry:

a 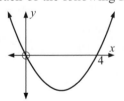   **b** 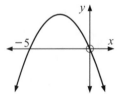   **c**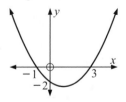

d 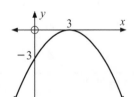   **e** 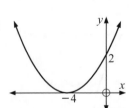   **f**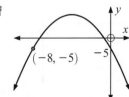

4 For each of the following quadratic functions:
  i sketch the graph using axes intercepts and hence find
  ii the equation of the axis of symmetry **iii** the coordinates of the vertex.

  a $y = x^2 + 4x$ **b** $y = x(x-4)$ **c** $y = 3(x-2)^2$
  d $y = 2(x-1)(x+3)$ **e** $y = -2(x-1)^2$ **f** $y = -3(x+2)(x-2)$

Example 4

Sketch the parabola which has x-intercepts -3 and 1, and y-intercept -2.
Find the equation of the axis of symmetry.

The axis of symmetry lies halfway
between the x-intercepts ∴ axis of
symmetry is $x = -1$.
$\{\dfrac{-3+1}{2} = -1\}$

Note: The graph is concave up.
Can you see why?

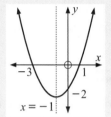

---

5 For each of the following:
  i sketch the parabola **ii** find the equation of the axis of symmetry.

  a x-intercepts 3 and -1, y-int. -4 **b** x-intercepts 2 and -2, y-int. 4
  c x-intercept -3 (touching), y-int. 6   **d** x-intercept 1 (touching), y-int. -4

6 Find all x-intercepts of the following graphs of quadratic functions:
  a cuts the x-axis at -1, axis of symmetry $x = -3$
  b touches the x-axis at 3.

C   COMPLETING THE SQUARE

If we wish to find the vertex of a quadratic given in general form $y = ax^2 + bx + c$ then one approach is to convert it to the form $y = a(x-h)^2 + k$ where we can read off the vertex $(h,\ k)$. To do this we may choose to '**complete the square**'.

Consider a case where $a = 1$; $y = x^2 - 4x + 1$.

$$y = x^2 - 4x + 1$$
$$\therefore \quad y = x^2 - 4x + 2^2 + 1 - 2^2$$
$$\therefore \quad y = x^2 - 4x + 2^2 - 3$$
$$\therefore \quad y = (x-2)^2 - 3$$

So, $y = x^2 - 4x + 1$ is really $y = (x-2)^2 - 3$

and therefore the graph of $y = x^2 - 4x + 1$ can be considered as the graph of $y = x^2$ after it has been translated 2 units to the right and 3 units down, i.e., $\begin{bmatrix} 2 \\ -3 \end{bmatrix}$.

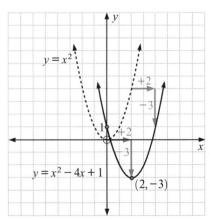

Example 5

Write $y = x^2 + 4x + 3$ in the form $y = (x - h)^2 + k$ using completing the square and hence sketch $y = x^2 + 4x + 3$, stating the coordinates of the vertex.

$y = x^2 + 4x + 3$

$\therefore \quad y = x^2 + 4x + 2^2 + 3 - 2^2$

$\therefore \quad y = (x + 2)^2 - 1$

shift 2
units left

shift 1
unit down

Vertex is $(-2, -1)$ and the y-intercept is 3

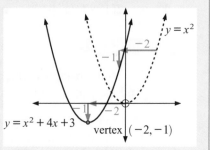

EXERCISE 7C

1 Write the following quadratics in the form $y = (x - h)^2 + k$ using 'completing the square' and hence sketch each function, stating the vertex:

a $y = x^2 - 2x + 3$

b $y = x^2 + 4x - 2$

c $y = x^2 - 4x$

d $y = x^2 + 3x$

e $y = x^2 + 5x - 2$

f $y = x^2 - 3x + 2$

g $y = x^2 - 6x + 5$

h $y = x^2 + 8x - 2$

i $y = x^2 - 5x + 1$

Example 6

Convert $y = 3x^2 - 4x + 1$ into the form $y = a(x - h)^2 + k$ by 'completing the square'. Hence, write down the coordinates of its vertex and sketch the graph of the function.

$y = 3x^2 - 4x + 1$

$= 3[x^2 - \frac{4}{3}x + \frac{1}{3}]$ {take out a factor of 3}

$= 3[x^2 - 2(\frac{2}{3})x + (\frac{2}{3})^2 - (\frac{2}{3})^2 + \frac{1}{3}]$ {complete the square}

$= 3[(x - \frac{2}{3})^2 - \frac{4}{9} + \frac{1}{3}]$ {write as a perfect square}

$= 3[(x - \frac{2}{3})^2 - \frac{4}{9} + \frac{3}{9}]$ {get common denominator}

$= 3[(x - \frac{2}{3})^2 - \frac{1}{9}]$ {add fractions}

$= 3(x - \frac{2}{3})^2 - \frac{1}{3}$ {expand to put into desired form}

So the vertex is $(\frac{2}{3}, -\frac{1}{3})$

The y-intercept is 1.

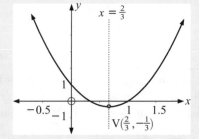

We can use technology to confirm this. For example:

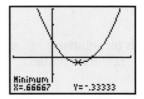

2   For each of the following quadratics:

> i   convert into the form $y = a(x - h)^2 + k$
> by 'completing the square'
> ii   state the coordinates of the vertex
> iii   find the y-intercept.
> iv   Hence, sketch the graph of the quadratic.
> v   Use technology to check your answer.

a is always the factor to be 'taken out'.

a	$y = 2x^2 + 4x + 5$	**b**	$y = 2x^2 - 8x + 3$
c	$y = 2x^2 - 6x + 1$	**d**	$y = 3x^2 - 6x + 5$
e	$y = -x^2 + 4x + 2$	**f**	$y = -2x^2 - 5x + 3$

3   By using your **graphing package** or **graphics calculator**, graph each of the following functions, and hence write each function in the form $y = a(x - h)^2 + k$:

a	$y = x^2 - 4x + 7$	**b**	$y = x^2 + 6x + 3$	**c**	$y = -x^2 + 4x + 5$
d	$y = 2x^2 + 6x - 4$	**e**	$y = -2x^2 - 10x + 1$	**f**	$y = 3x^2 - 9x - 5$

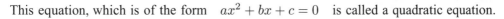

D   QUADRATIC EQUATIONS

Apex Leather Jacket Co. makes and sells x leather jackets each day and their revenue function is given by $R = 12.5x^2 - 550x + 8125$ dollars.

How many jackets must be made and sold each week in order to obtain income of $3000 each week?

Clearly we need to solve the equation:

$$12.5x^2 - 550x + 8125 = 3000$$
$$\text{i.e.,}\quad 12.5x^2 - 550x + 5125 = 0$$

This equation, which is of the form $ax^2 + bx + c = 0$ is called a quadratic equation.

> A **quadratic equation**, with variable x, is an equation of the form
> $ax^2 + bx + c = 0$ where $a \neq 0$.

To solve quadratic equations we can:

- **factorise** the quadratic and use the **Null Factor law**:   "if $ab = 0$ then $a = 0$
  or $b = 0$"
- **complete the square**
- use the **quadratic formula**
- use **technology**.

Definition:

The **roots** (or **solutions**) of $ax^2 + bx + c = 0$ are all the values of x which satisfy the equation (i.e., make it true).

For example, $x = 2$ is a root of $x^2 - 3x + 2 = 0$ since, when $x = 2$

$$x^2 - 3x + 2 = (2)^2 - 3(2) + 2 = 4 - 6 + 2 = 0 \quad \checkmark$$

SOLVING USING FACTORISATION

Step 1: Make one side of the equation 0 by transferring all terms to one side.

Step 2: Fully factorise the other side.

Step 3: Use the 'Null Factor law': "if $ab = 0$ then $a = 0$ or $b = 0$".

Step 4: Solve the resulting elementary linear equations.

Example 7

Solve for x: **a** $3x^2 + 5x = 0$ **b** $x^2 = 5x + 6$

a $3x^2 + 5x = 0$

$\therefore \quad x(3x + 5) = 0$

$\therefore \quad x = 0$ or $3x + 5 = 0$

$\therefore \quad x = 0$ or $x = -\frac{5}{3}$

b $x^2 = 5x + 6$

$\therefore \quad x^2 - 5x - 6 = 0$

$\therefore \quad (x - 6)(x + 1) = 0$

$\therefore \quad x - 6 = 0$ or $x + 1 = 0$

$\therefore \quad x = 6$ or -1

EXERCISE 7D.1

In each of the following, check answers with technology.

1 Solve the following using 'factorisation':

a	$4x^2 + 7x = 0$	**b**	$6x^2 + 2x = 0$	**c**	$3x^2 - 7x = 0$
d	$2x^2 - 11x = 0$	**e**	$3x^2 = 8x$	**f**	$9x = 6x^2$
g	$x^2 - 5x + 6 = 0$	**h**	$x^2 = 2x + 8$	**i**	$x^2 + 21 = 10x$
j	$9 + x^2 = 6x$	**k**	$x^2 + x = 12$	**l**	$x^2 + 8x = 33$

Example 8

Solve for x: **a** $4x^2 + 1 = 4x$ **b** $6x^2 = 11x + 10$

a $4x^2 + 1 = 4x$

$\therefore \quad 4x^2 - 4x + 1 = 0$

$\therefore \quad (2x - 1)^2 = 0$

$\therefore \quad x = \frac{1}{2}$

b $6x^2 = 11x + 10$

$\therefore \quad 6x^2 - 11x - 10 = 0$

$\therefore \quad (2x - 5)(3x + 2) = 0$ {using a factorisation technique}

$\therefore \quad x = \frac{5}{2}$ or $-\frac{2}{3}$

2 Solve the following using factorisation:

a $9x^2 - 12x + 4 = 0$ b $2x^2 - 13x - 7 = 0$ c $3x^2 = 16x + 12$

d $3x^2 + 5x = 2$ e $2x^2 + 3 = 5x$ f $3x^2 = 4x + 4$

g $3x^2 = 10x + 8$ h $4x^2 + 4x = 3$ i $4x^2 = 11x + 3$

j $12x^2 = 11x + 15$ k $7x^2 + 6x = 1$ l $15x^2 + 2x = 56$

Example 9

Solve for x:

$3x + \dfrac{2}{x} = -7$

$3x + \dfrac{2}{x} = -7$

$\therefore \quad x(3x + \dfrac{2}{x}) = -7x$ {multiply both sides by x to eliminate the fraction}

$\therefore \quad 3x^2 + 2 = -7x$ {clear the bracket}

$\therefore \quad 3x^2 + 7x + 2 = 0$ {equate to 0}

$\therefore \quad (x + 2)(3x + 1) = 0$ {on factorising}

$\therefore \quad x = -2 \text{ or } -\frac{1}{3}$

---

3 Solve for x:

a $(x + 1)^2 = 2x^2 - 5x + 11$ b $(x + 2)(1 - x) = -4$

c $5 - 4x^2 = 3(2x + 1) + 2$ d $x + \dfrac{2}{x} = 3$

e $2x - \dfrac{1}{x} = -1$ f $\dfrac{x + 3}{1 - x} = -\dfrac{9}{x}$

FINDING x GIVEN y IN $y = ax^2 + bx + c$

It is also possible to substitute a value for y to find a corresponding value for x. However, unlike linear functions, with quadratic functions there may be 0, 1 or 2 possible values for x for any one value of y.

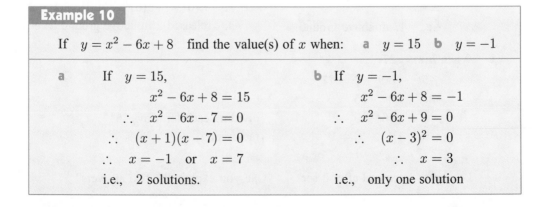

Example 10

If $y = x^2 - 6x + 8$ find the value(s) of x when: a $y = 15$ b $y = -1$

a   If $y = 15$,

$\qquad x^2 - 6x + 8 = 15$

$\therefore \quad x^2 - 6x - 7 = 0$

$\therefore \quad (x + 1)(x - 7) = 0$

$\therefore \quad x = -1 \text{ or } x = 7$

i.e., 2 solutions.

b   If $y = -1$,

$\qquad x^2 - 6x + 8 = -1$

$\therefore \quad x^2 - 6x + 9 = 0$

$\therefore \quad (x - 3)^2 = 0$

$\therefore \quad x = 3$

i.e., only one solution

4 Find the value(s) of x for the given value of y for each of the following quadratic functions:

  a $y = x^2 + 6x + 10$ $\{y = 1\}$
  b $y = x^2 + 5x + 8$ $\{y = 2\}$
  c $y = x^2 - 5x + 1$ $\{y = -3\}$
  d $y = 3x^2$ $\{y = -3\}$

Example 11

If $f(x) = x^2 + 4x + 11$ find x when   **a** $f(x) = 23$ **b** $f(x) = 7$

a   If $f(x) = 23$
$\therefore \quad x^2 + 4x + 11 = 23$
$\therefore \quad x^2 + 4x - 12 = 0$
$\therefore \quad (x + 6)(x - 2) = 0$ {factorising}
$\therefore \quad x = -6$ or 2
i.e., 2 solutions.

b   If $f(x) = 7$
$\therefore \quad x^2 + 4x + 11 = 7$
$\therefore \quad x^2 + 4x + 4 = 0$
$\therefore \quad (x + 2)^2 = 0$ {factorising}
$\therefore \quad x = -2$
i.e., one solution only.

---

5 Find the value(s) of x given that:

  a $f(x) = 3x^2 - 2x + 5$ and $f(x) = 5$
  b $f(x) = x^2 - x - 5$ and $f(x) = 1$
  c $f(x) = -2x^2 - 13x + 3$ and $f(x) = -4$
  d $f(x) = 2x^2 - 12x + 1$ and $f(x) = -17$

Example 12

A stone is thrown into the air and its height in metres above the ground is given by the function $h(t) = -5t^2 + 30t + 2$ where t is the time (in seconds) from when the stone is thrown.

  a How high above the ground is the stone at time $t = 3$ seconds?
  b How high above the ground was the stone released?
  c At what time was the stone's height above the ground 27 m?

a $h(3) = -5(3)^2 + 30(3) + 2$
$= -45 + 90 + 2$
$= 47$
i.e., 47 m above ground.

b The stone is released when
$t = 0$ sec
$\therefore \quad h(0) = -5(0)^2 + 30(0) + 2 = 2$
$\therefore$ released 2 m above ground level.

c When $h(t) = 27$
$-5t^2 + 30t + 2 = 27$
$\therefore \quad -5t^2 + 30t - 25 = 0$
$\therefore \quad t^2 - 6t + 5 = 0$ {dividing each term by -5}
$\therefore \quad (t - 1)(t - 5) = 0$ {factorising}
$\therefore \quad t = 1$ or 5

i.e., after 1 sec and after 5 sec.   Can you explain the two answers?

6 An object is projected into the air with a velocity of 30 m/s. Its height in metres, after t seconds, is given by the function $h(t) = 30t - 5t^2$.

    a Calculate the height after: **i** 1 second **ii** 5 seconds **iii** 3 seconds.

    b Calculate the time(s) at which the height is: **i** 40 m **ii** 0 m.

    c Explain your answers in part **b**.

7 A cake manufacturer finds that the profit in dollars, from making x cakes per day, is given by the function $P(x) = -\frac{1}{4}x^2 + 16x - 30$.

    a Calculate the profit if: **i** 0 cakes **ii** 10 cakes are made per day.

    b How many cakes per day are made if the profit is \$57?

SOLVING USING 'COMPLETING THE SQUARE'

As you would be aware by now, not all quadratics factorise easily. In fact, $x^2 + 4x + 1$ cannot be factorised by using a simple factorisation approach.

This means that we need a different approach in order to solve $x^2 + 4x + 1 = 0$.

One way is to use the 'completing the square' technique.

So, equations of the form $ax^2 + bx + c = 0$ can be converted to the form $(x + p)^2 = q$ from which the solutions are easy to obtain.

> Notice that if $X^2 = a$, then $X = \pm\sqrt{a}$ is used.

Example 13

Solve exactly for x: **a** $(x + 2)^2 = 7$ **b** $(x - 1)^2 = -5$

a $(x+2)^2 = 7$ $\therefore\quad x + 2 = \pm\sqrt{7}$ $\therefore\quad x = -2 \pm \sqrt{7}$	**b** $(x - 1)^2 = -5$ has no real solutions {the perfect square, $(x - 1)^2$ cannot be negative}

EXERCISE 7D.2

1 Solve for exact values of x:

    a $(x + 5)^2 = 2$ **b** $(x + 6)^2 = 11$ **c** $(x - 4)^2 = 8$

    d $(x - 8)^2 = 7$ **e** $2(x + 3)^2 = 10$ **f** $3(x - 2)^2 = 18$

    g $(x + 1)^2 + 1 = 11$ **h** $(2x + 1)^2 = 3$

Example 14

Solve for exact values of x: $x^2 + 4x + 1 = 0$

$x^2 + 4x + 1 = 0$	
$\therefore\quad x^2 + 4x = -1$	{put the constant on the RHS}
$\therefore\quad x^2 + 4x + 2^2 = -1 + 2^2$	{completing the square}
$\therefore\quad (x + 2)^2 = 3$	{factorising}
$\therefore\quad x + 2 = \pm\sqrt{3}$	{solving}
$\therefore\quad x = -2 \pm \sqrt{3}$	

> The squared number we add to both sides is $\left(\dfrac{\text{coefficient of } x}{2}\right)^2$

2 Solve for exact values of x by completing the square:

a $x^2 - 4x + 1 = 0$ 　　　**b** $x^2 + 6x + 2 = 0$ 　　　**c** $x^2 - 14x + 46 = 0$

d $x^2 = 4x + 3$ 　　　　　**e** $x^2 + 6x + 7 = 0$ 　　　**f** $x^2 = 2x + 6$

g $x^2 + 6x = 2$ 　　　　　**h** $x^2 + 10 = 8x$ 　　　　**i** $x^2 + 6x = -11$

3 If the coefficient of x^2 is not 1, we first divide throughout to make it 1.

For example,　$2x^2 + 10x + 3 = 0$ 　　becomes　$x^2 + 5x + \frac{3}{2} = 0$

$-3x^2 + 12x + 5 = 0$ 　becomes　$x^2 - 4x - \frac{5}{3} = 0$

Solve for exact values of x by completing the square:

a $2x^2 + 4x + 1 = 0$ 　　**b** $2x^2 - 10x + 3 = 0$ 　　**c** $3x^2 + 12x + 5 = 0$

d $3x^2 = 6x + 4$ 　　　　**e** $5x^2 - 15x + 2 = 0$ 　　**f** $4x^2 + 4x = 5$

E　　THE QUADRATIC FORMULA

Many quadratic equations cannot be solved by factorising, and completing the square is rather tedious. Consequently, the **quadratic formula** has been developed. This formula is:

$$\text{If }\ ax^2 + bx + c = 0, \quad \text{then}\quad x = \frac{-b \pm \sqrt{b^2 - 4ac}}{2a}.$$

Consider the Apex Leather Jacket Co. equation from page **131**. We need to solve:

$$12.5x^2 - 550x + 5125 = 0$$

Here we have $a = 12.5$, 　$b = -550$, 　$c = 5125$

Trying to factorise this equation or using 'completing the square' would not be easy.

$$\therefore\quad x = \frac{550 \pm \sqrt{(-550)^2 - 4(12.5)(5125)}}{2(12.5)}$$

$$= \frac{550 \pm \sqrt{46\,250}}{25}$$

$$\doteqdot 30.60 \quad \text{or} \quad 13.40$$

But as x needs to be a whole number, 　$x = 13$ or 31 would produce income of around \$3000 each week.

The following proof of the quadratic formula is worth careful examination.

Proof: 　　If　$ax^2 + bx + c = 0$,

then　$x^2 + \dfrac{b}{a}x + \dfrac{c}{a} = 0$ 　　　　　　　{dividing each term by a, as $a \neq 0$}

$\therefore \quad x^2 + \dfrac{b}{a}x \qquad = -\dfrac{c}{a}$

$\therefore \quad x^2 + \dfrac{b}{a}x + \left(\dfrac{b}{2a}\right)^2 = -\dfrac{c}{a} + \left(\dfrac{b}{2a}\right)^2$ 　　　　{completing the square on LHS}

$\therefore \quad \left(x + \dfrac{b}{2a}\right)^2 = -\dfrac{c}{a}\left(\dfrac{4a}{4a}\right) + \dfrac{b^2}{4a^2}$

$$\therefore \quad \left(x + \frac{b}{2a}\right)^2 = \frac{b^2 - 4ac}{4a^2}$$

$$\therefore \quad x + \frac{b}{2a} = \pm\sqrt{\frac{b^2 - 4ac}{4a^2}}$$

$$\therefore \quad x = -\frac{b}{2a} \pm \sqrt{\frac{b^2 - 4ac}{4a^2}}$$

$$\text{i.e.,} \quad x = \frac{-b \pm \sqrt{b^2 - 4ac}}{2a}$$

Example 15

Solve for x: **a** $x^2 - 2x - 2 = 0$ **b** $2x^2 + 3x - 4 = 0$

a $x^2 - 2x - 2 = 0$ has
$a = 1, \quad b = -2, \quad c = -2$

$$\therefore \quad x = \frac{-(-2) \pm \sqrt{(-2)^2 - 4(1)(-2)}}{2(1)}$$

$$\therefore \quad x = \frac{2 \pm \sqrt{4 + 8}}{2}$$

$$\therefore \quad x = \frac{2 \pm \sqrt{12}}{2}$$

$$\therefore \quad x = \frac{2 \pm 2\sqrt{3}}{2}$$

$$\therefore \quad x = 1 \pm \sqrt{3}$$

Solutions are: $1 + \sqrt{3}$ and $1 - \sqrt{3}$.

b $2x^2 + 3x - 4 = 0$ has
$a = 2, \quad b = 3, \quad c = -4$

$$\therefore \quad x = \frac{-3 \pm \sqrt{3^2 - 4(2)(-4)}}{2(2)}$$

$$\therefore \quad x = \frac{-3 \pm \sqrt{9 + 32}}{4}$$

$$\therefore \quad x = \frac{-3 \pm \sqrt{41}}{4}$$

Solutions are:

$$\frac{-3 + \sqrt{41}}{4} \quad \text{and} \quad \frac{-3 - \sqrt{41}}{4}.$$

EXERCISE 7E

1 Use the quadratic formula to solve for exact values of x:

   a $x^2 - 4x - 3 = 0$ **b** $x^2 + 6x + 7 = 0$ **c** $x^2 + 1 = 4x$

   d $x^2 + 4x = 1$ **e** $x^2 - 4x + 2 = 0$ **f** $2x^2 - 2x - 3 = 0$

   g $x^2 - 2\sqrt{2}x + 2 = 0$ **h** $(3x + 1)^2 = -2x$ **i** $(x + 3)(2x + 1) = 9$

2 Use the quadratic formula to solve for exact values of x:

   a $(x+2)(x-1) = 2-3x$ **b** $(2x + 1)^2 = 3 - x$ **c** $(x - 2)^2 = 1 + x$

   d $\dfrac{x - 1}{2 - x} = 2x + 1$ **e** $x - \dfrac{1}{x} = 1$ **f** $2x - \dfrac{1}{x} = 3$

Note: If asked to solve quadratic equations for **exact values** of x, use the quadratic formula.
     Use **completing the square** only when asked to do so.

F   SOLVING QUADRATIC EQUATIONS WITH TECHNOLOGY

A **graphics calculator** or **graphing package** could be used to solve quadratic equations.

However, exact solutions in square root form would be lost in most cases. Approximate decimal solutions are usually generated. At this stage we will find solutions using **graphs** of quadratics and examine intersections with the x-axis (to get zeros) or the intersection of two functions to find the x-coordinates of the points where they meet.

We have chosen to use this approach, even though it may not be the quickest, so that an understanding of the link between the algebra and the graphics is fully appreciated.

Consider the equation $2x^2 - 3x - 4 = 0$.

Our approach will be:

- draw the graph of $y = 2x^2 - 3x - 4$
- now $2x^2 - 3x - 4 = 0$ when $y = 0$ and this occurs at the x-intercepts of the graph.

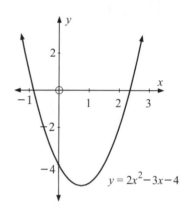

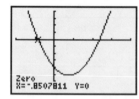 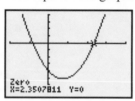

The solutions are: $x \doteqdot -0.8508$ or 2.351

Click on the appropriate icon for helpful instructions if using a **graphics calculator** and/or **graphing package**.

GRAPHING PACKAGE

EXERCISE 7F

1 Use technology to solve:

    a $x^2 + 4x + 2 = 0$ **b** $x^2 + 6x - 2 = 0$ **c** $2x^2 - 3x - 7 = 0$

    d $3x^2 - 7x - 11 = 0$ **e** $4x^2 - 11x - 13 = 0$ **f** $5x^2 + 6x - 17 = 0$

To solve a more complicated equation like $(x-2)(x+1) = 2 + 3x$ we could:

- make the RHS zero i.e., $(x-2)(x+1) - 2 - 3x = 0$.
  Plot $y = (x-2)(x+1) - 2 - 3x$ and find the x-intercepts.
- plot $y = (x-2)(x+1)$ and $y = 2 + 3x$ on the same axes and find the x-coordinates where the two graphs meet.

GRAPHING PACKAGE

If using a graphics calculator with

$Y_1 = (x-2)(x+1)$ and

$Y_2 = 2 + 3x$ we get

So, the solutions are

$x \doteqdot -0.8284$ or 4.8284

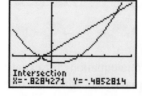 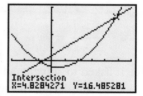

2 Use technology to solve:

a $(x+2)(x-1) = 2-3x$

b $(2x+1)^2 = 3 - x$

c $(x-2)^2 = 1 + x$

d $\dfrac{x-1}{2-x} = 2x + 1$

e $x - \dfrac{1}{x} = 1$

f $2x - \dfrac{1}{x} = 3$

G | PROBLEM SOLVING WITH QUADRATICS

When solving some problems algebraically, a quadratic equation results. Consequently, we are only interested in any **real solutions** which result as we are looking for real answers.

If the resulting quadratic equation has no real roots then the problem has no real solution.

Also, any answer must be checked to see if it is reasonable. For example:

- if you are finding a length then it must be positive, so reject any negative solutions
- if you are finding 'how many people present' then clearly a fractional answer would be unacceptable.

General problem solving method:

Step 1: If the information is given in words, translate it into algebra using x for the unknown, say. An equation results.

Step 2: Solve the equation by a suitable method.

Step 3: Examine the solutions carefully to see if they are acceptable.

Step 4: Give your answer in a sentence.

Example 16

A rectangle has length 3 cm longer than its width. Its area is 42 cm². Find its width.

If the width is x cm, then the length is $(x + 3)$ cm.

Therefore $x(x + 3) = 42$ {equating areas}

$\therefore \quad x^2 + 3x - 42 = 0$

$\therefore \quad x \doteqdot -8.15$ or 5.15 {using technology}

We reject the negative solution as lengths are positive $\therefore$ width $\doteqdot 5.15$ cm.

x cm

$(x + 3)$ cm

EXERCISE 7G

1 Two integers differ by 12 and the sum of their squares is 74. Find the integers.

2 The sum of a number and its reciprocal is $5\frac{1}{5}$. Find the number.

3 The sum of a natural number and its square is 210. Find the number.

4 The product of two consecutive even numbers is 360. Find the numbers.

5 The product of two consecutive odd numbers is 255. Find the numbers.

6 The number of diagonals of an n-sided polygon is given by the formula $D = \dfrac{n}{2}(n-3)$. A polygon has 90 diagonals. How many sides does it have?

7 The length of a rectangle is 4 cm longer than its width. Find its width given that its area is 26 cm².

8 A rectangular box has a square base and its height is 1 cm longer than the length of one side of its base.

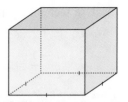

   a If x cm is the length of one side of its base, show that its total surface area, A, is given by $A = 6x^2 + 4x$ cm^2.

   b If the total surface area is 240 cm^2, find the dimensions of the box.

9

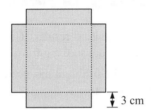

3 cm

An open box contains 80 cm^3 and is made from a square piece of tinplate with 3 cm squares cut from each of its 4 corners. Find the dimensions of the original piece of tinplate.

Example 17

Is it possible to bend a 12 cm length of wire to form the legs of a right angled triangle with area 20 cm^2?

i.e.,   ————   becomes

area 20 cm^2

$$\text{Area,} \quad A = \tfrac{1}{2}(12 - x)x$$

x

$12 - x$

$$\therefore \quad \tfrac{1}{2}x(12 - x) = 20$$
$$\therefore \quad x(12 - x) = 40$$
$$\therefore \quad 12x - x^2 - 40 = 0$$
$$\therefore \quad x^2 - 12x + 40 = 0 \quad \text{which becomes} \quad x = \frac{12 \pm \sqrt{-16}}{2}$$

Thus there are no real solutions, indicating the **impossibility**.

---

10 Is it possible to bend a 20 cm length of wire into the shape of a rectangle which has an area of 30 cm^2?

11 The *golden rectangle* is the rectangle defined by the following statement:

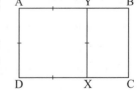

The golden rectangle can be divided into a square and a smaller rectangle by a line which is parallel to its shorter sides, and the smaller rectangle is **similar** to the original rectangle.

Thus, if ABCD is the golden rectangle, ADXY is a square and BCXY is similar to ABCD, (i.e., BCXY is a reduction of ABCD).

The ratio of $\dfrac{AB}{AD}$ for the golden rectangle is called the **golden ratio**.

Show that the golden ratio is $\dfrac{1 + \sqrt{5}}{2}$.   (**Hint:**   Let $AB = x$ units and $BC = 1$ unit.)

12

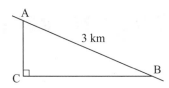

A triangular paddock has a road AB forming its hypotenuse. AB is 3 km long. The fences AC and CB are at right angles. If BC is 400 m longer than AC, find the area of the paddock in hectares.

13 Find the width of a uniform concrete path placed around a 30 m by 40 m rectangular lawn given that the concrete has area one quarter of the lawn.

Example 18

A wall is 12 m long and is timber panelled using vertical sheets of panelling of equal width. If the sheets had been 0.2 m wider, 2 less sheets would have been required. What is the width of the timber panelling used?

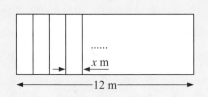

Let x m be the width of each panel used.

$\therefore \quad \dfrac{12}{x}$ is the number of sheets needed.

Now if the sheets are $\left(x + \frac{1}{5}\right)$ m in width

$\left(\dfrac{12}{x} - 2\right)$ sheets are needed.

So, $\left(x + \frac{1}{5}\right)\left(\dfrac{12}{x} - 2\right) = 12$ $\qquad$ {length of wall}

$\therefore \quad 12 - 2x + \dfrac{12}{5x} - \frac{2}{5} = 12$ $\qquad$ {expanding LHS}

$\therefore \quad -2x + \dfrac{12}{5x} - \frac{2}{5} = 0$

$\therefore \quad -10x^2 + 12 - 2x = 0$ $\qquad$ {$\times$ each term by $5x$}

$\therefore \quad 5x^2 + x - 6 = 0$ $\qquad$ {$\div$ each term by -2}

$\therefore \quad (5x + 6)(x - 1) = 0$

$\therefore \quad x = -\frac{6}{5}$ or 1 where $x > 0$

$\therefore$ each sheet is 1 m wide.

---

14 Chuong and Hassan both drive 40 km from home to work each day. One day Chuong said to Hassan, "If you drive home at your usual speed, I will average 40 kmph faster than you and arrive home in 20 minutes less time." Find Hassan's speed.

15 If the average speed of an aeroplane had been 120 kmph less, it would have taken a half an hour longer to fly 1000 km. Find the speed of the plane.

16 Two trains travel a 105 km track each day. The express travels 10 kmph faster and takes 30 minutes less than the normal train. Find the speed of the express.

17 A group of elderly citizens chartered a bus for $160. However, at the last minute, due to illness, 8 of them had to miss the trip. Consequently the other citizens had to pay an extra $1 each. How many elderly citizens went on the trip?

H   QUADRATIC GRAPHS (REVIEW)

REVIEW OF TERMINOLOGY

The equation of a **quadratic function** is given by $y = ax^2 + bx + c$, where $a \neq 0$.

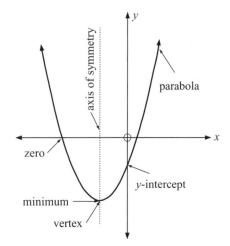

The graph of a quadratic function is called a **parabola**. The point where the graph 'turns' is called the **vertex**.

If the graph opens upward, the y coordinate of the vertex is the **minimum** (concave up), while if the graph opens downward, the y-coordinate of the vertex is the **maximum** (concave down).

The vertical line that passes through the vertex is called the **axis of symmetry**. All parabolas are symmetrical about the axis of symmetry.

The point where the graph crosses the y-axis is the y-**intercept**.

The points (if they exist) where the graph crosses the x-axis should be called the x-**intercepts**, but more commonly are called the **zeros** of the function.

OPENING UPWARDS OR DOWNWARDS?

If the coefficient of x^2:
- is positive, the graph is concave up $a > 0$
- is negative, the graph is concave down $a < 0$.

Quadratic form, $a \neq 0$	Graph	Facts
• $y = a(x - \alpha)(x - \beta)$ α, β are real	$x = \dfrac{\alpha + \beta}{2}$	x-intercepts are α and β axis of symmetry is $x = \frac{\alpha + \beta}{2}$
• $y = a(x - \alpha)^2$ α is real	$x = \alpha$ V $(\alpha, 0)$	touches x-axis at α vertex is $(\alpha, 0)$ axis of symmetry is $x = \alpha$
• $y = a(x - h)^2 + k$	$x = h$ V (h, k)	vertex is (h, k) axis of symmetry is $x = h$

Quadratic form, $a \neq 0$	Graph	Facts
• $y = ax^2 + bx + c$ (general quadratic form)	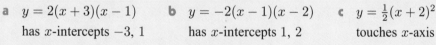	axis of symmetry is $$x = \frac{-b}{2a}$$ x-intercepts for $\Delta \geqslant 0$ are $$\frac{-b \pm \sqrt{\Delta}}{2a}$$ where $\Delta = b^2 - 4ac$

Notice that the axis of symmetry is always easily found.

Note: $\quad -\dfrac{b}{2a}$ is the **average** of $\dfrac{-b - \sqrt{\Delta}}{2a}$ and $\dfrac{-b + \sqrt{\Delta}}{2a}$.

$$\text{as the sum equals} \quad \frac{-b - \sqrt{\Delta}}{2a} + \frac{-b + \sqrt{\Delta}}{2a} = \frac{-2b}{2a} = \frac{-b}{a}$$

and so the average is $\dfrac{\text{the sum}}{2} = \dfrac{-b}{2a}$.

SKETCHING GRAPHS USING KEY FACTS

Example 19

Using axis intercepts only, sketch the graphs of:

a $y = 2(x + 3)(x - 1)$ **b** $y = -2(x - 1)(x - 2)$ **c** $y = \frac{1}{2}(x + 2)^2$

a $y = 2(x + 3)(x - 1)$

has x-intercepts -3, 1

when $x = 0$,
$y = 2(3)(-1)$
$= -6$

y-intercept is -6

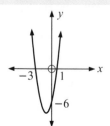

b $y = -2(x - 1)(x - 2)$

has x-intercepts 1, 2

when $x = 0$,
$y = -2(-1)(-2)$
$= -4$

y-intercept -4

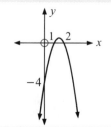

c $y = \frac{1}{2}(x + 2)^2$

touches x-axis at -2

when $x = 0$,
$y = \frac{1}{2}(2)^2$
$= 2$

has y-intercept 2

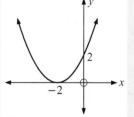

EXERCISE 7H

1 Using axis intercepts only, sketch the graphs of:

    a $y = (x - 4)(x + 2)$ **b** $y = -(x - 4)(x + 2)$ **c** $y = 2(x + 3)(x + 5)$

    d $y = -3x(x + 4)$ **e** $y = 2(x + 3)^2$ **f** $y = -\frac{1}{4}(x + 2)^2$

2 What is the axis of symmetry of each graph in question **1**?

Example 20

Use the vertex, axis of symmetry and y-intercept to graph $y = -2(x + 1)^2 + 4$.

The vertex is $(-1, 4)$.

The axis of symmetry is $x = -1$.

When $x = 0$, $y = -2(1)^2 + 4$
$$= 2$$

$a < 0$ $\therefore$ $\bigwedge$ shape

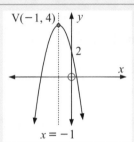

---

3 Use the vertex, axis of symmetry and y-intercept to graph:

    a $y = (x - 1)^2 + 3$ **b** $y = 2(x + 2)^2 + 1$ **c** $y = -2(x - 1)^2 - 3$

    d $y = \frac{1}{2}(x - 3)^2 + 2$ **e** $y = -\frac{1}{3}(x - 1)^2 + 4$ **f** $y = -\frac{1}{10}(x + 2)^2 - 3$

Example 21

For the quadratic $y = 2x^2 + 6x - 3$, find:
a the equation of the axis of symmetry   **b** the coordinates of the vertex
c the axes intercepts.   **d** Hence, sketch the graph.

For $y = 2x^2 + 6x - 3$, $a = 2$, $b = 6$, $c = -3$ $a > 0$ $\therefore$

a $\dfrac{-b}{2a} = \dfrac{-6}{4} = -\dfrac{3}{2}$

     $\therefore$ axis of symmetry is $x = -\frac{3}{2}$.

b   When $x = -\frac{3}{2}$,

     $y = 2(-\frac{3}{2})^2 + 6(-\frac{3}{2}) - 3$

        $= -7.5$ {simplifying}

     $\therefore$ vertex is $(-\frac{3}{2}, -7\frac{1}{2})$.

c   When $x = 0$, $y = -3$

     $\therefore$ y-intercept is -3.

When $y = 0$, $2x^2 + 6x - 3 = 0$

     $\therefore$ $x = \dfrac{-6 \pm \sqrt{36 - 4(2)(-3)}}{4}$

     $\therefore$ $x \doteqdot -3.44$ or 0.44

d

Example 22

Determine the coordinates of the vertex of $y = 2x^2 - 8x + 1$.

$y = 2x^2 - 8x + 1$ has $a = 2$, $b = -8$, $c = 1$

and so $\dfrac{-b}{2a} = \dfrac{-(-8)}{2 \times 2} = 2$

$\therefore$ equation of axis of symmetry is $x = 2$

and when $x = 2$, $y = 2(2)^2 - 8(2) + 1$

$= -7$

$\therefore$ the vertex has coordinates $(2, -7)$.

> The vertex is sometimes called the maximum turning point or the minimum turning point depending on whether the graph is concave down or concave up.

Note: A parabola opening upwards has a shape called **concave up**.
A parabola opening downwards has a shape called **concave down**.

4   Find the turning point (vertex) for the following quadratic functions:

   a $y = x^2 - 4x + 2$ **b** $y = x^2 + 2x - 3$

   c $y = 2x^2 + 4$ **d** $y = -3x^2 + 1$

   e $y = 2x^2 + 8x - 7$ **f** $y = -x^2 - 4x - 9$

   g $y = 2x^2 + 6x - 1$ **h** $y = 2x^2 - 10x + 3$

   i $y = -\frac{1}{2}x^2 + x - 5$ **j** $y = -2x^2 + 8x - 2$

5   Find the x-intercepts for:

   a $y = x^2 - 9$ **b** $y = 2x^2 - 6$ **c** $y = x^2 + 7x + 10$

   d $y = x^2 + x - 12$ **e** $y = 4x - x^2$ **f** $y = -x^2 - 6x - 8$

   g $y = -2x^2 - 4x - 2$ **h** $y = 4x^2 - 24x + 36$ **i** $y = x^2 - 4x + 1$

   j $y = x^2 + 4x - 3$ **k** $y = x^2 - 6x - 2$ **l** $y = x^2 + 8x + 11$

6   For the following quadratics, find:

   i   the equation of the axis of symmetry   **ii**   the coordinates of the vertex

   iii   the axes intercepts, if they exist   **iv**   Hence, sketch the graph.

   a $y = x^2 - 2x + 5$ **b** $y = x^2 + 4x - 1$ **c** $y = 2x^2 - 5x + 2$

   d $y = -x^2 + 3x - 2$ **e** $y = -3x^2 + 4x - 1$ **f** $y = -2x^2 + x + 1$

   g $y = 6x - x^2$ **h** $y = -x^2 - 6x - 8$ **i** $y = -\frac{1}{4}x^2 + 2x + 1$

THE DISCRIMINANT, Δ

In the quadratic formula, $b^2 - 4ac$,   which is under the square root sign, is called **the discriminant**.

The symbol **delta** Δ, is used to represent the discriminant,   i.e., $\Delta = b^2 - 4ac$.

The quadratic formula becomes $x = \dfrac{-b \pm \sqrt{\Delta}}{2a}$ if Δ replaces $b^2 - 4ac$.

Note: • if $\Delta = 0$, $x = \dfrac{-b}{2a}$ is the **only solution** (a **repeated** or **double root**)

• if $\Delta > 0$, $\sqrt{\Delta}$ is a positive real number and so there are **two distinct real roots**, $\dfrac{-b + \sqrt{\Delta}}{2a}$ and $\dfrac{-b - \sqrt{\Delta}}{2a}$

• if $\Delta < 0$, $\sqrt{\Delta}$ is not a real number and so there are **no real roots**.

Note: If a, b and c are rational and Δ is a **perfect square** then the equation has two rational roots which can be found by factorisation.

Example 23

Use the discriminant to determine the nature of the roots of:

a $2x^2 - 3x + 4 = 0$ **b** $4x^2 - 4x - 1 = 0$

a $\Delta = b^2 - 4ac$
$= (-3)^2 - 4(2)(4)$
$= -23$ which is < 0
$\therefore$ no real roots

b $\Delta = b^2 - 4ac$
$= (-4)^2 - 4(4)(-1)$
$= 32$ which is > 0
$\therefore$ has 2 distinct irrational roots

EXERCISE 7I.1

1 By using the discriminant only, state the nature of the solutions of:

a $x^2 + 7x - 2 = 0$ **b** $x^2 + 4\sqrt{2}x + 8 = 0$ **c** $2x^2 + 3x - 1 = 0$

d $6x^2 + 5x - 4 = 0$ **e** $x^2 + x + 6 = 0$ **f** $9x^2 + 6x + 1 = 0$

2 By using the discriminant only, determine which of the following quadratic equations have rational roots which can be found by factorisation.

a $2x^2 + 7x - 4 = 0$ **b** $3x^2 - 7x - 6 = 0$ **c** $2x^2 + 6x + 1 = 0$

d $6x^2 + 19x + 10 = 0$ **e** $4x^2 - 3x + 3 = 0$ **f** $8x^2 - 10x - 3 = 0$

Example 24

For $x^2 - 2x + m = 0$, find Δ and hence find the values of m for which the equation has: **a** a repeated root **b** 2 distinct real roots **c** no real roots.

$x^2 - 2x + m = 0$ has $a = 1$, $b = -2$ and $c = m$
$\therefore$ $\Delta = b^2 - 4ac = (-2)^2 - 4(1)(m) = 4 - 4m$

a For a repeated root
$\Delta = 0$
$\therefore$ $4 - 4m = 0$
$\therefore$ $4 = 4m$
$\therefore$ $m = 1$

b For 2 distinct real roots
$\Delta > 0$
$\therefore$ $4 - 4m > 0$
$\therefore$ $-4m > -4$
$\therefore$ $m < 1$

c For no real roots
$\Delta < 0$
$\therefore$ $4 - 4m < 0$
$\therefore$ $-4m < -4$
$\therefore$ $m > 1$

Note: 2 distinct real roots ⟵——— repeated ———⟶ imaginary roots m values
1

3 For the following quadratic equations, determine the discriminant in simplest form and hence find the values of m for which the equation has:

    i a repeated root   **ii** two distinct roots   **iii** no real roots.

    a $x^2 + 3x + m = 0$ **b** $x^2 - 5x + m = 0$ **c** $mx^2 - x + 1 = 0$

    d $mx^2 + 2x + 3 = 0$ **e** $2x^2 + 7x + m = 0$ **f** $mx^2 - 5x + 4 = 0$

THE DISCRIMINANT AND THE QUADRATIC GRAPH

Consider the graphs of: $y = x^2 - 2x + 3$, $y = x^2 - 2x + 1$, $y = x^2 - 2x - 3$.

All of these curves have axis of symmetry with equation $x = 1$.

$y = x^2 - 2x + 3$	$y = x^2 - 2x + 1$	$y = x^2 - 2x - 3$
(graph)	(graph)	(graph)
$\Delta = b^2 - 4ac$ $= (-2)^2 - 4(1)(3)$ $= -8$	$\Delta = b^2 - 4ac$ $= (-2)^2 - 4(1)(1)$ $= 0$	$\Delta = b^2 - 4ac$ $= (-2)^2 - 4(1)(-3)$ $= 16$
$\Delta < 0$	$\Delta = 0$	$\Delta > 0$
does not cut the x-axis	touches the x-axis	cuts the x-axis twice

Thus, the **discriminant** Δ, helps us to decide between the possibilities of:

- not cutting the x-axis $(\Delta < 0)$
- touching the x-axis $(\Delta = 0)$
- cutting the x-axis twice $(\Delta > 0)$.

Example 25

Use the discriminant to determine the relationship between the graph and the x-axis of: **a** $y = x^2 + 3x + 4$ **b** $y = -2x^2 + 5x + 1$

a $a = 1, \quad b = 3, \quad c = 4$

    $\therefore \quad \Delta = b^2 - 4ac$ $a > 0 \quad \therefore \quad$ concave up

          $= 9 - 4(1)(4)$

          $= -7$ which is < 0

    $\therefore$ graph does not cut the x-axis,   i.e.,   lies entirely above the x-axis.

b $a = -2, \quad b = 5, \quad c = 1$ $a < 0 \quad \therefore \quad$ concave down

    $\therefore \quad \Delta = b^2 - 4ac$

          $= 25 - 4(-2)(1)$

          $= 33$ which is > 0 $\therefore$ graph cuts the x-axis twice.

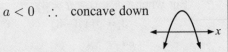

POSITIVE DEFINITE AND NEGATIVE DEFINITE QUADRATICS

Definitions:

Positive definite quadratics are quadratics which are definitely positive for all values of x, i.e., $ax^2 + bx + c > 0$ for all x.

Negative definite quadratics are quadratics which are definitely negative for all values of x, i.e., $ax^2 + bx + c < 0$ for all x.

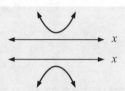

TESTS
- A quadratic is **positive definite** if $a > 0$ and $\Delta < 0$, i.e., $y > 0$ for all $x \in \mathcal{R}$.
- A quadratic is **negative definite** if $a < 0$ and $\Delta < 0$, i.e., $y < 0$ for all $x \in \mathcal{R}$.

EXERCISE 7I.2

1 Use the discriminant to determine the relationship between the graph and x-axis for:

   a $y = x^2 + 7x - 2$ **b** $y = x^2 + 4\sqrt{2}x + 8$ **c** $y = -2x^2 + 3x + 1$

   d $y = 6x^2 + 5x - 4$ **e** $y = -x^2 + x + 6$ **f** $y = 9x^2 + 6x + 1$

2 Show that:

   a $x^2 - 3x + 6 > 0$ for all x **b** $4x - x^2 - 6 < 0$ for all x

   c $2x^2 - 4x + 7$ is positive definite   **d** $-2x^2 + 3x - 4$ is negative definite

3 Explain why $3x^2 + kx - 1$ is never always positive for any value of k.

4 Under what conditions is $2x^2 + kx + 2$ positive definite?

J   DETERMINING THE QUADRATIC FROM A GRAPH

If we are given sufficient information on or about a graph we can determine the quadratic function in whatever form is required.

Example 26

Find the equation of the quadratic with graph:

a
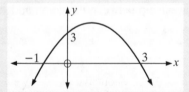

b
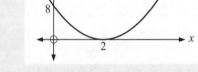

a Since the x-intercepts are -1 and 3
then $y = a(x + 1)(x - 3)$, $a < 0$.
But when $x = 0$, $y = 3$
$\therefore \quad 3 = a(1)(-3)$
$\therefore \quad a = -1$
So, $y = -(x + 1)(x - 3)$.

b Since it touches at 2, then
$y = a(x - 2)^2$, $a > 0$.
But when $x = 0$, $y = 8$
$\therefore \quad 8 = a(-2)^2$
$\therefore \quad a = 2$
So, $y = 2(x - 2)^2$.

EXERCISE 7J

1 Find the equation of the quadratic with graph:

a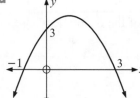

b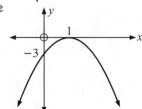

c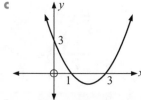

d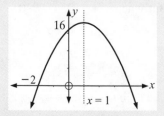

e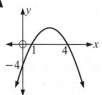

f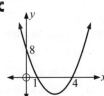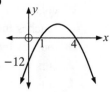

2 Match the given graphs to the possible formulae stated:

a $y = 2(x - 1)(x - 4)$ **b** $y = -(x + 1)(x - 4)$

c $y = (x - 1)(x - 4)$ **d** $y = (x + 1)(x - 4)$

e $y = 2(x + 4)(x - 1)$ **f** $y = -3(x + 4)(x - 1)$

g $y = -(x - 1)(x - 4)$ **h** $y = -3(x - 1)(x - 4)$

A 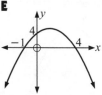   **B**   **C** 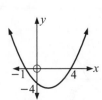   **D**

E 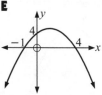   **F** 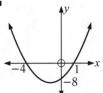   **G** 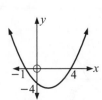   **H**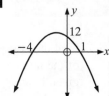

Example 27

Find the equation of the quadratic with graph:

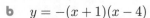

As the axis of symmetry is $x = 1$, the other x-intercept is 4

$$\therefore \quad y = a(x + 2)(x - 4)$$

But when $x = 0$, $y = 16$

$$\therefore \quad 16 = a(2)(-4)$$

$$\therefore \quad a = -2$$

$\therefore$ quadratic is $y = -2(x + 2)(x - 4)$

3 Find the quadratic with graph:

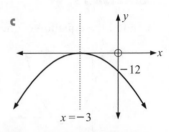

a

b

c

Example 28

Find, in the form $y = ax^2 + bx + c$, the equation of the quadratic whose graph cuts the x-axis at 4 and -3 and passes through the point $(2, -20)$.

Since the x-intercepts are 4 and -3, the equation is
$$y = a(x - 4)(x + 3) \quad \text{where} \quad a \neq 0.$$
But when $x = 2$, $y = -20$ $\qquad \therefore \quad -20 = a(2 - 4)(2 + 3)$
$$\therefore \quad -20 = a(-2)(5)$$
$$\therefore \quad a = 2$$
$\therefore$ equation is $y = 2(x - 4)(x + 3)$ i.e., $y = 2x^2 - 2x - 24$

---

4 Find, in the form $y = ax^2 + bx + c$, the equation of the quadratic whose graph:

a cuts the x-axis at 5 and 1, and passes through $(2, -9)$

b cuts the x-axis at 2 and $-\frac{1}{2}$, and passes through $(3, -14)$

c touches the x-axis at 3 and passes through $(-2, -25)$

d touches the x-axis at -2 and passes through $(-1, 4)$

e cuts the x-axis at 3, passes through $(5, 12)$ and has axis of symmetry $x = 2$

f cuts the x-axis at 5, passes through $(2, 5)$ and has axis of symmetry $x = 1$.

Example 29

Find the equation of the quadratic given its graph is:

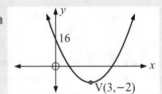

a

b

---

a For vertex $(3, -2)$
the quadratic has form
$y = a(x - 3)^2 - 2$

But when $x = 0$, $y = 16$

$\therefore \quad 16 = a(-3)^2 - 2$
$\therefore \quad 16 = 9a - 2$
$\therefore \quad 9a = 18$
$\therefore \quad a = 2$
i.e., $y = 2(x - 3)^2 - 2$

b For vertex $(-4, 2)$
the quadratic has form
$y = a(x + 4)^2 + 2$

But when $x = -2$, $y = 0$

$\therefore \quad 0 = a(2)^2 + 2$
$\therefore \quad 4a = -2$
$\therefore \quad a = -\frac{1}{2}$
i.e., $y = -\frac{1}{2}(x + 4)^2 + 2$

5 Find the equation of the quadratic given its graph is: (V is the vertex.)

a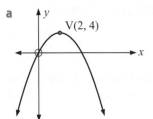

b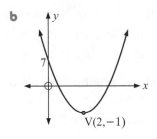

c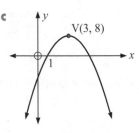

d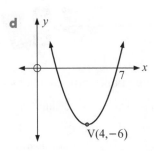

e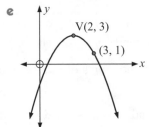

f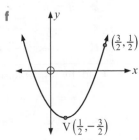

K WHERE FUNCTIONS MEET

Consider the graphs of a quadratic function and a linear function on the same set of axes.

Notice that we could have:

cutting

(2 points of intersection)

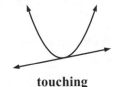

touching

(1 point of intersection)

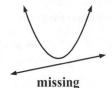

missing

(no points of intersection)

The graphs could meet and the coordinates of the points of intersection of the graphs of the two functions can be found by *solving the two equations simultaneously*.

Example 30

Find the coordinates of the points of intersection of the graphs with equations $y = x^2 - x - 18$ and $y = x - 3$.

$y = x^2 - x - 18$ meets $y = x - 3$ where
$$x^2 - x - 18 = x - 3$$
$$\therefore \quad x^2 - 2x - 15 = 0 \qquad \{\text{RHS} = 0\}$$
$$\therefore \quad (x - 5)(x + 3) = 0 \qquad \{\text{factorising}\}$$
$$\therefore \quad x = 5 \text{ or } -3$$

Substituting into $y = x - 3$, when $x = 5$, $y = 2$ and when $x = -3$, $y = -6$.

$\therefore$ graphs meet at $(5, 2)$ and $(-3, -6)$.

EXERCISE 7K

1   Find the coordinates of the point(s) of intersection of the graphs with equations:

  a $y = x^2 - 2x + 8$ and $y = x + 6$ **b** $y = -x^2 + 3x + 9$ and $y = 2x - 3$

  c $y = x^2 - 4x + 3$ and $y = 2x - 6$ **d** $y = -x^2 + 4x - 7$ and $y = 5x - 4$

2   Use a **graphing package** or a **graphics calculator** to find the coordinates of the points of intersection (to two decimal places) of the graphs with equations:

  a $y = x^2 - 3x + 7$ and $y = x + 5$

  b $y = x^2 - 5x + 2$ and $y = x - 7$

  c $y = -x^2 - 2x + 4$ and $y = x + 8$

  d $y = -x^2 + 4x - 2$ and $y = 5x - 6$

3   Find, by algebraic means, the points of intersection of the graphs with equations:

  a $y = x^2$ and $y = x + 2$ **b** $y = x^2 + 2x - 3$ and $y = x - 1$

  c $y = 2x^2 - x + 3$ and $y = 2 + x + x^2$ **d** $xy = 4$ and $y = x + 3$

4   Use technology to check your solutions to the questions in **3**.

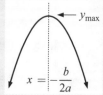
GRAPHING PACKAGE

L   QUADRATIC MODELLING

There are many situations in the real world where the relationship between two variables is a quadratic function.

This means that the graph of such a relationship will be either or ⌒ and the function will have a minimum or maximum value.

For $y = ax^2 + bx + c$:

  •   if $a > 0$,   the **minimum** value of y occurs at $x = -\dfrac{b}{2a}$

  •   if $a < 0$,   the **maximum** value of y occurs at $x = -\dfrac{b}{2a}$.

Note: we are optimising y, not x. $x = -\dfrac{b}{2a}$ helps us calculate this y-value.

The process of finding the maximum or minimum value of a function is called **optimisation**.

Optimisation is a very useful tool when looking at such issues as:

  •   maximising profits

  •   minimising costs

  •   maximising heights reached etc.

Example 31

The height H metres, of a rocket t seconds after it is fired vertically upwards is given by $H(t) = 80t - 5t^2$, $t \geqslant 0$.

a   How long does it take for the rocket to reach its maximum height?

b   What is the maximum height reached by the rocket?

c   How long does it take for the rocket to fall back to earth?

a
$$H(t) = 80t - 5t^2$$
$$\therefore \quad H(t) = -5t^2 + 80t \quad \text{where} \quad a = -5 \quad \therefore$$

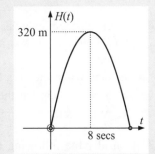

The maximum height reached occurs when $t = \dfrac{-b}{2a} = \dfrac{-80}{2(-5)} = 8$

i.e.,   the maximum height is reached after 8 seconds.

b $H(8) = 80 \times 8 - 5 \times 8^2$
$\qquad\quad = 640 - 320$
$\qquad\quad = 320$

i.e.,   the maximum height reached is 320 m.

c   The rocket falls back to earth when $H(t) = 0$
$$\therefore \quad 0 = 80t - 5t^2$$
$$\therefore \quad 5t^2 - 80t = 0$$
$$\therefore \quad 5t(t - 16) = 0 \quad \{\text{factorising}\}$$
$$\therefore \quad t = 0 \text{ or } t = 16$$

i.e.,   the rocket falls back to earth after 16 seconds.

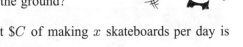

EXERCISE 7L

1   The height H metres, of a ball hit vertically upwards, t seconds after it is hit is given by $H(t) = 36t - 2t^2$.

   a   How long does it take for the ball to reach its maximum height?

   b   What is the maximum height of the ball?

   c   How long does it take for the ball to hit the ground?

2   A skateboard manufacturer finds that the cost $\$C$ of making x skateboards per day is given by $C(x) = x^2 - 24x + 244$.

   a   How many skateboards should be made per day to minimise the cost of production?

   b   What is the minimum cost?

   c   What is the cost if no skateboards are made in a day?

3   The driver of a car travelling downhill on a road applied the brakes. The velocity (v) of the car in m/s, t seconds after the brakes were applied was given by
$v(t) = -\frac{1}{2}t^2 + \frac{1}{2}t + 15$ m/s.

   a   How fast was the car travelling when the driver applied the brakes?

   b After how many seconds did the car reach its maximum velocity? Explain why this may have happened.

   c What was the maximum velocity reached?

   d How long does it take for the car to stop?

4 The hourly profit (P) obtained from operating a fleet of n taxis is given by $P(n) = 84n - 45 - 2n^2$.

   a What number of taxis gives the maximum hourly profit?

   b What is the maximum hourly profit?

   c How much money is lost per hour if no taxis are on the road?

5 The temperature T^o Celsius in a greenhouse t hours after dusk (7.00 pm) is given by $T(t) = \frac{1}{4}t^2 - 5t + 30, \quad (t \leqslant 20)$.

   a What was the temperature in the greenhouse at dusk?

   b At what time was the temperature at a minimum?

   c What was the minimum temperature?

6 A vegetable gardener has 40 m of fencing to enclose a rectangular garden plot where one side is an existing brick wall. If the width is x m as shown:

   a Show that the area (A) enclosed is given by $A = -2x^2 + 40x$ m^2.

   b Find x such that the vegetable garden has maximum area.

   c What is the maximum area?

7 Consider the following diagram of a bridge:

AB is the longest vertical support of a bridge which contains a parabolic arch. The vertical supports are 10 m apart. The arch meets the vertical end supports 6 m above the road.

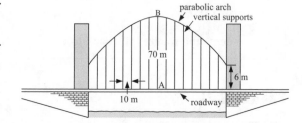

   a If axes are drawn on the diagram of the bridge above, with x-axis the road and y-axis on AB, find the equation of the parabolic arch in the form $y = ax^2 + c$.

   b Hence, determine the lengths of all other vertical supports.

GRAPHICS CALCULATOR INVESTIGATION   TUNNELS AND TRUCKS

A tunnel is parabolic in shape with dimensions shown:

A truck carrying a wide load is 4.8 m high and 3.9 m wide and needs to pass through the tunnel. Your task is to determine if the truck will fit through the tunnel.

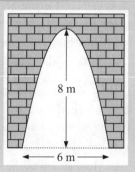

What to do:

1   If a set of axes is fitted to the parabolic tunnel as shown, state the coordinates of points A, B and C.

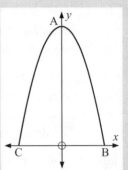

2   Using a **graphics calculator**:
    a   enter the x-coordinates of A, B and C into **List 1**
    b   enter the y-coordinates of A, B and C into **List 2.**

3   Draw a **scatterplot** of points A, B and C.

4   Set your calculator to display 4 decimal places and determine the equation of the parabolic boundary of the tunnel in the form $y = ax^2 + bx + c$, by fitting a **quadratic model** to the data.

5   Place the end view of the truck on the same set of axes as above.

    What is the equation of the truck's roofline?

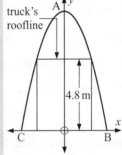

6   You should have found that the equation of the parabolic boundary of the tunnel is $y = -0.8889x^2 + 8$ and the equation of the truck's roofline is $y = 4.8$.

    Graph these equations on the same set of axes. Calculate the **points of intersection** of the graphs of these functions.

7   Using the points of intersection found in **6**, will the truck pass through the tunnel? What is the maximum width of a truck that is 4.8 m high if it is to pass through the tunnel?

8   Investigate the maximum width of a truck that is 3.7 m high if it is to pass through the tunnel.

9   What is the maximum width of a 4.1 m high truck if it is to pass through a parabolic tunnel 6.5 m high and 5 m wide?

REVIEW SET 7A

1   For $y = -2(x + 2)(x - 1)$:
    a   state the x-intercepts
    b   state the equation of the axis of symmetry
    c   find the coordinates of the vertex
    d   find the y-intercept
    e   sketch the graph of the function
    f   use technology to check your answers.

2   For $y = \frac{1}{2}(x - 2)^2 - 4$:
    a   state the equation of the axis of symmetry
    b   find the coordinates of the vertex
    c   find the y-intercept
    d   sketch the graph of the function
    e   use technology to check your answers.

3 For $y = x^2 - 4x - 1$:
  a convert into the form $y = (x - h)^2 + k$ by 'completing the square'
  b state the coordinates of the vertex   **c** find the y-intercept.
  d Hence sketch the graph.   **e** Use technology to check your answer.

4 For $y = 2x^2 + 6x - 3$:
  a convert into the form $y = (x - h)^2 + k$ by 'completing the square'
  b state the coordinates of the vertex   **c** find the y-intercept.
  d Hence sketch the graph.   **e** Use technology to check your answer.

5 Solve the following equations, giving exact answers:
  a $x^2 - 11x = 60$ **b** $3x^2 - x - 10 = 0$ **c** $3x^2 - 12x = 0$

6 Solve the following equations:
  a $x^2 + 10 = 7x$ **b** $x + \dfrac{12}{x} = 7$ **c** $2x^2 - 7x + 3 = 0$

7 Solve the following equation by completing the square: $x^2 + 7x - 4 = 0$

8 Solve the following equation by completing the square: $x^2 + 4x + 1 = 0$

9 Solve the following using the quadratic formula:
  a $x^2 - 7x + 3 = 0$ **b** $2x^2 - 5x + 4 = 0$

REVIEW SET 7B

1 Draw the graph of $y = -x^2 + 2x$.

2 Find the equation of the axis of symmetry and the vertex of $y = -3x^2 + 8x + 7$.

3 Find the equation of the axis of symmetry and the vertex of $y = 2x^2 + 4x - 3$.

4 Use the discriminant only to determine the number of solutions to:
  a $3x^2 - 5x + 7 = 0$ **b** $-2x^2 - 4x + 3 = 0$

5 Show that $5 + 7x + 3x^2$ is positive definite.

6 Find the maximum or minimum value of the relation $y = -2x^2 + 4x + 3$ and the value of x for which the maximum or minimum occurs.

7 Find the points of intersection of $y = x^2 - 3x$ and $y = 3x^2 - 5x - 24$.

8 For what values of k does the graph of $y = -2x^2 + 5x + k$ not cut the x-axis?

9 60 m of chicken wire is available for constructing a chicken enclosure against an existing wall. The enclosure is to be rectangular.

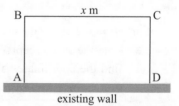

  a If $BC = x$ m, show that the area of rectangle ABCD is given by $A = (30x - \frac{1}{2}x^2)$ m².
  b Find the dimensions of the enclosure which will maximise the area enclosed.

REVIEW SET 7C, 7D, 7E
Click on the icon to obtain printable review sets and answers

REVIEW SET 7C   REVIEW SET 7D   REVIEW SET 7E

Chapter

Complex numbers and polynomials

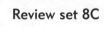

A   SOLUTIONS OF REAL QUADRATICS WITH $\Delta < 0$

From **Chapter 7**, we determined that:

If $ax^2 + bx + c = 0$, $a \neq 0$ and $a, b, c \in R$, then the solutions (roots) are found

using the formula $x = \dfrac{-b \pm \sqrt{\Delta}}{2a}$ where $\Delta = b^2 - 4ac$ is known as the **discriminant**.

Also, we observed that if:
- $\Delta > 0$ we have two real, distinct solutions
- $\Delta = 0$ we have two real, identical solutions
- $\Delta < 0$ we have no real solutions.

Now a most useful property for the development of polynomial theory is for quadratics (polynomials of degree 2) to have **exactly** 2 solutions even if repeated.

This is satisfied above where $\Delta \geqslant 0$.

However when $\Delta < 0$ we have no real solutions. But if we define $i = \sqrt{-1}$ (i being **imaginary**, i.e., it does not really exist) then when $\Delta < 0$ we do get 2 solutions, but they are not real because of the presence of i.

We say when i is present that we have 2 **complex number** roots of the quadratic equation.

Example 1

Solve the quadratic equations: **a** $x^2 = -4$ **b** $z^2 + z + 2 = 0$

a $x^2 = -4$

$\therefore \quad x = \pm\sqrt{-4}$

$\therefore \quad x = \pm\sqrt{4}\sqrt{-1}$

$\therefore \quad x = \pm 2i$

b $\Delta = 1 - 8 = -7$

Now $z = \dfrac{-1 \pm \sqrt{-7}}{2}$ {quadratic formula}

$\therefore \quad z = \dfrac{-1 \pm \sqrt{7}i}{2}$

$\therefore \quad z = -\frac{1}{2} \pm \frac{\sqrt{7}}{2}i$

Note 1: In each equation we have 2 solutions and $\Delta < 0$
($\Delta = -16$ and -7 respectively}

Note 2: Solutions to both equations are of the form $a + bi$ where a and b are real.

HISTORICAL NOTE

18th century mathematicians enjoyed playing with these new types of numbers but felt that they were little more than interesting curiosities, until **Gauss** (1777-1855), a German mathematician, astronomer and physicist, used them extensively in his work. For centuries mathematicians attempted to find a method of trisecting an angle using a compass and straight edge. Gauss put an end to this when he used complex numbers to prove the impossibility of such a construction. From his systematic use of complex numbers and the special results, he was able to convince mathematicians of their usefulness.

Early last century **Steinmetz** (an American engineer) used complex numbers to solve electrical problems, illustrating that complex numbers did have a practical application.

Currently complex numbers are used extensively in electronics, engineering and in various scientific fields, especially physics.

EXERCISE 8A

1 Write in terms of i:

    a $\sqrt{-9}$ **b** $\sqrt{-64}$ **c** $\sqrt{-\frac{1}{4}}$ **d** $\sqrt{-5}$ **e** $\sqrt{-8}$

Example 2

Write as a product of linear factors:	**a** $x^2 + 4$	**b** $x^2 + 11$
a x^2+4 **b** x^2+11	$= x^2 - 4i^2$	$= x^2 - 11i^2$
	$= (x+2i)(x-2i)$	$= (x+i\sqrt{11})(x-i\sqrt{11})$

---

2 Write as a product of linear factors:

    a $x^2 - 9$ **b** $x^2 + 9$ **c** $x^2 - 7$ **d** $x^2 + 7$

    e $4x^2 - 1$ **f** $4x^2 + 1$ **g** $2x^2 - 9$ **h** $2x^2 + 9$

    i $x^3 - x$ **j** $x^3 + x$ **k** $x^4 - 1$ **l** $x^4 - 16$

Example 3

Solve for x:	**a** $x^2 + 9 = 0$	**b** $x^3 + 2x = 0$
a $x^2 + 9 = 0$	$\therefore \quad x^2 - 9i^2 = 0$	$\therefore \quad x(x^2 + 2) = 0$
b $x^3 + 2x = 0$	$(x+3i)(x-3i) = 0$	$\therefore \quad x(x^2 - 2i^2) = 0$
	$\therefore \quad x = \pm 3i$	$x(x+i\sqrt{2})(x-i\sqrt{2}) = 0$
		$\therefore \quad x = 0 \text{ or } \pm i\sqrt{2}$

---

3 Solve for x:

    a $x^2 - 25 = 0$ **b** $x^2 + 25 = 0$ **c** $x^2 - 5 = 0$ **d** $x^2 + 5 = 0$

    e $4x^2 - 9 = 0$ **f** $4x^2 + 9 = 0$ **g** $x^3 - 4x = 0$ **h** $x^3 + 4x = 0$

    i $x^3 - 3x = 0$ **j** $x^3 + 3x = 0$ **k** $x^4 - 1 = 0$ **l** $x^4 = 81$

Example 4

Solve for x: $x^2 - 4x + 13 = 0$	$x^2 - 4x + 13 = 0 \quad \therefore \quad x = \dfrac{4 \pm \sqrt{16 - 4(1)(13)}}{2}$
	$\therefore \quad x = \dfrac{4 \pm \sqrt{-36}}{2}$
	$\therefore \quad x = \dfrac{4 \pm 6i}{2}$
	$\therefore \quad x = 2 + 3i \text{ or } 2 - 3i$

4 Solve for x:

    a $x^2 - 10x + 29 = 0$ **b** $x^2 + 6x + 25 = 0$ **c** $x^2 + 14x + 50 = 0$

    d $2x^2 + 5 = 6x$ **e** $x^2 - 2\sqrt{3}x + 4 = 0$ **f** $2x + \dfrac{1}{x} = 1$

Example 5

Solve for x:

$x^4 + x^2 = 6$

$$x^4 + x^2 = 6$$
$$\therefore \quad x^4 + x^2 - 6 = 0$$
$$\therefore \quad (x^2 + 3)(x^2 - 2) = 0$$
$$\therefore \quad (x + i\sqrt{3})(x - i\sqrt{3})(x + \sqrt{2})(x - \sqrt{2}) = 0$$
$$\therefore \quad x = \pm i\sqrt{3} \ \text{ or } \ \pm\sqrt{2}$$

---

5 Solve for x:

    a $x^4 + 2x^2 = 3$ **b** $x^4 = x^2 + 6$ **c** $x^4 + 5x^2 = 36$

    d $x^4 + 9x^2 + 14 = 0$ **e** $x^4 + 1 = 2x^2$ **f** $x^4 + 2x^2 + 1 = 0$

B   COMPLEX NUMBERS

FORMAL DEFINITION OF A COMPLEX NUMBER (IN CARTESIAN FORM)

Any number of the form $a + bi$ where **a and b are real** and $i = \sqrt{-1}$ is called a **complex number**.

Notice that **real** numbers are complex numbers. (The case where $b = 0$.)

A complex number of the form bi where $b \neq 0$ is called **purely imaginary.**

THE 'SUM OF TWO SQUARES'

Notice that:

$$a^2 + b^2$$
$$= a^2 - b^2 i^2 \qquad \{\text{as} \ \ i^2 = -1\}$$
$$= (a + bi)(a - bi)$$

Compare: $a^2 - b^2 = (a + b)(a - b)$ {the difference of two squares factorisation}

    and $a^2 + b^2 = (a + bi)(a - bi)$ {the sum of two squares factorisation}

REAL AND IMAGINARY PARTS OF COMPLEX NUMBERS

If we write $z = a + bi$ where **a and b are real** then:

-   a is the **real part** of z,   and we write $a = \mathcal{Re}(z)$,
-   b is the **imaginary part** of z,   and we write $b = \mathcal{Im}(z)$.

So,   if $z = 2 + 3i$, $\mathcal{Re}(z) = 2$ and $\mathcal{Im}(z) = 3$

      if $z = -\sqrt{2}i$, $\mathcal{Re}(z) = 0$ and $\mathcal{Im}(z) = -\sqrt{2}$.

OPERATIONS WITH COMPLEX NUMBERS

Notice that: for radicals, $(2 + \sqrt{3}) + (4 + 2\sqrt{3}) = (2 + 4) + (1 + 2)\sqrt{3} = 6 + 3\sqrt{3}$

and for complex numbers, $(2 + i) + (4 + 2i) = (2 + 4) + (1 + 2)i = 6 + 3i$

Also, notice that $(2 + \sqrt{3})(4 + 2\sqrt{3}) = 8 + 4\sqrt{3} + 4\sqrt{3} + 2(\sqrt{3})^2 = 8 + 8\sqrt{3} + 6$

and $(2 + i)(4 + 2i) = 8 + 4i + 4i + 2i^2 = 8 + 8i - 2$

In fact the operations with complex numbers are identical to those for radicals, with the $i^2 = -1$ rather than $(\sqrt{2})^2 = 2$ or $(\sqrt{3})^2 = 3$.

So: We can **add**, **subtract**, **multiply** and **divide** complex numbers in the same way we perform these operations with radicals, always remembering that $i^2 = -1$.

$$(a + bi) + (c + di) = (a + c) + (b + d)i \qquad \textbf{addition}$$

$$(a + bi) - (c + di) = (a - c) + (b - d)i \qquad \textbf{subtraction}$$

$$(a + bi)(c + di) = ac + adi + bci + bdi^2 \qquad \textbf{multiplication}$$

$$\frac{a + bi}{c + di} = \left(\frac{a + bi}{c + di}\right)\left(\frac{c - di}{c - di}\right) = \frac{ac - adi + bci - bdi^2}{c^2 + d^2} \qquad \textbf{division}$$

Example 6

If $z = 3 + 2i$ and $w = 4 - i$ find:

a $z + w$ **b** $z - w$ **c** zw

a $z + w$
$= (3 + 2i) + (4 - i)$
$= 7 + i$

b $z - w$
$= (3 + 2i) - (4 - i)$
$= 3 + 2i - 4 + i$
$= -1 + 3i$

c zw
$= (3 + 2i)(4 - i)$
$= 12 - 3i + 8i - 2i^2$
$= 12 + 5i + 2$
$= 14 + 5i$

EXERCISE 8B.1

1   Copy and complete:

z	$\mathcal{Re}(z)$	$\mathcal{Im}(z)$	z	$\mathcal{Re}(z)$	$\mathcal{Im}(z)$
$3 + 2i$			$-3 + 4i$		
$5 - i$			$-7 - 2i$		
3			$-11i$		
0			$i\sqrt{3}$		

2   If $z = 5 - 2i$ and $w = 2 + i$,   find in simplest form:

a $z + w$ **b** $2z$ **c** iw **d** $z - w$

e $2z - 3w$ **f** zw **g** w^2 **h** z^2

3   For $z = 1 + i$ and $w = -2 + 3i$,   find in simplest form:

a $z + 2w$ **b** z^2 **c** z^3 **d** iz

e w^2 **f** zw **g** $z^2 w$ **h** izw

4 Simplify i^n for $n = 0, 1, 2, 3, 4, 5, 6, 7, 8, 9$ and also for $n = -1, -2, -3, -4,$ and -5. Hence, simplify i^{4n+3} where n is any integer.

5 Suppose $z = \cos\theta + i\sin\theta$. Show that:

    a $z^2 = \cos 2\theta + i\sin 2\theta$ **b** $\dfrac{1}{z} = \cos\theta - i\sin\theta$

6 Write $(1 + i)^4$ in simplest form and hence find $(1 + i)^{101}$ in simplest form.

7 Suppose $(a + bi)^2 = -16 - 30i$ where a and b are real.
Find the possible values of a and b, given that $a > 0$.

Example 7

If $z = 3 + 2i$ and $w = 4 - i$ find $\dfrac{z}{w}$ in the form $a + bi$, where a and b are real.

$$\frac{z}{w} = \frac{3 + 2i}{4 - i}$$

$$= \left(\frac{3 + 2i}{4 - i}\right)\left(\frac{4 + i}{4 + i}\right)$$

$$= \frac{12 + 3i + 8i + 2i^2}{16 - i^2}$$

$$= \frac{10 + 11i}{17} \quad \text{i.e.,} \quad \tfrac{10}{17} + \tfrac{11}{17}i$$

---

8 For $z = 2 - i$ and $w = 1 + 3i$, find in the form $a + bi$, where a and b are real:

    a $\dfrac{z}{w}$ **b** $\dfrac{i}{z}$ **c** $\dfrac{w}{iz}$ **d** z^{-2}

9 Simplify: **a** $\dfrac{i}{1 - 2i}$ **b** $\dfrac{i(2 - i)}{3 - 2i}$ **c** $\dfrac{1}{2 - i} - \dfrac{2}{2 + i}$

10 If $z = 2 + i$ and $w = -1 + 2i$, find:

    a $\mathcal{Im}(4z - 3w)$ **b** $\mathcal{Re}(zw)$ **c** $\mathcal{Im}(iz^2)$ **d** $\mathcal{Re}\left(\dfrac{z}{w}\right)$

11 Check your answers to questions **1** - **4**, **8** - **10** using technology.

EQUALITY OF COMPLEX NUMBERS

Two complex numbers are **equal** when their **real parts** are equal and their **imaginary parts** are equal,

          i.e., if $a + bi = c + di$, then $a = c$ and $b = d$.

Proof: Suppose $b \neq d$. Now if $a + bi = c + di$, where a, b, c and d are real,

$$\text{then} \quad bi - di = c - a$$

$$\therefore \quad i(b - d) = c - a$$

$$\therefore \quad i = \frac{c - a}{b - d} \quad \{\text{as } b - d \neq 0\}$$

and this is false as the RHS is real and the LHS is imaginary.

Thus, the supposition is false and hence $b = d$, and $a = c$ follows immediately.

Example 8

If $(x + yi)(2 - i) = -i$ and x, y are real, determine the values of x and y.

If $(x + yi)(2 - i) = -i$, then $x + yi = \dfrac{-i}{2 - i}$

i.e., $x + yi = \left(\dfrac{-i}{2 - i}\right)\left(\dfrac{2 + i}{2 + i}\right)$

$\therefore \quad x + yi = \dfrac{-2i - i^2}{4 + 1} = \dfrac{1 - 2i}{5}$

$\therefore \quad x + yi = \tfrac{1}{5} - \tfrac{2}{5}i$

and so $x = \tfrac{1}{5}$, $y = -\tfrac{2}{5}$ Check this answer
using technology.

EXERCISE 8B.2

1 Find real numbers x and y such that:

    a $2x + 3yi = -x - 6i$
    b $x^2 + xi = 4 - 2i$

    c $(x + yi)(2 - i) = 8 + i$
    d $(3 + 2i)(x + yi) = -i$

Example 9

Find real numbers x and y for which $(x + 2i)(1 - i) = 5 + yi$

$(x + 2i)(1 - i) = 5 + yi$

$\therefore \quad x - xi + 2i + 2 = 5 + yi$

$\therefore \quad [x + 2] + [2 - x]i = 5 + yi$

$\therefore \quad x + 2 = 5 \quad \text{and} \quad 2 - x = y \qquad \{\text{equating real and imaginary parts}\}$

$\therefore \quad x = 3 \quad \text{and} \quad y = -1.$

2 Find x and y if:

    a $2(x + yi) = x - yi$
    b $(x + 2i)(y - i) = -4 - 7i$

    c $(x + i)(3 - iy) = 1 + 13i$
    d $(x + yi)(2 + i) = 2x - (y + 1)i$

COMPLEX CONJUGATES

> Complex numbers $a + bi$ and $a - bi$ are called **complex conjugates**.
> If $z = a + bi$ we write its conjugate as $z^* = a - bi$.

Complex conjugates appear as the solutions of real quadratic equations of the form
$ax^2 + bx + c = 0$ where the discriminant, $\Delta = b^2 - 4ac$ is **negative**.

For example: • $x^2 - 2x + 5 = 0$ has $\Delta = (-2)^2 - 4(1)(5) = -16$
                                          and the solutions are $x = 1 + 2i$ and $1 - 2i$

              • $x^2 + 4 = 0$ has $\Delta = 0^2 - 4(1)(4) = -16$
                                          and the solutions are $x = 2i$ and $-2i$

Note:
- Quadratics with real coefficients are called **real quadratics**.
- If a quadratic equation has **rational coefficients** and a **radical root** of the form $c + d\sqrt{n}$ then $c - d\sqrt{n}$ is also a root.
  (These roots are called irrational roots.)
- If a real quadratic equation has $\Delta < 0$ and $c + di$ is a complex root then $c - di$ is also a root.

Theorem: If $c + di$ and $c - di$ are roots of a quadratic equation, then the quadratic equation is $x^2 - 2cx + (c^2 + d^2) = 0$ if the coefficient of x is unity.

Proof: the sum of the roots is $= 2c$

and the product is $= (c + di)(c - di)$ and as $x^2 - (\text{sum})x + (\text{product}) = 0$
$$= c^2 + d^2 \qquad \text{then} \quad x^2 - 2cx + (c^2 + d^2) = 0$$

An alternative argument is

If $c + di$ and $c - di$ are roots then
$x - [c + di]$ and $x - [c - di]$ are factors
$\therefore \quad (x - [c + di])(x - [c - di]) = 0$
i.e., $(x - c - di)(x - c + di) = 0$
or $(x - c)^2 - d^2 i^2 = 0$
i.e., $x^2 - 2cx + c^2 + d^2 = 0$

Example 10

Find all quadratic equations with real coefficients having $1 - 2i$ as a root.

sum of roots	$= 1 - 2i + 1 + 2i$	product of roots	$= (1 - 2i)(1 + 2i)$
	$= 2$		$= 1 + 4$
			$= 5$

as $x^2 - (\text{sum})x + (\text{product}) = 0$
$\therefore \quad a(x^2 - 2x + 5) = 0, \ a \neq 0$ gives all equations.

Note: The sum of complex conjugates $c + di$ and $c - di$ is $2c$ which is **real**.
The product is $(c + di)(c - di) = c^2 + d^2$ which is also **real**.

EXERCISE 8B.3

1 Find all quadratic equations with real coefficients and roots of:

a $3 \pm i$	b $1 \pm 3i$	c $-2 \pm 5i$	d $\sqrt{2} \pm i$
e $2 \pm \sqrt{3}$	f 0 and $-\frac{2}{3}$	g $\pm i\sqrt{2}$	h $-6 \pm i$

Example 11

Find exact values of a and b if $\sqrt{2} + i$ is a root of $x^2 + ax + b = 0, \ a, b \in \mathcal{R}$.

Since a and b are real, the quadratic has real coefficients, $\therefore \ \sqrt{2} - i$ is also a root
$\therefore$ sum of roots $= \sqrt{2} + i + \sqrt{2} - i = 2\sqrt{2}$
product of roots $= (\sqrt{2} + i)(\sqrt{2} - i) = 2 + 1 = 3$
Thus $a = -2\sqrt{2}$ and $b = 3$.

2 Find exact values of a and b if:

    a $3 + i$ is a root of $x^2 + ax + b = 0$, where a and b are real

    b $1 - \sqrt{2}$ is a root of $x^2 + ax + b = 0$, where a and b are rational

    c $a + ai$ is a root of $x^2 + 4x + b = 0$ where a and b are real. [Careful!]

INVESTIGATION 1   PROPERTIES OF CONJUGATES

The purpose of this investigation is to discover any properties that complex conjugates might have.

What to do:

1 Given $z_1 = 1 - i$ and $z_2 = 2 + i$ find:

    a $z_1^{\,*}$ **b** $z_2^{\,*}$ **c** $(z_1^{\,*})^*$ **d** $(z_2^{\,*})^*$ **e** $(z_1 + z_2)^*$ **f** $z_1^{\,*} + z_2^{\,*}$

    g $(z_1 - z_2)^*$ **h** $z_1^{\,*} - z_2^{\,*}$ **i** $(z_1 z_2)^*$ **j** $z_1^{\,*} z_2^{\,*}$ **k** $\left(\dfrac{z_1}{z_2}\right)^*$ **l** $\dfrac{z_1^{\,*}}{z_2^{\,*}}$

    m $\left(z_1^2\right)^*$ **n** $\left(z_1^{\,*}\right)^2$ **o** $\left(z_2^3\right)^*$ **p** $\left(z_2^{\,*}\right)^3$

2 Repeat **1** with z_1 and z_2 of your choice.

3 From **1** and **2** formulate possible rules of conjugates.

PROPERTIES OF CONJUGATES

From the investigation you probably formulated the following rules for complex conjugates:

- $(z^*)^* = z$

- $(z_1 + z_2)^* = z_1^{\,*} + z_2^{\,*}$ and $(z_1 - z_2)^* = z_1^{\,*} - z_2^{\,*}$

- $(z_1 z_2)^* = z_1^{\,*} \times z_2^{\,*}$ and $\left(\dfrac{z_1}{z_2}\right)^* = \dfrac{z_1^{\,*}}{z_2^{\,*}}$, $z_2 \neq 0$

- $(z^n)^* = (z^*)^n$ for integers $n = 1$, 2 and 3

- $z + z^*$ and zz^* are real.

Example 12

Show that $(z_1 + z_2)^* = z_1^{\,*} + z_2^{\,*}$ for all complex numbers z_1 and z_2.

Let $z_1 = a + bi$ and $z_2 = c + di$ $\therefore$ $z_1^* = a - bi$ and $z_2^* = c - di$

Now $z_1 + z_2 = (a + c) + (b + d)i$ $\therefore$ $(z_1 + z_2)^* = (a + c) - (b + d)i$

$$= a + c - bi - di$$
$$= a - bi + c - di$$
$$= z_1^{\,*} + z_2^{\,*}$$

EXERCISE 8B.4

1 Show that $(z_1 - z_2)^* = z_1^{\,*} - z_2^{\,*}$ for all complex numbers z_1 and z_2.

2 Simplify the expression $(w^* - z)^* - (w - 2z^*)$ using the properties of conjugates.

3   It is known that a complex number z satisfies the equation $z^* = -z$.
Show that either z is purely imaginary or zero.

Example 13

Show that $(z_1 z_2)^* = z_1{}^* \times z_2{}^*$ for all complex numbers z_1 and z_2.	Let $z_1 = a + bi$ and $z_2 = c + di$

$$\therefore \quad z_1 z_2 = (a + bi)(c + di)$$
$$= ac + adi + bci + bdi^2$$
$$= [ac - bd] + i[ad + bc]$$

Thus $(z_1 z_2)^* = [ac - bd] - i[ad + bc]$ ...... (1)

Now $z_1{}^* \times z_2{}^* = (a - bi)(c - di)$
$$= ac - adi - bci + bdi^2$$
$$= [ac - bd] - i[ad + bc] \quad ...... (2)$$

From (1) and (2), $(z_1 z_2)^* = z_1{}^* \times z_2{}^*$

---

4   If $z_1 = a + bi$ and $z_2 = c + di$:

a find $\dfrac{z_1}{z_2}$ (in form $X + Yi$)   **b** show that $\left(\dfrac{z_1}{z_2}\right)^* = \dfrac{z_1{}^*}{z_2{}^*}$ for all z_1 and $z_2 \neq 0$.

5   An easier way of proving $\left(\dfrac{z_1}{z_2}\right)^* = \dfrac{z_1{}^*}{z_2{}^*}$ is to start with $\left(\dfrac{z_1}{z_2}\right)^* \times z_2{}^*$.

Show how this can be done, remembering that you have already proved that "the conjugate of a product is the product of the conjugates" in **Example 13**.

6   Prove that for all complex numbers z and w:

a $zw^* + z^*w$ is always real   **b** $zw^* - z^*w$ is purely imaginary or zero.

7   **a** If $z = a + bi$ find z^2 in the form $X + Yi$.

   b Hence, show that $\left(z^2\right)^* = (z^*)^2$ for all complex numbers z.

   c Repeat **a** and **b** but for z^3 instead of z^2.

8 $w = \dfrac{z - 1}{z^* + 1}$ where $z = a + bi$.   Find the conditions under which:

a w is real   **b** w is purely imaginary.

CONJUGATE GENERALISATIONS

Notice that $(z_1 + z_2 + z_3)^* = (z_1 + z_2)^* + z_2{}^*$ {treating $z_1 + z_2$ as one complex number}
$$= z_1{}^* + z_2{}^* + z_3{}^* \quad ...... (1)$$

Likewise $(z_1 + z_2 + z_3 + z_4)^* = (z_1 + z_2 + z_3)^* + z_4{}^*$
$$= z_1{}^* + z_2{}^* + z_3{}^* + z_4{}^* \quad \{\text{from (1)}\}$$

Since there is no reason why this process cannot continue for the conjugate of 5, 6, 7, ...
complex numbers we generalise to:

$$(z_1 + z_2 + z_3 + \ldots\ldots + z_n)^* = z_1{}^* + z_2{}^* + z_3{}^* + \ldots\ldots + z_n{}^*.$$

The process of obtaining the general case from observing the simpler cases when $n = 1, 2, 3, 4, \ldots$ is called **mathematical induction**.

Proof by the Principle of Mathematical Induction is an exercise that could be undertaken after the completion of **Chapter 10**. This is a more formal treatment and constitutes a proper proof.

EXERCISE 8B.5

1 **a** Assuming $(z_1 z_2)^* = z_1^* z_2^*$, explain why $(z_1 z_2 z_3)^* = z_1^* z_2^* z_3^*$.

    b Show that $(z_1 z_2 z_3 z_4)^* = z_1^* z_2^* z_3^* z_4^*$ from **a**.

    c What is the inductive generalisation of your results in **a** and **b**?

    d What is the result of letting all z_i values be equal to z in **c**?

SUMMARY OF CONJUGATE DISCOVERIES

- If z is any complex number then $z + z^*$ is real and zz^* is real.
- $(z^*)^* = z$
- If z_1 and z_2 are any complex numbers then
$$(z_1 + z_2)^* = z_1^* + z_2^* \quad \text{and} \quad (z_1 - z_2)^* = z_1^* - z_2^*$$
$$\text{and} \quad (z_1 z_2)^* = z_1^* z_2^* \quad \text{and} \quad \left(\frac{z_1}{z_2}\right)^* = \frac{z_1^*}{z_2^*}$$
- $(z^n)^* = (z^*)^n$ for all positive integers n
- $(z_1 + z_2 + z_3 + \ldots + z_n)^* = z_1^* + z_2^* + z_3^* + \ldots + z_n^*$
$$\text{and} \quad (z_1 z_2 z_3 \ldots z_n)^* = z_1^* z_2^* z_3^* \ldots z_n^*$$

C   REAL POLYNOMIALS

Up to this point we have studied linear and quadratic polynomial functions at some depth with perhaps occasional reference to cubic and quartic polynomials.

Some definitions:

The **degree** of a polynomial is its highest power of the variable.

Recall that:

a, b, c, d and e are all constants.

Polynomials	Degree	Name
$ax + b, \quad a \neq 0$	1	**linear**
$ax^2 + bx + c, \quad a \neq 0$	2	**quadratic**
$ax^3 + bx^2 + cx + d, \quad a \neq 0$	3	**cubic**
$ax^4 + bx^3 + cx^2 + dx + e, \quad a \neq 0$	4	**quartic**

a is the **leading coefficient** and the term not containing the **variable** x is called the **constant term**.

> A **real polynomial** has all its coefficients as real numbers (i.e., do not contain i where $i = \sqrt{-1}$).

OPERATIONS WITH POLYNOMIALS (REVIEW)

We are familiar with the techniques for adding, subtracting and multiplying with polynomials.

ADDITION AND SUBTRACTION

To **add** (or **subtract**) two polynomials we **add** (or **subtract**) 'like terms'.

Example 14

If $P(x) = x^3 - 2x^2 + 3x - 5$ and $Q(x) = 2x^3 + x^2 - 11$ find:

a $P(x) + Q(x)$ b $P(x) - Q(x)$

> It is a good idea to place brackets around expressions which are subtracted.

a $P(x) + Q(x)$

$\quad x^3 - 2x^2 + 3x - 5$

$\quad + 2x^3 + x^2 - 11$

$= 3x^3 - x^2 + 3x - 16$

b $P(x) - Q(x)$

$= x^3 - 2x^2 + 3x - 5 - [2x^3 + x^2 - 11]$

$= x^3 - 2x^2 + 3x - 5 - 2x^3 - x^2 + 11$

$= -x^3 - 3x^2 + 3x + 6$

SCALAR MULTIPLICATION

To **multiply** a polynomial by a **scalar** (constant) we multiply each term of the polynomial by the scalar.

Example 15

If $P(x) = x^4 - 2x^3 + 4x + 7$ find: a $3P(x)$ b $-2P(x)$

a $3P(x)$

$= 3(x^4 - 2x^3 + 4x + 7)$

$= 3x^4 - 6x^3 + 12x + 21$

b $-2P(x)$

$= -2(x^4 - 2x^3 + 4x + 7)$

$= -2x^4 + 4x^3 - 8x - 14$

POLYNOMIAL MULTIPLICATION

To **multiply** two polynomials, we multiply every term of the first polynomial by every term of the second polynomial and then collect like terms.

Example 16

If $P(x) = x^3 - 2x + 4$ and $Q(x) = 2x^2 + 3x - 5$, find $P(x)Q(x)$.

$$P(x)Q(x) = (x^3 - 2x + 4)(2x^2 + 3x - 5)$$

$$= x^3(2x^2 + 3x - 5) - 2x(2x^2 + 3x - 5) + 4(2x^2 + 3x - 5)$$

$$= 2x^5 + 3x^4 - 5x^3$$

$$ - 4x^3 - 6x^2 + 10x$$

$$ + 8x^2 + 12x - 20$$

$$= 2x^5 + 3x^4 - 9x^3 + 2x^2 + 22x - 20$$

EXERCISE 8C.1

1 If $P(x) = x^2 + 2x + 3$ and $Q(x) = 4x^2 + 5x + 6,$ find in simplest form:

    a $3P(x)$ **b** $P(x) + Q(x)$ **c** $P(x) - 2Q(x)$ **d** $P(x)Q(x)$

2 If $f(x) = x^2 - x + 2$ and $g(x) = x^3 - 3x + 5,$ find in simplest form:

    a $f(x) + g(x)$ **b** $g(x) - f(x)$ **c** $2f(x) + 3g(x)$

    d $g(x) + xf(x)$ **e** $f(x)g(x)$ **f** $[f(x)]^2$

3 Expand and simplify:

    a $(x^2 - 2x + 3)(2x + 1)$ **b** $(x - 1)^2(x^2 + 3x - 2)$

    c $(x + 2)^3$ **d** $(2x^2 - x + 3)^2$

    e $(2x - 1)^4$ **f** $(3x - 2)^2(2x + 1)(x - 4)$

SYNTHETIC MULTIPLICATION

Polynomial multiplication can be performed using the coefficients only.

For example, for $(x^3 + 2x - 5)(2x + 3)$ we detach coefficients and multiply as in ordinary multiplication of large numbers.

	1	0	2	-5	$\longleftarrow$	coefficients of $x^3 + 2x - 5$
	$\times$		2	3	$\longleftarrow$	coefficients of $2x + 3$
	3	0	6	-15		
2	0	4	-10			
2	3	4	-4	-15		

    x^4 x^3 x^2 x constants

So $(x^3 + 2x - 5)(2x + 3)$
$= 2x^4 + 3x^3 + 4x^2 - 4x - 15.$

4 Use the method above to find the following products:

    a $(2x^2 - 3x + 5)(3x - 1)$ **b** $(4x^2 - x + 2)(2x + 5)$

    c $(2x^2 + 3x + 2)(5 - x)$ **d** $(x - 2)^2(2x + 1)$

    e $(x^2 - 3x + 2)(2x^2 + 4x - 1)$ **f** $(3x^2 - x + 2)(5x^2 + 2x - 3)$

    g $(x^2 - x + 3)^2$ **h** $(2x^2 + x - 4)^2$

    i $(2x + 5)^3$ **j** $(x^3 + x^2 - 2)^2$

DIVISION OF POLYNOMIALS

The division of polynomials is a more difficult process. We can divide a polynomial by another polynomial using an algorithm (process) which is very similar to that used for division of whole numbers.

The division process is only sensible if we divide a polynomial of degree n by another of degree n or less.

DIVISION BY LINEARS

Consider $(2x^2 + 3x + 4)(x + 2) + 7.$

If we expand this expression we get $(2x^2 + 3x + 4)(x + 2) + 7 = 2x^3 + 7x^2 + 10x + 15.$

Now consider $2x^3 + 7x^2 + 10x + 15$ divided by $x + 2$

i.e., $$\frac{2x^3 + 7x^2 + 10x + 15}{x + 2} = \frac{(2x^2 + 3x + 4)(x + 2) + 7}{x + 2}$$

$\therefore$ $$\frac{2x^3 + 7x^2 + 10x + 15}{x + 2} = \frac{(2x^2 + 3x + 4)\cancel{(x + 2)}}{\cancel{x + 2}} + \frac{7}{x + 2}$$

$\therefore$ $$\frac{2x^3 + 7x^2 + 10x + 15}{x + 2} = 2x^2 + 3x + 4 + \frac{7}{x + 2}$$

We compare this with $\frac{25}{9} = 2 + \frac{7}{9}$ ⟵ remainder
                                                  ⟵ divisor

quotient

DIVISION ALGORITHM

Division may be performed directly using the following **algorithm** (process):

$$
\begin{array}{r}
2x^2 \quad +3x \quad +4 \\
x + 2 \enclose{longdiv}{2x^3 \ +7x^2 \ +10x \ +15} \\
-(2x^3 \ +4x^2) \\
\hline
3x^2 \ +10x \\
-(3x^2 \ + 6x) \\
\hline
4x \ +15 \\
-(4x \ + 8) \\
\hline
7
\end{array}
$$

x^3s x^2s xs   constants

Step 1:   What do we multiply x by to get $2x^3$?
Answer $2x^2$.
Then $2x^2(x + 2) = \underline{2x^3 + 4x^2}$.

Step 2:   Subtract $2x^3 + 4x^2$ from $2x^3 + 7x^2$.
The answer is $3x^2$.

Step 3:   Bring down the $10x$ to obtain $3x^2 + 10x$
and ask the question, "What must we
multiply x by to get $3x^2$?"   Answer $3x$.
Then $3x(x + 2) = 3x^2 + 6x$ etc.

This result is easily achieved by leaving
out the variable.

$$
\begin{array}{r}
\quad\ 2 \quad 3 \quad 4 \\
1 \ 2 \enclose{longdiv}{2 \quad 7 \quad 10 \quad 15} \\
-(2 \quad 4) \\
\hline
3 \quad 10 \\
-(3 \quad 6) \\
\hline
4 \quad 15 \\
-(4 \quad 8) \\
\hline
7
\end{array}
$$

Either way, $$\frac{2x^3 + 7x^2 + 10x + 15}{x + 2} = 2x^2 + 3x + 4 + \frac{7}{x + 2},$$

where $x + 2$ is called the **divisor**,
$2x^2 + 3x + 4$ is called the **quotient**,
and 7 is called the **remainder**.

In general,   if $P(x)$ is divided by $ax + b$ until a constant remainder R is obtained,

$$\frac{P(x)}{ax + b} = Q(x) + \frac{R}{ax + b}$$ where $ax + b$ is the **divisor**,
$Q(x)$ is the **quotient**, and
R is the **remainder**.

Notice that $P(x) = Q(x) \times (ax + b) + R$.

Example 17

Find the quotient and remainder for $\dfrac{x^3 - x^2 - 3x - 5}{x - 3}$.

$$
\begin{array}{r}
x^2 \ +2x \ +3 \\
x-3 \ \overline{\smash{\big)}\ x^3 - \ x^2 - \ 3x - 5} \\
\underline{-(x^3 -3x^2)} \quad \downarrow \\
2x^2 \ -3x \\
\underline{-(2x^2 \ -6x)} \\
3x \ -5 \\
\underline{-(3x \ -9)} \\
4
\end{array}
$$

$\therefore$ quotient is $x^2 + 2x + 3$ and remainder is 4.

Thus $\dfrac{x^3 - x^2 - 3x - 5}{x - 3} = x^2 + 2x + 3 + \dfrac{4}{x - 3}$

So, $x^3 - x^2 - 3x - 5 = (x^2 + 2x + 3)(x - 3) + 4.$

(Check by expanding and simplifying the RHS.)

EXERCISE 8C.2

1 Find the quotient and remainder for:

a $\dfrac{x^2 + 2x - 3}{x + 2}$ **b** $\dfrac{x^2 - 5x + 1}{x - 1}$ **c** $\dfrac{2x^3 + 6x^2 - 4x + 3}{x - 2}$

2 Perform the divisions:

a $\dfrac{x^2 - 3x + 6}{x - 4}$ **b** $\dfrac{x^2 + 4x - 11}{x + 3}$ **c** $\dfrac{2x^2 - 7x + 2}{x - 2}$

d $\dfrac{2x^3 + 3x^2 - 3x - 2}{2x + 1}$ **e** $\dfrac{3x^3 + 11x^2 + 8x + 7}{3x - 1}$ **f** $\dfrac{2x^4 - x^3 - x^2 + 7x + 4}{2x + 3}$

Example 18

Perform the division $\dfrac{x^4 + 2x^2 - 1}{x + 3}$.

> Notice the insertion of $0x^3$ and $0x$.
> Why?

$$
\begin{array}{r}
x^3 \ -3x^2 \ +11x \ -33 \\
x+3 \ \overline{\smash{\big)}\ x^4 \ \ +0x^3 +2x^2 + 0x \ -1} \\
\underline{-(x^4 \ \ +3x^3)} \quad \downarrow \\
-3x^3 +2x^2 \\
\underline{-(-3x^3 \ -9x^2)} \quad \downarrow \\
11x^2 \ + 0x \\
\underline{-(11x^2 \ +33x)} \quad \downarrow \\
-33x \ -1 \\
\underline{-(-33x \ -99)} \\
98
\end{array}
$$

$\therefore \quad \dfrac{x^4 + 2x - 1}{x + 3}$

$= x^3 - 3x^2 + 11x - 33 + \dfrac{98}{x + 3}$

So, $x^4 + 2x - 1$

$= (x^3 - 3x^2 + 11x - 33)(x + 3) + 98$

3 Perform the divisions:

a $\dfrac{x^2 + 5}{x - 2}$

b $\dfrac{2x^2 + 3x}{x + 1}$

c $\dfrac{3x^2 + 2x - 5}{x + 2}$

d $\dfrac{x^3 + 2x^2 - 5x + 2}{x - 1}$

e $\dfrac{2x^3 - x}{x + 4}$

f $\dfrac{x^3 + x^2 - 5}{x - 2}$

DIVISION BY QUADRATICS

As with division by linears we can use the **division algorithm** to divide polynomials by quadratics. Notice that the division process will stop when the remainder has degree less than that of the divisor,

i.e., $\qquad \dfrac{P(x)}{a^2 + bx + c} = Q(x) + \dfrac{ex + f}{ax^2 + bx + c}.$

The remainder could be linear if $e \neq 0$ or constant if $e = 0$.

Example 19

Find the quotient and remainder for $\dfrac{x^4 + 4x^3 - x + 1}{x^2 - x + 1}$.

$$
\begin{array}{r}
x^2 \;+5x\; +4 \\
x^2 - x + 1 \;\big|\; x^4\; +4x^3\; +0x^2\; -x\; +1 \\
-(x^4\; -x^3\; +x^2) \\
\hline
5x^3\; -x^2\; -x \\
-(5x^3\; -5x^2\; +5x) \\
\hline
4x^2\; -6x\; +1 \\
-(4x^2\; -4x\; +4) \\
\hline
-2x\; -3
\end{array}
$$

$\therefore$ quotient is $x^2 + 5x + 4$

and remainder is $-2x - 3$

So, $x^4 + 4x^3 - x + 1$
$= (x^2 - x + 1)(x^2 + 5x + 4) - 2x - 3$

EXERCISE 8C.3

1 Find the quotient and remainder for:

a $\dfrac{x^3 + 2x^2 + x - 3}{x^2 + x + 1}$

b $\dfrac{3x^2 - x}{x^2 - 1}$

c $\dfrac{3x^3 + x - 1}{x^2 + 1}$

d $\dfrac{x - 4}{x^2 + 2x - 1}$

2 Carry out the following divisions and also write each in the form $P(x) = D(x)Q(x) + R(x)$:

a $\dfrac{x^2 - x + 1}{x^2 + x + 1}$

b $\dfrac{x^3}{x^2 + 2}$

c $\dfrac{x^4 + 3x^2 + x - 1}{x^2 - x + 1}$

d $\dfrac{2x^3 - x + 6}{(x - 1)^2}$

e $\dfrac{x^4}{(x + 1)^2}$

f $\dfrac{x^4 - 2x^3 + x + 5}{(x - 1)(x + 2)}$

3 $P(x) = (x - 2)(x^2 + 2x + 3) + 7$. What is the quotient and remainder when $P(x)$ is divided by $x - 2$?

SYNTHETIC DIVISION (Optional)

When dividing a polynomial by a factor of the form $x - k$ or $x + k$ a quick form of division is possible, and this process is known as **synthetic division**.

For example, consider the division of $2x^3 + 7x^2 + 10x + 15$ by $x + 2$.

We set up the following:

Step 1:

-2 $\boxed{2 \quad 7 \quad 10 \quad 15}$ ← coefficients of $P(x)$

On dividing by $x + 2$ we write -2 here.

Step 2:

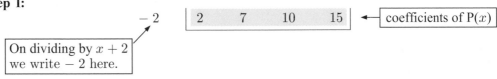

| -2 | 2 | 7 | 10 | 15 |

0 is always written here.

add

This number is the product of the two shaded numbers

Step 3: Repeat the process: Continue adding then multiplying across the array.

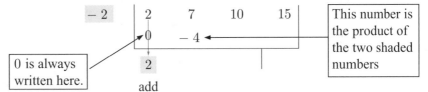

quotient ← remainder

Step 4: $\therefore \quad \dfrac{2x^3 + 7x^2 + 10x + 15}{x + 2} = 2x^2 + 3x + 4 + \dfrac{7}{x + 2}.$

To see why this produces the required result examine the following.

In **Example 17** we showed: $\dfrac{x^3 - x^2 - 3x - 5}{x - 3} = x^2 + 2x + 3 + \dfrac{4}{x - 3}$ {division algorithm}

$$
\begin{array}{r}
x^2 + 2x + 3 \\
x - 3 \overline{\smash{)}\, x^3 - x^2 - 3x - 5} \\
-(x^3 - 3x^2) \\
\hline
2x^2 - 3x \\
-(2x^2 - 6x) \\
\hline
3x - 5 \\
-(3x - 9) \\
\hline
4
\end{array}
$$

or

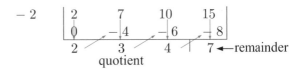

Examine:

A more rigorous argument might be worth considering.

Suppose $P(x) = a_3 x^3 + a_2 x^2 + a_1 x + a_0$ is divided by $x - k$ to give a quotient of $Q(x) = b_2 x^2 + b_1 x + b_0$ and a **constant remainder** R, i.e., $\dfrac{a_3x^3 + a_2x^2 + a_1x + a_0}{x-k} = b_2x^2 + b_1x + b_0 + \dfrac{R}{x-k}$

$\therefore \quad a_3x^3 + a_2x^2 + a_1x + a_0 = (b_2x^2 + b_1x + b_0)(x-k) + R$

$\therefore \quad a_3x^3 + a_2x^2 + a_1x + a_0 = b_2x^3 + [b_1 - kb_2]x^2 + [b_0 - kb_1]x + [R - kb_0]$

$\therefore \quad a_3 = b_2, \quad a_2 = b_1 - kb_2, \quad a_1 = b_0 - kb_1, \quad a_0 = R - kb_0$

$\therefore \quad b_2 = a_3, \quad b_1 = a_2 + kb_2, \quad b_0 = a_1 + kb_1, \quad R = a_0 + kb_0,$

which can be set up in the following array,

$$\begin{array}{c|cccc} k & a_3 & a_2 & a_1 & a_0 \\ & 0 & kb_2 & kb_1 & kb_0 \\ \hline & b_2 & b_1 & b_0 & R \end{array}$$

Example 20

Carry out the division:

$$\dfrac{x^3 - 2x^2 + 3}{x + 2}$$

$$\begin{array}{c|cccc} -2 & 1 & -2 & 0 & 3 \\ & 0 & -2 & 8 & -16 \\ \hline & 1 & -4 & 8 & -13 \end{array}$$

$\therefore \quad \dfrac{x^3 - 2x^2 + 3}{x+2} = x^2 - 4x + 8 + \dfrac{-13}{x+2}$

i.e., $= x^2 - 4x + 8 - \dfrac{13}{x+2}$

EXERCISE 8C.4

1 Use synthetic division, or otherwise, to divide:

a $\dfrac{3x^2 - 2x - 3}{x - 1}$

b $\dfrac{x^3 + 5x^2 + 6x + 5}{x + 3}$

c $\dfrac{3z^2 - z + 2}{z + 1}$

d $\dfrac{x^3 + 27}{x + 3}$

e $\dfrac{z^4 - 2z^3 + z^2 - 4}{z - 3}$

f $\dfrac{z^4 + z^2 - z}{z + 1}$

2 Find $P(x)$ for the following synthetic divisions:

a $\begin{array}{c|cccc} 2 & & P(x) & & \\ & & & & \\ \hline & 3 & -2 & 1 & 4 \end{array}$

b $\begin{array}{c|cccc} -3 & & P(x) & & \\ & & & & \\ \hline & 1 & -7 & 8 & -5 \end{array}$

D   ROOTS, ZEROS AND FACTORS

ROOTS AND ZEROS

A **zero** of a polynomial is a value of the variable which makes the polynomial equal to zero. The **roots** of a polynomial **equation** are values of the variable which satisfy the equation, i.e., are its solutions.

The **roots** of $P(x) = 0$ are the **zeros** of $P(x)$.

If $x = 2$, $x^3 + 2x^2 - 3x - 10$

$\qquad = 8 + 8 - 6 - 10$ $\therefore$ 2 is a zero of $x^3 + 2x^2 - 3x - 10$

$\qquad = 0$ and   2 is a root of $x^3 + 2x^2 - 3x - 10 = 0$.

Note: α is a **zero** of polynomial $P(x) \Leftrightarrow P(\alpha) = 0$.

α is a **root** (or **solution**) of $P(x) = 0 \Leftrightarrow P(\alpha) = 0$.

Example 21

Find the zeros of: **a** $x^2 - 4x + 53$ **b** $z^3 + 3z$

a We wish to find x such that

$$x^2 - 4x + 53 = 0$$

i.e., $x = \dfrac{4 \pm \sqrt{16 - 4(1)(53)}}{2}$

$\therefore \quad x = \dfrac{4 \pm 14i}{2} = 2 \pm 7i$

b We wish to solve for z such that

$$z^3 + 3z = 0$$

i.e., $z(z^2 + 3) = 0$

i.e., $z(z + i\sqrt{3})(z - i\sqrt{3}) = 0$

$\therefore \quad z = 0$ or $\pm i\sqrt{3}$

If $P(x) = (x + 1)(2x - 1)(x + 2)$, then $(x + 1)$, $(2x - 1)$ and $(x + 2)$ are its **linear factors**.

Likewise $P(x) = (x + 3)^2(2x + 3)$ has been factorised into 3 linear factors, one of which is repeated.

In general, $(x - \alpha)$ is a **factor** of polynomial $P(x) \Leftrightarrow$ there exists a polynomial $Q(x)$ such that $P(x) = (x - \alpha)Q(x)$.

EXERCISE 8D.1

1 Find the zeros of:

a $2x^2 - 5x - 12$ **b** $x^2 + 6x + 10$ **c** $z^2 - 6z + 6$

d $x^3 - 4x$ **e** $z^3 + 2z$ **f** $z^4 + 4z^2 - 5$

2 Find the roots of:

a $5x^2 = 3x + 2$ **b** $(2x + 1)(x^2 + 3) = 0$ **c** $-2z(z^2 - 2z + 2) = 0$

d $x^3 = 5x$ **e** $z^3 + 5z = 0$ **f** $z^4 = 3z^2 + 10$

Example 22

What are the linear factors of: **a** $z^2 + 4z + 9$ **b** $2z^3 + 5z^2 - 3z$?

a $z^2 + 4z + 9$ is zero when

$\therefore \quad z = \dfrac{-4 \pm \sqrt{16 - 4(1)(9)}}{2} = -2 \pm i\sqrt{5}$

$\therefore \quad z^2 + 4z + 9 = (z - [-2 + i\sqrt{5}])(z - [-2 - i\sqrt{5}])$

$= (z + 2 - i\sqrt{5})(z + 2 + i\sqrt{5})$

b $2z^3 + 5z^2 - 3z$

$= z(2z^2 + 5z - 3)$

$= z(2z - 1)(z + 3)$

3 Find the linear factors of:

a $2x^2 - 7x - 15$ **b** $z^2 - 6z + 16$ **c** $x^3 + 2x^2 - 4x$

d $6z^3 - z^2 - 2z$ **e** $z^4 - 6z^2 + 5$ **f** $z^4 - z^2 - 2$

4 If $P(x) = a(x - \alpha)(x - \beta)(x - \gamma)$ then α, β and γ are its zeros.

Check that the above statement is correct by finding $P(\alpha)$, $P(\beta)$ and $P(\gamma)$.

Example 23

Find *all* cubic polynomials with zeros $\frac{1}{2}$, $-3 \pm 2i$.

The zeros $-3 \pm 2i$ have   sum $= -3 + 2i - 3 - 2i = -6$ and

$$\text{product} = (-3 + 2i)(-3 - 2i) = 13$$

and $\therefore$ come from the quadratic factor $z^2 + 6z + 13$

$\frac{1}{2}$ comes from the linear factor $2z - 1$

$\therefore$ $P(z) = a(2z - 1)(z^2 + 6z + 13)$, $a \neq 0$.

---

5 Find *all* cubic polynomials with zeros of:

   a $\pm 2, 3$ **b** $-2, \pm i$ **c** $3, -1 \pm i$ **d** $-1, -2 \pm \sqrt{2}$.

Example 24

Find *all* quartic polynomials with zeros of $2, -\frac{1}{3}$, $-1 \pm \sqrt{5}$.

The zeros $-1 \pm \sqrt{5}$ have   sum $= -1 + \sqrt{5} - 1 - \sqrt{5} = -2$ and

$$\text{product} = (-1 + \sqrt{5})(-1 - \sqrt{5}) = -4$$

and $\therefore$ come from the quadratic factor $z^2 + 2z - 4$

zeros 2 and $-\frac{1}{3}$ come from the linear factors $(z - 2)$ and $(3z + 1)$

$\therefore$ $P(z) = a(z - 2)(3z + 1)(z^2 + 2z - 4)$, $a \neq 0$.

---

6 Find *all* quartic polynomials with zeros of:

   a $\pm 1, \pm \sqrt{2}$ **b** $2, -1, \pm i\sqrt{3}$ **c** $\pm \sqrt{3}, 1 \pm i$ **d** $2 \pm \sqrt{5}, -2 \pm 3i$.

POLYNOMIAL EQUALITY

Polynomials are equal if and only if they generate the same y-value for each x-value. This means that graphs of equal polynomials should be identical.

> Two polynomials are **equal** if and only if they have the **same degree** (order) and corresponding terms have equal coefficients.

For example,   if $2x^3 + 3x^2 - 4x + 6 = ax^3 + bx^2 + cx + d$,   then
$$a = 2, \quad b = 3, \quad c = -4 \quad \text{and} \quad d = 6.$$

EQUATING COEFFICIENTS

If we know that two polynomials are **equal** we can use the principle of 'equating coefficients' in order to find unknown coefficients.

Example 25

Find constants a, b and c given that:
$$6x^3 + 7x^2 - 19x + 7 = (2x - 1)(ax^2 + bx + c) \quad \text{for all } x.$$

If $6x^3 + 7x^2 - 19x + 7 = (2x - 1)(ax^2 + bx + c)$

then $6x^3 + 7x^2 - 19x + 7 = 2ax^3 + 2bx^2 + 2cx - ax^2 - bx - c$

i.e., $6x^3 + 7x^2 - 19x + 7 = 2ax^3 + [2b - a]x^2 + [2c - b]x - c$

Since this is true for all x, we equate coefficients

$\therefore$ $\underbrace{2a = 6,}_{x^3 \text{ s}} \quad \underbrace{2b - a = 7,}_{x^2 \text{ s}} \quad \underbrace{2c - b = -19}_{x \text{ s}}$ and $\underbrace{7 = -c}_{\text{constants}}$

$\therefore$ $a = 3$ and $c = -7$ and consequently $\underbrace{2b - 3 = 7 \quad \text{and} \quad -14 - b = -19}$

$\qquad\qquad\qquad\qquad\qquad\qquad\qquad\qquad\qquad\qquad\quad b = 5$

So, $a = 3$, $b = 5$ and $c = -7$. $\qquad$ in both equations

EXERCISE 8D.2

1   Find constants a, b and c given that:

a $2x^2 + 4x + 5 = ax^2 + [2b - 6]x + c$ for all x

b $2x^3 - x^2 + 6 = (x - 1)^2(2x + a) + bx + c$ for all x.

Example 26

Find a and b if $z^4 + 9 = (z^2 + az + 3)(z^2 + bz + 3)$ for all z.

$z^4 + 9 = (z^2 + az + 3)(z^2 + bz + 3)$ for all z

$\therefore$ $z^4 + 9 = z^4 + bz^3 + 3z^2$
$\qquad\qquad\qquad + az^3 + abz^2 + 3az$
$\qquad\qquad\qquad\qquad + 3z^2 + 3bz + 9$

i.e., $z^4 + 9 = z^4 + [a + b]z^3 + [ab + 6]z^2 + [3a + 3b]z + 9$ for all z

Equating coefficients gives $\begin{cases} a + b = 0 & \text{...... (1)} \quad \{z^3 \text{ s}\} \\ ab + 6 = 0 & \text{...... (2)} \quad \{z^2 \text{ s}\} \\ 3a + 3b = 0 & \text{...... (3)} \quad \{z \text{ s}\} \end{cases}$

From (1) (and (3)) we see that $b = -a$

So, in (2) $\qquad\qquad a(-a) + 6 = 0$

$\qquad\qquad\qquad \therefore \quad a^2 = 6$

$\qquad\qquad\qquad\qquad \therefore \quad a = \pm\sqrt{6}$ and so $b = \mp\sqrt{6}$

i.e., $a = \sqrt{6}$, $b = -\sqrt{6}$ or $a = -\sqrt{6}$, $b = \sqrt{6}$

2   Find a and b if:

a $z^4 + 4 = (z^2 + az + 2)(z^2 + bz + 2)$ for all z

b $2z^4 + 5z^3 + 4z^2 + 7z + 6 = (z^2 + az + 2)(2z^2 + bz + 3)$ for all z

3 Show that $z^4 + 64$ can be factorised into two real quadratic factors of the form $z^2 + az + 8$ and $z^2 + bz + 8$, but cannot be factorised into two real quadratic factors of the form $z^2 + az + 16$ and $z^2 + bz + 4$.

4 Find real numbers a and b such that $x^4 - 4x^2 + 8x - 4 = (x^2 + ax + 2)(x^2 + bx - 2)$, and hence solve the equation $x^4 + 8x = 4x^2 + 4$.

Example 27

$x + 3$ is a factor of $P(x) = x^3 + ax^2 - 7x + 6$. Find a and the other factors.

As $x + 3$ is a factor then
$$x^3 + ax^2 - 7x + 6 = (x + 3)(x^2 + bx + 2)$$
$$= x^3 + bx^2 + 2x + 3x^2 + 3bx + 6$$
$$= x^3 + [b + 3]x^2 + [3b + 2]x + 6$$

Equating coefficients $3b + 2 = -7$ and $a = b + 3$
$$\therefore \quad b = -3 \quad \text{and} \quad \therefore \quad a = 0$$

$$\therefore \quad P(x) = (x + 3)(x^2 - 3x + 2)$$
$$= (x + 3)(x - 1)(x - 2)$$

---

5 a $2z - 3$ is a factor of $2z^3 - z^2 + az - 3$. Find a and all zeros of the cubic.

  b $3z + 2$ is a factor of $3z^3 - z^2 + [a + 1]z + a$. Find a and all the zeros of the cubic.

Example 28

$2x + 3$ and $x - 1$ are factors of $2x^4 + ax^3 - 3x^2 + bx + 3$.
Find a and b and all zeros of the polynomial.

Since $2x + 3$ and $x - 1$ are factors then
$$2x^4 + ax^3 - 3x^2 + bx + 3 = (2x + 3)(x - 1) \text{ (a quadratic)}$$
$$= (2x^2 + x - 3)(x^2 + cx - 1)$$

Equating coefficients of x^2 gives: $-3 = -2 + c - 3$
$$\text{i.e.,} \quad c = 2$$

Equating coefficients of x^3: $a = 2c + 1$
$$\therefore \quad a = 4 + 1 = 5$$

Equating coefficients of x: $b = -1 - 3c$
$$\therefore \quad b = -1 - 6 = -7$$

and $P(x) = (2x + 3)(x - 1)(x^2 + 2x - 1)$ which has zeros of:
$$-\tfrac{3}{2}, 1 \quad \text{and} \quad \frac{-2 \pm \sqrt{4 - 4(1)(-1)}}{2} = \frac{-2 \pm 2\sqrt{2}}{2} = -1 \pm \sqrt{2}$$

i.e., zeros are $-\tfrac{3}{2}$, 1 and $-1 \pm \sqrt{2}$.

6 **a** Both $2x + 1$ and $x - 2$ are factors of $P(x) = 2x^4 + ax^3 + bx^2 - 12x - 8$.
Find a and b and all zeros of $P(x)$.

 b $x + 3$ and $2x - 1$ are factors of $2x^4 + ax^3 + bx^2 + ax + 3$.
Find a and b and hence determine all zeros of the quartic.

7 **a** $x^3 + 3x^2 - 9x + c$ has two identical linear factors. Prove that c is either 5 or -27 and factorise the cubic into linear factors in each case.

 b $3x^3 + 4x^2 - x + m$ has two identical linear factors. Find m and find the zeros of the polynomial in all possible cases.

THE REMAINDER THEOREM

Consider the following division: $\dfrac{x^3 + 5x^2 - 11x + 3}{x - 2}$.   We can show by long division that

$$\frac{x^3 + 5x^2 - 11x + 3}{x - 2} = x^2 + 7x + 3 + \frac{9}{x - 2} \;\longleftarrow \text{ remainder.}$$

i.e.,   on division by $x - 2$ its remainder is 9.

Notice also that if $\qquad P(x) = x^3 + 5x^2 - 11x + 3$
then $\qquad\qquad P(2) = 8 + 20 - 22 + 3$
$\qquad\qquad\qquad\quad = 9,$ which is the remainder.

After considering other examples like the one above we formulate the **Remainder theorem**.

THE REMAINDER THEOREM

> When polynomial $P(x)$ is divided by $x - k$ until a constant remainder R is obtained then $R = P(k)$.

Proof: By the division algorithm, $\quad P(x) = Q(x)(x - k) + R$
$\qquad\qquad\qquad$ Now if $x = k$, $\quad P(k) = Q(k) \times 0 + R$
$\qquad\qquad\qquad\qquad\qquad \therefore \qquad P(k) = R$

Example 29

Use the Remainder theorem to find the remainder when $x^4 - 3x^3 + x - 4$
is divided by $x + 2$.

If $P(x) = x^4 - 3x^3 + x - 4,$ then
$$P(-2) = (-2)^4 - 3(-2)^3 + (-2) - 4$$
$$= 16 + 24 - 2 - 4$$
$$= 34$$

$\therefore$ when $P(x)$ is divided by $x + 2$,   the remainder is 34.   {Remainder theorem}

It is important to realise when doing Remainder theorem questions that
$P(x) = (x + 2)Q(x) + 3$, $P(-2) = 3$ and   '$P(x)$ divided by $x + 2$ leaves a remainder of 3' are all **equivalent statements**.

EXERCISE 8D.3

1 Write two equivalent statements for:

    a If $P(2) = 7$, then ......
    b If $P(x) = (x + 3)Q(x) - 8$, then ......

    c If $P(x)$ when divided by $x - 5$ has a remainder of 11 then ......

2 Without performing division, find the remainder when:

    a $x^3 + 2x^2 - 7x + 5$ is divided by $x - 1$
    b $x^4 - 2x^2 + 3x - 1$ is divided by $x + 2$.

3 Find a given that:

    a when $x^3 - 2x + a$ is divided by $x - 2$, the remainder is 7
    b when $2x^3 + x^2 + ax - 5$ is divided by $x + 1$, the remainder is -8.

4 Find a and b given that when $x^3 + 2x^2 + ax + b$ is divided by $x - 1$ the remainder is 4 and when divided by $x + 2$ the remainder is 16.

5 If $2x^n + ax^2 - 6$ leaves a remainder of -7 when divided by $x - 1$ and 129 when divided by $x + 3$, find a and n.

Example 30

When $P(x)$ is divided by $x^2 - 3x + 7$ the quotient is $x^2 + x - 1$ and the remainder is unknown. However, when $P(x)$ is divided by $x - 2$ the remainder is 29 and when divided by $x + 1$ the remainder is -16. If the remainder has the form $ax + b$, find a and b.

As the divisor is $x^2 - 3x + 7$ and the remainder has form $ax + b$,

$$\text{then} \quad P(x) = \underbrace{(x^2 + x - 1)}_{Q(x)}\underbrace{(x^2 - 3x + 7)}_{D(x)} + \underbrace{ax + b}_{R(x)}$$

But $P(2) = 29$ and $P(-1) = -16$ {Remainder theorem}

$$\therefore \quad (2^2 + 2 - 1)(2^2 - 6 + 7) + 2a + b = 29$$
$$\text{and} \quad ((-1)^2 + (-1) - 1)((-1)^2 - 3(-1) + 7) + (-a + b) = -16$$

$$\therefore \quad \begin{cases} (5)(5) + 2a + b = 29 \\ (-1)(11) - a + b = -16 \end{cases}$$

$$\therefore \quad \begin{cases} 2a + b = 4 \\ -a + b = -5 \end{cases}$$

Solving these gives $a = 3$ and $b = -2$.

---

6 When $P(z)$ is divided by $z^2 - 3z + 2$ the remainder is $4z - 7$.
Find the remainder when $P(z)$ is divided by: **a** $z - 1$ **b** $z - 2$.

7 When $P(z)$ is divided by $z + 1$ the remainder is -8 and when divided by $z - 3$ the remainder is 4. Find the remainder when $P(z)$ is divided by $(z - 3)(z + 1)$.

8 If $P(x)$ is divided by $(x - a)(x - b)$, prove that the remainder is: $\left(\dfrac{P(b) - P(a)}{b - a} \right) \times (x - a) + P(a)$.

9 If $P(x)$ is divided by $(x-a)^2$, prove that the remainder is $P'(a)(x-a)+P(a)$, where $P'(x)$ is the derivative of $P(x)$.

An immediate consequence of the Remainder theorem is the **Factor theorem**.

THE FACTOR THEOREM

$$k \text{ is a zero of } P(x) \Leftrightarrow (x-k) \text{ is a factor of } P(x).$$

Proof: k is a zero of $P(x)$ $\Leftrightarrow P(k)=0$ {definition of a zero}
$\qquad\qquad\qquad\qquad\qquad\quad \Leftrightarrow R=0$ {Remainder theorem}
$\qquad\qquad\qquad\qquad\qquad\quad \Leftrightarrow P(x)=Q(x)(x-k)$ {division algorithm}
$\qquad\qquad\qquad\qquad\qquad\quad \Leftrightarrow (x-k) \text{ is a factor of } P(x)$ {definition of factor}

The **Factor theorem** says that if 2 is a zero of $P(x)$ then $(x-2)$ is a factor of $P(x)$ and vice versa.

Example 31

Find k given that $x-2$ is a factor of x^3+kx^2-3x+6 and then fully factorise x^3+kx^2-3x+6.

Let $P(x)=x^3+kx^2-3x+6$

By the Factor theorem, as $x-2$ is a factor then $P(2)=0$
$$\therefore \quad 2^3+k2^2-3(2)+6=0$$
$$\therefore \quad 8+4k=0 \quad \text{and so} \quad k=-2$$

Now $x^3-2x^2-3x+6=(x-2)(x^2+ax-3)$

Equating coefficients of x^2 gives: $-2=-2+a$ i.e., $a=0$
Equating coefficients of x gives: $-3=-2a-3$ i.e., $a=0$

$$\therefore \quad x^3-2x^2-3x+6=(x-2)(x^2-3)$$
$$=(x-2)(x+\sqrt{3})(x-\sqrt{3})$$

or Using synthetic division

$$
\begin{array}{r|cccc}
2 & 1 & k & -3 & 6 \\
 & 0 & 2 & 2k+4 & 4k+2 \\
\hline
 & 1 & k+2 & 2k+1 & 4k+8
\end{array}
$$

$\therefore \quad P(2)=4k+8$ and since $P(2)=0$, $k=-2$

Now $P(x)=(x-2)(x^2+[k+2]x+[2k+1])$
$$=(x-2)(x^2-3)$$
$$=(x-2)(x+\sqrt{3})(x-\sqrt{3})$$

EXERCISE 8D.4

1 Find k and hence factorise the polynomial if:

  a $2x^3+x^2+kx-4$ has a factor of $x+2$

  b $x^4-3x^3-kx^2+6x$ has a factor of $x-3$.

2 Find a and b given that $2x^3 + ax^2 + bx + 5$ has factors of $x - 1$ and $x + 5$.

3 **a** 3 is a zero of $P(z) = z^3 - z^2 + [k - 5]z + [k^2 - 7]$.
Find k and hence find all zeros of $P(z)$.

    b Show that $z - 2$ is a factor of $P(z) = z^3 + mz^2 + (3m - 2)z - 10m - 4$ for all values of m. For what values of m is $(z - 2)^2$ a factor of $P(z)$?

4 **a** Consider $P(x) = x^3 - a^3$ where a is real.

    i Find $P(a)$. What is the significance of this result?

    ii Factorise $x^3 - a^3$ as a product of a real linear and quadratic factor.

    b Now consider $P(x) = x^3 + a^3$, where a is real.

    i Find $P(-a)$. What is the significance of this result?

    ii Factorise $x^3 + a^3$ as a product of a real linear and quadratic factor.

5 **a** Prove that "$x + 1$ is a factor of $x^n + 1$ $\Leftrightarrow$ n is odd."

    b Find real number a such that $x - 1 - a$ is a factor of $P(x) = x^3 - 3ax - 9$.

E   GRAPHING POLYNOMIALS

In this section we are obviously only concerned with graphing **real** polynomials. Do you remember what is meant by a real polynomial?

Graphing using a **graphics calculator** or the **graphing package** provided would be invaluable.

INVESTIGATION 2   CUBIC GRAPHING

   Possible types to consider are:

    Type 1: $P(x) = a(x - \alpha)(x - \beta)(x - \gamma)$, $a \neq 0$

    Type 2: $P(x) = a(x - \alpha)(x - \beta)^2$, $a \neq 0$

    Type 3: $P(x) = (x - \alpha)(ax^2 + bx + c)$, $\Delta = b^2 - 4ac < 0$, $a \neq 0$

    Type 4: $P(x) = a(x - \alpha)^3$, $a \neq 0$

What to do: (Use transformations of **Chapter 6** wherever possible)

1 Experiment with *Type 1* graphs of cubics. Clearly state the effect of changing a (in size and sign). What is the geometrical significance of α, β and γ?

2 Experiment with *Type 2* graphs of cubics. What is the geometrical significance of the squared factor?

3 Experiment with *Type 3* graphs of cubics. What is the geometric significance of α and the quadratic factor which has imaginary zeros?

4 Experiment with *Type 4* graphs of cubics. What is the geometric significance of α? Do not forget to consider $a > 0$ and $a < 0$.

From the **Investigation** you should have discovered that:

- If $a > 0$, the graph's shape is or , if $a < 0$ it is or .

- For a cubic in the form $P(x) = a(x - \alpha)(x - \beta)(x - \gamma)$ the graph has three distinct x-intercepts α, β and γ and the graph crosses over or **cuts** the x-axis at these points.
- For a cubic in the form $P(x) = a(x - \alpha)^2(x - \beta)$ the graph **touches** the x-axis at α and **cuts** it at β.
- For a cubic in the form $P(x) = (x-\alpha)(ax^2+bx+c)$ where $\Delta < 0$ the graph cuts the x-axis **once only**. The imaginary zeros do not show up on a real graph.
- For a cubic of the form $P(x) = a(x - \alpha)^3$, the graph has x-intercept α and at α the tangent is horizontal and crosses over the curve at α.
- All cubics are continuous smooth curves.

Example 32

Find the equation of the cubic with graph:

a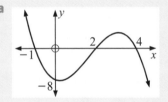

b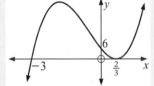

a The x-intercepts are $-1, 2, 4$

$\therefore \quad y = a(x + 1)(x - 2)(x - 4)$

But when $x = 0$, $y = -8$

$\therefore \quad a(1)(-2)(-4) = -8$

$\therefore \quad a = -1$

So, $y = -(x + 1)(x - 2)(x - 4)$

b Touching at $\frac{2}{3}$ indicates a squared factor $(3x - 2)^2$ and x-intercept is -3, $\therefore \quad y = a(3x - 2)^2(x + 3)$

But when $x = 0$, $y = 6$

So, $a(-2)^2(3) = 6$ and $\therefore \quad a = \frac{1}{2}$

So, $y = \frac{1}{2}(3x - 2)^2(x + 3)$

Note:
- Given,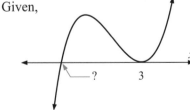

where an x-intercept is not given, then $P(x) = (x - 3)^2 \underbrace{(ax + b)}$.

most general form of a linear

Note: $P(x) = a(x - 3)^2(x + b)$ is more complicated.

- Given,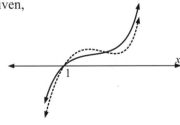

where there is clearly only one x-intercept and that is given, then $P(x) = (x + 1) \underbrace{(ax^2 + bx + c)}$.

most general form of a quadratic

What can you say about this quadratic?

EXERCISE 8E.1

1   What is the geometrical significance of:

    a a single factor in $P(x)$, such as $(x - \alpha)$

    b a squared factor in $P(x)$, such as $(x - \alpha)^2$

    c a cubed factor in $P(x)$, such as $(x - \alpha)^3$?

2   Find the equation of the cubic with graph:

  a

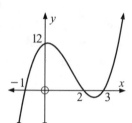

  b

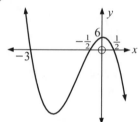

  c

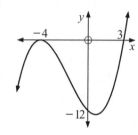

  d

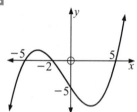

  e

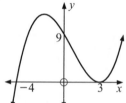

  f

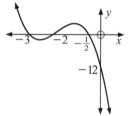

Example 33

Find the equation of the cubic which cuts the x-axis at 2, -3 and -4 and passes through the point $(1, -40)$.

Zeros of the cubic are 2, -3 and -4

$\therefore \ y = a(x - 2)(x + 3)(x + 4), \quad a \neq 0$

But when $x = 1, \quad y = -40 \qquad \therefore \quad a(-1)(4)(5) = -40$

$\qquad\qquad\qquad\qquad\qquad\qquad\qquad \therefore \qquad -20a = -40$

$\qquad\qquad\qquad\qquad\qquad\qquad\qquad \therefore \qquad a = 2$

So, the equation is $\ y = 2(x - 2)(x + 3)(x + 4)$.

---

3   Find the equation of the cubic whose graph:

    a cuts the x-axis at 3, 1, -2 and passes through $(2, -4)$

    b cuts the x-axis at -2, 0 and $\frac{1}{2}$ and passes through $(-3, -21)$

    c touches the x-axis at 1, cuts the x-axis at -2 and passes through $(4, 54)$

    d touches the x-axis at $-\frac{2}{3}$, cuts the x-axis at 4 and passes through $(-1, -5)$.

4 Match the given graphs to the corresponding cubic function:

a $y = 2(x-1)(x+2)(x+4)$ **b** $y = -(x+1)(x-2)(x-4)$

c $y = (x-1)(x-2)(x+4)$ **d** $y = -2(x-1)(x+2)(x+4)$

e $y = -(x-1)(x+2)(x+4)$ **f** $y = 2(x-1)(x-2)(x+4)$

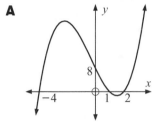
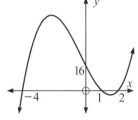
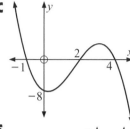

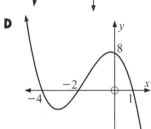
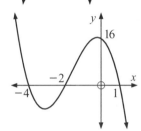
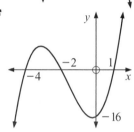

5 Find the equation of a real cubic polynomial which cuts:

a the x-axis at $\frac{1}{2}$ and -3, cuts the y-axis at 30 and passes through $(1, -20)$

b the x-axis at 1, touches the x-axis at -2 and cuts the y-axis at $(0, 8)$

c the x-axis at 2, the y-axis at -4 and passes through $(1, -1)$ and $(-1, -21)$.

INVESTIGATION 3   **QUARTIC GRAPHING**

There are considerably more possible factor types for quartic functions, to consider. Instead we will consider quartics containing certain types of factors.

What to do:

1 Experiment with quartics which have:

  a four linear real factors

  b a squared real linear factor and two different real linear factors

  c two squared real linear factors

  d a cubed factor and one real linear factor

  e a real linear factor raised to the fourth power

  f one real quadratic factor with $\Delta < 0$ and two real linear factors

  g two real quadratic factors each with $\Delta < 0$.

From the **Investigation** you should have discovered that:

> •   If $a > 0$ the graph opens upwards.   } a is the coefficient of x^4
>   If $a < 0$ the graph opens downwards.

Can you explain why?

- If a quartic with $a > 0$ is fully factored into real linear factors, for:

  ▶ a **single factor** $(x - \alpha)$, the graph **cuts** the x-axis at α

  e.g.

  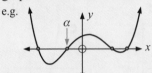

  ▶ a **squared factor** $(x - \alpha)^2$, the graph **touches** the x-axis at α

  e.g.

  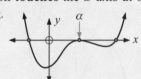

  ▶ a **cubed factor** $(x - \alpha)^3$, the graph **cuts** the x-axis at α, but is 'flat' at α

  e.g.

  ▶ a **quadruple factor** $(x - \alpha)^4$, the graph **touches** the x-axis but is 'flat' at that point.

  e.g.

  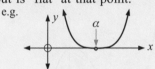

- If a quartic with $a > 0$ has one real quadratic factor with $\Delta < 0$ we could have

  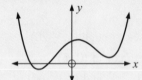

- If a quartic with $a > 0$ has two real quadratic factors both with $\Delta < 0$ we have

  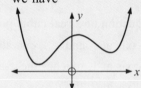

  i.e., does not cut the x-axis.

Example 34

Find the equation of the quartic with graph:

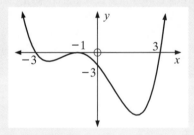

Since the graph touches the x-axis at -1 and cuts it at -3 and 3 then

$$y = a(x + 1)^2(x + 3)(x - 3)$$

But when $x = 0$, $y = -3$

$$\therefore \quad -3 = a(1)^2(3)(-3)$$

$$\therefore \quad -3 = -9a \text{ and so } a = \tfrac{1}{3}$$

$$\therefore \quad y = \tfrac{1}{3}(x + 1)^2(x + 3)(x - 3)$$

EXERCISE 8E.2

1 Find the equation of the quartic with graph:

a

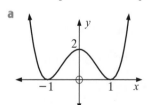

b

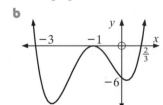

c

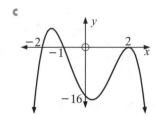

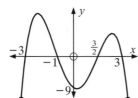

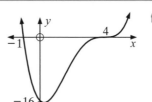

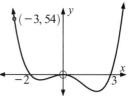

2 Match the given graphs to the corresponding quartic function:

    a $y = (x-1)^2(x+1)(x+3)$ **b** $y = -2(x-1)^2(x+1)(x+3)$

    c $y = (x-1)(x+1)^2(x+3)$ **d** $y = (x-1)(x+1)^2(x-3)$

    e $y = -\frac{1}{3}(x-1)(x+1)(x+3)^2$ **f** $y = -(x-1)(x+1)(x-3)^2$

A
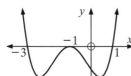

B
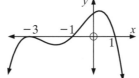

C
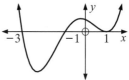

D
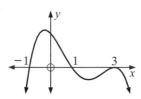

E
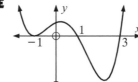

F
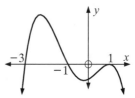

Example 35

Find the quartic which touches the x-axis at 2, cuts it at -3 and also passes through $(1, -12)$ and $(3, 6)$.

$(x-2)^2$ is a factor as the graph *touches* the x-axis at 2.

$(x+3)$ is a factor as the graph *cuts* the x-axis at -3.

So $P(x) = (x-2)^2(x+3)(ax+b)$ {$(ax+b)$ is required as the 4th factor}

Now $P(1) = -12$, $\therefore$ $(-1)^2(4)(a+b) = -12$ i.e., $a+b = -3$ ...... (1)

and $P(3) = 6$, $\therefore$ $1^2(6)(3a+b) = 6$ i.e., $3a+b = 1$ ...... (2)

Solving (1) and (2) simultaneously gives $a = 2$, $b = -5$

$\therefore$ $P(x) = (x-2)^2(x+3)(2x-5)$

---

3 Find the equation of the quartic whose graph:

    a cuts the x-axis at -4 and $\frac{1}{2}$, touches it at 2 and passes through the point $(1, 5)$

    b touches the x-axis at $\frac{2}{3}$ and -3, and passes through the point $(-4, 49)$

    c cuts the x-axis at $\pm\frac{1}{2}$ and ± 2 and passes through the point $(1, -18)$

    d touches the x-axis at 1, cuts the y-axis at -1 and passes through the points $(-1, -4)$ and $(2, 15)$.

Note: What happens to $P(x) = a_n x^n + a_{n-1} x^{n-1} + \ldots + a_1 x + a_0, \quad a_n \neq 0$
a polynomial of degree n, $n \in N$ as $|x|$ gets large? We consider, as $|x|$ gets large, really means as $|x| \to \infty$, i.e., as $x \to -\infty$ and as $x \to +\infty$.

Now as $|x| \to \infty$, the term $a_n x^n$ dominates the value of $P(x)$ and the values of the other terms become insignificant.

Hence if:
- $a_n > 0$, and n is even, $P(x) \to +\infty$, as $x \to +\infty$
   and $P(x) \to +\infty$, as $x \to -\infty$

- $a_n > 0$ and n is odd, $P(x) \to +\infty$, as $x \to +\infty$
   and $P(x) \to -\infty$ as $x \to -\infty$

- $a_n < 0$ and n is even, $P(x) \to -\infty$, as $x \to +\infty$
   and $P(x) \to +\infty$, as $x \to -\infty$

- $a_n < 0$ and n is odd, $P(x) \to -\infty$, as $x \to +\infty$
   and $P(x) \to +\infty$, as $n \to -\infty$

Summary of facts you should have discovered so far about **cubics** with **integer coefficients**:

▶ Every cubic polynomial must cut the x-axis at least once and so has at least one real zero. The other two zeros could be:
- real and rational
- real and irrational and appear as radical conjugates
- imaginary and appear as a complex conjugate pair.

▶ Real zeros are x-intercepts, so a cubic can have:
- 3 real zeros, *or*
  for example:
- 1 real and 2 imaginary *or*
  zeros, for example:
- 2 real zeros (one repeated)
  for example:

For **quartics** with **integer coefficients** there are many more cases to consider.

DISCUSSION

Read the above summary for cubics and then construct a summary like it for quartics. Cover all possible cases. Write a report which includes sketch graphs. Could you do this for quintic polynomials, i.e., degree 5?

We will use a **graphics calculator** to find a rational zero for cubics and two rational zeros for quartics.

Example 36

Find all zeros of $P(x) = 3x^3 - 14x^2 + 5x + 2$.

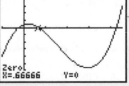

Using the calculator we search for any rational zero.

In this case $x = 0.666\,667$ or $0.\overline{6}$ indicates $x = \frac{2}{3}$ is a zero and $\therefore$ $(3x - 2)$ is a factor

and so, $3x^3 - 14x^2 + 5x + 2 = (3x - 2)(x^2 + ax - 1)$
$\qquad\qquad\qquad\qquad\qquad\qquad = 3x^3 + [3a - 2]x^2 + [-3 - 2a]x + 2$

Equating coefficients: $3a - 2 = -14$ and $-3 - 2a = 5$

i.e., $3a = -12$ and $-2a = 8$

i.e., $a = -4$

$\therefore \quad P(x) = (3x - 2)(x^2 - 4x - 1)$

which has zeros $\frac{2}{3}$ and $2 \pm \sqrt{5}$ {quadratic formula}

GRAPHING PACKAGE

Clearly, for a quartic $P(x)$ we need to identify **two rational** zeros before trying to find the other two, which may be *rational* or *complex*.

EXERCISE 8E.3

1 Find all zeros of:

  a $x^3 - 3x^2 - 3x + 1$

  b $x^3 - 3x^2 + 4x - 2$

  c $2x^3 - 3x^2 - 4x - 35$

  d $2x^3 - x^2 + 20x - 10$

  e $4x^4 - 4x^3 - 25x^2 + x + 6$

  f $x^4 - 6x^3 + 22x^2 - 48x + 40$

Example 37

Find all roots of $6x^3 + 13x^2 + 20x + 3 = 0$

$x = -0.16666667$ is a zero, that is, $x = -\frac{1}{6}$

$\therefore \quad (6x + 1)$ is a factor

i.e., $(6x + 1)(x^2 + ax + 3) = 0$

    Equating coefficients of x^2: $\quad 1 + 6a = 13$

        $\therefore \quad 6a = 12$ i.e., $a = 2$

    Equating coefficients of x: $\quad a + 18 = 20$ ✓

$\therefore \quad (6x + 1)(x^2 + 2x + 3) = 0 \quad x = -\frac{1}{6}$ or $-1 \pm i\sqrt{2}$ {quadratic formula}

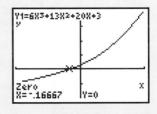

---

2 Find the roots of:

  a $x^3 + 2x^2 + 3x + 6 = 0$

  b $2x^3 + 3x^2 - 3x - 2 = 0$

  c $x^3 - 6x^2 + 12x - 8 = 0$

  d $2x^3 + 18 = 5x^2 + 9x$

  e $x^4 - x^3 - 9x^2 + 11x + 6 = 0$

  f $2x^4 - 13x^3 + 27x^2 = 13x + 15$

3 Factorise into linear factors:

  a $x^3 - 3x^2 + 4x - 2$

  b $x^3 + 3x^2 + 4x + 12$

  c $2x^3 - 9x^2 + 6x - 1$

  d $x^3 - 4x^2 + 9x - 10$

  e $4x^3 - 8x^2 + x + 3$

  f $3x^4 + 4x^3 + 5x^2 + 12x - 12$

  g $2x^4 - 3x^3 + 5x^2 + 6x - 4$

  h $2x^3 + 5x^2 + 8x + 20$

4 The following cubics will not factorise. Find their zeros using technology.

  a $x^3 + 2x^2 - 6x - 6$

  b $x^3 + x^2 - 7x - 8$

F | THEOREMS FOR REAL POLYNOMIALS

The following theorems are formal statements of discoveries we have made:

- **Unique Factorisation theorem**

  Every real polynomial of degree n can be factorised into n complex linear factors, some of which may be repeated. [**Reminder:** Real zeros are complex zeros.]

- Every real polynomial can be expressed as a product of real linear and irreducible quadratic factors (where $\Delta < 0$).

- If $p + qi$ $(q \neq 0)$ is a zero of a real polynomial then its complex conjugate $p - qi$ is also a zero.

- Every polynomial of odd degree has at least one real zero. Why?

- All real polynomials of degree n have n zeros, some of which may be repeated. These zeros are real and/or complex zeros that occur in conjugate pairs. **Be careful** of the **distinction** between **zeros** and **factors**.

Example 38

If $-3 + i$ is a zero of $P(x) = ax^3 + 9x^2 + ax - 30$ where a is real, find a and hence find all zeros of the cubic.

As $P(x)$ is real (coefficients are real) both $-3 + i$ and $-3 - i$ are zeros.

These have sum of -6 and product of $(-3 + i)(-3 - i) = 10$

So, $-3 \pm i$ come from the quadratic $x^2 + 6x + 10$.

Consequently, $ax^3 + 9x^2 + ax - 30 = (x^2 + 6x + 10)(ax - 3)$.

To find a we equate coefficients of x^2 and x

$\therefore$ $9 = 6a - 3$ and $a = 10a - 18$ and $a = 2$ in both cases

$\therefore$ $a = 2$ and the other two zeros are $-3 - i$ and $\frac{3}{2}$.

the linear factor is $(ax - 3)$ i.e., $(2x - 3)$

EXERCISE 8F.1

1 Find all third degree real polynomials with zeros of $-\frac{1}{2}$ and $1 - 3i$.

2 $p(x)$ is a real cubic polynomial in which $p(1) = p(2 + i) = 0$ and $p(0) = -20$. Find $p(x)$ in expanded form.

3 $2 - 3i$ is a zero of $P(z) = z^3 + pz + q$ where p and q are real. Using conjugate pairs, find p and q and the other two zeros. Check your answer by solving for p and q using $P(2 - 3i) = 0$.

4 $3 + i$ is a root of $z^4 - 2z^3 + az^2 + bz + 10 = 0$, where a and b are real. Find a and b and the other roots of the equation.

Example 39

One zero of $ax^3 + [a+1]x^2 + 10x + 15$, $a \in \mathcal{R}$, is purely imaginary. Find a and the zeros of the polynomial.

Let the purely imaginary zero be bi, $b \neq 0$.

Since $P(x)$ is real (coefficients are all real) $-bi$ is also a zero.

For bi and $-bi$, their sum $= 0$ and   product $= -b^2i^2 = b^2$

$\therefore$ these two zeros come from $x^2 + b^2$.

So, $ax^3 + [a+1]x^2 + 10x + 15 = (x^2 + b^2)(ax + \dfrac{15}{b^2})$

$$= ax^3 + \left[\dfrac{15}{b^2}\right]x^2 + b^2ax + 15$$

Consequently $a + 1 = \dfrac{15}{b^2}$ ...... (1)   and $b^2a = 10$ ...... (2)

$\therefore$ $b^2a + b^2 = 15$ from (1)

$\therefore$ $10 + b^2 = 15$

$\therefore$ $b^2 = 5$ and so $b = \pm\sqrt{5}$

In (2),   as $b^2 = 5$, $5a = 10$ $\therefore$ $a = 2$.

The linear factor is $ax + \dfrac{15}{b^2}$ i.e., $2x + 3$

$\therefore$ $a = 2$ and the zeros are $\pm i\sqrt{5}$, $-\frac{3}{2}$.

5 One zero of $P(z) = z^3 + az^2 + 3z + 9$ is purely imaginary. If a is real, find a and hence factorise $P(z)$ into linear factors.

6 At least one zero of $P(x) = 3x^3 + kx^2 + 15x + 10$ is purely imaginary. Given that k is real, find k and hence resolve $P(x)$ into a product of linear factors.

EXERCISE 8F.2 PROBLEM SOLVING WITH POLYNOMIALS

Use a **graphics calculator** or **graphing package** with this exercise.

1 A scientist working for Crash Test Barriers, Inc. is trying to design a crash test barrier whose ideal characteristics are shown graphically below. The independent variable is the time after impact, measured in milliseconds. The dependent variable is the distance that the barrier has been depressed because of the impact, measured in millimetres.

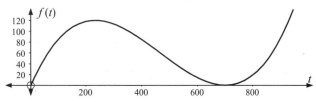

a The equation for this graph is of the form $f(t) = kt(t - a)^2$. From the graph, what is the value of a? What does it represent?

   b If the ideal crash barrier is depressed by 85 mm after 100 milliseconds, find the value of k, and hence find the equation of the graph given.

   c What is the maximum amount of depression, and when does it occur?

2 In the last year (starting 1st January), the volume of water (in megalitres) in a particular dam after t months could be described by the model $V(t) = -t^3 + 30t^2 - 131t + 250$.

The dam authority rules that if the volume falls below 100 ML, irrigation is prohibited. During which months, if any, was irrigation prohibited in the last twelve months? Include in your answer a neat sketch of any graphs you may have used.

3 A ladder of length 10 metres is leaning up against a wall such that it is just touching a cube of edge length one metre, that is resting on the ground against the wall.

What height up the wall does the ladder reach?

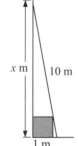

G INEQUALITIES

We have experienced at some depth what it means to solve an equation of the type (1) $f(x) = 0$ or type (2) $f(x) = g(x)$.

Simply, it means we are finding all possible values of the pronumeral, x in this case, that make the equation true.

Graphically, we can do this by graphing $f(x)$ in type (1) and finding where the graph meets the x-axis.

In type (2) we can graph $f(x)$ and $g(x)$ separately and find the x-coordinate(s) of the point(s) of intersection.

Example 40

Solve for x: **a** $e^x = 2x^2 + x + 1$ **b** $e^x \geqslant 2x^2 + x + 1$

  a We graph $f(x) = e^x$
        and $g(x) = 2x^2 + x + 1$

using technology we see that
$\therefore$ $x = 0$ and $x \doteqdot 3.21$ are solutions

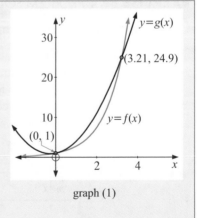

Note:

We need to be sure that the graphs will not meet again. We could graph $f(x) - g(x)$ and find where the graph meets the x-axis.

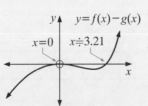

graph (1)

> **b** Using graph (1) above the solution is $x = 0$, $x \geqslant 3.21$
>
> This is where the graph of $f(x)$ meets the graph of $g(x)$ or is higher than the graph of $g(x)$.   We could even graph the
> solution set
>
> and could describe it as $x = 0$ *or* $x \in [3.21, \infty[$.

Note: When solving inequalities, only real number solutions are possible.

EXERCISE 8G.1

1 Solve for x:

   a $x^2 > 4$

   b $-x^2 + 4x + 1 < 0$

   c $x^2 \geqslant 4x - 4$

   d $x^2(x - 2) \leqslant 0$

   e $\dfrac{x - 5}{x + 1} \geqslant 3$

   f $\dfrac{x^2}{2 - 3x} \leqslant 1$

2 State the domain if $f : x \longmapsto x^2 \ln x$.   Hence find where $f(x) \leqslant 0$.

3 **a** Use technology to sketch the graph of $f : x \longmapsto \dfrac{2}{x} - e^{2x^2 - x + 1}$.

   b State the domain and range of this function.

   c Hence find all $x \in \mathcal{R}$, for which $e^{2x^2 - x + 1} > \dfrac{2}{x}$.

4 Let $g : x \longmapsto \sqrt{5 - \dfrac{1}{x^2}}$.

   a Solve $5 \geqslant \dfrac{1}{x^2}$.   **b** Hence find real values of x for which g is real and finite.

Sometimes, we require **exact** solutions for an inequality and consequently may need to use an analytical method for finding the solutions. Thus we need to remember some **basic** rules for manipulation of inequalities. Below is a summary:

- If we **add** or **subtract** the same number to both sides of an inequality, the inequality sign is maintained,   i.e., $a > b \;\Rightarrow\; a + c > b + c$.

- If we **multiply** or **divide** both sides by a positive number the inequality sign is **maintained**,   i.e., $a > b$, $c > 0 \;\Rightarrow\; ac > bc$ and $\dfrac{a}{c} > \dfrac{b}{c}$.

- If we multiply or divide both sides by a negative number, the inequality sign is **reversed**,   i.e., $a > b$, $c < 0 \;\Rightarrow\; ac < bc$ and $\dfrac{a}{c} < \dfrac{b}{c}$.

- If both sides of an inequality are non-negative we can square both sides, maintaining the inequality sign,   i.e., $a > b \geqslant 0 \;\Rightarrow\; a^2 > b^2$.

To solve inequalities using an analytical approach, the use of **sign diagrams** is most helpful.

SIGN DIAGRAMS

Sign diagrams give the signs ($+$ or $-$) of the function under consideration for all values of x in the domain of the function.

For example:

If $y = x^2 - 2x - 3$
$\quad = (x - 3)(x + 1)$

If $y = x^2 - 2x + 1$
$\quad = (x - 1)^2$

If $y = x^2 - 2x + 4$
$\quad = (x - 1)^2 + 3$

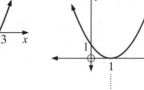

Sign diagrams:

Likewise, the rational function $y = \dfrac{3x + 2}{x - 1}$

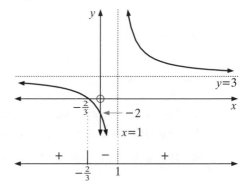

has vertical asymptote $x = 1$,   and graph
  horizontal asymptote $y = 3$
  x-intercept $-\frac{2}{3}$ and
  y-intercept -2

with sign diagram:

Reminders:

- The **horizontal line** of a sign diagram corresponds to the x-axis.
- The **critical values** (C.V.) are values of x when the function is **zero** or **undefined** (dotted lines indicating vertical asymptotes).
- A positive sign $(+)$ corresponds to the fact that the graph is *above* the x-axis. A negative sign $(-)$ corresponds to the fact that the graph is *below* the x-axis.
- When a factor has an **odd power** there is a change of sign about that critical value. When a factor has an **even power** there is no sign change about that critical value.
- For a quadratic factor $ax^2 + bx + c$ where $\Delta = b^2 - 4ac < 0$;
  $ax^2 + bx + c > 0$, for all x if $a > 0$,   ⎱ So there is no C.V. from
  $ax^2 + bx + c < 0$, for all x if $a < 0$.   ⎰ this quadratic.

Example 41

Draw sign diagrams for: **a** $(3 - 2x)(x + 2)^2$ **b** $\dfrac{-x(x - 3)}{(x + 2)^3}$

a $(3 - 2x)(x + 2)^2$ has critical
values $\frac{3}{2}$ and -2

when $x = 10$, say
$f(x) = - \times + = -$

First we substitute $x = 10$, say,
to find the sign for $x > \frac{3}{2}$

- $\frac{3}{2}$ comes from $(3 - 2x)^1$
  $\therefore$ sign change
- -2 comes from $(x + 2)^2$
  $\therefore$ no sign change

b $\dfrac{-x(x-3)}{(x+2)^3}$ has critical values 0, 3 and -2 is a VA value

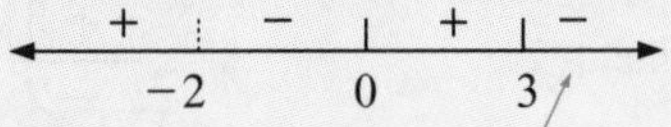

{all powers of factors are odd

∴ signs alternate}

when $x = 10$, say

$f(x) = \dfrac{- \times +}{+}$ ∴ $f(x) < 0$

EXERCISE 8G.2

1 Draw sign diagrams for:

a $4 - x^2$

b $3x^2 + x$

c $x^2 + x - 12$

d $x^2 + 2x - 2$

e $-x^2 + 4x + 1$

f $-2x^2 + x - 2$

g $-x(1-x)(2x+1)$

h $\dfrac{x-2}{3+x}$

i $\dfrac{3-x}{2x+1}$

j $4x - 4 - x^2$

k $x^2(x-2)$

l $\dfrac{x(x+2)}{x-1}$

m $2x^3 - 5x^2 + 10x$

n $(3-x)(x^2+2)$

o $x^4 - 5x^2 + 4$

p $\dfrac{x^2}{x+3}$

q $\dfrac{x-5}{x+1} + 3$

r $\dfrac{x^2}{2-3x} + 1$

SOLUTION SETS

We adopt the following procedure:

- Make the RHS **zero** by transferring all terms on the RHS to the LHS.
- Fully factorise the LHS.
- Draw a **sign diagram** of the LHS.
- Ask the question.   (e.g.,   For what values of x is ...... $\leqslant 0$?)

Example 42	
Solve for x: $\dfrac{3x+1}{x-1} > \dfrac{3x}{x+1}$	Since $\dfrac{3x+1}{x-1} > \dfrac{3x}{x+1}$

Since $\dfrac{3x+1}{x-1} > \dfrac{3x}{x+1}$

∴ $\dfrac{3x+1}{x-1} - \dfrac{3x}{x+1} > 0$

∴ $\dfrac{(3x+1)(x+1) - 3x(x-1)}{(x-1)(x+1)} > 0$

∴ $\dfrac{7x+1}{(x-1)(x+1)} > 0$

Discussion:

Why can't we cross multiply at the first step?

Sign diagram of LHS is:

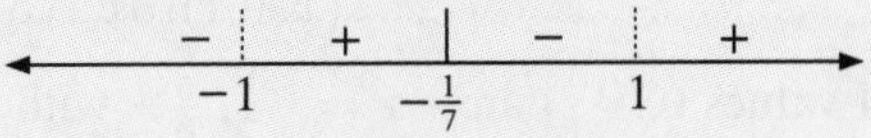

Thus $-1 < x < -\frac{1}{7}$ or $x > 1$.

EXERCISE 8G.3

1 Solve for x:

   a $(2x - 5)^2(x + 3) < 0$
   b $x^2 \geqslant 4x + 7$
   c $\dfrac{x + 3}{x - 2} > 2$

   d $\dfrac{3x + 1}{2 - x} \leqslant 1$
   e $x^3 \geqslant x$
   f $\dfrac{2x - 3}{x + 2} < \dfrac{2x}{x - 2}$

   g $x \geqslant \dfrac{1}{x}$
   h $x^2 \leqslant \dfrac{8}{x}$
   i $\dfrac{x^2}{3x - 2} \leqslant 1$

2 The equation $kx^2 + 2x - (k + 1) = 0$ has complex roots. Find the possible values of k.

3 Find the *exact* values of x for which $e^{2x} + 2e^x \geqslant 6 + 3e^x$.

The **modulus** of x, $|x|$ is defined by: $\quad |x| = \begin{cases} x & \text{if } x \geqslant 0 \\ -x & \text{if } x < 0 \end{cases} \quad \text{if } x \in \mathcal{R}$

PROPERTIES OF $|x|$, $x \in \mathcal{R}$

- $|x|$ is the distance from 0 (zero) to x on the number line.

- $|x| \geqslant 0$ for all x.

- $|-x| = |x|$ for all x.

- $|x^n| = |x|^n$ for all integers n.

- $|x - y| \geqslant |x| - |y|$ for all x and y.

- $|x - y| = |y - x|$

- $|x| = \sqrt{x^2}$ for all x, and thus $|x^2| = x^2$ for all x.

- $|x| \geqslant x$ for all x.

- $|xy| = |x|\,|y|$ for all x and y, and $\left| \dfrac{x}{y} \right| = \dfrac{|x|}{|y|}$ for all x and for all $y \neq 0$.

- $|x + y| \leqslant |x| + |y|$ for all x and y.

- $|x - a|$ is the distance between x and a on the real number line.

The first five of these properties are clearly true from the basic definition of $|x|$.

The others require proof and will be covered in the chapters on Mathematical Induction (**Chapter 10**) and Complex numbers (revisited **Chapter 16**).

Consequently, $\quad |f(x)| = \begin{cases} f(x) & \text{if } f(x) \geqslant 0 \\ -f(x) & \text{if } f(x) < 0 \end{cases} \quad$ see **Chapter 6F**.

Example 43	Find exactly where $2|x - 1| \geqslant |3 - x|$.

As both sides are positive in $\qquad 2|x - 1| \geqslant |3 - x|$

we square both sides to get $\qquad 4|x - 1|^2 \geqslant |3 - x|^2$

$\therefore \quad 4(x - 1)^2 - (3 - x)^2 \geqslant 0 \quad \{\text{as } |a|^2 = a^2 \text{ for } a \in \mathcal{R}\}$

$\therefore \quad [2(x - 1) + (3 - x)][2(x - 1) - (3 - x)] \geqslant 0$

$\therefore \quad (x + 1)(3x - 5) \geqslant 0$

critical values (CV's) are $\quad x = -1, \frac{5}{3}$ with sign diagram:

$\therefore \quad x \leqslant -1, \quad x \geqslant \frac{5}{3} \quad$ (check with graphics calculator)

EXERCISE 8G.4

1 Solve:

  a $|x - 3| \leqslant 4$ **b** $|2x - 1| \leqslant 3$ **c** $|3x + 1| > 2$ **d** $|5 - 2x| \geqslant 7$

  e $|x| \geqslant |2 - x|$ **f** $3|x| \leqslant |1 - 2x|$ **g** $\left|\dfrac{x}{x - 2}\right| \geqslant 3$ **h** $\left|\dfrac{2x + 3}{x - 1}\right| \geqslant 2$

Example 44	Solve graphically: $|1 - 2x| > x + 1$.

We draw graphs of $y = |1 - 2x|$ and $y = x + 1$ on the same set of axes.

$$y = |1 - 2x| = \begin{cases} 1 - 2x & \text{for } 1 - 2x \geqslant 0, \quad \text{i.e., } x \leqslant \tfrac{1}{2} \\ -1 + 2x & \text{for } 1 - 2x < 0, \quad \text{i.e., } x > \tfrac{1}{2} \end{cases}$$

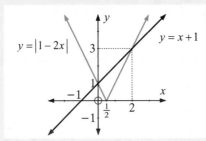

Now $|1 - 2x| > x + 1$

when the graph of $y = |1 - 2x|$ lies
above $y = x + 1$,

$\therefore \quad x < 0 \quad \text{or} \quad x > 2$.

i.e., $x \in \,] -\infty, 0 \, [\quad \text{or} \quad x \in \,] 2, \infty \, [$

---

2 Solve graphically:

  a $|2x - 3| < x$ **b** $2x - 3 < |x|$ **c** $|x^2 - x| > 2$ **d** $|x| - 2 \geqslant |4 - x|$

3 Graph the function $f(x) = \dfrac{|x|}{x - 2}$, and hence find all values of x for which $\dfrac{|x|}{x - 2} \geqslant -\tfrac{1}{2}$.

4 **a** Draw the graph of $y = |x + 5| + |x + 2| + |x| + |x - 3|$.

  b

P, Q and R are factories which are 5, 2 and 3 km away from factory O respectively.

A security service wishes to know where it should locate its premises along AB so
that the total length of cable to the 4 factories is a minimum.

  i Explain why the total length of cable is given by

  $|x + 5| + |x + 2| + |x| + |x - 3|$ where x is the position of the security service
  on AB.

  ii Where should the security service set up to minimise the length of cable to all
  4 factories? What is the minimum length of cable?

  iii If a fifth factory at S, located 7 km right of O, also requries the security service,
  where should the security service locate its premises for minimum cable length?

REVIEW SET 8A

1 Find real numbers a and b such that:

    a $a + ib = 4$ **b** $(1 - 2i)(a + bi) = -5 - 10i$ **c** $(a + 2i)(1 + bi) = 17 - 19i$

2 If $z = 3 + i$ and $w = -2 - i$, find in simplest form:

    a $2z - 3w$ **b** $\dfrac{z^*}{w}$ **c** z^3

3 Prove the following: $zw^* - z^*w$ is purely imaginary or zero for all complex numbers z and w.

4 Expand and simplify: **a** $(3x^3 + 2x - 5)(4x - 3)$ **b** $(2x^2 - x + 3)^2$

5 Carry out the following divisions: **a** $\dfrac{x^3}{x + 2}$ **b** $\dfrac{x^3}{(x + 2)(x + 3)}$

6 State and prove the Remainder theorem.

7 $-2 + bi$ is a solution to $z^2 + az + [3 + a] = 0$. Find a and b given that they are real.

8 Find all zeros of $2z^4 - 5z^3 + 13z^2 - 4z - 6$.

9 Factorise $z^4 + 2z^3 - 2z^2 + 8$ into linear factors.

10 Find a quartic polynomial with rational coefficients having $2 - i\sqrt{3}$ and $\sqrt{2} + 1$ as two of its zeros.

11 If $f(x) = x^3 - 3x^2 - 9x + b$ has $(x - k)^2$ as a factor, show that there are two possible values of k. For each of these two values of k, find the corresponding value for b and hence solve $f(x) = 0$.

12 Find exact x-values when: **a** $x^2 + 2x \geqslant 5$ **b** $x < \dfrac{9}{x}$ **c** $\left| \dfrac{x}{8 - x} \right| \leqslant 2$

13 Find k if the line with equation $y = 2x + k$ does not meet the circle with equation $x^2 + y^2 + 8x - 4y + 2 = 0$.

    Hint: Solve simultaneously to get a quadratic and find k for which $\Delta < 0$.

14 When $P(x) = x^n + 3x^2 + kx + 6$ is divided by $x + 1$ the remainder is 12. When $P(x)$ is divided by $x - 1$ the remainder is 8. Find k and n given that $34 < n < 38$.

15 If α and β are two of the roots of $x^3 - x + 1 = 0$, show that $\alpha\beta$ is a root of $x^3 + x^2 - 1 = 0$. [**Hint:** Let $x^3 - x + 1 = (x - \alpha)(x - \beta)(x - \gamma)$.]

REVIEW SET 8B, 8C, 8D
Click on the icon to obtain printable review sets and answers

REVIEW SET 8B REVIEW SET 8C REVIEW SET 8D

Chapter 9

Counting and binomial theorem

OPENING PROBLEM

At the 2004 IB Mathematics Teachers' Conference there were 273 delegates present. The organising committee consisted of 10 people.

- If each committee member shakes hands with every other committee member, how many handshakes take place?

  Can a 10-sided convex polygon be used to solve this problem?

- If all 273 delegates shake hands with all other delegates, how many handshakes take place now?

The opening problem is a counting problem. The following exercise helps us to count without actually listing and counting one by one. To do this we examine:

- the product principle   • counting permutations   • counting combinations

A   THE PRODUCT PRINCIPLE

Suppose that there are three towns A, B and C and that 4 different roads could be taken from A to B and two different roads from B to C.

Diagrammatically we have:

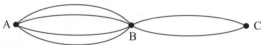

The question arises: "How many different pathways are there from A to C going through B?"

If we take road 1, there are two alternative roads to complete our trip.

If we take road 2, there are two alternative roads to complete our trip.   ...... etc.

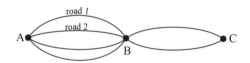

So there are $2 + 2 + 2 + 2 = 4 \times 2$ different pathways.

However, we notice that the 4 corresponds to the number of roads from A to B and the 2 corresponds to the number of roads from B to C.

Similarly, for

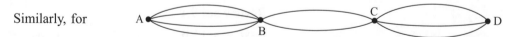

there would be $4 \times 2 \times 3 = 24$ different pathways from A to D passing through B and C.

THE PRODUCT PRINCIPLE

The **product principle** is:

If there are m different ways of performing an operation and for each of these there are n different ways of performing a second **independent** operation, then there are mn different ways of performing the two operations in succession."

The product principle can be extended to three or more successive operations.

> ### Example 1
>
>
>
> It is possible to take five different paths from Pauline's to Quinton's, 4 different paths from Quinton's to Reiko's and 3 different paths from Reiko's to Sam's. How many different pathways could be taken from Pauline's to Sam's via Quinton's and Reiko's?
>
> The total number of different pathways $= 5 \times 4 \times 3 = 60$. {product principle}

EXERCISE 9A

1 The illustration shows the possible map routes for a bus service which goes from P to S through both Q and R.

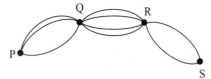

How many different routes are possible?

2  It is decided to label the vertices of a rectangle with the letters A, B, C and D.

In how many ways is this possible if:

   a they are to be in clockwise alphabetical order

   b they are to be in alphabetical order

   c they are to be in random order?

3 The figure alongside is box-shaped and made of wire. An ant crawls along the wire from A to B.

How many different paths of shortest length lead from A to B?

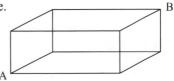

4 In how many different ways can the top two positions be filled in a table tennis competition of 7 teams?

5 A football competition is organised between 8 teams. In how many ways is it possible to fill the top 4 places in order of premiership points obtained?

6 How many 3-digit numbers can be formed using the digits 2, 3, 4, 5 and 6:

   a as often as desired   **b** once only?

7 How many different alpha-numeric plates for motor car registration can be made if the first 3 places are English alphabet letters and those remaining are 3 digits from 0 to 9?

8 In how many ways can:

   a 2 letters be mailed into 2 mail boxes   **b** 2 letters be mailed into 3 mail boxes

   c 4 letters be mailed into 3 mail boxes?

B   COUNTING PATHS

Consider the following road system leading from
P to Q:

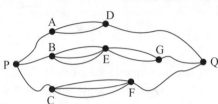

From A to Q there are 2 paths.
From B to Q there are $3 \times 2 = 6$ paths.
From C to Q there are 3 paths.

Thus, from P to Q there are $2 + 6 + 3 = 11$ paths.

Notice that: ▶   when going from B to G, we go from B to E **and** then from E to G,
and we multiply the possibilities,

▶   when going from P to Q, we must first go from P to A, **or** P to B
or P to C, and we add the possibilities.

Consequently: • the word **and** suggests multiplying the possibilities
• the word **or** suggests adding the possibilities.

Example 2

How many different paths
lead from P to Q?

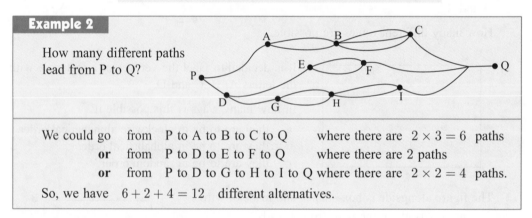

We could go   from   P to A to B to C to Q   where there are $2 \times 3 = 6$ paths
or   from   P to D to E to F to Q   where there are 2 paths
or   from   P to D to G to H to I to Q where there are $2 \times 2 = 4$ paths.

So, we have $6 + 2 + 4 = 12$ different alternatives.

EXERCISE 9B

1   How many different paths lead from P to Q?

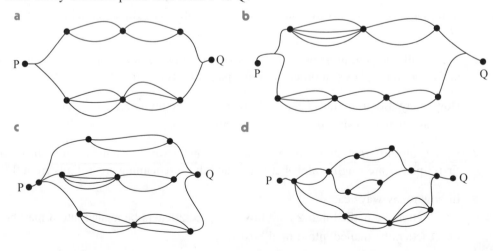

a

b

c

d

C FACTORIAL NOTATION

In problems involving counting, products and consecutive positive integers are common.

For example, $8 \times 7 \times 6$ or $6 \times 5 \times 4 \times 3 \times 2 \times 1$, etc.

FACTORIAL NOTATION

For convenience, we introduce **factorial numbers**, where numbers such as $6 \times 5 \times 4 \times 3 \times 2 \times 1$ are written as $6!$.

In general, $n!$ is the product of the first n positive integers for $n \geqslant 1$

i.e., $n! = n(n-1)(n-2)(n-3).... \times 3 \times 2 \times 1$, for $n \geqslant 1$

and $n! = 1$ for $n = 0$.

$n!$ is read "n factorial".

Notice that $8 \times 7 \times 6$ can be written using factorial numbers only as

$$8 \times 7 \times 6 = \frac{8 \times 7 \times 6 \times 5 \times 4 \times 3 \times 2 \times 1}{5 \times 4 \times 3 \times 2 \times 1} = \frac{8!}{5!}$$

PROPERTIES OF FACTORIAL NUMBERS

The **factorial rule** is $n! = n \times (n-1)!$

which can be extended to $n! = n(n-1)(n-2)!$,   etc.

Notice that, although 0! cannot be included in the original definition of factorial numbers, we can now give it a value.

Using the factorial rule with $n = 1$,   we have $1! = 1 \times 0!$ i.e., $1 = 0!$

So we define $0! = 1$,   and this is consistent with $n! = n \times (n-1)!$

Example 3

What integer is equal to: **a** $4!$ **b** $\dfrac{5!}{3!}$ **c** $\dfrac{7!}{4! \times 3!}$?

a $4! = 4 \times 3 \times 2 \times 1 = 24$ **b** $\dfrac{5!}{3!} = \dfrac{5 \times 4 \times \cancel{3 \times 2 \times 1}}{\cancel{3 \times 2 \times 1}} = 5 \times 4 = 20$

c $\dfrac{7!}{4! \times 3!} = \dfrac{7 \times 6 \times 5 \times \cancel{4 \times 3 \times 2 \times 1}}{\cancel{4 \times 3 \times 2 \times 1} \times 3 \times 2 \times 1} = 35$

EXERCISE 9C

1 Find $n!$ for $n = 0, 1, 2, 3, ..., 10$.

2 Simplify without using a calculator:

a $\dfrac{6!}{5!}$ **b** $\dfrac{6!}{4!}$ **c** $\dfrac{6!}{7!}$ **d** $\dfrac{4!}{6!}$ **e** $\dfrac{100!}{99!}$ **f** $\dfrac{7!}{5! \times 2!}$

3 Simplify: **a** $\dfrac{n!}{(n-1)!}$ **b** $\dfrac{(n+2)!}{n!}$ **c** $\dfrac{(n+1)!}{(n-1)!}$

Example 4

Express in factorial form: **a** $10 \times 9 \times 8 \times 7$ **b** $\dfrac{10 \times 9 \times 8 \times 7}{4 \times 3 \times 2 \times 1}$

a $10 \times 9 \times 8 \times 7 = \dfrac{10 \times 9 \times 8 \times 7 \times 6 \times 5 \times 4 \times 3 \times 2 \times 1}{6 \times 5 \times 4 \times 3 \times 2 \times 1} = \dfrac{10!}{6!}$

b $\dfrac{10 \times 9 \times 8 \times 7}{4 \times 3 \times 2 \times 1} = \dfrac{10 \times 9 \times 8 \times 7 \times 6 \times 5 \times 4 \times 3 \times 2 \times 1}{4 \times 3 \times 2 \times 1 \times 6 \times 5 \times 4 \times 3 \times 2 \times 1} = \dfrac{10!}{4! \times 6!}$

4 Express in factorial form:

a $7 \times 6 \times 5$

b 10×9

c $11 \times 10 \times 9 \times 8 \times 7$

d $\dfrac{13 \times 12 \times 11}{3 \times 2 \times 1}$

e $\dfrac{1}{6 \times 5 \times 4}$

f $\dfrac{4 \times 3 \times 2 \times 1}{20 \times 19 \times 18 \times 17}$

Example 5

Write the following sums/differences as a product by factorising:
a $8! + 6!$ **b** $10! - 9! + 8!$

a $8! + 6!$
$= 8 \times 7 \times 6! + 6!$
$= 6!(8 \times 7 + 1)$
$= 6! \times 57$

b $10! - 9! + 8!$
$= 10 \times 9 \times 8! - 9 \times 8! + 8!$
$= 8!(90 - 9 + 1)$
$= 8! \times 82$

5 Write as a product (using factorisation):

a $5! + 4!$ **b** $11! - 10!$ **c** $6! + 8!$ **d** $12! - 10!$

e $9! + 8! + 7!$ **f** $7! - 6! + 8!$ **g** $12! - 2 \times 11!$ **h** $3 \times 9! + 5 \times 8!$

Example 6

Simplify $\dfrac{7! - 6!}{6}$ using factorisation.

$\dfrac{7! - 6!}{6} = \dfrac{7 \times 6! - 6!}{6}$

$= \dfrac{6!(7 - 1)^{1}}{6_{1}}$

$= 6!$

6 Simplify using factorisation:

a $\dfrac{12! - 11!}{11}$

b $\dfrac{10! + 9!}{11}$

c $\dfrac{10! - 8!}{89}$

d $\dfrac{10! - 9!}{9!}$

e $\dfrac{6! + 5! - 4!}{4!}$

f $\dfrac{n! + (n-1)!}{(n-1)!}$

g $\dfrac{n! - (n-1)!}{n-1}$

h $\dfrac{(n+2)! + (n+1)!}{n+3}$

COUNTING PERMUTATIONS

> A **permutation** of a group of symbols is *any arrangement* of those symbols in a definite *order*.

For example, BAC is a permutation on the symbols A, B and C when all three of them are used, i.e., taken 3 at a time.

Notice that ABC, ACB, BAC, BCA, CAB, CBA are all the different permutations on the symbols A, B and C taken 3 at a time.

In this exercise we are concerned with listings of all permutations, and counting how many permutations there are, without having to list them all.

Example 7

List all the permutations on the symbols P, Q and R when they are taken:
a   1 at a time   b   2 at a time   c   3 at a time.

a   P, Q, R   b   PQ   QP   RP   c   PQR   QPR   RPQ
                         PR   QR   RQ   PRQ   QRP   RQP

Example 8

List all permutations on the symbols W, X, Y and Z taken 4 at a time.

WXYZ   WXZY   WYXZ   WYZX   WZXY   WZYX
XWYZ   XWZY   XYWZ   XYZW   XZYW   XZWY
YWXZ   YWZX   YXWZ   YXZW   YZWX   YZXW
ZWXY   ZWYX   ZXWY   ZXYW   ZYWX   ZYXW   i.e.,   24 of them.

For large numbers of symbols listing the complete set of permutations is absurd. However, we can still count them in the following way.

Consider **Example 8** again:

There are 4 positions to fill

1st	2nd	3rd	4th

Into the 1st position, any of the 4 symbols could be used.

> This leaves any 3 symbols to go into the 2nd position, which in turn leaves any 2 symbols to go into the 3rd position, and finally leaves the remaining 1 symbol to go into the 4th position.

Consequently,

4	3	2	1
1st	2nd	3rd	4th

and so the total number $= 4 \times 2 \times 2 \times 1$ {product
                      $= 24$ principle}

EXERCISE 9D

1   List the set of all permutations on the symbols W, X, Y and Z taken
    a   1 at a time   b   two at a time   c   three at a time.

(**Note: Example 8** has them taken 4 at a time.)

2 List the set of all permutations on the symbols A, B, C, D and E taken:

    a   2 at a time   **b**   3 at a time.

Example 9

If a chess association has 16 teams, in how many different ways could the top 8 positions be filled on the competition ladder?

Any of the 16 teams could fill the 'top' position.
Any of the remaining 15 teams could fill the 2nd position.
Any of the remaining 14 teams could fill the 3rd position.
     ⋮
Any of the remaining 9 teams could fill the 8th position.

i.e.,

16	15	14	13	12	11	10	9
1st	2nd	3rd	4th	5th	6th	7th	8th

∴ total number $= 16 \times 15 \times 14 \times 13 \times 12 \times 11 \times 10 \times 9$
$$= 518\,918\,400$$

---

3 In how many ways can:

    a   5 different books be arranged on a shelf

    b   3 different paintings, from a collection of 8, be hung in a row

    c   a signal consisting of 4 coloured flags be made if there are 10 different flags to choose from?

4 Suppose you have 4 different coloured flags. How many different signals could you make using:

    a   2 flags only   **b**   3 flags only   **c**   2 or 3 flags?

Example 10

You have available the alphabet blocks A, B, C, D and E and they are placed in a row. For example you could have: ☐D☐A☐E☐C☐B☐

    a   How many different permutations could you have?
    b   How many permutations end in C?
    c   How many permutations have form ☐...A...B...☐ ?
    d   How many begin and end with a vowel, i.e., A or E?

    a   There are 5 letters taken 5 at a time.

         ∴ total number $= 5 \times 4 \times 3 \times 2 \times 1 = 120.$

    b | 4 | 3 | 2 | 1 | 1 |

        any others here   C here

        C goes into the last position (i.e., 1 way) and the other 4 letters could go into the remaining 4 places in 4! ways.

        ∴ total number $= 1 \times 4! = 24$ ways.

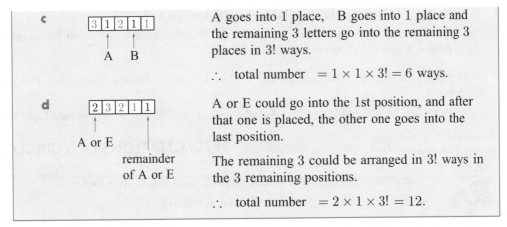

c

A goes into 1 place,   B goes into 1 place and the remaining 3 letters go into the remaining 3 places in 3! ways.

∴   total number $= 1 \times 1 \times 3! = 6$ ways.

d

A or E could go into the 1st position, and after that one is placed, the other one goes into the last position.

The remaining 3 could be arranged in 3! ways in the 3 remaining positions.

∴   total number $= 2 \times 1 \times 3! = 12$.

5 How many different permutations of the letters A, B, C, D, E and F are there if each letter can be used once only? How many of these:

    a   end in ED   **b**   begin with F and end with A
    c   begin and end with a vowel (i.e., A or E)?

6 How many 3-digit numbers can be constructed from digits 1, 2, 3, 4, 5, 6 and 7 if each digit may be used:

    a   as often as desired   **b**   only once   **c**   once only and the number is odd?

7 In how many ways can 3 boys and 3 girls be arranged in a row of 6 seats? In how many of these ways do the boys and girls alternate?

8 Numbers of 3 different digits are constructed from the digits 0, 1, 2, 3, 4, 5, 6, 7, 8 and 9 using a digit once only. How many such numbers:

    a   can be constructed   **b**   end in 5   **c**   end in 0   **d**   are divisible by 5?

Example 11

There are 6 different books arranged in a row on a shelf. In how many ways can two of the books, A and B be together?

Method 1:   We could have any of the following locations for A and B

A	B	×	×	×	×
B	A	×	×	×	×
×	A	B	×	×	×
×	B	A	×	×	×
×	×	A	B	×	×
×	×	B	A	×	×
×	×	×	A	B	×
×	×	×	B	A	×
×	×	×	×	A	B
×	×	×	×	B	A

⎫ 10 of these

If we consider any one of these, the remaining 4 books could be placed in 4! different orderings

∴   total number of ways
$= 10 \times 4! = 240$.

Method 2:

A and B can be put together in 2! ways   (i.e., AB or BA).

Now consider this pairing as one symbol (tie a string around them) which together with the other 4 books (i.e., 5 symbols) can be ordered in 5! different ways.

∴   total number $= 2! \times 5! = 240$.

9 In how many ways can 5 different books be arranged on a shelf if:

    a there are no restrictions   **b** books X and Y must be together

    c books X and Y are never together?

10 A group of 10 students randomly sit in a row of 10 chairs. In how many ways can this be done if:

    a there are no restrictions   **b** 3 students A, B and C are always seated together?

INVESTIGATION 1   PERMUTATIONS IN A CIRCLE

There are 6 permutations on the symbol A, B and C **in a line**.

These are: ABC ACB BAC BCA CAB CBA.

However **in a circle** there are only 2 different permutations on these 3 symbols. These are:

 and   as they are the only possibilities with different right-hand and left-hand neighbours.

        are the same cyclic permutations.

What to do:

1 Draw diagrams showing different cyclic permutations for:

    a one symbol;   A   **b** two symbols;   A and B

    c three symbols;   A, B and C   **d** four symbols;   A, B, C and D

2 Copy and complete:

Number of symbols	Permutations in a line	Permutations in a circle
1		
2		
3	$6 = 3!$	$2 = 2!$
4		

3 If there are n symbols to be permuted in a circle, how many different orderings are possible?

E   COMBINATIONS

A **combination** is a selection of objects *without* regard to order or arrangement.

For example, the possible teams of 3 people selected from A, B, C, D and E are

    ABC ABD ABE ACD ACE ADE

    BCD BCE BDE

    CDE   i.e.,   10 different combinations.

C_r^n is the number of combinations on n distinct/different symbols taken r at a time.

From the above example we therefore have $C_3^5 = 10$.

But   the number of permutations $= 5 \times 4 \times 3 = 60$,   and why is this answer 6 (or 3!) times larger than C_3^5 ?

This can be seen if we consider one of these teams, ABC say.

ABC say, is placed in order, this can be done in 3! ways,

i.e.,   ABC, ACB, BAC, BCA, CAB, CBA and if this is done for all 10 teams we get all possible permutations of the 5 people taken 3 at a time.

So, $5 \times 4 \times 3 = C_3^5 \times 3!$ $\therefore$ $C_3^5 = \dfrac{5 \times 4 \times 3}{3 \times 2 \times 1}$ or $\dfrac{5!}{3! \times 2!}$.

In **general,** $C_r^n = \dfrac{n\,(n-1)(n-2) \,..... \,(n-r+3)\,(n-r+2)\,(n-r+1)}{r\,(r-1)\,(r-2)\,.....\qquad 3 \qquad\quad 2 \qquad\quad 1} = \dfrac{n!}{r!(n-r)!}$

$\uparrow$ Factor form $\uparrow$ Factorial form

Values of C_r^n can be calculated from your calculator.

So, to find C_3^{10} or $_{10}C_3$ press e.g.,   10 **MATH** **PRB** 3 **ENTER** 2 **ENTER**.
The answer is   120.

Note: The following may prove useful: C_r^n ⟋ the number up for selection
                                                                    ⟍ the number of positions needed to be filled.

Example 12

How many different teams of 4 can be selected from a squad of 7 if:
a   there are no restrictions   b   the teams must include the captain?

a   This can be done in $C_4^7 = 35$ ways.
   {7 up for selection and we want any 4 of them}

b   If the captain must be included *and* we need any 3 of the other 6, this can be done in $C_1^1 \times C_3^6 = 20$ ways.

EXERCISE 9E

1   Evaluate using factor form: a C_1^8 b C_2^8 c C_3^8 d C_6^8 e C_8^8.
   Check each answer using your calculator.

2   In question **1** you probably noticed that $C_2^8 = C_6^8$.
   In general, $C_r^n = C_{n-r}^n$.   Prove that this statement is true.   (**Hint:** Use factorial form.)

3   List the different teams of 3 that can be chosen from a squad of 5 (named A, B, C, D and E). Check that the formula for C_r^n gives the total number of teams.

4   How many different teams of 11 can be chosen from a squad of 17?

5   Candidates for an examination are required to do 5 questions out of 9. In how many ways can this be done? If question 1 was compulsory, how many selections would be possible?

6   How many different committees of 3 can be selected from 13?

How many of these committees consist of the president and 2 others?

Example 13

A committee of 4 is chosen from 7 men and 6 women. How many different committees can be chosen if:

a   there are no restrictions   **b**   there must be 2 of each sex

c   at least one of each sex is needed?

---

a   For no restrictions there are $7 + 6 = 13$ people up for selection and we want any 4 of them. $\therefore$ total number $= C_4^{13} = 715.$

b   The 2 men can be chosen in C_2^7 ways *and* the 2 women can be chosen in C_2^6 ways.

$$\therefore \quad \text{total number} = C_2^7 \times C_2^6 = 315.$$

c   Total number

= number with   (3 M *and* 1 W)   *or*   (2 M *and* 2 W)   *or*   (1 M *and* 3 W)

$= C_3^7 \times C_1^6 \quad + \quad C_2^7 \times C_2^6 \quad + \quad C_1^7 \times C_3^6$

$= 665$

Alternatively,   total number $=$ $C_4^{13} - C_4^7 \times C_0^6 - C_0^7 \times C_4^6.$ *Why?*

---

7   How many different teams of 5 can be selected from a squad of 12?

How many of these teams contain:

a   the captain and vice-captain   **b**   exactly one of the captain or the vice-captain?

8   A team of 9 is selected from a squad of 15 of which 3 are *certainties*,   i.e.,   must be included, and another must be excluded because of injury. In how many ways can this be done?

9   In how many ways can 4 people be selected from 10 if:

a   one person is always in the selection   **b**   2 are excluded from every selection

c   1 is always included and 2 are always excluded?

10   A committee of 5 is chosen from 10 men and 6 women. Determine the number of ways of selecting the committee if:

a   there are no restrictions   **b**   it is to contain 3 men and 2 women

c   it is to contain all men   **d**   it is to contain at least 3 men

e   it is to contain at least one of each sex.

11   A committee of 5 is chosen from 6 doctors, 3 dentists and 7 others.

Determine the number of ways of selecting the committee if it is to contain:

a   2 doctors and 1 dentist   **b**   2 doctors   **c**   at least one of the two professions.

12   How many diagonals has a 20-sided convex polygon?

13   There are 12 distinct points A, B, C, D, ..., L, on a circle.

a   How many lines   **i**   are determined by the points   **ii**   pass through B?

b   How many triangles   **i**   are determined by the points   **ii**   have one vertex B?

14 How many 4-digit numbers can be constructed where the digits are in ascending order from left to right? **Note:** You cannot start with 0. Why?

15 **a** Give an example which demonstrates that:

$$C_0^5 \times C_4^6 \;+\; C_1^5 \times C_3^6 \;+\; C_2^5 \times C_2^6 \;+\; C_3^5 \times C_1^6 \;+\; C_4^5 \times C_0^6 \;=\; C_4^{11}.$$

b Copy and complete:

$$C_0^m \times C_r^n \;+\; C_1^m \times C_{r-1}^n \;+\; C_2^m \times C_{r-2}^n \;+\; .... \;+\; C_{r-1}^m \times C_1^n \;+\; C_r^m \times C_0^n \;=\; .....$$

16 In how many ways can 12 people be divided into:

  a two equal groups **b** three equal groups?

F   BINOMIAL EXPANSIONS

Consider the following algebraic expansions of the binomial $(a+b)^n$.

$(a+b)^1 = a+b$

$(a+b)^2 = a^2 + 2ab + b^2$

$(a+b)^3 = (a+b)(a+b)^2$

$\qquad\quad = (a+b)(a^2 + 2ab + b^2)$

$\qquad\quad = a^3 + 2a^2b + ab^2 + a^2b + 2ab^2 + b^3$

$\qquad\quad = a^3 + 3a^2b + 3ab^2 + b^3$

$(a+b)^4 = (a+b)(a+b)^3$

$\qquad\quad = (a+b)(a^3 + 3a^2b + 3ab^2 + b^3)$

$\qquad\qquad\qquad$ etc

$a^2 + 2ab + b^2$ is the binomial expansion of $(a+b)^2$

$a^3 + 3a^2b + 3ab^2 + b^3$ is the binomial expansion of $(a+b)^3$

INVESTIGATION 2 THE BINOMIAL EXPANSION OF $(a+b)^n$, $n \geqslant 4$

What to do:

1 Complete the expansion of $(a+b)^4$ as outlined above.

2 Similarly, expand algebraically $(a+b)^5$ using your answer for the expansion of $(a+b)^4$ from **1**.

3 Likewise, expand $(a+b)^6$ using your expansion for $(a+b)^5$.

4 The $(a+b)^3 = a^3 + 3a^2b + 3ab^2 + b^3$ expansion contains 4 terms; $a^3, 3a^2b, 3ab^2$ and b^3. The coefficients of these terms are: 1 3 3 1

  a What can be said about the powers of a and b in each term of the expansion of $(a+b)^n$ for $n = 0, 1, 2, 3, 4, 5$ and 6?

  b Write down the triangle of coefficients to row 6:

$n=0$			1			
$n=1$		1		1		
$n=2$	1		2		1	
$n=3$	1	3		3		1 ← row 3

$\qquad\qquad\qquad\qquad\qquad\vdots$ etc.

5 This triangle of coefficients is called **Pascal's triangle**. Investigate:

  a the predictability of each row from the previous one

  b a formula for finding the sum of the numbers in the nth row of Pascal's triangle.

6 Use your results from **5** to predict the elements of the 7th row of Pascal's triangle and hence write down the binomial expansion of $(a+b)^7$.

Check your result algebraically by using $(a+b)^7 = (a+b)(a+b)^6$ and your results from **3** above.

From the **Investigation** we obtained

$$(a+b)^4 = a^4 + 4a^3b + 6a^2b^2 + 4ab^3 + b^4$$
$$= a^4 + 4a^3b^1 + 6a^2b^2 + 4a^1b^3 + b^4$$

Notice that:
- As we look from left to right across the expansion, the powers of a decrease by 1 whilst the powers of b increase by 1.
- The sum of the powers of a and b in each term of the expansion is 4.
- The number of terms in the expansion is $4 + 1 = 5$.

In **general**, for the expansion of $(a+b)^n$ where $n = 1, 2, 3, 4, 5, \ldots$:

- As we look from left to right across the expansion, the powers of a decrease by 1 whilst the powers of b increase by 1.
- The sum of the powers of a and b in each term of the expansion is n.
- The number of terms in the expansion is $n + 1$.

Notice also that:

- $a + b$ is called a **binomial** as it contains two terms
- any expression of the form $(a+b)^n$ is called a **power of a binomial**.

The expansion of $(a+b)^3$, which is $a^3 + 3a^2b + 3ab^2 + b^3$ can be used to expand other cubes.

Example 14

Using $(a+b)^3 = a^3 + 3a^2b + 3ab^2 + b^3$, find the binomial expansion of:

a $(2x+3)^3$ **b** $(x-5)^3$

a In the expansion of $(a+b)^3$ we substitute $a = (2x)$, $b = (3)$

$\therefore$ $(2x+3)^3 = (2x)^3 + 3(2x)^2(3) + 3(2x)^1(3)^2 + (3)^3$

$= 8x^3 + 36x^2 + 54x + 27$ on simplifying

b This time, $a = (x)$ and $b = (-5)$

$\therefore$ $(x-5)^3 = (x)^3 + 3(x^2)(-5) + 3(x)(-5)^2 + (-5)^3$

$= x^3 - 15x^2 + 75x - 125$

EXERCISE 9F

1 Use the binomial expansion of $(a+b)^3$ to expand and simplify:

a $(x+1)^3$ **b** $(x+2)^3$ **c** $(x-4)^3$ **d** $(2x+1)^3$

e $(2x-1)^3$ **f** $(3x-1)^3$ **g** $(2x+5)^3$ **h** $\left(2x+\frac{1}{x}\right)^3$

2 Use $(a+b)^4 = a^4 + 4a^3b + 6a^2b^2 + 4ab^3 + b^4$ to expand and simplify:

    a $(x+2)^4$ **b** $(x-2)^4$ **c** $(2x+3)^4$

    d $(3x-1)^4$ **e** $\left(x+\frac{1}{x}\right)^4$ **f** $\left(2x-\frac{1}{x}\right)^4$

Example 15

Find the: **a** 5th row of Pascal's triangle **b** binomial expansion of $\left(x-\frac{2}{x}\right)^5$.

a
$$
\begin{array}{c}
1 \leftarrow \text{the 0th row, for } (a+b)^0 \\
1\quad 1 \leftarrow \text{the 1st row, for } (a+b)^1 \\
1\quad 2\quad 1 \\
1\quad 3\quad 3\quad 1 \\
1\quad 4\quad 6\quad 4\quad 1 \\
1\quad 5\quad 10\quad 10\quad 5\quad 1 \leftarrow \text{the 5th row}
\end{array}
$$

b So, $(a+b)^5 = a^5 + 5a^4b + 10a^3b^2 + 10a^2b^3 + 5ab^4 + b^5$

and we let $a = (x)$ and $b = \left(\frac{-2}{x}\right)$

$$\therefore \quad \left(x - \frac{2}{x}\right)^5 = (x)^5 + 5(x)^4\left(\frac{-2}{x}\right) + 10(x)^3\left(\frac{-2}{x}\right)^2 + 10(x)^2\left(\frac{-2}{x}\right)^3$$

$$+ 5(x)\left(\frac{-2}{x}\right)^4 + \left(\frac{-2}{x}\right)^5$$

$$= x^5 - 10x^3 + 40x - \frac{80}{x} + \frac{80}{x^3} - \frac{32}{x^5}$$

---

3 Expand and simplify:

    a $(x+2)^5$ **b** $(x-2)^5$ **c** $(2x+1)^5$ **d** $\left(2x-\frac{1}{x}\right)^5$

4 **a** Write down the 6th row of Pascal's triangle.

    b Find the binomial expansion of:

       i $(x+2)^6$ **ii** $(2x-1)^6$ **iii** $\left(x+\frac{1}{x}\right)^6$

5 Expand and simplify:

    a $(1+\sqrt{2})^3$ **b** $(1+\sqrt{5})^4$ **c** $(2-\sqrt{2})^5$

6 **a** Expand $(2+x)^6$.

    b Use the expansion of **a** to find the value of $(2.01)^6$.

7 Expand and simplify $(2x+3)(x+1)^4$.

8 Find the coefficient of:

    a a^3b^2 in the expansion of $(3a+b)^5$

    b a^3b^3 in the expansion of $(2a+3b)^6$.

Note: • C_r^n is also written as $\binom{n}{r}$

      • Values of C_r^n or $\binom{n}{r}$ can be found from **Pascal's triangle** or from your **calculator**.

G   THE GENERAL BINOMIAL THEOREM

$$(a+b)^n = \binom{n}{0}a^n + \binom{n}{1}a^{n-1}b + \binom{n}{2}a^{n-2}b^2 + \ldots + \binom{n}{n-1}ab^{n-1} + \binom{n}{n}b^n$$

where $\binom{n}{r}$ is the **binomial coefficient** of $a^{n-r}b^r$ and $r = 0, 1, 2, 3, \ldots, n$.

The **general term**, or $(r+1)$th term is $\quad T_{r+1} = \binom{n}{r}a^{n-r}b^r$.

Note: $\binom{n}{r}$ or C_r^n also represents the number of combinations of n objects when r are taken at a time.

For example: If we want to *select* any two people from Anna, Bob, Carlo and Davinda, we can do this in $C_2^4 = 6$ ways.   (These are: AB, AC, AD, BC, BD, CD)

Example 16

Write down the first 3 and last 2 terms of the expansion of $\left(2x + \dfrac{1}{x}\right)^{12}$.

$$\left(2x + \frac{1}{x}\right)^{12} = (2x)^{12} + \binom{12}{1}(2x)^{11}\left(\frac{1}{x}\right) + \binom{12}{2}(2x)^{10}\left(\frac{1}{x}\right)^2 + \ldots$$

$$+ \binom{12}{11}(2x)\left(\frac{1}{x}\right)^{11} + \binom{12}{12}\left(\frac{1}{x}\right)^{12}$$

EXERCISE 9G

1 Write down the first three and last two terms of the binomial expansion of:

   a $\quad (1 + 2x)^{11}$ **b** $\left(3x + \dfrac{2}{x}\right)^{15}$ **c** $\left(2x - \dfrac{3}{x}\right)^{20}$

Example 17

Find the 7th term of $\left(3x - \dfrac{4}{x^2}\right)^{14}$. Do not simplify.

For $\left(3x - \dfrac{4}{x^2}\right)^{14}$, $\quad a = (3x)\quad$ and $\quad b = \left(\dfrac{-4}{x^2}\right)$

So, as $T_{r+1} = \binom{n}{r}a^{n-r}b^r$, we let $r = 6$

$\therefore \quad T_7 = \binom{14}{6}(3x)^8\left(\dfrac{-4}{x^2}\right)^6$

---

2 Without simplifying, find:

   a   the 6th term of $\quad (2x + 5)^{15}$ **b**   the 4th term of $\left(x^2 + \dfrac{5}{x}\right)^9$

   c   the 10th term of $\left(x - \dfrac{2}{x}\right)^{17}$ **d**   the 9th term of $\left(2x^2 - \dfrac{1}{x}\right)^{21}$

Example 18

In the expansion of $\left(x^2 + \frac{4}{x}\right)^{12}$, find **a** the coefficient of x^6 **b** the constant term

$a = (x^2)$, $b = \left(\frac{4}{x}\right)$ and $n = 12$ $\therefore$ $T_{r+1} = \binom{12}{r}(x^2)^{12-r}\left(\frac{4}{x}\right)^r$

$$= \binom{12}{r}x^{24-2r}\frac{4^r}{x^r}$$

$$= \binom{12}{r}4^r x^{24-3r}$$

a Letting $24 - 3r = 6$

$\therefore$ $3r = 18$

$\therefore$ $r = 6$

and so, $T_7 = \binom{12}{6}4^6 x^6$

$\therefore$ the coefficient of x^6 is

$\binom{12}{6}4^6$ or $3\,784\,704$.

b Letting $24 - 3r = 0$

$\therefore$ $3r = 24$

$\therefore$ $r = 8$

and so, $T_9 = \binom{12}{8}4^8 x^0$

$\therefore$ the constant term is

$\binom{12}{8}4^8$ or $32\,440\,320$.

3 Find the coefficient of:

    a x^{10} in the expansion of $(3 + 2x^2)^{10}$

    b x^3 in the expansion of $\left(2x^2 - \frac{3}{x}\right)^6$

    c x^{12} in the expansion of $\left(2x^2 - \frac{1}{x}\right)^{12}$

4 Find the constant term in:

    a the expansion of $\left(x + \frac{2}{x^2}\right)^{15}$

    b the expansion of $\left(x - \frac{3}{x^2}\right)^9$

5 **a** Write down the first 5 rows of Pascal's triangle.

    b What is the sum of the numbers in:

        i row 1   **ii** row 2   **iii** row 3   **iv** row 4   **v** row 5?

    c Copy and complete: It seems that the sum of the numbers in row n
                       of Pascal's triangle is ......

    d Show that $(1 + x)^n = \binom{n}{0} + \binom{n}{1}x + \binom{n}{2}x^2 + ... + \binom{n}{n-1}x^{n-1} + \binom{n}{n}x^n$

       Hence deduce that $\binom{n}{0} + \binom{n}{1} + \binom{n}{2} + ... + \binom{n}{n-1} + \binom{n}{n} = 2^n$

Example 19

Find the coefficient
of x^5 in the expan-
sion of
$(x + 3)(2x - 1)^6$.

$(x + 3)(2x - 1)^6$

$= (x + 3)[(2x)^6 + \binom{6}{1}(2x)^5(-1) + \binom{6}{2}(2x)^4(-1)^2 + ...]$

$= (x + 3)(2^6 x^6 - \binom{6}{1}2^5 x^5 + \binom{6}{2}2^4 x^4 - ....)$

So terms containing x^5 are $\binom{6}{2}2^4 x^5$ from (1) and

$-3\binom{6}{1}2^5 x^5$ from (2)

$\therefore$ the coefficient of x^5 is $\binom{6}{2}2^4 - 3\binom{6}{1}2^5$ $= -336$

6 **a** Find the coefficient of x^5 in the expansion of $(x + 2)(x^2 + 1)^8$

  b Find the coefficient of x^6 in the expansion of $(2 - x)(3x + 1)^9$

7 **a** Show that $\binom{n}{1} = n$ and $\binom{n}{2} = \dfrac{n(n-1)}{2}$ are true statements.

  b The third term of $(1 + x)^n$ is $36x^2$. Find the fourth term.

  c If $(1 + kx)^n = 1 - 12x + 60x^2 - \dots$, find the values of k and n.

8 Find a if the coefficient of x^{11} in the expansion of $(x^2 + \dfrac{1}{ax})^{10}$ is 15.

REVIEW SET 9A

1 Alpha-numeric number plates have two letters followed by four digits. How many plates are possible if:

  a there are no restrictions   **b** the first letter must be a vowel

  c no letter or digit may be repeated?

2 Ten points are located on a 2-dimensional plane. If no three points are collinear,

  a how many line segments joining two points can be drawn

  b how many different triangles can be drawn by connecting all 10 points with line segments in any possible way?

3 Simplify: **a** $\dfrac{n!}{(n-2)!}$ **b** $\dfrac{n! + (n+1)!}{n!}$

4 How many committees of five can be selected from eight men and seven women?

  a How many of the committees contain two men and three women?

  b How many contain at least one man?

5 Eight people enter a room and each person shakes hands with every other person. How many hand shakes are possible?

6 A team of five is chosen from six men and four women.

  a How many different teams are possible with no restrictions?

  b How many contain at least one of each sex?

7 The letters P, Q, R, S and T are to be arranged in a row. How many of these arrangements

  a end with T **b** begin with P and end with T?

8 Use the binomial expansion to find   **a** $(x - 2y)^3$ **b** $(3x + 2)^4$

9 Find the coefficient of x^3 in the expansion of $(2x + 5)^6$.

10 Eight people enter a room and sit at random in a row of eight chairs. In how many ways can the sisters Cathy, Robyn and Jane sit together in the row?

11 **a** How many three digit numbers can be formed using the digits 0 to 9 only?

  b How many of these numbers are divisible by 5?

REVIEW SET 9B

REVIEW SET 9B

Click on the icon to obtain printable review sets and answers

Chapter **10**

Mathematical induction

Contents:

A   THE PROCESS OF INDUCTION

The process of formulating a general result from a close examination of the simplest cases is called **mathematical induction**.

For example,   the first positive even number is $2 = 2 \times 1$
the second positive even number is $4 = 2 \times 2$
the third positive even number is $6 = 2 \times 3$
the fourth positive even number is $8 = 2 \times 4$

and from these results we induce that

the nth positive even number is $2 \times n$ or $2n$.

The statement that "The nth positive even number is $2n$." is a summary of the observations of the simple cases $n = 1, 2, 3, 4$ and is a statement which we **believe** is true.

Now examine the following argument for finding the sum of the first n odd numbers:

$$1 = 1 = 1^2$$
$$1 + 3 = 4 = 2^2$$
$$1 + 3 + 5 = 9 = 3^2$$
$$1 + 3 + 5 + 7 = 16 = 4^2$$
$$\underbrace{1 + 3 + 5 + 7 + 9}_{\text{5 of these}} = 25 = 5^2$$

It seems that   "the sum of the first n odd numbers is n^2".

This pattern may continue or it may not. We require proof of the fact for all positive integers n. A formal statement of our proposition may be:

" $\underbrace{1 + 3 + 5 + 7 + 9 + ...}_{n \text{ of these}}$ $= n^2$ for all $n \in Z^+$ "

Note: The nth odd number is $(2n - 1)$, so we could rewrite the proposition as:

"$1 + 3 + 5 + 7 + 9 + ... + (2n - 1) = n^2$ for all $n \in Z^+$"

One direct proof of the proposition is to note that the series is arithmetic with $u_1 = 1$, $d = 2$ and "n" $= n$.

$$\text{Hence}\quad S_n = \frac{n}{2}(2(1) + (n - 1)2) \qquad \left\{ = \frac{\text{"}n\text{"}}{2}(2u_1 + (n - 1)d) \right\}$$

$$= \frac{n}{2} \times 2n$$

$$= n^2$$

Any proposition will remain a proposition until it is **proven true**.

Note:

> The result $1 + 2 + 3 + 4 + ... + n = \dfrac{n(n+1)}{2}$ for all n in Z^+
>
> is worth memorising.

Example 1

By examining the cases $n = 1$, 2, 3 and 4, make a proposition about the sum
of $S_n = \frac{1}{1\times 2} + \frac{1}{2\times 3} + \frac{1}{3\times 4} + \frac{1}{4\times 5} + ... + \frac{1}{n(n+1)}$.

$S_1 = \frac{1}{1\times 2} = \frac{1}{2}$

$S_2 = \frac{1}{1\times 2} + \frac{1}{2\times 3} = \frac{1}{2} + \frac{1}{6} = \frac{2}{3}$

$S_3 = \frac{1}{1\times 2} + \frac{1}{2\times 3} + \frac{1}{3\times 4} = \frac{2}{3} + \frac{1}{12} = \frac{3}{4}$

$S_4 = \frac{1}{1\times 2} + \frac{1}{2\times 3} + \frac{1}{3\times 4} + \frac{1}{4\times 5} = \frac{3}{4} + \frac{1}{20} = \frac{4}{5}$

From these results we propose that: $S_n = \dfrac{n}{n+1}$.

Note:

- If the result in **Example 1** is true, then:

  $\frac{1}{1\times 2} + \frac{1}{2\times 3} + \frac{1}{3\times 4} + \frac{1}{4\times 5} + ... + \frac{1}{1000\times 1001} = \frac{1000}{1001}$ {case $n = 1000$}

- The great Swiss mathematician **Euler** proposed that $P(n) = n^2 + n + 41$
  was a formula for generating prime numbers. People who read his statement
  probably checked it for $n = 1$, 2, 3, 4, 5, ..., 10 and agreed with him.

  However, it was found to be incorrect as, for example

  $P(41) = 41^2 + 41 + 41 = 41(41 + 1 + 1) = 41 \times 43$,   a composite.

  So, not all propositions are true.

EXERCISE 10A

1 By examining the following, for substitutions like $n = 1$, 2, 3, 4, ..., complete a
proposition.

   a The nth term of the sequence 3, 7, 11, 15, 19, ... is
for $n = 1$, 2, 3, 4, ...

   b $3^n > 1 + 2n$ for

   c $11^n - 1$ is divisible by   for

   d $2 + 4 + 6 + 8 + 10 + ... + 2n = $ for

   e $1! + 2 \times 2! + 3 \times 3! + 4 \times 4! + ... + n \times n! = $ for

   f $\dfrac{1}{2!} + \dfrac{2}{3!} + \dfrac{3}{4!} + \dfrac{4}{5!} + ... + \dfrac{n}{(n+1)!} = $ for

   g $7^n + 2$ is divisible by   for

   h $\left(1 - \frac{1}{2}\right)\left(1 - \frac{1}{3}\right)\left(1 - \frac{1}{4}\right) ..... \left(1 - \frac{1}{n+1}\right) = $ for

   i $\dfrac{1}{2\times 5} + \dfrac{1}{5\times 8} + \dfrac{1}{8\times 11} + ...$ to n terms $= $ for

2 n points are placed inside a triangle.

Non-intersecting line segments are drawn connecting the 3 vertices of the triangle and the points within it, to partition the given triangle into smaller triangles. Make a proposition concerning the number of triangles obtained in the general case.

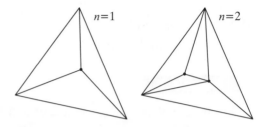

B THE PRINCIPLE OF MATHEMATICAL INDUCTION

Proposition notation

We use P_n to represent a proposition which is defined for every integer a where $n \geqslant a$.

For example, in the case of **Example 1**, our proposition P_n is

$$\text{``} \frac{1}{1 \times 2} + \frac{1}{2 \times 3} + \frac{1}{3 \times 4} ..... + \frac{1}{n(n+1)} = \frac{n}{n+1} \quad \text{for} \quad n \in Z^+ \text{''}$$

Notice that $\quad P_1$ is $\quad \text{``} \dfrac{1}{1 \times 2} = \dfrac{1}{2} \text{''}\quad$ and $\quad P_2$ is $\quad \text{``} \dfrac{1}{1 \times 2} + \dfrac{1}{2 \times 3} = \dfrac{2}{3} \text{''}$

and $\quad P_k$ is $\quad \text{``} \dfrac{1}{1 \times 2} + \dfrac{1}{2 \times 3} + \dfrac{1}{3 \times 4} + ... + \dfrac{1}{k(k+1)} = \dfrac{k}{k+1} \text{''}$.

THE PRINCIPLE OF MATHEMATICAL INDUCTION

> Suppose P_n is a proposition which is defined for every integer $n \geqslant a$, $a \in Z$.
>
> Now if • P_a is true, and
>
> • P_{k+1} is true whenever P_k is true,
>
> then P_n is true for all $n \geqslant a$.

This means that for $a = 1$, say, and the two above conditions hold, then

the truth of P_1 implies that P_2 is true, which implies that P_3 is true, which implies that P_4 is true, etc.

We use this method to prove that a particular proposition is true.

One can liken the principle of mathematical induction to the **domino effect**. We imagine an infinite set of dominoes all lined up.

Provided that

DEMO

• the first one topples to the right

• and we know that in general, the $(k+1)$th domino will topple if the kth domino topples, then eventually, all will topple,

i.e., 1st topples makes 2nd topple, which makes 3rd topple, etc.

SUMS OF SERIES

Example 2

a Prove that $1^2 + 2^2 + 3^2 + 4^2 + \ldots + n^2 = \dfrac{n(n+1)(2n+1)}{6}$ for all $n \in Z^+$.

b Find $1^2 + 2^2 + 3^2 + 4^2 + \ldots + 100^2$.

a P_n is: "$1^2 + 2^2 + 3^2 + 4^2 + \ldots + n^2 = \dfrac{n(n+1)(2n+1)}{6}$ for all $n \in Z^+$.

Proof: (By the principle of mathematical induction)

(1) If $n = 1$, LHS $= 1^2 = 1$ and RHS $= \dfrac{1 \times 2 \times 3}{6} = 1$

$\therefore$ P_1 is true

(2) If P_k is true, then

$1^2 + 2^2 + 3^2 + 4^2 + \ldots + k^2 = \dfrac{k(k+1)(2k+1)}{6}$ $\ldots$ (*)

Thus $1^2 + 2^2 + 3^2 + 4^2 + \ldots + k^2 + (k+1)^2$

$= \dfrac{k(k+1)(2k+1)}{6} + (k+1)^2$ {using *}

$= \dfrac{k(k+1)(2k+1)}{6} + (k+1)^2 \times \dfrac{6}{6}$

Note:

Always look for common factors.

$= \dfrac{(k+1)[k(2k+1) + 6(k+1)]}{6}$

$= \dfrac{(k+1)(2k^2 + k + 6k + 6)}{6}$

$= \dfrac{(k+1)(2k^2 + 7k + 6)}{6}$

$= \dfrac{(k+1)(k+2)(2k+3)}{6}$

$= \dfrac{(k+1)([k+1]+1)(2[k+1]+1)}{6}$

Thus P_{k+1} is true whenever P_k is true. Since P_1 is true, P_n is true for all $n \in Z^+$. {Principle of mathematical induction}

b $1^2 + 2^2 + 3^2 + 4^2 + \ldots + 100^2 = \dfrac{100 \times 101 \times 201}{6} = 338\,350$ {as $n = 100$}

EXERCISE 10B

1 Prove that the following propositions are true for all positive integers n:

a $1 + 2 + 3 + 4 + 5 + \ldots + n = \dfrac{n(n+1)}{2}$

b $1 \times 2 + 2 \times 3 + 3 \times 4 + 4 \times 5 + \ldots + n(n+1) = \dfrac{n(n+1)(n+2)}{3}$

c $3 \times 5 + 6 \times 6 + 9 \times 7 + 12 \times 8 + ... + 3n(n+4) = \dfrac{n(n+1)(2n+13)}{2}$

d $1^3 + 2^3 + 3^3 + 4^3 + ... + n^3 = \dfrac{n^2(n+1)^2}{4}$

e $1 + 2 \times 2 + 3 \times 2^2 + 4 \times 2^3 + ... + n \times 2^{n-1} = (n-1) \times 2^n + 1$

Example 3

Prove that:

$\dfrac{1}{2 \times 5} + \dfrac{1}{5 \times 8} + \dfrac{1}{8 \times 11} + ... + \dfrac{1}{(3n-1)(3n+2)} = \dfrac{n}{6n+4}$ for all $n \in Z^+$.

P_n is: "$\dfrac{1}{2 \times 5} + \dfrac{1}{5 \times 8} + \dfrac{1}{8 \times 11} + ... + \dfrac{1}{(3n-1)(3n+2)} = \dfrac{n}{6n+4}$, $n \in Z^+$."

Proof: (By the principle of mathematical induction)

(1) If $n = 1$,   LHS $= \dfrac{1}{2 \times 5} = \tfrac{1}{10}$ and RHS $= \dfrac{1}{6 \times 1 + 4} = \tfrac{1}{10}$

   $\therefore$ P_1 is true.

(2) If P_k is true, then

$\dfrac{1}{2 \times 5} + \dfrac{1}{5 \times 8} + \dfrac{1}{8 \times 11} + ... + \dfrac{1}{(3k-1)(3k+2)} = \dfrac{k}{6k+4}$ ..... (*)

Now $\dfrac{1}{2 \times 5} + \dfrac{1}{5 \times 8} + \dfrac{1}{8 \times 11} + ... + \dfrac{1}{(3k-1)(3k+2)} + \dfrac{1}{(3k+2)(3k+5)}$

$= \dfrac{k}{6k+4} + \dfrac{1}{(3k+2)(3k+5)}$ {using *}

$= \dfrac{k}{2(3k+2)} + \dfrac{1}{(3k+2)(3k+5)}$

$= \dfrac{k}{2(3k+2)} \times \left(\dfrac{3k+5}{3k+5}\right) + \dfrac{1}{(3k+2)(3k+5)} \times \left(\dfrac{2}{2}\right)$

> **Note:**
> Always look for common factors.

$= \dfrac{3k^2 + 5k + 2}{2(3k+2)(3k+5)}$

$= \dfrac{(3k+2)(k+1)}{2(3k+2)(3k+5)}$

$= \dfrac{k+1}{6k+10}$

$= \dfrac{[k+1]}{6[k+1]+4}$

Thus P_{k+1} is true whenever P_k is true and P_1 is true.

$\therefore$ P_n is true   {Principle of mathematical induction}

2 Prove that the following propositions are true for $n \in Z^+$:

a $\dfrac{1}{1 \times 2} + \dfrac{1}{2 \times 3} + \dfrac{1}{3 \times 4} + ... + \dfrac{1}{n(n+1)} = \dfrac{n}{n+1}$

and hence find $\dfrac{1}{10 \times 11} + \dfrac{1}{11 \times 12} + \dfrac{1}{12 \times 13} + ... + \dfrac{1}{20 \times 21}$

b $\dfrac{1}{1 \times 2 \times 3} + \dfrac{1}{2 \times 3 \times 4} + ... + \dfrac{1}{n(n+1)(n+2)} = \dfrac{n(n+3)}{4(n+1)(n+2)}$

3 Prove the following propositions true, for $n \in Z^+$:

a $1 \times 1! + 2 \times 2! + 3 \times 3! + 4 \times 4! + ... + n \times n! = (n+1)! - 1$

[$n!$ is the product of the first n positive integers, e.g., $4! = 4 \times 3 \times 2 \times 1$]

b $\dfrac{1}{2!} + \dfrac{2}{3!} + \dfrac{3}{4!} + \dfrac{4}{5!} + ... + \dfrac{n}{(n+1)!} = \dfrac{(n+1)! - 1}{(n+1)!}$,   and hence find the sum

$\dfrac{1}{2!} + \dfrac{2}{3!} + \dfrac{3}{4!} + \dfrac{4}{5!} + ... + \dfrac{9}{10!}$ in rational form.

4 Prove that the following proposition is true:

$1 \times n + 2 \times (n-1) + 3 \times (n-2) + ... + (n-2) \times 3 + (n-1) \times 2 + n \times 1$

$= \dfrac{n(n+1)(n+2)}{6}$ for all integers $n \geqslant 1$.

[**Hint:** $1 \times 6 + 2 \times 5 + 3 \times 4 + 4 \times 3 + 5 \times 2 + 6 \times 1$
$= 1 \times 5 + 2 \times 4 + 3 \times 3 + 4 \times 2 + 5 \times 1 + (1 + 2 + 3 + 4 + 5 + 6).$]

DIVISIBILITY

Consider the expression $4^n + 2$ for $n = 0, 1, 2, 3, 4, 5, ...$

$4^0 + 2 = 3 = 3 \times 1$

$4^1 + 2 = 6 = 3 \times 2$

$4^2 + 2 = 18 = 3 \times 6$ We observe that each of the answers is divisible

$4^3 + 2 = 66 = 3 \times 22$ by 3 and so we make the proposition

$4^4 + 2 = 258 = 3 \times 86$ P_n is: "$4^n + 2$ is divisible by 3 for all $n \in Z^+$."

This proposition may, or may not, be true. If it is true, then we should be able to prove it by using the principle of mathematical induction.

Note: $4^n + 2$ can be proven to be divisible by 3 by using the binomial expansion.

We observe that
$4^n + 2$

$= (1+3)^n + 2$

$= 1^n + \binom{n}{1}3 + \binom{n}{2}3^2 + \binom{n}{3}3^3 + \binom{n}{4}3^4 + ... + \binom{n}{n-1}3^{n-1} + \binom{n}{n}3^n + 2$

$= 3 + \binom{n}{1}3 + \binom{n}{2}3^2 + \binom{n}{3}3^3 + \binom{n}{4}3^4 + ... + \binom{n}{n-1}3^{n-1} + \binom{n}{n}3^n$

$= 3\left(1 + \binom{n}{1} + \binom{n}{2}3 + \binom{n}{3}3^2 + \binom{n}{4}3^3 + ... + \binom{n}{n-1}3^{n-2} + \binom{n}{n}3^{n-1}\right)$

where the contents of the brackets is an integer,   etc.

Example 4

Prove that $4^n + 2$ is divisible by 3 for $n \in Z$, $n \geqslant 0$.

P_n is: "$4^n + 2$ is divisible by 3 for all $n \in Z$, $n \geqslant 0$."

Proof: (By the principle of mathematical induction)

(1)   If $n = 0$, $4^0 + 2 = 3 = 1 \times 3$ $\therefore$ P_0 is true.

(2)   If P_k is true, then $4^k + 2 = 3A$ where A is an integer   ..... $(*)$

Now $4^{k+1} + 2$

$= 4^1 \times 4^k + 2$

$= 4(3A - 2) + 2$ $\{$as $4^k = 3A - 2$ using $*\}$

$= 12A - 8 + 2$

$= 12A - 6$

$= 3(4A - 2)$ where $4A - 2$ is an integer
as A is an integer.

Thus $4^{k+1} + 2$ is divisible by 3 if $4^k + 2$ is divisible by 3.

Hence, P_{k+1} is true whenever P_k is true and P_0 is true.

$\therefore$ P_n is true   {Principle of mathematical induction}

5   Use the principle of mathematical induction to prove that:

a $n^3 + 2n$ is divisible by 3 for all positive integers n

b $n(n^2 + 5)$ is divisible by 6 for all integers $\in Z^+$

c $6^n - 1$ is divisible by 5 for all integers $n \geqslant 0$

d $7^n - 4^n - 3^n$ is divisible by 12 for all $n \in Z^+$.

6   Use the principle of mathematical induction to prove that $\dfrac{2^n - (-1)^n}{3}$ is an odd number for all $n \in Z^+$.

[**Hint:**   An odd number has form $2A + 1$ where A is an integer.]

OTHER APPLICATIONS

Proof by the principle of mathematical induction is used in several other areas of mathematics. For example, in establishing truths dealing with:

- **inequalities**
- **sequences**
- **differential calculus**
- **matrices**
- **geometrical generalisations**
- **products**
- **complex numbers**.

Some proofs with these topics will be observed in the chapters containing them.

Example 5

Prove that a convex n-sided polygon has $\frac{1}{2}n(n-3)$ diagonals for all $n \geqslant 3$.

P_n is: "A convex n-sided polygon has $\frac{1}{2}n(n-3)$ diagonals for all $n \geqslant 3$."

Proof: (By the principle of mathematical induction)

(1)   If $n = 3$,   i.e., a triangle   there are 0 diagonals

and $\frac{1}{2} \times 0 \times (-3) = 0$

∴ P_3 is true.

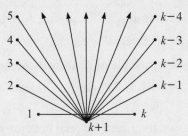

(2)   If P_k is true, a convex k-sided polygon has $\frac{1}{2}k(k-3)$ diagonals.

If we label the vertices

$1, 2, 3, 4, 5, \ldots, k-1, k$

and $k+1$ as an additional vertex

then

$$P_{k+1} = P_k + k - 2 + 1$$

$\left\{ \begin{array}{l} \text{the number of diagonals} \\ \text{from } k+1 \text{ to the vertices} \\ 2, 3, 4, 5, \ldots, k-1 \end{array} \right.$ $\left\{ \begin{array}{l} \text{the line from 1 to } k \text{ was} \\ \text{once a side and is now a} \\ \text{diagonal} \end{array} \right.$

$$\begin{aligned} \therefore \quad P_{k+1} &= \tfrac{1}{2}k(k-3) + k - 1 \\ &= \tfrac{1}{2}k(k-3) + \tfrac{2}{2}(k-1) \\ &= \tfrac{1}{2}[k^2 - 3k + 2k - 2] \\ &= \tfrac{1}{2}[k^2 - k - 2] \\ &= \tfrac{1}{2}(k+1)(k-2) \\ &= \tfrac{1}{2}(k+1)([k+1]-3) \end{aligned}$$

Try it for
$k = 3, 4, \ldots$

Thus P_{k+1} is true whenever P_k is true and P_3 is true.

∴ P_n is true   {Principle of mathematical induction}

---

7   Use the principle of mathematical induction to prove the following propositions:

a $\left(1 - \dfrac{1}{2}\right)\left(1 - \dfrac{1}{3}\right)\left(1 - \dfrac{1}{4}\right)\left(1 - \dfrac{1}{5}\right) \ldots \left(1 - \dfrac{1}{n+1}\right) = \dfrac{1}{n+1}, \quad n \in Z^+$.

b   If n straight lines are drawn such that each line intersects every other line and no three lines have a common point of intersection, then the plane is divided into $\dfrac{n(n+1)}{2} + 1$ regions.

c   If n points are placed inside a triangle and non-intersecting lines are drawn connecting the 3 vertices of the triangle and the points within it to partition the triangle into smaller triangles, then the number of triangles resulting is $2n + 1$.

d $\left(1 - \dfrac{1}{2^2}\right)\left(1 - \dfrac{1}{3^2}\right)\left(1 - \dfrac{1}{4^2}\right)\ .....\ \left(1 - \dfrac{1}{n^2}\right) = \dfrac{n+1}{2n}$ for all integers $n \geqslant 2$.

INVESTIGATION   SEQUENCES, SERIES AND INDUCTION

This investigation involves the use of mathematical induction as well as concepts from sequences, series and counting.

What to do:

1 The sequence of numbers $\{u_n\}$ is defined by $u_1 = 1 \times 1!$, $u_2 = 2 \times 2!$, $u_3 = 3 \times 3!$, etc.   What is the nth term of the sequence?

2 Let $S_n = a_1 + a_2 + a_3 + ... + a_n$. Investigate S_n for several different values of n.

3 Based on your results from **2**, conjecture an expression for S_n.

4 Prove your conjecture to be true using the principle of mathematical induction.

5 Show that u_n can be written as $(n+1)! - n!$ and devise an alternative, direct proof of your conjecture for S_n.

6 Let $C_n = u_n + u_{n+1}$. Write an expression for C_n in factorial notation and simplify it.

7 Let $T_n = C_1 + C_2 + C_3 + ... + C_n$ and find T_n for $n = 1$, 2, 3, 4 and 5.

8 Conjecture an expression for T_n.

9 Prove your conjecture for T_n by any method.

C   INDIRECT PROOF (EXTENSION)

Some propositions may be proven to be true by using an **indirect proof** such as **proof by contradiction**. In such proofs we suppose the opposite of the statement to be true and on using correct argument hope to obtain a contradiction.

Example 6

Prove that the sum of any positive real number and its reciprocal is at least 2.

Proof: (by contradiction)

Suppose that $x + \dfrac{1}{x} < 2$ where x is > 0

then $x\left(x + \dfrac{1}{x}\right) < 2x$ {multiplying both sides by x, $x > 0$}

$\therefore \quad x^2 + 1 < 2x$

$\therefore \quad x^2 - 2x + 1 < 0$

$\therefore \quad (x - 1)^2 < 0$

which is a contradiction as no perfect square of a real number can be negative.

So, the supposition is false and its opposite $x + \dfrac{1}{x} \geqslant 2$, $x > 0$ must be true.

Example 7

Prove that the solution of $2^x = 3$ is an irrational number.

Proof: (by contradiction)

Suppose that if $2^x = 3$ then x is rational

$\therefore \quad 2^{\frac{p}{q}} = 3$ for positive integers p, q $\ (q \neq 0)$

$\therefore \quad (2^{\frac{p}{q}})^q = 3^q$

$\therefore \quad 2^p = 3^q$

which is clearly a contradiction, as for example, the LHS $= 2^p$ is even and the RHS $= 3^q$ is odd.

$\therefore$ the supposition is false and its opposite is true

i.e.,   if $2^x = 3$ then x is irrational.

Note: A **rational number** can be written in the form $\dfrac{p}{q}$ where p and q are integers, $q \neq 0$ and p, q have no common factors.

EXERCISE 10C

Use proof by contradiction to prove that:

1 The sum of a positive number and nine times its reciprocal is at least 6.

2 Prove that the solution of $3^x = 4$ is an irrational number.

3 Prove that $\log_2 5$ is irrational.

4 **Challenge:** Prove that $\sqrt{2}$ is irrational.

REVIEW SET 10A

Prove the following propositions, using the principle of mathematical induction:

1 $1 + 3 + 5 + 7 + ... + (2n - 1) = n^2$, $\ n \in Z^+$.

2 $7^n + 2$ is divisible by 3, $\ n \in Z^+$.

3 $1 \times 2 \times 3 + 2 \times 3 \times 4 + 3 \times 4 \times 5 + ... + n(n+1)(n+2) = \dfrac{n(n+1)(n+2)(n+3)}{4}$, $n \in Z^+$.

4 $1 + r + r^2 + r^3 + r^4 + ... + r^{n-1} = \dfrac{1 - r^n}{1 - r}$, $\ n \in Z^+$, provided that $r \neq 1$.

5 $5^{2n} - 1$ is divisible by 24, $\ n \in Z^+$.

REVIEW SET 10B

Prove the following propositions, using the principle of mathematical induction:

1 $1^2 + 3^2 + 5^2 + 7^2 + ... + (2n-1)^2 = \dfrac{n(2n+1)(2n-1)}{3}$ $n \in Z^+, \quad n \geqslant 1$.

2 $3^{2n+2} - 8n - 9$ is divisible by 64, for all positive integers n.

3 $3 + 5 \times 2 + 7 \times 2^2 + 9 \times 2^3 + ... + (2n+1)2^{n-1} = 1 + (2n-1) \times 2^n$ for all positive integers n.

4 $5^n + 3$ is divisible by 4 for all integers $n \geqslant 0$.

5 $1 \times 2^2 + 2 \times 3^2 + 3 \times 4^2 + 4 \times 5^2 + ... + n(n+1)^2 = \dfrac{n(n+1)(n+2)(3n+5)}{12}$,
for all positive integers n.

REVIEW SET 10C

Prove the following propositions, using the principle of mathematical induction:

1 $1 \times 3 + 2 \times 4 + 3 \times 5 + 4 \times 6 + ... + n(n+2) = \dfrac{n(n+1)(2n+7)}{6}$, $n \in Z^+$.

2 $7^n - 1$ is divisible by 6, $n \in Z^+$.

3 $1^3 + 3^3 + 5^3 + 7^3 + ... + (2n-1)^3 = n^2(2n^2 - 1)$ for all positive integers $n \geqslant 1$.

4 $3^n - 1 - 2n$ is always divisible by 4,   for non-negative integers n.

5 $\dfrac{1}{1 \times 3} + \dfrac{1}{3 \times 5} + \dfrac{1}{5 \times 7} + ... + \dfrac{1}{(2n-1)(2n+1)} = \dfrac{n}{2n+1}$ for all positive integers n.

Chapter 11

The unit circle and radian measure

Contents:

Before starting this chapter you can make sure that you have a good understanding of the necessary background knowledge in trigonometry and Pythagoras.

BACKGROUND KNOWLEDGE

Click on the icon alongside to obtain a printable set of exercises and answers on this background knowledge.

OPENING PROBLEM

Consider an equilateral triangle with sides 10 cm long. All its angles are of size $60°$. Altitude AN bisects side BC and the vertical angle BAC.

a Can you see from this figure that $\sin 30° = \frac{1}{2}$?

b Use your calculator to find the values of $\sin 30°$, $\sin 150°$, $\sin 390°$, $\sin 1110°$ and $\sin(-330°)$. What do you notice? Can you explain why this result occurs even though the angles are not between $0°$ and $90°$?

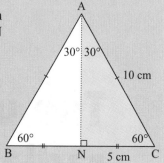

By the end of this chapter you should be able to answer the above question.

A   THE UNIT QUARTER CIRCLE

The unit quarter circle is the part of a circle centre $(0, 0)$ and radius 1 unit that lies in the first quadrant. Suppose P(x, y) can move anywhere on this arc from A to B.

Notice that: $\cos\theta = \dfrac{ON}{OP} = \dfrac{x}{1} = x$

and $\sin\theta = \dfrac{PN}{OP} = \dfrac{y}{1} = y.$

So:

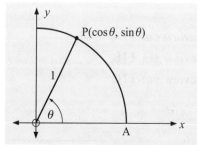

On the unit quarter circle, if $\angle AOP = \theta°$, then the coordinates of P are $(\cos\theta, \sin\theta)$.

The x- and y-coordinates of P each have a special name.

- The y-coordinate is called "the sine of angle θ" or $\sin\theta$.
- The x-coordinate is called "the cosine of angle θ" or $\cos\theta$.

Notice also that in $\triangle ONP$, $x^2 + y^2 = 1$ {Pythagoras}

and so $[\cos\theta]^2 + [\sin\theta]^2 = 1$ or $\mathbf{\cos^2\theta + \sin^2\theta = 1}$

Note: We use $\cos^2\theta$ for $[\cos\theta]^2$ and $\sin^2\theta$ for $[\sin\theta]^2$.

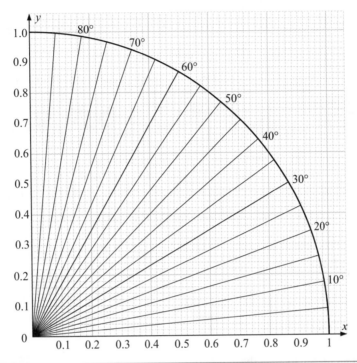

Example 1

Use the unit quarter circle above to find:

a $\sin 40^o$ b $\cos 30^o$ c   the coordinates of P if $\theta = 50^o$

a   The y-coordinate at 40° is about   b   The x-coordinate at 30° is about

  0.64, $\therefore$ $\sin 40^o \doteqdot 0.64$ 0.87, $\therefore$ $\cos 30^o \doteqdot 0.87$

c   For $\theta = 50^o$,   P is $(\cos 50^o, \sin 50^o) \doteqdot (0.64, 0.77)$

You have probably already noticed the difficulty of obtaining accurate values from the unit circle and the impossibility of estimating beyond 2 decimal places.

EXERCISE 11A

1   Use the unit quarter circle to find the value of:

a $\sin 0^o$ b $\sin 15^o$ c $\sin 25^o$ d $\sin 30^o$

e $\sin 45^o$ f $\sin 60^o$ g $\sin 75^o$ h $\sin 90^o$

2   Use your calculator to check your answers to question 1.

3   Use the unit quarter circle diagram to find the value of:

a $\cos 0^o$ b $\cos 15^o$ c $\cos 25^o$ d $\cos 30^o$

e $\cos 45^o$ f $\cos 60^o$ g $\cos 75^o$ h $\cos 90^o$

4 Use your calculator to check your answers to question **3**.

5 Use the unit quarter circle diagram to find the coordinates of the point on the unit circle where OP makes an angle of 55° with the x-axis. Use your calculator to check this answer.

6 Draw a sketch of a unit quarter circle and on it show how to locate the point with coordinates: **a** $(\cos 20^o, \sin 20^o)$ **b** $(\cos 75^o, \sin 75^o)$ **c** $(\cos \phi, \sin \phi)$

7 **a** If $\cos \theta = 0.8$ and $0^o < \theta < 90^o$, find $\sin \theta$.
   b If $\sin \theta = 0.7$ and $0^o < \theta < 90^o$, find $\cos \theta$ correct to 3 sig. figs.

B   OBTUSE ANGLES

So far we have only considered angles between 0° and 90°, i.e., acute angles. **Obtuse angles** have measurement between 90° and 180°. In order to display obtuse angles we can extend the unit quarter circle into the second quadrant. So we have the unit semicircle.

We will now apply the definitions for $\sin \theta$ and $\cos \theta$ to obtuse angles.

Definition: If P is any point on the unit circle and θ is the angle measured from the positive x-axis then

$\cos \theta$ is the x-coordinate of P and
$\sin \theta$ is the y-coordinate of P.

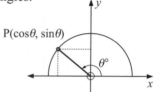

EXERCISE 11B

1 Use your calculator to find the value of:

   a $\sin 100^o$ **b** $\sin 80^o$ **c** $\sin 120^o$ **d** $\sin 60^o$
   e $\sin 150^o$ **f** $\sin 30^o$ **g** $\sin 180^o$ **h** $\sin 0^o$

2 **a** Use your results from question **1** to copy and complete: $\sin(180 - \theta)^o = ...$
   b Justify your answer using the diagram alongside.

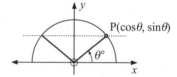

3 Use your calculator to find the value of:

   a $\cos 110^o$ **b** $\cos 70^o$ **c** $\cos 130^o$ **d** $\cos 50^o$
   e $\cos 140^o$ **f** $\cos 40^o$ **g** $\cos 180^o$ **h** $\cos 0^o$

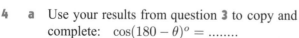

4 **a** Use your results from question **3** to copy and complete: $\cos(180 - \theta)^o = ...$
   b Justify your answer using the diagram alongside.

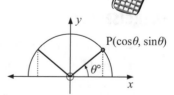

5 Find the obtuse angle which has the same sine as:
   a 45° **b** 51° **c** 74° **d** 82°

6 Find the acute angle which has the same sine as:
   a 130° **b** 146° **c** 162° **d** 171°

7 Without using your calculator find:

a $\sin 137^\circ$ if $\sin 43^\circ \doteqdot 0.6820$

b $\sin 59^\circ$ if $\sin 121^\circ \doteqdot 0.8572$

c $\cos 143^\circ$ if $\cos 37^\circ \doteqdot 0.7986$

d $\cos 24^\circ$ if $\cos 156^\circ \doteqdot -0.9135$

e $\sin 115^\circ$ if $\sin 65^\circ \doteqdot 0.9063$

f $\cos 132^\circ$ if $\cos 48^\circ \doteqdot 0.6691$

8 a   If angle AOP $= \theta$ and angle BOQ $= \theta$ also, what is the measure of angle AOQ?

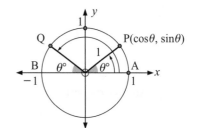

b   Copy and complete:
OQ is a reflection of OP in the ......
and so Q has coordinates ......

c   Now using **a** and **b**, what trigonometric formulae can be deduced?

In the exercises above you should have discovered that:

- If θ is acute, then $\cos \theta$ and $\sin \theta$ are both positive.
- If θ is obtuse, then $\cos \theta$ is negative and $\sin \theta$ is positive.
- $\sin(180 - \theta) = \sin \theta$ and $\cos(180 - \theta) = -\cos \theta$

These facts are particularly important in the next chapter.

ANGLE MEASUREMENT

Suppose P lies anywhere on the unit circle and A is $(1, 0)$. Let θ be the angle measured from OA, on the positive x-axis.

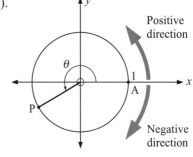

θ is   **positive** for anticlockwise rotations and **negative** for clockwise rotations.

For example, $\theta = 210^\circ$ and $\phi = -150^\circ$.

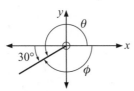

Consequently, we can easily find the coordinates of any point on the unit circle for a particular angle measured from the positive x-axis.

For example,

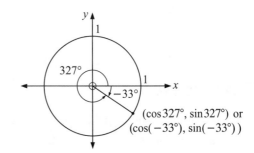

C   THE UNIT CIRCLE

The **unit circle** is the circle with centre (0, 0) and radius 1 unit.

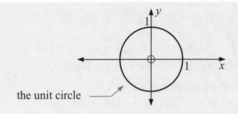

the unit circle

CIRCLES WITH CENTRE (0, 0)

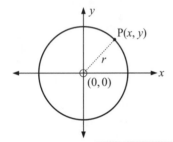

Consider a circle with centre (0, 0) and radius r units, and suppose P(x, y) is any point on this circle.

Since   OP $= r$,   then

$$\sqrt{(x-0)^2 + (y-0)^2} = r \qquad \text{\{distance formula\}}$$

$$\therefore \quad x^2 + y^2 = r^2$$

We say that $x^2 + y^2 = r^2$ is the equation of a circle with centre (0, 0) and radius r.

So,   the **equation** of the **unit circle** is $x^2 + y^2 = 1$.   {as $r = 1$}

If we allow the definitions of $\cos\theta$ and $\sin\theta$ to apply to any angle we see that on the unit circle, for example:

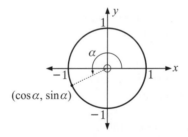

$(\cos\alpha, \sin\alpha)$

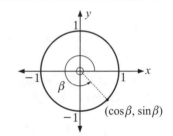

$(\cos\beta, \sin\beta)$

So, as point P moves anywhere on the unit circle,

its x-coordinate is $\cos\theta$
its y-coordinate is $\sin\theta$

provided that θ is the angle made by OP with the positive x-axis.

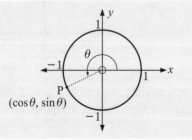

$(\cos\theta, \sin\theta)$

Notice that: as $-1 \leqslant x \leqslant 1$ and $-1 \leqslant y \leqslant 1$ for all points on the unit circle,

then $-1 \leqslant \cos\theta \leqslant 1$ and $-1 \leqslant \sin\theta \leqslant 1$ for all θ.

EXERCISE 11C

1 Sketch the graph of the curve with equation:

    a $x^2 + y^2 = 1$ **b** $x^2 + y^2 = 4$ **c** $x^2 + y^2 = 1, \quad y \geqslant 0$

2 For each angle illustrated:
- **i** write down the actual coordinates of points A, B and C
- **ii** use your calculator to give the coordinates of A, B and C correct to 3 significant figures.

a

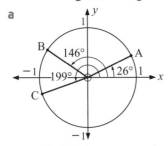

b

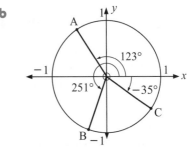

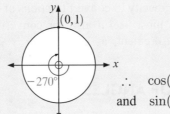

Example 2

Use a unit circle diagram to find the values of $\cos(-270^o)$ and $\sin(-270^o)$.

$\therefore \quad \cos(-270^o) = 0 \quad$ {the x-coordinate}

and $\quad \sin(-270^o) = 1 \quad$ {the y-coordinate}

---

3 Use a unit circle diagram to find:

- **a** $\cos 0^o$ and $\sin 0^o$
- **b** $\cos 90^o$ and $\sin 90^o$
- **c** $\cos 180^o$ and $\sin 180^o$
- **d** $\cos 270^o$ and $\sin 270^o$
- **e** $\cos(-90^o)$ and $\sin(-90^o)$
- **f** $\cos 450^o$ and $\sin 450^o$

INVESTIGATION   PARAMETRIC EQUATIONS

Usually we write functions in the form $y = f(x)$.

For example: $y = 3x + 7$, $y = x^2 - 6x + 8$, $y = \sin x$

However, sometimes it is useful to express **both** x and y in terms of one convenient variable, t say, called the **parameter**.

The purpose of this investigation is to use technology to graph a set of ordered pairs defined in **parametric form**, for example, $x = \cos t$ and $y = \sin t$.

GRAPHING PACKAGE

What to do:

1 Either click on the icon, or use your graphics calculator (with the same scale on both axes) to plot $\{(x, y): \ x = \cos t, \ y = \sin t, \ 0^o \leqslant t \leqslant 360^o\}$

Note: Set up your calculator in degrees.

2 Describe the resulting graph.

3 What is the equation of this graph? (Two possible answers).

4 If using a graphics calculator, use the *trace* key to move along the curve. What do you notice?

RADIAN MEASURE AND PERIODIC PROPERTIES OF CIRCLES

DEGREE MEASUREMENT OF ANGLES

Recall that one full revolution makes an angle of 360° and a straight angle is 180°. Hence, one *degree*, 1°, can be defined as $\frac{1}{360}$th of one full revolution. This measure of angle is probably most useful for surveyors, architects etc. and is the one you most probably have used in earlier years.

For greater accuracy we define *one minute*, $1'$, as $\frac{1}{60}$th *of one degree* and *one second*, $1''$, as $\frac{1}{60}$th of *one minute*. Obviously a minute and a second are very small angles.

Most graphics calculators have the capacity to convert fractions of angles measured in degrees into minutes and seconds. This is most useful also for converting fractions of hours into minutes and seconds for time measurement, as *one minute is $\frac{1}{60}$th of one hour*, and *one second is $\frac{1}{60}$th of one minute*.

RADIAN MEASUREMENT OF ANGLES

The term radian comes from the word radius referring to the fixed distance of any point on the circumference of a circle to its centre. Hence, one radian, 1^c, is defined as the angle that subtends an arc of length equal to the radius.

Now the circumference of a circle has length $C = 2\pi r$ which means that there are 2π radians (radii) in one full revolution.

This gives us the equivalence relationships

- $2\pi^c$ (radians) $\equiv 360^o$ (degrees)   or
- π^c (radians) $\equiv 180^o$ (degrees).

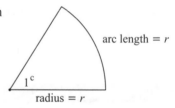

The advantage of using radian measure for an angle is that it measures the angle in terms of arc length. Trigonometric functions (using degrees) are now called **circular functions** (using radians) and the domain and range have the same units of measurement. Scientists probably find this measure more useful.

To convert from degrees to radians it may be best to remember that

$$180^o \equiv \pi^c.$$

EXERCISE 11D.1

1   Find the angle θ (in degrees) which is equivalent to an arc length of:

   a $\frac{\pi}{4}$ b $\frac{\pi}{6}$ c $\frac{2\pi}{3}$ d $\frac{3\pi}{2}$ e $\frac{5\pi}{3}$

Example 3

What arc length on the unit circle is equivalent to $\theta = 120^o$?

Since 120° is $\frac{1}{3}$ of 360°,   the arc length $= \frac{1}{3}$ of $2\pi = \frac{2\pi}{3}$ units.

2 Find the arc length on the unit circle which is equivalent to:

  a $\theta = 30^o$ **b** $\theta = 60^o$ **c** $\theta = 90^o$ **d** $\theta = 120^o$

  e $\theta = 135^o$ **f** $\theta = 150^o$ **g** $\theta = 225^o$ **h** $\theta = 270^o$

3

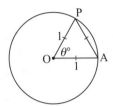

  a What is the value of θ in the given diagram?

  b Find arc length AP for the value of θ in **a**.

  c If θ changes so that arc AP $= 1$, will $\theta = 60$ increase or decrease?

  d If arc AP $= 1$, find θ correct to 1 decimal place.

From question **3** above we observe that:

> One **radian** is the angle subtended at the centre of a circle by an arc equal in length to the radius of the circle. 1 radian $\doteqdot 57.3^o$

It is the angle subtended at the centre of a circle by an arc of length equal to the radius.

Notice that 1 radian is exactly the same angle regardless of how the radius of the circle changes.

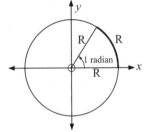

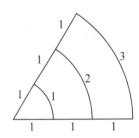

Notation: One radian could be written as 1^R or 1^c or just 1.

DEGREE-RADIAN CONVERSIONS

A full revolution is measured as 360° using degrees and 2π when using radians.

So, 2π radians is equivalent to 360° and consequently

> π radians is equivalent to 180°.

The following diagram is useful for converting from one system of measure to the other:

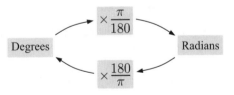

If degrees are used we use a small ^{o} to indicate this. For radians a small ^{c}. For example, 2.3^c can be used but usually no symbol for radians is inserted.

In higher mathematics radian measure is mostly used as it is a distance measure and so both axes on a graph use the same units. For example, the graph of $y = \sin x$ (x in radians) would have the same units on the x and y axes.

Notice that:

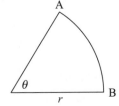

using degrees

$$\text{arc AB} = \left(\frac{\theta}{360}\right) \times 2\pi r,$$

using radians

arc AB $= r\theta$. Why?

Example 4

Convert $45°$ to radians in terms of π.

Notice that angles in radians are either in terms of π or as decimals.

$$45° = \left(45 \times \tfrac{\pi}{180}\right) \text{ radians} \quad or \quad 180° = \pi \text{ radians}$$
$$= \tfrac{\pi}{4} \text{ radians} \qquad \therefore \quad \left(\tfrac{180}{4}\right)° = \tfrac{\pi}{4} \text{ radians}$$
$$\text{i.e., } 45° = \tfrac{\pi}{4} \text{ radians}$$

EXERCISE 11D.2

1 Convert to radians, in terms of π:

a	$90°$	b	$60°$	c	$30°$	d	$18°$	e	$9°$
f	$135°$	g	$225°$	h	$270°$	i	$360°$	j	$720°$
k	$315°$	l	$540°$	m	$36°$	n	$80°$	o	$230°$

Example 5

Convert $126.5°$ to radians.

$126.5°$
$= \left(126.5 \times \tfrac{\pi}{180}\right)$ radians
$\doteqdot 2.21$ radians   (3 s.f.)

To convert degrees to radians, multiply by $\tfrac{\pi}{180}$.

2 Convert to radians (correct to 3 s.f.):

a	$36.7°$	b	$137.2°$	c	$317.9°$	d	$219.6°$	e	$396.7°$

Example 6

Convert $\tfrac{5\pi}{6}$ to degrees.

$\tfrac{5\pi}{6}$
$= \tfrac{5 \times 180°}{6}$
$= 150°$

Replace π radians by $180°$.

3 Convert the following radian measure to degrees:

a	$\tfrac{\pi}{5}$	b	$\tfrac{3\pi}{5}$	c	$\tfrac{3\pi}{4}$	d	$\tfrac{\pi}{18}$	e	$\tfrac{\pi}{9}$
f	$\tfrac{7\pi}{9}$	g	$\tfrac{\pi}{10}$	h	$\tfrac{3\pi}{20}$	i	$\tfrac{5\pi}{6}$	j	$\tfrac{\pi}{8}$

Example 7

Convert 0.638 radians to degrees.

0.638 radians
$= \left(0.638 \times \tfrac{180}{\pi}\right)°$
$\doteqdot 36.55°$

To convert radians to degrees, multiply by $\tfrac{180}{\pi}$.

4 Convert the following radians to degrees (to 2 decimal places):

a	2	b	1.53	c	0.867	d	3.179	e	5.267

5 Copy and complete:

a

Degrees	0	45	90	135	180	225	270	315	360
Radians									

b

Degrees	0	30	60	90	120	150	180	210	240	270	300	330	360
Radians													

E | THE BASIC TRIGONOMETRIC RATIOS

Recall that: If $P(x, y)$ moves around the unit circle (circle centre $(0, 0)$, radius 1) such that OP makes an angle of θ with the positive x-axis then:

the x-coordinate of P is $\cos\theta$
and
the y-coordinate of P is $\sin\theta$.

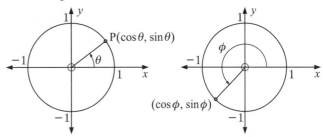

Example 8

Use a unit circle diagram to find the values of $\cos\left(\frac{3\pi}{2}\right)$ and $\sin\left(\frac{3\pi}{2}\right)$.

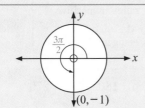

$$\therefore \quad \cos\left(\tfrac{3\pi}{2}\right) = 0 \quad \{x\text{-coordinate}\}$$

$$\sin\left(\tfrac{3\pi}{2}\right) = -1 \quad \{y\text{-coordinate}\}$$

EXERCISE 11E.1

1 Use a unit circle diagram to find:

a $\cos\left(\frac{\pi}{2}\right)$ and $\sin\left(\frac{\pi}{2}\right)$

b $\cos 2\pi$ and $\sin 2\pi$

c $\cos\left(-\frac{\pi}{2}\right)$ and $\sin\left(-\frac{\pi}{2}\right)$

d $\cos\left(\frac{7\pi}{2}\right)$ and $\sin\left(\frac{7\pi}{2}\right)$

Example 9

Find the possible values of $\cos\theta$ for $\sin\theta = \frac{2}{3}$. Illustrate.

Since $\cos^2\theta + \sin^2\theta = 1$, then

$$\cos^2\theta + \left(\tfrac{2}{3}\right)^2 = 1$$

$$\therefore \quad \cos^2\theta = \tfrac{5}{9}$$

$$\therefore \quad \cos\theta = \pm\tfrac{\sqrt{5}}{3}$$

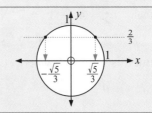

2 Find the possible values of $\cos\theta$ for:

    a $\sin\theta = \frac{1}{2}$ **b** $\sin\theta = -\frac{1}{3}$ **c** $\sin\theta = 0$ **d** $\sin\theta = -1$

3 Find the possible values of $\sin\theta$ for:

    a $\cos\theta = \frac{4}{5}$ **b** $\cos\theta = -\frac{3}{4}$ **c** $\cos\theta = 1$ **d** $\cos\theta = 0$

4 The diagram alongside shows the 4 quadrants. They are numbered anticlockwise.

    a Copy and complete:

Quadrant	Degree measure	Radian measure	$\cos\theta$	$\sin\theta$
1	$0 < \theta < 90$	$0 < \theta < \frac{\pi}{2}$	positive	positive
2				
3				
4				

    b In which quadrants are the following true?
        i $\cos\theta$ is positive   **ii** $\cos\theta$ is negative
        iii $\cos\theta$ and $\sin\theta$ are both negative
        iv $\cos\theta$ is negative and $\sin\theta$ is positive

> **Useful:**
>
>
>
> **All Silly Turtles Crawl**
> indicates which trig ratios are positive
> **A** - all, **S** - sine,
> **T** - tangent, **C** - cosine

Example 10

If $\sin\theta = -\frac{3}{4}$ and $\pi < \theta < \frac{3\pi}{2}$, find $\cos\theta$ without using a calculator.

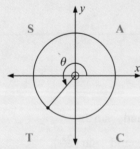

Since $\pi < \theta < \frac{3\pi}{2}$, then $180^o < \theta < 270^o$.

So, θ is a quad. 3 angle and $\therefore$ $\cos\theta$ is *negative*.

Now $\cos^2\theta + \sin^2\theta = 1$

$\therefore \quad \cos^2\theta + \frac{9}{16} = 1$

$\therefore \quad \cos^2\theta = \frac{7}{16}$

$\therefore \quad \cos\theta = \pm\frac{\sqrt{7}}{4}$

and since $\cos\theta$ is negative, $\cos\theta = -\frac{\sqrt{7}}{4}$.

or   using a **working angle**, the angle symmetrical with θ in quadrant 1.

Suppose α is a quad 1 where $\sin\alpha = \frac{3}{4}$

then $n^2 = 4^2 - 3^2 = 7$ {Pythagoras}

$\therefore \quad n = \sqrt{7}$ and so $\cos\alpha = \frac{\sqrt{7}}{4}$

But θ is in quad 3 where $\cos\theta$ is negative

so $\cos\theta = -\frac{\sqrt{7}}{4}$.

5 Without using a calculator, find:

   a $\sin\theta$ if $\cos\theta = \frac{2}{3}$, $0 < \theta < \frac{\pi}{2}$

   b $\cos\theta$ if $\sin\theta = \frac{2}{5}$, $\frac{\pi}{2} < \theta < \pi$

   c $\cos\theta$ if $\sin\theta = -\frac{3}{5}$, $\frac{3\pi}{2} < \theta < 2\pi$

   d $\sin\theta$ if $\cos\theta = -\frac{5}{13}$, $\pi < \theta < \frac{3\pi}{2}$

MULTIPLES OF 30° AND 45°

MULTIPLES OF 45° OR $\frac{\pi}{4}$

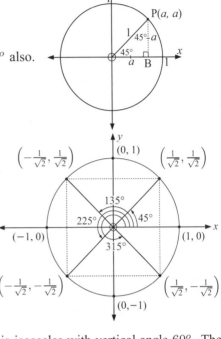

Consider $\theta = 45°$:

Triangle OBP is isosceles as angle OPB measures $45°$ also.

$\therefore$ OB = BP = a,   say

and $a^2 + a^2 = 1^2$ {Pythagoras}

     $\therefore$ $2a^2 = 1$

     $\therefore$ $a^2 = \frac{1}{2}$

     $\therefore$ $a = \frac{1}{\sqrt{2}}$ as $a > 0$

Hence,   P is $(\frac{1}{\sqrt{2}}, \frac{1}{\sqrt{2}})$ where $\frac{1}{\sqrt{2}} \doteqdot 0.7$.

Consequently we can find the coordinates corresponding to angles of $135°$, $225°$ and $315°$ using suitable rotations and reflections.

So, we have:

MULTIPLES OF 30° OR $\frac{\pi}{6}$

Consider $\theta = 60°$:

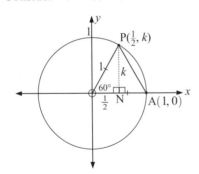

Triangle OAP is isosceles with vertical angle $60°$. The remaining angles are therefore $60°$ and so triangle AOP is equilateral. The altitude PN bisects base OA,

         $\therefore$ ON $= \frac{1}{2}$.

If P is $(\frac{1}{2}, k)$, then $(\frac{1}{2})^2 + k^2 = 1$

           $\therefore$ $k^2 = \frac{3}{4}$

           $\therefore$ $k = \frac{\sqrt{3}}{2}$ {as $k > 0$}

$\therefore$ P is $(\frac{1}{2}, \frac{\sqrt{3}}{2})$ where $\frac{\sqrt{3}}{2} \doteqdot 0.9$.

Consequently, we can find the coordinates of all points on the unit circle corresponding to multiples of $30°$ using rotations/reflections.

So we have:

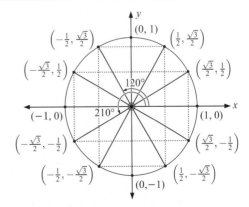

Summary:

- If θ is a **multiple of 90°**, the coordinates of the points on the unit circle involve 0 and ± 1.

- If θ is a **multiple of 45°**, (but not a multiple of 90°), the coordinates involve $\pm\frac{1}{\sqrt{2}}$.

- If θ is a **multiple of 30°**, (but not a multiple of 90°), the coordinates involve $\pm\frac{1}{2}$ and $\pm\frac{\sqrt{3}}{2}$.

You should not try to memorise the coordinates on the above circles for multiples of 30° and 45°, but rather use the summary.

For example: for 215° $215° = 5 \times 45°$
i.e., a multiple of 45°

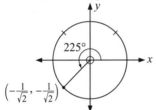

as in quad 3, signs are both negative and both have $\frac{1}{\sqrt{2}}$ size

for 300° $300° = 10 \times 30°$
i.e., a multiple of 30°

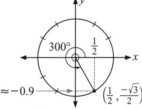

as in quad 4, signs are $(+, -)$ and from the diagram the x-value is $\frac{1}{2}$

Example 11

Use a unit circle to find the exact values of $\sin\alpha$ and $\cos\alpha$ for $\alpha = \frac{3\pi}{4}$.

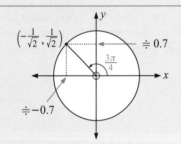

$\alpha = \frac{3\pi}{4} = \frac{3}{4}$ of $180° = 135°$

$\therefore \cos(\frac{3\pi}{4}) = -\frac{1}{\sqrt{2}}, \quad \sin(\frac{3\pi}{4}) = \frac{1}{\sqrt{2}}$

EXERCISE 11E.2

1 Use a unit circle diagram to find $\sin\theta$ and $\cos\theta$ for θ equal to:

a $\frac{\pi}{4}$ b $\frac{5\pi}{4}$ c $\frac{7\pi}{4}$ d π e $\frac{-3\pi}{4}$

Example 12

Use a unit circle diagram to find the exact values of $\sin A$ and $\cos A$ for $A = \frac{4\pi}{3}$.

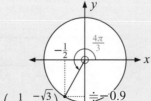

$\frac{4\pi}{3} = \frac{4}{3} \times 180° = 240°$

$\therefore \cos(\frac{4\pi}{3}) = -\frac{1}{2}$

and $\sin(\frac{4\pi}{3}) = -\frac{\sqrt{3}}{2}$

2 Use a unit circle diagram to find $\sin \beta$ and $\cos \beta$ for β equal to:

    a $\frac{\pi}{6}$ **b** $\frac{2\pi}{3}$ **c** $\frac{7\pi}{6}$ **d** $\frac{5\pi}{3}$ **e** $\frac{11\pi}{6}$

Example 13

Without using a calculator, find the value of $8\sin\left(\frac{\pi}{3}\right)\cos\left(\frac{5\pi}{6}\right)$.

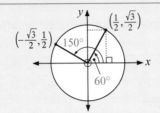

$\sin\left(\frac{\pi}{3}\right) = \frac{\sqrt{3}}{2}$ and $\cos\left(\frac{5\pi}{6}\right) = -\frac{\sqrt{3}}{2}$

$\therefore \quad 8\sin\left(\frac{\pi}{3}\right)\cos\left(\frac{5\pi}{6}\right) = 8\left(\frac{\sqrt{3}}{2}\right)\left(-\frac{\sqrt{3}}{2}\right)$

$= 2(-3)$

$= -6$

---

3 Without using a calculator, evaluate:

    a $\sin^2 60^o$ **b** $\sin 30^o \cos 60^o$ **c** $4\sin 60^o \cos 30^o$

    d $1 - \cos^2\left(\frac{\pi}{6}\right)$ **e** $\sin^2\left(\frac{2\pi}{3}\right) - 1$ **f** $\cos^2\left(\frac{\pi}{4}\right) - \sin\left(\frac{7\pi}{6}\right)$

    g $\sin\left(\frac{3\pi}{4}\right) - \cos\left(\frac{5\pi}{4}\right)$ **h** $1 - 2\sin^2\left(\frac{7\pi}{6}\right)$ **i** $\cos^2\left(\frac{5\pi}{6}\right) - \sin^2\left(\frac{5\pi}{6}\right)$

Check all answers using your calculator.

Example 14

Use a unit circle diagram to find all angles in $[0, 2\pi]$ with a cosine of $\frac{1}{2}$.

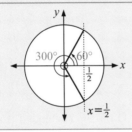

As the cosine is $\frac{1}{2}$, we draw the vertical line $x = \frac{1}{2}$.

Because $\frac{1}{2}$ is involved we know the required angles are multiples of 30°.

They are $\frac{\pi}{3}$ and $\frac{5\pi}{3}$.

---

4 Use a unit circle diagram to find all angles between 0° and 360° with:

    a a sine of $\frac{1}{2}$ **b** a sine of $\frac{\sqrt{3}}{2}$ **c** a cosine of $\frac{1}{\sqrt{2}}$

    d a cosine of $-\frac{1}{2}$ **e** a cosine of $-\frac{1}{\sqrt{2}}$ **f** a sine of $-\frac{\sqrt{3}}{2}$

5 Use a unit circle diagram to find all angles between 0° and 720° with:

    a a cosine of $\frac{\sqrt{3}}{2}$ **b** a sine of $-\frac{1}{2}$ **c** a sine of -1

6 Find θ in radians if $0 \leqslant \theta \leqslant 2\pi$ and:

    a $\cos\theta = \frac{1}{2}$ **b** $\sin\theta = \frac{\sqrt{3}}{2}$ **c** $\cos\theta = -1$ **d** $\sin\theta = 1$

    e $\cos\theta = -\frac{1}{\sqrt{2}}$ **f** $\sin^2\theta = 1$ **g** $\cos^2\theta = 1$ **h** $\cos^2\theta = \frac{1}{2}$

F   AREAS OF TRIANGLES

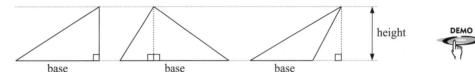

height

DEMO

If we know the base and height measurements of a triangle we can calculate the area using **area** $= \frac{1}{2}$ **base** $\times$ **height**.

However, cases arise where we do not know the height but we can still calculate the area.

These cases are:
- knowing two sides and the angle between them (called the **included angle**)
- knowing all three sides

For example:

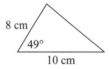

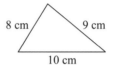

LABELLING TRIANGLES

If triangle ABC has angles of size A^o, B^o, C^o, the sides opposite these angles are labelled a, b and c respectively.

Using trigonometry, we can develop an alternative formula that does not depend on a perpendicular height. Any triangle that is not right angled must be either acute or obtuse.

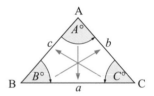

We will consider both cases.

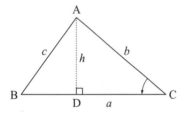

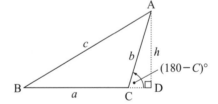

In both triangles a perpendicular is constructed from A to D on BC (extended if necessary).

$$\sin C = \frac{h}{b} \qquad\qquad \sin(180 - C) = \frac{h}{b}$$

$$\therefore \quad h = b\sin C \qquad\qquad \therefore \quad h = b\sin(180 - C)$$

$$\text{but} \quad \sin(180 - C) = \sin C$$

$$\therefore \quad h = b\sin C$$

So, as area $= \frac{1}{2}ah$ then   area $= \frac{1}{2}ab\sin C$.

Using different altitudes we could also show that the area is $\frac{1}{2}bc\sin A$ or $\frac{1}{2}ac\sin B$.

Summary:

Given the lengths of two sides of a triangle and the angle between them (called the **included angle**), the area of the triangle is

*a half of the product of two sides and the **sine of the included angle***.

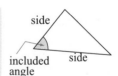

Example 15

Find the area of triangle ABC:

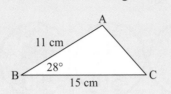

Area $= \frac{1}{2}ac\sin B$

$= \frac{1}{2} \times 15 \times 11 \times \sin 28^o$

$\doteqdot 38.7$ cm^2

EXERCISE 11F

1 Find the area of:

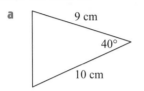

a 9 cm, 40°, 10 cm

b 31 km, 82°, 25 km

c 10.2 cm, 125°, 6.4 cm

2 If triangle ABC has area 150 cm^2, find the value of x:

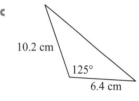

17 cm, B, 68°, A, x cm, C

3 A parallelogram has two adjacent sides of length 4 cm and 6 cm respectively. If the included angle measures 52°, find the area of the parallelogram.

4 A rhombus has side lengths 12 cm and an angle of 72°. Find its area.

5 Find the area of a regular hexagon with sides of length 12 cm.

6 A rhombus has an area of 50 cm^2 and an internal angle of size 63°. Find the length of its sides.

7 A regular pentagonal garden plot has centre of symmetry O and an area of 338 m^2. Find the distance OA.

Example 16

A triangle has sides of length 10 cm and 11 cm and an area of 50 cm^2.
Show that the included angle may take two different possible sizes.

If the included angle measures θ^o, then $\frac{1}{2} \times 10 \times 11 \times \sin\theta = 50$

$\therefore$ $\sin\theta = \frac{50}{55}$

Now $\arcsin\left(\frac{50}{55}\right) \doteqdot 65.4$

$\therefore$ $\theta = 65.4$ or $180 - 65.4$

i.e., $\theta = 65.4$ or 114.6

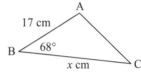

So, the two different possible angles are 65.4^o and 114.6^o

Reminder: $\sin\theta = \sin(180 - \theta)$ was established in the previous chapter.

8 Find the possible values of the included angle of a triangle with:

    a sides 5 cm and 8 cm, and area 15 cm^2

    b sides 45 km and 53 km, and area 800 km^2.

9 The Australian 50 cent coin has the shape of a dodecagon (12 sides).

Eight of these 50 cent coins will fit exactly on an Australian $10 note as shown below. What fraction of the $10 note is *not* covered?

10 Heron of Alexandria, in the first century A.D., showed that if a triangle has sides of length a, b and c, then its area can be calculated using $A = \sqrt{s(s-a)(s-b)(s-c)}$

where $s = \dfrac{a+b+c}{2}$.

    a Find the area of the right angled triangle with sides 3 cm, 4 cm and 5 cm:

        i without using Heron's formula

       ii using Heron's formula.

    b Find the area of a triangle with sides of length:

        i 6 cm, 8 cm and 12 cm   **ii** 7.2 cm, 8.9 cm and 9.7 cm

G   SECTORS AND SEGMENTS

Reminder:

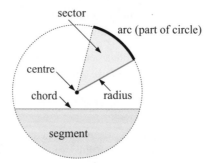

SECTORS

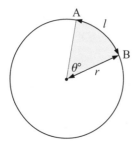

Consider a sector of a circle of radius r and angle $\theta°$ at the centre.

If l is the length of the arc from A to B then:

-     $l = \left(\dfrac{\theta}{360}\right) \times 2\pi r$

-     $\text{area} = \left(\dfrac{\theta}{360}\right) \times \pi r^2$

Note: $\dfrac{\theta}{360}$ is the fraction of the full circle occupied by the sector.

If θ is in **radians** the arc length and area formula become $l = r\theta$ and $\textbf{area} = \frac{1}{2}r^2\theta$.

These are easily obtained by substituting 2π for 360.

Example 17

A sector has radius 12 cm and angle $65°$. Find:
a   its arc length   b   its area

a   arc length $= \left(\dfrac{\theta}{360}\right) \times 2\pi r$ b   area $= \left(\dfrac{\theta}{360}\right) \times \pi r^2$

$\qquad\qquad = \dfrac{65}{360} \times 2 \times \pi \times 12$ $\qquad = \dfrac{65}{360} \times \pi \times 12^2$

$\qquad\qquad \doteqdot 13.6$ cm $\qquad \doteqdot 81.7$ cm^2

EXERCISE 11G

1 Find   **i**   the arc length   **ii**   the area of a sector of a circle of:
    a   radius 9 cm and angle $41.6°$ **b**   radius 4.93 cm and angle $122°$

2 A sector has an angle of $107.9°$ and an arc length of 5.92 m. Find:
    a   its radius   **b**   its area.

3 A sector has an angle of $68.2°$ and an area of 20.8 cm^2. Find:
    a   its radius   **b**   its perimeter.

Example 18

A sector has radius 8.2 cm and arc length 13.3 cm. Find its angle, in degrees.

arc length $= \left(\dfrac{\theta}{360}\right) \times 2\pi r$ *or*   arc length $= r\theta$ {θ in radians}

$\therefore\ \theta = \dfrac{360 \times \text{arc length}}{2\pi r}$ $\therefore\ \theta = \dfrac{\text{arc length}}{r} = \dfrac{13.3}{8.2}$

$\qquad = \dfrac{360 \times 13.3}{2 \times \pi \times 8.2}$ $\therefore\ \theta = \dfrac{13.3}{8.2} \times \dfrac{180}{\pi}$

$\qquad \doteqdot 92.93$ So, its angle is $92.9°$. $\therefore\ \theta \doteqdot 92.9°$

4 Find the angle of a sector of:
    a   radius 4.3 m and arc length 2.95 m   **b**   radius 10 cm and area 30 cm^2.

5 Find θ (in radians) for each of:

a

b
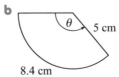

c
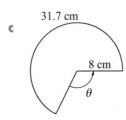

6 Find the shaded area of:

a

5 cm
0.7

b

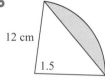

12 cm
1.5

c

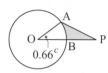

OA = 12 cm, BP = 18 cm

7 Find the arc length and area of a sector of radius 5 cm and angle 2 radians.

8 If a sector has radius 10 cm and arc length 13 cm, find its area.

9 This cone 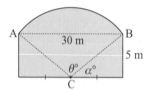 is made from this sector.

10 cm s cm

12 cm

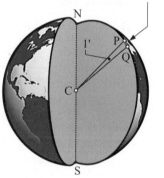

$\theta°$

r

Find correct to 3 significant figures:
  a the slant length (s cm)
  b the value of r
  c the arc length of the sector
  d the sector angle ($\theta°$)

10

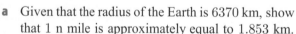

A   30 m   B

5 m

$\theta°$ $\alpha°$
C

The end wall of a building has the shape illustrated, where the centre of arc AB is at C. Find:
  a α to 4 significant figures
  b θ to 4 significant figures
  c the area of the wall.

11 A **nautical mile** (n mile) is the distance on the Earth's surface that subtends an angle of 1 minute (where 1 minute = $\frac{1}{60}$ degree) of the Great Circle arc measured from the centre of the Earth. A **knot** is a speed of 1 nautical mile per hour.

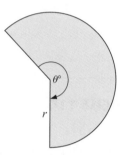

1 nautical mile (Nm)

N
1'
P
Q
C
S

  a Given that the radius of the Earth is 6370 km, show that 1 n mile is approximately equal to 1.853 km.
  b Calculate how long it would take a plane to fly from Perth to Adelaide (a distance of 2130 km) if the plane can fly at 480 knots.

12

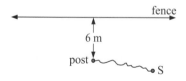

fence

6 m

post   S

A sheep is tethered to a post which is 6 m from a long fence. The length of rope is 9 m. Find the area which is available for the sheep to feed on.

13 A belt fits tightly around two pulleys of radii 4 cm and 6 cm respectively and the distance between their centres is 20 cm. Find, correct to 4 significant figures:
  a α **b** θ
  c ϕ **d** the length of the belt

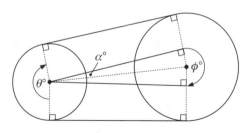

$\alpha°$
$\phi°$
$\theta°$

REVIEW SET 11A

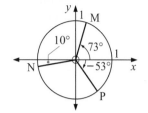

1 Use your calculator to find: **a** $\sin 70^{\circ}$ **b** $\cos 35^{\circ}$

2 Find the coordinates of the points
M, N and P on the unit circle.

3 Find θ if the value of the x-coordinate
of the point A on the unit circle is -0.222.

4 Find the acute angles that would have the same sine as: **a** 120° **b** 165° **c** 95°

5 Find the obtuse angles which have the same sine as: **a** 47° **b** 8° **c** 86°

6 Without using your calculator, find:
    a $\sin 159^{\circ}$ if $\sin 21^{\circ} \doteqdot 0.358$
    b $\cos 92^{\circ}$ if $\cos 88^{\circ} \doteqdot 0.035$
    c $\cos 75^{\circ}$ if $\cos 105^{\circ} \doteqdot -0.259$
    d $\sin 227^{\circ}$ if $\sin 47^{\circ} \doteqdot 0.731$

7 Use a unit circle diagram to find:
    a $\cos 360^{\circ}$ and $\sin 360^{\circ}$
    b $\cos(-180^{\circ})$ and $\sin(-180^{\circ})$

8 Find the acute angles that would have the same sine as: **a** 101° **b** 127° **c** 168°

9 Find the acute angles that would have the same cosine as: **a** 276° **b** 298° **c** 357°

10 If $\sin 74^{\circ} \doteqdot 0.961$,   without using a calculator, find the value of:
    a $\sin 106^{\circ}$ **b** $\sin 254^{\circ}$ **c** $\sin 286^{\circ}$ **d** $\sin 646^{\circ}$

11 If $\cos 42^{\circ} \doteqdot 0.743$,   without using a calculator, find the value of:
    a $\cos 138^{\circ}$ **b** $\cos 222^{\circ}$ **c** $\cos 318^{\circ}$ **d** $\cos(-222^{\circ})$

REVIEW SET 11B

1 Determine the area of:

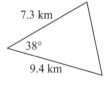

2 Determine the area of:
    a   a sector of angle 80° and radius 13 cm
    b   a triangle with sides 11 cm,
       9 cm and included angle 65°.

3 Find the perimeter and area of a sector of radius 11 cm and angle 63°.

4 Find the radius and hence the area of a sector of perimeter 36 cm if the angle is $\left(\frac{2\pi}{3}\right)^{c}$.

5 A triangle has sides of length 7 cm and 13 cm and its area is 42 cm^2. Find the size of its included angle.

6 Find the value of x if the area is
80 cm^2. Hence, find the length of AC.

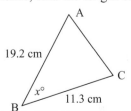

7 Determine the shaded area:

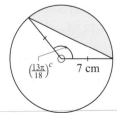

8 Anke and Lucas are considering buying a block of land and the land agent supplies them with the given accurate sketch. Find the area of the property giving your answer in:

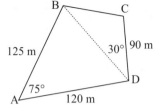

   a m^2

   b hectares.

9

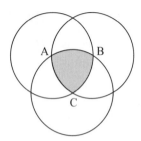

Three equal circles with radius r are drawn as shown, each with its centre on the circumference of the other two circles. A, B and C are the centres of the three circles. Prove that an expression for the area of the shaded region is:

$$A = \frac{r^2}{2}(\pi - \sqrt{3})$$

10 Convert these to radians in terms of π: **a** $120°$ **b** $225°$ **c** $150°$ **d** $540°$

11 Convert to radians (to 4 sig. figs.): **a** $71°$ **b** $124.6°$ **c** $-142°$ **d** $-25.3°$

12 Convert these radian measure to degrees: **a** $\frac{2\pi}{5}$ **b** $\frac{5\pi}{4}$ **c** $\frac{7\pi}{9}$ **d** $\frac{11\pi}{6}$

13 Convert these radian measure to degrees (to 2 decimal places):

   a 3   **b** 1.46   **c** 0.435   **d** -5.271

REVIEW SET 11C

1 Use your calculator to determine the coordinates of the point on the unit circle corresponding to an angle of: **a** $320°$ **b** $163°$

2 Illustrate the regions where $\sin\theta$ and $\cos\theta$ have the same sign.

3 Use a unit circle diagram to find exact values for $\sin\theta$ and $\cos\theta$ for θ equal to:

   a $\frac{2\pi}{3}$ **b** $\frac{8\pi}{3}$

4 Explain how to use the unit circle to find θ when $\cos\theta = -\sin\theta$.

5 Use a unit circle diagram to find:

   a $\cos\left(\frac{3\pi}{2}\right)$ and $\sin\left(\frac{3\pi}{2}\right)$ **b** $\cos\left(-\frac{\pi}{2}\right)$ and $\sin\left(-\frac{\pi}{2}\right)$

6 If $\cos\theta = \frac{3}{4}$ find the possible values of $\sin\theta$.

7 If $\cos\theta = -\frac{3}{4}$, $\frac{\pi}{2} < \theta < \pi$ find $\sin\theta$.

8 Without a calculator, evaluate: **a** $\sin^2\left(\frac{2\pi}{3}\right)$ **b** $\cos\left(\frac{3\pi}{4}\right) - \sin\left(\frac{3\pi}{4}\right)$

9 Without a calculator evaluate:

   a $2\sin\left(\frac{\pi}{3}\right)\cos\left(\frac{\pi}{3}\right)$ **b** $\sin^2\left(\frac{\pi}{4}\right) - 1$ **c** $\cos^2\left(\frac{\pi}{6}\right) - \sin^2\left(\frac{\pi}{6}\right)$

10 Use a unit circle diagram to find all angles between $0°$ and $360°$ which have:

   a a cosine of $-\frac{\sqrt{3}}{2}$ **b** a sine of $\frac{1}{\sqrt{2}}$

11 Find θ in radians if: **a** $\cos\theta = -1$ **b** $\sin^2\theta = \frac{3}{4}$

Chapter 12

Non right angled triangle trigonometry

Contents:

A   THE COSINE RULE

The **cosine rule** involves the sides and angles of a triangle.

In any $\triangle ABC$:

$$a^2 = b^2 + c^2 - 2bc\cos A$$
$$or \quad b^2 = a^2 + c^2 - 2ac\cos B$$
$$or \quad c^2 = a^2 + b^2 - 2ab\cos C$$

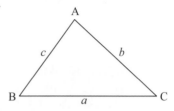

We will develop the first formula for both an acute and an obtuse triangle.

Proof:

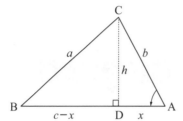 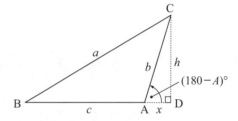

In both triangles drop a perpendicular from C to meet AB (extended if necessary) at D.

Let $AD = x$ and let $CD = h$.

Apply the theorem of Pythagoras in $\triangle BCD$:

$$a^2 = h^2 + (c - x)^2 \qquad\qquad a^2 = h^2 + (c + x)^2$$
$$\therefore \quad a^2 = h^2 + c^2 - 2cx + x^2 \qquad\qquad \therefore \quad a^2 = h^2 + c^2 + 2cx + x^2$$

In both cases, applying Pythagoras to $\triangle ADC$: $h^2 + x^2 = b^2$ and substitute for h^2.

$$\therefore \quad a^2 = b^2 + c^2 - 2cx \qquad\qquad \therefore \quad a^2 = b^2 + c^2 + 2cx$$

In ADC: $\cos A = \dfrac{x}{b}$ $\qquad\qquad$ Now $\cos(180 - A) = \dfrac{x}{b}$

$$\therefore \quad b\cos A = x \qquad\qquad\quad \therefore \quad b\cos(180 - A) = x$$
$$\therefore \quad a^2 = b^2 + c^2 - 2bc\cos A \qquad But, \quad \cos(180 - A) = -\cos A$$
$$\therefore \quad -b\cos A = x$$
$$\therefore \quad a^2 = b^2 + c^2 - 2bc\cos A$$

The other variations of the cosine rule could be developed by rearranging the vertices of $\triangle ABC$.

Note that if $A = 90^o$, $\cos A = 0$ and $a^2 = b^2 + c^2 - 2bc\cos A$ reduces to $a^2 = b^2 + c^2$, the Pythagoras' Rule.

The **cosine rule** can be used to solve triangles given:
- two sides and an included angle
- three sides.

There is no ambiguity possible using the cosine rule.

Example 1

Find, correct to 2 decimal places, the length of BC.

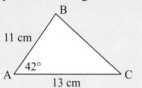

By the cosine rule:
$$BC^2 = 11^2 + 13^2 - 2 \times 11 \times 13 \times \cos 42^o$$
$$\therefore \quad BC \doteqdot \sqrt{(11^2 + 13^2 - 2 \times 11 \times 13 \times \cos 42^o)}$$
$$\therefore \quad BC \doteqdot 8.801.....$$
$$\therefore \quad BC \text{ is } 8.80 \text{ cm in length.}$$

EXERCISE 12A

1 Find the length of the remaining side in the given triangle:

a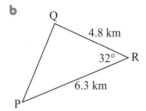

b

c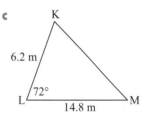

Rearrangement of the original cosine rule formulae can be used for angle finding if we know all three sides. The formulae for finding the angles are:

$$\cos A = \frac{b^2 + c^2 - a^2}{2bc} \qquad \cos B = \frac{c^2 + a^2 - b^2}{2ca} \qquad \cos C = \frac{a^2 + b^2 - c^2}{2ab}$$

Example 2

In triangle ABC, if AB = 7 cm, BC = 8 cm and CA = 5 cm, find the measure of angle BCA.

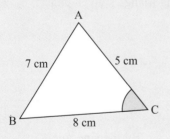

By the cosine rule:
$$\cos C = \frac{(5^2 + 8^2 - 7^2)}{(2 \times 5 \times 8)}$$
$$\therefore \quad C = \cos^{-1}\left(\frac{(5^2 + 8^2 - 7^2)}{(2 \times 5 \times 8)}\right)$$
$$\therefore \quad C = 60$$

So, angle BCA measures 60°.

2 Find the measure of all angles of:

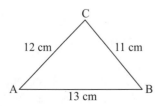

3 Find the measure of obtuse angle PQR.

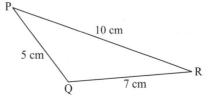

4 Find:

  a the smallest angle of a triangle with sides 11 cm, 13 cm and 17 cm

  b the largest angle of a triangle with sides 4 cm, 7 cm and 9 cm.

The smallest angle is opposite the shortest side.

5 Find:

  a $\cos\theta$ but not θ

  b the value of x.

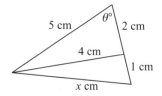

B   THE SINE RULE

The **sine rule** is a set of equations which connects the lengths of the sides of any triangle with the sines of the angles of the triangle. The triangle does not have to be right angled for the sine rule to be used.

In any triangle ABC with sides a, b and c units in length, and opposite angles A, B and C respectively,

$$\frac{\sin A}{a} = \frac{\sin B}{b} = \frac{\sin C}{c} \quad \text{or} \quad \frac{a}{\sin A} = \frac{b}{\sin B} = \frac{c}{\sin C}$$

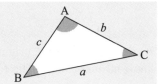

Proof: The area of any triangle ABC is given by

$\frac{1}{2}bc\sin A = \frac{1}{2}ac\sin B = \frac{1}{2}ab\sin C$.

Dividing each expression by $\frac{1}{2}abc$ gives

$\dfrac{\sin A}{a} = \dfrac{\sin B}{b} = \dfrac{\sin C}{c}$.

Note: The sine rule is used to solve problems involving triangles given either:

  • **two angles** and **one side**, or

  • **two sides** and a **non-included** angle.

FINDING SIDES

Example 3

Find the length of AC correct to two decimal places.

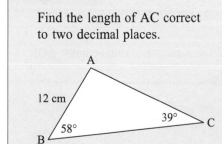

By the sine rule

$$\therefore \quad \frac{b}{\sin 58^o} = \frac{12}{\sin 39^o}$$

$$\therefore \quad b = \frac{12 \times \sin 58^o}{\sin 39^o}$$

$$\therefore \quad b \doteqdot 16.170\,74$$

$\therefore$ AC is 16.2 cm long.

EXERCISE 12B.1

1 Find the value of x:

a

b

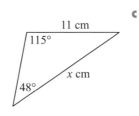

c

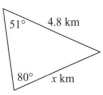

2 In triangle ABC find:

    a a if A $= 63°$, B $= 49°$ and $b = 18$ cm

    b b if A $= 82°$, C $= 25°$ and $c = 34$ cm

    c c if B $= 21°$, C $= 48°$ and $a = 6.4$ cm

FINDING ANGLES

The problem of finding angles using the sine rule is more complicated because there may be two possible answers.

In this investigation you should have discovered that when you are given two sides and a non-included angle there are a number of different possibilities. You could get two triangles, one triangle or it may be impossible to draw any triangles from the given data.

Let us consider the calculations involved in each of the cases of the investigation.

Task 1: · Given: $c = 10$ cm, $a = 6$ cm, $A = 30°$

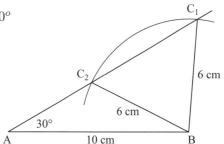

Finding C: $\dfrac{\sin C}{c} = \dfrac{\sin A}{a}$

$\therefore \quad \sin C = \dfrac{c \sin A}{a}$

$\therefore \quad \sin C = \dfrac{10 \times \sin 30°}{6} = 0.8333$

Because $\sin\theta \doteqdot \sin(180^o - \theta)$ there are two possible angles:

$$C = 56.44^o \quad or \quad 180^o - 56.44^o = 123.56^o$$

On your calculator check that the sine ratio of both of these angles is 0.8333.

Task 2:   Given: $c = 10$ cm, $a = 5$ cm, $A = 30^o$

Finding C: $\dfrac{\sin C}{c} = \dfrac{\sin A}{a}$

$\therefore \quad \sin C = \dfrac{c\sin A}{a}$

$\therefore \quad \sin C = \dfrac{10 \times \sin 30^o}{5} = 1$

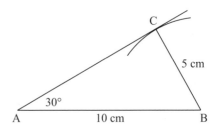

There is only one possible solution for C in the range from 0° to 180° and that is $C = 90^o$.
So only one triangle (i.e., one set of solutions) is possible. Complete the solution of the
triangle yourself.

Task 3:   Given: $c = 10$ cm, $a = 3$ cm, $A = 30^o$

Finding C: $\dfrac{\sin C}{c} = \dfrac{\sin A}{a}$

$\therefore \quad \sin C = \dfrac{c\sin A}{a}$

$\therefore \quad \sin C = \dfrac{10 \times \sin 30^o}{3}$

$\therefore \quad \sin C = 1.6667$

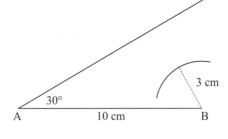

There is no angle that has a sine ratio > 1. Therefore there is *no solution* for this given data,
i.e., *no possible* triangle can be drawn.

Task 4:   Given: $c = 10$ cm, $a = 12$ cm, $A = 30^o$

Finding C:

$\dfrac{\sin C}{c} = \dfrac{\sin A}{a}$

$\therefore \quad \sin C = \dfrac{c\sin A}{a}$

$\therefore \quad \sin C = \dfrac{10 \times \sin 30^o}{12}$

$\therefore \quad \sin C = 0.4167$

Two angles have a sine
ratio of 0.4167

$C = 24.62^o \quad or$
    $180^o - 24.62^o$

$C = 24.62^o \quad or \quad 155.38^o$

However, in this case only one of these two angles is valid.   If $A = 30^o$ then C cannot
possibly equal 155.38^o because $30^o + 155.38^o > 180^o$.

Therefore, there is only one solution, $C = 24.62^o$. Once again, you may wish to carry on and complete the solution.

Conclusion: Each situation using the sine rule with two sides and a non-included angle must be examined very carefully.

Example 4

Find the measure of angle C in triangle ABC if AC is 7 cm, AB is 11 cm and angle B measures 25°.

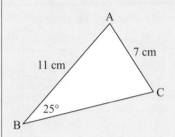

By the sine rule

$$\frac{\sin C}{c} = \frac{\sin B}{b}$$

$$\therefore \quad \frac{\sin C}{11} = \frac{\sin 25^o}{7}$$

$$\therefore \quad \sin C = \frac{11 \times \sin 25^o}{7}$$

$$\therefore \quad C = \sin^{-1}\left(\frac{11 \times \sin 25^o}{7}\right) \quad \text{or its supplement}$$

$$\therefore \quad C \doteqdot 41.6^o \text{ or } 180^o - 41.6^o$$

$$\{\text{as } C \text{ may be obtuse}\}$$

$$\therefore \quad C \doteqdot 41.6^o \text{ or } 138.4^o$$

$$\therefore \quad C \text{ measures } 41.6^o \text{ if angle } C \text{ is acute}$$

$$\text{or } C \text{ measures } 138.4^o \text{ if angle } C \text{ is obtuse.}$$

In this example there is insufficient information to determine the actual shape of the triangle.

Note: Sometimes there is information in the question which enables us to **reject** one of the answers.

Example 5

Find the measure of angle L in triangle KLM given that angle LKM measures 56°, LM = 16.8 m and KM = 13.5 m.

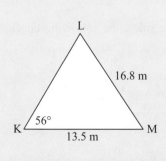

$$\frac{\sin L}{13.5} = \frac{\sin 56^o}{16.8} \quad \{\text{the sine rule}\}$$

$$\therefore \quad \sin L = \frac{13.5 \times \sin 56^o}{16.8}$$

$$\therefore \quad L = \sin^{-1}\left(\frac{13.5 \times \sin 56^o}{16.8}\right) \quad \text{or its supplement}$$

$$\therefore \quad L \doteqdot 41.8^o \quad \text{or} \quad 180^o - 41.8^o$$

$$\therefore \quad L \doteqdot 41.8^o \quad \text{or} \quad 138.2^o$$

But reject $L = 138.2^o$ as $138.2^o + 56^o > 180^o$ which is impossible. $\therefore \quad \angle L \doteqdot 41.8^o$.

EXERCISE 12B.2

1   Triangle ABC has $\angle B = 40^o$, $b = 8$ cm and $c = 11$ cm. Find the two possible values for angle C.

2   In triangle ABC, find the measure of:
   a   angle A if $a = 14.6$ cm, $b = 17.4$ cm and $\angle ABC = 65^o$
   b   angle B if $b = 43.8$ cm, $c = 31.4$ cm and $\angle ACB = 43^o$
   c   angle C if $a = 6.5$ km, $c = 4.8$ km and $\angle BAC = 71^o$.

3   Is it possible to have a triangle with measurements as shown? Explain!

4   Find the magnitude of the angle ABC and hence BD in the given figure.

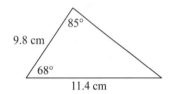

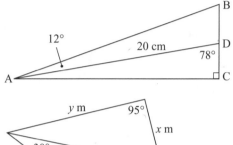

5   Find x and y in the given figure.

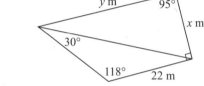

6   Triangle ABC has $\widehat{A} = 58^o$, AB $= 10$ cm and AC $= 5.1$ cm. Find:
   a $\widehat{C}$ correct to the nearest tenth of a degree using the sine rule
   b $\widehat{C}$ correct to the nearest tenth of a degree using the cosine rule.
   c   Copy and complete: "When faced with using either the sine rule or the cosine rule it is better to use the .... as it avoids ...."

C | USING THE SINE AND COSINE RULES

First decide which rule to use.

If the triangle is right angled then the trigonometric ratios or Pythagoras' Theorem can be used, and for some problems adding an extra line or two to the diagram may result in a right triangle.

However, if you have to choose between the sine and cosine rules, the following checklist may assist you.

Use the **cosine rule** when given
   • three sides
   • two sides and an included angle.

Use the **sine rule** when given

   • one side and two angles
   • two sides and a non-included angle (but beware of the *ambiguous case* which can occur when the smaller of the two given sides is opposite the given angle).

Example 6

The angles of elevation to the top of a mountain are measured from two beacons A and B, at sea.

These angles are as shown on the diagram.

If the beacons are 1473 m apart, how high is the mountain?

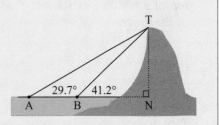

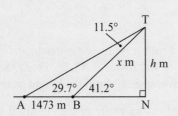

$\angle ATB = 41.2° - 29.7°$ {exterior angle of Δ}
$\qquad = 11.5°$

We can now find x in ΔABT using the sine rule,

i.e., $\quad \dfrac{x}{\sin 29.7} = \dfrac{1473}{\sin 11.5}$

$\therefore \quad x = \dfrac{1473}{\sin 11.5} \times \sin 29.7$

$\qquad \doteqdot 3660.62.....$

Now, in ΔBNT, $\sin 41.2° = \dfrac{h}{x} = \dfrac{h}{3660.62....}$

$\therefore \quad h = \sin 41.2° \times 3660.62....$

$\therefore \quad h \doteqdot 2410$

So, the mountain is about 2410 m high.

EXERCISE 12C

1   Manny wishes to determine the height of a flag pole. He takes a sighting of the top of the flagpole from point P. He then moves further away from the flagpole by 20 metres to point Q and takes a second sighting. The information is shown in the diagram alongside. How high is the flagpole?

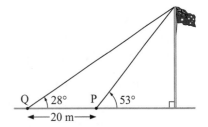

2

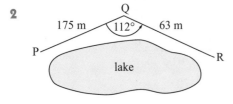

To get from P to R, a park ranger had to walk along a path to Q and then to R as shown.

What is the distance in a straight line from P to R?

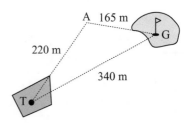

3   A golfer played his tee shot a distance of 220 m to a point A. He then played a 165 m six iron to the green. If the distance from tee to green is 340 m, determine the number of degrees the golfer was off line with his tee shot.

4 A Communications Tower is constructed on
top of a building as shown. Find the height
of the tower.

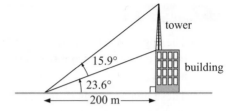

5

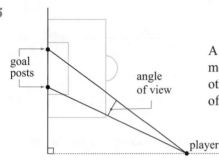

A soccer goal is 5 metres wide. When a player is 21
metres from one goal post and 19 metres from the
other, he shoots for goal. What is the angle of view
of the goals that the player sees?

6 A tower 42 metres high, stands on top of a hill. From a point some distance from the
base of the hill, the angle of elevation to the top of the tower is $13.2°$. From the same
point the angle of elevation to the bottom of the tower is $8.3°$. Find the height of the hill.

7 From the foot of a building I have to look upwards at an angle of $22°$ to sight the top
of a tree. From the top of the building, 150 metres above ground level, I have to look
down at an angle of $50°$ below the horizontal to sight the tree top.

  a How high is the tree?   **b** How far from the building is this tree?

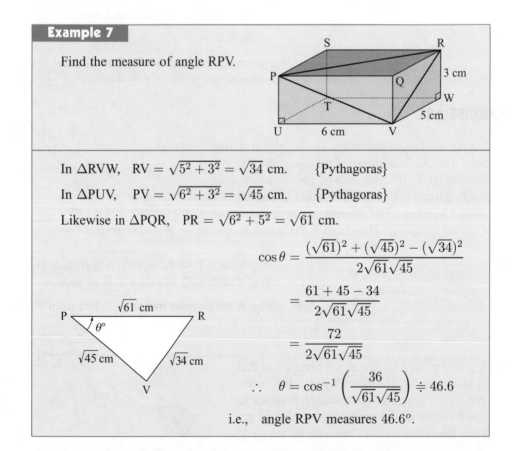

Example 7

Find the measure of angle RPV.

In $\triangle$RVW, RV $= \sqrt{5^2 + 3^2} = \sqrt{34}$ cm.   {Pythagoras}

In $\triangle$PUV,   PV $= \sqrt{6^2 + 3^2} = \sqrt{45}$ cm.   {Pythagoras}

Likewise in $\triangle$PQR,   PR $= \sqrt{6^2 + 5^2} = \sqrt{61}$ cm.

$$\cos \theta = \frac{(\sqrt{61})^2 + (\sqrt{45})^2 - (\sqrt{34})^2}{2\sqrt{61}\sqrt{45}}$$

$$= \frac{61 + 45 - 34}{2\sqrt{61}\sqrt{45}}$$

$$= \frac{72}{2\sqrt{61}\sqrt{45}}$$

$$\therefore \quad \theta = \cos^{-1}\left(\frac{36}{\sqrt{61}\sqrt{45}}\right) \doteqdot 46.6$$

i.e.,   angle RPV measures $46.6°$.

8

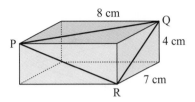

Find the measure of angle PQR in the rectangular box shown.

9 Two observation posts are 12 km apart at A and B. From A, a third observation post C is located such that angle CAB is $42°$ while angle CBA is $67°$. Find the distance of C from both A and B.

10 Stan and Olga are considering buying a sheep farm and the land agent supplies them with the given accurate sketch. Find the area of the property giving your answer in:

    a km^2 **b** hectares.

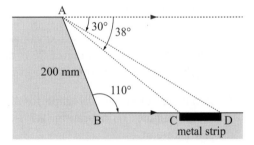

11 Thabo and Palesa start at point A. They each walk in a straight line at an angle of $120°$ to each other. Thabo walks at 6 kmph and Palesa walks at 8 kmph. How far apart are they after 45 minutes?

12 The design of the kerbing cross-section for a driverless-bus roadway is given. The metal strip is inlaid into the concrete and is used to control the direction of travel and speed of the bus. Find the width of the metal strip.

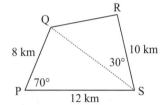

13 An orienteer runs for $4\frac{1}{2}$ km and then turns through an angle of $32°$ and runs another 6 km. How far is she from her starting point?

14 Sam and Markus are standing on level ground 100 metres apart. A large tree is due North of Markus and on a bearing of $065°$ from Sam. The top of the tree appears at an angle of elevation of $25°$ to Sam and $15°$ to Markus. Find the height of the tree.

15 A helicopter A, flying at 4000 m, observes two ships B and C. B is 23.8 km from the helicopter and C is 31.9 km from it. The angle of view from the helicopter to B and C (angle BAC) is $83.6°$. How far are the ships apart?

REVIEW SET 12

1 Determine the value of x:

    a

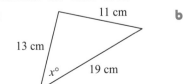

    b

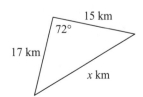

2 Find the value of x:

a

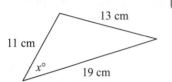

b

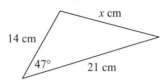

3 Find the unknown sides and angles:

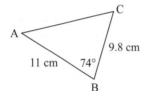

4 Find the area of quadrilateral ABCD:

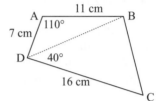

5 A vertical tree is growing on the side of a hill with slope of $10°$ to the horizontal. From a point 50 m downhill from the tree, the angle of elevation to the top of the tree is $18°$. Find the height of the tree.

6 From point A, the angle of elevation to the top of a tall building is $20°$. On walking 80 m towards the building the angle of elevation is now $23°$. How tall is the building?

7 Peter, Sue and Alix are sea-kayaking. Peter is 430 m from Sue on a bearing of $113°$ while Alix is on a bearing of $203°$ and a distance 310 m from Sue. Find the distance and bearing of Peter from Alix.

8 A rally car drives at 140 kmph for 45 minutes on a bearing of $032°$ and then 180 kmph for 40 minutes on a bearing $317°$. Find the distance and bearing of the car from its starting point.

9 You are given details of a triangle such that you could use either the cosine rule or the sine rule to find an unknown. Which rule should you use? Explain your answer.

10 Kady was asked to draw accurately a triangle, a rough sketch of which is shown below:

   a Use the cosine rule to find x.

   b What should Kady's response be?

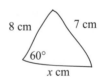

11 Frank, a soil contractor was given the following dimensions over the telephone:

The triangular garden plot ABC has angle CAB measuring $44°$, AC is 8 m long and BC is 6 m long. Soil to a depth of 10 cm is required.

   a Explain why Frank needed extra information from his client.

   b What is the maximum volume of soil needed if his client was not able to supply additional information?

Chapter 13

Periodic phenomena

Contents:

INTRODUCTION

Periodic phenomena occur in the physical world in:

- seasonal variations in our climate
- variations in the average maximum and minimum monthly temperatures at a place
- the number of daylight hours at a place
- variations in the depth of water in a harbour due to tidal movement
- the phases of the moon   etc.

Periodic phenomena also occur in the living world in animal populations.

These phenomena illustrate variable behaviour which is repeated over time. This repetition may be called periodic, oscillatory or cyclic in different situations.

In this topic we will consider various data sets which display periodic behaviour.

OPENING PROBLEM

 A Ferris wheel rotates at a constant speed. The wheel's radius is 10 m and the bottom of the wheel is 2 m above ground level. From a point in front of the wheel Andrew is watching a green light on the perimeter of the wheel. Andrew notices that the green light moves in a circle. He then considers how high the light is above ground level at two second intervals and draws a scatterplot of his results.

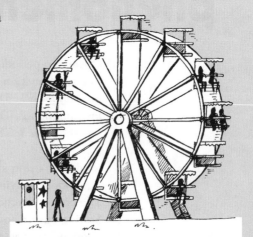

- What would his scatterplot look like?
- Could a known function be used to model the data?
- How could this function be used to find the light's position at any point in time?
- How could this function be used to find the time when the light is at a maximum (or minimum) height?
- What part of the function would indicate the time interval over which one complete cycle occurs?

Click on the icon to visit a simulation of the Ferris wheel.

You are to view the light on the Ferris wheel:

- from a position in front of the wheel
- from a side-on position
- from above the wheel.

DEMO

Now observe the graph of height above (or below) the wheel's axis over time as the wheel rotates at a constant rate.

A   OBSERVING PERIODIC BEHAVIOUR

Consider the table below which shows the mean monthly maximum temperature (^oC) for Cape Town.

Month	Jan	Feb	Mar	Apr	May	Jun	Jul	Aug	Sep	Oct	Nov	Dec
Temp	28	27	$25\frac{1}{2}$	22	$18\frac{1}{2}$	16	15	16	18	21	24	26

If this data is graphed using a scatterplot, assigning January $= 1$, February $= 2$ etc., for the 12 months of the year, the graph shown is obtained.

(**Note:** The points are not joined as interpolation has no meaning here.)

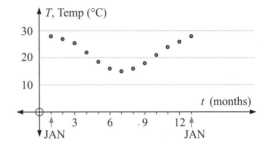

The temperature shows a variation from an average of 28^oC in January through a range of values across the months and the cycle will repeat itself for the next 12 months.

It is worthwhile noting that later we will be able to establish a function which approximately fits this set of points.

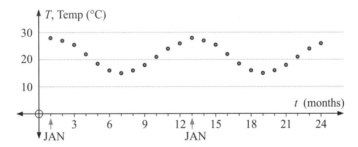

HISTORICAL NOTE

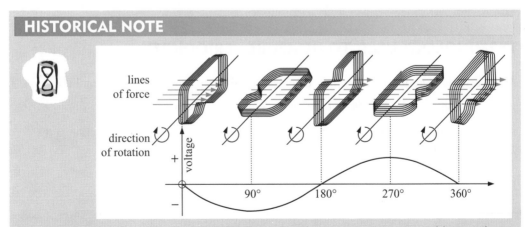

In 1831 **Michael Faraday** discovered that an electric current was generated by rotating a coil of wire in a magnetic field. The electric current produced showed a voltage which varied between positive and negative values as the coil rotated through 360°.

Graphs which have this basic shape where the cycle is repeated over and over are called **sine waves**.

GATHERING PERIODIC DATA

- Maximum and minimum monthly temperatures are obtained from appropriate internet sites. (e.g. http://www.bom.gov.au/silo/)
- Tidal details can be obtained from daily newspapers or http://www.ntf.flinders.edu.au/TEXT/TIDES/tides.html

ACTIVITY   **BICYCLE DATA**

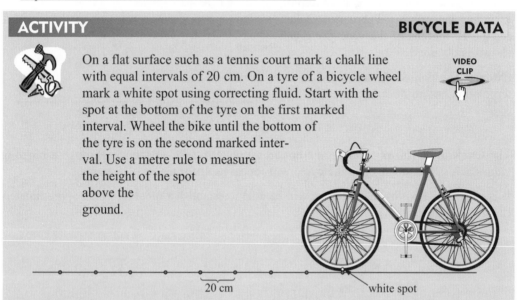

On a flat surface such as a tennis court mark a chalk line with equal intervals of 20 cm. On a tyre of a bicycle wheel mark a white spot using correcting fluid. Start with the spot at the bottom of the tyre on the first marked interval. Wheel the bike until the bottom of the tyre is on the second marked interval. Use a metre rule to measure the height of the spot above the ground.

a Record your result and continue until you have 20 or more data values.

b Plot this data on a set of axes.

c Are you entitled to fit a smooth curve through these points or should they be left as discrete points? Keep your results for future analysis.

TERMINOLOGY USED TO DESCRIBE PERIODICITY

A **periodic function** is one which repeats itself over and over in a horizontal direction.

The **period** of a periodic function is the length of one repetition or cycle.

If $f(x)$ is a periodic function with period p then $f(x + p) = f(x)$ for all x and p is the smallest positive value for this to be true.

Use a **graphing package** to examine the following function:

$$f : x \longmapsto x - [x]$$

GRAPHING PACKAGE

where $[x]$ is the largest integer less than or equal to x.

Is $f(x)$ periodic?   What is its period?

A **cardioid** is also an example of a periodic function. It is the curve traced out by a point on a circle as the circle moves along a flat surface.

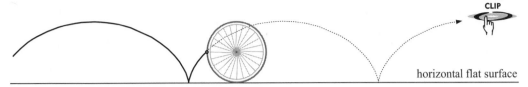

VIDEO CLIP

horizontal flat surface

Unfortunately the cardioid function cannot be written as $y = \ldots\ldots$ or $f(x) = \ldots\ldots$

In this course we are mainly concerned with periodic phenomena which show a wave pattern when graphed.

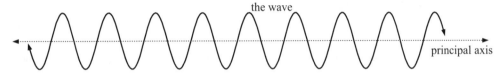

the wave

principal axis

The wave oscillates about a horizontal line called the **principal axis** (or **mean line**).

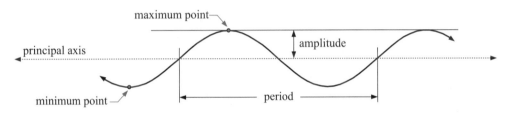

maximum point

principal axis

amplitude

minimum point

period

A **maximum point** occurs at the top of a crest and a **minimum point** at the bottom of a trough.

The **amplitude** is the distance between a maximum (or minimum) point and the principal axis.

EXERCISE 13A

1   For each set of data below, draw a scatterplot and decide whether or not the data exhibits approximately periodic behaviour.

a

x	0	1	2	3	4	5	6	7	8	9	10	11	12
y	0	1	1.4	1	0	-1	-1.4	-1	0	1	1.4	1	0

b

x	0	1	2	3	4
y	4	1	0	1	4

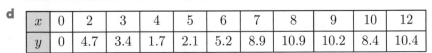

c

x	0	0.5	1.0	1.5	2.0	2.5	3.0	3.5
y	0	1.9	3.5	4.5	4.7	4.3	3.4	2.4

d

x	0	2	3	4	5	6	7	8	9	10	12
y	0	4.7	3.4	1.7	2.1	5.2	8.9	10.9	10.2	8.4	10.4

2 The following tabled values show actual bicycle wheel data as determined by the method described earlier.

Distance travelled (cm)	0	20	40	60	80	100	120	140	160
Height above ground (cm)	0	6	23	42	57	64	59	43	23

Distance travelled (cm)	180	200	220	240	260	280	300	320	340
Height above ground (cm)	7	1	5	27	40	55	63	60	44

Distance travelled (cm)	360	380	400
Height above ground (cm)	24	9	3

a Plot the graph of height against distance.

b Is the data periodic, and if so find estimates of:

    i   the equation of the principal axis   **ii**   the maximum value

   iii   the period   **iv**   the amplitude

c Is it reasonable to fit a curve to this data, or should we leave it as discrete points?

3 Which of these graphs show periodic behaviour?

a
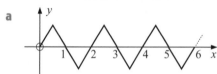

b
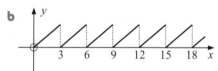

c
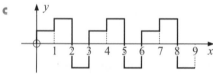

d

e
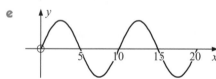

f
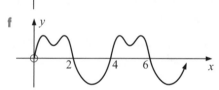

PERIODIC FUNCTIONS FROM CIRCLES

In previous studies of trigonometry we have only considered right angled triangles, or static situations, where the angle θ is fixed. However, when an object moves in a circle the situation is dynamic, with θ (the angle between the radius OP and the horizontal axis) continually changing.

Once again consider the Ferris wheel of radius 10 m revolving at constant speed.

The height of P, the point representing the person on the wheel relative to the principal axis at any given time, can be determined by using right angle triangle trigonometry.

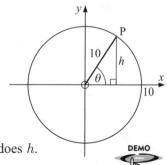

$$\text{As} \quad \sin\theta = \frac{h}{10}, \quad \text{then} \quad h = 10\sin\theta.$$

From this it is obvious that as time goes by θ changes and so does h.

So, h is a function of θ, but more importantly h is a function of time t.

DEMO

B ┃ THE SINE FUNCTION

Returning to the Ferris wheel we will examine the graph obtained when plotting the height of the light above or below the principal axis against the time in seconds. We do this for a wheel of radius 10 m which takes 100 seconds for one full revolution.

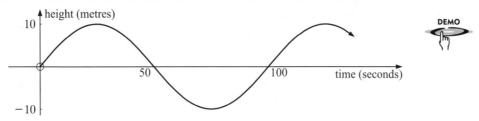

We observe that the amplitude is 10 and the period is 100 seconds.

The family of sine curves can have different amplitudes and different periods. We will examine such families in this section.

THE BASIC SINE CURVE

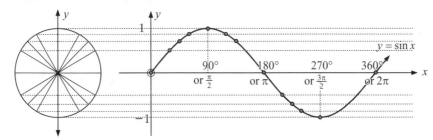

If we project the values of $\sin \theta$ from the unit circle to the set of axes on the right we obtain the graph of $y = \sin x$.

The wave of course can be continued beyond $0 \leqslant x \leqslant 2\pi$.

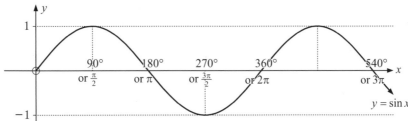

We expect the *period* to be 2π, as for example, the Ferris wheel repeats its positioning after one full revolution.

The *maximum* value is 1 and the *minimum* is -1 as $-1 \leqslant y \leqslant 1$ on the unit circle.

The *amplitude* is 1.

Use your **graphics calculator** or **graphing package** to obtain the graph of $y = \sin x$ to check these features.

When patterns of variation can be identified and quantified in terms of a formula (or equation) predictions may be made about behaviour in the future. Examples of this include tidal movement which can be predicted many months ahead, and the date of the full moon in the future.

INVESTIGATION 1   THE FAMILY $y = A\sin x$

What to do:

1 Use technology to graph on the same set of axes:

    a $y = \sin x$ and $y = 2\sin x$ **b** $y = \sin x$ and $y = 0.5\sin x$

    c $y = \sin x$ and $y = -\sin x$ $(A = -1)$

GRAPHING PACKAGE

If using a graphics calculator, make sure that the mode is set in **radians** and that your viewing window is appropriate.

2 For each of $y = \sin x$, $y = 2\sin x$, $y = 0.5\sin x$, $y = -\sin x$ record the maximum and minimum values and state the period and amplitude. If using a calculator use the built in functions to find the maximum and minimum values.

3 How does A affect the function $y = A\sin x$?

4 State the amplitude of: **a** $y = 3\sin x$ **b** $y = \sqrt{7}\sin x$ **c** $y = -2\sin x$

INVESTIGATION 2   THE FAMILY $y = \sin Bx$, $B > 0$

What to do:

1 Use technology to graph on the same set of axes:

    a $y = \sin x$ and $y = \sin 2x$ **b** $y = \sin x$ and $\sin(\frac{1}{2}x)$

2 For each of $y = \sin x$, $y = \sin 2x$, $y = \sin(\frac{1}{2}x)$ record the maximum and minimum values and state the period and amplitude.

GRAPHING PACKAGE

3 How does B affect the function $y = \sin Bx$?

4 State the period of:

    a $y = \sin 3x$ **b** $y = \sin(\frac{1}{3}x)$ **c** $y = \sin(1.2x)$ **d** $y = \sin Bx$

From the previous investigations you should have observed that:

- in $y = A\sin x$, A affects the amplitude and the amplitude is $|A|$
- in $y = \sin Bx$, $B > 0$, B affects the period and the period is $\dfrac{2\pi}{B}$.

Recall $|x|$ is the modulus of x, the size of x ignoring its sign.

The modulus sign ensures that the final answer is non-negative and this needs to be so for amplitudes.

Example 1

Without using technology sketch the graphs of:

a $y = 2\sin x$ **b** $y = -2\sin x$ for $0 \leqslant x \leqslant 2\pi$.

a   The amplitude is 2,   and the period is 2π.

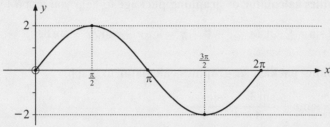

We place the 5 points as shown and fit the sine wave to them.

b   The amplitude is 2,   the period is 2π,   and it is the reflection of $y = 2\sin x$ in the x-axis.

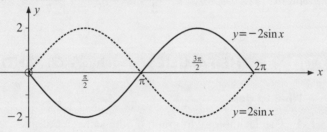

EXERCISE 13B.1

1   Without using technology draw the graphs of the following for $0 \leqslant x \leqslant 2\pi$:

   a $y = 3\sin x$ **b** $y = -3\sin x$ **c** $y = \frac{3}{2}\sin x$ **d** $y = -\frac{3}{2}\sin x$

Example 2

Without using technology sketch the graph of $y = \sin 2x$, $0 \leqslant x \leqslant 2\pi$.

The period is $\frac{2\pi}{2} = \pi$.

So, for example, the maximum values are π units apart.

> As $\sin 2x$ has half the period of $\sin x$, the first maximum is at $\frac{\pi}{4}$ not $\frac{\pi}{2}$.

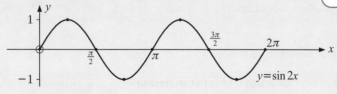

2   Without using technology sketch the graphs of the following for $0 \leqslant x \leqslant 3\pi$:

   a $y = \sin 3x$ **b** $y = \sin\left(\frac{x}{2}\right)$ **c** $y = \sin(-2x)$

3 State the period of:

    a $y = \sin 4x$ **b** $y = \sin(-4x)$ **c** $y = \sin\left(\frac{x}{3}\right)$ **d** $y = \sin(0.6x)$

4 Find B given that the function $y = \sin Bx$, $B > 0$ has period:

    a 5π **b** $\frac{2\pi}{3}$ **c** 12π **d** 4   **e** 100

5 Use a **graphics calculator** or **graphing package** to help you graph for $0 \leqslant x \leqslant 720$:

    a $y = 2\sin x + \sin 2x$ **b** $y = \sin x + \sin 2x + \sin 3x$ **c** $y = \dfrac{1}{\sin x}$

6 Use a **graphing package** or **graphics calculator** to graph:

    a $f(x) = \sin x + \dfrac{\sin 3x}{3} + \dfrac{\sin 5x}{5}$

    b $f(x) = \sin x + \dfrac{\sin 3x}{3} + \dfrac{\sin 5x}{5} + \dfrac{\sin 7x}{7} + \dfrac{\sin 9x}{9} + \dfrac{\sin 11x}{11}$

    Predict the graph of $f(x) = \sin x + \dfrac{\sin 3x}{3} + \dfrac{\sin 5x}{5} + \dfrac{\sin 7x}{7} + \ldots\ldots + \dfrac{\sin 1001x}{1001}$

INVESTIGATION 3   THE FAMILIES $y = \sin(x - C)$ AND $y = \sin x + D$

What to do:

1 Use technology to graph on the same set of axes:

    a $y = \sin x$ and $y = \sin(x - 2)$ GRAPHING PACKAGE

    b $y = \sin x$ and $y = \sin(x + 2)$

    c $y = \sin x$ and $y = \sin\left(x - \frac{\pi}{3}\right)$

2 For each of $y = \sin x$, $y = \sin(x - 2)$, $y = \sin(x + 2)$, $y = \sin\left(x - \frac{\pi}{3}\right)$ record the maximum and minimum values and state the period and amplitude.

3 What transformation moves $y = \sin x$ to $y = \sin(x - C)$?

4 Use technology to graph on the same set of axes:

    a $y = \sin x$ and $y = \sin x + 3$ **b** $y = \sin x$ and $y = \sin x - 2$

5 For each of $y = \sin x$, $y = \sin x + 3$ and $y = \sin x - 2$ record the maximum and minimum values and state the period and amplitude.

6 What transformation moves $y = \sin x$ to $y = \sin x + D$?

7 What transformation would move $y = \sin x$ to $y = \sin(x - C) + D$?

From **Investigation 3** we observe that:

- $y = \sin(x - C)$ is a **horizontal translation** of $y = \sin x$ through C units.
- $y = \sin x + D$ is a **vertical translation** of $y = \sin x$ through D units.
- $y = \sin(x - C) + D$ is a **translation** of $y = \sin x$ through vector $\begin{bmatrix} C \\ D \end{bmatrix}$.

Example 3

On the same set of axes graph for $0 \leqslant x \leqslant 4\pi$:

a $y = \sin x$ and $y = \sin(x - 1)$ **b** $y = \sin x$ and $y = \sin x - 1$

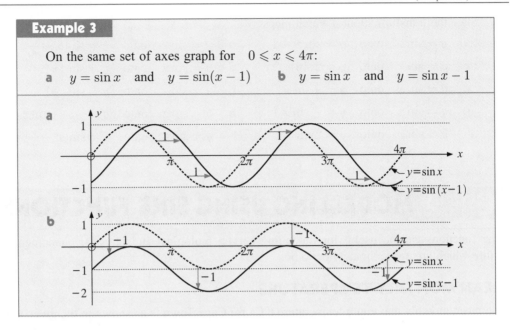

THE GENERAL SINE FUNCTION

$y = A \sin B(x - C) + D$ is called the **general sine function**.

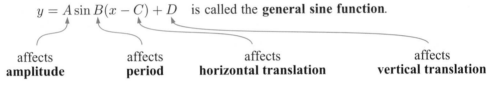

affects	affects	affects	affects
amplitude	**period**	**horizontal translation**	**vertical translation**

Note: The **principal axis** of $y = A \sin B(x - C) + D$ is $y = D$.

Consider $y = 2\sin 3(x - \frac{\pi}{4}) + 1$.   It is a translation of $y = 2 \sin 3x$ under $\begin{bmatrix} \frac{\pi}{4} \\ 1 \end{bmatrix}$.

So starting with $y = \sin x$ we would:

- first double the amplitude to produce $y = 2\sin x$,   then
- the period is divided by 3 to produce $y = 2\sin 3x$,   then
- translate $\begin{bmatrix} \frac{\pi}{4} \\ 1 \end{bmatrix}$ to produce $y = 2\sin 3\left(x - \frac{\pi}{4}\right) + 1$.

Actually doing these multiple transformations is unimportant compared with using the facts in modelling data which is periodic.

EXERCISE 13B.2

1   Draw sketch graphs of:

   a $y = \sin x - 2$ **b** $y = \sin(x - 2)$ **c** $y = \sin(x + 2)$

   d $y = \sin x + 2$ **e** $y = \sin(x + \frac{\pi}{4})$ **f** $y = \sin(x - \frac{\pi}{6}) + 1$

2   Check your answers to **1** using technology.

3   State the period of:

   a $y = \sin 5t$ **b** $y = \sin\left(\frac{t}{4}\right)$ **c** $y = \sin(-2t)$

GRAPHING PACKAGE

4   Find B where $B > 0$,   in $y = \sin Bx$ if the period is:

   a 3π **b** $\frac{\pi}{10}$ **c** 100π **d** 50

5 State the transformation(s) which maps:

a $y = \sin x$ onto $y = \sin x - 1$

b $y = \sin x$ onto $y = \sin(x - \frac{\pi}{4})$

c $y = \sin x$ onto $y = 2\sin x$

d $y = \sin x$ onto $y = \sin 4x$

e $y = \sin x$ onto $y = \frac{1}{2}\sin x$

f $y = \sin x$ onto $y = \sin\left(\frac{x}{4}\right)$

g $y = \sin x$ onto $y = -\sin x$

h $y = \sin x$ onto $y = -3 + \sin(x + 2)$

i $y = \sin x$ onto $y = 2\sin 3x$

j $y = \sin x$ onto $y = \sin(x - \frac{\pi}{3}) + 2$

C   MODELLING USING SINE FUNCTIONS

Sine functions can be useful for modelling certain biological and physical phenomena in nature which are approximately periodic.

MEAN MONTHLY TEMPERATURE

The mean monthly maximum temperature ($^\circ$C) for Cape Town is as shown in the given table

Month	Jan	Feb	Mar	Apr	May	Jun	Jul	Aug	Sep	Oct	Nov	Dec
Temp	28	27	$25\frac{1}{2}$	22	$18\frac{1}{2}$	16	15	16	18	$21\frac{1}{2}$	24	26

and the graph over a two year period is as follows:

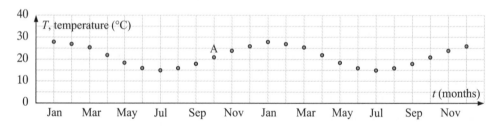

We will attempt to model this data   to $y = A\sin B(x - C) + D$

i.e., $T = A\sin B(t - C) + D$.

Now the period is 12 months, so $\dfrac{2\pi}{B} = 12$ and $\therefore$ $B = \frac{\pi}{6}$.

The amplitude $= \dfrac{\text{max.} - \text{min.}}{2} \doteqdot \dfrac{28 - 15}{2} \doteqdot 6.5$, so $A = 6.5$.

The principal axis is midway between max. and min., $\therefore$ $D = \dfrac{28 + 15}{2} = 21.5$.

So, the model is $T = 6.5\sin\frac{\pi}{6}(t - C) + 21.5$

Viewing A on the original graph as $(10, 21.5)$ means that C is 10.

So $T \doteqdot 6.5\sin\frac{\pi}{6}(t - 10) + 21.5$ is the model.

The model is therefore $T = 6.5\sin\frac{\pi}{6}(t - 10) + 21.5$ and is superimposed on the original data as follows.

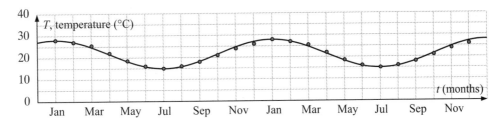

TIDAL MODELS

At Juneau, in Alaska, on one day it was noticed that:

> high tide occurred at 1.18 pm
>
> low tides occurred at 6.46 am and at 7.13 pm,

and on the next day   high tides occurred at 1.31 am and 2.09 pm

> low tides occurred at 7.30 am and 7.57 pm.

Suppose high tide corresponds to 1 and low tide to -1.

Plotting these times (where t is the time after midnight before the first low tide), we get:

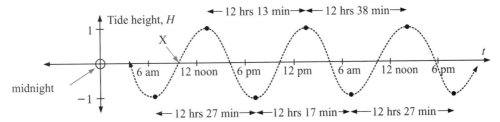

We will attempt to model this periodic data to $y = A \sin B(x - C) + D$

or $H = A \sin B(t - C) + D.$

Since the principal axis appears to be $H = 0$,   then $D = 0$.

The amplitude is 1,   so $A = 1$.

The graph shows that the 'average' period is about 12 hours 24 min $\doteqdot$ 12.4 hours.

But the period is $\dfrac{2\pi}{B}$. $\therefore$ $\dfrac{2\pi}{B} \doteqdot 12.4$ and so $B \doteqdot \dfrac{2\pi}{12.4} \doteqdot 0.507$.

The model is now $H \doteqdot \sin 0.507(t - C)$ and so we have to find C.

Point X is midway between a maximum and a minimum value,

i.e., between $t = 6.77$ and $t = 13.3$ $\therefore$ $C = \dfrac{13.3 + 6.77}{2} \doteqdot 10.0$.

So, finally the model is $H \doteqdot \sin 0.507(t - 10.04)$.

Below is our original graph of seven plotted points and our model which attempts to fit them.

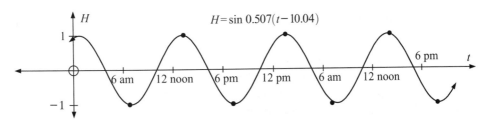

Use your **graphics calculator** to check this result.

Times must be given in hours after midnight,

i.e., $(6.77, -1)$, $(13.3, 1)$, $(19.22, -1)$,   etc.

EXERCISE 13C

1 Below is a table which shows the mean monthly maximum temperature (^oC) for a city in Greece.

Month	Jan	Feb	Mar	Apr	May	Jun	July	Aug	Sept	Oct	Nov	Dec
Temp	15	14	15	18	21	25	27	26	24	20	18	16

    a A sine function of the form $T \doteq A \sin B(t - C) + D$ is used to model the data. Find good estimates of the constants A, B, C and D without using technology. Use Jan $\equiv 1$, Feb $\equiv 2$, etc.

    b Use technology to check your answer to **a**. How well does your model fit?

2 The data in the table is of the mean monthly temperature for Christchurch.

Month	Jan	Feb	Mar	Apr	May	Jun	July	Aug	Sept	Oct	Nov	Dec
Temp	15	16	$14\frac{1}{2}$	12	10	$7\frac{1}{2}$	7	$7\frac{1}{2}$	$8\frac{1}{2}$	$10\frac{1}{2}$	$12\frac{1}{2}$	14

    a Find a sine model for this data in the form $T \doteq A \sin B(t - C) + D$.   Do not use technology and assume Jan $\equiv 1$, Feb $\equiv 2$, etc.

    b Use technology to check your answer to **a**.

3 At the Mawson base in Antarctica, the mean monthly temperatures for the last 30 years are as follows:

Month	Jan	Feb	Mar	Apr	May	Jun	July	Aug	Sept	Oct	Nov	Dec
Temp	0	−4	−10	−15	−16	−17	−18	−19	−17	−13	−6	−1

Find a sine model for this data using your calculator. Use Jan $\equiv 1$, Feb $\equiv 2$, etc. How appropriate is the model?

4 In Canada's Bay of Fundy, some of the largest tides are observed. The difference between high and low tide is 14 metres and the average time difference between high tides is about 12.4 hours.

    a Find a sine model for the height of the tide H, in terms of the time t.

    b Sketch the graph of the model over one period.

5 Revisit the **Opening Problem** on page **264**.

The wheel takes 100 seconds to complete one revolution. Find the sine model which gives the height of the light above the ground at any point in time. Assume at time $t = 0$, the light is at its lowest point.

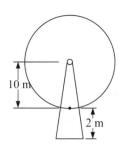

D   EQUATIONS INVOLVING SINE

Linear equations such as $2x + 3 = 11$ have exactly one solution and quadratic equations, i.e., equations of the form $ax^2 + bx + c = 0$, $a \neq 0$ have at most two real solutions.

Trigonometric equations generally have infinitely many solutions unless a restrictive domain such as $0 \leqslant x \leqslant 3\pi$ is given.

We will examine solving sine equations using:
- preprepared graphs
- technology
- algebraic methods.

For the Ferris Wheel **Opening Problem** the model is $H = 10 \sin \frac{\pi}{50}(t - 25) + 12$.

We can easily check this by substituting $t = 0, 25, 50, 75$

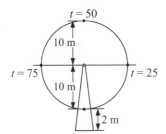

$H(0) = 10 \sin\left(-\frac{\pi}{2}\right) + 12 = -10 + 12 = 2$ ✓

$H(25) = 10 \sin 0 + 12 = 12$ ✓

$H(50) = 10 \sin\left(\frac{\pi}{2}\right) + 12 = 22$ ✓

etc.

However, we may be interested in the times when the light is 16 m above the ground, which means that we need to solve the equation

$10 \sin \frac{\pi}{50}(t - 25) + 12 = 16$ which is of course a **sine equation**.

GRAPHICAL SOLUTION OF SINE EQUATIONS

Sometimes simple sine graphs on grid paper are available and estimates of solutions can be obtained.

To solve $\sin x = 0.3$, we observe where the horizontal line $y = 0.3$ meets the graph $y = \sin x$.

EXERCISE 13D.1

1

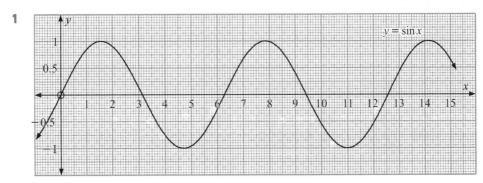

Use the graph of $y = \sin x$ to find correct to 1 decimal place the solutions of:

a $\sin x = 0.3$ for $0 \leqslant x \leqslant 15$

b $\sin x = -0.4$ for $5 \leqslant x \leqslant 15$

2

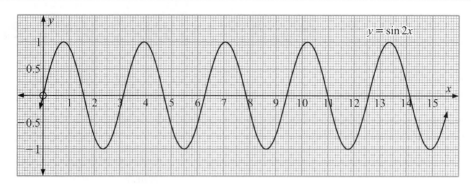

Use the graph of $y = \sin 2x$ to find correct to 1 decimal place the solutions of:

a $\sin 2x = 0.7$ **b** $\sin 2x = -0.3$

SOLVING SINE EQUATIONS USING TECHNOLOGY

To solve $\sin x = 0.3$ we could use either a **graphing package** or **graphics calculator**.

If using a graphics calculator make sure the **mode** is set to **radians**.

Graph $Y_1 = \sin X$ and $Y_2 = 0.3$

Use the built-in functions to find the first two points of intersection. These are $X = 0.3047$ and $X = 2.8369$.

So, as $\sin x$ has period 2π, the general solution is

$$x = \left. \begin{array}{c} 0.3047 \\ 2.8369 \end{array} \right\} + k2\pi, \quad k \text{ any integer.}$$

Note: We are entitled to substitute any integers for k,   i.e., $k = 0, \pm 1, \pm 2$, etc.

For a restricted domain like $0 \leqslant x \leqslant 15$ the solutions would be

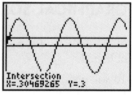

$$x = 0.3047, \quad 2.8369, \quad 6.5879, \quad 9.1201, \quad 12.8711, \quad \overset{\displaystyle\nearrow}{15.4033}$$
$$\qquad\qquad\qquad\quad \underset{k=1}{\uparrow} \qquad \underset{k=1}{\uparrow} \qquad \underset{k=2}{\uparrow} \qquad \underset{k=2}{\uparrow}$$

So, we have five solutions in this domain.

EXERCISE 13D.2

1   Use technology to solve for $0 \leqslant x \leqslant 8$, giving answers to 4 sig. figs.

    a $\sin x = 0.414$ **b** $\sin x = -0.673$ **c** $\sin x = 1.289$

    d $\sin 2x = 0.162$ **e** $\sin\left(\frac{x}{2}\right) = -0.606$ **f** $\sin(x + 2) = 0.0652$

    g $\sin(x - 1.3) = 0.866$ **h** $\sin\left(x - \frac{\pi}{3}\right) = 0.7063$ **i** $\sin\left(\frac{2x}{3}\right) = -0.9367$

SOLVING SINE EQUATIONS ALGEBRAICALLY (ANALYTICAL SOLUTIONS)

Using a calculator we get approximate decimal solutions to trigonometric equations.

Sometimes exact solutions are needed in terms of π, and these arise when the solutions are multiples of $\frac{\pi}{6}$ or $\frac{\pi}{4}$.

Reminder:

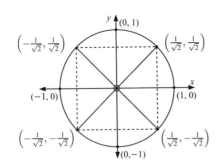
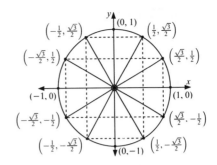

Example 4

Use the unit circle to find the exact solutions of x, $0 \leqslant x \leqslant 3\pi$ for:

a $\sin x = -\frac{1}{2}$ **b** $\sin 2x = -\frac{1}{2}$ **c** $\sin\left(x - \frac{\pi}{6}\right) = -\frac{1}{2}$

---

a $\sin x = -\frac{1}{2}$,   so from the unit circle

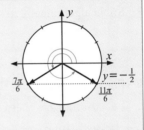

$$x = \left. \begin{array}{c} \frac{7\pi}{6} \\[2mm] \frac{11\pi}{6} \end{array} \right\} + k2\pi, \quad k \text{ an integer}$$

$\therefore \quad x = \dfrac{7\pi}{6}, \quad \dfrac{11\pi}{6}, \quad \dfrac{19\pi}{6}$ i.e.,   2 solutions

$\qquad\qquad\quad \uparrow \qquad\quad \uparrow \qquad\quad \uparrow$
$\qquad\qquad k = 0 \quad k = 0 \quad k = 1$

Substituting $k = 1, 2, 3, \ldots$ gives answers outside the required domain.
Likewise $k = -1, -2, \ldots$ gives answers outside the required domain.

b $\sin 2x = -\frac{1}{2}$ is solved exactly the same way only this time

$$2x = \left. \begin{array}{c} \frac{7\pi}{6} \\[2mm] \frac{11\pi}{6} \end{array} \right\} + k2\pi, \quad k \text{ an integer}$$

$$\therefore \quad x = \left. \begin{array}{c} \frac{7\pi}{12} \\[2mm] \frac{11\pi}{12} \end{array} \right\} + k\pi \qquad \{\text{divide each term by 2}\}$$

$\therefore \quad x = \frac{7\pi}{12}, \frac{11\pi}{12}, \frac{19\pi}{12}, \frac{23\pi}{12}, \frac{31\pi}{12}, \frac{35\pi}{12}$ $\{$obtained by letting $k = 0, 1, 2, 3\}$

c $\sin\left(x - \frac{\pi}{6}\right) = -\frac{1}{2}$ is solved the same way, but this time

> Don't forget to try
> $k = -1, -2$, etc. as
> sometimes we get
> solutions from them.

$$x - \frac{\pi}{6} = \left. \begin{array}{c} \frac{7\pi}{6} \\[2mm] \frac{11\pi}{6} \end{array} \right\} + k2\pi$$

$$\therefore \quad x = \left. \begin{array}{c} \frac{8\pi}{6} \\[2mm] 2\pi \end{array} \right\} + k2\pi \qquad \{\text{adding } \frac{\pi}{6} \text{ to both sides}\}$$

$\therefore \quad x = \quad \dfrac{4\pi}{3}, \qquad 2\pi, \qquad \dfrac{10\pi}{3} \quad \text{too big,} \qquad 0$

$\qquad\qquad\quad \uparrow \qquad\quad \uparrow \qquad\quad \uparrow \qquad\qquad\qquad \uparrow$
$\qquad\qquad k = 0 \quad\ k = 0 \quad\ k = 1 \qquad\qquad\qquad k = -1$

So, $x = 0, \quad \frac{4\pi}{3}, \quad 2\pi$ which is *three* solutions.

EXERCISE 13D.3

1 List the possible answers if k is an integer and:

    a $x = \frac{\pi}{6} + k2\pi, \quad 0 \leqslant x \leqslant 6\pi$
        b $x = -\frac{\pi}{3} + k2\pi, \quad -2\pi \leqslant x \leqslant 2\pi$

    c $x = -\frac{\pi}{2} + k\pi, \quad -4\pi \leqslant x \leqslant 4\pi$
        d $x = \frac{5\pi}{6} + k\left(\frac{\pi}{2}\right), \quad 0 \leqslant x \leqslant 4\pi$

2 Solve algebraically giving answers in terms of π:

    a $2\sin x = 1, \quad 0 \leqslant x \leqslant 6\pi$
        b $\sqrt{2}\sin x = 1, \quad 0 \leqslant x \leqslant 4\pi$

    c $2\sin x - 1 = 0, \quad -2\pi \leqslant x \leqslant 2\pi$
        d $\sqrt{2}\sin x - 1 = 0, \quad -4\pi \leqslant x \leqslant 0$

    e $\sin x = -1, \quad 0 \leqslant x \leqslant 6\pi$
        f $\sin^2 x = 1, \quad 0 \leqslant x \leqslant 4\pi$

    g $\sin 2x = \frac{1}{2}, \quad 0 \leqslant x \leqslant 3\pi$
        h $\sqrt{2}\sin 3x + 1 = 0, \quad 0 \leqslant x \leqslant 2\pi$

    i $2\sin 2x - \sqrt{3} = 0, \quad 0 \leqslant x \leqslant 3\pi$
        j $2\sin\left(x + \frac{\pi}{3}\right) = 1, \quad -3\pi \leqslant x \leqslant 3\pi$

3 Solve algebraically giving answers in terms of π, for $-2\pi \leqslant x \leqslant 2\pi$:

    a $\sin^2 x + \sin x - 2 = 0$
        b $4\sin^2 x = 3$

    c $2\sin^2 x = \sin x + 1$
        d $2\sin^2 x + 1 = 3\sin x$

4 Find the zeros of: (The zeros of $y = \sin 2x$ are the solutions of $\sin 2x = 0$.)

    a $y = \sin 2x$ between 0 and π (inclusive)

    b $y = \sin(x - \frac{\pi}{4})$ between 0 and 3π (inclusive)

USING SINE MODELS

Example 5

The height $h(t)$ metres of the tide above mean sea level on January 24th at Cape Town is modelled approximately by $h(t) = 3\sin\left(\frac{\pi t}{6}\right)$ where t is the number of hours after midnight.

    a Graph $y = h(t)$ for $0 \leqslant t \leqslant 24$.

    b When was high tide and what was the maximum height?

    c What was the height at 2 pm?

    d If a ship can cross the harbour provided the tide is at least 2 m above mean sea level, when is crossing possible on January 24?

    a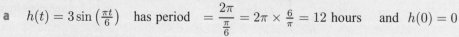

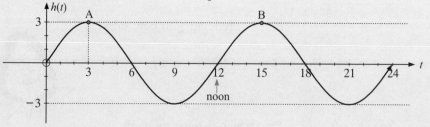

b High tide is at 3 am and 3 pm, and maximum height is 3 m above the mean as seen at points A and B.

c At 2 pm, $t = 14$ and $h(14) = 3\sin\left(\frac{14\pi}{6}\right) \doteqdot 2.60$ (3 significant figures)

So the tide is 2.6 m above the mean.

d

We need to solve $h(t) = 2$ i.e., $3\sin\left(\frac{\pi t}{6}\right) = 2$.

Using a graphics calculator with $Y_1 = 3\sin\left(\frac{\pi X}{6}\right)$ and $Y_2 = 2$

we obtain $t_1 = 1.39$, $t_2 = 4.61$, $t_3 = 13.39$, $t_4 = 16.61$

or you could **trace** across the graph to find these values.

Now 1.39 hours = 1 hour 23 minutes, etc.

$\therefore$ can cross between 1:23 am and 4:37 am or 1:23 pm and 4:37 pm.

EXERCISE 13D.4

1 The population estimate of grass-hoppers after t weeks where $0 \leqslant t \leqslant 12$ is given by $P(t) = 7500 + 3000\sin\left(\frac{\pi t}{8}\right)$.

  a What was: **i** the initial estimate **ii** the estimate after 5 weeks?

  b What was the greatest population size over this interval and when did it occur?

  c When is the population **i** 9000 **ii** 6000?

  d During what time interval(s) does the population size exceed 10 000?

2 The model for the height of a light on a Ferris Wheel is $H(t) = 20 - 19\sin\left(\frac{2\pi t}{3}\right)$, where H is the height in metres above the ground, t is in minutes.

  a Where is the light at time $t = 0$?

  b At what time was the light at its lowest in the first revolution of the wheel?

  c How long does the wheel take to complete one revolution?

  d Sketch the graph of the $H(t)$ function over one revolution.

3 The population of water buffalo is given by $P(t) = 400 + 250\sin\left(\frac{\pi t}{2}\right)$ where t is the number of years since the first estimate was made.

  a What was the initial estimate?

  b What was the population size after:

    i 6 months **ii** two years?

  c Find $P(1)$. What is the significance of this value?

  d Find the smallest population size and when it first occurs.

  e Find the first time interval when the herd exceeds 500.

4 Over a 28 day period, the cost per litre of petrol is modelled by

$C(t) = 9.2 \sin \frac{\pi}{7}(t-4) + 107.8$ cents/L.

a True or false?

  i "The cost/litre oscillates about 107.8 cents with maximum price \$1.17."

  ii "Every 14 days, the cycle repeats itself."

b What is the cost at day 7?

c On what days was the petrol priced at \$1.10/L?

d What is the minimum cost per litre and when does it occur?

E   THE COSINE FUNCTION

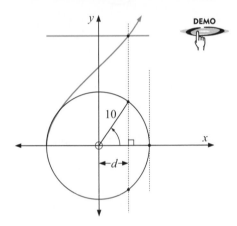

DEMO

We return to the Ferris wheel to see the cosine function being generated.

Click on the icon to inspect a simulation of the view from above the wheel.

The graph being generated over time is a **cosine function**.

This is no surprise as $\cos \theta = \dfrac{d}{10}$

i.e., $d = 10 \cos \theta.$

DEMO

Now view the relationship between the sine and cosine functions.

Notice that the functions are identical in shape, but the cosine function is $\frac{\pi}{2}$ units left of the sine function under a horizontal translation.

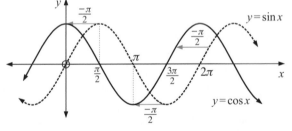

This suggests that $\cos x = \sin \left(x + \frac{\pi}{2}\right).$

Use your graphing package or graphics calculator to check this by graphing $y = \cos x$ and $y = \sin \left(x + \frac{\pi}{2}\right).$

GRAPHING PACKAGE

Example 6

On the same set of axes graph: $y = \cos x$ and $y = \cos \left(x - \frac{\pi}{3}\right)$

$y = \cos \left(x - \frac{\pi}{3}\right)$ comes from $y = \cos x$ under a horizontal translation through $\frac{\pi}{3}$.

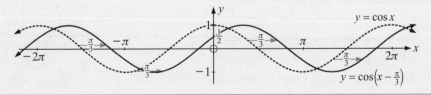

Note: You could use technology to help draw your sketch graphs as in **Example 6**.

EXERCISE 13E

1 Given the graph of $y = \cos x$, sketch the graphs of:

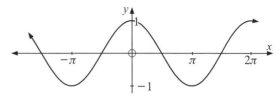

  a $y = \cos x + 2$ **b** $y = \cos x - 1$ **c** $y = \cos(x - \frac{\pi}{4})$

  d $y = \cos(x + \frac{\pi}{6})$ **e** $y = \frac{2}{3}\cos x$ **f** $y = \frac{3}{2}\cos x$

  g $y = -\cos x$ **h** $y = \cos(x - \frac{\pi}{6}) + 1$ **i** $y = \cos(x + \frac{\pi}{4}) - 1$

  j $y = \cos 2x$ **k** $y = \cos\left(\frac{x}{2}\right)$ **l** $y = 3\cos 2x$

2 Without graphing them, state the periods of:

  a $y = \cos 3x$ **b** $y = \cos\left(\frac{x}{3}\right)$ **c** $y = \cos\left(\frac{\pi}{50}x\right)$

3 The general cosine function is $y = A \cos B(x - C) + D$.

State the geometrical significance of A, B, C and D.

4 For the following graphs, find the cosine function representing them:

  a

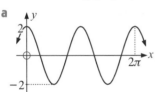

  b

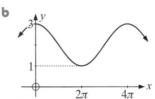

  c

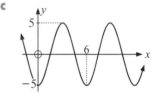

F SOLVING COSINE EQUATIONS

We could use a graph to find approximate solutions for trigonometric equations such as $\cos\theta = 0.4$ for $0 \leqslant \theta \leqslant 10$ radians. We draw the graph of $y = \cos\theta$ for $0 \leqslant \theta \leqslant 10$ and find all values of θ where the y-coordinate of any point of the graph is 0.4.

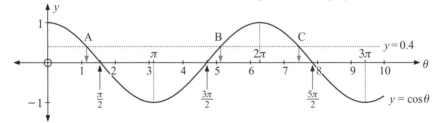

$y = 0.4$ meets $y = \cos\theta$ at A, B and C and hence $\theta \doteqdot 1.2$, 5.1 or 7.4.

So, the solutions of $\cos\theta = 0.4$ for $0 \leqslant \theta \leqslant 10$ radians are 1.2, 5.1 and 7.4.

DISCUSSION

- How many solutions does $\cos\theta = 1.3$ have for $0 \leqslant \theta \leqslant 10$?
- How many solutions does $\cos\theta = 0.4$ have with no restrictions for θ?

Once again we could solve cosine equations: • from given graphs   • using technology

                                                • algebraically.

The techniques are the same as those used for sine equations.

EXERCISE 13F

1

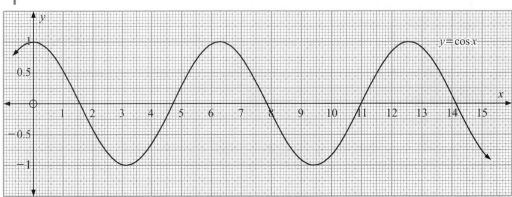

Use the graph of $y = \cos x$ to find to 1 decimal place, the approximate solutions of:

  a $\cos x = 0.4, \ x \in [0, 10]$ **b** $\cos x = -0.3, \ x \in [4, 12]$

2 Use technology to solve the following to 3 decimal places:

  a $\cos x = 0.561, \ x \in [0, 10]$ **b** $\cos 2x = 0.782, \ x \in [0, 6]$

  c $\cos(x - 1.3) = -0.609, \ x \in [0, 12]$ **d** $4\cos 3x + 1 = 0, \ x \in [0, 5]$

Example 7

Find exact solutions of $\sqrt{2}\cos\left(x - \frac{3\pi}{4}\right) + 1 = 0$ for $x \in [0, 6\pi]$.

As $\sqrt{2}\cos\left(x - \frac{3\pi}{4}\right) + 1 = 0$ then $\sqrt{2}\cos\left(x - \frac{3\pi}{4}\right) = -1$

$$\therefore \ \cos\left(x - \tfrac{3\pi}{4}\right) = -\tfrac{1}{\sqrt{2}}$$

We recognise $\frac{1}{\sqrt{2}}$ as a special

fraction (for multiples of $\frac{\pi}{4}$)

$$\therefore \quad x - \frac{3\pi}{4} = \left. \begin{matrix} \frac{3\pi}{4} \\ \frac{5\pi}{4} \end{matrix} \right\} + k2\pi$$

$$\therefore \quad x = \left. \begin{matrix} \frac{3\pi}{2} \\ 2\pi \end{matrix} \right\} + k2\pi$$

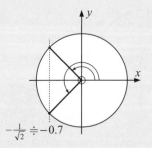

$-\frac{1}{\sqrt{2}} \doteqdot -0.7$

If $k = -1$, $x = -\frac{\pi}{2}$ or 0.   If $k = 0$, $x = \frac{3\pi}{2}$ or 2π.

If $k = 1$, $x = \frac{7\pi}{2}$ or 4π.   If $k = 2$, $x = \frac{11\pi}{2}$ or 6π.

If $k = 3$,   the answers are greater than 6π.

So, the solutions are: $x = 0, \frac{3\pi}{2}, 2\pi, \frac{7\pi}{2}, 4\pi, \frac{11\pi}{2}$ or 6π.

3 Find the exact solutions of:

a $\cos x = \frac{1}{\sqrt{2}}$, $x \in [0, 4\pi]$

b $\cos x = -\frac{1}{2}$, $x \in [0, 5\pi]$

c $2\cos x + \sqrt{3} = 0$, $x \in [0, 3\pi]$

d $\cos\left(x - \frac{2\pi}{3}\right) = \frac{1}{2}$, $x \in [-2\pi, 2\pi]$

e $\sqrt{2}\cos\left(x - \frac{\pi}{4}\right) + 1 = 0$, $x \in [0, 3\pi]$

f $\cos 2x + 1 = 0$, $x \in [0, 2\pi]$

4 A paint spot X lies on the outer rim of the wheel of a paddle-steamer. The wheel has radius 3 m and as it rotates at a constant rate, X is seen entering the water every 4 seconds. H is the distance of X above the bottom of the boat. At time $t = 0$, X is at its highest point.

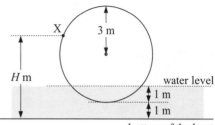

a Find the cosine model,
   $H(t) = A\cos B(t - C) + D$.

b At what time does X first enter the water?

G   TRIGONOMETRIC RELATIONSHIPS

There are a vast number of trigonometric relationships. However, we will use only a few of them. First of all we will look at how to simplify trigonometric expressions.

SIMPLIFYING TRIGONOMETRIC EXPRESSIONS

Since for a given angle θ, $\sin\theta$ and $\cos\theta$ are real numbers, the algebra of trigonometry is identical to the algebra of real numbers.

Consequently, expressions like $2\sin\theta + 3\sin\theta$ compare with $2x + 3x$ when we wish to do simplification.   So, $2\sin\theta + 3\sin\theta = 5\sin\theta$.

Example 8
Simplify: **a** $3\cos\theta + 4\cos\theta$ **b** $\sin\alpha - 3\sin\alpha$
a $\quad 3\cos\theta + 4\cos\theta$ $\quad$ **b** $\quad \sin\alpha - 3\sin\alpha$ $\quad = 7\cos\theta$ $\qquad\qquad\quad = -2\sin\alpha$ $\quad \{3x + 4x = 7x\}$ $\qquad\quad \{x - 3x = -2x\}$

EXERCISE 13G.1

1 Simplify:

a $\sin\theta + \sin\theta$

b $2\cos\theta + \cos\theta$

c $3\sin\theta - \sin\theta$

d $3\sin\theta - 2\sin\theta$

e $\cos\theta - 3\cos\theta$

f $2\cos\theta - 5\cos\theta$

To simplify more complicated trigonometric expressions involving $\sin\theta$ and $\cos\theta$ we often use

$$\sin^2\theta + \cos^2\theta = 1 \qquad \text{(See pages } \textbf{230} \text{ and } \textbf{231}\text{)}$$

It is worth graphing $y = \sin^2 \theta$, $y = \cos^2 \theta$ and $y = \sin^2 \theta + \cos^2 \theta$ using technology.

Notice that:

$\sin^2 \theta + \cos^2 \theta$	could be replaced by	1
1	could be replaced by	$\sin^2 \theta + \cos^2 \theta$
$\sin^2 \theta$	could be replaced by	$1 - \cos^2 \theta$
$1 - \cos^2 \theta$	could be replaced by	$\sin^2 \theta$
$\cos^2 \theta$	could be replaced by	$1 - \sin^2 \theta$
$1 - \sin^2 \theta$	could be replaced by	$\cos^2 \theta$.

GRAPHING
PACKAGE

Example 9

Simplify:

a $2 - 2\cos^2 \theta$

b $\sin^2 \theta \cos \theta + \cos^3 \theta$

a $\quad 2 - 2\cos^2 \theta$
$= 2(1 - \cos^2 \theta)$
$= 2\sin^2 \theta$
$\{\cos^2 \theta + \sin^2 \theta = 1\}$

b $\quad \sin^2 \theta \cos \theta + \cos^3 \theta$
$= \cos \theta \, (\sin^2 \theta + \cos^2 \theta)$
$= \cos \theta \times 1$
$= \cos \theta$

2 Simplify:

a $3\sin^2 \theta + 3\cos^2 \theta$

b $-2\sin^2 \theta - 2\cos^2 \theta$

c $-\cos^2 \theta - \sin^2 \theta$

d $3 - 3\sin^2 \theta$

e $4 - 4\cos^2 \theta$

f $\sin^3 \theta + \sin \theta \cos^2 \theta$

g $\cos^2 \theta - 1$

h $\sin^2 \theta - 1$

i $2\cos^2 \theta - 2$

j $\dfrac{1 - \sin^2 \theta}{\cos^2 \theta}$

k $\dfrac{1 - \cos^2 \theta}{\sin \theta}$

l $\dfrac{\cos^2 \theta - 1}{-\sin \theta}$

As with ordinary algebraic expressions we can **expand** trigonometric products.

Sometimes simplication of these expansions is possible.

$\sin \theta$ and $\cos \theta$ are simply numbers and so the algebra of trigonometry is exactly the same as ordinary algebra.

Example 10

Expand and simplify if possible: $(\cos \theta - \sin \theta)^2$

$(\cos \theta - \sin \theta)^2$
$= \cos^2 \theta - 2\cos \theta \sin \theta + \sin^2 \theta$ $\{$using $(a - b)^2 = a^2 - 2ab + b^2\}$
$= \cos^2 \theta + \sin^2 \theta - 2\cos \theta \sin \theta$
$= 1 - 2\cos \theta \sin \theta$

3 Expand and simplify if possible:

a $(1 + \sin \theta)^2$

b $(\sin \alpha - 2)^2$

c $(\cos \alpha - 1)^2$

d $(\sin \alpha + \cos \alpha)^2$

e $(\sin \beta - \cos \beta)^2$

f $-(2 - \cos \alpha)^2$

Factorisation of trigonometric expressions is also possible.

Example 11

Factorise: **a** $\cos^2 \alpha - \sin^2 \alpha$ **b** $\sin^2 \theta - 3\sin \theta + 2$

a $\cos^2 \alpha - \sin^2 \alpha$
$= (\cos \alpha + \sin \alpha)(\cos \alpha - \sin \alpha)$
$\{$as $a^2 - b^2 = (a+b)(a-b)\}$

b $\sin^2 \theta - 3\sin \theta + 2$
$= (\sin \theta - 2)(\sin \theta - 1)$
as $\{x^2 - 3x + 2 = (x-2)(x-1)\}$

4   Factorise:

   a $1 - \sin^2 \theta$ **b** $\sin^2 \alpha - \cos^2 \alpha$ **c** $\cos^2 \alpha - 1$

   d $2\sin^2 \beta - \sin \beta$ **e** $2\cos \phi + 3\cos^2 \phi$ **f** $3\sin^2 \theta - 6\sin \theta$

   g $\sin^2 \theta + 5\sin \theta + 6$ **h** $2\cos^2 \theta + 7\cos \theta + 3$ **i** $6\cos^2 \alpha - \cos \alpha - 1$

Example 12

Simplify: **a** $\dfrac{2 - 2\cos^2 \theta}{1 + \cos \theta}$ **b** $\dfrac{\cos \theta - \sin \theta}{\cos^2 \theta - \sin^2 \theta}$

a $\dfrac{2 - 2\cos^2 \theta}{1 + \cos \theta}$

$= \dfrac{2(1 - \cos^2 \theta)}{1 + \cos \theta}$

$= \dfrac{2(1 + \cos \theta)(1 - \cos \theta)}{(1 + \cos \theta)}$

$= 2(1 - \cos \theta)$

b $\dfrac{\cos \theta - \sin \theta}{\cos^2 \theta - \sin^2 \theta}$

$= \dfrac{(\cos \theta - \sin \theta)}{(\cos \theta + \sin \theta)(\cos \theta - \sin \theta)}$

$= \dfrac{1}{\cos \theta + \sin \theta}$

5   Simplify:

   a $\dfrac{1 - \sin^2 \alpha}{1 - \sin \alpha}$ **b** $\dfrac{\cos^2 \beta - 1}{\cos \beta + 1}$ **c** $\dfrac{\cos^2 \phi - \sin^2 \phi}{\cos \phi + \sin \phi}$

   d $\dfrac{\cos^2 \phi - \sin^2 \phi}{\cos \phi - \sin \phi}$ **e** $\dfrac{\sin \alpha + \cos \alpha}{\sin^2 \alpha - \cos^2 \alpha}$ **f** $\dfrac{3 - 3\sin^2 \theta}{6\cos \theta}$

6   Show that:

   a $(\cos \theta + \sin \theta)^2 + (\cos \theta - \sin \theta)^2$ simplifies to 2

   b $(2\sin \theta + 3\cos \theta)^2 + (3\sin \theta - 2\cos \theta)^2$ simplifies to 13

   c $(1 - \cos \theta)\left(1 + \dfrac{1}{\cos \theta}\right)$ simplifies to $\dfrac{\sin^2 \theta}{\cos \theta}$

   d $\left(1 + \dfrac{1}{\sin \theta}\right)(\sin \theta - \sin^2 \theta)$ simplifies to $\cos^2 \theta$

   e $\dfrac{\sin \theta}{1 + \cos \theta} + \dfrac{1 + \cos \theta}{\sin \theta}$ simplifies to $\dfrac{2}{\sin \theta}$

GRAPHING PACKAGE

Use a graphing package to check these.

INVESTIGATION 4 NEGATIVE AND COMPLEMENTARY ANGLE FORMULAE

The purpose of this investigation is to discover relationships (if they exist) between:

- $\cos(-\theta)$, $\sin(-\theta)$, $\cos\theta$ and $\sin\theta$
- $\cos(\frac{\pi}{2} - \theta)$, $\sin(\frac{\pi}{2} - \theta)$, $\cos\theta$ and $\sin\theta$

Note: $-\theta$ is the **negative** of θ and $(\frac{\pi}{2} - \theta)$ is the **complement** of θ.

What to do:

1 Copy and complete, adding angles of your choice to the table:

θ	$\sin\theta$	$\cos\theta$	$\sin(-\theta)$	$\cos(-\theta)$	$\sin(\frac{\pi}{2} - \theta)$	$\cos(\frac{\pi}{2} - \theta)$
2.67						
0.642						
$\frac{\pi}{6}$						
etc						

2 From your table in **1** make a prediction on how to simplify $\sin(-\theta)$, $\cos(-\theta)$, $\sin(\frac{\pi}{2} - \theta)$ and $\cos(\frac{\pi}{2} - \theta)$.

NEGATIVE ANGLE FORMULAE

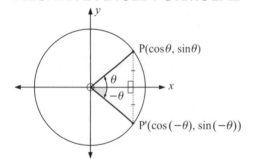

Notice that P and P′ have the same x-coordinate, whereas their y-coordinates are negatives.

Hence $\cos(-\theta) = \cos\theta$

and $\sin(-\theta) = -\sin\theta$

GRAPHING PACKAGE

So, $\mathbf{cos}\,(-\theta) = \mathbf{cos}\,\theta$

$\mathbf{sin}\,(-\theta) = -\mathbf{sin}\,\theta.$

COMPLEMENTARY ANGLE FORMULAE

Consider P′ on the unit circle, which corresponds to the angle $(\frac{\pi}{2} - \theta)$.

Then P′ is $(\cos(\frac{\pi}{2} - \theta),\ \sin(\frac{\pi}{2} - \theta))$ ...... (1)

But P′ is the image of P under a reflection in the line $y = x$.

So, P′ is $(\sin\theta, \cos\theta)$ ...... (2)

Comparing (1) and (2) gives

$\cos(\frac{\pi}{2} - \theta) = \sin\theta$ and $\sin(\frac{\pi}{2} - \theta) = \cos\theta$.

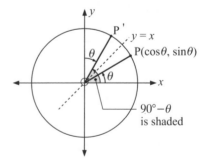

90°−θ is shaded

$\mathbf{cos}\,(\frac{\pi}{2} - \theta) = \mathbf{sin}\,\theta$

$\mathbf{sin}\,(\frac{\pi}{2} - \theta) = \mathbf{cos}\,\theta$

GRAPHING PACKAGE

Example 13

Simplify:

a $2\sin(-\theta) + 3\sin\theta$

b $2\cos\theta + \cos(-\theta)$

a $2\sin(-\theta) + 3\sin\theta$
$= -2\sin\theta + 3\sin\theta$
$= \sin\theta$

b $2\cos\theta + \cos(-\theta)$
$= 2\cos\theta + \cos\theta$
$= 3\cos\theta$

EXERCISE 13G.2

1 Simplify:

a $\sin\theta + \sin(-\theta)$ b $\sin(-\theta) - \sin\theta$ c $2\cos\theta + \cos(-\theta)$

d $3\sin\theta - \sin(-\theta)$ e $\cos^2(-\alpha)$ f $\sin^2(-\alpha)$

g $\cos(-\alpha)\cos\alpha - \sin(-\alpha)\sin\alpha$

Example 14

Simplify:

$3\sin\left(\frac{\pi}{2} - \theta\right) + 2\cos\theta$

$3\sin(\frac{\pi}{2} - \theta) + 2\cos\theta$
$= 3\cos\theta + 2\cos\theta$
$= 5\cos\theta$

---

2 Simplify:

a $2\sin\theta - \cos(90° - \theta)$ b $\sin(-\theta) - \cos(90° - \theta)$ c $\sin(90° - \theta) - \cos\theta$

d $3\cos(-\theta) - 4\sin(\frac{\pi}{2} - \theta)$ e $3\cos\theta + \sin(\frac{\pi}{2} - \theta)$ f $\cos(\frac{\pi}{2} - \theta) + 4\sin\theta$

3 Explain why $\sin(\theta - \phi) = -\sin(\phi - \theta)$, $\cos(\theta - \phi) = \cos(\phi - \theta)$.

H | COMPOUND ANGLE FORMULAE

INVESTIGATION 5   COMPOUND ANGLE FORMULAE

What to do:

1 Copy and complete for angles A and B in radians or degrees:

A	B	$\cos A$	$\cos B$	$\cos(A-B)$	$\cos A - \cos B$	$\cos A\cos B + \sin A\sin B$
$47°$	$24°$					
$138°$	$49°$					
3 rad	2 rad					
⋮	⋮			Make sure you use some angles of your choosing.		

2 What do you suspect from the results of this table?

3 Make another table with columns A, B, $\sin A$, $\sin B$, $\sin(A+B)$,
$\sin A + \sin B$, $\sin A\cos B + \cos A\sin B$ and complete it for four sets of angles of
your choosing. What is your conclusion?

If A and B are **any** two angles then:

$$\cos(A + B) = \cos A \cos B - \sin A \sin B$$
$$\cos(A - B) = \cos A \cos B + \sin A \sin B$$
$$\sin(A + B) = \sin A \cos B + \cos A \sin B$$
$$\sin(A - B) = \sin A \cos B - \cos A \sin B$$

These are known as the **compound angle formulae**. There are many ways of establishing these formulae but most of these methods are unsatisfactory as the arguments limit the angles A and B to being acute.

Proof:

Consider $P(\cos A, \sin A)$ and $Q(\cos B, \sin B)$ as any two points on the unit circle, as shown.

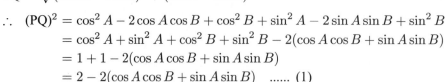

Angle POQ is $A - B$.

Using the distance formula:

$PQ = \sqrt{(\cos A - \cos B)^2 + (\sin A - \sin B)^2}$

$$\begin{aligned}
\therefore \quad (PQ)^2 &= \cos^2 A - 2\cos A \cos B + \cos^2 B + \sin^2 A - 2\sin A \sin B + \sin^2 B \\
&= \cos^2 A + \sin^2 A + \cos^2 B + \sin^2 B - 2(\cos A \cos B + \sin A \sin B) \\
&= 1 + 1 - 2(\cos A \cos B + \sin A \sin B) \\
&= 2 - 2(\cos A \cos B + \sin A \sin B) \quad \ldots\ldots \ (1)
\end{aligned}$$

But, by the *cosine rule* in $\triangle POQ$,

$$\begin{aligned}
(PQ)^2 &= 1^2 + 1^2 - 2(1)(1)\cos(A - B) \\
&= 2 - 2\cos(A - B) \quad \ldots\ldots \ (2)
\end{aligned}$$

$\therefore \quad \cos(A - B) = \cos A \cos B + \sin A \sin B \qquad$ {comparing (1) and (2)}

From this formula the other three formulae can be established.

$$\begin{aligned}
\cos(A + B) &= \cos(A - (-B)) \\
&= \cos A \cos(-B) + \sin A \sin(-B) \\
&= \cos A \cos B + \sin A(-\sin B) \qquad \{\cos(-\theta) = \cos\theta \ \text{ and } \ \sin(-\theta) = -\sin\theta\} \\
&= \cos A \cos B - \sin A \sin B
\end{aligned}$$

Also
$$\begin{aligned}
\sin(A - B) \\
&= \cos(\tfrac{\pi}{2} - (A - B)) \\
&= \cos((\tfrac{\pi}{2} - A) + B) \\
&= \cos(\tfrac{\pi}{2} - A)\cos B - \sin(\tfrac{\pi}{2} - A)\sin B \\
&= \sin A \cos B - \cos A \sin B
\end{aligned}$$

$$\begin{aligned}
\sin(A + B) \\
&= \sin(A - (-B)) \\
&= \sin A \cos(-B) - \cos A \sin(-B) \\
&= \sin A \cos B - \cos A(-\sin B) \\
&= \sin A \cos B + \cos A \sin B
\end{aligned}$$

Example 15

Expand:

a $\sin(\theta - \phi)$ **b** $\cos(\theta + \alpha)$

a $\sin(\theta - \phi) = \sin\theta\cos\phi - \cos\theta\sin\phi$

b $\cos(\theta + \alpha) = \cos\theta\cos\alpha - \sin\theta\sin\alpha$

EXERCISE 13H

1 Expand the following:

a $\sin(M + N)$ **b** $\cos(T - S)$ **c** $\sin(\alpha - \beta)$

d $\sin(\phi + \theta)$ **e** $\cos(\alpha + \beta)$ **f** $\cos(2\theta - \alpha)$

g $\sin(\alpha - 2\beta)$ **h** $\cos(3A + B)$ **i** $\cos(B - 2C)$

Example 16

Expand and simplify $\sin(270^o + \alpha)$.

$\sin(270^o + \alpha)$

$= \sin 270^o \cos\alpha + \cos 270^o \sin\alpha$

$= -1 \times \cos\alpha \ + \ 0 \times \sin\alpha$

$= -\cos\alpha$

2 Expand and simplify:

   a $\sin(90° + \theta)$ **b** $\cos(90° + \theta)$ **c** $\sin(180° - \alpha)$

   d $\cos(\pi + \alpha)$ **e** $\sin(2\pi - A)$ **f** $\cos\left(\frac{3\pi}{2} - \theta\right)$

3 Expand, then simplify and write your answer in the form $A\sin\theta + B\cos\theta$:

   a $\sin\left(\theta + \frac{\pi}{3}\right)$ **b** $\cos\left(\frac{2\pi}{3} - \theta\right)$ **c** $\cos\left(\theta + \frac{\pi}{4}\right)$ **d** $\sin\left(\frac{\pi}{6} - \theta\right)$

Example 17

Simplify:
$\cos 3\theta \cos \theta - \sin 3\theta \sin \theta$

$\cos 3\theta \cos \theta - \sin 3\theta \sin \theta$
$= \cos(3\theta + \theta)$ {compound formula in reverse}
$= \cos 4\theta$

---

4 Simplify using appropriate compound formulae (in reverse):

   a $\cos 2\theta \cos \theta + \sin 2\theta \sin \theta$ **b** $\sin 2A \cos A + \cos 2A \sin A$

   c $\cos A \sin B - \sin A \cos B$ **d** $\sin \alpha \sin \beta + \cos \alpha \cos \beta$

   e $\sin \phi \sin \theta - \cos \phi \cos \theta$ **f** $2\sin \alpha \cos \beta - 2\cos \alpha \sin \beta$

5 Simplify using compound formulae:

   a $\cos(\alpha + \beta)\cos(\alpha - \beta) - \sin(\alpha + \beta)\sin(\alpha - \beta)$

   b $\sin(\theta - 2\phi)\cos(\theta + \phi) - \cos(\theta - 2\phi)\sin(\theta + \phi)$

   c $\cos \alpha \cos(\beta - \alpha) - \sin \alpha \sin(\beta - \alpha)$

Example 18

Without using your calculator,

show that $\sin 75° = \frac{\sqrt{6}+\sqrt{2}}{4}$.

$\sin 75° = \sin(45° + 30°)$
$= \sin 45° \cos 30° + \cos 45° \sin 30°$
$= \left(\frac{1}{\sqrt{2}}\right)\left(\frac{\sqrt{3}}{2}\right) + \left(\frac{1}{\sqrt{2}}\right)\left(\frac{1}{2}\right)$
$= \left(\frac{\sqrt{3}+1}{2\sqrt{2}}\right)\frac{\sqrt{2}}{\sqrt{2}}$
$= \frac{\sqrt{6}+\sqrt{2}}{4}$

---

6 Without using your calculator, show that the following are true:

   a $\cos 75° = \frac{\sqrt{6}-\sqrt{2}}{4}$ **b** $\sin 105° = \frac{\sqrt{6}+\sqrt{2}}{4}$ **c** $\cos\left(\frac{13\pi}{12}\right) = \frac{-\sqrt{6}-\sqrt{2}}{4}$

7 **a** Show that, $\sqrt{2}\cos\left(\theta + \frac{\pi}{4}\right)$, expanded and simplified, is $\cos\theta - \sin\theta$.

   b Show that, $2\cos\left(\theta - \frac{\pi}{3}\right)$, expanded and simplified, is $\cos\theta + \sqrt{3}\sin\theta$.

   c Show that $\cos(\alpha + \beta) - \cos(\alpha - \beta)$ simplifies to $-2\sin \alpha \sin \beta$.

   d Show that $\cos(\alpha + \beta)\cos(\alpha - \beta)$ simplifies to $\cos^2 \alpha - \sin^2 \beta$.

8 **a** Show that: $\sin(A + B) + \sin(A - B) = 2\sin A \cos B$

   b From **a** we notice that $\sin A \cos B = \frac{1}{2}\sin(A + B) + \frac{1}{2}\sin(A - B)$ and this formula enables us to convert a product into a sum. Use the formula to write the following as sums:

   i $\sin 3\theta \cos \theta$ **ii** $\sin 6\alpha \cos \alpha$ **iii** $2\sin 5\beta \cos \beta$

   iv $4\cos \theta \sin 4\theta$ **v** $6\cos 4\alpha \sin 3\alpha$ **vi** $\frac{1}{3}\cos 5A \sin 3A$

9   **a**   Show that $\cos(A+B) + \cos(A-B) = 2\cos A \cos B$

     b   From **a** we notice that $\cos A \cos B = \frac{1}{2}\cos(A+B) + \frac{1}{2}\cos(A-B)$.

        Use this formula to convert the following to a *sum* of cosines:

        i $\cos 4\theta \cos \theta$ **ii** $\cos 7\alpha \cos \alpha$ **iii** $2\cos 3\beta \cos \beta$

        iv $6\cos x \cos 7x$ **v** $3\cos P \cos 4P$ **vi** $\frac{1}{4}\cos 4x \cos 2x$

10   **a**   Show that $\cos(A-B) - \cos(A+B) = 2\sin A \sin B$.

     b   From **a** we notice that $\sin A \sin B = \frac{1}{2}\cos(A-B) - \frac{1}{2}\cos(A+B)$.

        Use this formula to convert the following to a *difference* of cosines:

        i $\sin 3\theta \sin \theta$ **ii** $\sin 6\alpha \sin \alpha$ **iii** $2\sin 5\beta \sin \beta$

        iv $4\sin \theta \sin 4\theta$ **v** $10\sin 2A \sin 8A$ **vi** $\frac{1}{5}\sin 3M \sin 7M$

11

$$\sin A \cos B = \tfrac{1}{2}\sin(A+B) + \tfrac{1}{2}\sin(A-B) \quad \ldots\ldots (1)$$

$$\cos A \cos B = \tfrac{1}{2}\cos(A+B) + \tfrac{1}{2}\cos(A-B) \quad \ldots\ldots (2)$$

$$\sin A \sin B = \tfrac{1}{2}\cos(A-B) - \tfrac{1}{2}\cos(A+B) \quad \ldots\ldots (3)$$

are called **products to sums formulae**.   What formulae result if we replace B by A in each of these formulae?

12 Suppose $A + B = S$ and $A - B = D$.

    a   Show that $A = \frac{S+D}{2}$ and $B = \frac{S-D}{2}$.

    b   For the substitution $A + B = S$ and $A - B = D$, show that equation (1) in question **11** becomes $\sin S + \sin D = 2\sin\left(\frac{S+D}{2}\right)\cos\left(\frac{S-D}{2}\right)$ $\ldots\ldots$ (4)

    c   In (4) replace D by $(-D)$ and simplify to obtain

$$\sin S - \sin D = 2\cos\left(\tfrac{S+D}{2}\right)\sin\left(\tfrac{S-D}{2}\right).$$

    d   What results when the substitution $A = \frac{S+D}{2}$ and $B = \frac{S-D}{2}$ is made into (2) of question **11**?

    e   What results when the substitution $A = \frac{S+D}{2}$ and $B = \frac{S-D}{2}$ is made into (3) of question **11**?

13 From question **12** we obtain the formulae:

$$\sin S + \sin D = 2\sin\left(\tfrac{S+D}{2}\right)\cos\left(\tfrac{S-D}{2}\right) \qquad \cos S + \cos D = 2\cos\left(\tfrac{S+D}{2}\right)\cos\left(\tfrac{S-D}{2}\right)$$

$$\sin S - \sin D = 2\cos\left(\tfrac{S+D}{2}\right)\sin\left(\tfrac{S-D}{2}\right) \qquad \cos S - \cos D = -2\sin\left(\tfrac{S+D}{2}\right)\sin\left(\tfrac{S-D}{2}\right)$$

and these are called the **factor formulae** as they convert sums and differences into factored (factorised) forms. Use these formulae to convert the following to products:

   a $\sin 5x + \sin x$ **b** $\cos 8A + \cos 2A$ **c** $\cos 3\alpha - \cos \alpha$

   d $\sin 5\theta - \sin 3\theta$ **e** $\cos 7\alpha - \cos \alpha$ **f** $\sin 3\alpha + \sin 7\alpha$

   g $\cos 2B - \cos 4B$ **h** $\sin(x+h) - \sin x$ **i** $\cos(x+h) - \cos x$

I | DOUBLE ANGLE FORMULAE

What to do:

1 Copy and complete using angles of your choice as well:

A	$\sin 2A$	$2 \sin A$	$2 \sin A \cos A$	$\cos 2A$	$2 \cos A$	$\cos^2 A - \sin^2 A$
0.631						
57.81^o						
-3.697						

2 Write down any discoveries from your table of values in **1**.

The **double angle** formulae are:

$$\sin 2A = 2 \sin A \cos A \qquad \cos 2A = \begin{cases} \cos^2 A - \sin^2 A \\ 2 \cos^2 A - 1 \\ 1 - 2 \sin^2 A \end{cases}$$

GRAPHING
PACKAGE

GRAPHING
PACKAGE

Example 19

Given that $\sin \alpha = \frac{3}{5}$
and $\cos \alpha = -\frac{4}{5}$ find:

a $\sin 2\alpha$ **b** $\cos 2\alpha$

a $\sin 2\alpha$
$= 2 \sin \alpha \cos \alpha$
$= 2(\frac{3}{5})(-\frac{4}{5})$
$= -\frac{24}{25}$

b $\cos 2\alpha$
$= \cos^2 \alpha - \sin^2 \alpha$
$= (-\frac{4}{5})^2 - (\frac{3}{5})^2$
$= \frac{7}{25}$

EXERCISE 13I

1 If $\sin A = \frac{4}{5}$ and $\cos A = \frac{3}{5}$ find the values of: **a** $\sin 2A$ **b** $\cos 2A$

2 If $\cos A = \frac{1}{3}$, find $\cos 2A$.   **3** If $\sin \phi = -\frac{2}{3}$, find $\cos 2\phi$.

Example 20

If $\sin \alpha = \frac{5}{13}$ where $\frac{\pi}{2} < \alpha < \pi$, find the value of $\sin 2\alpha$.

First we need to find $\cos \alpha$ where α
is in quad 2 $\therefore$ $\cos \alpha$ is negative.
Now $\cos^2 \alpha + \sin^2 \alpha = 1$
$\therefore$ $\cos^2 \alpha + \frac{25}{169} = 1$
$\therefore$ $\cos^2 \alpha = \frac{144}{169}$
$\therefore$ $\cos \alpha = -\frac{12}{13}$

But $\sin 2\alpha = 2 \sin \alpha \cos \alpha$
$= 2(\frac{5}{13})(-\frac{12}{13})$
$= -\frac{120}{169}$

4 a If $\sin \alpha = -\frac{2}{3}$ where $\pi < \alpha < \frac{3\pi}{2}$ find the value of $\cos \alpha$ and hence the value of $\sin 2\alpha$.

b If $\cos \beta = \frac{2}{5}$ where $\frac{3\pi}{2} < \beta < 2\pi$, find the value of $\sin \beta$ and hence the value of $\sin 2\beta$.

Example 21

If α is acute and $\cos 2\alpha = \frac{3}{4}$ find the values of **a** $\cos \alpha$ **b** $\sin \alpha$.

a $\cos 2\alpha = 2\cos^2 \alpha - 1$

$\therefore \quad \frac{3}{4} = 2\cos^2 \alpha - 1$

$\therefore \quad \cos^2 \alpha = \frac{7}{8}$

$\therefore \quad \cos \alpha = \pm \frac{\sqrt{7}}{2\sqrt{2}}$

$\therefore \quad \cos \alpha = \frac{\sqrt{7}}{2\sqrt{2}}$

{as α is acute, $\cos \alpha$ is > 0}

b $\sin \alpha = \sqrt{1 - \cos^2 \alpha}$

{as α is acute, $\sin \alpha$ is positive}

$\therefore \quad \sin \alpha = \sqrt{1 - \frac{7}{8}}$

$\therefore \quad \sin \alpha = \sqrt{\frac{1}{8}}$

$\therefore \quad \sin \alpha = \frac{1}{2\sqrt{2}}$

---

5 If α is acute and $\cos 2\alpha = -\frac{7}{9}$, find without a calculator: **a** $\cos \alpha$ **b** $\sin \alpha$

Example 22

Use an appropriate 'double angle formula' to simplify:

a $3\sin \theta \cos \theta$ **b** $4\cos^2 2B - 2$

a $3\sin \theta \cos \theta$

$= \frac{3}{2}(2\sin \theta \cos \theta)$

$= \frac{3}{2}\sin 2\theta$

b $4\cos^2 2B - 2$

$= 2(2\cos^2 2B - 1)$

$= 2\cos 2(2B)$

$= 2\cos 4B$

---

6 Use an appropriate 'double angle' formula to simplify:

a $2\sin \alpha \cos \alpha$
b $4\cos \alpha \sin \alpha$
c $\sin \alpha \cos \alpha$

d $2\cos^2 \beta - 1$
e $1 - 2\cos^2 \phi$
f $1 - 2\sin^2 N$

g $2\sin^2 M - 1$
h $\cos^2 \alpha - \sin^2 \alpha$
i $\sin^2 \alpha - \cos^2 \alpha$

j $2\sin 2A \cos 2A$
k $2\cos 3\alpha \sin 3\alpha$
l $2\cos^2 4\theta - 1$

m $1 - 2\cos^2 3\beta$
n $1 - 2\sin^2 5\alpha$
o $2\sin^2 3D - 1$

p $\cos^2 2A - \sin^2 2A$
q $\cos^2(\frac{\alpha}{2}) - \sin^2(\frac{\alpha}{2})$
r $2\sin^2 3P - 2\cos^2 3P$

7 Show that:

a $(\sin \theta + \cos \theta)^2$ simplifies to $1 + \sin 2\theta$

b $\cos^4 \theta - \sin^4 \theta$ simplifies to $\cos 2\theta$

GRAPHING
PACKAGE

J | THE TANGENT FUNCTION

Consider the unit circle diagram given.

$P(\cos \theta, \sin \theta)$ is a point which is free to move around the circle.

In the first quadrant we extend OP to meet the tangent at A(1, 0) so that it meets this tangent at Q.

As P moves, so does Q.

Q's position relative to A is defined as the **tangent function**.

Now Δ's ONP and OAQ are equiangular and therefore similar.

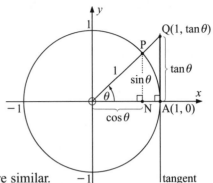

Consequently, $\dfrac{AQ}{OA} = \dfrac{NP}{ON}$ i.e., $\dfrac{AQ}{1} = \dfrac{\sin \theta}{\cos \theta}$ which suggests that $\boxed{\tan \theta = \dfrac{\sin \theta}{\cos \theta}}$.

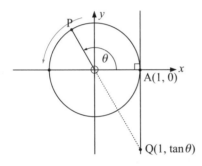

The question arises: "if P does not lie in the first quadrant, how is $\tan \theta$ defined"?

For θ obtuse, since $\sin \theta$ is positive and $\cos \theta$ is negative,

$\tan \theta = \dfrac{\sin \theta}{\cos \theta}$ is negative and PO is extended

to meet the tangent at A at Q(1, $\tan \theta$).

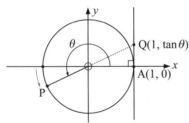

For θ in quadrant 3, $\sin \theta$ and $\cos \theta$ are both negative and so $\tan \theta$ is positive and this is clearly demonstrated as Q returns above the x-axis.

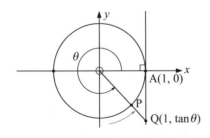

For θ in quadrant 4, $\sin \theta$ is negative and $\cos \theta$ is positive. So, $\tan \theta$ is negative.

DISCUSSION

- What is $\tan \theta$ when P is at (0, 1)?

- What is $\tan \theta$ when P is at (0, −1)?

EXERCISE 13J.1

1 Use your calculator to find the value of:

    a $\tan 0^\circ$ **b** $\tan 15^\circ$ **c** $\tan 20^\circ$ **d** $\tan 25^\circ$

    e $\tan 35^\circ$ **f** $\tan 45^\circ$ **g** $\tan 50^\circ$ **h** $\tan 55^\circ$

2 Explain why $\tan 45^\circ = 1$ exactly.

Now click on the icon to see the graph of $y = \tan\theta$ demonstrated from its unit circle definition.

DEMO

THE GRAPH OF $y = \tan x$

The graph of $y = \tan x$ is

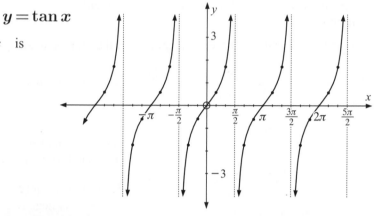

DISCUSSION

- Is the tangent function periodic? If so, what is its period?
- For what values of x does the graph not exist? What physical characteristics are shown near these values? Explain why these values must occur when $\cos x = 0$.
- Discuss how to find the x-intercepts of $y = \tan x$.
- What must $\tan(x - \pi)$ simplify to?
- How many solutions can the equation $\tan x = 2$ have?

EXERCISE 13J.2

1   **a**   Use a transformation approach to *sketch* the graphs of these functions, $x \in [0, 3\pi]$:

       i $y = \tan(x - \frac{\pi}{2})$ **ii** $y = -\tan x$ **iii** $y = \tan 2x$

    GRAPHING PACKAGE

   b   Use technology to check your answers to **a**.

       Look in particular for: •   asymptotes   • x-axis intercepts.

2 Use the graphing package to graph, on the same set of axes:

    a $y = \tan x$ and $y = \tan(x - 1)$ **b** $y = \tan x$ and $y = -\tan x$

    c $y = \tan x$ and $y = \tan\left(\frac{x}{2}\right)$

    GRAPHING PACKAGE

Describe the transformation which moves the first curve to the second in each case.

3 The graph of $y = \tan x$ is illustrated.

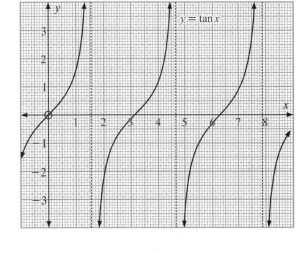

  a Use the graph to find estimates of:

   i $\tan 1$ **ii** $\tan 2.3$

  b Check your answers from a calculator.

  c Find, correct to 1 decimal place, the solutions of:

   i $\tan x = 2$ for $0 \leqslant x \leqslant 8$

   ii $\tan x = -1.4$ for $2 \leqslant x \leqslant 7$

4 What is the period of:

  a $y = \tan x$ **b** $y = \tan 2x$ **c** $y = \tan nx$?

K   TANGENT EQUATIONS

In question **3** of the previous exercise we solved tangent equations graphically. Unfortunately the solutions by this method are not very accurate.

Consider solving these similar looking equations

$$\begin{cases} \tan x = 2.61 \\ \tan(x - 2) = 2.61 \\ \tan 2x = 2.61 \end{cases}$$

ALGEBRAIC SOLUTION

Since the tangent function is periodic with period π we see that $\tan(x + \pi) = \tan x$ for all values of x. This means that equal tan values are π units apart.

Notice all equations are of the form $\tan X = 2.61$.

If $\tan X = 2.61$
∴ $X = \tan^{-1}(2.61)$
∴ $X \doteqdot 1.205$

So, if $\tan x = 2.61$, then
$x = 1.205 + k\pi$, (k any integer)

If $\tan(x - 2) = 2.61$
then $x - 2 \doteqdot 1.205 + k\pi$
∴ $x \doteqdot 3.205 + k\pi$

If $\tan 2x = 2.61$
then $2x \doteqdot 1.205 + k\pi$
∴ $x \doteqdot \dfrac{1.205}{2} + \dfrac{k\pi}{2}$
∴ $x \doteqdot 0.602 + \dfrac{k\pi}{2}$

Notice that the period of $\tan 2x$ is $\frac{\pi}{2}$.

EXERCISE 13K.1

1 If $\tan X = 2$, find *all* solutions for X.   Hence, solve the equations:

  a $\tan 2x = 2$ **b** $\tan\left(\dfrac{x}{3}\right) = 2$ **c** $\tan(x + 1.2) = 2$

2 If $\tan X = -3$, find *all* solutions for X.   Hence, solve the equations:

  a $\tan(x - 2) = -3$ **b** $\tan 3x = -3$ **c** $\tan\left(\dfrac{x}{2}\right) = -3$

3 Find the exact solutions of $\tan X = \sqrt{3}$ in terms of π only. Hence solve the equations:

    a $\tan\left(x - \frac{\pi}{6}\right) = \sqrt{3}$ **b** $\tan 4x = \sqrt{3}$ **c** $\tan^2 x = 3$

SOLUTION FROM TECHNOLOGY

Consider once again the equation $\tan x = 2.61$.

Graphing $y = \tan x$ and $y = 2.61$ on the same set of axes and finding the x-values where they intersect leads us to the solutions.

GRAPHICS CALCULATOR

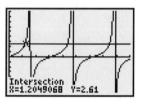

Graph $Y_1 = \tan X$ and $Y_2 = 2.61$.

Use built-in functions to find the first positive point of intersection.

It is $X \doteq 1.205$. So, the solutions are $x = 1.205 + k\pi$ as the period of $y = \tan x$ is π.

Note: • To solve $\tan(x - 2) = 2.61$ use $Y_1 = \tan(X - 2)$.

       • To solve $\tan 2x = 2.61$ use $Y_1 = \tan 2X$.

GRAPHING PACKAGE

Graph $y = \tan x$ and $y = 2.61$ on the same set of axes and find the first positive point of intersection, etc.

What to do: Repeat question **1** from **Exercise 13K.1** using your technology.   GRAPHING PACKAGE

TANGENT CALCULATIONS AND SIMPLIFICATIONS

As $\tan x = \dfrac{\sin x}{\cos x}$, we can use the unit circle to find the exact value(s) of $\tan x$.

Example 23

Use a unit circle diagram to find the exact value of $\tan\left(\frac{2\pi}{3}\right)$.

We see that $\cos\left(\frac{2\pi}{3}\right) = -\frac{1}{2}$ and $\sin\left(\frac{2\pi}{3}\right) = \frac{\sqrt{3}}{2}$

$\therefore\ \tan\left(\frac{2\pi}{3}\right) = \dfrac{\frac{\sqrt{3}}{2}}{-\frac{1}{2}} = -\sqrt{3}$

EXERCISE 13K.2

1 Use a unit circle diagram to find the exact value of:

    a $\tan 0$ **b** $\tan\left(\frac{\pi}{4}\right)$ **c** $\tan\left(\frac{\pi}{6}\right)$ **d** $\tan\left(\frac{\pi}{3}\right)$ **e** $\tan\left(\frac{\pi}{2}\right)$

    f $\tan\left(\frac{3\pi}{4}\right)$ **g** $\tan\left(\frac{5\pi}{3}\right)$ **h** $\tan\left(\frac{3\pi}{2}\right)$ **i** $\tan\left(-\frac{\pi}{3}\right)$ **j** $\tan\left(\frac{-3\pi}{4}\right)$

2 Use a unit circle diagram to find all angles between 0 and 2π which have:

    a a tangent of 1   **b** a tangent of -1 **c** a tangent of $\sqrt{3}$

    d a tangent of 0   **e** a tangent of $\frac{1}{\sqrt{3}}$ **f** a tangent of $-\sqrt{3}$

Often expressions containing $\tan x$ can be simplified by replacing $\tan x$ by $\dfrac{\sin x}{\cos x}$.

3 Simplify:

    a $3\tan x - \tan x$ **b** $\tan x - 4\tan x$ **c** $\tan x \cos x$

    d $\dfrac{\sin x}{\tan x}$ **e** $3\sin x + 2\cos x \tan x$ **f** $\dfrac{2\tan x}{\sin x}$

Given the exact values of $\sin x$ or $\cos x$ we can determine $\tan x$ without a calculator.

Example 24

If $\sin x = -\frac{1}{3}$ and $\pi < x < \frac{3\pi}{2}$, find the value of $\tan x$, without finding x.

Consider $\sin X = \frac{1}{3}$.   So

{X is the *working angle* and is acute}

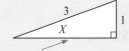

                                This side is $\sqrt{8}$ {Pythagoras}

$\therefore$ $\tan X = \frac{1}{\sqrt{8}}$

$\therefore$ $\tan x = \frac{1}{\sqrt{8}}$

{as we know that x lies in quad. 3, when tan is > 0}

---

4   **a**   If $\sin x = \frac{1}{3}$ and $\frac{\pi}{2} < x < \pi$, find $\tan x$ in radical (surd) form.

      b   If $\cos x = \frac{1}{5}$ and $\frac{3\pi}{2} < x < 2\pi$, find $\tan x$ in radical (surd) form.

      c   If $\sin x = -\frac{1}{\sqrt{3}}$ and $\pi < x < \frac{3\pi}{2}$, find $\tan x$ in radical (surd) form.

      d   If $\cos x = -\frac{3}{4}$ and $\frac{\pi}{2} < x < \pi$, find $\tan x$ in radical (surd) form.

Example 25

If $\tan x = \frac{3}{4}$ and $\pi < x < \frac{3\pi}{2}$, find $\sin x$ and $\cos x$.

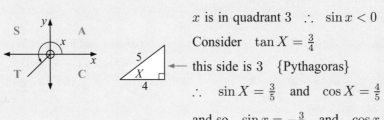

x is in quadrant 3 $\therefore$ $\sin x < 0$ and $\cos x < 0$.

Consider $\tan X = \frac{3}{4}$

this side is 3   {Pythagoras}

$\therefore$ $\sin X = \frac{3}{5}$ and $\cos X = \frac{4}{5}$

and so $\sin x = -\frac{3}{5}$ and $\cos x = -\frac{4}{5}$

---

5   Find $\sin x$ and $\cos x$ given that:

     a $\tan x = \frac{2}{3}$ and $0 < x < \frac{\pi}{2}$ **b** $\tan x = -\frac{4}{3}$ and $\frac{\pi}{2} < x < \pi$

     c $\tan x = \frac{\sqrt{5}}{3}$ and $\pi < x < \frac{3\pi}{2}$ **d** $\tan x = -\frac{12}{5}$ and $\frac{3\pi}{2} < x < 2\pi$

L   OTHER EQUATIONS INVOLVING $\tan x$

Example 26

Find the exact solutions of $\sqrt{3}\sin x = \cos x$ for $0 \leqslant x \leqslant 2\pi$.

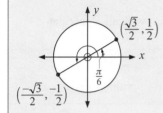

$$\sqrt{3}\sin x = \cos x$$

$$\therefore \quad \frac{\sin x}{\cos x} = \frac{1}{\sqrt{3}} \quad \{\text{dividing both sides by } \sqrt{3}\cos x\}$$

$$\therefore \quad \tan x = \frac{1}{\sqrt{3}}$$

$$\therefore \quad x = \frac{\pi}{6} \text{ or } \frac{7\pi}{6}$$

EXERCISE 13L

1   a Use your graphics calculator to sketch the graphs of $y = \sin x$ and $y = \cos x$ on the same set of axes on the domain $x \in [0, 2\pi]$.

b Find the x values of the points of intersection of the two graphs.

c Confirm that these values are the solutions of $\sin x = \cos x$ on $x \in [0, 2\pi]$.

2 Find the exact solutions to these equations for $0 \leqslant x \leqslant 2\pi$.

a $\sin x = -\cos x$ **b** $\sin(3x) = \cos(3x)$ **c** $\sin(2x) = \sqrt{3}\cos(2x)$

3 Check your answers to question **2** using a graphics calculator.

Find the points of intersection of appropriate graphs.

4 Solve on $0 \leqslant x \leqslant 10$: **a** $\sin x = 5\cos x$ **b** $4\sin x + 3\cos x = 0$

Check your answers to question **4** using a graphics calculator and appropriate graphs.

M   QUADRATIC TRIGONOMETRIC EQUATIONS

$2\sin^2 x + \sin x = 0$ and $2\cos^2 x + \cos x - 1 = 0$ are clearly quadratic equations when the variable is $\sin x$ and $\cos x$ respectively.

These equations can be factorised and then solved.

That is: $\qquad 2\sin^2 x + \sin x = 0 \qquad$ and $\qquad 2\cos^2 x + \cos x + 1 = 0$

$\qquad \therefore \quad \sin x(2\sin x + 1) = 0 \qquad \therefore \quad (2\cos x - 1)(\cos x + 1) = 0$

$\qquad \qquad \therefore \quad \sin x = 0 \text{ or } -\frac{1}{2} \qquad \qquad \therefore \quad \cos x = \frac{1}{2} \text{ or } -1$

$\qquad \qquad \qquad \text{etc.} \qquad \qquad \qquad \qquad \qquad \text{etc.}$

The use of the **quadratic formula** is often necessary.

EXERCISE 13M

1 Solve for $x \in [0, 2\pi]$:

a $2\sin^2 x + \sin x = 0$ **b** $2\cos^2 x = \cos x$ **c** $2\cos^2 x + \cos x - 1 = 0$

d $2\sin^2 x + 3\sin x + 1 = 0$ **e** $\sin^2 x = 2 - \cos x$ **f** $2\cos^2 x = \sin x$

2 Solve for $x \in [0, 2\pi]$:

a $\sin 2x + \sin x = 0$ **b** $\sin 2x - 2\cos x = 0$ **c** $\cos 2x - \cos x = 0$

d $\cos 2x + 3\cos x = 1$ **e** $\cos 2x + 5\sin x = 0$ **f** $\sin 2x + 3\sin x = 0$

N ▌ RECIPROCAL TRIGONOMETRIC FUNCTIONS

We define cosec x, secant x and cotangent x as:

$$\csc x = \frac{1}{\sin x}, \qquad \sec x = \frac{1}{\cos x} \qquad \text{and} \qquad \cot x = \frac{1}{\tan x} = \frac{\cos x}{\sin x}$$

Two important identities: $1 + \tan^2 x = \sec^2 x$ and $1 + \cot^2 x = \csc^2 x$

Example 27

Use sketching techniques from **Chapter 6** to sketch the graph of $y = \dfrac{1}{\sin x}$ from the graph of $y = \sin x$ for $x \in [-2\pi, 2\pi]$. Check using your calculator.

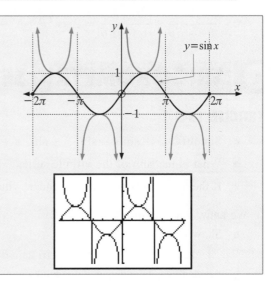

EXERCISE 13N

1 Without using a calculator, find $\csc x$, $\sec x$ and $\cot x$ for:

a $\sin x = \frac{3}{5}, \quad 0 \leqslant x \leqslant \frac{\pi}{2}$ **b** $\cos x = \frac{2}{3}, \quad \frac{3\pi}{2} < x < 2\pi$

2 Without using a calculator, find:

a $\csc\left(\frac{\pi}{3}\right)$ **b** $\cot\left(\frac{2\pi}{3}\right)$ **c** $\sec\left(\frac{5\pi}{6}\right)$ **d** $\cot\left(\pi\right)$

3 Find the other *five* trigonometric ratios if:

a $\cos x = \frac{3}{4}$ and $\frac{3\pi}{2} < x < 2\pi$ **b** $\sin x = -\frac{2}{3}$ and $\pi < x < \frac{3\pi}{2}$

c $\sec x = 2\frac{1}{2}$ and $0 < x < \frac{\pi}{2}$ **d** $\csc x = 2$ and $\frac{\pi}{2} < x < \pi$

e $\tan x = \frac{1}{2}$ and $\pi < x < \frac{3\pi}{2}$ **f** $\cot x = \frac{4}{3}$ and $\pi < \theta < \frac{3\pi}{2}$

4 Simplify:

a $\tan x \cot x$ **b** $\sin x \csc x$ **c** $\csc x \cot x$

d $\sin x \cot x$ **e** $\dfrac{\cot x}{\csc x}$ **f** $\dfrac{2\sin x \cot x + 3\cos x}{\cot x}$

5 Use technology to help sketch graphs on $[-2\pi, 2\pi]$ of: **a** $y = \sec x$ **b** $y = \cot x$

6 Solve for x when $x \in [0, 2\pi]$:

    a $\sec x = 2$ **b** $\csc x = -\sqrt{2}$ **c** $\cot x = 4$

    d $\sec 2x = \frac{1}{3}$ **e** $\csc 3x = -\frac{2}{3}$ **f** $\cot\left(2x - \frac{\pi}{4}\right) + 3 = 0$

7 Prove that: **a** $1 + \tan^2 x = \sec^2 x$ **b** $1 + \cot^2 x = \csc^2 x$

    Hint: In both cases start with $\sin^2 x + \cos^2 x = 1$

8 Show that:

    a $\sin^2 x + \cot^2 x \sin^2 x = 1$ **b** $\tan x + \cot x = \csc x \sec x$

    c $\sec x - \tan x \sin x = \cos x$ **d** $\dfrac{\sin \theta}{1 - \cos \theta} - \dfrac{\sin \theta}{1 + \cos \theta} = 2 \cot \theta$

    e $\dfrac{1}{1 - \sin \theta} + \dfrac{1}{1 + \sin \theta} = 2 \sec^2 \theta$ **f** $\dfrac{(1 - \cot \theta)^2}{\csc^2 \theta} + \sin 2\theta = 1$

⊙ TRIGONOMETRIC SERIES AND PRODUCTS

EXERCISE 13O

1   **a** Simplify $1 + \sin x + \sin^2 x + \sin^3 x + \sin^4 x + \,.....\, + \sin^{n-1} x$.

    b What is the sum of the infinite series $1 + \sin x + \sin^2 x + \sin^3 x + \,.....$?

    c If the series in **b** has sum $\frac{2}{3}$, find x when $x \in [0, 2\pi]$.

2 We know that $2 \sin x \cos x = \sin 2x$.

    a Show that:

        i $2 \sin x(\cos x + \cos 3x) = \sin 4x$ **ii** $2 \sin x(\cos x + \cos 3x + \cos 5x) = \sin 6x$

    b What do you suspect the following would simplify to?

        i $2 \sin x(\cos x + \cos 3x + \cos 5x + \cos 7x)$

       ii $\cos x + \cos 3x + \cos 5x + \,.....\, + \cos 19x$ (i.e.,   10 terms)

    c Write down the possible generalisation of **b ii** to n terms.

3 From $\sin 2x = 2 \sin x \cos x$ we observe that $\sin x \cos x = \dfrac{\sin 2x}{2} = \dfrac{\sin(2^1 x)}{2^1}$

    a Prove that:

        i $\sin x \cos x \cos 2x = \dfrac{\sin(2^2 x)}{2^2}$ **ii** $\sin x \cos x \cos 2x \cos 4x = \dfrac{\sin(2^3 x)}{2^3}$

    b If the pattern observed in **a** continues:

        i what would $\sin x \cos x \cos 2x \cos 4x \cos 8x$ simplify to

       ii what would $\sin x \cos x \cos 2x .... \cos 32x$ simplify to?

    c What is the generalisation of the results in **a** and **b**?

4   **a** Use the principle of mathematical induction to prove that:

$$\cos \theta + \cos 3\theta + \cos 5\theta + \,......\, + \cos(2n-1)\theta = \frac{\sin 2n\theta}{2 \sin \theta}, \quad n \in Z^+.$$

    b What does $\cos \theta + \cos 3\theta + \cos 5\theta + \,......\, + \cos 31\theta$ simplify to?

5 Use the principle of mathematical induction to prove that:

$$\sin\theta + \sin 3\theta + \sin 5\theta + \ldots\ldots + \sin(2n-1)\theta = \frac{1 - \cos 2n\theta}{2\sin\theta}$$

for all positive integers n, and hence find the value of

$$\sin\tfrac{\pi}{7} + \sin\tfrac{3\pi}{7} + \sin\tfrac{5\pi}{7} + \sin\pi + \sin\tfrac{9\pi}{7} + \sin\tfrac{11\pi}{7} + \sin\tfrac{13\pi}{7}.$$

6 Use the principle of mathematical induction to prove that:

$$\cos x \times \cos 2x \times \cos 4x \times \cos 8x\ldots\ldots \cos(2^{n-1}x) = \frac{\sin(2^n x)}{2^n \times \sin x} \quad \text{for all } n \in \mathbb{Z}^+.$$

REVIEW SET 13A

1 Without using technology draw the graph of $\;y = 4\sin x\;$ for $\;0 \leqslant x \leqslant 2\pi$.

2 Without using technology draw the graph of $\;y = \sin 3x\;$ for $\;0 \leqslant x \leqslant 2\pi$.

3 State the period of:

    a $y = 4\sin\left(\tfrac{x}{3}\right)$ **b** $y = -2\sin 4x$

4 Without using technology draw a sketch graph of $\;y = \sin\left(x - \tfrac{\pi}{3}\right) + 2$.

5 The table below gives the mean monthly maximum temperature (°C) for Perth Airport in Western Australia.

Month	Jan	Feb	Mar	Apr	May	Jun	Jul	Aug	Sept	Oct	Nov	Dec
Temp	31.5	31.8	29.5	25.4	21.5	18.8	17.7	18.3	20.1	22.4	25.5	28.8

    a   A sine function of the form $\;T \doteq A\sin B(t - C) + D\;$ is used to model the data. Find good estimates of the constants A, B, C and D without using technology. Use Jan $\equiv 1$, Feb $\equiv 2$, etc.

    b   Check your answer to **a** using your technology. How well does your model fit?

6 Use technology to solve for $\;x \in [0,\,8]$:

    a $\sin x = 0.382$ **b** $\sin\left(\tfrac{x}{2}\right) = -0.458$

7 Use technology to solve for $\;x \in [0,\,8]$:

    a $\sin(x - 2.4) = 0.754$ **b** $\sin\left(x + \tfrac{\pi}{3}\right) = 0.6049$

8 Solve algebraically in terms of π:

    a $2\sin x = -1\;$ for $\;x \in [0,\,4\pi]$ **b** $\sqrt{2}\sin x - 1 = 0\;$ for $\;x \in [-2\pi,\,2\pi]$

9 Solve algebraically in terms of π:

    a $2\sin 3x + \sqrt{3} = 0\;$ for $\;x \in [0,\,2\pi]$ **b** $\sqrt{2}\sin\left(x + \tfrac{\pi}{4}\right) = 0\;$ for $\;x \in [0,\,3\pi]$

10 The population estimate, in thousands, of a species of water beetle where $\;0 \leqslant t \leqslant 8$ and t is the number of weeks after the initial population estimate was made, is given by $P(t) = 5 + 2\sin\left(\tfrac{\pi t}{3}\right)$.

    a   What was the initial population?   **b**   What were the smallest and largest populations?

    b   During what time interval(s) did the population size exceed 6000?

REVIEW SET 13B

1 Solve algebraically, giving answers in terms of π:

    a $\sin^2 x - \sin x - 2 = 0$ **b** $4 \sin^2 x = 1$

2 **a** On the same set of axes, sketch the graphs of $y = \cos x$ and $y = \cos x - 3$.

    b On the same set of axes, sketch the graphs of $y = \cos x$ and $y = \cos\left(x - \frac{\pi}{4}\right)$.

    c On the same set of axes, sketch the graphs of $y = \cos x$ and $y = 3\cos 2x$.

    d On the same set of axes, sketch $y = \cos x$ and $y = 2\cos\left(x - \frac{\pi}{3}\right) + 3$.

3 In an industrial city, the amount of pollution in the air becomes greater during the working week when factories are operating, and lessens over the weekend. The number of milligrams of pollutants in a cubic metre of air is given by

$$P(t) = 40 + 12 \sin \frac{2\pi}{7} \left(t - \frac{37}{12}\right)$$

where t is the number of days after midnight on Saturday night.

    a What was the minimum level of pollution?

    b At what time during the week does this minimum level occur?

4 For the following graphs, find the cosine function representing them:

    a 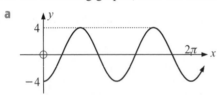   **b**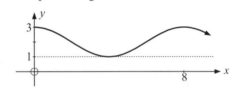

5 Use technology to solve:

    a $\cos x = 0.4379$ for $0 \leqslant x \leqslant 10$ **b** $\cos(x - 2.4) = -0.6014$ for $0 \leqslant x \leqslant 6$.

6 Use technology to solve:

    a $\cos 4x = 0.3$ for all x **b** $4\cos 2x + 1 = 0$ for $0 \leqslant x \leqslant 5$.

7 Find the exact solutions of:

    a $\cos x = -\frac{1}{\sqrt{2}}$, $x \in [0, 4\pi]$ **ii** $\cos\left(x + \frac{2\pi}{3}\right) = \frac{1}{2}$, $x \in [-2\pi, 2\pi]$.

8 Find the exact solutions of:

    a $\sqrt{2}\cos\left(x + \frac{\pi}{4}\right) - 1 = 0$, $x \in [0, 4\pi]$.   **b** $2\cos 2x - 1 = 0$ for all x.

9 Simplify: **a** $\cos^3 \theta + \sin^2 \theta \cos \theta$ **b** $\dfrac{\cos^2 \theta - 1}{\sin \theta}$ **c** $3\cos\theta - \cos\theta$

              d $5 - 5\sin^2\theta$ **e** $\dfrac{\sin^2\theta - 1}{\cos\theta}$

10 Expand and simplify if possible: **a** $(2\sin\alpha - 1)^2$ **b** $(\cos\alpha - \sin\alpha)^2$

REVIEW SET 13C, 13D
Click on the icon to obtain printable review sets and answers

REVIEW SET 13C   REVIEW SET 13D

Chapter 14

Matrices

Contents:

INTRODUCTION

You have been using matrices for many years without realising it.

For example:

July 2001						
M	T	W	T	F	S	S
						1
2	3	4	5	6	7	8
9	10	11	12	13	14	15
16	17	18	19	20	21	22
23	24	25	26	27	28	29
30	31					

	Won	*Lost*	*Drew*	*Points*
Arsenal	24	2	4	76
Liverpool	23	3	4	73
Chelsea	21	4	5	68
Leeds	20	5	5	65

Ingredients	*Amount*
sugar	1 tspn
flour	1 cup
milk	200 mL
salt	1 pinch

In general:

A **matrix** is a rectangular array of numbers arranged in **rows** and **columns**.

Consider these two items of information:

Shopping list

Bread	2 loaves
Juice	1 carton
Eggs	6
Cheese	1

Furniture inventory			
	chairs	tables	beds
Flat	6	1	2
Unit	9	2	3
House	10	3	4

It is usual to put square or round brackets around a matrix. We could write the shopping list and furniture inventory as:

$$
\begin{array}{c|c}
 & \text{number} \\
B & 2 \\
J & 1 \\
E & 6 \\
C & 1
\end{array}
\quad \text{and} \quad
\begin{array}{c|ccc}
 & C & T & B \\
F & 6 & 1 & 2 \\
U & 9 & 2 & 3 \\
H & 10 & 3 & 4
\end{array}
\quad \text{or simply} \quad
\begin{bmatrix} 2 \\ 1 \\ 6 \\ 1 \end{bmatrix}
\quad \text{and} \quad
\begin{bmatrix} 6 & 1 & 2 \\ 9 & 2 & 3 \\ 10 & 3 & 4 \end{bmatrix}
$$

In $\begin{bmatrix} 2 \\ 1 \\ 6 \\ 1 \end{bmatrix}$ we have 4 rows and 1 column and we say that this is a 4×1 **column matrix** or **column vector**.

In $\begin{bmatrix} 6 & 1 & 2 \\ 9 & 2 & 3 \\ 10 & 3 & 4 \end{bmatrix}$ we have 3 rows and 3 columns and we have a 3×3 **square matrix**.

This **element**, 3, is in row 3, column 2.

$\begin{bmatrix} 3 & 0 & -1 & 2 \end{bmatrix}$ has 1 row and 4 columns and is called a 1×4 **row matrix** or **row vector**.

Note: • An $m \times n$ matrix has m rows and n columns.

rows   columns

• $m \times n$ specifies the **order** of a matrix.

USES OF MATRICES

Following are a few of many uses for the mathematics of matrices:

- **Solving of systems of equations** in business, physics, engineering, etc.

- **Linear programming** where, for example, we may wish to optimise a linear expression subject to linear constraints. For example, optimising profits of a business.

- **Business inventories** involving stock control, cost, revenue and profit calculations. Matrices form the basis of business computer software.

- **Markov chains**, for predicting long term probabilities such as in weather.

- **Strategies in games** where we wish to maximise our chance of winning.

- **Economic modelling** where the input from various suppliers is needed to help a business be successful.

- **Graph (network) theory** which is used in truck and airline route determination to minimise distance travelled and therefore minimise costs.

- **Assignment problems** where we have to direct resources in industrial situations in the most cost effective way.

- **Forestry and fisheries management** where we need to select an appropriate sustainable harvesting policy.

- **Cubic spline interpolation** which is used to construct fonts used in desktop publishing. Each font is stored in matrix form in the memory of a computer.

- **Computer graphics**, **flight simulation**, **Computer Aided Tomography** (CAT scanning) and **Magnetic Resonance Imaging** (MRI), **Fractals**, **Chaos**, **Genetics**, **Cryptography** (coding, code breaking, computer confidentiality), etc.

A matrix can be used to represent numbers of items to be purchased, prices of items to be purchased, numbers of people involved in the construction of a building, etc.

Example 1

Lisa goes shopping at store A to buy 2 loaves of bread at $2.65 each, 3 litres of milk at $1.55 per litre, a 500 g tub of butter at $2.35.

Represent the quantities purchased in a row matrix and the costs in a column matrix.

Quantities matrix is $\begin{bmatrix} 2 & 3 & 1 \end{bmatrix}$

bread   milk   butter

Costs matrix is $\begin{bmatrix} 2.65 \\ 1.55 \\ 2.35 \end{bmatrix}$ ← bread, ← milk, ← butter

---

Note: If Lisa goes to a different supermarket (store B) and finds that the prices for the same items are $2.25 for bread, $1.50 for milk, and $2.20 for butter, then the costs matrix to show prices from both stores is:

$\begin{bmatrix} 2.65 & 2.25 \\ 1.55 & 1.50 \\ 2.35 & 2.20 \end{bmatrix}$ ← bread, ← milk, ← butter

store A   store B

EXERCISE 14A

1 Write down the order of:

a
$$\begin{bmatrix} 5 & 1 & 0 & 2 \end{bmatrix}$$

b
$$\begin{bmatrix} 2 \\ 7 \end{bmatrix}$$

c
$$\begin{bmatrix} 2 & -1 \\ 1 & 3 \end{bmatrix}$$

d
$$\begin{bmatrix} 1 & 2 & 3 \\ 2 & 0 & 4 \\ 5 & 1 & 0 \end{bmatrix}$$

2 A grocery list consists of 2 loaves of bread, 1 kg of butter, 6 eggs and 1 carton of cream. The cost of each grocery item is $1.95, $2.35, $0.15 and $0.95 respectively.

a Construct a row matrix showing quantities.

b Construct a column matrix showing prices.

c What is the significance of $(2 \times 1.95) + (1 \times 2.35) + (6 \times 0.15) + (1 \times 0.95)$?

3 Big Bart's Baked Beans factory produces cans of baked beans in 3 sizes;   200 g, 300 g and 500 g. In February they produced respectively:

1000, 1500 and 1250 cans of each in week 1;   1500, 1000 and 1000 of each in week 2
800, 2300 and 1300 cans of each in week 3;   and 1200 cans of each in week 4.

Construct a matrix to show February's production levels.

4 Over a long weekend holiday period, a baker produced the following food items. On Friday he baked 40 dozen pies, 50 dozen pasties, 55 dozen rolls and 40 dozen buns. On Saturday 25 dozen pies, 65 dozen pasties, 30 dozen buns and 44 dozen rolls were made. On Sunday 40 dozen pasties, 40 dozen rolls, 35 dozen of each of pies and buns were made. On Monday the totals were 40 dozen pasties, 50 dozen buns and 35 dozen of each of pies and rolls. Represent this information as a matrix.

B   ADDITION AND SUBTRACTION OF MATRICES

Before attempting to add and subtract matrices it is necessary to define what we mean by **matrix equality**.

EQUALITY

Two matrices are **equal** if they have exactly the same shape (order) and elements in corresponding positions are equal.

For example, if $\begin{bmatrix} a & b \\ c & d \end{bmatrix} = \begin{bmatrix} w & x \\ y & z \end{bmatrix}$ then $a = w$, $b = x$, $c = y$ and $d = z$.

ADDITION

Thao has three stores (A, B and C). Her stock levels for dresses, skirts and blouses are given by the matrix:

	Store A	B	C
dresses	23	41	68
skirts	28	39	79
blouses	46	17	62

Some newly ordered stock has just arrived. For each store 20 dresses, 30 skirts and 50 blouses must be added to stock levels.

Her stock order is given by the matrix
$$\begin{bmatrix} 20 & 20 & 20 \\ 30 & 30 & 30 \\ 50 & 50 & 50 \end{bmatrix}$$

Clearly the new levels are shown as:
$$\begin{bmatrix} 23+20 & 41+20 & 68+20 \\ 28+30 & 39+30 & 79+30 \\ 46+50 & 17+50 & 62+50 \end{bmatrix}$$

or
$$\begin{bmatrix} 23 & 41 & 68 \\ 28 & 39 & 79 \\ 46 & 17 & 62 \end{bmatrix} + \begin{bmatrix} 20 & 20 & 20 \\ 30 & 30 & 30 \\ 50 & 50 & 50 \end{bmatrix} = \begin{bmatrix} 43 & 61 & 88 \\ 58 & 69 & 109 \\ 96 & 67 & 112 \end{bmatrix}$$

So,   to **add** two matrices they must be of the **same order** and then we simply **add corresponding elements**.

Example 2

If $A = \begin{bmatrix} 1 & 2 & 3 \\ 6 & 5 & 4 \end{bmatrix}$, $B = \begin{bmatrix} 2 & 1 & 6 \\ 0 & 3 & 5 \end{bmatrix}$ and $C = \begin{bmatrix} 3 & 1 \\ 2 & 4 \end{bmatrix}$ find:

a $A + B$ **b** $A + C$

a $A + B = \begin{bmatrix} 1 & 2 & 3 \\ 6 & 5 & 4 \end{bmatrix} + \begin{bmatrix} 2 & 1 & 6 \\ 0 & 3 & 5 \end{bmatrix}$

$ = \begin{bmatrix} 1+2 & 2+1 & 3+6 \\ 6+0 & 5+3 & 4+5 \end{bmatrix}$

$ = \begin{bmatrix} 3 & 3 & 9 \\ 6 & 8 & 9 \end{bmatrix}$

b $A + C$ cannot be found as A and C are not the same sized matrices

i.e.,   they have different orders.

SUBTRACTION

If Thao's stock levels were $\begin{bmatrix} 29 & 51 & 19 \\ 31 & 28 & 32 \\ 40 & 17 & 29 \end{bmatrix}$ and her sales matrix for the week is

$\begin{bmatrix} 15 & 12 & 6 \\ 20 & 16 & 19 \\ 19 & 8 & 14 \end{bmatrix}$ what are the current stock levels?

It is obvious that we subtract corresponding elements.

That is $\begin{bmatrix} 29 & 51 & 19 \\ 31 & 28 & 32 \\ 40 & 17 & 29 \end{bmatrix} - \begin{bmatrix} 15 & 12 & 6 \\ 20 & 16 & 19 \\ 19 & 8 & 14 \end{bmatrix} = \begin{bmatrix} 14 & 39 & 13 \\ 11 & 12 & 13 \\ 21 & 9 & 15 \end{bmatrix}$

So,   to **subtract** matrices they must be of the **same order** and then we simply subtract corresponding elements.

Example 3

If $A = \begin{bmatrix} 3 & 4 & 8 \\ 2 & 1 & 0 \\ 1 & 4 & 7 \end{bmatrix}$

and $B = \begin{bmatrix} 2 & 0 & 6 \\ 3 & 0 & 4 \\ 5 & 2 & 3 \end{bmatrix}$

find $A - B$.

$A - B = \begin{bmatrix} 3 & 4 & 8 \\ 2 & 1 & 0 \\ 1 & 4 & 7 \end{bmatrix} - \begin{bmatrix} 2 & 0 & 6 \\ 3 & 0 & 4 \\ 5 & 2 & 3 \end{bmatrix}$

$= \begin{bmatrix} 3-2 & 4-0 & 8-6 \\ 2-3 & 1-0 & 0-4 \\ 1-5 & 4-2 & 7-3 \end{bmatrix}$

$= \begin{bmatrix} 1 & 4 & 2 \\ -1 & 1 & -4 \\ -4 & 2 & 4 \end{bmatrix}$

EXERCISE 14B

1 If $A = \begin{bmatrix} 3 & 4 \\ 5 & 2 \end{bmatrix}$, $B = \begin{bmatrix} 6 & -3 \\ -2 & 1 \end{bmatrix}$ and $C = \begin{bmatrix} -3 & 7 \\ -4 & -2 \end{bmatrix}$, find:

   a $A + B$ b $A + B + C$ c $B + C$ d $C + B - A$

2 If $P = \begin{bmatrix} 3 & 5 & -11 \\ 10 & 2 & 6 \\ -2 & -1 & 7 \end{bmatrix}$ and $Q = \begin{bmatrix} 17 & -4 & 3 \\ -2 & 8 & -8 \\ 3 & -4 & 11 \end{bmatrix}$, find:

   a $P + Q$
   b $P - Q$
   c $Q - P$

3 A restaurant served 85 men, 92 women and 52 children on Friday night. On Saturday night they served 102 men, 137 women and 49 children.

   a Express this information in *two* column matrices.

   b Use the matrices to find the totals of men, women and children served over the Friday-Saturday period.

4 On Monday David bought shares in five companies and on Friday he sold them. The details are:

   a Write down David's

       i   cost price column matrix

       ii selling price column matrix.

   b What matrix operation is needed to find David's profit/loss matrix?

   c Find David's profit/loss matrix.

	Cost price/share	Selling price/share
A	$1.72	$1.79
B	$27.85	$28.75
C	$0.92	$1.33
D	$2.53	$2.25
E	$3.56	$3.51

5 In November, Lou E Gee sold 23 fridges, 17 stoves and 31 microwave ovens and his partner Rose A Lee sold 19 fridges, 29 stoves and 24 microwave ovens.

   In December Lou's sales were: 18 fridges, 7 stoves and 36 microwaves while Rose's sales were: 25 fridges, 13 stoves and 19 microwaves.

   a Write their sales for November as a 3×2 matrix.

   b Write their sales for December as a 3×2 matrix.

   c Write their total sales for November and December as a 3×2 matrix.

6 Find x and y if:

a $\begin{bmatrix} x & x^2 \\ 3 & -1 \end{bmatrix} = \begin{bmatrix} y & 4 \\ 3 & y+1 \end{bmatrix}$

b $\begin{bmatrix} x & y \\ y & x \end{bmatrix} = \begin{bmatrix} -y & x \\ x & -y \end{bmatrix}$

7 **a** If $A = \begin{bmatrix} 2 & 1 \\ 3 & -1 \end{bmatrix}$ and $B = \begin{bmatrix} -1 & 2 \\ 2 & 3 \end{bmatrix}$ find $A + B$ and $B + A$.

b Explain why $A + B = B + A$ for all 2×2 matrices A and B.

8 **a** For $A = \begin{bmatrix} -1 & 0 \\ 1 & 5 \end{bmatrix}$, $B = \begin{bmatrix} 3 & 4 \\ -1 & -2 \end{bmatrix}$ and $C = \begin{bmatrix} 4 & -1 \\ -1 & 3 \end{bmatrix}$ find

$(A + B) + C$ and $A + (B + C)$.

b Prove that, if A, B and C are any 2×2 matrices then

$(A + B) + C = A + (B + C)$.

(**Hint:** Let $A = \begin{bmatrix} a & b \\ c & d \end{bmatrix}$, $B = \begin{bmatrix} p & q \\ r & s \end{bmatrix}$ and $C = \begin{bmatrix} w & x \\ y & z \end{bmatrix}$, say.)

C — MULTIPLES OF MATRICES

In the pantry there are 6 cans of peaches, 4 cans of apricots and 8 cans of pears.

This information could be represented by the column vector $C = \begin{bmatrix} 6 \\ 4 \\ 8 \end{bmatrix}$.

Doubling these cans in the pantry we would have $\begin{bmatrix} 12 \\ 8 \\ 16 \end{bmatrix}$ which is $C + C$.

Now if we let $C + C$ be $2C$ we notice that to get $2C$ from C we simply multiply all matrix elements by 2.

Likewise, trebling the fruit cans in the pantry is $3C = \begin{bmatrix} 3 \times 6 \\ 3 \times 4 \\ 3 \times 8 \end{bmatrix} = \begin{bmatrix} 18 \\ 12 \\ 24 \end{bmatrix}$ and halving them is $\frac{1}{2}C = \begin{bmatrix} \frac{1}{2} \times 6 \\ \frac{1}{2} \times 4 \\ \frac{1}{2} \times 8 \end{bmatrix} = \begin{bmatrix} 3 \\ 2 \\ 4 \end{bmatrix}$

In general,

> if a scalar t is multiplied by a matrix A the result is matrix tA obtained by multiplying every element of A by t.

Example 4

If A is $\begin{bmatrix} 1 & 2 & 5 \\ 2 & 0 & 1 \end{bmatrix}$

find **a** $3A$

b $\frac{1}{2}A$

a $3A = 3\begin{bmatrix} 1 & 2 & 5 \\ 2 & 0 & 1 \end{bmatrix}$

$= \begin{bmatrix} 3 & 6 & 15 \\ 6 & 0 & 3 \end{bmatrix}$

b $\frac{1}{2}A = \frac{1}{2}\begin{bmatrix} 1 & 2 & 5 \\ 2 & 0 & 1 \end{bmatrix}$

$= \begin{bmatrix} \frac{1}{2} & 1 & 2\frac{1}{2} \\ 1 & 0 & \frac{1}{2} \end{bmatrix}$

EXERCISE 14C

1 If $\mathbf{B} = \begin{bmatrix} 6 & 12 \\ 24 & 6 \end{bmatrix}$ find: **a** $2\mathbf{B}$ **b** $\frac{1}{3}\mathbf{B}$ **c** $\frac{1}{12}\mathbf{B}$ **d** $-\frac{1}{2}\mathbf{B}$

2 If $\mathbf{A} = \begin{bmatrix} 2 & 3 & 5 \\ 1 & 6 & 4 \end{bmatrix}$ and $\mathbf{B} = \begin{bmatrix} 1 & 2 & 1 \\ 1 & 2 & 3 \end{bmatrix}$ find:

   a $\mathbf{A} + \mathbf{B}$ **b** $\mathbf{A} - \mathbf{B}$ **c** $2\mathbf{A} + \mathbf{B}$ **d** $3\mathbf{A} - \mathbf{B}$

3 Isabelle sells clothing made by four different companies which we will call A, B, C and D. Her usual monthly order is:

$$\begin{array}{c} \\ \text{skirt} \\ \text{dress} \\ \text{evening} \\ \text{suit} \end{array} \begin{array}{cccc} A & B & C & D \\ \begin{bmatrix} 30 & 40 & 40 & 60 \\ 50 & 40 & 30 & 75 \\ 40 & 40 & 50 & 50 \\ 10 & 20 & 20 & 15 \end{bmatrix} \end{array}$$

Find her order, to the nearest whole number, if:

   a she increases her total order by 15%

   b she decreases her total order by 15%.

4 During weekdays a video store finds that its average hirings are: 75 movies (VHS), 27 movies (DVD) and 102 video/computer games. On the weekends the average figures are: 43 DVD movies, 136 VHS movies and 129 games.

   a Represent the data using *two* column matrices.

   b Find the sum of the matrices in **a**.

   c What does the sum matrix of **b** represent?

$$\begin{bmatrix} \ \\ \ \\ \ \end{bmatrix} \begin{array}{l} \longleftarrow \text{VHS} \\ \longleftarrow \text{DVD} \\ \longleftarrow \text{games} \end{array}$$

5 A builder builds a block of 12 identical flats. Each flat is to contain 1 table, 4 chairs, 2 beds and 1 wardrobe.

   If $\mathbf{F} = \begin{bmatrix} 1 \\ 4 \\ 2 \\ 1 \end{bmatrix}$ is the matrix representing the furniture in one flat, what, in terms of $\mathbf{F}$, is the matrix representing the furniture in **all** flats?

ZERO MATRIX (SOMETIMES CALLED NULL MATRIX)

For real numbers, it is true that $a + 0 = 0 + a = a$ for all values of a.

The question: "Is there a matrix $\mathbf{O}$ in which $\mathbf{A} + \mathbf{O} = \mathbf{O} + \mathbf{A} = \mathbf{A}$ for any matrix $\mathbf{A}$?"

Simple examples like: $\begin{bmatrix} 2 & 3 \\ 4 & -1 \end{bmatrix} + \begin{bmatrix} 0 & 0 \\ 0 & 0 \end{bmatrix} = \begin{bmatrix} 2 & 3 \\ 4 & -1 \end{bmatrix}$ suggest that $\mathbf{O}$ consists of all zeros.

> A **zero matrix** is a matrix in which all elements are zero.

For example, the 2×2 zero matrix is $\begin{bmatrix} 0 & 0 \\ 0 & 0 \end{bmatrix}$, the 2×3 zero matrix is $\begin{bmatrix} 0 & 0 & 0 \\ 0 & 0 & 0 \end{bmatrix}$.

Zero matrices have the property that:

> If $\mathbf{A}$ is a matrix of any order and $\mathbf{O}$ is the corresponding **zero matrix**, then $\mathbf{A} + \mathbf{O} = \mathbf{O} + \mathbf{A} = \mathbf{A}$.

NEGATIVE MATRICES

> The **negative** matrix **A**, denoted $-\mathbf{A}$ is actually $-1\mathbf{A}$.

So, if $\quad \mathbf{A} = \begin{bmatrix} 3 & -1 \\ 2 & 4 \end{bmatrix}$, then $\quad -\mathbf{A} = \begin{bmatrix} -1 \times 3 & -1 \times -1 \\ -1 \times 2 & -1 \times 4 \end{bmatrix} = \begin{bmatrix} -3 & 1 \\ -2 & -4 \end{bmatrix}$

Thus $-\mathbf{A}$ is obtained from **A** by simply reversing the sign of each element of **A**.

Notice that the addition of a matrix and its negative always produces a zero matrix. For example,

$$\begin{bmatrix} 3 & -1 \\ 2 & 4 \end{bmatrix} + \begin{bmatrix} -3 & 1 \\ -2 & -4 \end{bmatrix} = \begin{bmatrix} 0 & 0 \\ 0 & 0 \end{bmatrix}$$

Thus, in general, $\qquad \mathbf{A} + (-\mathbf{A}) = (-\mathbf{A}) + \mathbf{A} = \mathbf{O}.$

D   MATRIX ALGEBRA FOR ADDITION

Compare our discoveries about matrices so far with ordinary algebra. We will assume the matrices have the same order.

Ordinary algebra	Matrix algebra
• If a and b are real numbers then $a + b$ is also a real number.	• If **A** and **B** are matrices then $\mathbf{A} + \mathbf{B}$ is also a matrix.
• $a + b = b + a$	• $\mathbf{A} + \mathbf{B} = \mathbf{B} + \mathbf{A}$
• $(a + b) + c = a + (b + c)$	• $(\mathbf{A} + \mathbf{B}) + \mathbf{C} = \mathbf{A} + (\mathbf{B} + \mathbf{C})$
• $a + 0 = 0 + a = a$	• $\mathbf{A} + \mathbf{O} = \mathbf{O} + \mathbf{A} = \mathbf{A}$
• $a + (-a) = (-a) + a = 0$	• $\mathbf{A} + (-\mathbf{A}) = (-\mathbf{A}) + \mathbf{A} = \mathbf{O}$
• a half of a is $\dfrac{a}{2}$	• a half of **A** is $\frac{1}{2}\mathbf{A}$ $\left(\text{not } \dfrac{\mathbf{A}}{2}\right)$ (Dividing a matrix by a real number has no meaning in matrix algebra.)

Note: The notation we use is capital letters for matrices and lower-case letters for scalars.

Remember: You can only add (subtract) matrices that have the same order (shape).

Example 5

Explain why it is true that:

a if $\mathbf{X} + \mathbf{A} = \mathbf{B}$ then $\mathbf{X} = \mathbf{B} - \mathbf{A}$ **b** if $3\mathbf{X} = \mathbf{A}$ then $\mathbf{X} = \frac{1}{3}\mathbf{A}$

a $\qquad$ if $\mathbf{X} + \mathbf{A} = \mathbf{B}$

then $\mathbf{X} + \mathbf{A} + (-\mathbf{A}) = \mathbf{B} + (-\mathbf{A})$

$\therefore \quad \mathbf{X} + \mathbf{O} = \mathbf{B} - \mathbf{A}$

i.e., $\mathbf{X} = \mathbf{B} - \mathbf{A}$

b $\qquad$ if $3\mathbf{X} = \mathbf{A}$

then $\frac{1}{3}(3\mathbf{X}) = \frac{1}{3}\mathbf{A}$

$\therefore \quad 1\mathbf{X} = \frac{1}{3}\mathbf{A}$

$\therefore \quad \mathbf{X} = \frac{1}{3}\mathbf{A}$

Notice that the rules for addition (and subtraction) of matrices are identical to those of real numbers but we must be careful with scalar multiplication in matrix equations.

EXERCISE 14D

1 Simplify:

a $\mathbf{A} + 2\mathbf{A}$

b $3\mathbf{B} - 3\mathbf{B}$

c $\mathbf{C} - 2\mathbf{C}$

d $-\mathbf{B} + \mathbf{B}$

e $2(\mathbf{A} + \mathbf{B})$

f $-(\mathbf{A} + \mathbf{B})$

g $-(2\mathbf{A} - \mathbf{C})$

h $3\mathbf{A} - (\mathbf{B} - \mathbf{A})$

i $\mathbf{A} + 2\mathbf{B} - (\mathbf{A} - \mathbf{B})$

2 Find $\mathbf{X}$ in terms of $\mathbf{A}$, $\mathbf{B}$ and $\mathbf{C}$ if:

a $\mathbf{X} + \mathbf{B} = \mathbf{A}$

b $\mathbf{B} + \mathbf{X} = \mathbf{C}$

c $4\mathbf{B} + \mathbf{X} = 2\mathbf{C}$

d $2\mathbf{X} = \mathbf{A}$

e $3\mathbf{X} = \mathbf{B}$

f $\mathbf{A} - \mathbf{X} = \mathbf{B}$

g $\frac{1}{2}\mathbf{X} = \mathbf{C}$

h $2(\mathbf{X} + \mathbf{A}) = \mathbf{B}$

i $\mathbf{A} - 4\mathbf{X} = \mathbf{C}$

3   a   If $\mathbf{M} = \begin{bmatrix} 1 & 2 \\ 3 & 6 \end{bmatrix}$,   find $\mathbf{X}$ if $\frac{1}{3}\mathbf{X} = \mathbf{M}$.

b   If $\mathbf{N} = \begin{bmatrix} 2 & -1 \\ 3 & 5 \end{bmatrix}$,   find $\mathbf{X}$ if $4\mathbf{X} = \mathbf{N}$.

c   If $\mathbf{A} = \begin{bmatrix} 1 & 0 \\ -1 & 2 \end{bmatrix}$,   and $\mathbf{B} = \begin{bmatrix} 1 & 4 \\ -1 & 1 \end{bmatrix}$,   find $\mathbf{X}$ if $\mathbf{A} - 2\mathbf{X} = 3\mathbf{B}$.

E   MATRIX MULTIPLICATION

Suppose you go to a shop and purchase 3 soft drink cans, 4 chocolate bars and 2 icecreams

and the prices are

soft drink cans	chocolate bars	ice creams
$1.30	$0.90	$1.20

Each of these can be represented using matrices,

i.e., $\mathbf{A} = \begin{bmatrix} 3 \\ 4 \\ 2 \end{bmatrix}$ and $\mathbf{B} = \begin{bmatrix} 1.30 & 0.90 & 1.20 \end{bmatrix}$.

To work out the total cost, the following *product* could be found:

$$\mathbf{BA} = \begin{bmatrix} 1.30 & 0.90 & 1.20 \end{bmatrix} \begin{bmatrix} 3 \\ 4 \\ 2 \end{bmatrix}$$

$$= (1.30 \times 3) + (0.9 \times 4) + (1.20 \times 2)$$

$$= 3.90 + 3.60 + 2.40$$

$$= 9.90 \qquad \text{Thus the total cost is} \quad \$9.90.$$

Notice that we write the **row matrix** first and the **column matrix** second

and that $\begin{bmatrix} a & b & c \end{bmatrix} \begin{bmatrix} p \\ q \\ r \end{bmatrix} = ap + bq + cr.$

EXERCISE 14E.1

1 Determine:

   a $\begin{bmatrix} 3 & -1 \end{bmatrix} \begin{bmatrix} 5 \\ 4 \end{bmatrix}$
   b $\begin{bmatrix} 1 & 3 & 2 \end{bmatrix} \begin{bmatrix} 5 \\ 1 \\ 7 \end{bmatrix}$
   c $\begin{bmatrix} 6 & -1 & 2 & 3 \end{bmatrix} \begin{bmatrix} 1 \\ 0 \\ -1 \\ 4 \end{bmatrix}$

2 Show that the sum of w, x, y and z is given by $\begin{bmatrix} w & x & y & z \end{bmatrix} \begin{bmatrix} 1 \\ 1 \\ 1 \\ 1 \end{bmatrix}$.

   Represent the average of w, x, y and z in the same way.

3 Lucy buys 4 shirts, 3 skirts and 2 blouses costing $27, $35 and $39 respectively.

   a Write down a quantities matrix **Q** and a price matrix **P**.

   b Show how to use **P** and **Q** to determine the total cost.

4 In the interschool public speaking competition a first place is awarded 10 points, second place 6 points, third place 3 points and fourth place 1 point. One school won 3 first places, 2 seconds, 4 thirds and 2 fourths.

   a Write down this information in terms of points matrix **P**, and numbers matrix **N**.

   b Show how to use **P** and **N** to find the total number of points awarded to the school.

Now consider more complicated matrix multiplication.

In **Example 1,**   Lisa needed $\begin{bmatrix} 2 & 3 & 1 \end{bmatrix}$ and at store A, the costs matrix was $\begin{bmatrix} 2.65 \\ 1.55 \\ 2.35 \end{bmatrix}$.

                      bread   milk   butter

To find the *total cost* Lisa needs to multiply the number of items by their respective cost,

      i.e., $2 \times \$2.65 + 3 \times \$1.55 + 1 \times \$2.35 = \$12.30$

As the quantities do not change, her total cost in Store B is

      $2 \times \$2.25 + 3 \times \$1.50 + 1 \times \$2.20 = \$11.20$

To do this using matrices notice that:

$$\begin{bmatrix} 2 & 3 & 1 \end{bmatrix} \times \begin{bmatrix} 2.65 & 2.25 \\ 1.55 & 1.50 \\ 2.35 & 2.20 \end{bmatrix} = \begin{bmatrix} 12.30 & 11.20 \end{bmatrix}$$

orders: 1×3 3×2 1×2

                    the same

                resultant matrix

Now suppose Lisa's friend Olu needs 1 bread, 2 milk and 2 butter.

The quantities matrix for both Lisa and Olu would be $\begin{bmatrix} 2 & 3 & 1 \\ 1 & 2 & 2 \end{bmatrix}$ ← Lisa
                                                ← Olu

                      bread   milk   butter

Lisa's *total cost* at   Store A is $12.30 and at store B is $11.20

Olu's *total cost* at   Store A is $1 \times \$2.65 + 2 \times \$1.55 + 2 \times \$2.35 = \$10.45$

                Store B is $1 \times \$2.25 + 2 \times \$1.50 + 2 \times \$2.20 = \$9.65$

So, using matrices we require that

row 1 × column 1

$$\begin{bmatrix} 2 & 3 & 1 \\ 1 & 2 & 2 \end{bmatrix} \times \begin{bmatrix} 2.65 & 2.25 \\ 1.55 & 1.50 \\ 2.35 & 2.20 \end{bmatrix} = \begin{bmatrix} 12.30 & 11.20 \\ 10.45 & 9.65 \end{bmatrix}$$

row 1 × column 2

row 2 × column 1

row 2 × column 2

2×3 3×2 2×2

the same

resultant matrix

We are now ready to give a formal definition of a matrix product.

MATRIX PRODUCTS

As a consequence of observing the usefulness of multiplying matrices as in the contextual examples we are now in a position to define multiplication more formally.

> The **product** of an $m \times n$ matrix **A** with an $n \times p$ matrix **B**, is the $m \times p$ matrix (called **AB**) in which the element in the rth row and cth column is the sum of the products of the elements in the rth row of **A** with the corresponding elements in the cth column of **B**.

For example,

if $\mathbf{A} = \begin{bmatrix} a & b \\ c & d \end{bmatrix}$ and $\mathbf{B} = \begin{bmatrix} p & q \\ r & s \end{bmatrix}$, then $\mathbf{AB} = \begin{bmatrix} ap + br & aq + bs \\ cp + dr & cq + ds \end{bmatrix}$,

and if $\mathbf{C} = \begin{bmatrix} a & b & c \\ d & e & f \end{bmatrix}$ and $\mathbf{D} = \begin{bmatrix} x \\ y \\ z \end{bmatrix}$, then $\mathbf{CD} = \begin{bmatrix} ax + by + cz \\ dx + ey + fz \end{bmatrix}$

2×3 3×1 2×1

i.e., to get the matrix AB you multiply **rows by columns**. To get the element in the 5th row and 3rd column of AB (if it exists) multiply the 5th row of A by the 3rd column of B. If any number in a row of A does not correspond to a number in a column of B, then you cannot multiply the matrices.

Example 6

If $\mathbf{A} = \begin{bmatrix} 1 & 3 & 5 \end{bmatrix}$, $\mathbf{B} = \begin{bmatrix} 2 \\ 4 \\ 7 \end{bmatrix}$, and $\mathbf{C} = \begin{bmatrix} 1 & 0 \\ 2 & 3 \\ 1 & 4 \end{bmatrix}$

find: **a AB b AC**

---

a A is 1×3 and B is 3×1 $\therefore$ **AB** is 1×1

$\checkmark$

$\mathbf{AB} = \begin{bmatrix} 1 & 3 & 5 \end{bmatrix} \begin{bmatrix} 2 \\ 4 \\ 7 \end{bmatrix}$

$= [1 \times 2 + 3 \times 4 + 5 \times 7]$

$= [49]$

b   **A** is 1×3 and **C** is 3×2 $\therefore$ **AC** is 1×2

$$\mathbf{AC} = \begin{bmatrix} 1 & 3 & 5 \end{bmatrix} \begin{bmatrix} 1 & 0 \\ 2 & 3 \\ 1 & 4 \end{bmatrix} = \begin{bmatrix} 1 \times 1 + 3 \times 2 + 5 \times 1 & 1 \times 0 + 3 \times 3 + 5 \times 4 \end{bmatrix}$$
$$= \begin{bmatrix} 12 & 29 \end{bmatrix}$$

EXERCISE 14E.2

1   Explain why **AB** cannot be found for $\mathbf{A} = \begin{bmatrix} 4 & 2 & 1 \end{bmatrix}$ and $\mathbf{B} = \begin{bmatrix} 1 & 2 & 1 \\ 0 & 1 & 0 \end{bmatrix}$.

2   If **A** is $2 \times n$ and **B** is $m \times 3$:

   a   When can we find **AB**?   **b**   If **AB** can be found, what is its order?

   c   Why can **BA** never be found?

3   **a**   For $\mathbf{A} = \begin{bmatrix} 2 & 1 \\ 3 & 4 \end{bmatrix}$ and $\mathbf{B} = \begin{bmatrix} 5 & 6 \end{bmatrix}$,   find **BA**.

   b   For $\mathbf{A} = \begin{bmatrix} 2 & 0 & 3 \end{bmatrix}$ and $\mathbf{B} = \begin{bmatrix} 1 \\ 4 \\ 2 \end{bmatrix}$ find   **i** **AB**   **ii** **BA**.

4   Find: **a** $\begin{bmatrix} 1 & 2 & 1 \end{bmatrix} \begin{bmatrix} 2 & 3 & 1 \\ 0 & 1 & 0 \\ 1 & 0 & 2 \end{bmatrix}$ **b** $\begin{bmatrix} 1 & 0 & -1 \\ -1 & 1 & 0 \\ 0 & -1 & 1 \end{bmatrix} \begin{bmatrix} 2 \\ 3 \\ 4 \end{bmatrix}$

5      At the Fair, tickets for the Ferris Wheel are $12.50 per adult and $9.50 per child. On the first day of the Fair, 2375 adults and 5156 children ride this wheel. On the second day the figures are 2502 adults and 3612 children.

   a   Write the costs matrix **C** as a 2×1 matrix and the numbers matrix **N** as a 2×2 matrix.

   b   Find **NC** and interpret the resulting matrix.

   c   Find the total income for the two days.

6   You and your friend each go to your local hardware stores A and B to price items you wish to purchase. You want to buy 1 hammer, 1 screwdriver and 2 cans of white paint and your friend wants 1 hammer, 2 screwdrivers and 3 cans of white paint. The prices of these goods are:

	Hammer	Screwdriver	Can of paint
Store A	$7	$3	$19
Store B	$6	$2	$22

   a   Write the requirements matrix **R** as a 3×2 matrix.

   b   Write the prices matrix **P** as a 2×3 matrix.

   c   Find **PR**.

   d   What are your costs at store A and your friend's costs at store B?

   e   Should you buy from store A or store B?

USING TECHNOLOGY

USING A GRAPHICS CALCULATOR FOR MATRIX OPERATIONS

Click on the icon for your calculator to assist you to enter and perform operations on matrices.

USING A SPREADSHEET FOR MATRIX OPERATIONS

ADDING MATRICES

Adding matrices by hand can be tedious, particularly for matrices of higher order. A spreadsheet can significantly speed up the process.

Consider the addition:
$$\begin{bmatrix} 3 & 0 & 3 & 2 \\ 2 & 1 & 1 & 5 \\ 2 & 5 & 0 & 3 \\ 1 & 4 & 2 & 8 \end{bmatrix} + \begin{bmatrix} 2 & 2 & 3 & 4 \\ 8 & 1 & 5 & 2 \\ 7 & 3 & 2 & 0 \\ 4 & 4 & 4 & 1 \end{bmatrix}$$

SPREADSHEET

What to do:

1 Enter the two matrices on the spreadsheet. For example:

2 Highlight the cells in the range E7:H10 as shown. The addition will appear in these cells.

3 With the cells still highlighted, type =B2:E5+G2:J5   To enter the formula hold down CTRL and SHIFT together and while doing this press ENTER .

	A	B	C	D	E	F	G	H	I	J
1										
2		3	0	3	2		2	2	3	4
3		2	1	1	5		8	1	5	2
4		2	5	0	3		7	3	2	0
5		1	4	2	8		4	4	4	1
6										
7										
8										
9										
10										
11										

SUBTRACTING MATRICES

This is identical to addition except for the formula which should now be   =B2:E5-G2:J5

SCALAR MULTIPLICATION

Consider finding $3.5 \begin{bmatrix} 2 & 3 & 1 & 4 \\ 8 & 5 & 3 & 2 \\ 4 & 2 & 5 & 1 \end{bmatrix}$

	A	B	C	D	E	F	G	H
1								
2		3.5		2	3	1	4	
3				8	5	3	2	
4				4	2	5	1	
5								
6								
7								
8								
9								

What to do:

1 Enter 3.5 into B2 and the given matrix in the range D2:G4 say.

2 Highlight the cells C6:F8 and while still highlighted type =B2*D2:G4.

3 Enter the formula by holding down CTRL and SHIFT together and while doing this press ENTER .

MULTIPLYING MATRICES

Multiplying matrices by hand can be very tedious, particularly with real life matrices which could be very large. The formula = MMULT is used.

Consider finding
$$\begin{bmatrix} 1 & 3 & 2 & 5 & 6 \\ 3 & 0 & 2 & 1 & 2 \\ 0 & 1 & 3 & 2 & 4 \end{bmatrix} \times \begin{bmatrix} 2 & 3 & 1 & 2 \\ 1 & 2 & 0 & 5 \\ 1 & 0 & 0 & 1 \\ 0 & 1 & 3 & 0 \\ 4 & 5 & 2 & 7 \end{bmatrix}$$

What to do:

SPREADSHEET

1 First notice that we are multiplying a 3×5 and a 5×4 matrix. So the result is a 3×4 matrix.

2 Enter the matrices on a spreadsheet. For example:

	A	B	C	D	E	F	G	H	I	J	K	L
1												
2		1	3	2	5	6		2	3	1	2	
3		3	0	2	1	2		1	2	0	5	
4		0	1	3	2	4		1	0	0	1	
5								0	1	3	0	
6								4	5	2	7	
7												
8												
9												
10												
11												

3 Highlight the cells C8:F10 as shown and while these cells are highlighted type

$$=\text{MMULT}(\underbrace{\text{B2:F4}}_{\substack{\text{first}\\\text{matrix}}}, \underbrace{\text{H2:K6}}_{\substack{\text{second}\\\text{matrix}}})$$

4 Enter the formula by holding down CTRL and SHIFT together and while doing this press ENTER .

EXERCISE 14F

1 Use technology to find:

a $\begin{bmatrix} 13 & 12 & 4 \\ 11 & 12 & 8 \\ 7 & 9 & 7 \end{bmatrix} + \begin{bmatrix} 3 & 6 & 11 \\ 2 & 9 & 8 \\ 3 & 13 & 17 \end{bmatrix}$

b $\begin{bmatrix} 13 & 12 & 4 \\ 11 & 12 & 8 \\ 7 & 9 & 7 \end{bmatrix} - \begin{bmatrix} 3 & 6 & 11 \\ 2 & 9 & 8 \\ 3 & 13 & 17 \end{bmatrix}$

c $22\begin{bmatrix} 1 & 0 & 6 & 8 & 9 \\ 2 & 7 & 4 & 5 & 0 \\ 8 & 2 & 4 & 4 & 6 \end{bmatrix}$

d $\begin{bmatrix} 2 & 6 & 0 & 7 \\ 3 & 2 & 8 & 6 \\ 1 & 4 & 0 & 2 \\ 3 & 0 & 1 & 8 \end{bmatrix}\begin{bmatrix} 4 \\ 5 \\ 6 \\ 11 \end{bmatrix}$

Use technology to assist in solving the following problems:

2 For their holiday, Lars and Simke are planning to spend time at a popular tourist resort. They will need accommodation at one of the local motels and they are not certain how long they will stay. Their initial planning is for three nights and includes three breakfasts and two dinners. They have gathered prices from three different motels.

The Bay View has rooms at $125 per night. A full breakfast costs $22 per person (and therefore $44 for them both). An evening meal for two usually costs $75 including drinks.

By contrast, 'The Terrace' has rooms at \$150 per night, breakfast at \$40 per double and dinner costs on average \$80.

Things seem to be a little better at the Staunton Star Motel. Accommodation is \$140 per night, full breakfast (for two) is \$40, while an evening meal for two usually costs \$65.

a Write down a 'numbers' matrix as a 1×3 row matrix.

b Write down a 'prices' matrix in 3×3 form.

c Use matrix multiplication to establish total prices for each venue.

d Instead of the couple staying three nights, the alternative is to spend two nights. In that event Lars and Simke d ecide on having breakfast just once and one evening meal before moving on. Recalculate prices for each venue.

e Now remake the 'numbers' matrix (2×3) so that it includes both scenarios and recalculate the product with the 'prices' matrix.

3 A bus company runs four tours. Tour A costs \$125, Tour B costs \$315, Tour C costs \$405, and Tour D costs \$375. The numbers of clients they had over the summer period are shown in the table below.

	Tour A	Tour B	Tour C	Tour D
November	50	42	18	65
December	65	37	25	82
January	120	29	23	75
February	42	36	19	72

Use the information and matrix methods to find the total income for the tour company.

4 The Bay View Motel has three types of suites for guests.

Standard suites cost \$125 per night. They have 20 suites.

Deluxe suites cost \$195 per night. They have 15 suites.

Executive suites cost \$225 per night. They have 5 suites.

The rooms which are occupied also have a maintenance

cost: Standard suites cost \$85 per day to maintain.

Deluxe suites cost \$120 per day to maintain.

Executive suites cost \$130 per day to maintain.

The hotel has confirmed room bookings for the next week.

	M	T	W	Th	F	S	Su
Standard	15	12	13	11	14	16	8
Deluxe	4	3	6	2	0	4	7
Executive	3	1	4	4	3	2	0

By using a process outlined below we can see that

(income from room) $\times$ (bookings per day)

   $-$ (maintenance cost per room) $\times$ (bookings per day)

= (total expected income per day) $-$ (expected costs per day)

= profit per day

a Create the matrices required to show how the profit per week can be found.

b How would the results alter if the hotel maintained (cleaned) all rooms every day? Show calculations.

c Produce a profit per room matrix and show how **a** could be done with a single matrix product.

G SOME PROPERTIES OF MATRIX MULTIPLICATION

In the following exercise we should discover the properties of 2×2 matrix multiplication which are like those of ordinary number multiplication, and those which are not.

EXERCISE 14G

1 For ordinary arithmetic $2 \times 3 = 3 \times 2$ and in algebra $ab = ba$.

For matrices, is $\mathbf{AB} = \mathbf{BA}$ always?

Hint: Try $\mathbf{A} = \begin{bmatrix} 1 & 0 \\ 1 & 2 \end{bmatrix}$ and $\mathbf{B} = \begin{bmatrix} -1 & 1 \\ 0 & 3 \end{bmatrix}$ say.

2 If $\mathbf{A} = \begin{bmatrix} a & b \\ c & d \end{bmatrix}$ and $\mathbf{O} = \begin{bmatrix} 0 & 0 \\ 0 & 0 \end{bmatrix}$ find $\mathbf{AO}$ and $\mathbf{OA}$.

3 For all real numbers a, b and c it is true that $a(b + c) = ab + ac$ and this is known as the **distributive law**.

  a 'Make up' three 2×2 matrices $\mathbf{A}$, $\mathbf{B}$ and $\mathbf{C}$ and verify that
$\mathbf{A(B + C)} = \mathbf{AB} + \mathbf{AC}$.

  b Now let $\mathbf{A} = \begin{bmatrix} a & b \\ c & d \end{bmatrix}$, $\mathbf{B} = \begin{bmatrix} p & q \\ r & s \end{bmatrix}$ and $\mathbf{C} = \begin{bmatrix} w & x \\ y & z \end{bmatrix}$

    and prove that in general $\mathbf{A(B + C)} = \mathbf{AB} + \mathbf{AC}$.

  c Use the matrices you 'made up' in **a** to verify that $\mathbf{(AB)C} = \mathbf{A(BC)}$

  d As in **b** prove that $\mathbf{(AB)C} = \mathbf{A(BC)}$

4 **a** If $\begin{bmatrix} a & b \\ c & d \end{bmatrix} \begin{bmatrix} w & x \\ y & z \end{bmatrix} = \begin{bmatrix} a & b \\ c & d \end{bmatrix}$ i.e., $\mathbf{AX} = \mathbf{A}$,
deduce that $w = z = 1$ and $x = y = 0$.

  b For any real number a, it is true that $a \times 1 = 1 \times a = a$.
Is there a matrix $\mathbf{I}$, say, such that $\mathbf{AI} = \mathbf{IA} = \mathbf{A}$ for all 2×2 matrices $\mathbf{A}$?
[**Hint:** Use the results of **a** above.]

5 Suppose $\mathbf{A}^2 = \mathbf{AA}$, i.e., $\mathbf{A}$ multiplied by itself, and that $\mathbf{A}^3 = \mathbf{AAA}$.

  a Find $\mathbf{A}^2$ if $\mathbf{A} = \begin{bmatrix} 2 & 1 \\ 3 & -2 \end{bmatrix}$ **b** Find $\mathbf{A}^3$ if $\mathbf{A} = \begin{bmatrix} 5 & -1 \\ 2 & 4 \end{bmatrix}$.

6 **a** If $\mathbf{A} = \begin{bmatrix} 1 & 2 \\ 3 & 4 \\ 5 & 6 \end{bmatrix}$ try to find $\mathbf{A}^2$.

  b When can $\mathbf{A}^2$ be found, i.e., under what conditions can we square a matrix?

7 Show that if $\mathbf{I} = \begin{bmatrix} 1 & 0 \\ 0 & 1 \end{bmatrix}$ then $\mathbf{I}^2 = \mathbf{I}$ and $\mathbf{I}^3 = \mathbf{I}$.

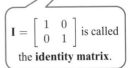

$\mathbf{I} = \begin{bmatrix} 1 & 0 \\ 0 & 1 \end{bmatrix}$ is called the **identity matrix**.

You should have discovered from the above exercise that:

Ordinary algebra	Matrix algebra
• If a and b are real numbers then so is ab.	• If **A** and **B** are matrices that can be multiplied then **AB** is also a matrix. {closure}
• $ab = ba$ for all a, b	• In general **AB** $\neq$ **BA**. {non-commutative}
• $a0 = 0a = 0$ for all a	• If **O** is a zero matrix then **AO** = **OA** = **O** for all **A**.
• $a(b + c) = ab + ac$	• **A**(**B** + **C**) = **AB** + **AC** {distributive law}
• $a \times 1 = 1 \times a = a$	• If $\mathbf{I} = \begin{bmatrix} 1 & 0 \\ 0 & 1 \end{bmatrix}$ then **AI** = **IA** = **A** for all 2×2 matrices **A**. {identity law}
• a^n exists for all $a \geqslant 0$	• $\mathbf{A}^n$ for $n \geqslant 2$ can be determined provided that **A** is a square and n is an integer.

Example 7

Expand and simplify where possible: a $(\mathbf{A} + 2\mathbf{I})^2$ b $(\mathbf{A} - \mathbf{B})^2$

a $(\mathbf{A} + 2\mathbf{I})^2$

$= (\mathbf{A} + 2\mathbf{I})(\mathbf{A} + 2\mathbf{I})$ $\{\mathbf{X}^2 = \mathbf{XX}$ by definition$\}$

$= (\mathbf{A} + 2\mathbf{I})\mathbf{A} + (\mathbf{A} + 2\mathbf{I})2\mathbf{I}$ $\{\mathbf{B}(\mathbf{C} + \mathbf{D}) = \mathbf{BC} + \mathbf{BD}\}$

$= \mathbf{A}^2 + 2\mathbf{IA} + 2\mathbf{AI} + 4\mathbf{I}^2$ $\{\mathbf{B}(\mathbf{C} + \mathbf{D}) = \mathbf{BC} + \mathbf{BD}$ again, twice$\}$

$= \mathbf{A}^2 + 2\mathbf{A} + 2\mathbf{A} + 4\mathbf{I}$ $\{\mathbf{AI} = \mathbf{IA} = \mathbf{A}$ and $\mathbf{I}^2 = \mathbf{I}\}$

$= \mathbf{A}^2 + 4\mathbf{A} + 4\mathbf{I}$

b $(\mathbf{A} - \mathbf{B})^2$

$= (\mathbf{A} - \mathbf{B})(\mathbf{A} - \mathbf{B})$ $\{\mathbf{X}^2 = \mathbf{XX}$ by definition$\}$

$= (\mathbf{A} - \mathbf{B})\mathbf{A} - (\mathbf{A} - \mathbf{B})\mathbf{B}$ $\{\mathbf{C}(\mathbf{D} - \mathbf{E}) = \mathbf{CD} - \mathbf{CE}$, three times$\}$

$= \mathbf{A}^2 - \mathbf{BA} - \mathbf{AB} + \mathbf{B}^2$

Note: b cannot be simplified further as in general **AB** $\neq$ **BA**.

8 Given that all matrices are 2×2 and **I** is the identity matrix, explain and simplify:

a **A**(**A** + **I**)   b (**B** + 2**I**)**B**   c **A**($\mathbf{A}^2$ − 2**A** + **I**)

d **A**($\mathbf{A}^2$ + **A** − 2**I**)   e (**A** + **B**)(**C** + **D**)   f $(\mathbf{A} + \mathbf{B})^2$

g (**A** + **B**)(**A** − **B**)   h $(\mathbf{A} + \mathbf{I})^2$ i $(3\mathbf{I} - \mathbf{B})^2$

Example 8

If $\mathbf{A}^2 = 2\mathbf{A} + 3\mathbf{I}$, find $\mathbf{A}^3$ and $\mathbf{A}^4$ in the form $k\mathbf{A} + l\mathbf{I}$, ($k$ and l are scalars).

$\mathbf{A}^2 = 2\mathbf{A} + 3\mathbf{I}$, $\therefore$ $\mathbf{A}^3 = \mathbf{A} \times \mathbf{A}^2$ and $\mathbf{A}^4 = \mathbf{A} \times \mathbf{A}^3$

$\qquad\qquad\qquad = \mathbf{A}(2\mathbf{A} + 3\mathbf{I})$ $\qquad\qquad\qquad = \mathbf{A}(7\mathbf{A} + 6\mathbf{I})$

$\qquad\qquad\qquad = 2\mathbf{A}^2 + 3\mathbf{AI}$ $\qquad\qquad\qquad = 7\mathbf{A}^2 + 6\mathbf{AI}$

$\qquad\qquad\qquad = 2(2\mathbf{A} + 3\mathbf{I}) + 3\mathbf{AI}$ $\qquad\qquad = 7(2\mathbf{A} + 3\mathbf{I}) + 6\mathbf{A}$

$\qquad\qquad\qquad = 7\mathbf{A} + 6\mathbf{I}$ $\qquad\qquad\qquad\quad = 20\mathbf{A} + 21\mathbf{I}$

9 **a** If $A^2 = 2A - I$, find A^3 and A^4 in linear form, $kA + lI$, (k and l are scalars).

 b If $B^2 = 2I - B$, find B^3, B^4 and B^5 in linear form.

 c If $C^2 = 4C - 3I$, find C^3 and C^5 in linear form.

10 **a** If $A^2 = I$, simplify:

 i $A(A + 2I)$ **ii** $(A - I)^2$ **iii** $A(A + 3I)^2$

 b If $A^3 = I$, simplify $A^2(A + I)^2$

 c If $A^2 = O$, simplify:

 i $A(2A - 3I)$ **ii** $A(A + 2I)(A - I)$ **iii** $A(A + I)^3$

11 The result "if $ab = 0$ then $a = 0$ or $b = 0$" for real numbers does not have an equivalent result for matrices.

 a If $A = \begin{bmatrix} 1 & 0 \\ 0 & 0 \end{bmatrix}$ and $B = \begin{bmatrix} 0 & 0 \\ 0 & 1 \end{bmatrix}$ find AB.

 This example provides us with evidence that
 "If $AB = O$ then $A = O$ or $B = O$" is a false statement.

 b If $A = \begin{bmatrix} \frac{1}{2} & \frac{1}{2} \\ \frac{1}{2} & \frac{1}{2} \end{bmatrix}$ determine A^2.

 c Comment on the following argument for a 2×2 matrix A:

 It is known that $A^2 = A$, $\therefore$ $A^2 - A = O$
 $\therefore$ $A(A - I) = O$
 $\therefore$ $A = O$ or $A - I = O$
 $\therefore$ $A = O$ or I

 d Find **all** 2×2 matrices A for which $A^2 = A$. (**Hint:** Let $A = \begin{bmatrix} a & b \\ c & d \end{bmatrix}$.)

12 Give **one** example which shows that "if $A^2 = O$ then $A = O$" is a *false* statement.

Example 9

Find constants a and b such that $A^2 = aA + bI$ for A equal to $\begin{bmatrix} 1 & 2 \\ 3 & 4 \end{bmatrix}$.

Since $A^2 = aA + bI$, $\therefore$ $\begin{bmatrix} 1 & 2 \\ 3 & 4 \end{bmatrix}\begin{bmatrix} 1 & 2 \\ 3 & 4 \end{bmatrix} = a\begin{bmatrix} 1 & 2 \\ 3 & 4 \end{bmatrix} + b\begin{bmatrix} 1 & 0 \\ 0 & 1 \end{bmatrix}$

$\therefore$ $\begin{bmatrix} 1+6 & 2+8 \\ 3+12 & 6+16 \end{bmatrix} = \begin{bmatrix} a & 2a \\ 3a & 4a \end{bmatrix} + \begin{bmatrix} b & 0 \\ 0 & b \end{bmatrix}$

$\begin{bmatrix} 7 & 10 \\ 15 & 22 \end{bmatrix} = \begin{bmatrix} a+b & 2a \\ 3a & 4a+b \end{bmatrix}$

Thus $a + b = 7$ and $2a = 10$
$\therefore$ $a = 5$ and $b = 2$

Checking for consistency $3a = 3(5) = 15$ ✓ $4a + b = 4(5) + (2) = 22$ ✓

13 Find constants a and b such that $\mathbf{A}^2 = a\mathbf{A} + b\mathbf{I}$ for $\mathbf{A}$ equal to:

    a $\begin{bmatrix} 1 & 2 \\ -1 & 2 \end{bmatrix}$ **b** $\begin{bmatrix} 3 & 1 \\ 2 & -2 \end{bmatrix}$

14 If $\mathbf{A} = \begin{bmatrix} 1 & 2 \\ -1 & -3 \end{bmatrix}$, find constants p and q such that $\mathbf{A}^2 = p\mathbf{A} + q\mathbf{I}$.

    a Hence, write $\mathbf{A}^3$ in linear form, $r\mathbf{A} + s\mathbf{I}$ where r and s are scalars.

    b Also write $\mathbf{A}^4$ in linear form.

H   THE INVERSE OF A 2×2 MATRIX

We can solve $\begin{cases} 2x + 3y = 4 \\ 5x + 4y = 17 \end{cases}$ algebraically to get $x = 5, \quad y = -2$.

Notice that this system can be written as a matrix equation $\begin{bmatrix} 2 & 3 \\ 5 & 4 \end{bmatrix} \begin{bmatrix} x \\ y \end{bmatrix} = \begin{bmatrix} 4 \\ 17 \end{bmatrix}$.

The solution $x = 5, \quad y = -2$ is easily checked as

$$\begin{bmatrix} 2 & 3 \\ 5 & 4 \end{bmatrix} \begin{bmatrix} 5 \\ -2 \end{bmatrix} = \begin{bmatrix} 2(5) + 3(-2) \\ 5(5) + 4(-2) \end{bmatrix} = \begin{bmatrix} 4 \\ 17 \end{bmatrix} \quad \checkmark$$

Notice that these matrix equations have form $\mathbf{AX} = \mathbf{B}$ where $\mathbf{A}$ is the matrix of coefficients, $\mathbf{X}$ is the unknown column matrix and $\mathbf{B}$ is the column matrix of constants.

The question arises: If $\mathbf{AX} = \mathbf{B}$, how can we find $\mathbf{X}$ using matrices only?

To answer this question, suppose there exists a matrix $\mathbf{C}$ such that $\mathbf{CA} = \mathbf{I}$.

    If we *pre-multiply* each side of $\mathbf{AX} = \mathbf{B}$ by $\mathbf{C}$ we get

$$\mathbf{C(AX)} = \mathbf{CB}$$
$$\therefore \quad \mathbf{(CA)X} = \mathbf{CB}$$
$$\therefore \quad \mathbf{IX} = \mathbf{CB}$$
$$\text{and so} \quad \mathbf{X} = \mathbf{CB}$$

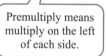

Premultiply means multiply on the left of each side.

If it exists, we will call $\mathbf{C}$ such that $\mathbf{CA} = \mathbf{I}$, the **multiplication inverse** of $\mathbf{A}$ and we will use the notation $\mathbf{C} = \mathbf{A}^{-1}$.

In general,   the **multiplication inverse of A**, if it exists, satisfies $\mathbf{A}^{-1}\mathbf{A} = \mathbf{AA}^{-1} = \mathbf{I}$.

    Notice that $\begin{bmatrix} 3 & 1 \\ 5 & 2 \end{bmatrix} \begin{bmatrix} 2 & -1 \\ -5 & 3 \end{bmatrix} = \begin{bmatrix} 1 & 0 \\ 0 & 1 \end{bmatrix} = \mathbf{I}$

Notice also that $\begin{bmatrix} 1 & 2 \\ 3 & 4 \end{bmatrix} \begin{bmatrix} 4 & -2 \\ -3 & 1 \end{bmatrix} = \begin{bmatrix} -2 & 0 \\ 0 & -2 \end{bmatrix} = -2 \begin{bmatrix} 1 & 0 \\ 0 & 1 \end{bmatrix} = 2\mathbf{I}$

    and that $\begin{bmatrix} 5 & 11 \\ -2 & 3 \end{bmatrix} \begin{bmatrix} 3 & -11 \\ 2 & 5 \end{bmatrix} = \begin{bmatrix} 37 & 0 \\ 0 & 37 \end{bmatrix} = 37 \begin{bmatrix} 1 & 0 \\ 0 & 1 \end{bmatrix} = 37\mathbf{I}$

Notice that all answers are scalar multiples of $\mathbf{I}$.

These results suggest that $\begin{bmatrix} a & b \\ c & d \end{bmatrix} \begin{bmatrix} d & -b \\ -c & a \end{bmatrix} = k\mathbf{I}$ for some scalar k.

On expanding this product $\begin{bmatrix} ad - bc & 0 \\ 0 & ad - bc \end{bmatrix} = k\mathbf{I}$

$$\therefore \quad (ad - bc) \begin{bmatrix} 1 & 0 \\ 0 & 1 \end{bmatrix} = k\mathbf{I}$$

i.e., $(ad - bc)\mathbf{I} = k\mathbf{I}$
and so $k = ad - bc$.

Consequently, $\begin{bmatrix} a & b \\ c & d \end{bmatrix} \times \dfrac{1}{ad - bc} \begin{bmatrix} d & -b \\ -c & a \end{bmatrix} = \begin{bmatrix} 1 & 0 \\ 0 & 1 \end{bmatrix}$.

which suggests that   if $\mathbf{A} = \begin{bmatrix} a & b \\ c & d \end{bmatrix}$ then $\mathbf{A}^{-1} = \dfrac{1}{ad - bc} \begin{bmatrix} d & -b \\ -c & a \end{bmatrix}$.

We also notice that $\mathbf{A}^{-1}$ exists provided $ad - bc \neq 0$, otherwise $\dfrac{1}{ad - bc}$ would be undefined. If $ad - bc \neq 0$, we say that $\mathbf{A}$ is **invertible** or **non-singular**.

So the value of $ad - bc$ *determines* whether or not a 2×2 matrix has an inverse.

Consequently, for $\mathbf{A} = \begin{bmatrix} a & b \\ c & d \end{bmatrix}$ the value of $ad - bc$ is called the **determinant** of $\mathbf{A}$.

It is denoted by $|\mathbf{A}|$ or $\det \mathbf{A}$.

> $\mathbf{A}$ has an **inverse** if $|\mathbf{A}| \neq 0$,   i.e., $\mathbf{A}$ is non-singular

Hence,   if $\mathbf{A} = \begin{bmatrix} a & b \\ c & d \end{bmatrix}$,   then $\mathbf{A}^{-1} = \dfrac{1}{|\mathbf{A}|} \begin{bmatrix} d & -b \\ -c & a \end{bmatrix}$ where $|\mathbf{A}| = ad - bc$.

EXERCISE 14H

1   **a**   Find $\begin{bmatrix} 5 & 6 \\ 2 & 3 \end{bmatrix} \begin{bmatrix} 3 & -6 \\ -2 & 5 \end{bmatrix}$ and hence find the inverse of $\begin{bmatrix} 5 & 6 \\ 2 & 3 \end{bmatrix}$.

   b   Find $\begin{bmatrix} 3 & -4 \\ 1 & 2 \end{bmatrix} \begin{bmatrix} 2 & 4 \\ -1 & 3 \end{bmatrix}$ and hence find the inverse of $\begin{bmatrix} 3 & -4 \\ 1 & 2 \end{bmatrix}$.

   c   Find $\begin{bmatrix} 2 & 0 & 3 \\ 1 & 5 & 2 \\ 1 & -3 & 1 \end{bmatrix} \begin{bmatrix} -11 & 9 & 15 \\ -1 & 1 & 1 \\ 8 & -6 & -10 \end{bmatrix}$ and hence find the inverse of $\begin{bmatrix} 2 & 0 & 3 \\ 1 & 5 & 2 \\ 1 & -3 & 1 \end{bmatrix}$.

2   Find $|\mathbf{A}|$ for $\mathbf{A}$ equal to:

   a $\begin{bmatrix} 3 & 7 \\ 2 & 4 \end{bmatrix}$ **b** $\begin{bmatrix} -1 & 3 \\ 1 & -2 \end{bmatrix}$ **c** $\begin{bmatrix} 0 & 0 \\ 0 & 0 \end{bmatrix}$ **d** $\begin{bmatrix} 1 & 0 \\ 0 & 1 \end{bmatrix}$

3   Find $\det \mathbf{B}$ for $\mathbf{B}$ equal to:

   a $\begin{bmatrix} 3 & -2 \\ 7 & 4 \end{bmatrix}$ **b** $\begin{bmatrix} 3 & 0 \\ 0 & 2 \end{bmatrix}$ **c** $\begin{bmatrix} 0 & 1 \\ 1 & 0 \end{bmatrix}$ **d** $\begin{bmatrix} a & -a \\ 1 & a \end{bmatrix}$

4 For $\mathbf{A} = \begin{bmatrix} 2 & -1 \\ -1 & -1 \end{bmatrix}$ find: **a** $|\mathbf{A}|$ **b** $|\mathbf{A}|^2$ **c** $|2\mathbf{A}|$

5 Prove that, if $\mathbf{A}$ is any 2×2 matrix and k is a constant, then $|k\mathbf{A}| = k^2|\mathbf{A}|$.

6 By letting $\mathbf{A} = \begin{bmatrix} a & b \\ c & d \end{bmatrix}$ and $\mathbf{B} = \begin{bmatrix} w & x \\ y & z \end{bmatrix}$

   a find $|\mathbf{A}|$ and $|\mathbf{B}|$ **b** find $\mathbf{AB}$ and $|\mathbf{AB}|$, and hence
   c show that $|\mathbf{AB}| = |\mathbf{A}| |\mathbf{B}|$ for all 2×2 matrices $\mathbf{A}$ and $\mathbf{B}$.

7 $\mathbf{A} = \begin{bmatrix} 1 & 2 \\ 3 & 4 \end{bmatrix}$ and $\mathbf{B} = \begin{bmatrix} -1 & 2 \\ 0 & 1 \end{bmatrix}$.

   a Using the results of **5** and **6** above and the calculated values of $|\mathbf{A}|$ and $|\mathbf{B}|$, find:
      i $|\mathbf{A}|$ **ii** $|2\mathbf{A}|$ **iii** $|-\mathbf{A}|$ **iv** $|-3\mathbf{B}|$ **v** $|\mathbf{AB}|$
   b Check your answers without using the results of **5** and **6** above.

8 Find, if it exists, the inverse matrix of:

   a $\begin{bmatrix} 2 & 4 \\ -1 & 5 \end{bmatrix}$ **b** $\begin{bmatrix} 1 & 0 \\ 1 & -1 \end{bmatrix}$ **c** $\begin{bmatrix} 2 & 4 \\ 1 & 2 \end{bmatrix}$ **d** $\begin{bmatrix} 1 & 0 \\ 0 & 1 \end{bmatrix}$

   e $\begin{bmatrix} 3 & 5 \\ -6 & -10 \end{bmatrix}$ **f** $\begin{bmatrix} -1 & 2 \\ 4 & 7 \end{bmatrix}$ **g** $\begin{bmatrix} 3 & 4 \\ -1 & 2 \end{bmatrix}$ **h** $\begin{bmatrix} -1 & -1 \\ 2 & 3 \end{bmatrix}$

SOLVING A PAIR OF LINEAR EQUATIONS

Example 10

a If $\mathbf{A} = \begin{bmatrix} 2 & 1 \\ 3 & 4 \end{bmatrix}$ find $|\mathbf{A}|$.   **b** Does $\begin{cases} 2x + y = 4 \\ 3x + 4y = -1 \end{cases}$ have a unique solution?

a $|\mathbf{A}| = 2(4) - 1(3)$ **b** The system in matrix form is
   $\phantom{|\mathbf{A}|} = 8 - 3$ $\begin{bmatrix} 2 & 1 \\ 3 & 4 \end{bmatrix} \begin{bmatrix} x \\ y \end{bmatrix} = \begin{bmatrix} 4 \\ -1 \end{bmatrix}$
   $\phantom{|\mathbf{A}|} = 5$

   Now as $|\mathbf{A}| = 5 \neq 0$, $\mathbf{A}^{-1}$ exists and so we
   can solve for x and y,   i.e., a unique solution.

Example 11

If $\mathbf{A} = \begin{bmatrix} 2 & 3 \\ 5 & 4 \end{bmatrix}$,   find $\mathbf{A}^{-1}$ and hence solve $\begin{cases} 2x + 3y = 4 \\ 5x + 4y = 17 \end{cases}$.

Now in matrix form the system is: $\begin{bmatrix} 2 & 3 \\ 5 & 4 \end{bmatrix} \begin{bmatrix} x \\ y \end{bmatrix} = \begin{bmatrix} 4 \\ 17 \end{bmatrix}$

i.e., $\mathbf{AX} = \mathbf{B}$ where $|\mathbf{A}| = 8 - 15 = -7$

Now $\mathbf{A}^{-1}\mathbf{AX} = \mathbf{A}^{-1}\mathbf{B}$

$$\therefore \; \mathbf{IX} = \frac{1}{-7} \begin{bmatrix} 4 & -3 \\ -5 & 2 \end{bmatrix} \begin{bmatrix} 4 \\ 17 \end{bmatrix}$$

$$\therefore \; \mathbf{X} = \frac{1}{-7} \begin{bmatrix} -35 \\ 14 \end{bmatrix}$$

$$\therefore \; \mathbf{X} = \begin{bmatrix} 5 \\ -2 \end{bmatrix} \quad \text{and so} \; x = 5, \; y = -2$$

> Notice that both sides of the matrix equation are multiplied by the inverse matrix in the front or pre-position. This is called pre-multiplication

EXERCISE 14I

1 Convert into matrix equations:

a $3x - y = 8$
$2x + 3y = 6$

b $4x - 3y = 11$
$3x + 2y = -5$

c $3a - b = 6$
$2a + 7b = -4$

2 Use matrix algebra to solve the system:

a $2x - y = 6$
$x + 3y = 14$

b $5x - 4y = 5$
$2x + 3y = -13$

c $x - 2y = 7$
$5x + 3y = -2$

d $3x + 5y = 4$
$2x - y = 11$

e $4x - 7y = 8$
$3x - 5y = 0$

f $7x + 11y = 18$
$11x - 7y = -11$

3 **a** Show that if $\mathbf{AX} = \mathbf{B}$ then $\mathbf{X} = \mathbf{A}^{-1}\mathbf{B}$ whereas if $\mathbf{XA} = \mathbf{B}$ then $\mathbf{X} = \mathbf{BA}^{-1}$.

b Find $\mathbf{X}$ if:

i $\mathbf{X} \begin{bmatrix} 1 & 2 \\ 5 & -1 \end{bmatrix} = \begin{bmatrix} 14 & -5 \\ 22 & 0 \end{bmatrix}$

ii $\begin{bmatrix} 1 & 3 \\ 2 & -1 \end{bmatrix} \mathbf{X} = \begin{bmatrix} 1 & -3 \\ 4 & 2 \end{bmatrix}$

Example 12

Find $\mathbf{A}^{-1}$ when $\mathbf{A} = \begin{bmatrix} 4 & k \\ 2 & -1 \end{bmatrix}$ and state k when $\mathbf{A}^{-1}$ exists.

> If $|\mathbf{A}| = 0$, the matrix $\mathbf{A}$ is singular and is not invertible.

$$\mathbf{A}^{-1} = \frac{1}{-4 - 2k} \begin{bmatrix} -1 & -k \\ -2 & 4 \end{bmatrix} = \begin{bmatrix} \dfrac{1}{2k+4} & \dfrac{k}{2k+4} \\ \dfrac{2}{2k+4} & \dfrac{-4}{2k+4} \end{bmatrix}$$

So $\mathbf{A}^{-1}$ exists provided that $2k + 4 \neq 0$, i.e., $k \neq -2$.

4 For **a** $\mathbf{A} = \begin{bmatrix} k & 1 \\ -6 & 2 \end{bmatrix}$

b $\mathbf{A} = \begin{bmatrix} 3 & -1 \\ 0 & k \end{bmatrix}$

c $\mathbf{A} = \begin{bmatrix} k+1 & 2 \\ 1 & k \end{bmatrix}$

i find the values of k for which the matrix $\mathbf{A}$ is singular

ii find $\mathbf{A}^{-1}$ when $\mathbf{A}$ is non-singular.

5   **a**   If $\mathbf{A} = \begin{bmatrix} 1 & 0 & 2 \\ -1 & 1 & 3 \end{bmatrix}$ and $\mathbf{B} = \begin{bmatrix} -1 & 2 \\ -4 & 6 \\ 1 & -1 \end{bmatrix}$,   find **AB**.

   b   Does your result in **a** imply that **A** and **B** are inverses?   [**Hint:**   Find **BA**.]

   The above example illustrates that only square matrices can have inverses. Why?

6   Given $\mathbf{A} = \begin{bmatrix} 2 & 1 \\ 0 & 1 \end{bmatrix}$, $\mathbf{B} = \begin{bmatrix} 1 & 2 \\ -1 & 0 \end{bmatrix}$ and $\mathbf{C} = \begin{bmatrix} 0 & 3 \\ 1 & 2 \end{bmatrix}$, find **X** if **AXB** = **C**.

7   **a**   Consider the system $\begin{cases} 2x - 3y = 8 \\ 4x - y = 11 \end{cases}$

   i   Write the equations in the form $\mathbf{AX} = \mathbf{B}$ and find $|\mathbf{A}|$.
   ii   Does the system have a unique solution? If so, find it.

   b   Consider the system $\begin{cases} 2x + ky = 8 \\ 4x - y = 11 \end{cases}$

   i   Write the system in the form $\mathbf{AX} = \mathbf{B}$ and find $|\mathbf{A}|$.
   ii   For what value(s) of k does the system have a unique solution? Find the unique solution.
   iii   Find k when the system does not have a unique solution. How many solutions does it have in this case?

8   If a matrix **A** is its own inverse, then $\mathbf{A} = \mathbf{A}^{-1}$.

   For example, if $\mathbf{A} = \begin{bmatrix} 0 & -1 \\ -1 & 0 \end{bmatrix}$ then $\mathbf{A}^{-1} = \dfrac{1}{-1} \begin{bmatrix} 0 & 1 \\ 1 & 0 \end{bmatrix} = \begin{bmatrix} 0 & -1 \\ -1 & 0 \end{bmatrix} = \mathbf{A}.$

   a   Show that, if $\mathbf{A} = \mathbf{A}^{-1}$, then $\mathbf{A}^2 = \mathbf{I}$.

   b   If $\begin{bmatrix} a & b \\ b & a \end{bmatrix}$ is its own inverse, show that there are exactly 4 matrices of this form.

9   **a**   If $\mathbf{A} = \begin{bmatrix} 1 & 2 \\ -1 & 0 \end{bmatrix}$ find $\mathbf{A}^{-1}$ and $(\mathbf{A}^{-1})^{-1}$.

   b   If **A** is any square matrix which has inverse $\mathbf{A}^{-1}$, simplify $(\mathbf{A}^{-1})^{-1} \cdot (\mathbf{A}^{-1})$ and $(\mathbf{A}^{-1})(\mathbf{A}^{-1})^{-1}$ by replacing $\mathbf{A}^{-1}$ by   **B**.

   c   What can be deduced from **b**?

10   **a**   If $\mathbf{A} = \begin{bmatrix} 1 & 1 \\ 2 & -1 \end{bmatrix}$ and $\mathbf{B} = \begin{bmatrix} 0 & 1 \\ 2 & -3 \end{bmatrix}$ find in simplest form:

   i $\mathbf{A}^{-1}$ **ii** $\mathbf{B}^{-1}$ **iii** $(\mathbf{AB})^{-1}$
   iv $(\mathbf{BA})^{-1}$ **v** $\mathbf{A}^{-1}\mathbf{B}^{-1}$ **vi** $\mathbf{B}^{-1}\mathbf{A}^{-1}$

   b   Choose any two invertible matrices and repeat question **a**.
   c   What do the results of **a** and **b** suggest?
   d   Simplify $(\mathbf{AB})(\mathbf{B}^{-1}\mathbf{A}^{-1})$ and $(\mathbf{B}^{-1}\mathbf{A}^{-1})(\mathbf{AB})$ given that $\mathbf{A}^{-1}$ and $\mathbf{B}^{-1}$ exist.
   Conclusion?

11 If k is a non-zero number, and $\mathbf{A}^{-1}$ exists, simplify $(k\mathbf{A})(\frac{1}{k}\mathbf{A}^{-1})$ and $(\frac{1}{k}\mathbf{A}^{-1})(k\mathbf{A})$.
What conclusion follows from your results?

12 If $\mathbf{X} = \mathbf{AY}$ and $\mathbf{Y} = \mathbf{BZ}$ where $\mathbf{A}$ and $\mathbf{B}$ are invertible, find:
   a $\mathbf{X}$ in terms of $\mathbf{Z}$ **b** $\mathbf{Z}$ in terms of $\mathbf{X}$.
   [$\mathbf{X}$, $\mathbf{Y}$ and $\mathbf{Z}$ are 2×1 and $\mathbf{A}$, $\mathbf{B}$ are 2×2]

Example 13

If $\mathbf{A}^2 = 2\mathbf{A} + 3\mathbf{I}$, find $\mathbf{A}^{-1}$ in linear form $r\mathbf{A} + s\mathbf{I}$, where r and s are scalars.

$$\mathbf{A}^2 = 2\mathbf{A} + 3\mathbf{I}$$
$$\therefore \quad \mathbf{A}^{-1}\mathbf{A}^2 = \mathbf{A}^{-1}(2\mathbf{A} + 3\mathbf{I}) \qquad \{\text{premultiply both sides by } \mathbf{A}^{-1}\}$$
$$\therefore \quad \mathbf{A}^{-1}\mathbf{AA} = 2\mathbf{A}^{-1}\mathbf{A} + 3\mathbf{A}^{-1}\mathbf{I}$$
$$\therefore \quad \mathbf{IA} = 2\mathbf{I} + 3\mathbf{A}^{-1}$$
$$\therefore \quad \mathbf{A} - 2\mathbf{I} = 3\mathbf{A}^{-1}$$
$$\therefore \quad \mathbf{A}^{-1} = \tfrac{1}{3}(\mathbf{A} - 2\mathbf{I}) \qquad \text{i.e., } \mathbf{A}^{-1} = \tfrac{1}{3}\mathbf{A} - \tfrac{2}{3}\mathbf{I}$$

13 Find $\mathbf{A}^{-1}$ in linear form given that
   a $\mathbf{A}^2 = 4\mathbf{A} - \mathbf{I}$ **b** $5\mathbf{A} = \mathbf{I} - \mathbf{A}^2$ **c** $2\mathbf{I} = 3\mathbf{A}^2 - 4\mathbf{A}$

14 If $\mathbf{A} = \begin{bmatrix} 3 & 2 \\ -2 & -1 \end{bmatrix}$, write $\mathbf{A}^2$ in the form $p\mathbf{A} + q\mathbf{I}$ where p and q are scalars.
   Hence write $\mathbf{A}^{-1}$ in the form $r\mathbf{A} + s\mathbf{I}$ where r and s are scalars.

15 It is known that $\mathbf{AB} = \mathbf{A}$ and $\mathbf{BA} = \mathbf{B}$ where the matrices $\mathbf{A}$ and $\mathbf{B}$ are not necessarily invertible.
   Prove that $\mathbf{A}^2 = \mathbf{A}$. [**Note:** From $\mathbf{AB} = \mathbf{A}$, you cannot deduce that $\mathbf{B} = \mathbf{I}$. Why?]

16 Under what condition is it true that   "if $\mathbf{AB} = \mathbf{AC}$ then $\mathbf{B} = \mathbf{C}$"?

17 If $\mathbf{X} = \mathbf{P}^{-1}\mathbf{AP}$ and $\mathbf{A}^3 = \mathbf{I}$, prove that $\mathbf{X}^3 = \mathbf{I}$.

18 If $a\mathbf{A}^2 + b\mathbf{A} + c\mathbf{I} = \mathbf{O}$ and $\mathbf{X} = \mathbf{P}^{-1}\mathbf{AP}$, prove that $a\mathbf{X}^2 + b\mathbf{X} + c\mathbf{I} = \mathbf{O}$.

J   THE 3×3 DETERMINANT

The **determinant** of $\mathbf{A} = \begin{bmatrix} a_1 & b_1 & c_1 \\ a_2 & b_2 & c_2 \\ a_3 & b_3 & c_3 \end{bmatrix}$ is defined as

$$|\mathbf{A}| = a_1 \begin{vmatrix} b_2 & c_2 \\ b_3 & c_3 \end{vmatrix} + b_1 \begin{vmatrix} c_2 & a_2 \\ c_3 & a_3 \end{vmatrix} + c_1 \begin{vmatrix} a_2 & b_2 \\ a_3 & b_3 \end{vmatrix}$$

Example 14

Find $|\mathbf{A}|$ for

$$\mathbf{A} = \begin{bmatrix} 1 & 2 & 4 \\ 2 & 0 & 1 \\ 3 & -1 & 2 \end{bmatrix}$$

$$|\mathbf{A}| = 1\begin{vmatrix} 0 & 1 \\ -1 & 2 \end{vmatrix} + 2\begin{vmatrix} 1 & 2 \\ 2 & 3 \end{vmatrix} + 4\begin{vmatrix} 2 & 0 \\ 3 & -1 \end{vmatrix}$$

same   same

same

$$= 1(0 - -1) + 2(3 - 4) + 4(-2 - 0)$$
$$= 1 - 2 - 8$$
$$= -9 \quad \{\text{which checks with the earlier example}\}$$

Once again we observe that a 3×3 system of linear equations in matrix form $\mathbf{AX} = \mathbf{B}$ will have a **unique solution** if $|\mathbf{A}| \neq 0$.

Note: A graphics calculator or spreadsheet can be used to find the value of a determinant.

EXERCISE 14J

1 Evaluate:

a $\begin{vmatrix} 2 & 3 & 0 \\ -1 & 2 & 1 \\ 2 & 0 & 5 \end{vmatrix}$

b $\begin{vmatrix} -1 & 2 & -3 \\ 1 & 0 & 0 \\ -1 & 2 & 1 \end{vmatrix}$

c $\begin{vmatrix} 2 & 1 & 3 \\ -1 & 1 & 2 \\ 2 & 1 & 3 \end{vmatrix}$

d $\begin{vmatrix} 1 & 0 & 0 \\ 0 & 2 & 0 \\ 0 & 0 & 3 \end{vmatrix}$

e $\begin{vmatrix} 0 & 0 & 2 \\ 0 & 1 & 0 \\ 3 & 0 & 0 \end{vmatrix}$

f $\begin{vmatrix} 4 & 1 & 3 \\ -1 & 0 & 2 \\ -1 & 1 & 1 \end{vmatrix}$

2 a Find the values of x for which the matrix $\begin{bmatrix} x & 2 & 9 \\ 3 & 1 & 2 \\ -1 & 0 & x \end{bmatrix}$ is singular.

b What does your answer to **a** mean?

3 Evaluate:

a $\begin{vmatrix} a & 0 & 0 \\ 0 & b & 0 \\ 0 & 0 & c \end{vmatrix}$

b $\begin{vmatrix} 0 & x & y \\ -x & 0 & z \\ -y & -z & 0 \end{vmatrix}$

c $\begin{vmatrix} a & b & c \\ b & c & a \\ c & a & b \end{vmatrix}$

4 For what values of k does $\begin{cases} x + 2y - 3z = 5 \\ 2x - y - z = 8 \\ kx + y + 2z = 14 \end{cases}$ have a unique solution?

5 For what values of k does $\begin{cases} 2x - y - 4z = 8 \\ 3x - ky + z = 1 \\ 5x - y + kz = -2 \end{cases}$ have a unique solution?

6 Find k given that: a $\begin{vmatrix} 1 & k & 3 \\ k & 1 & -1 \\ 3 & 4 & 2 \end{vmatrix} = 7$ b $\begin{vmatrix} k & 2 & 1 \\ 2 & k & 2 \\ 1 & 2 & k \end{vmatrix} = 0$

7 Use technology to find the determinant and inverse of:

a
$$\begin{bmatrix} 1 & 2 & 3 & 1 \\ 2 & 0 & 1 & 2 \\ 3 & 1 & 4 & 0 \\ 1 & 2 & 0 & 5 \end{bmatrix}$$

b
$$\begin{bmatrix} 1 & 2 & 3 & 4 & 6 \\ 2 & 3 & 4 & 5 & 0 \\ 1 & 2 & 0 & 1 & 4 \\ 2 & 1 & 0 & 1 & 5 \\ 3 & 0 & 1 & 2 & 1 \end{bmatrix}$$

Note: In MSEXCEL, = MDETERM( ) gives the determinant and = MINVERSE( ) gives the inverse matrix.

A7	▼		= {=MINVERSE(A1:D4)}		
	A	**B**	**C**	**D**	**E**	**F**
1	2	3	1	3		
2	4	4	3	2		determinant
3	3	1	1	0		4
4	1	2	2	1		
5						
6						
7	0.25	-0.5	0.75	0.25		
8	-1.25	3.5	-2.75	-3.25		
9	0.5	-2	1.5	2.5		
10	1.25	-2.5	1.75	2.25		

the inverse of
$$\begin{bmatrix} 2 & 3 & 1 & 3 \\ 4 & 4 & 3 & 2 \\ 3 & 1 & 1 & 0 \\ 1 & 2 & 2 & 1 \end{bmatrix}$$

is

$$\begin{bmatrix} \frac{1}{4} & -\frac{2}{4} & \frac{3}{4} & \frac{1}{4} \\ -\frac{5}{4} & \frac{14}{4} & -\frac{11}{4} & -\frac{13}{4} \\ \frac{2}{4} & -\frac{8}{4} & \frac{6}{4} & \frac{10}{4} \\ \frac{5}{4} & -\frac{10}{4} & \frac{7}{4} & \frac{9}{4} \end{bmatrix}$$

8 If Jan bought one orange, two apples, a pear, a cabbage and a lettuce the total cost would be $6.30. Two oranges, one apple, two pears, one cabbage and one lettuce would cost a total of $6.70. One orange, two apples, three pears, one cabbage and one lettuce would cost a total of $7.70. Two oranges, two apples, one pear, one cabbage and three lettuces would cost a total of $9.80. Three oranges, three apples, five pears, two cabbages and two lettuces would cost a total of $10.90.

a Write this information in $\mathbf{AX = B}$ form where $\mathbf{A}$ is the quantities matrix, $\mathbf{X}$ is the cost per item column matrix and $\mathbf{B}$ is the total costs column matrix.

b Explain why $\mathbf{X}$ cannot be found from the given information.

c If the last lot of information is deleted and in its place "three oranges, one apple, two pears, two cabbages and one lettuce cost a total of $9.20" is substituted, can the system be solved now, and if so, what is the solution?

Note: If a solution can be found use $\mathbf{A}^{-1}$.

K   THE INVERSE OF A 3×3 MATRIX

We will use a graphics calculator to find the inverse of a 3×3 matrix.

For example, if $\mathbf{A} = \begin{bmatrix} 1 & 2 & 4 \\ 2 & 0 & 1 \\ 3 & -1 & 2 \end{bmatrix}$ what is $\mathbf{A}^{-1}$?

We obtain $\mathbf{A}^{-1} = \begin{bmatrix} -0.111 & 0.888 & -0.222 \\ 0.111 & 1.111 & -0.777 \\ 0.222 & -0.777 & 0.444 \end{bmatrix}$ which converts to $\begin{bmatrix} -\frac{1}{9} & \frac{8}{9} & -\frac{2}{9} \\ \frac{1}{9} & \frac{10}{9} & -\frac{7}{9} \\ \frac{2}{9} & -\frac{7}{9} & \frac{4}{9} \end{bmatrix}$

EXERCISE 14K

1   Use technology to find $\mathbf{A}^{-1}$ for: **a** $\mathbf{A} = \begin{bmatrix} 3 & 2 & 3 \\ 1 & -1 & 2 \\ 2 & 1 & 3 \end{bmatrix}$ **b** $\mathbf{A} = \begin{bmatrix} 2 & 0 & 3 \\ 1 & 5 & 2 \\ 1 & -3 & 1 \end{bmatrix}$

2   Find $\mathbf{B}^{-1}$ for: **a** $\mathbf{B} = \begin{bmatrix} 13 & 43 & -11 \\ 16 & 9 & 27 \\ -8 & 31 & -13 \end{bmatrix}$ **b** $\mathbf{B} = \begin{bmatrix} 1.61 & 4.32 & 6.18 \\ 0.37 & 6.02 & 9.41 \\ 7.12 & 5.31 & 2.88 \end{bmatrix}$

L   3×3 SYSTEMS WITH UNIQUE SOLUTIONS

EXERCISE 14L

1   Write as a matrix equation:

  a $x - y - z = 2$
      $x + y + 3z = 7$
      $9x - y - 3z = -1$

  b $2x + y - z = 3$
      $y + 2z = 6$
      $x - y + z = 13$

  c $a + b - c = 7$
      $a - b + c = 6$
      $2a + b - 3c = -2$

2   For $\mathbf{A} = \begin{bmatrix} 2 & 1 & -1 \\ -1 & 2 & 1 \\ 0 & 6 & 1 \end{bmatrix}$ and $\mathbf{B} = \begin{bmatrix} 4 & 7 & -3 \\ -1 & -2 & 1 \\ 6 & 12 & -5 \end{bmatrix}$,

  calculate $\mathbf{AB}$ and hence solve the system of equations $4a + 7b - 3c = -8$
                                                                                            $-a - 2b + c = 3$
                                                                                            $6a + 12b - 5c = -15.$

3   For $\mathbf{M} = \begin{bmatrix} 5 & 3 & -7 \\ -1 & -3 & 3 \\ -3 & -1 & 5 \end{bmatrix}$ and $\mathbf{N} = \begin{bmatrix} 3 & 2 & 3 \\ 1 & -1 & 2 \\ 2 & 1 & 3 \end{bmatrix}$,

  calculate $\mathbf{MN}$ and hence solve the system $3u + 2v + 3w = 18$
                                                                          $u - v + 2w = 6$
                                                                          $2u + v + 3w = 16.$

Example 15

Solve the system $\begin{aligned} x - y - z &= 2 \\ x + y + 3z &= 7 \\ 9x - y - 3z &= -1 \end{aligned}$ using matrix methods and a graphics calculator.

In matrix form the system is:

$\begin{bmatrix} 1 & -1 & -1 \\ 1 & 1 & 3 \\ 9 & -1 & -3 \end{bmatrix} \begin{bmatrix} x \\ y \\ z \end{bmatrix} = \begin{bmatrix} 2 \\ 7 \\ -1 \end{bmatrix}$ (i.e., $\mathbf{AX} = \mathbf{B}$)

$\therefore \quad \begin{bmatrix} x \\ y \\ z \end{bmatrix} = \begin{bmatrix} 1 & -1 & -1 \\ 1 & 1 & 3 \\ 9 & -1 & -3 \end{bmatrix}^{-1} \begin{bmatrix} 2 \\ 7 \\ -1 \end{bmatrix}$

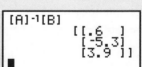

Into a calculator we enter $\mathbf{A}$ and $\mathbf{B}$ and calculate $[\mathbf{A}]^{-1}[\mathbf{B}]$
i.e., $x = 0.6$, $y = -5.3$, $z = 3.9$

4 Use matrix methods and technology to solve:

a $3x + 2y - z = 14$
   $x - y + 2z = -8$
   $2x + 3y - z = 13$

b $x - y - 2z = 4$
   $5x + y + 2z = -6$
   $3x - 4y - z = 17$

c $x + 3y - z = 15$
   $2x + y + z = 7$
   $x - y - 2z = 0$

5 Use your graphics calculator to solve:

a $x + y + z = 6$
   $2x + 4y + z = 5$
   $2x + 3y + z = 6$

b $x + 4y + 11z = 7$
   $x + 6y + 17z = 9$
   $x + 4y + 8z = 4$

c $2x - y + 3z = 17$
   $2x - 2y - 5z = 4$
   $3x + 2y + 2z = 10$

d $x + 2y - z = 23$
   $x - y + 3z = -23$
   $7x + y - 4z = 62$

e $10x - y + 4z = -9$
   $7x + 3y - 5z = 89$
   $13x - 17y + 23z = -309$

f $1.3x + 2.7y - 3.1z = 8.2$
   $2.8x - 0.9y + 5.6z = 17.3$
   $6.1x + 1.4y - 3.2z = -0.6$

Example 16

Rent-a-car has three different makes of vehicles, P, Q and R, for hire. These cars are located at yards A and B on either side of a city. Some cars are out (being rented). In total they have 150 cars. At yard A they have 20% of P, 40% of Q and 30% of R which is 46 cars in total. At yard B they have 40% of P, 20% of Q and 50% of R which is 54 cars in total. How many of each car type does Rent-a-car have?

Suppose Rent-a-car has x of P, y of Q and z of R.

Then as it has 150 cars in total, $x + y + z = 150$ ...... (1)

But yard A has 20% of P + 40% of Q + 30% of R and this is 46.

$$\therefore \quad \tfrac{2}{10}x + \tfrac{4}{10}y + \tfrac{3}{10}z = 46$$

$$\text{i.e.,} \quad 2x + 4y + 3z = 460 \quad ...... (2)$$

And, yard B has 40% of P + 20% of Q + 50% of R and this is 54.

$$\therefore \quad \tfrac{4}{10}x + \tfrac{2}{10}y + \tfrac{5}{10}z = 54$$

$$\text{i.e.,} \quad 4x + 2y + 5z = 540 \quad ...... (3)$$

We need to solve the system $x + y + z = 150$
   $2x + 4y + 3z = 460$
   $4x + 2y + 5z = 540$

i.e., $\begin{bmatrix} 1 & 1 & 1 \\ 2 & 4 & 3 \\ 4 & 2 & 5 \end{bmatrix} \begin{bmatrix} x \\ y \\ z \end{bmatrix} = \begin{bmatrix} 150 \\ 460 \\ 540 \end{bmatrix}$

So $\begin{bmatrix} x \\ y \\ z \end{bmatrix} = \begin{bmatrix} 1 & 1 & 1 \\ 2 & 4 & 3 \\ 4 & 2 & 5 \end{bmatrix}^{-1} \begin{bmatrix} 150 \\ 460 \\ 540 \end{bmatrix}$

$\therefore$ $\begin{bmatrix} x \\ y \\ z \end{bmatrix} = \begin{bmatrix} 45 \\ 55 \\ 50 \end{bmatrix}$

```
[A]⁻¹[B]
           [[45]
            [55]
            [50]]
```

Thus, Rent-a-car has
45 of P, 55 of Q and 50 of R.

6 Westwood School bought two footballs, one baseball and three basketballs for a total cost of $90. Sequoia School bought three footballs, two baseballs and a basketball for $81. Lamar School bought five footballs and two basketballs for $104.

    a State clearly what the variables x, y and z must represent if this situation is to be described by the set of equations: $2x + y + 3z = 90$, $3x + 2y + z = 81$, $5x + 2z = 104$.

    b If Kato International School needs 4 footballs, 5 baseballs and wishes to order as many basketballs as they can afford, how many basketballs will they be able to purchase if there is a total of $315 to be spent?

7 Managers, clerks and labourers are paid according to an industry award.

Xenon employs 2 managers, 3 clerks and 8 labourers with a total salary bill of $352 000. Xanda employs 1 manager, 5 clerks and 4 labourers with a total salary bill of $274 000. Xylon employs 1 manager, 2 clerks and 11 labourers with a total salary bill of $351 000.

    a If x, y and z represent the salaries (in thousands of dollars) for managers, clerks and labourers respectively, show that the above information can be represented by a system of three equations.

    b Solve the above system of equations.

    c Determine the total salary bill for Xulu company which employs 3 managers, 8 clerks and 37 labourers.

8 A mixed nut company uses cashews, macadamias and brazil nuts to make three gourmet mixes. The table along side indicates the weight in hundreds of grams of each kind of nut required to make a kilogram of mix.

	Mix A	Mix B	Mix C
Cashews	5	2	6
Macas.	3	4	1
Brazils	2	4	3

If 1 kg of mix A costs $12.50 to produce, 1 kg of mix B costs $12.40 and 1 kg of mix C costs $11.70, determine the cost per kilogram of each of the different kinds of nuts.

Hence, find the cost per kilogram to produce a mix containing 400 grams of cashews, 200 grams of macadamias and 400 grams of brazil nuts.

9 Klondike High has 76 students in total in classes P, Q and R. There are p students in P, q in Q and r in R.

One-third of P, one-third of Q and two-fifths of R study Chemistry.

One-half of P, two-thirds of Q and one-fifth of R study Maths.

One-quarter of P, one-third of Q and three-fifths of R study Geography.

Given that 27 study Chemistry, 35 study Maths and 30 study Geography:

    a find a system of equations which contains this information, making sure that the coefficients of p, q and r are integers.

    b Solve for p, q and r.

10 Susan and James opened a new business in 1997. Their annual profit was $160 000 in 2000, $198 000 in 2001 and $240 000 in 2002. Based on the information from these three years they believe that their annual profit could be predicted by the model

$$P(t) = at + b + \frac{c}{t+4} \text{ dollars}$$

where t is the number of years after 2000,   i.e., $t = 0$ gives 2000 profit.

    a Determine the values of a, b and c which fit the profits for 2000, 2001 and 2002.

   b If the profit in 1999 was $130 000, does this profit fit the model in **a**?

   c Susan and James believe their profit will continue to grow according to this model. Predict their profit in 2003 and 2005.

INVESTIGATION   USING MATRICES IN CRYPTOGRAPHY

 Cryptography is the study of encoding and decoding messages. Cryptography was first developed to send secret messages in written form. However, today it is used to maintain privacy when information is being transmitted via public communication services (by line or by satellite).

Messages are sent in **code** or **cipher** form. The method of converting text to ciphertext is called **enciphering** and the reverse process is called **deciphering**.

The operations of matrix addition and multiplication can be used to create codes and the coded messages are transmitted. Decoding using additive or multiplicative inverses is required by the receiver in order to read the message.

The letters of the alphabet are first assigned integer values.

Notice that Z is assigned 0.

A	B	C	D	E	F	G	H	I	J	K	L	M
1	2	3	4	5	6	7	8	9	10	11	12	13
N	O	P	Q	R	S	T	U	V	W	X	Y	Z
14	15	16	17	18	19	20	21	22	23	24	25	0

The coded form of the word SEND is therefore 19 5 14 4 which we could put in 2×2 matrix form $\begin{bmatrix} 19 & 5 \\ 14 & 4 \end{bmatrix}$.

An encoding matrix of your choice could be added to this matrix. Suppose it is $\begin{bmatrix} 2 & 7 \\ 13 & 5 \end{bmatrix}$.

The matrix to be transmitted is then $\begin{bmatrix} 19 & 5 \\ 14 & 4 \end{bmatrix} + \begin{bmatrix} 2 & 7 \\ 13 & 5 \end{bmatrix} = \begin{bmatrix} 21 & 12 \\ 27 & 9 \end{bmatrix}$

Now $\begin{bmatrix} 21 & 12 \\ 27 & 9 \end{bmatrix}$ becomes $\begin{bmatrix} 21 & 12 \\ 1 & 9 \end{bmatrix}$ as any number not in the range 0 to 25 is adjusted to be in it by adding or subtracting multiples of 26.

So, $\begin{bmatrix} 21 & 12 \\ 1 & 9 \end{bmatrix}$ is sent as 21 12 1 9.

The message SEND MONEY PLEASE could be broken into groups of four letters and each group is encoded.

       SEND|MONE|YPLE|ASEE ⟵ repeat the last letter to make group of 4.
                               This is a dummy letter.

For MONE the matrix required is $\begin{bmatrix} 13 & 15 \\ 14 & 5 \end{bmatrix} + \begin{bmatrix} 2 & 7 \\ 13 & 5 \end{bmatrix} = \begin{bmatrix} 15 & 22 \\ 27 & 10 \end{bmatrix}$ i.e., $\begin{bmatrix} 15 & 22 \\ 1 & 10 \end{bmatrix}$

For YPLE the matrix required is $\begin{bmatrix} 25 & 16 \\ 12 & 5 \end{bmatrix} + \begin{bmatrix} 2 & 7 \\ 13 & 5 \end{bmatrix} = \begin{bmatrix} 27 & 23 \\ 25 & 10 \end{bmatrix}$ i.e., $\begin{bmatrix} 1 & 23 \\ 25 & 10 \end{bmatrix}$

For ASEE the matrix required is $\begin{bmatrix} 1 & 19 \\ 5 & 5 \end{bmatrix} + \begin{bmatrix} 2 & 7 \\ 13 & 5 \end{bmatrix} = \begin{bmatrix} 3 & 26 \\ 18 & 10 \end{bmatrix}$ i.e., $\begin{bmatrix} 3 & 0 \\ 18 & 10 \end{bmatrix}$

So the whole message is   21 12 1 9 15 22 1 10 1 23 25 10 3 0 18 10

The decoder requires the additive inverse matrix $\begin{bmatrix} -2 & -7 \\ -13 & -5 \end{bmatrix}$ to decode the message.

What to do:

1 Use the decoder matrix to check that the original message is obtained.

2 Use the code given to decode the message:

    21 12   1   9 22 15 18 25 20 22   2 21 21   1   2
    25 10 12   0 20 23   1 21 20   8   1 21 10 15   2
     5 23   3   6 12   4

3 Create your own matrix addition code. Encode a short message. Supply the decoding matrix to a friend so that he/she can decode it.

4 Breaking codes where matrix multiplication is used is much more difficult.

A chosen encoder matrix is required. Suppose it is $\begin{bmatrix} 2 & 3 \\ 1 & 2 \end{bmatrix}$.

The word   SEND   is encoded as $\begin{bmatrix} 19 & 5 \\ 14 & 4 \end{bmatrix} \begin{bmatrix} 2 & 3 \\ 1 & 2 \end{bmatrix} = \begin{bmatrix} 43 & 67 \\ 32 & 50 \end{bmatrix}$

which is converted to $\begin{bmatrix} 17 & 15 \\ 6 & 24 \end{bmatrix}$

a What is the coded form of   SEND MONEY PLEASE?

b What decoder matrix needs to be supplied to the receiver so that the message can be read?

c Check by decoding the message.

d Create your own code using matrix multiplication using a matrix $\begin{bmatrix} a & b \\ c & d \end{bmatrix}$ where $ad - bc = 1$.   Why?

e What are the problems in using a 2×2 matrix when $ad - bc \neq 1$? How can these problems be overcome?

5 Research **Hill ciphers** and explain how they differ from the methods given previously.

M   SOLVING USING ROW OPERATIONS

The system of equations $2x + y = -1$ is called a 2×2 system,
$$x - 3y = 17$$
i.e., **2 equations** in **2 unknowns**.

In the method of 'elimination' used to solve these equations, we observe that the following operations produce equations with the same solutions as the original pair.

- The equations can be interchanged without affecting the solutions.

    For example, $2x + y = -1$ has the same solutions as $x - 3y = 17$.
    $$x - 3y = 17 \qquad\qquad\qquad 2x + y = -1$$

- An equation can be replaced by a non-zero multiple of itself.

  For example, $2x + y = -1$ could be replaced by $-6x - 3y = 3$

  (obtained by multiplying each term of -3).

- Any equation can be replaced by a multiple of itself plus (or minus) a multiple of another equation.

  For example, $\begin{aligned} E_1: \\ E_2: \end{aligned} \left\{ \begin{aligned} 2x - 3y &= 1 \\ 3x + y &= 7 \end{aligned} \right.$ becomes $\left\{ \begin{aligned} 2x - 3y &= 1 \\ 11y &= 11 \end{aligned} \right.$ if $E_2 \rightarrow 2E_2 - 3E_1$.

  [$E_2 \rightarrow 2E_2 - 3E_1$ reads: equation 2 is replaced by twice equation 2 $-$ three times equation 1.]

AUGMENTED MATRICES

We will now solve systems of equation with non-unique solutions using row operations on the augmented matrix.

Instead of writing $\begin{aligned} 2x + y &= -1 \\ -3y + x &= 17 \end{aligned}$ we detach the coefficients and write the system

in **augmented matrix** form $\left[\begin{array}{cc|c} 2 & 1 & -1 \\ 1 & -3 & 17 \end{array} \right]$,   as $\left\{ \begin{aligned} 2x + y &= -1 \\ x - 3y &= 17 \end{aligned} \right.$.

In this form we can use **elementary row operations** equivalent to the three legitimate operations with equations,

i.e.,
- interchange rows
- replace any row by a non-zero multiple of itself
- replace any row by itself plus (or minus) a multiple of another row.

Interchanging rows is equivalent to writing the equations in a different order and it is often desirable to have 1 where possible in the *top left hand corner*.

So, $\left[\begin{array}{cc|c} 2 & 1 & -1 \\ 1 & -3 & 17 \end{array} \right]$ becomes $\left[\begin{array}{cc|c} 1 & -3 & 17 \\ 2 & 1 & -1 \end{array} \right]$.

We now attempt to eliminate one of the variables in the second equation, i.e., obtain a 0 in its place. To do this we replace R_2 by $R_2 - 2R_1$ {(row 2) $-$ 2 $\times$ (row 1)}

So, $\left[\begin{array}{cc|c} 1 & -3 & 17 \\ 2 & 1 & -1 \end{array} \right]$ becomes $\left[\begin{array}{cc|c} 1 & -3 & 17 \\ 0 & 7 & -35 \end{array} \right]$

$$\begin{array}{rrrl} 2 & 1 & -1 & \leftarrow R_2 \\ -2 & 6 & -34 & \leftarrow -2R_1 \\ \hline 0 & 7 & -35 & \text{adding} \end{array}$$

The second row of the matrix is really $7y = -35$

$\therefore \quad y = -5$

and substituting $y = -5$ into the first equation, $x - 3(-5) = 17$

$\therefore \quad x + 15 = 17$

$\therefore \quad x = 2$

So, the solution is $x = 2$, $y = -5$.

We may not see the benefit of this method right now but we will certainly appreciate it when solving 3×3 or higher order systems.

Example 17

Use elementary row operations to solve: $\begin{cases} 2x + 3y = 4 \\ 5x + 4y = 17 \end{cases}$

In augmented matrix form the system is:

$$\left[\begin{array}{cc|c} 2 & 3 & 4 \\ 5 & 4 & 17 \end{array} \right]$$

We can eliminate x if we replace R_2 by $\underbrace{5R_1 - 2R_2}$

$$\sim \left[\begin{array}{cc|c} 2 & 3 & 4 \\ 0 & 7 & -14 \end{array} \right]$$

Re-introducing the variables we have
$$7y = -14$$
$$\therefore \quad y = -2$$

$\sim$ is read as "which has the same solution as"

and on 'back substituting' into the first equation we have
$$2x + 3(-2) = 4$$
$$\therefore \quad 2x - 6 = 4$$
$$\therefore \quad 2x = 10$$
$$\therefore \quad x = 5$$

Don't forget to check your solution

So the solution is $x = 5$, $y = -2$.

In two dimensional geometry $ax + by = c$ where a, b and c are constants is the equation of a straight line. Now there are three different cases which could occur. These are:

The lines could be

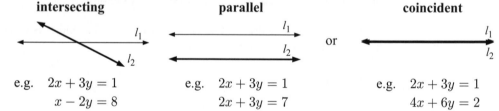

| **intersecting** | **parallel** | | **coincident** |

e.g. $2x + 3y = 1$ $\quad$ e.g. $2x + 3y = 1$ $\quad$ e.g. $2x + 3y = 1$
$x - 2y = 8$ $\qquad\qquad$ $2x + 3y = 7$ $\qquad\qquad$ $4x + 6y = 2$

one point of intersection, so, a **unique solution**

no points of intersection so, **no solution**

infinitely many points of intersection, so, one equation is an exact multiple of the other, so, **infinitely many solutions**

EXERCISE 14M.1

1 Solve using elementary row operations:

  a $\quad x - 2y = 8$
$\quad\quad 4x + y = 5$

  b $\quad 4x + 5y = 21$
$\quad\quad 5x - 3y = -20$

  c $\quad 3x + y = -10$
$\quad\quad 2x + 5y = -24$

2 By inspection, classify the following pairs of equations as either intersecting, parallel or coincident lines:

  a $\quad x - 3y = 2$
$\quad\quad 3x + y = 8$

  b $\quad x + y = 7$
$\quad\quad 3x + 3y = 1$

  c $\quad 4x - y = 8$
$\quad\quad\quad\quad y = 2$

  d $\quad x - 2y = 4$
$\quad\quad 2x - 4y = 8$

  e $\quad 5x - 11y = 2$
$\quad\quad 6x + y = 8$

  f $\quad 3x - 4y = 5$
$\quad\quad -3x + 4y = 2$

3 Consider the equation pair $\begin{cases} x + 2y = 3 \\ 2x + 4y = 6 \end{cases}$.

    a Explain why there are infinitely many solutions giving geometric evidence.

    b Explain why the second equation can be ignored when finding all solutions.

    c Give all solutions in the form:

        i $x = t, \quad y = \ldots\ldots$ **ii** $y = s, \quad x = \ldots\ldots$

4 **a** Use elementary row operations on the system $\begin{cases} 2x + 3y = 5 \\ 2x + 3y = 11 \end{cases}$ to show that it

    reduces to $\begin{bmatrix} 2 & 3 & | & 5 \\ 0 & 0 & | & 6 \end{bmatrix}$ What does the second row indicate? What is the geometrical significance of your result?

    b Use elementary row operations on the system $\begin{cases} 2x + 3y = 5 \\ 4x + 6y = 10 \end{cases}$ to show that it

    reduces to $\begin{bmatrix} 2 & 3 & | & 5 \\ 0 & 0 & | & 0 \end{bmatrix}$.   Explain geometrically.

5 **a** By using augmented matrices show that $\begin{cases} 3x - y = 2 \\ 6x - 2y = 4 \end{cases}$ has infinitely many

    solutions of the form $x = t, \ y = 3t - 2$.

    b Discuss the solutions to $\begin{cases} 3x - y = 2 \\ 6x - 2y = k \end{cases}$ where k can take any real value.

Example 18

Find all solutions to $\begin{cases} x + 3y = 5 \\ 4x + 12y = k \end{cases}$ where k is a constant, by using elementary row operations.

In augmented matrix form, the system is:

$$\begin{bmatrix} 1 & 3 & | & 5 \\ 4 & 12 & | & k \end{bmatrix}$$

$$\sim \begin{bmatrix} 1 & 3 & | & 5 \\ 0 & 0 & | & k - 20 \end{bmatrix} \begin{matrix} \longleftarrow R_1 \to R_1 \\ \longleftarrow R_2 \to R_2 - 4R_1 \end{matrix}$$

$$\begin{array}{rrr} 4 & 12 & k \\ -4 & -12 & -20 \\ \hline 0 & 0 & k - 20 \end{array}$$

The second equation actually reads $0x + 0y = k - 20$

So, if $k \neq 20$ we have $0 = $ a non-zero number, which is absurd,

$\therefore$ no solution exists

and if $k = 20$ we have $0 = 0$.

This means that all solutions come from $x + 3y = 5$ alone.

Letting $y = t$, $x = 5 - 3t$ for all values of t

$\therefore$ there are infinitely many solutions of the form $x = 5 - 3t, \ y = t, \ t$ real.

6 Consider $\begin{cases} 3x - y = 8 \\ 6x - 2y = k \end{cases}$ where k is any real number.

   a Use elementary row operations to reduce the system to: $\begin{bmatrix} 3 & -1 & | & 8 \\ 0 & 0 & | & .... \end{bmatrix}$

   b For what value of k is there infinitely many solutions?

   c What form do the infinite number of solutions have?

   d When does the system have no solutions?

7 Consider $\begin{cases} 4x + 8y = 1 \\ 2x - ay = 11 \end{cases}$

   a Use elementary row operations to reduce the system to: $\begin{bmatrix} 4 & 8 & | & 1 \\ 0 & .... & | & .... \end{bmatrix}$

   b For what values of a does the system have a unique solution?

   c Show that the unique solution is $x = \dfrac{a + 88}{4a + 16}$, $y = \dfrac{-21}{2a + 8}$

   d What is the solution in all other cases?

8 Use elementary row operations to find the values of m when the system $\begin{cases} mx + 2y = 6 \\ 2x + my = 6 \end{cases}$ has a unique solution.

   a Find the unique solution.

   b Discuss the solutions in the other *two* cases.

USING A GRAPHICS CALCULATOR

Click on the appropriate icon to obtain instructions on how to enter a number array called an **augmented matrix** and then obtain the **reduced row-echelon form**.

In the example $\begin{cases} 2x + y = -1 \\ x - 3y = 17 \end{cases}$

we obtained reduced row-echelon form when $\begin{bmatrix} 2 & 1 & | & -1 \\ 1 & -3 & | & 17 \end{bmatrix}$ becomes $\begin{bmatrix} 1 & 0 & | & 2 \\ 0 & 1 & | & -5 \end{bmatrix}$

Consequently $x = 2$ and $y = -5$.

Try solving other 2×2 systems: **a** $\begin{cases} 3x + 5y = 4 \\ 6x - y = -11 \end{cases}$ **b** $\begin{cases} 0.83x + 1.72y = 13.76 \\ 1.65x - 2.77y = 3.49 \end{cases}$

USING ROW OPERATIONS TO SOLVE A 3 × 3 SYSTEM

A general 3×3 system in variables x, y and z has form $\begin{aligned} a_1x + b_1y + c_1z &= d_1 \\ a_2x + b_2y + c_2z &= d_2 \\ a_3x + b_3y + c_3z &= d_3 \end{aligned}$

where the coefficients of x, y and z are constants.

$\begin{bmatrix} a_1 & b_1 & c_1 & | & d_1 \\ a_2 & b_2 & c_2 & | & d_2 \\ a_3 & b_3 & c_3 & | & d_3 \end{bmatrix}$ is the system's **augmented matrix form** which we need to reduce to **echelon form**, $\begin{bmatrix} a & b & c & | & d \\ 0 & e & f & | & g \\ 0 & 0 & h & | & i \end{bmatrix}$, by using **elementary row operations**.

Notice the creation, where possible, of a **triangle of zeros** in the **bottom left hand corner**. In this form we can easily solve the system. The last row is really $hz = i$.

- If $h \neq 0$ (i may or may not be 0) we can determine z uniquely ($z = \dfrac{i}{h}$) and likewise y and x from the other two rows. Thus we arrive at a **unique solution**.

- If $h = 0$ and $i \neq 0$, the last row reads $0 \times z = i$ where $i \neq 0$ which is absurd. Hence, there is **no solution** and we say that the system is **inconsistent**.

- If $h = 0$ and $i = 0$, the last row is all zeros .

  Consequently, there are **infinitely many** solutions of the form $x = p + kt$, $y = q + lt$ and $z = t$ where t is any real number.

Example 19

Solve the system
$$\begin{aligned} x + 3y - z &= 15 \\ 2x + y + z &= 7 \\ x - y - 2z &= 0. \end{aligned}$$

In augmented matrix form, the system is

$$\begin{bmatrix} 1 & 3 & -1 & \vline & 15 \\ 2 & 1 & 1 & \vline & 7 \\ 1 & -1 & -2 & \vline & 0 \end{bmatrix} \quad R_2 \to R_2 - 2R_1$$

$$\begin{array}{rrrr} 2 & 1 & 1 & 7 \\ -2 & -6 & 2 & -30 \\ \hline 0 & -5 & 3 & -23 \end{array}$$

$$\sim \begin{bmatrix} 1 & 3 & -1 & \vline & 15 \\ 0 & -5 & 3 & \vline & -23 \\ 0 & -4 & -1 & \vline & -15 \end{bmatrix} \quad R_3 \to R_3 - R_1$$

$$\begin{array}{rrrr} 1 & -1 & -2 & 0 \\ -1 & -3 & 1 & -15 \\ \hline 0 & -4 & -1 & -15 \end{array}$$

$$\sim \begin{bmatrix} 1 & 3 & -1 & \vline & 15 \\ 0 & -5 & 3 & \vline & -23 \\ 0 & 0 & -17 & \vline & 17 \end{bmatrix} \quad R_3 \to 5R_3 - 4R_2$$

$$\begin{array}{rrrr} 0 & -20 & -5 & -75 \\ 0 & 20 & -12 & 92 \\ \hline 0 & 0 & -17 & 17 \end{array}$$

The last row gives $-17z = 17$
$$\therefore \quad z = -1$$

Thus in row 2, as $-5y + 3z = -23$
$$\therefore \quad -5y - 3 = -23$$
$$\therefore \quad -5y = -20$$
$$\therefore \quad y = 4$$

and $\therefore$ from row 1 $x + 3y - z = 15$
$$\therefore \quad x + 12 + 1 = 15$$
$$\therefore \quad x = 2$$

A typical graphics calculator solution:

```
rref([A])
    [[1 0 0 2 ]
     [0 1 0 4 ]
     [0 0 1 -1]]
```

Thus we have a unique solution $x = 2$, $y = 4$, $z = -1$.

Remember: Rows are really equations.

Note: You can use matrix algebra to find unique solutions,

i.e., $\begin{bmatrix} x \\ y \\ z \end{bmatrix} = \begin{bmatrix} 1 & 3 & -1 \\ 2 & 1 & 1 \\ 1 & -1 & -2 \end{bmatrix}^{-1} \begin{bmatrix} 15 \\ 7 \\ 0 \end{bmatrix}$ Try it on your calculator.

EXERCISE 14M.2

1 Without using technology, solve using row operations on the augmented matrix:

a $x + y + z = 6$
$2x + 4y + z = 5$
$2x + 3y + z = 6$

b $x + 4y + 11z = 7$
$x + 6y + 17z = 9$
$x + 4y + 8z = 4$

c $2x - y + 3z = 17$
$2x - 2y - 5z = 4$
$3x + 2y + 2z = 10$

2 Use technology to check your answers to **1 a** and **1 c**.

CASES WITH NON-UNIQUE SOLUTIONS

As with 2×2 systems of linear equations, 3×3 systems may have **a unique solution** where a single value of each variable satisfies all three equations simultaneously or it could have

- **no solutions**   or
- **infinitely many solutions**.

We will now consider examples which show each of these situations.

Example 20

Solve the system $\begin{cases} x + 2y + z = 3 \\ 2x - y + z = 8 \\ 3x - 4y + z = 18 \end{cases}$.

In augmented matrix form, the system is:

$$\left[\begin{array}{ccc|c} 1 & 2 & 1 & 3 \\ 2 & -1 & 1 & 8 \\ 3 & -4 & 1 & 18 \end{array}\right]$$

$R_2 \to R_2 - 2R_1$

$$\begin{array}{cccc} 2 & -1 & 1 & 8 \\ -2 & -4 & -2 & -6 \\ \hline 0 & -5 & -1 & 2 \end{array}$$

$$\sim \left[\begin{array}{ccc|c} 1 & 2 & 1 & 3 \\ 0 & -5 & -1 & 2 \\ 0 & -10 & -2 & 9 \end{array}\right]$$

$R_3 \to R_3 - 3R_1$

$$\begin{array}{cccc} 3 & -4 & 1 & 18 \\ -3 & -6 & -3 & -9 \\ \hline 0 & -10 & -2 & 9 \end{array}$$

$$\sim \left[\begin{array}{ccc|c} 1 & 2 & 1 & 3 \\ 0 & -5 & -1 & 2 \\ 0 & 0 & 0 & 5 \end{array}\right]$$

$R_3 \to R_3 - 2R_2$

$$\begin{array}{cccc} 0 & -10 & -2 & 9 \\ 0 & 10 & 2 & -4 \\ \hline 0 & 0 & 0 & 5 \end{array}$$

The last equation is really $0x + 0y + 0z = 5$ i.e., $0 = 5$ which is absurd,
$\therefore$ the system has no solution.

Using a **graphics calculator:**

Once again, $0 = 1$
So, no solution.

```
rref([A])
    [[1 0 .6 0]
     [0 1 .2 0]
     [0 0 0  1]]
```

Example 21

Solve the system:
$$\begin{cases} 2x - y + z = 5 \\ x + y - z = 2 \\ 3x - 3y + 3z = 8 \end{cases}$$

In augmented matrix form, the system is:

$$\begin{bmatrix} 1 & 1 & -1 & | & 2 \\ 2 & -1 & 1 & | & 5 \\ 3 & -3 & 3 & | & 8 \end{bmatrix}$$

Notice the swapping of R_1 and R_2.

$$\begin{array}{rrrr} 2 & -1 & 1 & 5 \\ -2 & -2 & 2 & -4 \\ \hline 0 & -3 & 3 & 1 \end{array}$$

$$\sim \begin{bmatrix} 1 & 1 & -1 & | & 2 \\ 0 & -3 & 3 & | & 1 \\ 0 & -6 & 6 & | & 2 \end{bmatrix} \quad \begin{array}{l} \longleftarrow R_2 \to R_2 - 2R_1 \\ \longleftarrow R_3 \to R_3 - 3R_1 \end{array}$$

$$\begin{array}{rrrr} 3 & -3 & 3 & 8 \\ -3 & -3 & 3 & -6 \\ \hline 0 & -6 & 6 & 2 \end{array}$$

$$\sim \begin{bmatrix} 1 & 1 & -1 & | & 2 \\ 0 & -3 & 3 & | & 1 \\ 0 & 0 & 0 & | & 0 \end{bmatrix} \quad \longleftarrow R_3 \to R_3 - 2R_2$$

$$\begin{array}{rrrr} 0 & -6 & 6 & 2 \\ 0 & 6 & -6 & -2 \\ \hline 0 & 0 & 0 & 0 \end{array}$$

The row of zeros indicates infinitely many solutions.

If we let $z = t$ in row 2,
$$-3y + 3t = 1$$
$$-3y = 1 - 3t$$
$$\therefore \quad y = \frac{1 - 3t}{-3}$$
$$\therefore \quad y = -\tfrac{1}{3} + t$$

```
rref([A])▶Frac
  [[1 0 0   7/3 ]
   [0 1 -1  -1/3]
   [0 0 0    0  ]]
```

Thus in equation 1,
$$x + (-\tfrac{1}{3} + t) - t = 2$$
$$\therefore \quad x - \tfrac{1}{3} = 2$$
$$\therefore \quad x = \tfrac{7}{3}$$

$\therefore$ the solutions have form: $x = \tfrac{7}{3}$, $y = -\tfrac{1}{3} + t$, $z = t$ (t real)

EXERCISE 14M.3

1 Solve the following systems:

a
$$x - 2y + 5z = 1$$
$$2x - 4y + 8z = 2$$
$$-3x + 6y + 7z = -3$$

b
$$x + 2y - z = 4$$
$$3x + 2y + z = 7$$
$$5x + 2y + 3z = 11$$

c
$$2x + 4y + z = 1$$
$$3x + 5y = 1$$
$$5x + 13y + 7z = 4$$

d
$$2x + 3y + 4z = 1$$
$$5x + 6y + 7z = 2$$
$$8x + 9y + 10z = 4$$

Example 22

Consider the system $\begin{cases} x - 2y - z = -1 \\ 2x + y + 3z = 13 \\ x + 8y + 9z = a \end{cases}$ where a takes all real values.

a Use elementary row operations to reduce the system to echelon form.

b When does the system have no solutions?

c When does the system have infinitely many solutions? What are the solutions?

a In augmented matrix form, the system is:

$$\left[\begin{array}{ccc|c} 1 & -2 & -1 & -1 \\ 2 & 1 & 3 & 13 \\ 1 & 8 & 9 & a \end{array} \right]$$

$$\sim \left[\begin{array}{ccc|c} 1 & -2 & -1 & -1 \\ 0 & 5 & 5 & 15 \\ 0 & 10 & 10 & a+1 \end{array} \right] \begin{array}{l} R_2 \to R_2 - 2R_1 \\ \\ \leftarrow R_3 \to R_3 - R_1 \end{array}$$

$$\sim \left[\begin{array}{ccc|c} 1 & -2 & -1 & -1 \\ 0 & 5 & 5 & 15 \\ 0 & 0 & 0 & a-29 \end{array} \right] \leftarrow R_3 \to R_3 - 2R_2$$

$$\begin{array}{rrrr} 2 & 1 & 3 & 13 \\ -2 & 4 & 2 & 2 \\ \hline 0 & 5 & 5 & 15 \end{array}$$

$$\begin{array}{rrrr} 1 & 8 & 9 & a \\ -1 & 2 & 1 & 1 \\ \hline 0 & 10 & 10 & a+1 \end{array}$$

$$\begin{array}{rrrr} 0 & 10 & 10 & a+1 \\ 0 & -10 & -10 & -30 \\ \hline 0 & 0 & 0 & a-29 \end{array}$$

b Now if $a \neq 29$, we have an inconsistent system   {as zero = non-zero} and $\therefore$ no solutions.

c And if $a = 29$, the last row is all zeros indicating infinitely many solutions.

Letting $z = t$, in equation 2 gives

$$5y + 5t = 15$$
$$\therefore \quad y = 3 - t$$

and in the first equation,

$$x - 2y - z = -1$$
$$\therefore \quad x - 2(3 - t) - t = -1$$
$$\therefore \quad x - 6 + 2t - t = -1$$
$$\therefore \quad x = 5 - t$$

Thus we have infinitely many solutions, in the form:
$$x = 5 - t, \quad y = 3 - t, \quad z = t \quad (t \text{ being real}).$$

2 Write the system of equations $\quad x + 2y + z = 3$
$$2x - y + 4z = 1$$
$$x + 7y - z = k \quad \text{in augmented matrix form.}$$

a Use elementary row operations to reduce the system to echelon form as shown:

b Show that the system has either no solutions or infinitely many solutions and write down these solutions.

$$\left[\begin{array}{ccc|c} \bullet & \bullet & \bullet & \bullet \\ 0 & \bullet & \bullet & \bullet \\ 0 & 0 & \bullet & \bullet \end{array} \right]$$

c Why does the system not have a unique solution?

3 Consider the system of equations $x + 2y - 2z = 5$
$$x - y + 3z = -1$$
$$x - 7y + kz = -k.$$

a Reduce the system to echelon form,   i.e., $\begin{bmatrix} \bullet & \bullet & \bullet & | & \bullet \\ 0 & \bullet & \bullet & | & \bullet \\ 0 & 0 & \bullet & | & \bullet \end{bmatrix}$.

b Show that for one value of k the system has infinitely many solutions and find the solutions in this case.

c Show that, for any other values of k, a unique solution exists. Find the unique solution.

4 A system of equations is $x + 3y + 3z = a - 1$
$$2x - y + z = 7$$
$$3x - 5y + az = 16.$$

a Reduce the system by using elementary row operations to echelon form.

b Show that if $a = -1$ the system has infinitely many solutions, and find their form.

c If $a \neq -1$, find the unique solution, in terms of a.

5 Reduce the system of equations $2x + y - z = 3$
$$mx - 2y + z = 1$$
$$x + 2y + mz = -1$$

to a form in which the solutions may be determined for all real values of m.

a Show that the system has no solutions for one value of m ($m = m_1$, say).

b Show that the system has infinitely many solutions for another value of m ($m = m_2$, say).

c For what values of m does the system have a unique solution?

Show that the unique solution is $x = \dfrac{7}{m + 5}$, $y = \dfrac{3(m - 2)}{m + 5}$, $z = \dfrac{-7}{m + 5}$.

6 Consider the system of equations $x + 3y + kz = 2$
$$kx - 2y + 3z = k$$
$$4x - 3y + 10z = 5.$$

a Write the system in augmented matrix form and reduce it by elementary row operations to the form $\begin{bmatrix} 1 & 3 & k & | & 2 \\ 0 & \bullet & \bullet & | & \bullet \\ 0 & 0 & \bullet & | & \bullet \end{bmatrix}$

b Show that for one value of k the system has infinitely many solutions and find the form of these solutions.

c For what value(s) of k does the system have no solutions?

d For what values of k does the system have a unique solution? [There is no need to find the unique solution.]

NOT ENOUGH EQUATIONS

$\begin{cases} x + y + 2z = 2 \\ 2x + y - z = 4 \end{cases}$ is a 2×3 system of two linear equations in three unknowns and has infinitely many solutions.

It requires a further equation if a unique solution is to be obtained.

We call this an **underspecified system**.

Example 23

a Solve: $\begin{cases} x + y + 2z = 2 \\ 2x + y - z = 4 \end{cases}$

b What can be deduced if the following equation is added to the system
   i $3x - y - 4z = 18$ **ii** $3x + y - 4z = 18$?

---

a The augmented matrix is

$$\begin{bmatrix} 1 & 1 & 2 & | & 2 \\ 2 & 1 & -1 & | & 4 \end{bmatrix}$$

$$\sim \begin{bmatrix} 1 & 1 & 2 & | & 2 \\ 0 & -1 & -5 & | & 0 \end{bmatrix} \longleftarrow R_2 \to R_2 - 2R_1 \qquad \begin{array}{rrrr} 2 & 1 & -1 & 4 \\ -2 & -2 & -4 & -4 \\ \hline 0 & -1 & -5 & 0 \end{array}$$

So, $-y - 5z = 0$ and if $z = t$, $y = -5t$

and as $x + y + 2z = 2$,

$\qquad x - 5t + 2t = 2$

That is, $x = 2 + 3t$. So, $x = 2 + 3t$, $y = -5t$, $z = t$ for all real t.

b i If in addition $3x - y - 4z = 18$
   then $3(2 + 3t) - (-5t) - 4t = 18$
   $\therefore \quad 6 + 9t + 5t - 4t = 18$
   i.e., $10t = 12$
   $\qquad \quad t = 1.2$

and when $t = 1.2$, $x = 5.6$, $y = -6$, $z = 1.2$, a unique solution.

ii If in addition $3x + y - 4z = 18$
   then $3(2 + 3t) + (-5t) - 4t = 18$
   i.e., $6 = 18$ which is absurd, so no solution exists.

Note: Unspecified systems (not enough equations) may have no solutions. This will be evident by any inconsistency.

EXERCISE 14M.4

1 Solve the systems:

a $2x + y + z = 5$
     $x - y + z = 3$

b $3x + y + 2z = 10$
     $x - 2y + z = -4$

c $x + 2y + z = 5$
     $2x + 4y + 2z = 16$

2 Solve $\begin{array}{l} x - 3y + z = 0 \\ 2x + y - 2z = 0 \end{array}$ and hence solve the system $\begin{array}{l} x - 3y + z = 0 \\ 2x + y - 2z = 0 \\ 3x - y + z = 18. \end{array}$

3 Solve $\begin{array}{l} 2x + 3y + z = 0 \\ x - y + 2z = 0 \end{array}$ and hence solve $\begin{array}{l} 2x + 3y + z = 0 \\ x - y + 2z = 0 \\ ax + y - z = 0 \end{array}$ for all real numbers a.

4 An economist producing x thousand items attempts to model a profit function as a quadratic model $P(x) = ax^2 + bx + c$ thousand dollars. She notices that for producing 1000 items the profit is \$8000 and when producing 4000 items the profit is \$17 000.

a Using the supplied information show that $\begin{cases} a + b + c = 8 \\ 16a + 4b + c = 17 \end{cases}$

b Show that $a = t$, $b = 3 - 5t$, $c = 5 + 4t$ represents the possible solutions for the system.

c If she discovers that the profit for producing 2500 items is \$19 750, find the actual profit function.

d What is the maximum profit to be made and what level of production is needed to achieve it?

Conditions for the existence of a unique solution, no solution or infinitely many solutions:

Step 1: To quickly determine if a system of equations has a unique solution, for example,

$$\begin{aligned} 3x - 2y + z &= 3 \\ 2x + 3y - 2z &= -3 \\ x - 2y + 5z &= 2 \end{aligned} \qquad \begin{aligned} \text{we convert} \\ \text{to matrix} \\ \text{form,} \end{aligned} \qquad \begin{bmatrix} 3 & -2 & 1 \\ 2 & 3 & -2 \\ 1 & -2 & 5 \end{bmatrix} \begin{bmatrix} x \\ y \\ z \end{bmatrix} = \begin{bmatrix} 3 \\ -3 \\ 2 \end{bmatrix}$$

If $\det \begin{bmatrix} 3 & -2 & 1 \\ 2 & 3 & -2 \\ 1 & -2 & 5 \end{bmatrix} \neq 0$, $\begin{bmatrix} 3 & -2 & 1 \\ 2 & 3 & -2 \\ 1 & -2 & 5 \end{bmatrix}^{-1}$ exists and we have a **unique solution**.

Step 2: If $\det \begin{bmatrix} 3 & -2 & 1 \\ 2 & 3 & -2 \\ 1 & -2 & 5 \end{bmatrix} = 0$,   we either have
- no solutions   *or*
- infinitely many solutions.

To determine which, use row operations on the augmented matrix.

If the augmented matrix reduces to $\left[\begin{array}{ccc|c} a & b & c & d \\ 0 & e & f & g \\ 0 & 0 & 0 & h \end{array}\right]$ with

- $h \neq 0$,   the system is inconsistent and **no solutions** exist
- $h = 0$,   the system has **infinitely many solutions**   {as in **Example 22 c**}

If you have infinite solutions, you should give them in parametric form.

A 3×3 system may collapse to one equation in 3 unknowns $\left[\begin{array}{ccc|c} a & b & c & d \\ 0 & 0 & 0 & 0 \\ 0 & 0 & 0 & 0 \end{array}\right]$

in which case there are infinite solutions that can be expressed in terms of two parameters s and t, say:

If we let $z = s$ and $y = t$ then $x = \dfrac{d - bt - cs}{a}$, $s, t \in \mathcal{R}$

Note: A geometric interpretation of equations in 3 unknowns can be given after studying **Chapter 15**   (**Vectors in 2 and 3-dimensions**)

N   INDUCTION WITH MATRICES

EXERCISE 14N

1 Let $M = \begin{bmatrix} 1 & 2 \\ 0 & 1 \end{bmatrix}$.

    a Find M^2, M^3, M^4.   **b** State a proposition for M^n.

    c Prove your conjecture true using mathematical induction.

2   **a** Given $A = \begin{bmatrix} 1 & 2 \\ 0 & 3 \end{bmatrix}$, find A^2, A^3, A^4, A^5.

    b Conjecture a value for A^n, i.e., express A^n in terms of n, where $n \in Z^+$.

    c Use mathematical induction to prove your conjecture is true.

    d Is the result true when $n = -1$?

3 Let the matrix $P = \begin{bmatrix} 2 & 1 \\ -1 & 0 \end{bmatrix}$.

    a Find P^2, P^3, P^4.

    b **i** Give a proposition (conjecture) for P^n where $n \in Z^+$.

        ii Prove your proposition true by mathematical induction.

4 For the sequence $1, 1, 2, 3, 5, 8, 13, ...$ where $u_1 = u_2 = 1$ and $u_{n+2} = u_n + u_{n+1}$,

    $n \in Z^+$, and the matrix $A = \begin{bmatrix} 1 & 1 \\ 1 & 0 \end{bmatrix}$, prove by the principle of mathematical

    induction that $\quad A^{n+1} = \begin{bmatrix} u_{n+2} & u_{n+1} \\ u_{n+1} & u_n \end{bmatrix}$ for all integers $n \geqslant 1$.

REVIEW SET 14A

1 If $A = \begin{bmatrix} 3 & 2 \\ 0 & -1 \end{bmatrix}$ and $B = \begin{bmatrix} 1 & 0 \\ -2 & 4 \end{bmatrix}$ find:

    a $A + B$ **b** $3A$ **c** $-2B$ **d** $A - B$

    e $B - 2A$ **f** $3A - 2B$ **g** AB **h** BA

    i A^{-1} **j** A^2 **k** ABA **l** $(AB)^{-1}$

2 Find a, b, c and d if:

    a $\begin{bmatrix} a & b-2 \\ c & d \end{bmatrix} = \begin{bmatrix} -a & 3 \\ 2-c & -4 \end{bmatrix}$ **b** $\begin{bmatrix} 3 & 2a \\ b & -2 \end{bmatrix} + \begin{bmatrix} b & -a \\ c & d \end{bmatrix} = \begin{bmatrix} a & 2 \\ 2 & 6 \end{bmatrix}$

3 Make Y the subject of:

    a $B - Y = A$ **b** $2Y + C = D$ **c** $AY = B$

    d $YB = C$ **e** $C - AY = B$ **f** $AY^{-1} = B$

4 Solve using matrix methods:

    a $\begin{array}{l} 3x - 4y = 2 \\ 5x + 2y = -1 \end{array}$ **b** $\begin{array}{l} 4x - y = 5 \\ 2x + 3y = 9 \end{array}$

c $\quad \mathbf{X} \begin{bmatrix} 3 & 4 \\ 1 & 1 \end{bmatrix} = \begin{bmatrix} 5 & 4 \\ 0 & -2 \end{bmatrix}$

d $\quad \begin{bmatrix} 2 & 0 \\ -1 & 1 \end{bmatrix} \mathbf{X} = \begin{bmatrix} -1 \\ 2 \end{bmatrix}$

e $\quad \begin{bmatrix} 1 & 1 \\ 1 & -2 \end{bmatrix} \mathbf{X} = \begin{bmatrix} 5 \\ 4 \end{bmatrix}$

f $\quad \begin{bmatrix} 1 & 1 \\ -1 & 1 \end{bmatrix} \mathbf{X} \begin{bmatrix} 2 & 1 \\ 1 & -1 \end{bmatrix} = \begin{bmatrix} 5 & 1 \\ 0 & 3 \end{bmatrix}$

5 If **A** is $\begin{bmatrix} 1 & 2 & 3 \end{bmatrix}$ and **B** is $\begin{bmatrix} 2 & 4 \\ 0 & 1 \\ 3 & 2 \end{bmatrix}$ find, if possible:

a $\quad 2\mathbf{B}$

b $\quad \frac{1}{2}\mathbf{B}$

c $\quad \mathbf{AB}$

d $\quad \mathbf{BA}$

6 For $\mathbf{P} = \begin{bmatrix} 1 & 2 \\ 1 & 0 \\ 2 & 3 \end{bmatrix}$ and $\mathbf{Q} = \begin{bmatrix} 3 & 0 \\ 1 & 4 \\ 1 & 1 \end{bmatrix}$ find:

a $\quad \mathbf{P} + \mathbf{Q}$

b $\quad \mathbf{Q} - \mathbf{P}$

c $\quad \frac{3}{2}\mathbf{P} - \mathbf{Q}$

7 When does the system $\begin{array}{c} x + 4y = 2 \\ kx + 3y = -6 \end{array}$ have a unique solution?

Comment on the solutions for the non-unique cases.

8 Solve the system $\begin{array}{c} 3x - y + 2z = 3 \\ 2x + 3y - z = -3 \\ x - 2y + 3z = 2. \end{array}$

9 The two points $(-2, 4)$ and $(1, 3)$ lie on a circle with equation in the form
$$x^2 + y^2 + ax + by + c = 0.$$

a $\quad$ Find two equations in a, b and c and solve the system of equations.

b $\quad$ Explain why infinitely many solutions are obtained in **a**.

c $\quad$ If $(2, 2)$ is also on the circle, find the equation of the circle.

10 $\begin{array}{c} 2x + 3y - 4z = 13 \\ x - y + 3z = -1 \\ 3x + 7y - 11z = k \end{array}$ Solve the system using elementary row operations, and describe the solution set as k takes all real values.

11 Solve the system $\begin{array}{c} 3x + y - z = 0 \\ x + y + 2z = 0. \end{array}$

REVIEW SET 14B

1 What is the 2×2 matrix which when multiplied by $\begin{bmatrix} 1 & 0 \\ 1 & 1 \end{bmatrix}$ gives an answer of $\begin{bmatrix} 1 & 0 \\ 1 & 1 \end{bmatrix}$? **Hint:** Let the matrix be $\begin{bmatrix} a & b \\ c & d \end{bmatrix}$.

2 $\mathbf{A} = \begin{bmatrix} 4 & 3 & 2 \end{bmatrix}$, $\mathbf{B} = \begin{bmatrix} 1 \\ 2 \\ 0 \end{bmatrix}$ and $\mathbf{C} = \begin{bmatrix} 1 & 2 & 3 \\ 3 & 2 & 1 \\ 1 & 2 & 3 \end{bmatrix}$. Find, if possible:

a $\quad \mathbf{AB}$

b $\quad \mathbf{BA}$

c $\quad \mathbf{AC}$

d $\quad \mathbf{CA}$

e $\quad \mathbf{CB}$

3 Find, if they exist, the inverse matrices of each of the following:

a $\begin{bmatrix} 6 & 8 \\ 5 & 7 \end{bmatrix}$ 　　　　　**b** $\begin{bmatrix} 4 & -3 \\ 8 & -6 \end{bmatrix}$ 　　　　　**c** $\begin{bmatrix} 11 & 5 \\ -6 & -3 \end{bmatrix}$

4　**a** If $\mathbf{A} = 2\mathbf{A}^{-1}$, show that $\mathbf{A}^2 = 2\mathbf{I}$.

　　b If $\mathbf{A} = 2\mathbf{A}^{-1}$, simplify $(\mathbf{A} - \mathbf{I})(\mathbf{A} + 3\mathbf{I})$ giving your answer in the form $r\mathbf{A} + s\mathbf{I}$ where r and s are real numbers.

5 A café sells two types of cola drinks. The drinks each come in three sizes: small, medium and large. At the beginning of the day the fridge was stocked with the number of units of each as shown in the matrix below. At the end of the day the stock was again counted. The results are shown below:

Start of the day　　　　　　　　　　At the end of the day

	Brand C	Brand P
small ⟶	42	54
medium ⟶	36	27
large ⟶	34	30

	Brand C	Brand P
small ⟶	27	31
medium ⟶	28	15
large ⟶	28	22

The profit matrix is profit

small	medium	large
$0.75	$0.55	$1.20

Use matrix methods to calculate the profit made for the day from the sale of these drinks.

6 If $\mathbf{A} = \begin{bmatrix} 1 & 2 & 3 \\ 2 & 5 & 7 \\ -2 & -4 & -5 \end{bmatrix}$ and $\mathbf{B} = \begin{bmatrix} 3 & -2 & -1 \\ -4 & 1 & -1 \\ 2 & 0 & 1 \end{bmatrix}$, find $\mathbf{AB}$ and $\mathbf{BA}$ and

hence find $\mathbf{A}^{-1}$ in terms of $\mathbf{B}$.

7 Solve the system of equations
$$2x + y + z = 8$$
$$4x - 7y + 3z = 10$$
$$3x - 2y - z = 1.$$

8 Solve the system
$$x + 2y - 3z = 3$$
$$6x + 3y + 2z = 4.$$

9　**a** Show that the system
$$2x - 3y = 9$$
$$mx - 7y = n$$
has augmented matrix after elementary

row operations of $\begin{bmatrix} 2 & -3 & | & 9 \\ 14 - 3m & 0 & | & 63 - 3n \end{bmatrix}$

　　b Under what conditions does the system have a unique solution?

Chapter 15

Vectors in 2 and 3 dimensions

A VECTORS

OPENING PROBLEM

An aeroplane in calm conditions is flying due east. A cold wind suddenly blows in from the south west. The aeroplane, cruising at 800 km/h, is blown slightly off course by the 35 km/h wind.

- What effect does the wind have on the speed and direction of the aeroplane?
- How can we accurately determine the new speed and direction using mathematics?
- How much of the force of the wind operates in the direction of the aeroplane, and how does this affect fuel consumption and the time of the flight?

VECTORS AND SCALARS

In order to handle the **Opening Problem** and problems similar to it we need to examine the **size** or **magnitude** of the quantities under consideration as well as the direction in which they are acting.

For example, the effect of the wind on an aeroplane would be different if the wind was blowing from behind the plane rather than against it.

Consider the problem of forces acting at a point.

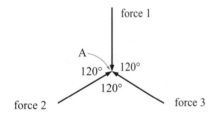

If three equal forces act on point A and they are from directions $120°$ apart then clearly A would not move.

(Imagine three people pushing a fourth person with equal force and $120°$ apart.)

Now suppose three forces act on the point A as shown. What is the resultant force acting on A and in what direction would A move under these three forces?

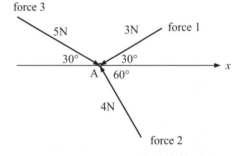

VECTORS

To handle these situations we need to consider quantities called **vectors** which have both size (magnitude) and direction.

> Quantities which have only magnitude are called **scalars**.
>
> Quantities which have both size (magnitude) and direction are called **vectors**.

For example,   velocity is a vector since it deals with speed (a scalar) in a particular direction.

Other examples of vector quantities are:
- acceleration
- force
- displacement
- momentum
- weight

DIRECTED LINE SEGMENT REPRESENTATION

Consider the following example where a car is travelling at 80 kmph in a NE direction.

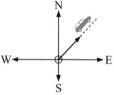

One good way of representing this is to use an arrow on a scale diagram.

Scale: 1 cm represents 40 kmph

The **length of the arrow** represents the size (magnitude) of the quantity and the **arrowhead** shows the direction of travel.

Consider the vector represented by the line segment from O to A.

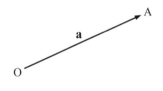

- This **vector** could be represented by

  $\overrightarrow{OA}$ or   **a**   or $\underline{a}$ or $\vec{a}$

  bold used   used by
  in text books   students

- The **magnitude (length)** could be represented by

  $|\overrightarrow{OA}|$ or   OA   or $|\mathbf{a}|$ or $|\underline{a}|$ or $|\vec{a}|$

For   the vector which **emanates** at A and **terminates** at B,

$\overrightarrow{AB}$ is the **position vector** of B relative to (from) A.

Example 1	
On a scale diagram, sketch the vector which represents "a force of 20 Newtons in a southerly direction".	*Scale:* 1 cm ≡ 10 Newtons 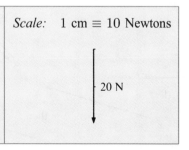

Example 2	
Draw a scaled arrow diagram representing '40 Newtons on a bearing 115°'.	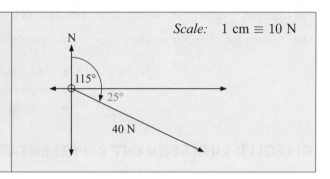

EXERCISE 15A.1

1   Using a scale of 1 cm represents 10 units, sketch a vector to represent:
   a   30 Newtons in a SE direction
   b   25 ms^{-1} in a northerly direction
   c   a displacement of 35 m in a direction 070°
   d   an aeroplane taking off at an angle of 10° to the runway with a speed of 50 m/s.

2   If ——————————➤ represents a velocity of 50 m/s due east, draw a directed line segment representing a velocity of:
   a   100 m/s due west   **b**   75 m/s north east.

3   Draw a scaled arrow diagram representing the following vectors:
   a   a force of 30 Newtons in the NW direction
   b   a velocity of 40 m/s in the direction 146°
   c   a displacement of 25 km in the direction S32°E
   d   an aeroplane taking off at an angle of 8° to the runway at a speed of 150 kmph.

VECTOR EQUALITY

Two vectors are **equal** if they have the same magnitude and direction.

So, if arrows are used to represent vectors, then equal vectors are **parallel** and **equal in length**.

This means that equal vector arrows are translations of one another.

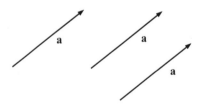

NEGATIVE VECTORS

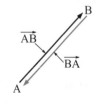

Notice that $\overrightarrow{AB}$ and $\overrightarrow{BA}$ have the same length but have opposite directions.

We say that $\overrightarrow{BA}$ is the negative of $\overrightarrow{AB}$ and write $\overrightarrow{BA} = -\overrightarrow{AB}$.

Also if 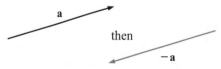 then

as these two vectors are parallel, equal in length, but opposite in direction.

Example 3

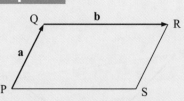

PQRS is a parallelogram, and $\overrightarrow{PQ} = \mathbf{a}$ and $\overrightarrow{QR} = \mathbf{b}$.

Find vector expressions for:

  a $\overrightarrow{QP}$ **b** $\overrightarrow{RQ}$ **c** $\overrightarrow{SR}$ **d** $\overrightarrow{SP}$

  a $\overrightarrow{QP} = -\mathbf{a}$ {the negative vector of $\overrightarrow{PQ}$}

  b $\overrightarrow{RQ} = -\mathbf{b}$ {the negative vector of $\overrightarrow{QR}$}

  c $\overrightarrow{SR} = \mathbf{a}$ {parallel to and the same length as $\overrightarrow{PQ}$}

  d $\overrightarrow{SP} = -\mathbf{b}$ {parallel to and the same length as $\overrightarrow{RQ}$}

EXERCISE 15A.2

1 State the vectors which are:

  a equal in magnitude   **b** parallel

  c in the same direction   **d** equal

  e negatives of one another.

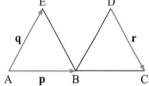

2 The figure shown consists of 2 congruent equilateral triangles. ABC lie on a straight line. $\overrightarrow{AB} = \mathbf{p}$, $\overrightarrow{AE} = \mathbf{q}$ and $\overrightarrow{DC} = \mathbf{r}$.

Which of the following statements is true?

  a $\overrightarrow{EB} = \mathbf{r}$ **b** $|\mathbf{p}| = |\mathbf{q}|$ **c** $\overrightarrow{BC} = \mathbf{r}$

  d $\overrightarrow{DB} = \mathbf{q}$ **e** $\overrightarrow{ED} = \mathbf{p}$ **f** $\mathbf{p} = \mathbf{q}$

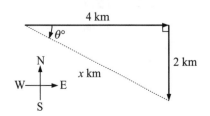

DISCUSSION

Could we have a zero vector?

What would its length be? What direction?

B   OPERATIONS WITH VECTORS

We have already been operating with vectors without realising it.

Bearing problems are an example of this. The vectors in this case are **displacements**.

A typical problem could be, "A runner runs in an easterly direction for 4 km and then in a southerly direction for 2 km.

How far is she from her starting point and in what direction?"

Notice that trigonometry and Pythagoras' rule are used to answer such problems as we need to find θ and x.

DISPLACEMENT VECTORS

Suppose we have three towns P, Q and R.

A trip from P to Q followed by a trip from Q to R is equivalent to a trip from P to R.

This can be expressed in a vector form as

$\overrightarrow{PQ} + \overrightarrow{QR} = \overrightarrow{PR}$ where the $+$ sign could mean '*followed by*'.

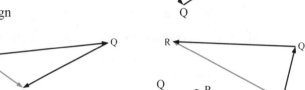

This triangular diagram could take all sorts of shapes. For example:

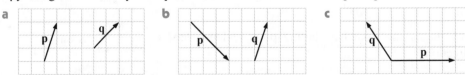

VECTOR ADDITION

After considering displacements in diagrams like those above, we define vector addition geometrically as:

To add **a** and **b**   *Step 1:*   first draw **a**, then
              Step 2:   at the arrowhead end of **a** draw **b**, and then
              Step 3:   join the beginning of **a** to the arrowhead end of **b** and this is vector **a + b**.

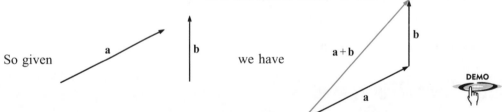

So given ... we have ...

DEMO

Example 4	
Given **a** and **b** as shown, construct **a + b**.	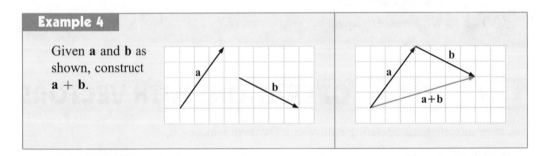

EXERCISE 15B.1

1   Copy the given vectors **p** and **q** and hence show how to find **p + q**:

d 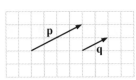   **e** 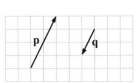   **f**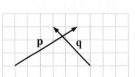

Example 5

Find a single vector which is equal to:

a $\overrightarrow{BC} + \overrightarrow{CA}$

b $\overrightarrow{BA} + \overrightarrow{AE} + \overrightarrow{EC}$

c $\overrightarrow{AB} + \overrightarrow{BC} + \overrightarrow{CA}$

d $\overrightarrow{AB} + \overrightarrow{BC} + \overrightarrow{CD} + \overrightarrow{DE}$

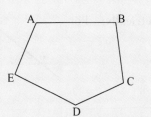

a $\overrightarrow{BC} + \overrightarrow{CA} = \overrightarrow{BA}$ {as shown}

b $\overrightarrow{BA} + \overrightarrow{AE} + \overrightarrow{EC} = \overrightarrow{BC}$

c $\overrightarrow{AB} + \overrightarrow{BC} + \overrightarrow{CA} = \overrightarrow{AA}$

d $\overrightarrow{AB} + \overrightarrow{BC} + \overrightarrow{CD} + \overrightarrow{DE} = \overrightarrow{AE}$

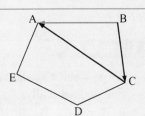

2 Find a single vector which is equal to:

  a $\overrightarrow{AB} + \overrightarrow{BC}$ **b** $\overrightarrow{BC} + \overrightarrow{CD}$ **c** $\overrightarrow{AB} + \overrightarrow{BC} + \overrightarrow{CD}$ **d** $\overrightarrow{AC} + \overrightarrow{CB} + \overrightarrow{BD}$

3 **a** Use vector diagrams to find   **i** $\mathbf{p} + \mathbf{q}$ **ii** $\mathbf{q} + \mathbf{p}$ given that:

  p is   and **q** is

  b For any two vectors **p** and **q**,   is $\mathbf{p} + \mathbf{q} = \mathbf{q} + \mathbf{p}$?

4 Consider: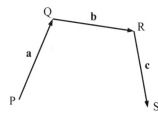

Notice that one way of finding $\overrightarrow{PS}$

is $\overrightarrow{PS} = \overrightarrow{PR} + \overrightarrow{RS}$

$= (\mathbf{a} + \mathbf{b}) + \mathbf{c}.$

Use the diagram to show that
$(\mathbf{a} + \mathbf{b}) + \mathbf{c} = \mathbf{a} + (\mathbf{b} + \mathbf{c}).$

Before defining vector subtraction it is necessary to look again at what we mean by **negative vectors**.

NEGATIVE VECTORS

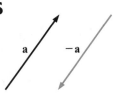

$-\mathbf{a}$ is the **negative** of **a**.

Notice that $-\mathbf{a}$ has the same magnitude as **a** but is in the opposite direction.

ZERO VECTOR

The **zero vector** is written as **0** and for any vector **a**, $\mathbf{a} + (-\mathbf{a}) = (-\mathbf{a}) + \mathbf{a} = \mathbf{0}$.

VECTOR SUBTRACTION

To subtract one vector from another, we simply **add its negative**, i.e., $\mathbf{a} - \mathbf{b} = \mathbf{a} + (-\mathbf{b})$.

Geometrically: For and then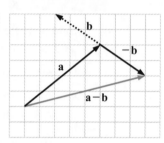

Example 6

For **r**, **s** and **t** as shown
find geometrically:

a $\mathbf{r} - \mathbf{s}$ **b** $\mathbf{s} - \mathbf{t} - \mathbf{r}$

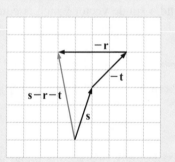

a

b

EXERCISE 15B.2

1 For the following vectors **p** and **q**, show how to construct $\mathbf{p} - \mathbf{q}$:

a 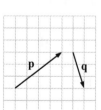   **b**   **c** 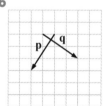   **d**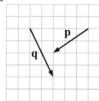

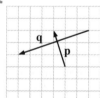

2 For the following vectors:

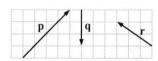

show how to construct: **a** $\mathbf{p} + \mathbf{q} - \mathbf{r}$ **b** $\mathbf{p} - \mathbf{q} - \mathbf{r}$ **c** $\mathbf{r} - \mathbf{q} - \mathbf{p}$

AN APPLICATION OF VECTOR SUBTRACTION

Vector subtraction is used in problem solving involving displacement, velocity and force.

Consider the following velocity application:

An aeroplane needs to fly due east from one city to another at a speed of 400 km/h. However a 50 km/h wind blows constantly from the north-east.

In what direction must the aeroplane head and at what speed must it travel?

Notice that on this occasion we know:

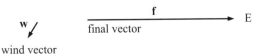

SIMULATION

wind vector

We also know that the aeroplane would have to head a little north of its final destination as the north-easterly would blow it back to its final direction.

So

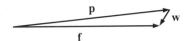

Even though the plane moves in the **f** direction it is actually lined up in the **p** direction.

Notice that $\mathbf{p} + \mathbf{w} = \mathbf{f}$ and   so $\mathbf{p} + \mathbf{w} + (-\mathbf{w}) = \mathbf{f} + (-\mathbf{w})$

$$\therefore \quad \mathbf{p} + \mathbf{0} = \mathbf{f} - \mathbf{w}$$

$$\text{i.e.,} \quad \mathbf{p} = \mathbf{f} - \mathbf{w}$$

The solution:

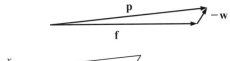

By the cosine rule,

$$x^2 = 50^2 + 400^2 - 2 \times 50 \times 400 \cos 135^o$$

gives $x \doteqdot 436.8$

By the sine rule

$$\frac{\sin \theta}{50} = \frac{\sin 135}{436.8} \quad \text{gives} \quad \theta \doteqdot 4.6$$

Consequently, the aeroplane must fly 4.6^o north of east at 436.8 km/h.

3 **a** Copy this diagram and on it mark the points:

    i X such that $\overrightarrow{MX} = \overrightarrow{MN} + \overrightarrow{MP}$

    ii Y such that $\overrightarrow{MY} = \overrightarrow{MN} - \overrightarrow{MP}$

    iii Z such that $\overrightarrow{PZ} = 2\overrightarrow{PM}$

  b What type of figure is MNYZ?

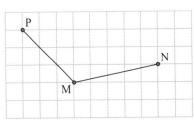

Example 7

For points A, B, C and D, simplify the following vector expressions:

a $\overrightarrow{AB} - \overrightarrow{CB}$

b $\overrightarrow{AC} - \overrightarrow{BC} - \overrightarrow{DB}$

a $\overrightarrow{AB} - \overrightarrow{CB}$

   $= \overrightarrow{AB} + \overrightarrow{BC}$ $\{$as $\overrightarrow{BC} = -\overrightarrow{CB}\}$

   $= \overrightarrow{AC}$

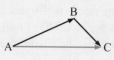

b $\overrightarrow{AC} - \overrightarrow{BC} - \overrightarrow{DB}$

   $= \overrightarrow{AC} + \overrightarrow{CB} + \overrightarrow{BD}$

   $= \overrightarrow{AD}$

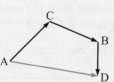

4   For points A, B, C and D, simplify the following vector expressions:

a $\overrightarrow{AC} + \overrightarrow{CB}$

b $\overrightarrow{AD} - \overrightarrow{BD}$

c $\overrightarrow{AC} + \overrightarrow{CA}$

d $\overrightarrow{AB} + \overrightarrow{BC} + \overrightarrow{CD}$

e $\overrightarrow{BA} - \overrightarrow{CA} + \overrightarrow{CB}$

f $\overrightarrow{AB} - \overrightarrow{CB} - \overrightarrow{DC}$

Example 8

Construct vector equations for:

a 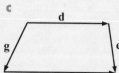   **b** 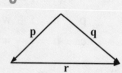   **c**

> We select any vector for the LHS and then take another path from its starting point to its finishing point.

a $\mathbf{t} = \mathbf{r} + \mathbf{s}$

b $\mathbf{r} = -\mathbf{p} + \mathbf{q}$

c $\mathbf{f} = -\mathbf{g} + \mathbf{d} + \mathbf{e}$

5   Construct vector equations for:

a 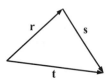   **b** 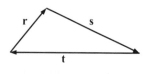   **c**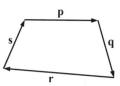

d   **e**   **f**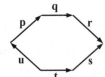

Example 9

For the given diagram, find, in terms
of **r**, **s** and **t**:

a $\overrightarrow{RS}$ **b** $\overrightarrow{SR}$ **c** $\overrightarrow{ST}$

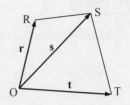

a $\overrightarrow{RS}$
$= \overrightarrow{RO} + \overrightarrow{OS}$
$= -\overrightarrow{OR} + \overrightarrow{OS}$
$= -\mathbf{r} + \mathbf{s}$
$= \mathbf{s} - \mathbf{r}$

b $\overrightarrow{SR}$
$= \overrightarrow{SO} + \overrightarrow{OR}$
$= -\overrightarrow{OS} + \overrightarrow{OR}$
$= -\mathbf{s} + \mathbf{r}$
$= \mathbf{r} - \mathbf{s}$

c $\overrightarrow{ST}$
$= \overrightarrow{SO} + \overrightarrow{OT}$
$= -\overrightarrow{OS} + \overrightarrow{OT}$
$= -\mathbf{s} + \mathbf{t}$
$= \mathbf{t} - \mathbf{s}$

6 **a** Find, in terms of **r**, **s** and **t**:

  i $\overrightarrow{OB}$ **ii** $\overrightarrow{CA}$ **iii** $\overrightarrow{OC}$

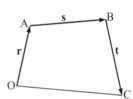

  b

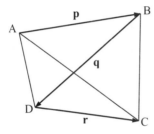

For $\overrightarrow{AB} = \mathbf{p}$, $\overrightarrow{BD} = \mathbf{q}$ and $\overrightarrow{DC} = \mathbf{r}$
find, in terms of **p**, **q** and **r**:

  i $\overrightarrow{AD}$ **ii** $\overrightarrow{BC}$ **iii** $\overrightarrow{AC}$

SCALAR MULTIPLICATION

Numbers such as 2 and -3 are also referred to as scalars. If **a** is a vector, what would $2\mathbf{a}$
and $-3\mathbf{a}$ mean?

By definition, $2\mathbf{a} = \mathbf{a} + \mathbf{a}$, $3\mathbf{a} = \mathbf{a} + \mathbf{a} + \mathbf{a}$, etc

$-3\mathbf{a} = 3(-\mathbf{a}) = (-\mathbf{a}) + (-\mathbf{a}) + (-\mathbf{a})$

So, if **a** is   then

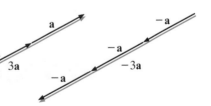

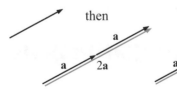

So, $2\mathbf{a}$ is in the direction of **a** but is twice as long as **a**

  $3\mathbf{a}$ is in the direction of **a** but is three times longer than **a**

  $-3\mathbf{a}$ is oppositely directed to **a** and is three times longer than **a**.

Note: If **a** is a vector and k is a scalar,

  $k\mathbf{a}$ is also a vector and we are performing **scalar multiplication**.

    If $k > 0$, $k\mathbf{a}$ and **a** have the same direction.

    If $k < 0$, $k\mathbf{a}$ and **a** have opposite directions.

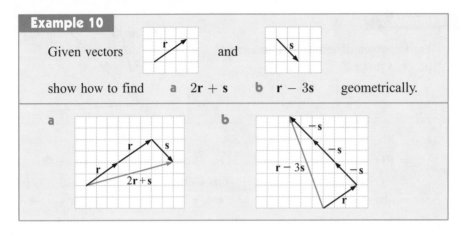

Example 10

Given vectors and show how to find   a $2\mathbf{r} + \mathbf{s}$ b $\mathbf{r} - 3\mathbf{s}$ geometrically.

EXERCISE 15B.3

1   Given vectors and , show how to find geometrically:

    a $-\mathbf{r}$
    b $2\mathbf{s}$
    c $\frac{1}{2}\mathbf{r}$
    d $-\frac{3}{2}\mathbf{s}$

    e $2\mathbf{r} - \mathbf{s}$
    f $2\mathbf{r} + 3\mathbf{s}$
    g $\frac{1}{2}\mathbf{r} + 2\mathbf{s}$
    h $\frac{1}{2}(\mathbf{r} + 3\mathbf{s})$

Example 11

Draw sketches of vectors $\mathbf{p}$ and $\mathbf{q}$ if   a $\mathbf{p} = 3\mathbf{q}$ b $\mathbf{p} = -\frac{1}{2}\mathbf{q}$.

Let $\mathbf{q}$ be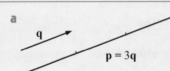

2   Draw sketches of $\mathbf{p}$ and $\mathbf{q}$ if:

    a $\mathbf{p} = \mathbf{q}$
    b $\mathbf{p} = -\mathbf{q}$
    c $\mathbf{p} = 2\mathbf{q}$
    d $\mathbf{p} = \frac{1}{3}\mathbf{q}$
    e $\mathbf{p} = -3\mathbf{q}$

C   2-D VECTORS IN COMPONENT FORM

So far we have examined vectors from their geometric representation.
We have used arrows where:

- the **length** of the arrow represents size (magnitude)
- the **arrowhead** indicates direction.

Consider a car travelling at 80 km/h in a NE direction.

The velocity vector could be represented by using the x and y-steps which are necessary to go from the start to the finish.

In this case the column vector $\begin{bmatrix} 56.6 \\ 56.6 \end{bmatrix}$ gives the x and y steps.

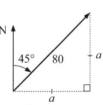

$$a^2 + a^2 = 80^2$$
$$\therefore \quad 2a^2 = 6400$$
$$\therefore \quad a^2 = 3200$$
$$\therefore \quad a \doteqdot 56.6$$

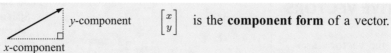

y-component $\quad \begin{bmatrix} x \\ y \end{bmatrix}\quad$ is the **component form** of a vector.

x-component

For example, given $\begin{bmatrix} 2 \\ 3 \end{bmatrix}$ we could draw and vice versa.

2 is the horizontal step and
3 is the vertical step.

EXERCISE 15C.1

1 Draw arrow diagrams to represent the vectors:

   a $\begin{bmatrix} 3 \\ 4 \end{bmatrix}$ **b** $\begin{bmatrix} 2 \\ 0 \end{bmatrix}$ **c** $\begin{bmatrix} 2 \\ -5 \end{bmatrix}$ **d** $\begin{bmatrix} -1 \\ -3 \end{bmatrix}$

2 Write the illustrated vectors in component form:

  a   **b** 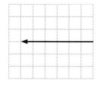   **c**

  d   **e**   **f**

VECTOR ADDITION

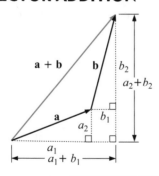

Consider adding vectors $\quad \mathbf{a} = \begin{bmatrix} a_1 \\ a_2 \end{bmatrix}\quad$ and $\quad \mathbf{b} = \begin{bmatrix} b_1 \\ b_2 \end{bmatrix}$.

Notice that the

horizontal step for $\mathbf{a} + \mathbf{b}$ is $a_1 + b_1$ and the
vertical step for $\mathbf{a} + \mathbf{b}$ is $a_2 + b_2$.

So,   if $\quad \mathbf{a} = \begin{bmatrix} a_1 \\ a_2 \end{bmatrix}\quad$ and $\quad \mathbf{b} = \begin{bmatrix} b_1 \\ b_2 \end{bmatrix}\quad$ then $\quad \mathbf{a} + \mathbf{b} = \begin{bmatrix} a_1 + b_1 \\ a_2 + b_2 \end{bmatrix}$.

Example 12		
If $\mathbf{a} = \begin{bmatrix} 1 \\ -3 \end{bmatrix}$ and $\mathbf{b} = \begin{bmatrix} 4 \\ 7 \end{bmatrix}$ find $\mathbf{a} + \mathbf{b}$. Check graphically.	$\mathbf{a} + \mathbf{b} = \begin{bmatrix} 1 \\ -3 \end{bmatrix} + \begin{bmatrix} 4 \\ 7 \end{bmatrix}$ $= \begin{bmatrix} 1 + 4 \\ -3 + 7 \end{bmatrix}$ $= \begin{bmatrix} 5 \\ 4 \end{bmatrix}$	*Check:* 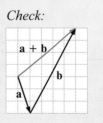

NEGATIVE VECTORS

Consider the vector $\mathbf{a} = \begin{bmatrix} 2 \\ 3 \end{bmatrix}$.

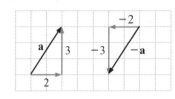

Start at the non-arrow end and move horizontally then vertically to the arrow end.

Notice that $-\mathbf{a} = \begin{bmatrix} -2 \\ -3 \end{bmatrix}$.

In general,   if $\mathbf{a} = \begin{bmatrix} a_1 \\ a_2 \end{bmatrix}$ then $-\mathbf{a} = \begin{bmatrix} -a_1 \\ -a_2 \end{bmatrix}$.

ZERO VECTOR

The zero vector is $\mathbf{0} = \begin{bmatrix} 0 \\ 0 \end{bmatrix}$ and for any vector $\mathbf{a}$, $\mathbf{a} + (-\mathbf{a}) = (-\mathbf{a}) + \mathbf{a} = \mathbf{0}$.

VECTOR SUBTRACTION

To subtract one vector from another, we simply **add its negative**, i.e., $\mathbf{a} - \mathbf{b} = \mathbf{a} + (-\mathbf{b})$.

Notice that, if $\mathbf{a} = \begin{bmatrix} a_1 \\ a_2 \end{bmatrix}$ and $\mathbf{b} = \begin{bmatrix} b_1 \\ b_2 \end{bmatrix}$ then $\mathbf{a} - \mathbf{b} = \mathbf{a} + (-\mathbf{b})$

$$= \begin{bmatrix} a_1 \\ a_2 \end{bmatrix} + \begin{bmatrix} -b_1 \\ -b_2 \end{bmatrix}$$

$$= \begin{bmatrix} a_1 - b_1 \\ a_2 - b_2 \end{bmatrix}$$

i.e.,   if $\mathbf{a} = \begin{bmatrix} a_1 \\ a_2 \end{bmatrix}$ and $\mathbf{b} = \begin{bmatrix} b_1 \\ b_2 \end{bmatrix}$ then $\mathbf{a} - \mathbf{b} = \begin{bmatrix} a_1 - b_1 \\ a_2 - b_2 \end{bmatrix}$.

EXERCISE 15C.2

1 If $\mathbf{a} = \begin{bmatrix} -3 \\ 2 \end{bmatrix}$ $\mathbf{b} = \begin{bmatrix} 1 \\ 4 \end{bmatrix}$, $\mathbf{c} = \begin{bmatrix} -2 \\ -5 \end{bmatrix}$ find:

a $\mathbf{a} + \mathbf{b}$	**b** $\mathbf{b} + \mathbf{a}$	**c** $\mathbf{b} + \mathbf{c}$	**d** $\mathbf{c} + \mathbf{b}$
e $\mathbf{a} + \mathbf{c}$	**f** $\mathbf{c} + \mathbf{a}$	**g** $\mathbf{a} + \mathbf{a}$	**h** $\mathbf{b} + \mathbf{a} + \mathbf{c}$

Example 13

Given $\mathbf{p} = \begin{bmatrix} 3 \\ -2 \end{bmatrix}$, $\mathbf{q} = \begin{bmatrix} 1 \\ 4 \end{bmatrix}$

and $\mathbf{r} = \begin{bmatrix} -2 \\ -5 \end{bmatrix}$ find:

a $\mathbf{q} - \mathbf{p}$

b $\mathbf{p} - \mathbf{q} - \mathbf{r}$

a $\mathbf{q} - \mathbf{p}$

$$= \begin{bmatrix} 1 \\ 4 \end{bmatrix} - \begin{bmatrix} 3 \\ -2 \end{bmatrix}$$

$$= \begin{bmatrix} 1 - 3 \\ 4 + 2 \end{bmatrix}$$

$$= \begin{bmatrix} -2 \\ 6 \end{bmatrix}$$

b $\mathbf{p} - \mathbf{q} - \mathbf{r}$

$$= \begin{bmatrix} 3 \\ -2 \end{bmatrix} - \begin{bmatrix} 1 \\ 4 \end{bmatrix} - \begin{bmatrix} -2 \\ -5 \end{bmatrix}$$

$$= \begin{bmatrix} 3 - 1 - -2 \\ -2 - 4 - -5 \end{bmatrix}$$

$$= \begin{bmatrix} 4 \\ -1 \end{bmatrix}$$

2 Given $\mathbf{p} = \begin{bmatrix} -4 \\ 2 \end{bmatrix}$, $\mathbf{q} = \begin{bmatrix} -1 \\ -5 \end{bmatrix}$ and $\mathbf{r} = \begin{bmatrix} 3 \\ -2 \end{bmatrix}$ find:

  a $\mathbf{p} - \mathbf{q}$ **b** $\mathbf{q} - \mathbf{r}$ **c** $\mathbf{p} + \mathbf{q} - \mathbf{r}$

  d $\mathbf{p} - \mathbf{q} - \mathbf{r}$ **e** $\mathbf{q} - \mathbf{r} - \mathbf{p}$ **f** $\mathbf{r} + \mathbf{q} - \mathbf{p}$

3 **a** Given $\overrightarrow{BA} = \begin{bmatrix} 2 \\ -3 \end{bmatrix}$ and $\overrightarrow{BC} = \begin{bmatrix} -3 \\ 1 \end{bmatrix}$ find $\overrightarrow{AC}$.   **Hint:** $\overrightarrow{AC} = \overrightarrow{AB} + \overrightarrow{BC}$
$$= -\overrightarrow{BA} + \overrightarrow{BC}.$$

  b If $\overrightarrow{AB} = \begin{bmatrix} -1 \\ 3 \end{bmatrix}$, $\overrightarrow{CA} = \begin{bmatrix} 2 \\ -1 \end{bmatrix}$, find $\overrightarrow{CB}$.

  c If $\overrightarrow{PQ} = \begin{bmatrix} -1 \\ 4 \end{bmatrix}$, $\overrightarrow{RQ} = \begin{bmatrix} 2 \\ 1 \end{bmatrix}$ and $\overrightarrow{RS} = \begin{bmatrix} -3 \\ 2 \end{bmatrix}$, find $\overrightarrow{SP}$.

SCALAR MULTIPLICATION

Recall the geometric approach for scalar multiplication.

For example:

> A **scalar** is a non-vector quantity.

The word scalar is also used for a constant number.

Consider $\mathbf{a} = \begin{bmatrix} 1 \\ 3 \end{bmatrix}$. $\quad \mathbf{a} + \mathbf{a} = \begin{bmatrix} 1 \\ 3 \end{bmatrix} + \begin{bmatrix} 1 \\ 3 \end{bmatrix} = \begin{bmatrix} 2 \\ 6 \end{bmatrix}$ and

$$\mathbf{a} + \mathbf{a} + \mathbf{a} = \begin{bmatrix} 1 \\ 3 \end{bmatrix} + \begin{bmatrix} 1 \\ 3 \end{bmatrix} + \begin{bmatrix} 1 \\ 3 \end{bmatrix} = \begin{bmatrix} 3 \\ 9 \end{bmatrix}$$

Examples like these suggest the following definition for **scalar multiplication**:

> If k is a scalar, then $k\mathbf{a} = \begin{bmatrix} ka_1 \\ ka_2 \end{bmatrix}$.

Notice that:

- $(-1)\mathbf{a} = \begin{bmatrix} (-1)a_1 \\ (-1)a_2 \end{bmatrix} = \begin{bmatrix} -a_1 \\ -a_2 \end{bmatrix} = -\mathbf{a}$

- $(0)\mathbf{a} = \begin{bmatrix} (0)a_1 \\ (0)a_2 \end{bmatrix} = \begin{bmatrix} 0 \\ 0 \end{bmatrix} = \mathbf{0}$

Example 14

For $\mathbf{p} = \begin{bmatrix} 4 \\ 1 \end{bmatrix}$, $\mathbf{q} = \begin{bmatrix} 2 \\ -3 \end{bmatrix}$ find: **a** $3\mathbf{q}$ **b** $\mathbf{p} + 2\mathbf{q}$ **c** $\frac{1}{2}\mathbf{p} - 3\mathbf{q}$

a $3\mathbf{q}$

$= 3\begin{bmatrix} 2 \\ -3 \end{bmatrix}$

$= \begin{bmatrix} 6 \\ -9 \end{bmatrix}$

b $\mathbf{p} + 2\mathbf{q}$

$= \begin{bmatrix} 4 \\ 1 \end{bmatrix} + 2\begin{bmatrix} 2 \\ -3 \end{bmatrix}$

$= \begin{bmatrix} 4 + 2(2) \\ 1 + 2(-3) \end{bmatrix}$

$= \begin{bmatrix} 8 \\ -5 \end{bmatrix}$

c $\frac{1}{2}\mathbf{p} - 3\mathbf{q}$

$= \frac{1}{2}\begin{bmatrix} 4 \\ 1 \end{bmatrix} - 3\begin{bmatrix} 2 \\ -3 \end{bmatrix}$

$= \begin{bmatrix} \frac{1}{2}(4) - 3(2) \\ \frac{1}{2}(1) - 3(-3) \end{bmatrix}$

$= \begin{bmatrix} -4 \\ 9\frac{1}{2} \end{bmatrix}$

EXERCISE 15C.3

1 For $\mathbf{p} = \begin{bmatrix} 1 \\ 5 \end{bmatrix}$, $\mathbf{q} = \begin{bmatrix} -2 \\ 4 \end{bmatrix}$ and $\mathbf{r} = \begin{bmatrix} -3 \\ -1 \end{bmatrix}$ find:

   a $-3\mathbf{p}$ **b** $\frac{1}{2}\mathbf{q}$ **c** $2\mathbf{p} + \mathbf{q}$ **d** $\mathbf{p} - 2\mathbf{q}$

   e $\mathbf{p} - \frac{1}{2}\mathbf{r}$ **f** $2\mathbf{p} + 3\mathbf{r}$ **g** $2\mathbf{q} - 3\mathbf{r}$ **h** $2\mathbf{p} - \mathbf{q} + \frac{1}{3}\mathbf{r}$

2 If $\mathbf{p} = \begin{bmatrix} 1 \\ 1 \end{bmatrix}$ and $\mathbf{q} = \begin{bmatrix} 2 \\ -1 \end{bmatrix}$ find by diagram (and comment on the results):

   a $\mathbf{p} + \mathbf{p} + \mathbf{q} + \mathbf{q} + \mathbf{q}$ **b** $\mathbf{p} + \mathbf{q} + \mathbf{p} + \mathbf{q} + \mathbf{q}$ **c** $\mathbf{q} + \mathbf{p} + \mathbf{q} + \mathbf{p} + \mathbf{q}$

LENGTH OF A VECTOR

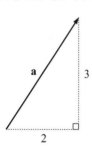

Consider vector $\mathbf{a} = \begin{bmatrix} 2 \\ 3 \end{bmatrix}$ as illustrated.

Recall that $|\mathbf{a}|$ represents the length of $\mathbf{a}$.

By Pythagoras $|\mathbf{a}|^2 = 2^2 + 3^2 = 4 + 9 = 13$

$$\therefore \quad |\mathbf{a}| = \sqrt{13} \text{ units}$$

In general, if $\mathbf{a} = \begin{bmatrix} a_1 \\ a_2 \end{bmatrix}$, then $|\mathbf{a}| = \sqrt{a_1{}^2 + a_2{}^2}$.

Example 15

If $\mathbf{p} = \begin{bmatrix} 3 \\ -5 \end{bmatrix}$ and $\mathbf{q} = \begin{bmatrix} -1 \\ -2 \end{bmatrix}$ find: **a** $|\mathbf{p}|$ **b** $|\mathbf{q}|$ **c** $|\mathbf{p} - 2\mathbf{q}|$

a $\mathbf{p} = \begin{bmatrix} 3 \\ -5 \end{bmatrix} \quad \therefore \quad |\mathbf{p}| = \sqrt{9 + 25}$
$$= \sqrt{34} \text{ units}$$

b $\mathbf{q} = \begin{bmatrix} -1 \\ -2 \end{bmatrix} \quad \therefore \quad |\mathbf{q}| = \sqrt{1 + 4}$
$$= \sqrt{5} \text{ units}$$

c $\mathbf{p} - 2\mathbf{q} = \begin{bmatrix} 3 \\ -5 \end{bmatrix} - 2\begin{bmatrix} -1 \\ -2 \end{bmatrix} = \begin{bmatrix} 5 \\ -1 \end{bmatrix}$ $\therefore \quad |\mathbf{p} - 2\mathbf{q}| = \sqrt{5^2 + (-1)^2}$
$$= \sqrt{26} \text{ units}$$

EXERCISE 15C.4

1 For $\mathbf{r} = \begin{bmatrix} 2 \\ 3 \end{bmatrix}$ and $\mathbf{s} = \begin{bmatrix} -1 \\ 4 \end{bmatrix}$ find:

   a $|\mathbf{r}|$ **b** $|\mathbf{s}|$ **c** $|\mathbf{r} + \mathbf{s}|$ **d** $|\mathbf{r} - \mathbf{s}|$ **e** $|\mathbf{s} - 2\mathbf{r}|$

2 If $\mathbf{p} = \begin{bmatrix} 1 \\ 3 \end{bmatrix}$, $\mathbf{q} = \begin{bmatrix} -2 \\ 4 \end{bmatrix}$ find:

   a $|\mathbf{p}|$ **b** $|2\mathbf{p}|$ **c** $|-2\mathbf{p}|$ **d** $|3\mathbf{p}|$ **e** $|-3\mathbf{p}|$

   f $|\mathbf{q}|$ **g** $|4\mathbf{q}|$ **h** $|-4\mathbf{q}|$ **i** $|\frac{1}{2}\mathbf{q}|$ **j** $|-\frac{1}{2}\mathbf{q}|$

3 From your answers in **2**, you should have noticed that $|k\mathbf{a}| = |k|\,|\mathbf{a}|$

   i.e., (the length of $k\mathbf{a}$) = (the modulus of k) $\times$ (the length of $\mathbf{a}$).

   By letting $\mathbf{a} = \begin{bmatrix} a_1 \\ a_2 \end{bmatrix}$, prove that $|k\mathbf{a}| = |k|\,|\mathbf{a}|$.

D   3-D COORDINATE GEOMETRY

To specify points in **space** (or **3-dimensional space**) we need a point of reference, O, called the **origin**.

Through O we draw 3 **mutually perpendicular** lines and call them the X, Y and Z-axes. The X-axis is considered to come directly out of the page.

In the diagram alongside the **coordinate planes** divide space into 8 regions, each pair of planes intersecting on the axes.

The **positive direction** of each axis is a solid line whereas the **negative direction** is 'dashed'.

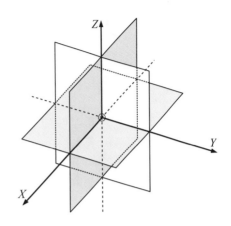

> Any point P, in space can be specified by an **ordered triple** of numbers (x, y, z) where x, y and z are the **steps** in the X, Y and Z directions from the origin O, to P.

The **position vector** of P is $\overrightarrow{OP} = \begin{bmatrix} x \\ y \\ z \end{bmatrix}$.

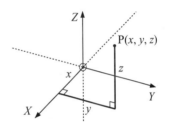

To help us visualise the 3-D position of a point on our 2-D paper, it is useful to complete a rectangular prism (or box) with the origin O as one vertex, the axes as sides adjacent to it, and P is at the vertex opposite O.

3-D POINT PLOTTER

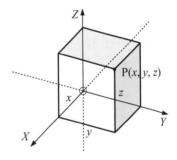

Example 16

Illustrate the points: a   A(0, 2, 0)   b   B(3, 0, 2)   c   C(−1, 2, 3)

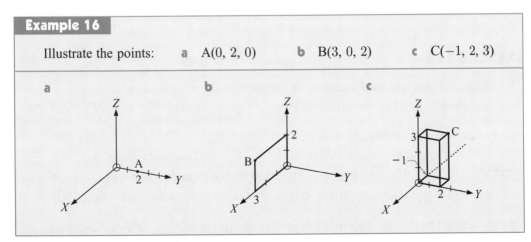

DISTANCE AND MIDPOINTS

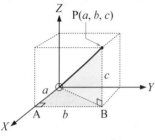

Triangle OAB is right angled at A

$\therefore$ $OB^2 = a^2 + b^2$ ...... (1)   {Pythagoras}

Triangle OBP is right angled at B

$\therefore$ $OP^2 = OB^2 + c^2$ {Pythagoras}

$\therefore$ $OP^2 = a^2 + b^2 + c^2$ {from (1)}

$\therefore$ $OP = \sqrt{a^2 + b^2 + c^2}$

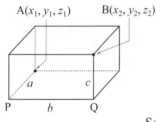

Now for two general points $A(x_1, y_1, z_1)$
and $B(x_2, y_2, z_2)$

a,   the x-step from A to B $= x_2 - x_1 = \Delta x$

b,   the y-step from A to B $= y_2 - y_1 = \Delta y$

c,   the z-step from A to B $= z_2 - z_1 = \Delta z$

So, $AB = \sqrt{(x_2 - x_1)^2 + (y_2 - y_1)^2 + (z_2 - z_1)^2}$

A simple extension from 2-D to 3-D geometry also gives the

$$\text{midpoint of AB} = \left(\frac{x_1 + x_2}{2}, \frac{y_1 + y_2}{2}, \frac{z_1 + z_2}{2} \right).$$

Note: As with the 2-D case, a proof of this rule can be done using similar triangles.

Example 17

If $A(-1, 2, 4)$ and $B(1, 0, -1)$ are two points in space, find:
a   the distance from A to B   b   the coordinates of the midpoint of AB.

a   AB

$= \sqrt{(1 - -1)^2 + (0 - 2)^2 + (-1 - 4)^2}$

$= \sqrt{4 + 4 + 25}$

$= \sqrt{33}$ units

b   midpoint is

$\left(\frac{-1 + 1}{2}, \frac{2 + 0}{2}, \frac{4 + (-1)}{2} \right)$

i.e., $(0, 1, \frac{3}{2})$

EXERCISE 15D

1   Illustrate P and find its distance to the origin O if P is:

   a $(0, 0, -3)$ b $(0, -1, 2)$ c $(3, 1, 4)$ d $(-1, -2, 3)$

2   For each of the following:

   i   find the distance AB   ii   find the midpoint of AB

   a $A(-1, 2, 3)$ and $B(0, -1, 1)$ b $A(0, 0, 0)$ and $B(2, -1, 3)$

   c $A(3, -1, -1)$ and $B(-1, 0, 1)$ d $A(2, 0, -3)$ and $B(0, 1, 0)$

3   Show that $P(0, 4, 4)$, $Q(2, 6, 5)$ and $R(1, 4, 3)$ are vertices of an isosceles triangle.

4 Determine the nature of triangle ABC using distances for:

  a A(2, −1, 7), B(3, 1, 4) and C(5, 4, 5)

  b A(0, 0, 3), B(2, 8, 1) and C(−9, 6, 18)

  c A(5, 6, −2), B(6, 12, 9) and C(2, 4, 2).

  d A(1, 0, −3), B(2, 2, 0) and C(4, 6, 6).

5 A sphere has centre C(−1, 2, 4) and diameter AB
where A is (−2, 1, 3).
Find the coordinates of B and the radius of the circle.

6 **a** State the coordinates of any point on the Y-axis.

  b Find the coordinates of two points on the Y-axis
which are $\sqrt{14}$ units from B(−1, −1, 2).

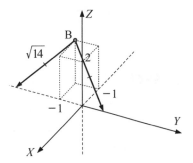

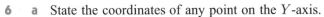

E   3-D VECTORS IN COMPONENT FORM

Consider a point $P(x_1, y_1, z_1)$.

The x, y and z-steps from the origin to P are x_1, y_1 and
z_1 respectively.

So $\overrightarrow{OP} = \begin{bmatrix} x_1 \\ y_1 \\ z_1 \end{bmatrix}$ is the vector which emanates

from O and terminates at P.

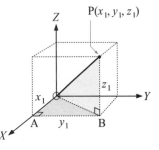

In general, if $A(x_1, y_1, z_1)$ and $B(x_2, y_2, z_2)$ are two
points in space then:

$$\overrightarrow{AB} = \begin{bmatrix} x_2 - x_1 \\ y_2 - y_1 \\ z_2 - z_1 \end{bmatrix} \begin{matrix} \leftarrow x\text{-step} \\ \leftarrow y\text{-step} \\ \leftarrow z\text{-step} \end{matrix} \quad \text{and} \quad \left|\overrightarrow{AB}\right| = \sqrt{(x_2 - x_1)^2 + (y_2 - y_1)^2 + (z_2 - z_1)^2}$$
$$\text{(Can you prove why?)}$$

$\overrightarrow{AB}$ is called 'vector AB' or 'the **position vector of B relative to A** (or from A)'

$\overrightarrow{OP}$, the position vector of P relative to O, is called the **position vector of the point** P (in
2-D and 3-D). Its usefulness is marked by the fact that its components are exactly the same
as the coordinates of the point P.

Example 18

If A is (3, −1, 2) and B is (1, 0, −2) find: **a** $\overrightarrow{OA}$ **b** $\overrightarrow{AB}$

  a $\overrightarrow{OA} = \begin{bmatrix} 3 - 0 \\ -1 - 0 \\ 2 - 0 \end{bmatrix} = \begin{bmatrix} 3 \\ -1 \\ 2 \end{bmatrix}$ **b** $\overrightarrow{AB} = \begin{bmatrix} 1 - 3 \\ 0 - (-1) \\ -2 - 2 \end{bmatrix} = \begin{bmatrix} -2 \\ 1 \\ -4 \end{bmatrix}$

Note: $\overrightarrow{OA}$ has length $\left|\overrightarrow{OA}\right|$ or simply OA, $\overrightarrow{AB}$ has length $\left|\overrightarrow{AB}\right|$ or simply AB.

Example 19

If P is $(-3, 1, 2)$ and Q is $(1, -1, 3)$, find $|\overrightarrow{PQ}|$.

$$\overrightarrow{PQ} = \begin{bmatrix} 1-(-3) \\ -1-1 \\ 3-2 \end{bmatrix} = \begin{bmatrix} 4 \\ -2 \\ 1 \end{bmatrix} \qquad \therefore \quad |\overrightarrow{PQ}| = \sqrt{4^2 + (-2)^2 + 1^2}$$
$$= \sqrt{21} \text{ units}$$

EXERCISE 15E.1

1 Consider the point T$(3, -1, 4)$.

   a Draw a diagram to locate the position of T in space.

   b Find $\overrightarrow{OT}$.   c How far is it from O to T?

2 Given A$(-3, 1, 2)$ and B$(1, 0, -1)$ find:

   a $\overrightarrow{AB}$ and $\overrightarrow{BA}$ b the length of $\overrightarrow{AB}$ and $\overrightarrow{BA}$.

3 Given A$(3, 1, 0)$ and B$(-1, 1, 2)$ find $\overrightarrow{OA}$, $\overrightarrow{OB}$, and $\overrightarrow{AB}$.

Example 20

If A is $(-1, 3, 2)$ and B$(2, 1, -4)$ find:
a the position vector of A from B   b the distance between A and B.

a The position vector of A from B is $\overrightarrow{BA} = \begin{bmatrix} -1-2 \\ 3-1 \\ 2-(-4) \end{bmatrix} = \begin{bmatrix} -3 \\ 2 \\ 6 \end{bmatrix}$

b $AB = |\overrightarrow{BA}|$

$= \sqrt{9 + 4 + 36}$

$= 7$ units

4 Given M$(4, -2, -1)$ and N$(-1, 2, 0)$ find:

   a the position vector of M from N   b the position vector of N from M

   c the distance between M and N.

5 For A$(-1, 2, 5)$, B$(2, 0, 3)$ and C$(-3, 1, 0)$ find the position vector of:

   a A from O and the distance of A from O

   b C from A and the distance of C from A

   c B from C and the distance of B from C.

6 Find the distance from Q$(3, 1, -2)$ to:

   a the Y-axis   b the origin   c the YOZ plane.

GEOMETRIC REPRESENTATION

As for 2-D vectors, 3-D vectors are represented by **directed line segments** (called **arrows**).
Consider the vector represented by the line segment from O to A.

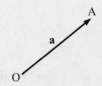

- This **vector** could be represented by

  $$\overrightarrow{OA} \quad \text{or} \quad \mathbf{a} \quad \text{or} \quad \underline{a} \text{ or } \vec{a}$$

  bold used   used by
  in text books   students

- The **magnitude (length)** could be shown as $|\overrightarrow{OA}|$,   OA, $|\mathbf{a}|$, $|\underline{a}|$ or $|\vec{a}|$.

  If $\mathbf{a} = \begin{bmatrix} a_1 \\ a_2 \\ a_3 \end{bmatrix}$ then $|\mathbf{a}| = \sqrt{a_1^2 + a_2^2 + a_3^2}$.

VECTOR EQUALITY

> Two vectors are **equal** if they have the same magnitude and direction.

So, if arrows are used to represent vectors, then equal
vectors are **parallel** and **equal in length**.

This means that equal vector arrows are translations
of one another, but in space.

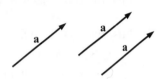

If $\mathbf{a} = \begin{bmatrix} a_1 \\ a_2 \\ a_3 \end{bmatrix}$ and $\mathbf{b} = \begin{bmatrix} b_1 \\ b_2 \\ b_3 \end{bmatrix}$,   then $\mathbf{a} = \mathbf{b} \iff a_1 = b_1, \ a_2 = b_2, \ a_3 = b_3$.

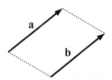

$\mathbf{a} = \mathbf{b}$ implies that vector $\mathbf{a}$ is parallel to vector $\mathbf{b}$,
and $|\mathbf{a}| = |\mathbf{b}|$.

Consequently, $\mathbf{a}$ and $\mathbf{b}$ are opposite sides of a
parallelogram, and certainly lie in the same plane.

DISCUSSION

- Do any three points in space define a plane? What about four points? Illustrate.

- What simple test(s) on four points in space enables us to deduce that the points
  are vertices of a parallelogram? Consider using vectors and not using vectors.

Example 21

Find a, b, and c if $\begin{bmatrix} a - 3 \\ b - 2 \\ c - 1 \end{bmatrix} = \begin{bmatrix} 1 - a \\ -b \\ -3 - c \end{bmatrix}$.

Equating components we get

$$\begin{array}{ccc} a - 3 = 1 - a & b - 2 = -b & c - 1 = -3 - c \\ \therefore \ 2a = 4 & 2b = 2 & 2c = -2 \\ \therefore \ a = 2 & b = 1 & c = -1 \end{array}$$

EXERCISE 15E.2

1 Find a, b and c if:

a $\begin{bmatrix} a - 4 \\ b - 3 \\ c + 2 \end{bmatrix} = \begin{bmatrix} 1 \\ 3 \\ -4 \end{bmatrix}$

b $\begin{bmatrix} a - 5 \\ b - 2 \\ c + 3 \end{bmatrix} = \begin{bmatrix} 3 - a \\ 2 - b \\ 5 - c \end{bmatrix}$

2 Find scalars a, b and c if:

a $\quad 2\begin{bmatrix} 1 \\ 0 \\ 3a \end{bmatrix} = \begin{bmatrix} b \\ c-1 \\ 2 \end{bmatrix}$
b $\quad \begin{bmatrix} 2 \\ a \\ 3 \end{bmatrix} = \begin{bmatrix} b \\ a^2 \\ a+b \end{bmatrix}$
c $\quad a\begin{bmatrix} 1 \\ 1 \\ 0 \end{bmatrix} + b\begin{bmatrix} 2 \\ 0 \\ -1 \end{bmatrix} + c\begin{bmatrix} 0 \\ 1 \\ 1 \end{bmatrix} = \begin{bmatrix} -1 \\ 3 \\ 3 \end{bmatrix}$

3 A$(-1, 3, 4)$, B$(2, 5, -1)$, C$(-1, 2, -2)$ and D (r, s, t) are four points in space.
Find r, s and t if: **a** $\overrightarrow{AC} = \overrightarrow{BD}$ **b** $\overrightarrow{AB} = \overrightarrow{DC}$

4 A quadrilateral has vertices A$(1, 2, 3)$, B$(3, -3, 2)$, C$(7, -4, 5)$ and D$(5, 1, 6)$.
a Find $\overrightarrow{AB}$ and $\overrightarrow{DC}$.   **b** What can be deduced about the quadrilateral ABCD?

Example 22

ABCD is a parallelogram. A is $(-1, 2, 1)$, B is $(2, 0, -1)$ and D is $(3, 1, 4)$.
Find the coordinates of C.

First we draw an axis free sketch:

Let C be (a, b, c).

Now as AB is parallel to DC and has the same
length then $\overrightarrow{DC} = \overrightarrow{AB}$,

i.e., $\begin{bmatrix} a-3 \\ b-1 \\ c-4 \end{bmatrix} = \begin{bmatrix} 3 \\ -2 \\ -2 \end{bmatrix}$

$\therefore \quad a - 3 = 3, \quad b - 1 = -2, \quad c - 4 = -2$
$\therefore \quad a = 6, \quad \therefore \quad b = -1, \quad \therefore \quad c = 2 \qquad$ So, C is $(6, -1, 2)$.

Check: midpoint of DB is   midpoint of AC is

$\left(\dfrac{3+2}{2}, \dfrac{1+0}{2}, \dfrac{4+-1}{2}\right)$ $\left(\dfrac{-1+6}{2}, \dfrac{2+-1}{2}, \dfrac{1+2}{2}\right)$

i.e., $\left(\dfrac{5}{2}, \dfrac{1}{2}, \dfrac{3}{2}\right)$ i.e., $\left(\dfrac{5}{2}, \dfrac{1}{2}, \dfrac{3}{2}\right)$

---

5 PQRS is a parallelogram. P is $(-1, 2, 3)$, Q$(1, -2, 5)$ and R$(0, 4, -1)$.
a Use vectors to find the coordinates of S.
b Use midpoints of diagonals to check your answer.

F | ALGEBRAIC OPERATIONS WITH VECTORS

For 3-D vectors:

If $\quad \mathbf{a} = \begin{bmatrix} a_1 \\ a_2 \\ a_3 \end{bmatrix}$ and $\mathbf{b} = \begin{bmatrix} b_1 \\ b_2 \\ b_3 \end{bmatrix}$ then $\mathbf{a} + \mathbf{b} = \begin{bmatrix} a_1 + b_1 \\ a_2 + b_2 \\ a_3 + b_3 \end{bmatrix}$, $\quad \mathbf{a} - \mathbf{b} = \begin{bmatrix} a_1 - b_1 \\ a_2 - b_2 \\ a_3 - b_3 \end{bmatrix}$

and $\quad k\mathbf{a} = \begin{bmatrix} ka_1 \\ ka_2 \\ ka_3 \end{bmatrix}$ for some scalar k

For 2-D vectors, it is the same with only 2 components.

SOME PROPERTIES OF VECTORS

- $\mathbf{a} + \mathbf{b} = \mathbf{b} + \mathbf{a}$
  $(\mathbf{a} + \mathbf{b}) + \mathbf{c} = \mathbf{a} + (\mathbf{b} + \mathbf{c})$
  $\mathbf{a} + \mathbf{0} = \mathbf{0} + \mathbf{a} = \mathbf{a}$
  $\mathbf{a} + (-\mathbf{a}) = (-\mathbf{a}) + \mathbf{a} = \mathbf{0}$

- $|k\mathbf{a}| = |k|\,|\mathbf{a}|$ where $k\mathbf{a}$ is parallel to $\mathbf{a}$
  length of $k\mathbf{a}$ length of $\mathbf{a}$
  modulus of k

The rules for solving vector equations are similar to those for solving real number equations except that there is no such thing as dividing a vector by a scalar.

We avoid this problem by multiplying by reciprocals.

So, for example,   if $2\mathbf{x} = \mathbf{a}$ then $\mathbf{x} = \frac{1}{2}\mathbf{a}$ and *not* $\dfrac{\mathbf{a}}{2}$.

$\dfrac{\mathbf{a}}{2}$ has no meaning in vector algebra.

Two useful rules are
- if $\mathbf{x} + \mathbf{a} = \mathbf{b}$ then $\mathbf{x} = \mathbf{b} - \mathbf{a}$
- if $k\mathbf{x} = \mathbf{a}$ then $\mathbf{x} = \frac{1}{k}\mathbf{a}$ $(k \neq 0)$

To establish these notice that:

if $\mathbf{x} + \mathbf{a} = \mathbf{b}$
then $\mathbf{x} + \mathbf{a} + (-\mathbf{a}) = \mathbf{b} + (-\mathbf{a})$
$\therefore$ $\mathbf{x} + \mathbf{0} = \mathbf{b} - \mathbf{a}$
$\therefore$ $\mathbf{x} = \mathbf{b} - \mathbf{a}$

and if $k\mathbf{x} = \mathbf{a}$
then $\frac{1}{k}(k\mathbf{x}) = \frac{1}{k}\mathbf{a}$
$\therefore$ $1\mathbf{x} = \frac{1}{k}\mathbf{a}$
$\therefore$ $\mathbf{x} = \frac{1}{k}\mathbf{a}$

Example 23

Solve for $\mathbf{x}$:
a $3\mathbf{x} - \mathbf{r} = \mathbf{s}$
b $\mathbf{c} - 2\mathbf{x} = \mathbf{d}$

a $3\mathbf{x} - \mathbf{r} = \mathbf{s}$
$\therefore$ $3\mathbf{x} = \mathbf{s} + \mathbf{r}$
$\therefore$ $\mathbf{x} = \frac{1}{3}(\mathbf{s} + \mathbf{r})$

b $\mathbf{c} - 2\mathbf{x} = \mathbf{d}$
$\therefore$ $\mathbf{c} - \mathbf{d} = 2\mathbf{x}$
$\therefore$ $\frac{1}{2}(\mathbf{c} - \mathbf{d}) = \mathbf{x}$

EXERCISE 15F

1 Solve the following vector equations for $\mathbf{x}$:

  a $2\mathbf{x} = \mathbf{q}$ **b** $\frac{1}{2}\mathbf{x} = \mathbf{n}$ **c** $-3\mathbf{x} = \mathbf{p}$

  d $\mathbf{q} + 2\mathbf{x} = \mathbf{r}$ **e** $4\mathbf{s} - 5\mathbf{x} = \mathbf{t}$ **f** $4\mathbf{m} - \frac{1}{3}\mathbf{x} = \mathbf{n}$

2 If $\mathbf{r} = \begin{bmatrix} -2 \\ 3 \end{bmatrix}$ and $\mathbf{s} = \begin{bmatrix} 1 \\ 2 \end{bmatrix}$,   find $\mathbf{y}$ if:

  a $2\mathbf{y} = \mathbf{r}$ **b** $\frac{1}{2}\mathbf{y} = \mathbf{s}$ **c** $\mathbf{r} + 2\mathbf{y} = \mathbf{s}$ **d** $3\mathbf{s} - 4\mathbf{y} = \mathbf{r}$

3 Show by equating components, that if $\mathbf{x} = \begin{bmatrix} x_1 \\ x_2 \end{bmatrix}$, $\mathbf{a} = \begin{bmatrix} a_1 \\ a_2 \end{bmatrix}$ and $k\mathbf{x} = \mathbf{a}$, then $\mathbf{x} = \frac{1}{k}\mathbf{a}$.

4 If $\mathbf{a} = \begin{bmatrix} -1 \\ 2 \\ 3 \end{bmatrix}$ and $\mathbf{b} = \begin{bmatrix} 2 \\ -2 \\ 1 \end{bmatrix}$ find $\mathbf{x}$ if:

  a $2\mathbf{a} + \mathbf{x} = \mathbf{b}$ **b** $3\mathbf{x} - \mathbf{a} = 2\mathbf{b}$ **c** $2\mathbf{b} - 2\mathbf{x} = -\mathbf{a}$

Notice that if $\overrightarrow{OA} = \mathbf{a}$ and $\overrightarrow{OB} = \mathbf{b}$ where O is the origin then $\overrightarrow{AB} = \mathbf{b} - \mathbf{a}$ and $\overrightarrow{BA} = \mathbf{a} - \mathbf{b}$.

Can you explain why?

5 If $\overrightarrow{OA} = \begin{bmatrix} -2 \\ -1 \\ 1 \end{bmatrix}$ and $\overrightarrow{OB} = \begin{bmatrix} 1 \\ 3 \\ -1 \end{bmatrix}$ find $\overrightarrow{AB}$ and hence find the distance from A to B.

6 The position vectors of A, B, C and D from O are $\begin{bmatrix} 2 \\ 1 \\ -2 \end{bmatrix}$, $\begin{bmatrix} 0 \\ 3 \\ -4 \end{bmatrix}$, $\begin{bmatrix} 1 \\ -2 \\ 1 \end{bmatrix}$ and $\begin{bmatrix} -2 \\ -3 \\ 2 \end{bmatrix}$ respectively. Deduce that $\overrightarrow{BD} = 2\overrightarrow{AC}$.

7

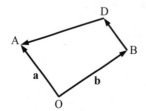

In the given figure BD is parallel to OA and half its length. Find in terms of $\mathbf{a}$ and $\mathbf{b}$ vector expressions for:

   a $\overrightarrow{BD}$ **b** $\overrightarrow{AB}$ **c** $\overrightarrow{BA}$

   d $\overrightarrow{OD}$ **e** $\overrightarrow{AD}$ **f** $\overrightarrow{DA}$

Example 24

If $\overrightarrow{AB} = \begin{bmatrix} -1 \\ 3 \\ 2 \end{bmatrix}$, $\overrightarrow{AC} = \begin{bmatrix} 2 \\ -1 \\ 4 \end{bmatrix}$ find $\overrightarrow{BC}$.

$\overrightarrow{BC} = \overrightarrow{BA} + \overrightarrow{AC}$

$= -\begin{bmatrix} -1 \\ 3 \\ 2 \end{bmatrix} + \begin{bmatrix} 2 \\ -1 \\ 4 \end{bmatrix}$

$= \begin{bmatrix} 3 \\ -4 \\ 2 \end{bmatrix}$

---

8 If $\overrightarrow{AB} = \begin{bmatrix} -1 \\ 3 \\ 2 \end{bmatrix}$, $\overrightarrow{AC} = \begin{bmatrix} 2 \\ -1 \\ 4 \end{bmatrix}$ and $\overrightarrow{BD} = \begin{bmatrix} 0 \\ 2 \\ -3 \end{bmatrix}$ find: **a** $\overrightarrow{AD}$ **b** $\overrightarrow{CB}$ **c** $\overrightarrow{CD}$

9 For $\mathbf{a} = \begin{bmatrix} 2 \\ -1 \\ 1 \end{bmatrix}$, $\mathbf{b} = \begin{bmatrix} 1 \\ 2 \\ -3 \end{bmatrix}$ and $\mathbf{c} = \begin{bmatrix} 0 \\ 1 \\ -3 \end{bmatrix}$, find:

  a $\mathbf{a} + \mathbf{b}$ **b** $\mathbf{a} - \mathbf{b}$ **c** $\mathbf{b} + 2\mathbf{c}$ **d** $\mathbf{a} - 3\mathbf{c}$

  e $\mathbf{a} + \mathbf{b} + \mathbf{c}$ **f** $\mathbf{c} - \frac{1}{2}\mathbf{a}$ **g** $\mathbf{a} - \mathbf{b} - \mathbf{c}$ **h** $2\mathbf{b} - \mathbf{c} + \mathbf{a}$

Example 25

If $\mathbf{a} = \begin{bmatrix} -1 \\ 3 \\ 2 \end{bmatrix}$, find $|\mathbf{a}|$.

$|\mathbf{a}| = \sqrt{(-1)^2 + 3^2 + 2^2}$

$= \sqrt{1 + 9 + 4}$

$= \sqrt{14}$ units

---

10 If $\mathbf{a} = \begin{bmatrix} -1 \\ 1 \\ 3 \end{bmatrix}$, $\mathbf{b} = \begin{bmatrix} 1 \\ -3 \\ 2 \end{bmatrix}$ and $\mathbf{c} = \begin{bmatrix} -2 \\ 2 \\ 4 \end{bmatrix}$ find: **a** $|\mathbf{a}|$ **b** $|\mathbf{b}|$ **c** $|\mathbf{b} + \mathbf{c}|$

                                          d $|\mathbf{a} - \mathbf{c}|$ **e** $|\mathbf{a}|\mathbf{b}$ **f** $\frac{1}{|\mathbf{a}|}\mathbf{a}$

G   VECTORS IN COORDINATE GEOMETRY

VECTORS BETWEEN TWO POINTS

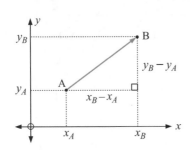

In 2-D: consider points $A(x_A, y_A)$ and $B(x_B, y_B)$

In going from A to B,

$\qquad x_B - x_A$ is the x-**step**,   and

$\qquad y_B - y_A$ is the y-**step**.

Consequently

$$\overrightarrow{AB} = \begin{bmatrix} x_B - x_A \\ y_B - y_A \end{bmatrix}.$$

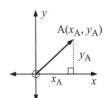

Notice that   if O is $(0, 0)$ and   A is (x_A, y_A) then $\overrightarrow{OA}$ is $\begin{bmatrix} x_A \\ y_A \end{bmatrix}$.

In 3-D: if the points are $A(x_A, y_A, z_A)$ and $B(x_B, y_B, z_B)$

$$\overrightarrow{AB} = \begin{bmatrix} x_B - x_A \\ y_B - y_A \\ z_B - z_A \end{bmatrix} \qquad \overrightarrow{OA} = \begin{bmatrix} x_A \\ y_A \\ z_A \end{bmatrix} \qquad \text{and note} \qquad \begin{aligned} \overrightarrow{AB} &= \overrightarrow{OB} - \overrightarrow{OA} \\ &= \mathbf{b} - \mathbf{a} \end{aligned}$$

where $\mathbf{a}, \mathbf{b}$ are the position vectors of A and B respectively.

DISTANCE BETWEEN TWO POINTS

The distance between two points A and B is the length of vector $\overrightarrow{AB}$ (or $\overrightarrow{BA}$), given by $| \overrightarrow{AB} |$.

Hence, the distance between points A and B is the length of vector $\overrightarrow{AB}$, given by $| \overrightarrow{AB} |$.

VECTOR EQUALITY

Two vectors are **equal** if they have the same length and direction.

Consequently, in 2-D   their x-steps are equal i.e., $p = r$

and   their y-steps are equal   i.e., $q = s$

i.e., $\begin{bmatrix} p \\ q \end{bmatrix} = \begin{bmatrix} r \\ s \end{bmatrix} \quad \Leftrightarrow \quad p = r \quad \text{and} \quad q = s.$

(where $\Leftrightarrow$ reads "if and only if")

In 3-D, $\begin{bmatrix} a \\ b \\ c \end{bmatrix} = \begin{bmatrix} p \\ q \\ r \end{bmatrix} \quad \Leftrightarrow \quad a = p, \quad b = q \quad \text{and} \quad c = r.$

EXERCISE 15G

1

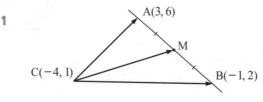

Find:

a   the coordinates of M

b   vectors $\overrightarrow{CA}, \overrightarrow{CM}$ and $\overrightarrow{CB}$.

c   Verify that $\overrightarrow{CM} = \frac{1}{2}\overrightarrow{CA} + \frac{1}{2}\overrightarrow{CB}$.

Example 26

Find the coordinates of C and D in:

$$\overrightarrow{AB} = \begin{bmatrix} 1 \\ 3 \\ -1 \end{bmatrix} \qquad \begin{aligned} \overrightarrow{OC} &= \overrightarrow{OA} + \overrightarrow{AC} \\ &= \overrightarrow{OA} + 2\overrightarrow{AB} \\ &= \begin{bmatrix} -2 \\ -5 \\ 3 \end{bmatrix} + \begin{bmatrix} 2 \\ 6 \\ -2 \end{bmatrix} \\ &= \begin{bmatrix} 0 \\ 1 \\ 1 \end{bmatrix} \end{aligned} \qquad \begin{aligned} \overrightarrow{OD} &= \overrightarrow{OA} + \overrightarrow{AD} \\ &= \overrightarrow{OA} + 3\overrightarrow{AB} \\ &= \begin{bmatrix} -2 \\ -5 \\ 3 \end{bmatrix} + \begin{bmatrix} 3 \\ 9 \\ -3 \end{bmatrix} \\ &= \begin{bmatrix} 1 \\ 4 \\ 0 \end{bmatrix} \end{aligned}$$

$$\text{C is } (0, 1, 1) \qquad \qquad \therefore \quad \text{D is } (1, 4, 0)$$

2   Find B if C is the centre of a circle with diameter AB:

   a   A is $(3, -2)$ and $C(1, 4)$ **b**   A is $(0, 5)$ and $C(-1, -2)$

   c   A is $(-1, -4)$ and $C(3, 0)$

3

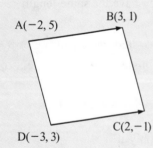

Find the coordinates of C, D and E.

Example 27

Use vectors to show that ABCD is a parallelogram where
A is $(-2, 5)$, $B(3, 1)$, $C(2, -1)$ and D is $(-3, 3)$.

$$\overrightarrow{AB} = \begin{bmatrix} 3 - (-2) \\ 1 - 5 \end{bmatrix} = \begin{bmatrix} 5 \\ -4 \end{bmatrix}$$

$$\overrightarrow{DC} = \begin{bmatrix} 2 - (-3) \\ -1 - 3 \end{bmatrix} = \begin{bmatrix} 5 \\ -4 \end{bmatrix}$$

i.e., $\overrightarrow{AB} = \overrightarrow{DC}$

$\therefore$ side AB is parallel to side DC
and is equal in length (magnitude) to
side DC.

Hence ABCD is a parallelogram.

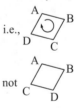

Given ABCD,
the ordering of
letters is cyclic,

i.e.,

not

4   Use vectors to find whether or not ABCD is a parallelogram:

   a $A(3, -1)$, $B(4, 2)$, $C(-1, 4)$ and $D(-2, 1)$

   b $A(5, 0, 3)$, $B(-1, 2, 4)$, $C(4, -3, 6)$ and $D(10, -5, 5)$

   c $A(2, -3, 2)$, $B(1, 4, -1)$, $C(-2, 6, -2)$ and $D(-1, -1, 2)$.

Example 28

Use vector methods to find the remaining vertex of:

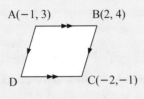

A(−1, 3)   B(2, 4)

D   C(−2, −1)

If D is (a, b) then

$$\overrightarrow{CD} = \begin{bmatrix} a - (-2) \\ b - (-1) \end{bmatrix} = \begin{bmatrix} a + 2 \\ b + 1 \end{bmatrix}$$

But $\overrightarrow{CD} = \overrightarrow{BA}$

$$\therefore \quad \begin{bmatrix} a + 2 \\ b + 1 \end{bmatrix} = \begin{bmatrix} -1 - 2 \\ 3 - 4 \end{bmatrix}$$

$\therefore \quad a + 2 = -3$ and $b + 1 = -1$

$\therefore \quad a = -5$ and $b = -2$

So,   D is $(-5, -2)$.

5 Use vector methods to find the remaining vertex of:

a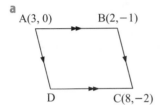

A(3, 0)   B(2, −1)

D   C(8, −2)

b

P(−1, 4, 3)   Q(−2, 5, 2)

S(4, 0, 7)   R

c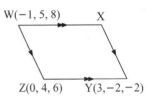

W(−1, 5, 8)   X

Z(0, 4, 6)   Y(3, −2, −2)

6 Find scalars r and s such that:

a $r \begin{bmatrix} 1 \\ -1 \end{bmatrix} + s \begin{bmatrix} 2 \\ 5 \end{bmatrix} = \begin{bmatrix} -8 \\ -27 \end{bmatrix}$

b $r \begin{bmatrix} 2 \\ -3 \\ 1 \end{bmatrix} + s \begin{bmatrix} 1 \\ 7 \\ 2 \end{bmatrix} = \begin{bmatrix} 7 \\ -19 \\ 2 \end{bmatrix}$

Three or more points are said to be **collinear** if they lie on the same straight line.

Notice that,   A, B and C are collinear if $\overrightarrow{AB} = k\overrightarrow{BC}$ for some scalar k.

Example 29

Prove that   A(−1, 2, 3), B(4, 0, −1) and C(14, −4, −9) are collinear and hence find the ratio in which B divides CA.

$$\overrightarrow{AB} = \begin{bmatrix} 5 \\ -2 \\ -4 \end{bmatrix} \qquad \overrightarrow{BC} = \begin{bmatrix} 10 \\ -4 \\ -8 \end{bmatrix} = 2\begin{bmatrix} 5 \\ -2 \\ -4 \end{bmatrix} \qquad \therefore \quad \overrightarrow{BC} = 2\overrightarrow{AB}$$

$\therefore$ BC is parallel to AB and since B is common to both, A, B and C are collinear.
To find the ratio in which B divides CA, we find

$$\overrightarrow{CB} : \overrightarrow{BA} = -2\begin{bmatrix} 5 \\ -2 \\ -4 \end{bmatrix} : -\begin{bmatrix} 5 \\ -2 \\ -4 \end{bmatrix} = 2 : 1$$

$\therefore$ B divides CA internally in the ratio $2 : 1$.

7 **a** Prove that A(−2, 1, 4), B(4, 3, 0) and C(19, 8, −10) are collinear and hence find the ratio in which A divides CB.

   b Prove that P(2, 1, 1), Q(5, −5, −2) and R(−1, 7, 4) are collinear and hence find the ratio in which Q divides PR.

8 **a** A(2, −3, 4), B(11, −9, 7) and C(−13, a, b) are collinear. Find a and b.

   b K(1, −1, 0), L(4, −3, 7) and M(a, 2, b) are collinear. Find a and b.

H   PARALLELISM

PARALLELISM

If two non-zero vectors are **parallel**, then one is a scalar multiple of the other and vice versa.

Note: • If **a** is parallel to **b**, then there exists a
               scalar, k say, such that   **a** = k**b**.

            • If   **a** = k**b**   for some scalar k,   then
               ▶ **a** is parallel to **b**,   and
               ▶ $|\mathbf{a}| = |k|\,|\mathbf{b}|$.

Notice that $\mathbf{a} = \begin{bmatrix} 2 \\ 6 \\ -4 \end{bmatrix}$ is parallel to $\mathbf{b} = \begin{bmatrix} 1 \\ 3 \\ -2 \end{bmatrix}$ and $\mathbf{c} = \begin{bmatrix} 4 \\ 12 \\ -8 \end{bmatrix}$ as $\mathbf{a} = 2\mathbf{b}$ and $\mathbf{a} = \frac{1}{2}\mathbf{c}$.

Also $\mathbf{a} = \begin{bmatrix} 2 \\ 6 \\ -4 \end{bmatrix}$ is parallel to $\mathbf{d} = \begin{bmatrix} -3 \\ -9 \\ 6 \end{bmatrix}$ as $\mathbf{a} = -\frac{3}{2}\mathbf{d}$.

Example 30

Find r and s given that $\mathbf{a} = \begin{bmatrix} 2 \\ -1 \\ r \end{bmatrix}$ is parallel to $\mathbf{b} = \begin{bmatrix} s \\ 2 \\ -3 \end{bmatrix}$.

Since **a** and **b** are parallel, then   **a** = k**b**   for some scalar k

$$\therefore \quad \begin{bmatrix} 2 \\ -1 \\ r \end{bmatrix} = k \begin{bmatrix} s \\ 2 \\ -3 \end{bmatrix}$$

$$\therefore \quad 2 = ks, \quad -1 = 2k \quad \text{and} \quad r = -3k$$

Consequently, $k = -\frac{1}{2}$ and $\therefore$ $2 = -\frac{1}{2}s$ and $r = -3\left(\frac{-1}{2}\right)$

$$\therefore \quad r = \frac{3}{2} \text{ and } s = -4$$

EXERCISE 15H

1 $\mathbf{a} = \begin{bmatrix} 2 \\ -1 \\ 3 \end{bmatrix}$ and $\mathbf{b} = \begin{bmatrix} -6 \\ r \\ s \end{bmatrix}$ are parallel. Find r and s.

2 Find scalars a and b, given that $\begin{bmatrix} 3 \\ -1 \\ 2 \end{bmatrix}$ and $\begin{bmatrix} a \\ 2 \\ b \end{bmatrix}$ are parallel.

3 **a** Find a vector of length 1 unit which is parallel to $\mathbf{a} = \begin{bmatrix} 2 \\ -1 \\ -2 \end{bmatrix}$.
        (**Hint:** Let the vector be $k\mathbf{a}$.)

   b Find a vector of length 2 units which is parallel to $\mathbf{b} = \begin{bmatrix} -2 \\ -1 \\ 2 \end{bmatrix}$.

4 What can be deduced from the following?

    a $\overrightarrow{AB} = 3\overrightarrow{CD}$ **b** $\overrightarrow{RS} = -\frac{1}{2}\overrightarrow{KL}$ **c** $\overrightarrow{AB} = 2\overrightarrow{BC}$ **d** $\overrightarrow{BC} = \frac{1}{3}\overrightarrow{AC}$

5 The position vectors of P, Q, R and S from O are $\begin{bmatrix} 3 \\ 2 \\ -1 \end{bmatrix}$, $\begin{bmatrix} 1 \\ 4 \\ -3 \end{bmatrix}$, $\begin{bmatrix} 2 \\ -1 \\ 2 \end{bmatrix}$ and $\begin{bmatrix} -1 \\ -2 \\ 3 \end{bmatrix}$ respectively.

    a Deduce that PR and QS are parallel.

    b What is the relationship between the lengths of PR and QS?

TRIANGLE INEQUALITY

In any triangle, the sum of any two sides must always be greater than the third side. This is based on the well known result "the shortest distance between two points is a straight line".

6 Prove that $|\mathbf{a} + \mathbf{b}| \leqslant |\mathbf{a}| + |\mathbf{b}|$ using a geometrical argument.

    [**Hint:** Consider **a** **a** is not parallel to **b** and use the triangle inequality

                     b **a** and **b** parallel   **c** any other cases.]

I   UNIT VECTORS

A **unit vector** is any vector which has a length of one unit.

For example,   • $\begin{bmatrix} 1 \\ 0 \\ 0 \end{bmatrix}$ is a unit vector as its length is $\sqrt{1^2 + 0^2 + 0^2} = 1$

              • $\begin{bmatrix} \frac{1}{\sqrt{2}} \\ 0 \\ -\frac{1}{\sqrt{2}} \end{bmatrix}$ is a unit vector as its length is $\sqrt{\left(\frac{1}{\sqrt{2}}\right)^2 + 0^2 + \left(-\frac{1}{\sqrt{2}}\right)^2} = 1$

              • $\mathbf{i} = \begin{bmatrix} 1 \\ 0 \\ 0 \end{bmatrix}$, $\mathbf{j} = \begin{bmatrix} 0 \\ 1 \\ 0 \end{bmatrix}$ and $\mathbf{k} = \begin{bmatrix} 0 \\ 0 \\ 1 \end{bmatrix}$ are special unit vectors in the direction of the positive X, Y and Z-axes respectively.

Notice that $\mathbf{a} = \begin{bmatrix} a_1 \\ a_2 \\ a_3 \end{bmatrix} \Leftrightarrow \mathbf{a} = \underbrace{a_1\mathbf{i} + a_2\mathbf{j} + a_3\mathbf{k}}.$

                         ↑   ↑

            component form   unit vector form

Thus, $\mathbf{a} = \begin{bmatrix} 2 \\ 3 \\ -5 \end{bmatrix}$ can be written as $\mathbf{a} = 2\mathbf{i} + 3\mathbf{j} - 5\mathbf{k}$ and vice versa.

We call **i**, **j** and **k** the **base** vectors as any vector can be written as a linear combination of the vectors **i**, **j** and **k**.

EXERCISE 15I

1 Express the following vectors in component form and find their length:

    a $\mathbf{i} - \mathbf{j} + \mathbf{k}$ **b** $3\mathbf{i} - \mathbf{j} + \mathbf{k}$ **c** $\mathbf{i} - 5\mathbf{k}$ **d** $\frac{1}{2}(\mathbf{j} + \mathbf{k})$

2 Find k for the unit vectors:

a $\begin{bmatrix} 0 \\ k \end{bmatrix}$ **b** $\begin{bmatrix} k \\ 0 \end{bmatrix}$ **c** $\begin{bmatrix} k \\ 1 \end{bmatrix}$ **d** $\begin{bmatrix} -\frac{1}{2} \\ k \\ \frac{1}{4} \end{bmatrix}$ **e** $\begin{bmatrix} k \\ \frac{2}{3} \\ -\frac{1}{3} \end{bmatrix}$

Example 31

Find the length of $2\mathbf{i} - 5\mathbf{j}$.	As $2\mathbf{i} - 5\mathbf{j} = \begin{bmatrix} 2 \\ -5 \end{bmatrix}$, its length is $$\sqrt{2^2 + (-5)^2}$$ $$= \sqrt{29} \text{ units}$$

---

3 Find the length of the vectors:

a $3\mathbf{i} + 4\mathbf{j}$ **b** $2\mathbf{i} - \mathbf{j} + \mathbf{k}$ **c** $\mathbf{i} + 2\mathbf{j} - 2\mathbf{k}$ **d** $-2.36\mathbf{i} + 5.65\mathbf{j}$

4 Find the unit vector in the direction of: **a** $\mathbf{i} + 2\mathbf{j}$ **b** $2\mathbf{i} - 3\mathbf{k}$ **c** $-2\mathbf{i} - 5\mathbf{j} - 2\mathbf{k}$

Example 32

Find a vector $\mathbf{b}$ of length 7 in the opposite direction to the vector $\mathbf{a} = \begin{bmatrix} 2 \\ -1 \\ 1 \end{bmatrix}$.

The unit vector in the direction of $\mathbf{a}$ is $\dfrac{1}{\sqrt{4 + 1 + 1}} \begin{bmatrix} 2 \\ -1 \\ 1 \end{bmatrix} = \dfrac{1}{\sqrt{6}} \begin{bmatrix} 2 \\ -1 \\ 1 \end{bmatrix}$.

We now multiply this unit vector by -7.   Thus $\mathbf{b} = -\dfrac{7}{\sqrt{6}} \begin{bmatrix} 2 \\ -1 \\ 1 \end{bmatrix}$.

---

5 Find a vector $\mathbf{b}$ if:

a it has the same direction as $\begin{bmatrix} 2 \\ -1 \end{bmatrix}$ and has length 3 units

b it has opposite direction to $\begin{bmatrix} -1 \\ -4 \end{bmatrix}$ and has length 2 units

c it has the same direction as $\begin{bmatrix} -1 \\ 4 \\ 1 \end{bmatrix}$ and has length 6 units

d it has opposite direction to $\begin{bmatrix} -1 \\ -2 \\ -2 \end{bmatrix}$ and has length 5 units

Note:
- vector $\mathbf{b}$ of length k, $k > 0$ in the same direction as $\mathbf{a}$ is $\mathbf{b} = \dfrac{k}{|\mathbf{a}|}\mathbf{a}$

- vector $\mathbf{b}$ of length k, $k > 0$ in the opposite direction to $\mathbf{a}$ is $\mathbf{b} = -\dfrac{k}{|\mathbf{a}|}\mathbf{a}$

- vector $\mathbf{b}$ of length k, $k > 0$ which is parallel to $\mathbf{a}$ is $\mathbf{b} = \pm\dfrac{k}{|\mathbf{a}|}\mathbf{a}$

J   THE SCALAR PRODUCT OF TWO VECTORS

Up to now, we have learned how to add, subtract and multiply vectors by a scalar. These operations have all been demonstrated to have practical uses, for example, **scalar multiplication** is used in the concept of **parallelism** and **finding unit** vectors.

We will now learn how to find the **product** of **two vectors** with practical applications being the reason for the definitions given.

Notation: With ordinary numbers numbers a and b we can write the product of a and b as
ab or $a \times b$.

Consequently, a^2, a^3 etc. makes sense as, for example, $a^3 = aaa$ or $a \times a \times a$. There is only one meaning for product.

With vectors, there are *two useful ways* for finding the product of two vectors that will be defined later. These are:

- The **scalar product** of 2 vectors which results in a **scalar** answer, and has the notation
  a • b   (read **a** dot **b**).

- The **vector product** of 2 vectors which results in a **vector** answer, and has the notation
  a × b   (read **a** cross **b**).

Consequently, for vector **a**, $\mathbf{a}^2$ or $(\mathbf{a})^2$ has no meaning, as it not clear whether we mean
a • a (a scalar answer)   *or*   **a × a** (a vector answer).

So we should **never** write $\mathbf{a}^n$ or $(\mathbf{a})^n$.

ANGLE BETWEEN VECTORS

Consider vectors: $\mathbf{a} = \begin{bmatrix} a_1 \\ a_2 \end{bmatrix}$ and $\mathbf{b} = \begin{bmatrix} b_1 \\ b_2 \end{bmatrix}$

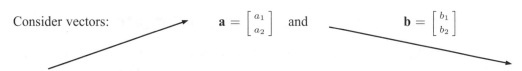

We translate one of the vectors so that they both emanate from the same point.

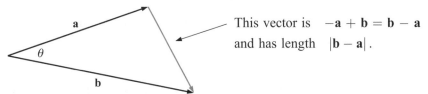

This vector is $-\mathbf{a} + \mathbf{b} = \mathbf{b} - \mathbf{a}$
and has length $|\mathbf{b} - \mathbf{a}|$.

Using the cosine rule, $|\mathbf{b} - \mathbf{a}|^2 = |\mathbf{a}|^2 + |\mathbf{b}|^2 - 2\,|\mathbf{a}|\,|\mathbf{b}|\cos\theta$

But $\mathbf{b} - \mathbf{a} = \begin{bmatrix} b_1 \\ b_2 \end{bmatrix} - \begin{bmatrix} a_1 \\ a_2 \end{bmatrix} = \begin{bmatrix} b_1 - a_1 \\ b_2 - a_2 \end{bmatrix}$

So $(b_1 - a_1)^2 + (b_2 - a_2)^2 = a_1{}^2 + a_2{}^2 + b_1{}^2 + b_2{}^2 - 2\,|\mathbf{a}|\,|\mathbf{b}|\cos\theta$

which simplifies to $a_1 b_1 + a_2 b_2 = |\mathbf{a}|\,|\mathbf{b}|\cos\theta$

So, $\cos\theta = \dfrac{a_1 b_1 + a_2 b_2}{|\mathbf{a}|\,|\mathbf{b}|}$ can be used to find the angle between two vectors **a** and **b**.

In 3-D, it can easily be shown that $\quad \cos \theta = \dfrac{a_1 b_1 + a_2 b_2 + a_3 b_3}{|\mathbf{a}|\,|\mathbf{b}|}, \quad$ where $\quad \mathbf{a} = \begin{bmatrix} a_1 \\ a_2 \\ a_3 \end{bmatrix}$

and $\quad \mathbf{b} = \begin{bmatrix} b_1 \\ b_2 \\ b_3 \end{bmatrix} \quad$ can be used to find the angle between two vectors $\mathbf{a}$ and $\mathbf{b}$.

Definition: If $\mathbf{a} = \begin{bmatrix} a_1 \\ a_2 \\ a_3 \end{bmatrix}$ and $\mathbf{b} = \begin{bmatrix} b_1 \\ b_2 \\ b_3 \end{bmatrix}$,

the **scalar product** of $\mathbf{a}$ and $\mathbf{b}$ (also known as the **dot product** or **inner product**) is defined as $\mathbf{a} \bullet \mathbf{b} = a_1 b_1 + a_2 b_2 + a_3 b_3$.

This definition is simply an extension of the 2-dimensional definition, adding the Z-component.

ALGEBRAIC PROPERTIES OF THE SCALAR PRODUCT

Dot product has the same algebraic properties for 3-D vectors as it has for its 2-D counterparts.

▶ $\qquad\qquad \mathbf{a} \bullet \mathbf{b} = \mathbf{b} \bullet \mathbf{a}$

▶ $\qquad\qquad \mathbf{a} \bullet \mathbf{a} = |\mathbf{a}|^2$

▶ $\qquad\quad \mathbf{a} \bullet (\mathbf{b} + \mathbf{c}) = \mathbf{a} \bullet \mathbf{b} + \mathbf{a} \bullet \mathbf{c}$ and
$\qquad (\mathbf{a} + \mathbf{b}) \bullet (\mathbf{c} + \mathbf{d}) = \mathbf{a} \bullet \mathbf{c} + \mathbf{a} \bullet \mathbf{d} + \mathbf{b} \bullet \mathbf{c} + \mathbf{b} \bullet \mathbf{d}$

These properties are proven in general by using vectors such as $\quad \mathbf{a} = \begin{bmatrix} a_1 \\ a_2 \\ a_3 \end{bmatrix} \quad \mathbf{b} = \begin{bmatrix} b_1 \\ b_2 \\ b_3 \end{bmatrix}, \quad$ etc.

Be careful not to confuse the **scalar product**, which is the product of two vectors to give a scalar answer, with **scalar multiplication**, which is the product of a scalar and a vector to give a parallel vector. They are both quite different.

GEOMETRIC PROPERTIES OF THE SCALAR PRODUCT

▶ If θ is the angle between vectors $\mathbf{a}$ and $\mathbf{b}$ then: $\quad \mathbf{a} \bullet \mathbf{b} = |\mathbf{a}|\,|\mathbf{b}| \cos \theta$

▶ For non-zero vectors $\mathbf{a}$ and $\mathbf{b}$: $\quad \mathbf{a} \bullet \mathbf{b} = 0 \quad \Leftrightarrow \quad \mathbf{a}$ and $\mathbf{b}$ are **perpendicular**.

$\mathbf{a} \bullet \mathbf{b} = \pm |\mathbf{a}|\,|\mathbf{b}| \quad \Leftrightarrow \quad \mathbf{a}$ and $\mathbf{b}$ are non-zero **parallel vectors**

The proofs of these results for 3-dimensions are identical for those in 2-dimensions.

Example 33

If $\mathbf{p} = \begin{bmatrix} 2 \\ 3 \\ -1 \end{bmatrix}$ and $\mathbf{q} = \begin{bmatrix} -1 \\ 0 \\ 2 \end{bmatrix}$, find: **a** $\mathbf{p} \bullet \mathbf{q}$ **b** the angle between $\mathbf{p}$ and $\mathbf{q}$.

a $\mathbf{p} \bullet \mathbf{q}$

$\quad = \begin{bmatrix} 2 \\ 3 \\ -1 \end{bmatrix} \bullet \begin{bmatrix} -1 \\ 0 \\ 2 \end{bmatrix}$

$\quad = 2(-1) + 3(0) + (-1)2$

$\quad = -2 + 0 - 2$

$\quad = -4$

b $\quad \mathbf{p} \bullet \mathbf{q} = |\mathbf{p}|\,|\mathbf{q}| \cos \theta$

$\therefore \quad -4 = \sqrt{4 + 9 + 1}\sqrt{1 + 0 + 4} \cos \theta$

$\therefore \quad -4 = \sqrt{14}\sqrt{5} \cos \theta$

$\therefore \quad -4 = \sqrt{70} \cos \theta$

$\therefore \quad \cos \theta = -\dfrac{4}{\sqrt{70}}$

$\therefore \quad \theta = \arccos\left(-\dfrac{4}{\sqrt{70}}\right) \doteqdot 118.56^{\circ}$

EXERCISE 15J.1

1 For $\mathbf{p} = \begin{bmatrix} 3 \\ 2 \end{bmatrix}$, $\mathbf{q} = \begin{bmatrix} -1 \\ 5 \end{bmatrix}$ and $\mathbf{r} = \begin{bmatrix} -2 \\ 4 \end{bmatrix}$, find:

     a $\mathbf{q} \bullet \mathbf{p}$ **b** $\mathbf{q} \bullet \mathbf{r}$ **c** $\mathbf{q} \bullet (\mathbf{p} + \mathbf{r})$ **d** $3\mathbf{r} \bullet \mathbf{q}$

     e $2\mathbf{p} \bullet 2\mathbf{p}$ **f** $\mathbf{i} \bullet \mathbf{p}$ **g** $\mathbf{q} \bullet \mathbf{j}$ **h** $\mathbf{i} \bullet \mathbf{i}$

2 For $\mathbf{a} = \begin{bmatrix} 2 \\ 1 \\ 3 \end{bmatrix}$, $\mathbf{b} = \begin{bmatrix} -1 \\ 1 \\ 1 \end{bmatrix}$ and $\mathbf{c} = \begin{bmatrix} 0 \\ -1 \\ 1 \end{bmatrix}$ find:

     a $\mathbf{a} \bullet \mathbf{b}$ **b** $\mathbf{b} \bullet \mathbf{a}$ **c** $|\mathbf{a}|^2$

     d $\mathbf{a} \bullet \mathbf{a}$ **e** $\mathbf{a} \bullet (\mathbf{b} + \mathbf{c})$ **f** $\mathbf{a} \bullet \mathbf{b} + \mathbf{a} \bullet \mathbf{c}$

3 Find: **a** $(\mathbf{i} + \mathbf{j} - \mathbf{k}) \bullet (2\mathbf{j} + \mathbf{k})$ **b** $\mathbf{i} \bullet \mathbf{i}$ **c** $\mathbf{i} \bullet \mathbf{j}$

4 Using $\mathbf{a} = \begin{bmatrix} a_1 \\ a_2 \\ a_3 \end{bmatrix}$, $\mathbf{b} = \begin{bmatrix} b_1 \\ b_2 \\ b_3 \end{bmatrix}$ and $\mathbf{c} = \begin{bmatrix} c_1 \\ c_2 \\ c_3 \end{bmatrix}$ prove that $\mathbf{a} \bullet (\mathbf{b} + \mathbf{c}) = \mathbf{a} \bullet \mathbf{b} + \mathbf{a} \bullet \mathbf{c}$.

Hence, prove that $(\mathbf{a} + \mathbf{b}) \bullet (\mathbf{c} + \mathbf{d}) = \mathbf{a} \bullet \mathbf{c} + \mathbf{a} \bullet \mathbf{d} + \mathbf{b} \bullet \mathbf{c} + \mathbf{b} \bullet \mathbf{d}$.

Example 34

> If two vectors are perpendicular then their scalar product is zero.

Find t such that $\mathbf{a} = \begin{bmatrix} -1 \\ 5 \end{bmatrix}$ and $\mathbf{b} = \begin{bmatrix} 2 \\ t \end{bmatrix}$ are perpendicular.

Since $\mathbf{a}$ and $\mathbf{b}$ are perpendicular, $\mathbf{a} \bullet \mathbf{b} = 0$

$\therefore \begin{bmatrix} -1 \\ 5 \end{bmatrix} \bullet \begin{bmatrix} 2 \\ t \end{bmatrix} = 0$

$\therefore (-1)(2) + 5t = 0$

$\therefore -2 + 5t = 0$

$\therefore 5t = 2$ and so $t = \frac{2}{5}$

---

5 Find t given that these vectors are perpendicular:

     a $\mathbf{p} = \begin{bmatrix} 3 \\ t \end{bmatrix}$ and $\mathbf{q} = \begin{bmatrix} -2 \\ 1 \end{bmatrix}$ **b** $\mathbf{r} = \begin{bmatrix} t \\ t+2 \end{bmatrix}$ and $\mathbf{s} = \begin{bmatrix} 3 \\ -4 \end{bmatrix}$

     c $\mathbf{a} = \begin{bmatrix} t \\ t+2 \end{bmatrix}$ and $\mathbf{b} = \begin{bmatrix} 2-3t \\ t \end{bmatrix}$ **d** $\mathbf{a} = \begin{bmatrix} 3 \\ -1 \\ t \end{bmatrix}$ and $\mathbf{b} = \begin{bmatrix} 2t \\ -3 \\ -4 \end{bmatrix}$

6 For question **5** find where possible the value(s) of t for which the given vectors are *parallel*. Explain why sometimes the vectors can never be parallel.

7 Show that $\mathbf{a} = \begin{bmatrix} 3 \\ 1 \\ 2 \end{bmatrix}$, $\mathbf{b} = \begin{bmatrix} -1 \\ 1 \\ 1 \end{bmatrix}$ and $\mathbf{c} = \begin{bmatrix} 1 \\ 5 \\ -4 \end{bmatrix}$ are mutually perpendicular.

8   **a** Show that $\begin{bmatrix} 1 \\ 1 \\ 5 \end{bmatrix}$ and $\begin{bmatrix} 2 \\ 3 \\ -1 \end{bmatrix}$ are perpendicular.

     b Find t if $\begin{bmatrix} 3 \\ t \\ -2 \end{bmatrix}$ is perpendicular to $\begin{bmatrix} 1-t \\ -3 \\ 4 \end{bmatrix}$.

9 Consider triangle ABC in which A is $(5, 1, 2)$, B$(6, -1, 0)$ and C$(3, 2, 0)$. Using scalar product only, show that the triangle is right angled.

10 A(2, 4, 2), B(−1, 2, 3), C(−3, 3, 6) and D(0, 5, 5) are vertices of a quadrilateral.

   a Prove that ABCD is a parallelogram.

   b Find $|\overrightarrow{AB}|$ and $|\overrightarrow{BC}|$.   What can be said about ABCD?

   c Find $\overrightarrow{AC} \bullet \overrightarrow{BD}$.   What property of figure ABCD has been found to be valid?

Example 35

Find the measure of the angle between the lines $2x + y = 5$ and $3x - 2y = 8$.

$2x + y = 5$ has slope $-\frac{2}{1}$ and $\therefore$ has direction vector $\begin{bmatrix} 1 \\ -2 \end{bmatrix} = \mathbf{a}$,   say.

$3x - 2y = 8$ has slope $\frac{3}{2}$ and $\therefore$ has direction vector $\begin{bmatrix} 2 \\ 3 \end{bmatrix} = \mathbf{b}$,   say.

If the angle between the lines is θ, then

$$\cos \theta = \frac{\mathbf{a} \bullet \mathbf{b}}{|\mathbf{a}|\,|\mathbf{b}|} = \frac{(1 \times 2) + (-2 \times 3)}{\sqrt{1+4}\sqrt{4+9}}$$

$$= \frac{-4}{\sqrt{5}\sqrt{13}}$$

$$\therefore \quad \theta = \arccos\left(\frac{-4}{\sqrt{65}}\right) \doteqdot 119.7^o$$

If a line has slope $\frac{b}{a}$ it has direction vector $\begin{bmatrix} a \\ b \end{bmatrix}$.

$\therefore$ the angle is 119.7^o or 60.3^o.

---

11 Find the measure of the angle between the lines:

   a $x - y = 3$ and $3x + 2y = 11$ **b** $y = x + 2$ and $y = 1 - 3x$

   c $y + x = 7$ and $x - 3y + 2 = 0$ **d** $y = 2 - x$ and $x - 2y = 7$

Notice that,   as $\mathbf{a} \bullet \mathbf{b} = |\mathbf{a}|\,|\mathbf{b}| \cos \theta$:

   if θ is acute, $\cos \theta > 0$ and $\therefore$ $\mathbf{a} \bullet \mathbf{b} > 0$ Can you

   if θ is obtuse, $\cos \theta < 0$ and $\therefore$ $\mathbf{a} \bullet \mathbf{b} < 0.$ explain why?

Note: Two vectors form two angles as in the diagram drawn,   i.e., θ and α. The angle between two vectors is always taken as the smaller angle, so we take θ to be the angle between the two vectors with $0 \leqslant \theta \leqslant 180^o$.

12 Find $\mathbf{p} \bullet \mathbf{q}$ for: **a** $|\mathbf{p}| = 2$, $|\mathbf{q}| = 5$ and $\theta = 60^o$ **b** $|\mathbf{p}| = 6$, $|\mathbf{q}| = 3$ and $\theta = 120^o$

Example 36

Find the form of all vectors which are perpendicular to $\begin{bmatrix} 3 \\ 4 \end{bmatrix}$.

$\begin{bmatrix} 3 \\ 4 \end{bmatrix} \bullet \begin{bmatrix} -4 \\ 3 \end{bmatrix} = -12 + 12 = 0.$

So, $\begin{bmatrix} -4 \\ 3 \end{bmatrix}$ is one such vector

$\therefore$ required vectors have form $k\begin{bmatrix} -4 \\ 3 \end{bmatrix}$, $k \neq 0.$

13 Find the form of all vectors which are perpendicular to:

a $\begin{bmatrix} 5 \\ 2 \end{bmatrix}$ b $\begin{bmatrix} -1 \\ -2 \end{bmatrix}$ c $\begin{bmatrix} 3 \\ -1 \end{bmatrix}$ d $\begin{bmatrix} -4 \\ 3 \end{bmatrix}$ e $\begin{bmatrix} 2 \\ 0 \end{bmatrix}$

PROJECTION (EXTENSION)

If **a** and **b** are two vectors then we say the projection of **a** on **b** is the length of the projection vector of **a** on **b**, i.e., the length of XO in the given diagram.

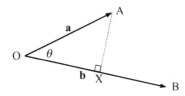

the **projection** of a on b $= |\mathbf{a}| \cos \theta$

$= |\mathbf{a}| \dfrac{\mathbf{a} \bullet \mathbf{b}}{|\mathbf{a}| \, |\mathbf{b}|}$

$= \dfrac{\mathbf{a} \bullet \mathbf{b}}{|\mathbf{b}|}$

If θ is obtuse, then the projection of **a** on **b** is given by $OX = -\dfrac{\mathbf{a} \bullet \mathbf{b}}{|\mathbf{b}|}$.   Prove this.

Hence,
- ▶ the **projection** of a on b is $\dfrac{|\mathbf{a} \bullet \mathbf{b}|}{|\mathbf{b}|}$

- ▶ the **projection vector** of a on b is $\underbrace{\left(\dfrac{\mathbf{a} \bullet \mathbf{b}}{|\mathbf{b}|} \right)}_{\substack{\text{the length and direction of} \\ \text{the projection vector}}} \underbrace{\dfrac{1}{|\mathbf{b}|} \mathbf{b}}_{\substack{\text{unit vector in the} \\ \text{direction of } \mathbf{b}}}$

Example 37

If $\mathbf{a} = \begin{bmatrix} 2 \\ 3 \\ 1 \end{bmatrix}$ and $\mathbf{b} = \begin{bmatrix} -1 \\ 0 \\ -3 \end{bmatrix}$, find

a $\mathbf{a} \bullet \mathbf{b}$ b the projection **a** and **b**   c the projection vector of **b** on **a**.

a $\mathbf{a} \bullet \mathbf{b}$

$= 2(-1) + 3(0) + 1(-3)$

$= -2 + 0 - 3$

$= -5$

b   the projection **a** and **b** $= \dfrac{|\mathbf{a} \bullet \mathbf{b}|}{|\mathbf{b}|}$

$= \dfrac{|-5|}{\sqrt{1 + 0 + 9}}$

$= \dfrac{5}{\sqrt{10}}$ units

c   the projection vector of **b** on **a** $= \left(\dfrac{\mathbf{b} \bullet \mathbf{a}}{|\mathbf{a}|} \right) \dfrac{1}{|\mathbf{a}|} \mathbf{a}$

$= \dfrac{-5}{\sqrt{14}} \dfrac{1}{\sqrt{14}} \mathbf{a}$

$= -\dfrac{5}{14} \mathbf{a}$ which is $\begin{bmatrix} -\frac{5}{7} \\ -\frac{15}{14} \\ -\frac{5}{14} \end{bmatrix}$

EXERCISE 15J.2

1 For $\mathbf{a} = -\mathbf{i} - \mathbf{j} + \mathbf{k}$ and $\mathbf{b} = \mathbf{i} + \mathbf{j} + \mathbf{k}$ find:

    a $\mathbf{a} \bullet \mathbf{b}$ **b** the angle between $\mathbf{a}$ and $\mathbf{b}$ **c** the projection vector of $\mathbf{a}$ on $\mathbf{b}$

    d the length of the projection vector of $\mathbf{a}$ on $\mathbf{b}$.

2 Find the angle ABC of triangle ABC for A(3, 0, 1), B(−3, 1, 2) and C(−2, 1, −1).

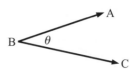

> **Reminder:** To find the angle at B, $\overrightarrow{BA}$ and $\overrightarrow{BC}$ are used.

What angle is found if $\overrightarrow{BA}$ and $\overrightarrow{CB}$ are used?

Example 38

Use vector methods to determine the measure of angle ABC.

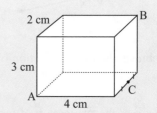

Placing the coordinate axes as illustrated,

A is (2, 0, 0), B is (0, 4, 3) and C is (1, 4, 0)

$\therefore$ $\overrightarrow{BA}$ is $\begin{bmatrix} 2 \\ -4 \\ -3 \end{bmatrix}$ and $\overrightarrow{BC}$ is $\begin{bmatrix} 1 \\ 0 \\ -3 \end{bmatrix}$

> Notice that vectors used must both be away from B (or towards B). If this is not done you will be finding the exterior angle at B.

and $\cos \angle ABC = \dfrac{\overrightarrow{BA} \bullet \overrightarrow{BC}}{|\overrightarrow{BA}| \; |\overrightarrow{BC}|}$

$= \dfrac{2(1) + (-4)(0) + (-3)(-3)}{\sqrt{4 + 16 + 9}\sqrt{1 + 0 + 9}}$

$= \dfrac{11}{\sqrt{290}}$

$\therefore$ $\angle ABC = \arccos\left(\dfrac{11}{\sqrt{290}}\right) \doteqdot 49.76°$

---

3 For the cube alongside with sides of length 2 cm, find using vector methods:

    a the measure of angle ABS

    b the measure of angle RBP

    c the measure of angle PBS.

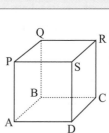

4 KL, LM and LX are 8, 5 and 3 units long respectively. P is the midpoint of KL. Find, using vector methods:

    a the measure of angle YNX

    b the measure of angle YNP.

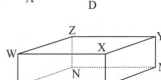
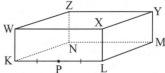

5 For the tetrahedron ABCD:

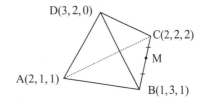

   a find the coordinates of M

   b find the measure of angle DMA.

6 **a** Find t if $2\mathbf{i} + t\mathbf{j} + (t-2)\mathbf{k}$ and $t\mathbf{i} + 3\mathbf{j} + t\mathbf{k}$ are perpendicular.

   b Find r, s and t if $\mathbf{a} = \begin{bmatrix} 1 \\ 2 \\ 3 \end{bmatrix}$, $\mathbf{b} = \begin{bmatrix} 2 \\ 2 \\ r \end{bmatrix}$ and $\mathbf{c} = \begin{bmatrix} s \\ t \\ 1 \end{bmatrix}$ are mutually perpendicular.

7 Find the angle made by:

   a the X-axis and $\begin{bmatrix} 1 \\ 2 \\ 3 \end{bmatrix}$ **b** a line parallel to the Y-axis and $\begin{bmatrix} -1 \\ 1 \\ 3 \end{bmatrix}$.

8 Find three vectors $\mathbf{a}$, $\mathbf{b}$ and $\mathbf{c}$ such that $\mathbf{a} \neq 0$ and $\mathbf{a} \bullet \mathbf{b} = \mathbf{a} \bullet \mathbf{c}$, but $\mathbf{b} \neq \mathbf{c}$.

9 Show, using $|\mathbf{x}|^2 = \mathbf{x} \bullet \mathbf{x}$, that:

   a $|\mathbf{a} + \mathbf{b}|^2 + |\mathbf{a} - \mathbf{b}|^2 = 2|\mathbf{a}|^2 + 2|\mathbf{b}|^2$ **b** $|\mathbf{a} + \mathbf{b}|^2 - |\mathbf{a} - \mathbf{b}|^2 = 4\,\mathbf{a} \bullet \mathbf{b}$

10 Given that $\mathbf{a}$ and $\mathbf{b}$ are the position vectors of two distinct points A and B (neither of which is the origin) show that if $|\mathbf{a} + \mathbf{b}| = |\mathbf{a} - \mathbf{b}|$ then $\mathbf{a}$ is perpendicular to $\mathbf{b}$ using:

   a a vector algebraic method   **b** a geometric argument.

11 If $|\mathbf{a}| = 3$ and $|\mathbf{b}| = 4$, find $(\mathbf{a} + \mathbf{b}) \bullet (\mathbf{a} - \mathbf{b})$.

12 Explain why $\mathbf{a} \bullet \mathbf{b} \bullet \mathbf{c}$ is meaningless.

K THE VECTOR PRODUCT OF TWO VECTORS

When scalar products are found the result is a scalar. However, there is another useful form of vector multiplication where a vector results and so is called **vector product**.

Vector product arises out of an attempt to find a vector which is *perpendicular to two other known vectors*. Following is such an attempt.

Suppose $\mathbf{x} = \begin{bmatrix} x \\ y \\ z \end{bmatrix}$ is perpendicular to both $\mathbf{a} = \begin{bmatrix} a_1 \\ a_2 \\ a_3 \end{bmatrix}$ and $\mathbf{b} = \begin{bmatrix} b_1 \\ b_2 \\ b_3 \end{bmatrix}$

$$\therefore \begin{cases} a_1 x + a_2 y + a_3 z = 0 \\ b_1 x + b_2 y + b_3 z = 0 \end{cases} \quad \text{\{as dot products are zero\}}$$

$$\therefore \begin{cases} a_1 x + a_2 y = -a_3 z \quad \text{...... (1)} \\ b_1 x + b_2 y = -b_3 z \quad \text{...... (2)} \end{cases}$$

We will now try to solve these two equations to get expressions for x and y in terms of z.

To eliminate x, we multiply (1) by $-b_1$ and (2) by a_1

$$-a_1 b_1 x - a_2 b_1 y = a_3 b_1 z$$
$$a_1 b_1 x + a_1 b_2 y = -a_1 b_3 z$$

Adding these gives $\quad (a_1 b_2 - a_2 b_1)y = (a_3 b_1 - a_1 b_3)z \qquad \therefore \quad \dfrac{y}{z} = \dfrac{a_3 b_1 - a_1 b_3}{a_1 b_2 - a_2 b_1}$

$$\therefore \quad y = (a_3b_1 - a_1b_3)t \quad \text{and} \quad z = (a_1b_2 - a_2b_1)t \quad \text{for all non-zero } t$$

Now in (1)
$$a_1x = -a_3(a_1b_2 - a_2b_1)t - a_2(a_3b_1 - a_1b_3)t$$
$$\therefore \quad a_1x = (-a_1a_3b_2 + a_2a_3b_1 - a_2a_3b_1 + a_1a_2b_3)t$$
$$\therefore \quad a_1x = a_1(a_2b_3 - a_3b_2)t$$
$$\therefore \quad x = (a_2b_3 - a_3b_2)t$$

The simplest vector perpendicular to both

$\begin{bmatrix} a_1 \\ a_2 \\ a_3 \end{bmatrix}$ and $\begin{bmatrix} b_1 \\ b_2 \\ b_3 \end{bmatrix}$ is obtained by letting $t = 1$ and is $\begin{bmatrix} a_2b_3 - a_3b_2 \\ a_3b_1 - a_1b_3 \\ a_1b_2 - a_2b_1 \end{bmatrix}$.

We call this vector the **cross product** of **a** and **b**, and it is written as $\mathbf{a} \times \mathbf{b}$.

That is, $\quad \mathbf{a} \times \mathbf{b} = \begin{bmatrix} a_2b_3 - a_3b_2 \\ a_3b_1 - a_1b_3 \\ a_1b_2 - a_2b_1 \end{bmatrix} = \begin{vmatrix} a_2 & a_3 \\ b_2 & b_3 \end{vmatrix} \mathbf{i} + \begin{vmatrix} a_3 & a_1 \\ b_3 & b_1 \end{vmatrix} \mathbf{j} + \begin{vmatrix} a_1 & a_2 \\ b_1 & b_2 \end{vmatrix} \mathbf{k}.$

Notice also that: $\quad \mathbf{a} \times \mathbf{b} = \begin{vmatrix} \mathbf{i} & \mathbf{j} & \mathbf{k} \\ a_1 & a_2 & a_3 \\ b_1 & b_2 & b_3 \end{vmatrix}$ —— This form is known as a **3 × 3 determinant**.

Example 39

If $\mathbf{a} = \begin{bmatrix} 2 \\ 3 \\ -1 \end{bmatrix}$

and $\mathbf{b} = \begin{bmatrix} -1 \\ 2 \\ 4 \end{bmatrix}$,

find $\mathbf{a} \times \mathbf{b}$.

$\mathbf{a} \times \mathbf{b}$

$= \begin{vmatrix} \mathbf{i} & \mathbf{j} & \mathbf{k} \\ 2 & 3 & -1 \\ -1 & 2 & 4 \end{vmatrix}$

$= \begin{vmatrix} 3 & -1 \\ 2 & 4 \end{vmatrix} \mathbf{i} + \begin{vmatrix} -1 & 2 \\ 4 & -1 \end{vmatrix} \mathbf{j} + \begin{vmatrix} 2 & 3 \\ -1 & 2 \end{vmatrix} \mathbf{k}$

$= 14\mathbf{i} - 7\mathbf{j} + 7\mathbf{k}$

EXERCISE 15K.1

1 Calculate:

a $\begin{bmatrix} 2 \\ -3 \\ 1 \end{bmatrix} \times \begin{bmatrix} 1 \\ 4 \\ -2 \end{bmatrix}$

b $\begin{bmatrix} -1 \\ 0 \\ 2 \end{bmatrix} \times \begin{bmatrix} 3 \\ -1 \\ -2 \end{bmatrix}$

c $(\mathbf{i} + \mathbf{j} - 2\mathbf{k}) \times (\mathbf{i} - \mathbf{k})$

d $(2\mathbf{i} - \mathbf{k}) \times (\mathbf{j} + 3\mathbf{k})$

2 Given $\mathbf{a} = \begin{bmatrix} 1 \\ 2 \\ 3 \end{bmatrix}$ and $\mathbf{b} = \begin{bmatrix} -1 \\ 3 \\ -1 \end{bmatrix}$, find $\mathbf{a} \times \mathbf{b}$ and hence determine

$\mathbf{a} \bullet (\mathbf{a} \times \mathbf{b})$ and $\mathbf{b} \bullet (\mathbf{a} \times \mathbf{b})$.   What has been verified from these results?

3 If **i**, **j** and **k** are the unit vectors parallel to the coordinate axes:

    a find $\mathbf{i} \times \mathbf{i}$, $\mathbf{j} \times \mathbf{j}$, and $\mathbf{k} \times \mathbf{k}$

    b find $\mathbf{i} \times \mathbf{j}$ and $\mathbf{j} \times \mathbf{i}$, $\mathbf{j} \times \mathbf{k}$ and $\mathbf{k} \times \mathbf{j}$, and $\mathbf{i} \times \mathbf{k}$ and $\mathbf{k} \times \mathbf{i}$.

What do you suspect $\mathbf{a} \times \mathbf{a}$ to simplify to, where **a** is any space vector?

What do you suspect is the relationship between $\mathbf{a} \times \mathbf{b}$ and $\mathbf{b} \times \mathbf{a}$?

4 Using $\mathbf{a} = \begin{bmatrix} a_1 \\ a_2 \\ a_3 \end{bmatrix}$ and $\mathbf{b} = \begin{bmatrix} b_1 \\ b_2 \\ b_3 \end{bmatrix}$, prove that:

    a $\mathbf{a} \times \mathbf{a} = \mathbf{0}$ for all space vectors $\mathbf{a}$

    b $\mathbf{a} \times \mathbf{b} = -\mathbf{b} \times \mathbf{a}$ for all space vectors $\mathbf{a}$ and $\mathbf{b}$.

Example 40

For $\mathbf{a} = \begin{bmatrix} 2 \\ 1 \\ -1 \end{bmatrix}$, $\mathbf{b} = \begin{bmatrix} 1 \\ 2 \\ 3 \end{bmatrix}$ and $\mathbf{c} = \begin{bmatrix} 2 \\ 0 \\ 4 \end{bmatrix}$ find:

    a $\mathbf{b} \times \mathbf{c}$ **b** $\mathbf{a} \bullet (\mathbf{b} \times \mathbf{c})$

a $\mathbf{b} \times \mathbf{c}$	**b** $\mathbf{a} \bullet (\mathbf{b} \times \mathbf{c})$
$= \begin{bmatrix} 1 \\ 2 \\ 3 \end{bmatrix} \times \begin{bmatrix} 2 \\ 0 \\ 4 \end{bmatrix}$	$= \begin{bmatrix} 2 \\ 1 \\ -1 \end{bmatrix} \bullet \begin{bmatrix} 8 \\ 2 \\ -4 \end{bmatrix}$
$= \begin{vmatrix} 2 & 3 \\ 0 & 4 \end{vmatrix} \mathbf{i} + \begin{vmatrix} 3 & 1 \\ 4 & 2 \end{vmatrix} \mathbf{j} + \begin{vmatrix} 1 & 2 \\ 2 & 0 \end{vmatrix} \mathbf{k}$	$= 16 + 2 + 4$
$= 8\mathbf{i} + 2\mathbf{j} - 4\mathbf{k}$	$= 22$

---

5 For $\mathbf{a} = \begin{bmatrix} 1 \\ 3 \\ 2 \end{bmatrix}$, $\mathbf{b} = \begin{bmatrix} 2 \\ -1 \\ 1 \end{bmatrix}$ and $\mathbf{c} = \begin{bmatrix} 0 \\ 1 \\ -2 \end{bmatrix}$ find:

    a $\mathbf{b} \times \mathbf{c}$ **b** $\mathbf{a} \bullet (\mathbf{b} \times \mathbf{c})$ **c** $\begin{vmatrix} 1 & 3 & 2 \\ 2 & -1 & 1 \\ 0 & 1 & -2 \end{vmatrix}$

Explain why the answers to **b** and **c** are the same.

6 Repeat **5** for vectors of your choosing.

7 If $\mathbf{a} = \mathbf{i} + 2\mathbf{k}$, $\mathbf{b} = -\mathbf{j} + \mathbf{k}$ and $\mathbf{c} = 2\mathbf{i} - \mathbf{k}$, determine:

    a $\mathbf{a} \times \mathbf{b}$ **b** $\mathbf{a} \times \mathbf{c}$ **c** $(\mathbf{a} \times \mathbf{b}) + (\mathbf{a} \times \mathbf{c})$ **d** $\mathbf{a} \times (\mathbf{b} + \mathbf{c})$

8 What do you suspect to be true from **7**?
Check with vectors $\mathbf{a}$, $\mathbf{b}$ and $\mathbf{c}$ of your choosing.

9 Prove that $\mathbf{a} \times (\mathbf{b} + \mathbf{c}) = \mathbf{a} \times \mathbf{b} + \mathbf{a} \times \mathbf{c}$ using $\mathbf{a} = \begin{bmatrix} a_1 \\ a_2 \\ a_3 \end{bmatrix}$, $\mathbf{b} = \begin{bmatrix} b_1 \\ b_2 \\ b_3 \end{bmatrix}$ and $\mathbf{c} = \begin{bmatrix} c_1 \\ c_2 \\ c_3 \end{bmatrix}$.

10 Use $\mathbf{a} \times (\mathbf{b} + \mathbf{c}) = (\mathbf{a} \times \mathbf{b}) + (\mathbf{a} \times \mathbf{c})$ to prove that
$(\mathbf{a} + \mathbf{b}) \times (\mathbf{c} + \mathbf{d}) = (\mathbf{a} \times \mathbf{c}) + (\mathbf{a} \times \mathbf{d}) + (\mathbf{b} \times \mathbf{c}) + (\mathbf{b} \times \mathbf{d})$.
[Notice that the order of the vectors must be maintained as $\mathbf{x} \times \mathbf{y} = -\mathbf{y} \times \mathbf{x}$.]

Example 41

Simplify $(\mathbf{a} + \mathbf{b}) \times (\mathbf{a} - \mathbf{b})$	$(\mathbf{a} + \mathbf{b}) \times (\mathbf{a} - \mathbf{b})$
	$= (\mathbf{a} \times \mathbf{a}) - (\mathbf{a} \times \mathbf{b}) + (\mathbf{b} \times \mathbf{a}) - (\mathbf{b} \times \mathbf{b})$
	$= \mathbf{0} + (\mathbf{b} \times \mathbf{a}) + (\mathbf{b} \times \mathbf{a}) - \mathbf{0}$
	$= 2(\mathbf{b} \times \mathbf{a})$

11 Simplify:

    a $\mathbf{a} \times (\mathbf{a} + \mathbf{b})$
        b $(\mathbf{a} + \mathbf{b}) \times (\mathbf{a} + \mathbf{b})$
        c $2\mathbf{a} \bullet (\mathbf{a} \times \mathbf{b})$

Example 42

Find *all* vectors perpendicular to both $\mathbf{a} = \begin{bmatrix} 1 \\ 2 \\ -1 \end{bmatrix}$ and $\mathbf{b} = \begin{bmatrix} 1 \\ 0 \\ -3 \end{bmatrix}$

$$\mathbf{a} \times \mathbf{b} = \begin{bmatrix} \mathbf{i} & \mathbf{j} & \mathbf{k} \\ 1 & 2 & -1 \\ 1 & 0 & -3 \end{bmatrix} = \begin{vmatrix} 2 & -1 \\ 0 & -3 \end{vmatrix} \mathbf{i} + \begin{vmatrix} -1 & 1 \\ -3 & 1 \end{vmatrix} \mathbf{j} + \begin{vmatrix} 1 & 2 \\ 1 & 0 \end{vmatrix} \mathbf{k}$$

$$= -6\mathbf{i} + 2\mathbf{j} - 2\mathbf{k}$$

$$= -2(3\mathbf{i} - \mathbf{j} + \mathbf{k})$$

$\therefore$ the vectors have form $k(3\mathbf{i} - \mathbf{j} + \mathbf{k})$, where k is any non-zero real number.

---

12 Find *all* vectors perpendicular to both:

    a $\begin{bmatrix} 2 \\ -1 \\ 3 \end{bmatrix}$ and $\begin{bmatrix} 1 \\ 1 \\ 1 \end{bmatrix}$
        b $\begin{bmatrix} -1 \\ 3 \\ 4 \end{bmatrix}$ and $\begin{bmatrix} 5 \\ 0 \\ 2 \end{bmatrix}$

    c $\mathbf{i} + \mathbf{j}$ and $\mathbf{i} - \mathbf{j} - \mathbf{k}$
        d $\mathbf{i} - \mathbf{j} - \mathbf{k}$ and $2\mathbf{i} + 2\mathbf{j} - 3\mathbf{k}$

13 Find all vectors perpendicular to both $\mathbf{a} = \begin{bmatrix} 2 \\ 3 \\ -1 \end{bmatrix}$ and $\mathbf{b} = \begin{bmatrix} 1 \\ -2 \\ 2 \end{bmatrix}$.

    Hence find a vector of length 5 units which is perpendicular to both **a** and **b**.

Example 43

Find a direction vector of a normal to the plane passing through the points
A(1, −1, 2), B(3, 1, 0) and C(−1, 2, −3).

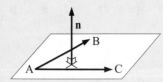
    $\overrightarrow{AB} = \begin{bmatrix} 2 \\ 2 \\ -2 \end{bmatrix}, \quad \overrightarrow{AC} = \begin{bmatrix} -2 \\ 3 \\ -5 \end{bmatrix}$

Now **n** is perpendicular to both $\overrightarrow{AB}$ and $\overrightarrow{AC}$.

{A normal is perpendicular to every line in the plane.}

$$\text{Thus}\quad \mathbf{n} = \begin{bmatrix} \mathbf{i} & \mathbf{j} & \mathbf{k} \\ 2 & 2 & -2 \\ -2 & 3 & -5 \end{bmatrix} = \begin{vmatrix} 2 & -2 \\ 3 & -5 \end{vmatrix} \mathbf{i} + \begin{vmatrix} -2 & 2 \\ -5 & -2 \end{vmatrix} \mathbf{j} + \begin{vmatrix} 2 & 2 \\ -2 & 3 \end{vmatrix} \mathbf{k}$$

$$= -4\mathbf{i} + 14\mathbf{j} + 10\mathbf{k}$$

$$= -2(2\mathbf{i} - 7\mathbf{j} - 5\mathbf{k})$$

Thus any non-zero multiple of $(2\mathbf{i} - 7\mathbf{j} - 5\mathbf{k})$ will do.

---

14 Find a direction vector of a normal to the plane passing through the points:

    a A(1, 3, 2), B(0, 2, −5) and C(3, 1, −4)

    b P(2, 0, −1), Q(0, 1, 3) and R(1, −1, 1).

In the above exercise you should have observed the following **properties** of **cross product**.

▶ $\mathbf{a} \times \mathbf{b}$ is a vector which is perpendicular to both **a** and **b**.

▶ $\mathbf{a} \times \mathbf{a} = \mathbf{0}$ for all space vectors **a**.

▶ $\mathbf{a} \times \mathbf{b} = -\mathbf{b} \times \mathbf{a}$ for all space vectors **a** and **b**,
   i.e., $\mathbf{a} \times \mathbf{b}$ and $\mathbf{b} \times \mathbf{a}$ have the same length, but in opposite directions.

▶ $\mathbf{a} \bullet (\mathbf{b} \times \mathbf{c}) = \begin{vmatrix} a_1 & a_2 & a_3 \\ b_1 & b_2 & b_3 \\ c_1 & c_2 & c_3 \end{vmatrix}$ and is called the **scalar triple product**.

▶ $\mathbf{a} \times (\mathbf{b} + \mathbf{c}) = (\mathbf{a} \times \mathbf{b}) + (\mathbf{a} \times \mathbf{c})$ and hence
   $(\mathbf{a} + \mathbf{b}) \times (\mathbf{c} + \mathbf{d}) = (\mathbf{a} \times \mathbf{c}) + (\mathbf{a} \times \mathbf{d}) + (\mathbf{b} \times \mathbf{c}) + (\mathbf{b} \times \mathbf{d}).$

DIRECTION OF $\mathbf{a} \times \mathbf{b}$

We have already observed that as $\mathbf{a} \times \mathbf{b} = -\mathbf{b} \times \mathbf{a}$
then $\mathbf{a} \times \mathbf{b}$ and $\mathbf{b} \times \mathbf{a}$ are oppositely directed.

But, what is the direction of each?

Consider $\mathbf{i} \times \mathbf{j}$ and $\mathbf{j} \times \mathbf{i}$. In the last Exercise,
we saw that $\mathbf{i} \times \mathbf{j} = \mathbf{k}$ and $\mathbf{j} \times \mathbf{i} = -\mathbf{k}$.

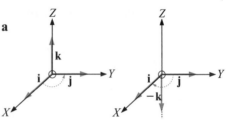

In general, the **direction**
of $\mathbf{a} \times \mathbf{b}$ is determined
by the **right hand rule**.

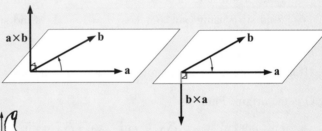

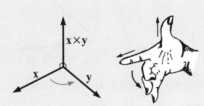

To determine the direction of $\mathbf{x} \times \mathbf{y}$ use the
right hand, where the fingers turn from $\mathbf{x}$ to $\mathbf{y}$
and the thumb points in the direction of $\mathbf{x} \times \mathbf{y}$.

THE LENGTH OF $\mathbf{a} \times \mathbf{b}$

As $\mathbf{a} \times \mathbf{b} = \begin{bmatrix} a_2b_3 - a_3b_2 \\ a_3b_1 - a_1b_3 \\ a_1b_2 - a_2b_1 \end{bmatrix}$, $|\mathbf{a} \times \mathbf{b}| = \sqrt{(a_2b_3 - a_3b_2)^2 + (a_3b_1 - a_1b_3)^2 + (a_1b_2 - a_2b_1)^2}$

However, another very useful form of the length of $\mathbf{a} \times \mathbf{b}$ exists. This is:

$$|\mathbf{a} \times \mathbf{b}| = |\mathbf{a}|\,|\mathbf{b}| \sin\theta \quad \text{where } \theta \text{ is the angle between } \mathbf{a} \text{ and } \mathbf{b}.$$

Proof: We start with $|\mathbf{a}|^2\,|\mathbf{b}|^2 \sin^2\theta$
$$= |\mathbf{a}|^2\,|\mathbf{b}|^2\,(1 - \cos^2\theta)$$
$$= |\mathbf{a}|^2\,|\mathbf{b}|^2 - |\mathbf{a}|^2\,|\mathbf{b}|^2 \cos^2\theta$$
$$= |\mathbf{a}|^2\,|\mathbf{b}|^2 - (\mathbf{a} \bullet \mathbf{b})^2$$

$$= (a_1{}^2 + a_2{}^2 + a_3{}^2)(b_1{}^2 + b_2{}^2 + b_3{}^2) - (a_1b_1 + a_2b_2 + a_3b_3)^2$$

which on expanding and then factorising

$$= (a_2b_3 - a_3b_2)^2 + (a_3b_1 - a_1b_3)^2 + (a_1b_2 - a_2b_1)^2$$

$$= |\mathbf{a} \times \mathbf{b}|^2$$

and so $|\mathbf{a} \times \mathbf{b}| = |\mathbf{a}|\,|\mathbf{b}|\sin\theta$ {as $\sin\theta > 0$}

Immediate consequences are:

> ▶ If **u** is a **unit vector** in the direction of $\mathbf{a} \times \mathbf{b}$ then $\mathbf{a} \times \mathbf{b} = |\mathbf{a}|\,|\mathbf{b}|\sin\theta\,\mathbf{u}$
> [In some texts this is the **geometric definition** of $\mathbf{a} \times \mathbf{b}$.]
>
> ▶ If **a** and **b** are non-zero vectors, then $\mathbf{a} \times \mathbf{b} = \mathbf{0}$ ⇔   **a** is parallel to **b**.

EXERCISE 15K.2

1 a   Find $\mathbf{i} \times \mathbf{k}$ and $\mathbf{k} \times \mathbf{i}$ using the original definition of $\mathbf{a} \times \mathbf{b}$.

b   Check that the **right-hand rule** correctly gives
the direction of $\mathbf{i} \times \mathbf{k}$ and $\mathbf{k} \times \mathbf{i}$.

c   Check that $\mathbf{a} \times \mathbf{b} = |\mathbf{a}|\,|\mathbf{b}|\sin\theta\,\mathbf{u}$ could be used
to find $\mathbf{i} \times \mathbf{k}$ and $\mathbf{k} \times \mathbf{i}$.

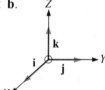

2 Consider $\mathbf{a} = \begin{bmatrix} 2 \\ -1 \\ 3 \end{bmatrix}$ and $\mathbf{b} = \begin{bmatrix} 1 \\ 0 \\ -1 \end{bmatrix}$.

a   Find $\mathbf{a} \bullet \mathbf{b}$ and $\mathbf{a} \times \mathbf{b}$.

b   Find $\cos\theta$ using $\mathbf{a} \bullet \mathbf{b} = |\mathbf{a}|\,|\mathbf{b}|\cos\theta$.

c   Find $\sin\theta$ using $\sin^2\theta + \cos^2\theta = 1$.

d   Find $\sin\theta$ using $|\mathbf{a} \times \mathbf{b}| = |\mathbf{a}|\,|\mathbf{b}|\sin\theta$.

3 Prove the property:

"If **a** and **b** are non-zero vectors then $\mathbf{a} \times \mathbf{b} = \mathbf{0}$ ⇔ **a** is parallel to **b**."

4 O is the origin. Find:

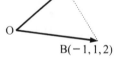

a $\overrightarrow{OA}$ and $\overrightarrow{OB}$ **b** $\overrightarrow{OA} \times \overrightarrow{OB}$ and $|\overrightarrow{OA} \times \overrightarrow{OB}|$.

c   Explain why the area of triangle OAB is $\frac{1}{2}\,|\overrightarrow{OA} \times \overrightarrow{OB}|$.

5 A, B and C are 3 distinct points with non-zero position vectors **a**, **b** and **c** respectively.

a   If $\mathbf{a} \times \mathbf{c} = \mathbf{b} \times \mathbf{c}$, what can be deduced about $\overrightarrow{OC}$ and $\overrightarrow{AB}$?

b   If $\mathbf{a} + \mathbf{b} + \mathbf{c} = \mathbf{0}$, what relationship exists between $\mathbf{a} \times \mathbf{b}$ and $\mathbf{b} \times \mathbf{c}$?

c   If $\mathbf{c} \neq \mathbf{0}$ and $\mathbf{b} \times \mathbf{c} = \mathbf{c} \times \mathbf{a}$, prove that $\mathbf{a} + \mathbf{b} = k\mathbf{c}$ for some scalar k.

AREAS AND VOLUMES

TRIANGLES

> If a triangle has defining vectors **a** and **b**
> then its area is $\frac{1}{2}\,|\mathbf{a} \times \mathbf{b}|$ units².

Proof: Area $= \frac{1}{2} \times$ product of two sides × sine of included angle $= \frac{1}{2} \times |\mathbf{a}|\,|\mathbf{b}|\sin\theta$

$$= \frac{1}{2}\,|\mathbf{a} \times \mathbf{b}|$$

Example 44

Find the area of $\triangle ABC$ given   A$(-1, 2, 3)$, B$(2, 1, 4)$ and C$(0, 5, -1)$.

$$\overrightarrow{AB} \times \overrightarrow{AC} = \begin{bmatrix} \mathbf{i} & \mathbf{j} & \mathbf{k} \\ 3 & -1 & 1 \\ 1 & 3 & -4 \end{bmatrix}$$

$$= \begin{vmatrix} -1 & 1 \\ 3 & -4 \end{vmatrix} \mathbf{i} + \begin{vmatrix} 1 & 3 \\ -4 & 1 \end{vmatrix} \mathbf{j} + \begin{vmatrix} 3 & -1 \\ 1 & 3 \end{vmatrix} \mathbf{k}$$

$$= \mathbf{i} + 13\mathbf{j} + 10\mathbf{k}$$

$$\therefore \quad \text{area} = \tfrac{1}{2} \, | \, \overrightarrow{AB} \times \overrightarrow{AC} \, | = \tfrac{1}{2}\sqrt{1 + 169 + 100}$$

$$= \tfrac{1}{2}\sqrt{270} \text{ units}^2$$

PARALLELOGRAMS

If a parallelogram has defining vectors
a and **b** then its area is $|\mathbf{a} \times \mathbf{b}|$ units^2.

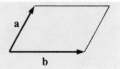

The proof follows directly from that of a triangle as the parallelogram consists of two congruent triangles with defining vectors **a** and **b**.

PARALLELEPIPED (EXTENSION)

If a parallelepiped has defining vectors **a**, **b** and **c** then
its volume is

$$\underbrace{|\mathbf{a} \bullet (\mathbf{b} \times \mathbf{c})|}_{\text{modulus}} = \underbrace{\begin{Vmatrix} a_1 & a_2 & a_3 \\ b_1 & b_2 & b_3 \\ c_1 & c_2 & c_3 \end{Vmatrix}}_{\text{modulus}} \overset{\text{determinant}}{} \text{ units}^3.$$

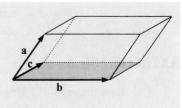

Proof:

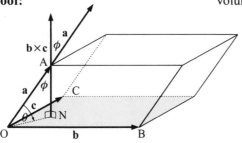

Volume $= (\text{area of base}) \times (\text{perp. height})$

$= |\mathbf{b} \times \mathbf{c}| \times AN$

$= |\mathbf{b} \times \mathbf{c}| \times |\mathbf{a}| \sin \theta \quad \{\text{as } \sin \theta = \dfrac{AN}{|\mathbf{a}|}\}$

$= |\mathbf{a}| \, |\mathbf{b} \times \mathbf{c}| \sin \theta$

$= |\mathbf{a}| \, |\mathbf{b} \times \mathbf{c}| \cos \phi$

where ϕ is the angle between **a** and $\mathbf{b} \times \mathbf{c}$

$= |\mathbf{a} \bullet (\mathbf{b} \times \mathbf{c})| \quad \text{as } \cos \phi > 0.$

TETRAHEDRON (EXTENSION)

If a tetrahedron has defining vectors **a**, **b** and **c**
then its volume is

$$\tfrac{1}{6} |\mathbf{a} \bullet (\mathbf{b} \times \mathbf{c})| = \tfrac{1}{6} \begin{Vmatrix} a_1 & a_2 & a_3 \\ b_1 & b_2 & b_3 \\ c_1 & c_2 & c_3 \end{Vmatrix} \text{ units}^3.$$

Proof:

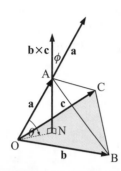

Volume $= \frac{1}{3}$(area of base) × (perp. height)

$= \frac{1}{3} \times \frac{1}{2} |\mathbf{b} \times \mathbf{c}| \times$ AN

$= \frac{1}{6} |\mathbf{b} \times \mathbf{c}| |\mathbf{a}| \sin\theta$ $\quad \{$as $\sin\theta = \dfrac{\text{AN}}{|\mathbf{a}|}\}$

$= \frac{1}{6} |\mathbf{a}| |\mathbf{b} \times \mathbf{c}| \cos\phi$

where ϕ is the angle between $\mathbf{a}$ and $\mathbf{b} \times \mathbf{c}$

$= \frac{1}{6} |\mathbf{a} \bullet (\mathbf{b} \times \mathbf{c})|$ $\quad$ as $\cos\phi > 0$.

Example 45

Find the volume of the tetrahedron with vertices P(0, 0, 1), Q(2, 3, 0),
R(−1, 2, 1) and S(1, −2, 4).

$\overrightarrow{PQ} = \begin{bmatrix} 2 \\ 3 \\ -1 \end{bmatrix}$, $\overrightarrow{PR} = \begin{bmatrix} -1 \\ 2 \\ 0 \end{bmatrix}$, $\overrightarrow{PS} = \begin{bmatrix} 1 \\ -2 \\ 3 \end{bmatrix}$ are the defining vectors from P

$\therefore$ volume $= \frac{1}{6} \begin{Vmatrix} 2 & 3 & -1 \\ -1 & 2 & 0 \\ 1 & -2 & 3 \end{Vmatrix}$

$= \frac{1}{6} \left| 2 \begin{vmatrix} 2 & 0 \\ -2 & 3 \end{vmatrix} + 3 \begin{vmatrix} 0 & -1 \\ 3 & 1 \end{vmatrix} - 1 \begin{vmatrix} -1 & 2 \\ 1 & -2 \end{vmatrix} \right|$

$= \frac{1}{6} |12 + 9 - 0|$

$= 3\frac{1}{2}$ units^3

EXERCISE 15K.3

1 Calculate the area of triangle ABC for:
   a A(2, 1, 1), B(4, 3, 0), C(1, 3, −2)
   b A(0, 0, 0), B(−1, 2, 3) and C(1, 2, 6)
   c A(1, 3, 2), B(2, −1, 0) and C(1, 10, 6)

2 Calculate the area of parallelogram ABCD for A(−1, 2, 2), B(2, −1, 4) and
   C(0, 1, 0).

3 ABCD is a parallelogram where A is (−1, 3, 2), B(2, 0, 4) and C(−1, −2, 5).
   Find the   a coordinates of D   b area of ABCD.

4 ABCD is a tetrahedron with A(1, −1, 0), B(2, 1, −1), C(0, 1, −3) and
   D(−1, 1, 2). Find the:
   a volume of the tetrahedron   b total surface area of the tetrahedron.

5 A(3, 0, 0), B(0, 1, 0) and C(1, 2, 3) are vertices of a parallelepiped, adjacent to vertex
   O(0, 0, 0). Find the:
   a coordinates of the other four vertices   b measure of ∠ABC
   c volume of the parallelepiped.

6 If A(−1, 1, 2), B(2, 0, 1) and C(k, 2, −1) are three points in space, find k if the area of triangle ABC is $\sqrt{88}$ units^2.

7 A, B and C are three points with position vectors **a**, **b** and **c** respectively. Find a formula for S, the total surface area of the tetrahedron OABC.

8 Three distinct points, A, B and C, have position vectors **a**, **b** and **c** respectively. Prove that A, B and C are collinear $\Leftrightarrow$ $(\mathbf{b} - \mathbf{a}) \times (\mathbf{c} - \mathbf{b}) = \mathbf{0}$.

TEST FOR COPLANAR POINTS

Four points in space are either coplanar or form the vertices of a tetrahedron. If they are coplanar, the volume of the tetrahedron is zero. So,

> if four points A, B, C and D have position vectors **a**, **b**, **c** and **d** respectively
> then A, B, C and D are coplanar $\Leftrightarrow$ $(\mathbf{b} - \mathbf{a}) \bullet (\mathbf{c} - \mathbf{a}) \times (\mathbf{d} - \mathbf{a}) = 0$.

Example 46

Are the points A(1, 2, −4), B(3, 2, 0), C(2, 5, 1) and D(5, −3, −1) coplanar?

$$\mathbf{b} - \mathbf{a} = \overrightarrow{AB} = \begin{bmatrix} 3-1 \\ 2-2 \\ 0--4 \end{bmatrix} = \begin{bmatrix} 2 \\ 0 \\ 4 \end{bmatrix} \qquad \mathbf{c} - \mathbf{a} = \overrightarrow{AC} = \begin{bmatrix} 2-1 \\ 5-2 \\ 1--4 \end{bmatrix} = \begin{bmatrix} 1 \\ 3 \\ 5 \end{bmatrix}$$

$$\mathbf{d} - \mathbf{a} = \overrightarrow{AD} = \begin{bmatrix} 5-1 \\ -3-2 \\ -1--4 \end{bmatrix} = \begin{bmatrix} 4 \\ -5 \\ 3 \end{bmatrix}$$

and $(\mathbf{b} - \mathbf{a}) \bullet (\mathbf{c} - \mathbf{a}) \times (\mathbf{d} - \mathbf{a}) = \begin{vmatrix} 2 & 0 & 4 \\ 1 & 3 & 5 \\ 4 & -5 & 3 \end{vmatrix}$

$$= 2(9 + 25) + 4(-5 - 12)$$
$$= 0$$

$\therefore$ A, B, C and D are coplanar.

---

9 Are these points coplanar?
- **a**   A(1, 1, 2), B(2, 4, 0), C(3, 1, 1) and D(4, 0, 1)
- **b**   P(2, 0, 5), Q(0, −1, 4), R(2, 1, 0), S(1, 1, 1)

10 Find k given that A(2, 1, 3), B(4, 0, 1), C(0, k, 2), D(1, 2, −1) are coplanar.

REVIEW SET 15A (MAINLY 2-D)

1 Using a scale of 1 cm represents 10 units, sketch a vector to represent:
- **a**   an aeroplane taking off at an angle of $8°$ to the runway with a speed of 60 m/s
- **b**   a displacement of 45 m in a direction $060°$.

2 Copy the given vectors and find geometrically:
- **a** $\mathbf{x} + \mathbf{y}$
- **b** $\mathbf{y} - 2\mathbf{x}$

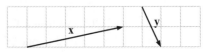

3 Find a single vector which is equal to: **a** $\overrightarrow{PR} + \overrightarrow{RQ}$ **b** $\overrightarrow{PS} + \overrightarrow{SQ} + \overrightarrow{QR}$

4 Dino walks for 9 km in a direction $246°$ and then for 6 km in a direction $096°$. Find his displacement from his starting point.

5 Simplify   **a** $\overrightarrow{AB} - \overrightarrow{CB}$ **b** $\overrightarrow{AB} + \overrightarrow{BC} - \overrightarrow{DC}$.

6 What geometrical facts can be deduced from the equations:
   a $\overrightarrow{AB} = \frac{1}{2}\overrightarrow{CD}$ **b** $\overrightarrow{AB} = 2\overrightarrow{AC}$?

7 Construct vector equations for: **a**   **b**

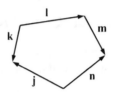

8

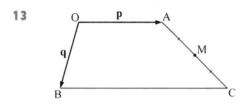

In the figure alongside $\overrightarrow{OP} = \mathbf{p}$, $\overrightarrow{OR} = \mathbf{r}$ and $\overrightarrow{RQ} = \mathbf{q}$.

If M and N are midpoints of the sides as shown, find in terms of $\mathbf{p}$, $\mathbf{q}$ and $\mathbf{r}$:

   a $\overrightarrow{OQ}$ **b** $\overrightarrow{PQ}$ **c** $\overrightarrow{ON}$ **d** $\overrightarrow{MN}$

9 Draw arrow diagrams to represent: **a** $\begin{bmatrix} 4 \\ 3 \end{bmatrix}$ **b** $\begin{bmatrix} 3 \\ -5 \end{bmatrix}$ **c** $\begin{bmatrix} 0 \\ -4 \end{bmatrix}$

10 If $\mathbf{p} = \begin{bmatrix} -3 \\ 1 \end{bmatrix}$, $\mathbf{q} = \begin{bmatrix} 2 \\ -4 \end{bmatrix}$, and $\mathbf{r} = \begin{bmatrix} 1 \\ 3 \end{bmatrix}$ find:

   a $2\mathbf{p} + \mathbf{q}$ **b** $\mathbf{q} - 3\mathbf{r}$ **c** $\mathbf{p} - \mathbf{q} + \mathbf{r}$

11 If $\overrightarrow{PQ} = \begin{bmatrix} -4 \\ 1 \end{bmatrix}$, $\overrightarrow{RQ} = \begin{bmatrix} -1 \\ 2 \end{bmatrix}$ and $\overrightarrow{RS} = \begin{bmatrix} 2 \\ -3 \end{bmatrix}$, find $\overrightarrow{SP}$.

12 If $\mathbf{r} = \begin{bmatrix} 4 \\ 1 \end{bmatrix}$ and $\mathbf{s} = \begin{bmatrix} -3 \\ 2 \end{bmatrix}$ find: **a** $|\mathbf{r}|$ **b** $|\mathbf{s}|$ **c** $|\mathbf{r} + \mathbf{s}|$ **d** $|2\mathbf{s} - \mathbf{r}|$

13

BC is parallel to OA and is twice its length. Find in terms of $\mathbf{p}$ and $\mathbf{q}$ vector expressions for   **a** $\overrightarrow{AC}$ **b** $\overrightarrow{OM}$.

14 If $\mathbf{p} = \begin{bmatrix} -3 \\ 1 \end{bmatrix}$, $\mathbf{q} = \begin{bmatrix} 2 \\ -4 \end{bmatrix}$ and $\mathbf{r} = \begin{bmatrix} 3 \\ 2 \end{bmatrix}$, find $\mathbf{x}$ if: **a** $\mathbf{p} - 3\mathbf{x} = \mathbf{0}$ **b** $2\mathbf{q} - \mathbf{x} = \mathbf{r}$

15 Use vectors to show that WYZX is a parallelogram if X is $(-2, 5)$, Y$(3, 4)$, W$(-3, -1)$, and Z$(4, 10)$.

16 Find scalars r and s such that $r\begin{bmatrix} -2 \\ 1 \end{bmatrix} + s\begin{bmatrix} 3 \\ -4 \end{bmatrix} = \begin{bmatrix} 13 \\ -24 \end{bmatrix}$.

17 AB and CD are diameters of a circle centre O. If $\overrightarrow{OC} = \mathbf{q}$ and $\overrightarrow{OB} = \mathbf{r}$, find:
   a $\overrightarrow{DB}$ in terms of $\mathbf{q}$ and $\mathbf{r}$ **b** $\overrightarrow{AC}$ in terms of $\mathbf{q}$ and $\mathbf{r}$.
   What can be deduced about DB and AC?

REVIEW SET 15B (MAINLY 3-D)

1 Given P(2, −5, 6) and Q(−1, 7, 9), find:

   a the position vector of Q from P   **b** the distance from P to Q

   c the distance from P to the x-axis.

2 For $\mathbf{m} = \begin{bmatrix} 6 \\ -3 \\ 1 \end{bmatrix}$, $\mathbf{n} = \begin{bmatrix} 2 \\ 3 \\ -4 \end{bmatrix}$ and $\mathbf{p} = \begin{bmatrix} -1 \\ 3 \\ 6 \end{bmatrix}$, find:

   a $\mathbf{m} - \mathbf{n} + \mathbf{p}$ **b** $2\mathbf{n} - 3\mathbf{p}$ **c** $|\mathbf{m} + \mathbf{p}|$

3 If $\overrightarrow{AB} = \begin{bmatrix} 2 \\ -7 \\ 4 \end{bmatrix}$ and $\overrightarrow{AC} = \begin{bmatrix} -6 \\ 1 \\ -3 \end{bmatrix}$, find $\overrightarrow{CB}$.

4 Find m and n if $\begin{bmatrix} 3 \\ m \\ n \end{bmatrix}$ and $\begin{bmatrix} -12 \\ -20 \\ 2 \end{bmatrix}$ are parallel vectors.

5 Prove that P(−6, 8, 2), Q(4, 6, 8) and R(19, 3, 17) are collinear. Hence find the ratio in which Q divides PR.

6 Find t if $\begin{bmatrix} -4 \\ t+2 \\ t \end{bmatrix}$ and $\begin{bmatrix} t \\ 1+t \\ -3 \end{bmatrix}$ are perpendicular vectors.

7 Determine the angle between $\begin{bmatrix} 2 \\ -4 \\ 3 \end{bmatrix}$ and $\begin{bmatrix} -1 \\ 1 \\ 3 \end{bmatrix}$.

8 Find the measure of angle GAC in the rectangular box alongside. Use vector methods.

9 For P(2, 3, −1) and Q(−4, 4, 2) find:

   a $\overrightarrow{PQ}$ **b** the distance between P and Q   **c** the midpoint of PQ.

10 For $\mathbf{p} = \begin{bmatrix} -1 \\ 2 \\ 1 \end{bmatrix}$, $\mathbf{q} = \begin{bmatrix} 3 \\ -1 \\ 4 \end{bmatrix}$ and $\mathbf{r} = \begin{bmatrix} 1 \\ 1 \\ 2 \end{bmatrix}$ find:

   a $\mathbf{p} \bullet \mathbf{q}$ **b** $\mathbf{p} + 2\mathbf{q} - \mathbf{r}$ **c** the angle between $\mathbf{p}$ and $\mathbf{r}$.

11 Find all angles of the triangle with vertices K(3, 1, 4), L(−2, 1, 3) and M(4, 1, 3).

12 Find the angle between $\begin{bmatrix} 3 \\ 1 \\ -2 \end{bmatrix}$ and $\begin{bmatrix} 2 \\ 5 \\ 1 \end{bmatrix}$.

13 If A(4, 2, −1), B(−1, 5, 2), C(3, −3, c) and triangle ABC is right angled at B, find possible values of c.

14 Explain why:

   a $\mathbf{a} \bullet \mathbf{b} \bullet \mathbf{c}$ is meaningless   **b** you do not need a bracket for $\mathbf{a} \bullet \mathbf{b} \times \mathbf{c}$.

15 Find k if the following are unit vectors: **a** $\begin{bmatrix} \frac{4}{7} \\ \frac{1}{k} \end{bmatrix}$ **b** $\begin{bmatrix} k \\ k \end{bmatrix}$

REVIEW SET 15C (MAINLY 2-D)

1 If $\mathbf{p} = \begin{bmatrix} 3 \\ -2 \end{bmatrix}$, $\mathbf{q} = \begin{bmatrix} -1 \\ 5 \end{bmatrix}$, and $\mathbf{r} = \begin{bmatrix} -3 \\ 4 \end{bmatrix}$ find: **a** $\mathbf{p} \bullet \mathbf{q}$ **b** $\mathbf{q} \bullet (\mathbf{p} - \mathbf{r})$

2 Using $\mathbf{p} = \begin{bmatrix} 3 \\ -2 \end{bmatrix}$, $\mathbf{q} = \begin{bmatrix} -2 \\ 5 \end{bmatrix}$ and $\mathbf{r} = \begin{bmatrix} 1 \\ -3 \end{bmatrix}$ verify that:

$\mathbf{p} \bullet (\mathbf{q} - \mathbf{r}) = \mathbf{p} \bullet \mathbf{q} - \mathbf{p} \bullet \mathbf{r}$.

3 Determine the value of t if $\begin{bmatrix} 3 \\ 3 - 2t \end{bmatrix}$ and $\begin{bmatrix} t^2 + t \\ -2 \end{bmatrix}$ are perpendicular.

4 Given A(2, 3), B(−1, 4) and C(3, k), find k if ∠BAC is a right angle.

5 Find all vectors which are perpendicular to the vector $\begin{bmatrix} -4 \\ 5 \end{bmatrix}$.

6 Find the measure of all angles of triangle KLM for K(−2, 1), L(3, 2) and M(1, −3).

7 Find the angle between the two lines with equations $4x - 5y = 11$ and $2x + 3y = 7$.

8   **a**   **Do not** assume any diagonal properties of parallelograms. OABC is a parallelogram with $\overrightarrow{OA} = \mathbf{p}$ and $\overrightarrow{OC} = \mathbf{q}$. M is the midpoint of AC.

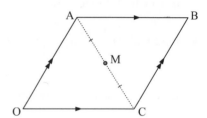

   i   Find in terms of $\mathbf{p}$ and $\mathbf{q}$:
   (1) $\overrightarrow{OB}$ **(2)** $\overrightarrow{OM}$

   ii   Show using **i** only that O, M and B are collinear and M is the midpoint of OB.

   b   AP and BQ are altitudes of triangle ABC.
   Let $\overrightarrow{OA} = \mathbf{p}$, $\overrightarrow{OB} = \mathbf{q}$ and $\overrightarrow{OC} = \mathbf{r}$.

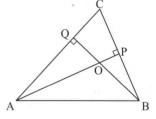

   i   Find vector expressions for $\overrightarrow{AC}$ and $\overrightarrow{BC}$ in terms of $\mathbf{p}$, $\mathbf{q}$ and $\mathbf{r}$.

   ii   Deduce that $\mathbf{q} \bullet \mathbf{r} = \mathbf{p} \bullet \mathbf{q} = \mathbf{p} \bullet \mathbf{r}$.

   iii   Hence prove that OC is perpendicular to AB.

9 If $\mathbf{a} = \begin{bmatrix} 2 \\ -3 \\ 1 \end{bmatrix}$, $\mathbf{b} = \begin{bmatrix} -1 \\ 2 \\ 3 \end{bmatrix}$, find:

   a $2\mathbf{a} - 3\mathbf{b}$ **b** $\mathbf{x}$ if $\mathbf{a} - 3\mathbf{x} = \mathbf{b}$ **c**   the projection vector of $\mathbf{a}$ on $\mathbf{b}$.

10 If $|\mathbf{a}| = 3$, $|\mathbf{b}| = \sqrt{7}$ and $\mathbf{a} \times \mathbf{b} = \mathbf{i} + 2\mathbf{j} - 3\mathbf{k}$ find:

   a $\mathbf{a} \bullet \mathbf{b}$ **b**   the area of triangle OAB given that $\overrightarrow{OA} = \mathbf{a}$ and $\overrightarrow{OB} = \mathbf{b}$

   c   the volume of tetrahedron OABC if C is the point (1, −1, 2).

REVIEW SET 15D (MAINLY 3-D)

REVIEW SET 15D

Click on the icon to obtain printable review sets and answers

Chapter 16

Complex numbers

Contents:

A ▌ COMPLEX NUMBERS AS 2-D VECTORS

Recall from **Chapter 8B** that a complex number can be written as $z = a + bi$ (Cartesian form) where $a = \text{Re}(z)$ and $b = \text{Im}(z)$ are both real numbers.

Hence, there exists a one-to-one relationship between any complex number $a + bi$ and any point (a, b) in the Cartesian Plane.

When we view points in the plane as complex numbers, we refer to the plane as the Argand diagram and the x-axis is called the "real axis" and y-axis is called the "imaginary axis".

Interestingly, all complex numbers with $b = 0$ (**real numbers**) lie on the **real** axis, and all complex numbers with $a = 0$ lie on the **imaginary** axis. The origin $(0, 0)$ lies on both axes and it corresponds to $z = 0$, a real number.

Consequently all points on the **imaginary** axis (y-axis) except for the origin are known as **pure imaginary** complex numbers i.e., $z = bi$, $b \neq 0$.

Complex numbers that are neither **real** nor **pure imaginary** lie in one of the four quadrants (a, b both $\neq 0$).

Now recall from **Chapter 15** that any point P in the plane corresponds uniquely to a vector. The position vector of the point P is $\overrightarrow{OP}$. We also learned that vectors have magnitude and direction so we can in turn attribute magnitude and direction to complex numbers.

Also, note that the operations of (1) multiples of vectors and (2) addition and subtraction of vectors, give answers that correspond to the same answers for complex numbers.

Note: For those studying the option "sets, relations and groups" this means there is an **isomorphic relationship** between complex numbers and 2-D vectors under the **binary** operation of $+$.

$$\text{So} \quad \begin{bmatrix} a \\ b \end{bmatrix} + \begin{bmatrix} c \\ d \end{bmatrix} = \begin{bmatrix} a + c \\ b + d \end{bmatrix} \qquad \text{for vectors}$$

$$\text{and} \quad (a + bi) + (c + di) = (a + c) + (b + d)i \quad \text{for complex numbers}$$

$$\text{and} \quad \begin{bmatrix} a + c \\ b + d \end{bmatrix} \equiv (a + c) + (b + d)i$$

Note: $\equiv$ means "is equivalent to" or "corresponds to"

> The **plane of complex numbers (complex plane**, or **Argand plane**), has a horizontal **real axis** and a vertical **imaginary axis**.

Notice that:

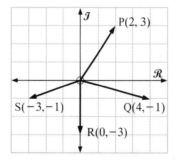

$\overrightarrow{OP} = \begin{bmatrix} 2 \\ 3 \end{bmatrix}$ represents $2 + 3i$

$\overrightarrow{OQ} = \begin{bmatrix} 4 \\ -1 \end{bmatrix}$ represents $4 - i$

$\overrightarrow{OR} = \begin{bmatrix} 0 \\ -3 \end{bmatrix}$ represents $-3i$

$\overrightarrow{OS} = \begin{bmatrix} -3 \\ -1 \end{bmatrix}$ represents $-3 - i$

$\mathcal{R}$ is the real axis, $\mathcal{J}$ is the imaginary axis.

Note: $a + bi$ is called the **Cartesian form** of a complex number as (a, b) is easily plotted on the **Cartesian plane**.

In general, 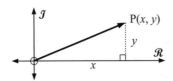 $\overrightarrow{OP} = \begin{bmatrix} x \\ y \end{bmatrix}$ represents $x + yi$

Example 1

Illustrate the position of $z_1 = 3$, $z_2 = 4 + 3i$, $z_3 = 5i$, $z_4 = -4 + 2i$, $z_5 = -3 - i$ and $z_6 = -2i$ in the complex plane.

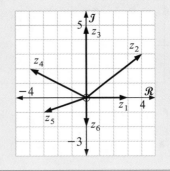

Example 2

If $z_1 = 3 + i$ and $z_2 = 1 - 4i$ find algebraically and vectorially:

a $z_1 + z_2$ **b** $z_1 - z_2$

a $z_1 + z_2$
$= 3 + i + 1 - 4i$
$= 4 - 3i$

b $z_1 - z_2$
$= 3 + i - (1 - 4i)$
$= 3 + i - 1 + 4i$
$= 2 + 5i$

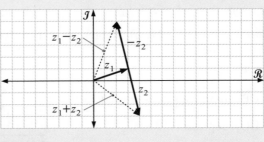

Reminder:
Draw z_1 first and at its arrow end draw z_2.
$z_1 + z_2$ goes from the start of z_1 to the end of z_2.

EXERCISE 16A.1

1 On an Argand diagram, illustrate the complex numbers:

   a $z_1 = 5$ **b** $z_2 = -1 + 2i$ **c** $z_3 = -6 - 2i$

   d $z_4 = -6i$ **e** $z_5 = 2 - i$ **f** $z_6 = 4i$

2 If $z = 1 + 2i$ and $w = 3 - i$, find both algebraically and vectorially:

   a $z + w$ **b** $z - w$ **c** $2z - w$ **d** $w - 3z$

Example 3

If $z = 1 + 2i$ and $w = 3 - i$, find both algebraically and vectorially:

a $2z + w$ **b** $z - 2w$

a $2z + w$
$$= 2(1 + 2i) + 3 - i$$
$$= 2 + 4i + 3 - i$$
$$= 5 + 3i$$

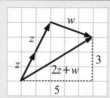

b $z - 2w$
$$= 1 + 2i - 2(3 - i)$$
$$= 1 + 2i - 6 + 2i$$
$$= -5 + 4i$$

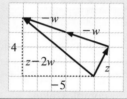

3 If $z_1 = 4 - i$ and $z_2 = 2 + 3i$ find both algebraically and vectorially:

   a $z_1 + 1$ **b** $z_1 + 2i$ **c** $z_2 + \frac{1}{2} z_1$ **d** $\dfrac{z_1 + 4}{2}$

4 If z is any complex number, explain with illustration how to find geometrically:

   a $3z$ **b** $-2z$ **c** z^* **d** $3i - z$

   e $2 - z$ **f** $z^* + i$ **g** $\dfrac{z + 2}{3}$ **h** $\dfrac{z - 4}{2}$

REPRESENTING CONJUGATES

If $z = x + iy$, then $z^* = x - iy$.

This means that if $\overrightarrow{OP} = [x, y]$ represents z then $\overrightarrow{OQ} = [x, -y]$ represents z^*.

For example:

$\overrightarrow{OP_1}$ represents $2 + 4i$ and

$\overrightarrow{OQ_1}$ represents $2 - 4i$

$\overrightarrow{OP_3}$ represents $-3i$ and

$\overrightarrow{OQ_3}$ represents $3i$ etc.

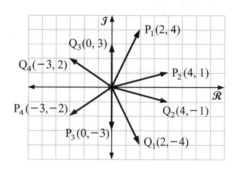

If z is $\overrightarrow{OP}$, its conjugate z^* is $\overrightarrow{OQ}$ where $\overrightarrow{OQ}$ is a reflection of $\overrightarrow{OP}$ in the real axis.

EXERCISE 16A.2

1 Show on an Argand diagram:

   a $z = 3 + 2i$ and its conjugate $z^* = 3 - 2i$

   b $z = -2 + 5i$ and its conjugate $z^* = -2 - 5i$

2 If $z = 2 - i$ we can add $z + z^*$ as shown in the diagram.
We notice that $z + z^*$ is 4 which is real.
Explain, by illustration, that $z + z^*$ is always real.

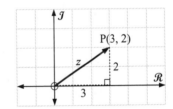

3 Explain, by illustration, that $z - z^*$ is always purely imaginary or zero. What distinguishes these two cases?

4 If z is real, what is z^*?

B   MODULUS, ARGUMENT, POLAR FORM

MODULUS

The modulus of the complex number z, written $|z|$, is the magnitude of the vector $\begin{bmatrix} a \\ b \end{bmatrix}$ where $z = a + bi$. So:

> The **modulus** of the complex number $z = a + bi$ is the real number $\sqrt{a^2 + b^2}$, and we write $|z| = \sqrt{a^2 + b^2}$ to represent the modulus of z.

Consider the complex number $z = 3 + 2i$.

The distance from P to O is its modulus, $|z|$.

So, $|z| = \sqrt{3^2 + 2^2}$ {Pythagoras}

Example 4

Find $|z|$ for z equal to:

a $3 + 2i$ **b** $3 - 2i$ **c** $-3 - 2i$

a	**b**	**c**
$|z|$	$|z|$	$|z|$
$= \sqrt{3^2 + 2^2}$	$= \sqrt{3^2 + (-2)^2}$	$= \sqrt{(-3)^2 + (-2)^2}$
$= \sqrt{13}$	$= \sqrt{9 + 4}$	$= \sqrt{9 + 4}$
	$= \sqrt{13}$	$= \sqrt{13}$

Note:
- $|z| = \sqrt{(\text{real part of } z)^2 + (\text{imaginary part of } z)^2}$, and is a positive real number.
- $|z|$ gives the distance of (a, b) from the origin if $z = a + bi$.

This is consistent with an earlier definition given for $|x|$ where $x \in \mathcal{R}$ as in **Chapter 8G**.

EXERCISE 16B.1

1 Find $|z|$ for z equal to:

     a $3 - 4i$ **b** $5 + 12i$ **c** $-8 + 2i$ **d** $3i$ **e** -4

2 If $z = 2 + i$ and $w = -1 + 3i$ find:

a $|z|$ b $|z^*|$ c $|z^*|^2$ d zz^*

e $|zw|$ f $|z||w|$ g $\left|\dfrac{z}{w}\right|$ h $\dfrac{|z|}{|w|}$

i $|z^2|$ j $|z|^2$ k $|z^3|$ l $|z|^3$

3 From **2**, suggest *five* possible rules for modulus.

4 If $z = a + bi$ is a complex number show that: a $|z^*| = |z|$ b $|z|^2 = zz^*$

Example 5

Prove that $|z_1 z_2| = |z_1| \times |z_2|$ for all complex numbers z_1 and z_2.

Let $z_1 = a + bi$ and $z_2 = c + di$ where a, b, c and d are real

$$\therefore \quad z_1 z_2 = (a + bi)(c + di)$$
$$= [ac - bd] + i[ad + bc]$$

Thus
$$|z_1 z_2| = \sqrt{(ac - bd)^2 + (ad + bc)^2}$$
$$= \sqrt{a^2 c^2 - 2abcd + b^2 d^2 + a^2 d^2 + 2abcd + b^2 c^2}$$
$$= \sqrt{a^2(c^2 + d^2) + b^2(c^2 + d^2)}$$
$$= \sqrt{(c^2 + d^2)(a^2 + b^2)}$$
$$= \sqrt{a^2 + b^2} \times \sqrt{c^2 + d^2}$$
$$= |z_1| \times |z_2|$$

---

5 Use the result $|z_1 z_2| = |z_1||z_2|$ to show that:

a $|z_1 z_2 z_3| = |z_1||z_2||z_3|$ and that $|z^3| = |z|^3$

b $|z_1 z_2 z_3 z_4| = |z_1||z_2||z_3||z_4|$ and that $|z^4| = |z|^4$.

6 What is the generalisation of the results in **5**?

7 Simplify $\left|\dfrac{z}{w}\right| \times |w|$ using the result of **Example 5** and use it to show that

$\left|\dfrac{z}{w}\right| = \dfrac{|z|}{|w|}$ provided that $w \neq 0$.

8 Given $|z| = 3$, use the rules $|zw| = |z||w|$ and $\left|\dfrac{z}{w}\right| = \dfrac{|z|}{|w|}$ to find:

a $|2z|$ b $|-3z|$ c $|(1 + 2i)z|$

d $|iz|$ e $\left|\dfrac{1}{z}\right|$ f $\left|\dfrac{2i}{z^2}\right|$

9 If $z = \cos\theta + i\sin\theta$, find $|z|$.

10 Use the result of **6** to find $|z^{20}|$ for $z = 1 - i\sqrt{3}$.

11 **a** If $w = \dfrac{z+1}{z-1}$ where $z = a + bi$, find w in the form $X + Yi$ when X and Y involve a and b.

  b If $w = \dfrac{z+1}{z-1}$ and $|z| = 1$, find Re(w).

12 Use the Principle of mathematical induction to prove that:

  a $|z_1 z_2 z_3 .... z_n| = |z_1| |z_2| |z_3| ..... |z_n|$, $n \in Z^+$ **b** $|z^n| = |z|^n$, $n \in Z^+$

SUMMARY OF MODULUS DISCOVERIES

- $|z^*| = |z|$ • $|z|^2 = zz^*$

- $|z_1 z_2| = |z_1| |z_2|$ and $\left| \dfrac{z_1}{z_2} \right| = \dfrac{|z_1|}{|z_2|}$ provided $z_2 \neq 0$

- $|z_1 z_2 z_3 .... z_n| = |z_1| |z_2| |z_3| ..... |z_n|$ and $|z^n| = |z|^n$ for n a positive integer.

DISTANCE IN THE NUMBER PLANE

Suppose P_1 and P_2 are two points in the complex plane which correspond to z_1 represented by $\overrightarrow{OP_1}$ and z_2 represented by $\overrightarrow{OP_2}$.

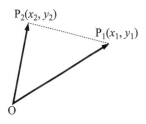

Now $\begin{aligned} |z_1 - z_2| &= |(x_1 + y_1 i) - (x_2 + y_2 i)| \\ &= |(x_1 - x_2) + (y_1 - y_2)i| \\ &= \sqrt{(x_1 - x_2)^2 + (y_1 - y_2)^2} \end{aligned}$ which we recognise as the distance between P_1 and P_2.

Alternatively:

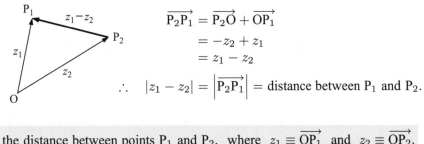

$\begin{aligned} \overrightarrow{P_2 P_1} &= \overrightarrow{P_2 O} + \overrightarrow{OP_1} \\ &= -z_2 + z_1 \\ &= z_1 - z_2 \end{aligned}$

$\therefore \quad |z_1 - z_2| = \left| \overrightarrow{P_2 P_1} \right| =$ distance between P_1 and P_2.

Thus,

$|z_1 - z_2|$ is the distance between points P_1 and P_2, where $z_1 \equiv \overrightarrow{OP_1}$ and $z_2 \equiv \overrightarrow{OP_2}$.

Note: The point corresponding to $z_1 - z_2$ can be found by drawing a vector equal to $\overrightarrow{P_2 P_1}$ emanating (starting) from the origin. Can you explain why?

CONNECTION TO COORDINATE GEOMETRY

There is a clear connection between complex numbers, vector geometry and coordinate geometry.

Consider the following:

Notice that $\overrightarrow{OR} \equiv w + z$ and $\overrightarrow{OM} \equiv \dfrac{w + z}{2}$

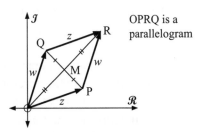

OPRQ is a parallelogram

as the diagonals of the parallelogram bisect each other.

$\overrightarrow{OR}$ and $\overrightarrow{PQ}$ give the diagonals of the parallelogram formed by w and z.

Example 6

P(2, 3) and Q(6, 1) are two points on the Cartesian plane. Use complex numbers
to find   **a** distance PQ   **b**   the midpoint of PQ.

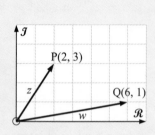

a   If $z = 2 + 3i$ and $w = 6 + i$

then $z - w = 2 + 3i - 6 - i$
$$= -4 + 2i$$

$\therefore$ $|z - w| = \sqrt{(-4)^2 + 2^2} = \sqrt{20}$

$\therefore$ PQ $= \sqrt{20}$ units

b $\dfrac{z + w}{2} = \dfrac{2 + 3i + 6 + i}{2} = 4 + 2i$

$\therefore$ the midpoint of PQ is (4, 2).

Example 7

What transformation moves z to iz?

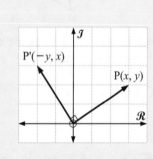

If $z = x + iy$

then $iz = i(x + iy)$
$$= xi + i^2 y$$
$$= -y + xi$$

we notice that $|z| = \sqrt{x^2 + y^2}$

and $|iz| = \sqrt{(-y)^2 + x^2}$
$$= \sqrt{x^2 + y^2}$$

So   OP$' = $ OP

$(x, y) \rightarrow (-y, x)$ under an anti-clockwise rotation of $\frac{\pi}{2}$ about O.

The transformation found in **Example 7** can be found more easily later. (See **Example 11**.)

EXERCISE 16B.2

1 Use complex numbers to find: **i** distance AB   **ii** the midpoint of AB   for
    a   A(3, 6) and B(−1, 2)   **b**   A(−4, 7) and B(1, −3)

2 OPQR is the parallelogram as shown. $\overrightarrow{OP}$
represents z and $\overrightarrow{OR}$ represents w where
z and w are complex numbers.
    a   In terms of z and w, what are:
        i $\overrightarrow{OQ}$ **ii** $\overrightarrow{PR}$?

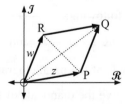

b Explain from triangle OPQ, why $|z + w| \leqslant |z| + |w|$.
It is important to discuss when the equality case occurs.

c Explain from triangle OPR, why $|z - w| \geqslant |w| - |z|$.
Once again discuss when the equality case occurs.

3 What transformation moves:

    a z to z^* **b** z to $-z^*$ **c** z to $-z$ **d** z to $-iz$?

ARGUMENT

The direction of the vector $\begin{bmatrix} a \\ b \end{bmatrix}$ can be described in a number of ways. One way is:

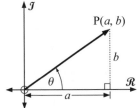

Suppose the complex number $z = a + bi$ is represented by vector $\overrightarrow{OP}$ as shown alongside.

$a + bi$ is the **Cartesian form** of z.

Suppose also that $\overrightarrow{OP}$ makes an angle of θ with the **positive real axis**.

> The angle θ is called the **argument** of z, or simply $\arg z$.

$\arg z = \theta$ has infinitely many possibilities i.e., $z \longmapsto \arg z = \theta$ is one-to-many and is not a function. Can you explain why?

To avoid the infinite number of possibilities for θ, we may choose to use $\theta \in]-\pi, \pi]$ which covers one full revolution and guarantees that $z \longmapsto \arg z = \theta$ is a function.

Note: • Real numbers have argument of 0 *or* π.

        • Pure imaginary numbers have argument of $\frac{\pi}{2}$ *or* $-\frac{\pi}{2}$.

POLAR FORM

Polar form is an alternative to Cartesian form, with many useful applications.

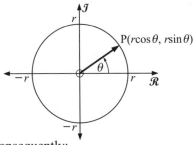

As P lies on a circle with centre O(0, 0) and radius r, its coordinates are $(r \cos \theta, \, r \sin \theta)$.

So, $z = r \cos \theta + ir \sin \theta$

i.e., $z = r(\cos \theta + i \sin \theta)$

But $r = |z|$ and if we represent $\cos \theta + i \sin \theta$ as $\text{cis } \theta$

then $z = |z| \text{ cis } \theta$.

Consequently:

> Any complex number z has **Cartesian form** $z = x + yi$ or **polar form** $z = |z| \text{ cis } \theta$
> where $|z|$ is the **modulus** of z, θ is the **argument** of z and $\text{cis } \theta = \cos \theta + i \sin \theta$.

As we develop this section we will observe that polar form is extremely powerful for dealing with multiplication and division of complex numbers as well as quickly finding powers and roots of numbers (see De Moivre's theorem). (Roots are really powers, why?)

z can also be written as $z = re^{i\theta}$ (**Euler form**) where $r = |z|$ and $\theta = \arg z$.

This form is discovered in **Chapter 29**.

Consider the complex number $z = 1 + i$.

$|z| = \sqrt{2}$ and $\theta = \frac{\pi}{4}$ $\therefore$ $1 + i = \sqrt{2}$ cis $\left(\frac{\pi}{4}\right)$

So, $\sqrt{2}$ cis $\left(\frac{\pi}{4}\right)$ is the polar form of $1 + i$.

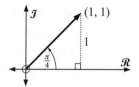

Example 8

Write in polar form: **a** $2i$ **b** -3 **c** $1 - i$

a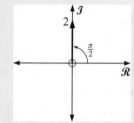

b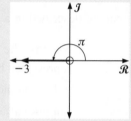

c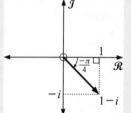

$|2i| = 2$	$|-3| = 3$	$|1 - i| = \sqrt{1 + 1} = \sqrt{2}$
$\theta = \frac{\pi}{2}$	$\theta = \pi$	$\theta = -\frac{\pi}{4}$
$\therefore$ $2i = 2$ cis $\frac{\pi}{2}$	$\therefore$ $-3 = 3$ cis π	$\therefore$ $1 - i = \sqrt{2}$ cis $\left(-\frac{\pi}{4}\right)$

EXERCISE 16B.3

1 Find the modulus and argument of the following complex numbers and hence write them in polar form:

   a 4 **b** $2i$ **c** -6 **d** $-3i$

   e $1 + i$ **f** $2 - 2i$ **g** $-\sqrt{3} + i$ **h** $2\sqrt{3} + 2i$

2 What complex number cannot be written in polar form? Why?

3 Convert $k + ki$ to polar form.   [Careful! You must consider $k > 0$, $k = 0$, $k < 0$.]

Example 9

Convert $\sqrt{3}$ cis $\left(\frac{5\pi}{6}\right)$ to Cartesian form.

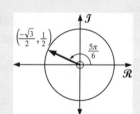

$\sqrt{3}$ cis $\left(\frac{5\pi}{6}\right)$

$= \sqrt{3}\left[\cos\left(\frac{5\pi}{6}\right) + i\sin\left(\frac{5\pi}{6}\right)\right]$

$= \sqrt{3}\left[-\frac{\sqrt{3}}{2} + i \times \frac{1}{2}\right]$

$= -\frac{3}{2} + \frac{\sqrt{3}}{2}i$

4 Convert to Cartesian form:

   a 2 cis $\left(\frac{\pi}{2}\right)$ **b** 8 cis $\left(\frac{\pi}{4}\right)$ **c** 4 cis $\left(\frac{\pi}{6}\right)$

   d $\sqrt{2}$ cis $\left(-\frac{\pi}{4}\right)$ **e** $\sqrt{3}$ cis $\left(\frac{2\pi}{3}\right)$ **f** 5 cis π

5 **a** Find the value of cis 0.   **b** Find the modulus of cis θ, i.e., $|$cis $\theta|$.

   c Show that   cis α cis $\beta =$ cis $(\alpha + \beta)$.

MULTIPLYING AND DIVIDING IN POLAR FORM

Cis θ has three useful properties. These are:

- $\text{cis } \theta \times \text{cis } \phi = \text{cis } (\theta + \phi)$
- $\dfrac{\text{cis } \theta}{\text{cis } \phi} = \text{cis } (\theta - \phi)$
- $\text{cis } (\theta + k2\pi) = \text{cis } \theta$ for all integers k.

The first two of these are similar to index laws: $a^\theta a^\phi = a^{\theta+\phi}$ and $\dfrac{a^\theta}{a^\phi} = a^{\theta - \phi}$.

The three properties are easily proved:

Proof:

- $\begin{aligned}
\text{cis } \theta \times \text{cis } \phi &= (\cos \theta + i \sin \theta)(\cos \phi + i \sin \phi) \\
&= [\cos \theta \cos \phi - \sin \theta \sin \phi] + i[\sin \theta \cos \phi + \cos \theta \sin \phi] \\
&= \cos(\theta + \phi) + i \sin(\theta + \phi) \\
&= \text{cis } (\theta + \phi)
\end{aligned}$

- $\begin{aligned}
\dfrac{\text{cis } \theta}{\text{cis } \phi} &= \dfrac{\text{cis } \theta}{\text{cis } \phi} \times \dfrac{\text{cis } (-\phi)}{\text{cis } (-\phi)} \\[2mm]
&= \dfrac{\text{cis } (\theta - \phi)}{\text{cis } 0} \\[2mm]
&= \text{cis } (\theta - \phi) \qquad \{\text{as} \quad \text{cis } 0 = 1\}
\end{aligned}$

- $\begin{aligned}
\text{cis } (\theta + k2\pi) &= \text{cis } \theta \times \text{cis } (k2\pi) \\
&= \text{cis } \theta \times 1 \\
&= \text{cis } \theta
\end{aligned}$

Example 10

Use the properties of cis to simplify: **a** $\text{cis } \left(\frac{\pi}{5}\right) \text{cis } \left(\frac{3\pi}{10}\right)$ **b** $\dfrac{\text{cis } \left(\frac{\pi}{5}\right)}{\text{cis } \left(\frac{7\pi}{10}\right)}$

a
$\begin{aligned}
&\text{cis } \left(\tfrac{\pi}{5}\right) \text{cis } \left(\tfrac{3\pi}{10}\right) \\
&= \text{cis } \left(\tfrac{\pi}{5} + \tfrac{3\pi}{10}\right) \\
&= \text{cis } \left(\tfrac{5\pi}{10}\right) \\
&= \text{cis } \tfrac{\pi}{2} \\
&= \cos \tfrac{\pi}{2} + i \sin \tfrac{\pi}{2} \\
&= 0 + i(1) \\
&= i
\end{aligned}$

b
$\begin{aligned}
&\dfrac{\text{cis } \left(\frac{\pi}{5}\right)}{\text{cis } \left(\frac{7\pi}{10}\right)} \\[2mm]
&= \text{cis } \left(\tfrac{\pi}{5} - \tfrac{7\pi}{10}\right) \\
&= \text{cis } \left(-\tfrac{\pi}{2}\right) \\
&= \cos \left(-\tfrac{\pi}{2}\right) + i \sin \left(-\tfrac{\pi}{2}\right) \\
&= 0 + i(-1) \\
&= -i
\end{aligned}$

Example 11

(see **Example 7** earlier)

What transformation moves z to iz?

$\text{Let}\quad z = r \text{ cis } \theta, \qquad i = 1 \text{ cis } \tfrac{\pi}{2}.$

$\therefore \quad \begin{aligned}[t]
iz &= r \text{ cis } \theta \times \text{cis } \tfrac{\pi}{2} \\
&= r \text{ cis } \left(\theta + \tfrac{\pi}{2}\right)
\end{aligned}$

So, z has been rotated anti-clockwise by $\tfrac{\pi}{2}$ about O.

EXERCISE 16B.4

1 Use the properties of cis to simplify:

    a $\text{cis } \theta \text{ cis } 2\theta$

    b $\dfrac{\text{cis } 3\theta}{\text{cis } \theta}$

    c $[\text{cis } \theta]^3$

    d $\text{cis } \left(\frac{\pi}{18}\right) \text{cis } \left(\frac{\pi}{9}\right)$

    e $2 \text{ cis } \left(\frac{\pi}{12}\right) \text{cis } \left(\frac{\pi}{6}\right)$

    f $2 \text{ cis } \left(\frac{2\pi}{5}\right) \times 4 \text{ cis } \left(\frac{8\pi}{5}\right)$

    g $\dfrac{4 \text{ cis } \left(\frac{\pi}{12}\right)}{2 \text{ cis } \left(\frac{7\pi}{12}\right)}$

    h $\dfrac{\sqrt{32} \text{ cis } \left(\frac{\pi}{8}\right)}{\sqrt{2} \text{ cis } \left(-\frac{7\pi}{8}\right)}$

    i $\left[\sqrt{2} \text{ cis } \left(\frac{\pi}{8}\right)\right]^4$

Example 12

Simplify $\text{cis } \left(\frac{107\pi}{6}\right)$.

$\frac{107\pi}{6} = 17\frac{5}{6}\pi = 18\pi - \frac{\pi}{6}$

$\therefore \;\; \text{cis}\left(\frac{107\pi}{6}\right) = \text{cis } \left(18\pi - \frac{\pi}{6}\right)$

$\qquad\qquad\quad = \text{cis } \left(-\frac{\pi}{6}\right) \quad \{\text{cis } (\theta + k2\pi) = \text{cis } \theta\}$

$\qquad\qquad\quad = \frac{\sqrt{3}}{2} - \frac{1}{2}i$

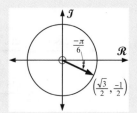

---

2 Use the property $\text{cis } (\theta + k2\pi) = \text{cis } \theta$ to evaluate:

    a $\text{cis } 17\pi$

    b $\text{cis } (-37\pi)$

    c $\text{cis } \left(\frac{91\pi}{3}\right)$

3 If $z = 2 \text{ cis } \theta$:

    a   What is $|z|$ and $\arg z$?

    b   Write z^* in polar form.

    c   Write $-z$ in polar form. [**Note:** $-2 \text{ cis } \theta$ is not in polar form as the coefficient of $\text{cis } \theta$ must be positive, as it is a length.]

    d   Write $-z^*$ in polar form.

Example 13

    a   Write $z = 1 + \sqrt{3}i$ in polar form and then multiply it by $2 \text{ cis } \left(\frac{\pi}{6}\right)$.

    b   Illustrate what has happened on an Argand diagram.

    c   What transformations have taken place when multiplying by $2 \text{ cis } \left(\frac{\pi}{6}\right)$?

a

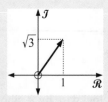

If $z = 1 + \sqrt{3}i$, then $|z| = \sqrt{1^2 + (\sqrt{3})^2}$

$\qquad\qquad\qquad\qquad\qquad\qquad = 2$

$\therefore \;\; z = 2 \left(\frac{1}{2} + \frac{\sqrt{3}}{2}i\right)$

i.e., $z = 2 \left(\cos \left(\frac{\pi}{3}\right) + i \sin \left(\frac{\pi}{3}\right)\right)$

$\qquad z = 2 \text{ cis } \frac{\pi}{3}$

$$(1 + \sqrt{3}i) \times 2 \text{ cis } \tfrac{\pi}{6} = 2 \text{ cis } \left(\tfrac{\pi}{3}\right) \times 2 \text{ cis } \left(\tfrac{\pi}{6}\right)$$

$$= 4 \text{ cis } \left(\tfrac{\pi}{3} + \tfrac{\pi}{6}\right)$$

$$= 4 \text{ cis } \left(\tfrac{\pi}{2}\right)$$

$$= 4(0 + 1i)$$

$$= 4i$$

b

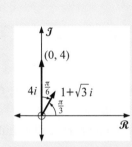

c When z was multiplied by $2 \text{ cis } \left(\tfrac{\pi}{6}\right)$ its modulus (length) was doubled and it was rotated through $\tfrac{\pi}{6}$.

Note: Multiplying by $r \text{ cis } \theta$ dilates the original complex number's vector representation by a factor of r and then rotates it through an angle of θ.

4 **a** Write i in polar form.

 b $z = r \text{ cis } \theta$ is any complex number. Write iz in polar form.

 c Explain why iz is the anti-clockwise rotation about 0 of z.

 d What transformation maps z onto $-iz$? Give reasoning in polar form.

5 Write in polar form: **a** $\cos \theta - i \sin \theta$ **b** $\sin \theta - i \cos \theta$

Use **a** above to complete this sentence:

If $z = r \text{ cis } \theta$ then $z^* = \text{.....}$ in polar form. Discuss.

Example 14

Use complex number methods to write $\cos \left(\tfrac{7\pi}{12}\right)$ and $\sin \left(\tfrac{7\pi}{12}\right)$ in simplest surd form.

$$\cos \left(\tfrac{7\pi}{12}\right) + i \sin \left(\tfrac{7\pi}{12}\right)$$

$$= \text{cis } \left(\tfrac{7\pi}{12}\right)$$

$$= \text{cis } \left(\tfrac{3\pi}{12} + \tfrac{4\pi}{12}\right)$$

$$= \text{cis } \tfrac{\pi}{4} \times \text{cis } \tfrac{\pi}{3} \quad \{\text{cis } (\theta + \phi) = \text{cis } \theta \times \text{cis } \phi\}$$

$$= \left(\tfrac{1}{\sqrt{2}} + \tfrac{1}{\sqrt{2}}i\right)\left(\tfrac{1}{2} + \tfrac{\sqrt{3}}{2}i\right)$$

$$= \left(\tfrac{1}{2\sqrt{2}} - \tfrac{\sqrt{3}}{2\sqrt{2}}\right) + i\left(\tfrac{\sqrt{3}}{2\sqrt{2}} + \tfrac{1}{2\sqrt{2}}\right)$$

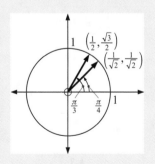

Equating real parts: $\cos \tfrac{7\pi}{12} = \left(\tfrac{1 - \sqrt{3}}{2\sqrt{2}}\right) \times \tfrac{\sqrt{2}}{\sqrt{2}} = \tfrac{\sqrt{2} - \sqrt{6}}{4}$

Equating imaginary parts: $\sin \tfrac{7\pi}{12} = \tfrac{\sqrt{3} + 1}{2\sqrt{2}} = \tfrac{\sqrt{6} + \sqrt{2}}{4}$

6 Use the method outlined above to find, in simplest surd form:

   a $\cos\left(\frac{\pi}{12}\right)$ and $\sin\left(\frac{\pi}{12}\right)$ **b** $\cos\left(\frac{11\pi}{12}\right)$ and $\sin\left(\frac{11\pi}{12}\right)$.

PROPERTIES OF ARGUMENT

The basic properties of argument are:

- $\arg(zw) = \arg z + \arg w$
- $\arg\left(\dfrac{z}{w}\right) = \arg z - \arg w$
- $\arg(z^n) = n \arg z$

Notice that they are *identical to the laws of logarithms*, with $\arg$ replaced by $\log$ or $\ln$.

Properties of modulus and argument can be proved jointly using polar form.

These properties lead to another form of expressing complex numbers, called Euler's form (see **Chapter 29**).

Example 15

Use polar form to establish that $|zw| = |z| \times |w|$ and $\arg(zw) = \arg z + \arg w$.

Let $z = |z| \operatorname{cis} \theta$ and $w = |w| \operatorname{cis} \phi$, say.

Now $zw = |z| \operatorname{cis} \theta \times |w| \operatorname{cis} \phi$

$ = \underbrace{|z|\,|w|}_{\text{non-negative}} \operatorname{cis}(\theta + \phi)$ {property of cis}

$\therefore \quad |zw| = |z|\,|w|$ {the non-negative number multiplied by cis (.....)}

and $\arg(zw) = \theta + \phi = \arg z + \arg w$.

Example 16

If $z = \sqrt{2} \operatorname{cis} \theta$, find the modulus and argument of:

  a $2z$ **b** iz **c** $(1-i)z$

a $2z = 2\sqrt{2} \operatorname{cis} \theta$ $\therefore \quad |2z| = 2\sqrt{2}$ and $\arg(2z) = \theta$

b $ i = \operatorname{cis} \frac{\pi}{2}$

$\therefore \quad iz = \operatorname{cis} \frac{\pi}{2} \times \sqrt{2} \operatorname{cis} \theta$

$ = \sqrt{2} \operatorname{cis}\left(\frac{\pi}{2} + \theta\right)$ So, $|iz| = \sqrt{2}$

$\phantom{\therefore \quad iz = \sqrt{2}} $ and $\arg(iz) = \frac{\pi}{2} + \theta$

c

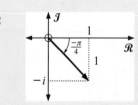

$1 - i = \sqrt{2} \operatorname{cis}\left(-\frac{\pi}{4}\right)$

$\therefore \quad (1-i)z = \sqrt{2} \operatorname{cis}\left(-\frac{\pi}{4}\right) \times \sqrt{2} \operatorname{cis} \theta$

$ = 2 \operatorname{cis}\left(-\frac{\pi}{4} + \theta\right)$

$\therefore \quad |(1-i)z| = 2$ and $\arg((1-i)z) = \theta - \frac{\pi}{4}$

EXERCISE 16B.5

1 Use polar form to establish:

$$\left|\frac{z}{w}\right| = \frac{|z|}{|w|} \quad \text{and} \quad \arg\left(\frac{z}{w}\right) = \arg z - \arg w, \quad \text{provided} \quad w \neq 0.$$

2 Suppose $z = 3 \operatorname{cis} \theta$. Determine the modulus and argument of:

 a $-z$ **b** z^* **c** iz **d** $(1+i)z$

Example 17

Suppose $z = \operatorname{cis} \phi$ where ϕ is acute. Find the modulus and argument of $z + 1$.

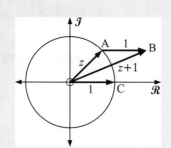

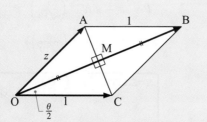

$|z| = 1$

$\therefore \;$ z lies on the unit circle

$z + 1$ is $\overrightarrow{OB}$ {found vectorially}

OABC is a rhombus

$\therefore \;$ $\arg(z + 1) = \frac{\theta}{2}$

{diagonals bisect the angles of the rhombus}

Also $\cos\left(\frac{\theta}{2}\right) = \dfrac{OM}{1}$

$\therefore \quad OM = \cos\left(\frac{\theta}{2}\right)$

$\therefore \quad OB = 2\cos\left(\frac{\theta}{2}\right)$

$\therefore \quad |z + 1| = 2\cos\left(\frac{\theta}{2}\right)$

---

3 **a**   If $z = \operatorname{cis}\phi$ where ϕ is acute, determine the modulus and argument of $z - 1$.

 b   Using **a**, write $z - 1$ in polar form.

 c   Now write $(z - 1)^*$ in polar form.

4   ABC is an equilateral triangle. Suppose z_1 represents $\overrightarrow{OA}$, z_2 represents $\overrightarrow{OB}$ and z_3 represents $\overrightarrow{OC}$.

 a   Explain what vectors represent $z_2 - z_1$ and $z_3 - z_2$.

 b   Find $\left|\dfrac{z_2 - z_1}{z_3 - z_2}\right|$.

 c   Determine $\arg\left(\dfrac{z_2 - z_1}{z_3 - z_2}\right)$.

 d   Use **b** and **c** to find the value of $\left(\dfrac{z_2 - z_1}{z_3 - z_2}\right)^3$.

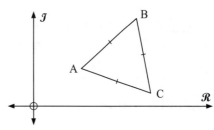

FURTHER CONVERSION BETWEEN CARTESIAN AND POLAR FORMS

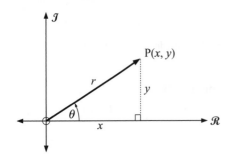

If $\;z = \underbrace{x + iy}_{\substack{\text{Cartesian} \\ \text{form}}} = \underbrace{r \operatorname{cis} \theta}_{\substack{\text{Polar} \\ \text{form}}}$

$$r = \sqrt{x^2 + y^2}, \qquad \tan\theta = \frac{y}{x},$$

$$\cos\theta = \frac{x}{\sqrt{x^2 + y^2}}, \qquad \sin\theta = \frac{y}{\sqrt{x^2 + y^2}}$$

Polar to cartesian

$$z = 2 \operatorname{cis}\left(\frac{\pi}{8}\right)$$
$$= 2\left(\cos\frac{\pi}{8} + i\sin\frac{\pi}{8}\right)$$
$$\doteqdot 1.85 + 0.765i$$

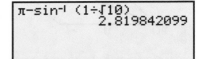

```
2×(cos (π÷8)+i×sin ((
π÷8))
            1.847759065
         +0.7653668647i



 i  Abs Arg Conj ReP ImP
```

Cartesian to polar

$$z = -3 + i \quad \text{has} \quad r = \sqrt{(-3)^2 + 1^2} = \sqrt{10} \quad \text{and} \quad \underbrace{\cos\theta = \frac{-3}{\sqrt{10}}, \quad \sin\theta = \frac{1}{\sqrt{10}}}$$

$$\theta = \pi - \sin^{-1}\left(\frac{1}{\sqrt{10}}\right)$$
$$\left(or\;\; \pi - \cos^{-1}\left(\frac{3}{\sqrt{10}}\right)\right)$$

$$\therefore \quad -3 + i \doteqdot \sqrt{10} \operatorname{cis}(2.82)$$

```
π-sin⁻¹ (1÷√10)
            2.819842099




 i  Abs Arg Conj ReP ImP
```

Alternatively:

MATH CPX takes us to the complex number menu.

Pressing 5 brings up **abs(** for calculating the **modulus** (absolute value).

To find the modulus of $-3 + i$, press

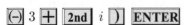

MATH CPX then 4 brings up **angle(** for calculating the **argument**. To find the argument of $-3 + i$, press

```
              √10
Abs (-3+i)
            3.16227766
Arg (-3+i)
            2.819842099

 i  Abs Arg Conj ReP ImP
```

EXERCISE 16B.6

1 Use your calculator to convert to Cartesian form:

   a $\;\sqrt{3} \operatorname{cis}(2.5187)$ **b** $\;\sqrt{11} \operatorname{cis}\left(-\frac{3\pi}{8}\right)$ **c** $\;2.83649 \operatorname{cis}(-2.68432)$

2 Use your calculator to convert to polar form:

    a $3 - 4i$ **b** $-5 - 12i$ **c** $-11.6814 + 13.2697i$

3 Add the following using $a + bi$ surd form and convert your answer to polar form:

    a $3 \text{ cis} \left(\frac{\pi}{4}\right) + \text{cis} \left(\frac{-3\pi}{4}\right)$ **b** $2 \text{ cis} \left(\frac{2\pi}{3}\right) + 5 \text{ cis} \left(\frac{-2\pi}{3}\right)$

4 Use the sum and product of roots to find the real quadratic equations with roots of:

    a $2 \text{ cis} \left(\frac{2\pi}{3}\right)$, $2 \text{ cis} \left(\frac{4\pi}{3}\right)$ **b** $\sqrt{2} \text{ cis} \left(\frac{\pi}{4}\right)$, $\sqrt{2} \text{ cis} \left(\frac{-\pi}{4}\right)$

    Note: Answers, if approximate, should be given to 3 significant figures.

C   De MOIVRE'S THEOREM

Squaring a complex number which is given in polar form gives us an indication of how we can find higher powers of that number.

We notice that if $z = |z| \text{ cis } \theta$

then $z^2 = |z| \text{ cis } \theta \times |z| \text{ cis } \theta$ and $z^3 = z^2 z$

$\qquad\quad = |z|^2 \text{ cis } (\theta + \theta)$ $= |z|^2 \text{ cis } 2\theta \times |z| \text{ cis } \theta$

$\qquad\quad = |z|^2 \text{ cis } 2\theta$ $= |z|^3 \text{ cis } (2\theta + \theta)$

$\qquad\qquad\qquad\qquad\qquad\qquad\qquad\qquad\quad = |z|^3 \text{ cis } 3\theta$

The generalisation of this process is: $(|z| \text{ cis } \theta)^n = |z|^n \text{ cis } n\theta$

Proof: (using mathematical induction)

P_n is: $(|z| \text{ cis } \theta)^n = |z|^n \text{ cis } n\theta$

  (1) If $n = 1$, then $(|z| \text{ cis } \theta)^1 = |z| \text{ cis } 1(\theta)$ $\therefore$ P_1 is true.

  (2) If P_k is true, then $(|z| \text{ cis } \theta)^k = |z|^k \text{ cis } k\theta$ ...... $(*)$

        Thus $(|z| \text{ cis } \theta)^{k+1} = (|z| \text{ cis } \theta)^k \times |z| \text{ cis } \theta$ {index law}

$\qquad\qquad\qquad\qquad\qquad\;\; = |z|^k \text{ cis } k\theta \times |z| \text{ cis } \theta$ {using $*$}

$\qquad\qquad\qquad\qquad\qquad\;\; = |z|^{k+1} \text{ cis } (k\theta + \theta)$ {index law and cis property}

$\qquad\qquad\qquad\qquad\qquad\;\; = |z|^{k+1} \text{ cis } (k + 1)\theta$

Thus P_{k+1} is true whenever P_k is true and P_1 is true.

  $\therefore$ P_n is true {Principle of mathematical induction}

We observe also that $\text{cis} (-n\theta) = \text{cis} (0 - n\theta) = \dfrac{\text{cis } 0}{\text{cis } n\theta}$ $\left\{\text{as} \;\; \dfrac{\text{cis } \theta}{\text{cis } \phi} = \text{cis} (\theta - \phi)\right\}$

$\qquad\qquad\;\; \therefore \;\; \text{cis} (-n\theta) = \dfrac{1}{\text{cis } n\theta}$ $\{\text{as} \;\; \text{cis } 0 = 1\}$

$\qquad\qquad\qquad\qquad\;\; = \dfrac{1}{[\text{cis } \theta]^n}$ $\{\text{for } n \text{ a positive integer}\}$

$\qquad\qquad\qquad\qquad\;\; = [\text{cis } \theta]^{-n}$

Also $[\operatorname{cis}\left(\frac{\theta}{n}\right)]^n = \operatorname{cis}\left(n\left(\frac{\theta}{n}\right)\right) = \operatorname{cis}\theta$ and so $[\operatorname{cis}\theta]^{\frac{1}{n}} = \operatorname{cis}\left(\frac{\theta}{n}\right)$

So DeMoivre's theorem seems to hold for any integer n and for $\frac{1}{n}$.

De MOIVRE'S THEOREM

$$(|z| \operatorname{cis}\theta)^n = |z|^n \operatorname{cis} n\theta \quad \text{for all rational } n.$$

Example 18

Find the exact value of $(\sqrt{3} + i)^8$ using De Moivre's theorem.
Check your answer by calculator.

$\sqrt{3} + i$ has modulus $\sqrt{(\sqrt{3})^2 + 1^2} = \sqrt{4} = 2$

$\therefore \quad \sqrt{3} + i = 2\left(\frac{\sqrt{3}}{2} + \frac{1}{2}i\right)$

$\qquad = 2 \operatorname{cis} \frac{\pi}{6}$

$\therefore \quad (\sqrt{3} + i)^8 = \left(2 \operatorname{cis} \frac{\pi}{6}\right)^8$

$\qquad = 2^8 \operatorname{cis} \left(\frac{8\pi}{6}\right)$

$\qquad = 2^8 \operatorname{cis} \left(\frac{4\pi}{3}\right)$

$\qquad = 2^8 \left(-\frac{1}{2} - \frac{\sqrt{3}}{2}i\right)$

$\qquad = -128 - 128\sqrt{3}i$

```
(√(3)+i)^8
-128-221.702503...
-128*√(3)
        -221.7025034
```

EXERCISE 16C

1 Using De Moivre's theorem to find a simple answer for:

   a $\left(\sqrt{2} \operatorname{cis} \frac{\pi}{5}\right)^{10}$ **b** $\left(\operatorname{cis} \frac{\pi}{12}\right)^{36}$ **c** $\left(\sqrt{2} \operatorname{cis} \frac{\pi}{8}\right)^{12}$

   d $\sqrt{5 \operatorname{cis} \frac{\pi}{7}}$ **e** $\sqrt[3]{8 \operatorname{cis} \frac{\pi}{2}}$ **f** $\left(8 \operatorname{cis} \frac{\pi}{5}\right)^{\frac{5}{3}}$

2 Use De Moivre's theorem to find the exact value of:

   a $(1 + i)^{15}$ **b** $(1 - i\sqrt{3})^{11}$ **c** $(\sqrt{2} - i\sqrt{2})^{-19}$

   d $(-1 + i)^{-11}$ **e** $(\sqrt{3} - i)^{\frac{1}{2}}$ **f** $(2 + 2i\sqrt{3})^{-\frac{5}{2}}$

3 Use your calculator to check the answers to **2**.

4   **a** Recall that if $z = |z| \operatorname{cis}\theta$ then $-\pi < \theta \leqslant \pi$.
      Use De Moivre's theorem to find $\sqrt{z}$ in terms of $|z|$ and θ.

  b What restrictions apply to $\theta = \arg(\sqrt{z})$?

  c True or false?   "$\sqrt{z}$ has non-negative real part."

5 Use De Moivre's theorem to explain why $|z^n| = |z|^n$ and $\arg(z^n) = n \arg z$.

6 Show that $\cos\theta - i\sin\theta = \text{cis}(-\theta)$. Hence, simplify $(\cos\theta - i\sin\theta)^{-3}$.

7 Write $z = 1 + i$ in polar form and hence write z^n in polar form. Find all values of n for which: **a** z^n is real **b** z^n is purely imaginary.

8 If $|z| = 2$ and $\arg z = \theta$, determine the modulus and argument of:

    a z^3 **b** iz^2 **c** $\dfrac{1}{z}$ **d** $-\dfrac{i}{z^2}$

9 If $z = \text{cis}\,\theta$, prove that $\dfrac{z^2 - 1}{z^2 + 1} = i\tan\theta$.

Example 19

By considering $\cos 2\theta + i\sin 2\theta$, deduce the double angle formulae: $\cos 2\theta$ and $\sin 2\theta$.	Now $\cos 2\theta + i\sin 2\theta$ $= \text{cis}\,2\theta$ $= [\text{cis}\,\theta]^2$ {De Moivre's theorem} $= [\cos\theta + i\sin\theta]^2$ $= [\cos^2\theta - \sin^2\theta] + i[2\sin\theta\cos\theta]$ Equating imaginary parts, $\sin 2\theta = 2\sin\theta\cos\theta$ Equating real parts, $\cos 2\theta = \cos^2\theta - \sin^2\theta$

---

10 By considering $\cos 3\theta + i\sin 3\theta$, deduce the formula:

    a $\sin 3\theta = 3\sin\theta - 4\sin^3\theta$ **b** $\cos 3\theta = 4\cos^3\theta - 3\cos\theta$

11 **a** If $z = \text{cis}\,\theta$ prove that $z^n + \dfrac{1}{z^n} = 2\cos n\theta$.

    b Hence, explain why $z + \dfrac{1}{z} = 2\cos\theta$.

    c Use the binomial theorem to expand $(z + \dfrac{1}{z})^3$, and simplify your result.

    d By using **a**, **b** and **c** above show that $\cos^3\theta = \frac{1}{4}\cos 3\theta + \frac{3}{4}\cos\theta$.

    e Hence show the exact value of $\cos^3\frac{13\pi}{12}$ is $\dfrac{-5\sqrt{2} - 3\sqrt{6}}{16}$ {**Note:** $\frac{13\pi}{12} = \frac{3\pi}{4} + \frac{\pi}{3}$}.

12 You are given that the points A, B, C in the Argand Diagram form an isosceles triangle with a right angle at B. Let the points A, B, and C be represented by the complex numbers z_1, z_2, and z_3 respectively.

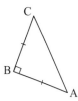

    a Show that $(z_1 - z_2)^2 = -(z_3 - z_2)^2$.

    b If ABCD forms a square, what complex number represents the point D? Give your answer in terms of z_1, z_2 and z_3.

13 **a** Find a formula for

        i $\cos 4\theta$ in terms of $\cos\theta$ **ii** $\sin 4\theta$ in terms of $\cos\theta$ and $\sin\theta$

    b Show that if $z = \text{cis}\,\theta$ then $z^n - \dfrac{1}{z^n} = 2i\sin n\theta$ and hence that

        $\sin^3\theta = \frac{3}{4}\sin\theta - \frac{1}{4}\sin 3\theta$? (See question **11** above.)

D | ROOTS OF COMPLEX NUMBERS

SOLVING $z^n = c$

We will examine solutions of equations of the form $z^n = c$ where n is a positive integer and c is either real or purely imaginary. However, the technique is satisfactory for all complex numbers c.

Definition: The nth roots of complex number c are the n solutions of $z^n = c$.

For example, the 4th roots of $2i$ are the four solutions of $z^4 = 2i$.

nth roots may be found by:
- factorisation
- using the 'nth root method' of complex numbers.

As factorisation can sometimes be very difficult or almost impossible, the 'nth root method' is most desirable in many cases.

Example 20

Find the four 4th roots of 1 by: **a** factorisation **b** the 'nth roots method'.

We need to find the 4 solutions of $z^4 = 1$.

a By factorisation $z^4 = 1$
$$\therefore \quad z^4 - 1 = 0$$
$$\therefore \quad (z^2 + 1)(z^2 - 1) = 0$$
$$(z + i)(z - i)(z + 1)(z - 1) = 0$$
$$\therefore \quad z = \pm i \quad \text{or} \quad \pm 1$$

b (By the 'nth roots method')
$$z^4 = 1$$
$$\therefore \quad z^4 = 1 \operatorname{cis}(0 + k2\pi) \quad \text{\{polar form\}}$$
$$\therefore \quad z = [\operatorname{cis}(k2\pi)]^{\frac{1}{4}}$$
$$\therefore \quad z = \operatorname{cis}\left(\frac{k2\pi}{4}\right) \quad \text{\{De Moivre\}}$$
$$\therefore \quad z = \operatorname{cis}\left(\frac{k\pi}{2}\right)$$
$$\therefore \quad z = \operatorname{cis} 0, \ \operatorname{cis} \frac{\pi}{2}, \ \operatorname{cis} \pi, \ \operatorname{cis} \frac{3\pi}{2}$$
$$\text{\{letting} \quad k = 0, 1, 2, 3\}$$
$$\therefore \quad z = 1, i, -1, -i$$

Note:
- The factorisation method is fine provided that the polynomial factorises easily, as in the example above.
- The substitution of $k = 0, 1, 2, 3$ to find the 4 roots could also be achieved by substituting any 4 consecutive integers for k. Why?

EXERCISE 16D

1 Find the three cube roots of 1 using: **a** factorisation **b** the 'nth roots method'.

2 Solve for z: **a** $z^3 = -8i$ **b** $z^3 = -27i$

3 Find the three cube roots of -1, and display them on an Argand diagram.

4 Solve for z: **a** $z^4 = 16$ **b** $z^4 = -16$

5 Find the four fourth roots of $-i$, and display them on an Argand diagram.

Example 21

Find the fourth roots of -4 in the form $a + bi$ and then factorise $z^4 + 4$ into linear factors. Hence, write $z^4 + 4$ as a product of real quadratic factors.

The fourth roots of -4 are solutions of

$$z^4 = -4$$

$$\therefore \quad z^4 = 4 \operatorname{cis}(\pi + k2\pi)$$

$$\therefore \quad z = [4 \operatorname{cis}(\pi + 2\pi)]^{\frac{1}{4}}$$

$$\therefore \quad z = 4^{\frac{1}{4}} \operatorname{cis}\left(\frac{\pi + k2\pi}{4}\right)$$

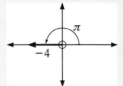

$$\therefore \quad z = 2^{\frac{1}{2}} \operatorname{cis} \frac{\pi}{4}, \quad 2^{\frac{1}{2}} \operatorname{cis} \frac{3\pi}{4}, \quad 2^{\frac{1}{2}} \operatorname{cis} \frac{5\pi}{4}, \quad 2^{\frac{1}{2}} \operatorname{cis} \frac{7\pi}{4} \quad \{\text{letting} \quad k = 0, 1, 2, 3\}$$

$$\therefore \quad z = \sqrt{2}\left(\frac{1}{\sqrt{2}} + \frac{1}{\sqrt{2}}i\right), \sqrt{2}\left(-\frac{1}{\sqrt{2}} + \frac{1}{\sqrt{2}}i\right), \sqrt{2}\left(-\frac{1}{\sqrt{2}} - \frac{1}{\sqrt{2}}i\right), \sqrt{2}\left(\frac{1}{\sqrt{2}} - \frac{1}{\sqrt{2}}i\right)$$

$$\therefore \quad z = 1 + i, \quad -1 + i, \quad -1 - i, \quad 1 - i$$

Roots $1 \pm i$ have sum $= 2$ and product $= (1 + i)(1 - i) = 2$ and $\therefore$ come from the quadratic factor $z^2 - 2z + 2$.

Roots $-1 \pm i$ have sum $= -2$ and product $= (-1 + i)(-1 - i) = 2$ and $\therefore$ come from the quadratic factor $z^2 + 2z + 2$.

Thus $z^4 + 4 = (z^2 - 2z + 2)(z^2 + 2z + 2)$

6 Find the four solutions of $z^4 + 1 = 0$ giving each of them in the form $a + bi$ and display them on an Argand diagram. Hence, write $z^4 + 1$ as the product of two real quadratic factors.

Recall that a **real** polynomial of degree n has **exactly** n zeros that are real and/or occur in conjugate pairs (see **Chapter 8F**).

SUMMARY OF SOLUTIONS OF $z^n = c$ (nth **roots of** c)

- There are **exactly** n nth roots of c.
- If $c \in \mathcal{R}$, the complex roots must occur in conjugate pairs.
- If $c \notin \mathcal{R}$, the complex roots do not all occur in conjugate pairs.
- All the roots of z^n will have the same modulus which is $|c|^{\frac{1}{n}}$. Why?

  Thus on an Argand diagram, all the roots will be the same distance from the origin and hence lie on a circle radius $= |c|^{\frac{1}{n}}$.

- All the roots on the circle $r = |c|^{\frac{1}{n}}$ will be equally spaced around the circle.

  If you join all the points you will get a geometric shape that is a regular polygon.

  For example, $n = 3$ (equilateral $\triangle$), $n = 4$ (square)

  $\qquad \qquad n = 5$ (regular pentagon) etc.

  $\qquad \qquad n = 6$ (regular hexagon)

E | THE nth ROOTS OF UNITY

The 'n**th roots of unity**' are the solutions of $z^n = 1$.

Example 22

Find the three cube roots of unity and display them on an Argand diagram. If w is the root with smallest positive argument, show that the roots are 1, w and w^2 and that $1 + w + w^2 = 0$.

The cube roots of unity are the solutions of $z^3 = 1$.

But $1 = \text{cis } 0 = \text{cis}(0 + k2\pi)$

$\therefore \quad z^3 = \text{cis }(k2\pi)$

$\therefore \quad z = [\text{cis}(k2\pi)]^{\frac{1}{3}}$ {De Moivre's theorem}

i.e., $z = \text{cis }\left(\frac{k2\pi}{3}\right)$

$\therefore \quad z = \text{cis } 0, \ \text{cis }\left(\frac{2\pi}{3}\right), \ \text{cis }\left(\frac{4\pi}{3}\right)$ {letting $k = 0, 1, 2$}

$\therefore \quad z = 1, \ -\frac{1}{2} + \frac{\sqrt{3}}{2}i, \ -\frac{1}{2} - \frac{\sqrt{3}}{2}i$

$w = \text{cis }\left(\frac{2\pi}{3}\right) \quad \text{and} \quad w^2 = [\text{cis }\left(\frac{2\pi}{3}\right)]^2 = \text{cis }\left(\frac{4\pi}{3}\right)$

$\therefore$ the roots are 1, w and w^2 where $w = \text{cis }\left(\frac{2\pi}{3}\right)$

and $1 + w + w^2 = 1 + \left(-\frac{1}{2} + \frac{\sqrt{3}}{2}i\right) + \left(-\frac{1}{2} - \frac{\sqrt{3}}{2}i\right) = 0$

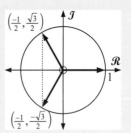

EXERCISE 16E

1 In **Example 22** we showed that the cube roots of 1 are 1, w, w^2 where $w = \text{cis }\left(\frac{2\pi}{3}\right)$.

  a Use this fact to solve the following equations, giving your answers in terms of w:

    i $(z + 3)^3 = 1$ **ii** $(z - 1)^3 = 8$ **iii** $(2z - 1)^3 = -1$

2 Show by vector addition that $1 + w + w^2 = 0$ if 1, w and w^2 are the cube roots of unity.

3 In **Example 20** we showed that the four fourth roots of unity were 1, i, -1, $-i$.

  a Is it true that the four fourth roots of unity can be written in the form 1, w, w^2, w^3 where $w = \text{cis }\frac{\pi}{2}$?

  b Show that $1 + w + w^2 + w^3 = 0$.

  c Show by vector addition that **b** is true.

4 **a** Find the 5 fifth roots of unity and display them on an Argand diagram.

  b If w is the root with smallest positive argument show that the roots are 1, w, w^2, w^3 and w^4.

  c Simplify $(1 + w + w^2 + w^3 + w^4)(1 - w)$ and hence show that $1 + w + w^2 + w^3 + w^4$ must be zero.

  d Show by vector addition that $1 + w + w^2 + w^3 + w^4 = 0$.

5 If w is the nth root of unity with the smallest positive argument, i.e., $w = \text{cis}\left(\frac{2\pi}{n}\right)$, show that:

    a   the n roots of $z^n = 1$ are $1, w, w^2, w^3, ..., w^n$

    b $1 + w + w^2 + w^3 + ... + w^{n-1} = 0$

    Note: The roots of unity lie on the unit circle, equally spaced around the unit circle. Why?

REVIEW SET 16A

1   Find the real and imaginary parts of $(i - \sqrt{3})^5$.

2   If $z = x + yi$ and $P(x, y)$ moves in the complex plane, find the cartesian equation for: **a** $|z - i| = |z + 1 + i|$ **b** $z^* + iz = 0$

3   Find $|z|$ if z is a complex number and $|z + 16| = 4|z + 1|$.

4   Points A and B are the representations in the complex plane of the numbers $z = 2 - 2i$ and $w = -1 - \sqrt{3}i$ respectively.

    a   Given that the origin is O, find the angle AOB in radians, expressing your answer in terms of π.

    b   Calculate the argument of zw in radians, again expressing your answer in terms of π.

5   Write in polar form:

    a $-5i$ **b** $2 - 2i\sqrt{3}$ **c** $k - ki$ where $k < 0$

6   Given that $z = (1 + bi)^2$, where b is real and positive, find the exact value of b if $\arg z = \frac{\pi}{3}$.

7   **a**   Prove that $\text{cis}\,\theta \times \text{cis}\,\phi = \text{cis}\,(\theta + \phi)$.

    b   Write $(1 - i)z$ in polar form if $z = 2\sqrt{2}\,\text{cis}\,\alpha$, and hence find $\arg[(1 - i)z]$.

8 $z_1 \equiv \overrightarrow{OA}$ and $z_2 \equiv \overrightarrow{OB}$ represent two sides of a right angled isosceles triangle OAB.

    a   Determine the modulus and argument of $\dfrac{z_1^{\,2}}{z_2^{\,2}}$.

    b   Hence, deduce that $z_1^{\,2} + z_2^{\,2} = 0$.

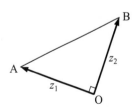

REVIEW SET 16B

1   Let $z_1 = \cos\frac{\pi}{6} + i\sin\frac{\pi}{6}$ and $z_2 = \cos\frac{\pi}{4} + i\sin\frac{\pi}{4}$.

    Express $\left(\dfrac{z_1}{z_2}\right)^3$ in the form $z = a + bi$.

2   If $z = 4 + i$ and $w = 2 - 3i$, find:

    a $2w^* - iz$ **b** $|w - z^*|$ **c** $|z^{10}|$ **d** $\arg(w - z)$

3 Find rationals a and b such that $\dfrac{2-3i}{2a+bi} = 3+2i$.

4 If $z = x + yi$ and P$(x,\ y)$ moves in the complex plane, find the Cartesian equation of the curve traced out by P if:

    a $\arg(z-i) = \frac{\pi}{2}$ **b** $\left|\dfrac{z+2}{z-2}\right| = 2$

5 Write $2 - 2\sqrt{3}i$ in polar form and hence find all values of n for which $(2-2\sqrt{3}i)^n$ is real.

6 Determine the cube roots of -27.

7 If $z = 4 \operatorname{cis} \theta$, find the modulus and argument of:

    a z^3 **b** $\dfrac{1}{z}$ **c** iz^*

8 If $z = \operatorname{cis} \phi$, prove that:

    a $|z| = 1$ **b** $z^* = \dfrac{1}{z}$ **c** $z^n - \dfrac{1}{z^n} = 2i \sin n\theta$

9 Prove the following:

    a $\arg(z^n) = n \arg z$ for all complex numbers z and rational n.

    b $\left(\dfrac{z}{w}\right)^* = \dfrac{z^*}{w^*}$ for all z and for all $w \neq 0$.

10 Find n given that each of the following can be written in the form $[\operatorname{cis} \theta]^n$:

    a $\cos 3\theta + i \sin 3\theta$ **b** $\dfrac{1}{\cos 2\theta + i \sin 2\theta}$ **c** $\cos \theta - i \sin \theta$

11 Determine the fifth roots of i.

12 If $z + \dfrac{1}{z}$ is real, prove that either $|z| = 1$ or z is real.

13 If w is the root of $z^5 = 1$ with smallest positive argument, find real quadratic equations with roots of:

    a w and w^4 **b** $w + w^4$ and $w^2 + w^3$.

14 If $|z + w| = |z - w|$ prove that $\arg z$ and $\arg w$ differ by $\frac{\pi}{2}$.

Chapter 17

Lines and planes in space

Contents:

INTRODUCTION

Suppose the vector $\begin{bmatrix} 1 \\ 0 \end{bmatrix}$ represents a displacement of 1 km due East and

$\begin{bmatrix} 0 \\ 1 \end{bmatrix}$ represents a displacement of 1 km due North.

The diagram shows the path of a yacht relative to a yacht club which is situated at $(0, 0)$. At 12:00 noon the yacht is at the point A(2, 20).

The yacht is travelling in the direction $\begin{bmatrix} 4 \\ -3 \end{bmatrix}$.

It has a constant speed of 5 km/h.

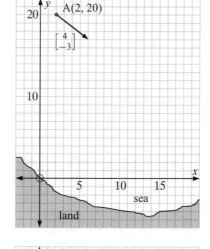

The following diagram shows the position of the yacht at 1:00 pm and 2:00 pm.

Since $\left| \begin{bmatrix} 4 \\ -3 \end{bmatrix} \right| = 5$ and the speed of the yacht is 5 km/h then $\begin{bmatrix} 4 \\ -3 \end{bmatrix}$ not only gives the direction of travel, but it also gives the distance travelled in one hour.

So, $\begin{bmatrix} 4 \\ -3 \end{bmatrix}$ is called the **velocity vector** of the yacht.

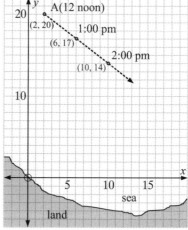

In order to define the position of the yacht at any time t hours after 12 noon, we can use the **parametric equations** $x = 2 + 4t$ and $y = 20 - 3t$ where t is called the **parameter**.

Note:
- If $t = 0$, $x = 2$ and $y = 20$, i.e., the yacht is at $(2, 20)$
  if $t = 1$, $x = 6$ and $y = 17$, i.e., the yacht is at $(6, 17)$
  if $t = 2$, $x = 10$ and $y = 14$, i.e., the yacht is at $(10, 14)$.
- t hours after 12 noon, the position is $(2 + 4t, 20 - 3t)$.
- $(2 + 4t, 20 - 3t)$ describes the position of the yacht at any time t hours.

The **cartesian equation** of the yacht's path can be found.

As $x = 2 + 4t$, $4t = x - 2$ and so $t = \dfrac{x - 2}{4}$

Substituting into the second equation, $y = 20 - 3t$ we get

$$y = 20 - 3\left(\frac{x - 2}{4}\right)$$

$$\therefore \quad 4y = 80 - 3(x - 2)$$
$$\text{i.e.,} \quad 4y = 80 - 3x + 6$$
$$\therefore \quad 3x + 4y = 86$$

The **vector equation** of the yacht's path can also be found.

Suppose the yacht is at R, t hours after 12:00 noon.

$$\text{Then} \quad \overrightarrow{OR} = \overrightarrow{OA} + \overrightarrow{AR}$$

$$\therefore \quad \mathbf{r} = \begin{bmatrix} 2 \\ 20 \end{bmatrix} + t \begin{bmatrix} 4 \\ -3 \end{bmatrix}$$

and if R is at (x, y), then

$$\begin{bmatrix} x \\ y \end{bmatrix} = \begin{bmatrix} 2 \\ 20 \end{bmatrix} + t \begin{bmatrix} 4 \\ -3 \end{bmatrix} \quad \text{and this is called the \textbf{vector equation} of the yacht's path.}$$

Note: The parametric equations are easily found from the vector equation,

i.e., if $\begin{bmatrix} x \\ y \end{bmatrix} = \begin{bmatrix} 2 \\ 20 \end{bmatrix} + t \begin{bmatrix} 4 \\ -3 \end{bmatrix}$ then $x = 2 + 4t$ and $y = 20 - 3t$.

Consequently, the coordinates of the yacht's position are expressed in terms of t, the time since 12:00 noon.

For example, at 3:00 pm, $t = 3$ and so $x = 14$ and $y = 11$,
i.e., the yacht is at (14, 11).

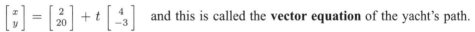

A   LINES IN A PLANE AND IN SPACE

In both 2-D and 3-D geometry a **fixed line** is determined when it has a **given direction** and passes through a **fixed point**.

So, if we know, or can find the direction of a line given by vector **b**, say, and if we know that the line passes through some given point A, then we can find the **equation of the line**. This applies in both 2-D and 3-D.

Suppose a line passes through a fixed point A (where $\overrightarrow{OA} = \mathbf{a}$) and has direction given by vector **b** (i.e., is parallel to **b**).

Let any point R move on the line so that $\overrightarrow{OR} = \mathbf{r}$.

$$\text{Then} \quad \overrightarrow{OR} = \overrightarrow{OA} + \overrightarrow{AR}$$

$$\therefore \quad \mathbf{r} = \mathbf{a} + t\mathbf{b} \quad \{\overrightarrow{AR} \parallel \mathbf{b}, \text{ so } \overrightarrow{AR} = t\mathbf{b}, \ t \in \mathcal{R}\}$$

a and **r** are the position vectors of A and R respectively.

So $\quad \mathbf{r} = \mathbf{a} + t\mathbf{b}, \quad t \in \mathcal{R}$ is the **vector equation** of the line.

In **2-D**, this means:

- $\begin{bmatrix} x \\ y \end{bmatrix} = \begin{bmatrix} a_1 \\ a_2 \end{bmatrix} + t \begin{bmatrix} b_1 \\ b_2 \end{bmatrix}$ is the **vector equation** of the line

  where   R(x, y) is any point on the line

  A(a_1, a_2) is the known (fixed) point on the line

  $\mathbf{b} = \begin{bmatrix} b_1 \\ b_2 \end{bmatrix}$ is the **direction vector** of the line.

Note: $\mathbf{b} = \begin{bmatrix} b_1 \\ b_2 \end{bmatrix}$ also enables us to calculate the slope of the line, $m = \dfrac{b_2}{b_1} \left(\dfrac{\text{rise}}{\text{run}} \right)$

- $\left. \begin{array}{l} x = a_1 + b_1 t \\ y = a_2 + b_2 t \end{array} \right\}, \ t \in \mathcal{R},$ are the **parametric equations** of the line.

  t is called the **parameter**.

  With these equations each point on the line corresponds to exactly one value of t, so every point forms a one-to-one mapping with real numbers.

- We can convert these equations into Cartesian form by equating t values.

  That is $t = \dfrac{x - a_1}{b_1} = \dfrac{y - a_2}{b_2}.$ So, $b_2 x - b_1 y = b_2 a_1 - b_1 a_2$ is

  the **Cartesian equation** of the line.

Example 1

Find **a** the vector   **b** the parametric   **c** the Cartesian   equation
of the line passing through the point (1, 5) with direction $\begin{bmatrix} 3 \\ 2 \end{bmatrix}$.

a $\mathbf{a} = \overrightarrow{OA} = \begin{bmatrix} 1 \\ 5 \end{bmatrix}$ and $\mathbf{b} = \begin{bmatrix} 3 \\ 2 \end{bmatrix}$

But $\mathbf{r} = \mathbf{a} + t\mathbf{b}$

$\therefore \ \begin{bmatrix} x \\ y \end{bmatrix} = \begin{bmatrix} 1 \\ 5 \end{bmatrix} + t \begin{bmatrix} 3 \\ 2 \end{bmatrix}, \ \ t \in \mathcal{R}$

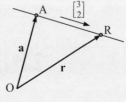

b   From **a**, $x = 1 + 3t$ and $y = 5 + 2t, \ \ t \in \mathcal{R}$

c   The Cartesian equation is $\dfrac{x - 1}{3} = \dfrac{y - 5}{2} \ \ (= t)$

$2x - 2 = 3y - 15$

$2x - 3y = -13$ {general form}

EXERCISE 17A.1

1 Find **i** the vector equation   **ii** the parametric equations of the lines:

  a passing through (3, -4) and in the direction $\begin{bmatrix} 1 \\ 4 \end{bmatrix}$

  b passing through (5, 2) and in the direction $\begin{bmatrix} -8 \\ 2 \end{bmatrix}$

  c cutting the x-axis at -6 and travelling in the direction $3\mathbf{i} + 7\mathbf{j}$

  d travelling in the direction $-2\mathbf{i} + \mathbf{j}$ and passing through (-1, 11)

2 Find the parametric equations of the line passing through $(-1, 4)$ with direction vector $\begin{bmatrix} 2 \\ -1 \end{bmatrix}$ and parameter λ. Find the points on the line when $\lambda = 0, 1, 3, -1, -4$.

3 **a** Does $(3, -2)$ lie on the line with parametric equations $x = t + 2$, $y = 1 - 3t$? Does $(0, 6)$ lie on this line?

    b $(k, 4)$ lies on the line with parametric equations $x = 1 - 2t$, $y = 1 + t$. Find k.

Example 2

A particle at $P(x(t), y(t))$ moves such that $x(t) = 2 - 3t$ and $y(t) = 2t + 4$, $t \geqslant 0$, t is in seconds. Distance units are metres.

a Find the initial position of P.

b Illustrate the motion showing points where $t = 0, 1, 2$ and 3.

c Find the speed of P.

a $x(0) = 2$, $y(0) = 4$

$\therefore$ the initial position of P is $(2, 4)$

b $x(1) = -1$, $y(1) = 6$

$x(2) = -4$, $y(2) = 8$

$x(3) = -7$, $y(3) = 10$

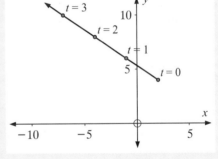

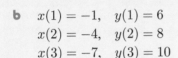

c Every second P moves with x-step -3 and y-step 2 a distance of $\sqrt{13}$ m.

$\therefore$ the speed is constant and is $\sqrt{13}$ m/s.

---

4 A particle at $P(x(t), y(t))$ moves such that $x(t) = 1 + 2t$ and $y(t) = 2 - 5t$, $t \geqslant 0$, t in seconds. Distance units are centimetres.

    a Find the initial position of P.

    b Illustrate the initial part of the motion of P where $t = 0, 1, 2, 3$.

    c Find the speed of P.

In 3-D:

- $\begin{bmatrix} x \\ y \\ z \end{bmatrix} = \begin{bmatrix} a_1 \\ a_2 \\ a_3 \end{bmatrix} + \lambda \begin{bmatrix} b_1 \\ b_2 \\ b_3 \end{bmatrix}$ is the **vector equation** of the line

    where $R(x, y, z)$ is any point on the line

                 $A(a_1, a_2, a_3)$ is the known (fixed) point on the line

                 $\mathbf{b} = \begin{bmatrix} b_1 \\ b_2 \\ b_3 \end{bmatrix}$ is the **direction vector** of the line.

- $\left. \begin{array}{l} x = a_1 + \lambda b_1 \\ y = a_2 + \lambda b_2 \\ z = a_3 + \lambda b_3 \end{array} \right\}$ are the **parametric equations** of the line.

   $\lambda \in \mathcal{R}$ is called the **parameter**.

Every point on the line corresponds to exactly one value of λ
i.e., λ values map one-to-one on the real numbers.

- $\dfrac{x - a_1}{b_1} = \dfrac{y - a_2}{b_2} = \dfrac{z - a_3}{b_3}$ $(= \lambda)$ are the **Cartesian equations** of the line.

   Note: In 3-D we do not have a gradient (or slope).

Example 3

Find the vector equation and the parametric equations of the line through
$(1, -2, 3)$ in the direction $4\mathbf{i} + 5\mathbf{j} - 6\mathbf{k}$.

The vector equation is $\begin{bmatrix} x \\ y \\ z \end{bmatrix} = \begin{bmatrix} 1 \\ -2 \\ 3 \end{bmatrix} + \lambda \begin{bmatrix} 4 \\ 5 \\ -6 \end{bmatrix}$, $\lambda \in \mathcal{R}$.

The parametric equations are: $x = 1 + 4\lambda$, $y = -2 + 5\lambda$, $z = 3 - 6\lambda$, λ in $\mathcal{R}$.

EXERCISE 17A.2

1 Find the vector equation of the line:

   a parallel to $\begin{bmatrix} 2 \\ 1 \\ 3 \end{bmatrix}$ and through the point $(1, 3, -7)$

   b through $(0, 1, 2)$ and with direction vector $\mathbf{i} + \mathbf{j} - 2\mathbf{k}$

   c parallel to the X-axis and through the point $(-2, 2, 1)$.

2 Find the parametric equations of the line:

   a parallel to $\begin{bmatrix} -1 \\ 2 \\ 6 \end{bmatrix}$ and through the point $(5, 2, -1)$

   b parallel to $2\mathbf{i} - \mathbf{j} + 3\mathbf{k}$ and through the point $(0, 2, -1)$

   c perpendicular to the XOY plane and through $(3, 2, -1)$.

Example 4

Find the parametric equations of the line through A$(2, -1, 4)$ and B$(-1, 0, 2)$.

We require a direction vector for the line $(\overrightarrow{AB}$ or $\overrightarrow{BA})$

$$\overrightarrow{AB} = \begin{bmatrix} -1 - 2 \\ 0 - -1 \\ 2 - 4 \end{bmatrix} = \begin{bmatrix} -3 \\ 1 \\ -2 \end{bmatrix}$$

Using the point A, the equations are: $x = 2 - 3\lambda$, $y = -1 + \lambda$, $z = 4 - 2\lambda$ (λ in $\mathcal{R}$)

[Using the point B, the equations are: $x = -1 - 3\mu$, $y = \mu$, $z = 2 - 2\mu$, (μ in $\mathcal{R}$)]

Note: Both sets of equations generate the same set of points and $\mu = \lambda - 1$.

3 Find the parametric equations of the line through:

    a A(1, 2, 1) and B(−1, 3, 2)   **b** C(0, 1, 3) and D(3, 1, −1)

    c E(1, 2, 5) and F(1, −1, 5)   **d** G(0, 1, −1) and H(5, −1, 3)

4 Find the coordinates of the point where the line with parametric equations
$x = 1 - \lambda$, $y = 3 + \lambda$ and $z = 3 - 2\lambda$ meets:

    a the XOY plane   **b** the YOZ plane   **c** the XOZ plane.

5 Find points on the line with parametric equations $x = 2 - \lambda$, $y = 3 + 2\lambda$ and
$z = 1 + \lambda$ which are $5\sqrt{3}$ units from the point $(1, 0, -2)$.

Example 5

Find the coordinates of the foot of the perpendicular from P(−1, 2, 3) to the line
with parametric equations $x = 1 + 2\lambda$, $y = -4 + 3\lambda$, $z = 3 + \lambda$.

A$(1 + 2t,\ -4 + 3t,\ 3 + t)$ is any point on the
given line.

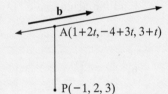

$$\overrightarrow{PA} = \begin{bmatrix} 1 + 2t - -1 \\ -4 + 3t - 2 \\ 3 + t - 3 \end{bmatrix} = \begin{bmatrix} 2 + 2t \\ -6 + 3t \\ t \end{bmatrix}$$

and $\mathbf{b} = \begin{bmatrix} 2 \\ 3 \\ 1 \end{bmatrix}$ is the direction vector of the line.

Now as $\overrightarrow{PA}$ and $\mathbf{b}$ are perpendicular, $\overrightarrow{PA} \bullet \mathbf{b} = 0$

$$\therefore \quad \begin{bmatrix} 2 + 2t \\ -6 + 3t \\ t \end{bmatrix} \bullet \begin{bmatrix} 2 \\ 3 \\ 1 \end{bmatrix} = 0$$

$$\therefore \quad 2(2 + 2t) + 3(-6 + 3t) + 1(t) = 0$$

$$\therefore \quad 4 + 4t - 18 + 9t + t = 0$$

$$\therefore \quad 14t = 14$$

$$\therefore \quad t = 1$$

and substituting $t = 1$ into the parametric equations we obtain the foot of the
perpendicular $(3, -1, 4)$.

Note: As $t = 1$, $\overrightarrow{PA} = [4, -3, 1]$ and $|\overrightarrow{PA}| = \sqrt{16 + 9 + 1}$
$$= \sqrt{26} \text{ units}$$

$\therefore$ the shortest distance from P to the line is $\sqrt{26}$ units.

---

6 Find the coordinates of the foot of the perpendicular:

    a from $(1, 1, 2)$ to the line with equations $x = 1 + \lambda$, $y = 2 - \lambda$, $z = 3 + \lambda$

    b from $(2, 1, 3)$ to the line with vector equation $\begin{bmatrix} x \\ y \\ z \end{bmatrix} = \begin{bmatrix} 1 \\ 2 \\ 0 \end{bmatrix} + \mu \begin{bmatrix} 1 \\ -1 \\ 2 \end{bmatrix}$.

7 Find the distance from:

    a $(3, 0, -1)$ to the line with equations $x = 2 + 3t$, $y = -1 + 2t$, $z = 4 + t$

    b $(1, 1, 3)$ to the line with vector equation $\begin{bmatrix} x \\ y \\ z \end{bmatrix} = \begin{bmatrix} 1 \\ -1 \\ 2 \end{bmatrix} + t \begin{bmatrix} 2 \\ 3 \\ 1 \end{bmatrix}$.

THE ANGLE BETWEEN 2-LINES (2-D and 3-D)

Clearly the angle between two lines is the angle between the direction vectors of these two lines. Now lines do not have a specific direction like vectors (lines go both ways).

As the angle between two direction vectors may be obtuse and we are really only interested in the smaller angle between two lines, we calculate the angle between two lines as θ,

$$\text{where}\quad \cos\theta = \frac{|\mathbf{b}_1 \bullet \mathbf{b}_2|}{|\mathbf{b}_1|\,|\mathbf{b}_2|}\quad\text{and}$$

$\mathbf{b}_1$ and $\mathbf{b}_2$ are the direction vectors of the given lines l_1 and l_2 respectively.

Example 6

Find the acute angle between the lines l_1: $x = 2 - 3t$, $y = -1 + t$ and
l_2: $x = 1 + 2s$, $y = -4 + 3s$

$$\mathbf{b}_1 = \begin{bmatrix} -3 \\ 1 \end{bmatrix} \qquad \mathbf{b}_2 = \begin{bmatrix} 2 \\ 3 \end{bmatrix} \qquad \therefore \quad \cos\theta = \frac{|-6 + 3|}{\sqrt{10}\sqrt{13}} \doteqdot 0.2631$$

$$\text{and so}\quad \theta = 74.7^o \qquad (1.30 \text{ radians})$$

Example 7

Find the acute angle between the lines l_1: $x = 2 - 3\lambda$, $y = -1 + \lambda$, $t = 4 - 2\lambda$

$$\text{and } l_2:\quad \frac{1-x}{3} = y = \frac{2-z}{2}$$

$$\mathbf{b}_1 = \begin{bmatrix} -3 \\ 1 \\ -2 \end{bmatrix} \quad\text{and}\quad \mathbf{b}_2 = \begin{bmatrix} -3 \\ 1 \\ -2 \end{bmatrix} \qquad \therefore \quad \cos\theta = \frac{|9+1+4|}{\sqrt{14}\sqrt{14}} = 1 \quad\text{and so}\quad \theta = 0^o$$

In fact these lines are coincident, i.e., l_1 and l_2 are the same line.

EXERCISE 17A.3

1 Find the angle between the lines: l_1 passing through $(-6, 3)$ parallel to $\begin{bmatrix} 4 \\ -3 \end{bmatrix}$ and l_2 cutting the y-axis at $(0, 8)$ with direction $5\mathbf{i} + 4\mathbf{j}$

2 Find the angle between the lines: l_1: $x = -4 + 12t$, $y = 3 + 5t$ and
l_2: $x = 3s$, $y = -6 - 4s$

3 Show that the lines: $x = 2 + 5p$, $y = 19 - 2p$ and
$x = 3 + 4r$, $y = 7 + 10r$ are perpendicular.

4 Find the angle between the lines: $\dfrac{x-8}{3} = \dfrac{9-y}{16} = \dfrac{z-10}{7}$ and

$x = 15 + 3\mu$, $y = 29 + 8\mu$, $z = 5 - 5\mu$

B | APPLICATIONS OF A LINE IN A PLANE

THE VELOCITY VECTOR OF A MOVING OBJECT

In **Example 2**, the particle moves $\begin{bmatrix} -3 \\ 2 \end{bmatrix}$ every second.

Hence, $\begin{bmatrix} -3 \\ 2 \end{bmatrix}$ is called the **velocity vector** of the particle

and as $\left\| \begin{bmatrix} -3 \\ 2 \end{bmatrix} \right\| = \sqrt{(-3)^2 + 2^2} = \sqrt{13}$,

the **velocity** of the particle is $\sqrt{13}$ metres per second in the direction $\begin{bmatrix} -3 \\ 2 \end{bmatrix}$.

The **speed** of the particle is $\sqrt{13}$ metres per second.

In general, if $\begin{bmatrix} a \\ b \end{bmatrix}$ is the velocity vector of a moving object, then it is travelling

at a speed of $\left\| \begin{bmatrix} a \\ b \end{bmatrix} \right\| = \sqrt{a^2 + b^2}$ in the direction of $\begin{bmatrix} a \\ b \end{bmatrix}$.

Example 8

$\begin{bmatrix} x \\ y \end{bmatrix} = \begin{bmatrix} 7 \\ 5 \end{bmatrix} + t \begin{bmatrix} 6 \\ -8 \end{bmatrix}$ is the vector equation of the path of an object where $t \geqslant 0$,

t in seconds. Distance units are metres. Find the
a object's initial position. **b** velocity vector of the object. **c** object's speed.

a At $t = 0$, $\begin{bmatrix} x \\ y \end{bmatrix} = \begin{bmatrix} 7 \\ 5 \end{bmatrix}$ ∴ the object is at $(7, 5)$.

b The velocity vector is $\begin{bmatrix} 6 \\ -8 \end{bmatrix}$ because the object moves $\begin{bmatrix} 6 \\ -8 \end{bmatrix}$ every second.

c The speed is $\left\| \begin{bmatrix} 6 \\ -8 \end{bmatrix} \right\| = \sqrt{36 + 64} = \sqrt{100} = 10$ m/s.

EXERCISE 17B.1

1 Each of the following vector equations represents the path of a moving object. t is measured in seconds and $t \geqslant 0$. Distance units are metres. For the object find the:
  i initial position **ii** velocity vector **iii** speed.

  a $\begin{bmatrix} x \\ y \end{bmatrix} = \begin{bmatrix} -4 \\ 3 \end{bmatrix} + t \begin{bmatrix} 12 \\ 5 \end{bmatrix}$ **b** $\begin{bmatrix} x \\ y \end{bmatrix} = \begin{bmatrix} 0 \\ -6 \end{bmatrix} + t \begin{bmatrix} 3 \\ -4 \end{bmatrix}$ **c** $\begin{bmatrix} x \\ y \end{bmatrix} = \begin{bmatrix} -2 \\ -7 \end{bmatrix} + t \begin{bmatrix} -6 \\ -4 \end{bmatrix}$

2 Given the following parametric equations for the path of a moving object (where t is measured in hours, $t \geqslant 0$ and distance is in kilometres), find:
  i the velocity vector **ii** the speed of the object
  a $x = 5 + 8t$ and $y = -5 + 4t$ **b** $x = 6t$ and $y = 3 + 2t$
  c $x(t) = -12 + 7t$ and $y(t) = 15 + 24t$

Example 9

Find the velocity vector of a speed boat moving parallel to $\begin{bmatrix} -5 \\ 12 \end{bmatrix}$ with a speed of 65 km/h.

$\left\| \begin{bmatrix} -5 \\ 12 \end{bmatrix} \right\| = \sqrt{(-5)^2 + 12^2}$ The speed of the boat is $65 = 5 \times 13$ km/h

$= \sqrt{25 + 144}$

$= 13$ $\therefore$ the velocity vector is $5 \begin{bmatrix} -5 \\ 12 \end{bmatrix} = \begin{bmatrix} -25 \\ 60 \end{bmatrix}$.

Note: $\left\| \begin{bmatrix} -25 \\ 60 \end{bmatrix} \right\| = \sqrt{(-25)^2 + 60^2} = \sqrt{4225} = 65$

3 Find the velocity vector of a speed boat moving parallel to:

a $\begin{bmatrix} 4 \\ -3 \end{bmatrix}$ with a speed of 150 km/h   **b** $\begin{bmatrix} 24 \\ 7 \end{bmatrix}$ with a speed of 12.5 km/h

c $2\mathbf{i} + \mathbf{j}$ with a speed of 50 km/h   **d** $-3\mathbf{i} + 4\mathbf{j}$ with a speed of 100 km/h.

CONSTANT VELOCITY PROBLEMS

Suppose a body (or object) moves with constant velocity $\mathbf{b}$. If the body is initially at A (when time, $t = 0$) and at time t it is at R, then

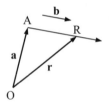

$$\overrightarrow{AR} = t\mathbf{b} \qquad \left\{ \text{time} \times \frac{\text{distance}}{\text{time}} = \text{distance} \right\}$$

Now $\mathbf{r} = \overrightarrow{OA} + \overrightarrow{AR}$

$\therefore$ $\mathbf{r} = \mathbf{a} + t\mathbf{b}$

Thus if a body has initial position vector $\mathbf{a}$, and moves with constant velocity $\mathbf{b}$, its position at time t is given by

$$\mathbf{r} = \mathbf{a} + t\mathbf{b} \quad \text{for} \quad t \geqslant 0.$$

Example 10

An object is initially at $(5, 10)$ and moves with velocity vector $3\mathbf{i} - \mathbf{j}$. Find:

a the position of the object at any time t (t in minutes)

b the position at $t = 3$ **c** the time when the object is due East of $(0, 0)$.

a

$\mathbf{r} = \mathbf{a} + t\mathbf{b}$

$\therefore$ $\begin{bmatrix} x \\ y \end{bmatrix} = \begin{bmatrix} 5 \\ 10 \end{bmatrix} + t \begin{bmatrix} 3 \\ -1 \end{bmatrix}$, $t \in \mathcal{R}$

$\therefore$ $\begin{bmatrix} x \\ y \end{bmatrix} = \begin{bmatrix} 5 + 3t \\ 10 - t \end{bmatrix}$

$\therefore$ P is at $(5 + 3t, 10 - t)$

b At $t = 3$, $5 + 3t = 14$ and $10 - t = 7$, $\therefore$ it is at $(14, 7)$.

c When the object is East of $(0, 0)$ y is zero,

$\therefore$ $10 - t = 0$

$\therefore$ $t = 10$ i.e., 10 minutes from the start.

EXERCISE 17B.2

1 A remote controlled toy car is initially at the point $(-3, -2)$ and moves with constant velocity $2\mathbf{i} + 4\mathbf{j}$. Distance units are centimetres and time is in seconds. Find:

    a the position vector of the car at any time, $t \geqslant 0$

    b the position of the car at $t = 2.5$

    c the time when the car is **i** due North **ii** due West of the observation point.

    d Plot the car's path at $t = 0, \frac{1}{2}, 1, 1\frac{1}{2}, 2, 2\frac{1}{2}, \dots$

2 For the following remote controlled toy cars, write vector equations for their positions in the form $\mathbf{r} = \mathbf{a} + t\mathbf{b}$ (**a** is the initial position vector, **b** is the velocity vector, **r** is the position vector at any time t sec, distances in cm):

    a the car is initially at $(8, -10)$ and travelling at 5 cm/s in the direction $\begin{bmatrix} 4 \\ -3 \end{bmatrix}$

    b the car is initially at $(-2, 6)$ and travelling at constant velocity reaches $(18, 21)$ in 10 seconds

    c the car is initially at $(-5, 0)$ and travelling parallel to the vector $2\mathbf{i} + \mathbf{j}$ at $\sqrt{5}$ cm/s

    d the car is travelling at 15 cm/s in the direction $3\mathbf{i} + 4\mathbf{j}$ and passing through the point $(1, -4)$ at the moment that $t = 1$ second.

3 Suppose $\begin{bmatrix} 1 \\ 0 \end{bmatrix}$ represents a 1 km displacement due East and $\begin{bmatrix} 0 \\ 1 \end{bmatrix}$ represents a 1 km displacement due North and

The point $(0, 0)$ is the position of the Port Del Ayvd.

The position vector $\mathbf{r}$ of a ship is given by $\mathbf{r} = \begin{bmatrix} -20 \\ 32 \end{bmatrix} + t \begin{bmatrix} 12 \\ -5 \end{bmatrix}$ where t is the time in hours since 6:00 am.

    a Find the distance between the ship and Port Del Ayvd at 6:00 am.

    b Find the speed of the ship.

    c Find the time when the ship will be due North of Port Del Ayvd.

4 Yacht A moves according to $x(t) = 4 + t$, $y(t) = 5 - 2t$ where the distance units are kilometres and the time units are hours. Yacht B moves according to $x(t) = 1 + 2t$, $y(t) = -8 + t$, $t \geqslant 0$.

    a Find the initial position of each yacht.   **b** Find the velocity vector of each yacht.

    c Show that the speed of each yacht is constant and state the speeds.

    d If they start at 6:00 am, find the time when the yachts are closest to each other.

    e Prove that the paths of the yachts are at right angles to each other.

5 Submarine P is at $(-5, 4)$ and fires a torpedo with velocity vector $\begin{bmatrix} 3 \\ -1 \end{bmatrix}$ at 1.34 pm.

Submarine Q is at $(15, 7)$ and a minutes later can fire a torpedo only in the direction $\begin{bmatrix} -4 \\ -3 \end{bmatrix}$. Distance units are kilometres and time units are minutes.

    a Show that the position of P's torpedo can be written as $P(x_1(t), y_1(t))$ where $x_1(t) = -5 + 3t$ and $y_1(t) = 4 - t$.

    b What is the speed of P's torpedo?

    c Show that the position of Q's torpedo can be written in the form $x_2(t) = 15 - 4(t - a)$, $y_2(t) = 7 - 3(t - a)$.

    d Q's torpedo is successful in knocking out P's torpedo. At what time did Q fire its torpedo and at what time did the explosion occur?

INVESTIGATION   THE TWO YACHTS PROBLEM

Yacht A has initial position $(-10, 4)$

and has velocity vector $\begin{bmatrix} 2 \\ -1 \end{bmatrix}$.

Yacht B has initial position $(3, -13)$

and has velocity vector $\begin{bmatrix} -1 \\ 3 \end{bmatrix}$.

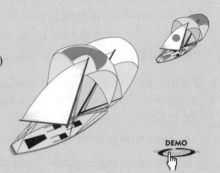

DEMO

In this investigation you will plot the path
of each yacht and determine the time when
they are nearest, and the shortest distance
they are apart.

What to do:

1   Explain why the position of each yacht at time t is given by

$$\mathbf{r}_A = \begin{bmatrix} -10 \\ 4 \end{bmatrix} + t \begin{bmatrix} 2 \\ -1 \end{bmatrix} \quad \text{and} \quad \mathbf{r}_B = \begin{bmatrix} 3 \\ -13 \end{bmatrix} + t \begin{bmatrix} -1 \\ 3 \end{bmatrix}.$$

2   On squared paper plot the path of the yachts when $t = 0, 1, 2, 3, 4, 5, \ldots$

3   Find the position vector of B relative to A, i.e., $\overrightarrow{AB}$.

4   Use **3** to show that if d is the distance between the yachts at any time t then
$d^2 = 25t^2 - 214t + 458$.

5   Show that d^2 is a minimum when $t = 4.28$.

6   Hence, find the time when d is a minimum and then find the shortest distance.

7   Investigate other situations with different initial positions and velocity vectors.
    You should be able to create a situation where the yachts will collide.

THE CLOSEST DISTANCE

A ship sails through point A in the direction **b**
past a port P. At that time will the ship R be
closest to the port?

This occurs when PR is perpendicular to AR,

i.e., $\overrightarrow{PR} \bullet \mathbf{b} = 0$.   {the scalar product is zero}

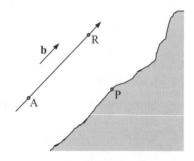

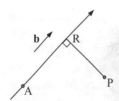

Example 11

If distances are measured in kilometres and a ship R is initially moving in the direction $\begin{bmatrix} 3 \\ 4 \end{bmatrix}$ at a speed of 10 km/h, find:

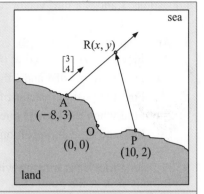

a an expression for the position of the ship in terms of t where t is the number of hours after leaving port A

b the time when it is closest to port P (10, 2).

a $\left| \begin{bmatrix} 3 \\ 4 \end{bmatrix} \right| = \sqrt{3^2 + 4^2} = 5$ and since the speed is 10 km/h, the ship's

velocity vector is $2 \begin{bmatrix} 3 \\ 4 \end{bmatrix} = \begin{bmatrix} 6 \\ 8 \end{bmatrix}$.

Relative to O(0, 0), $\overrightarrow{OR} = \overrightarrow{OA} + \overrightarrow{AR}$

$$\therefore \quad \begin{bmatrix} x \\ y \end{bmatrix} = \begin{bmatrix} -8 \\ 3 \end{bmatrix} + t \begin{bmatrix} 6 \\ 8 \end{bmatrix}$$

$\therefore$ R is at $(-8 + 6t, \, 3 + 8t)$

b The ship is closest to P when $\overrightarrow{PR} \perp \begin{bmatrix} 3 \\ 4 \end{bmatrix}$ $\therefore$ $\overrightarrow{PR} \bullet \begin{bmatrix} 3 \\ 4 \end{bmatrix} = 0$

$$\therefore \quad \begin{bmatrix} -8 + 6t - 10 \\ 3 + 8t - 2 \end{bmatrix} \bullet \begin{bmatrix} 3 \\ 4 \end{bmatrix} = 0$$

i.e., $3(6t - 18) + 4(1 + 8t) = 0$

i.e., $18t - 54 + 4 + 32t = 0$

i.e., $50t - 50 = 0$

i.e.,   1 hour after leaving A.   i.e., $t = 1$

EXERCISE 17B.3

1 Suppose **i** represents a displacement of 1 metre East and **j** represents a displacement of 1 m North. Time t, is measured in seconds.

A body has initial position $(-3, \, -2)$ and moves in a straight line with constant velocity $2\mathbf{i} + 4\mathbf{j}$. Find:

a the body's position at any time t, $t \geqslant 0$

b the times when it is   **i**   due East and   **ii**   due North of the origin

c the coordinates of the axes intercepts.

2 An object moves in a straight line with constant velocity vector $-\mathbf{i} - 3\mathbf{j}$. Unit vectors **i** and **j** represent a displacement of 1 metre. Time t is measured in seconds. Initially the object is at $(-2, \, 1)$. Find:

a the object's position at time t, $t \geqslant 0$

b the time when the object crosses the x-axis

c the coordinate where the object crosses the x-axis.

In questions **3** and **4** a unit vector represents a displacement of 1 km. Time t is in hours.

3 An ocean liner is at $(6, -6)$, cruising at 10 km/h in the direction $\begin{bmatrix} -3 \\ 4 \end{bmatrix}$.
A fishing boat is anchored at $(0, 0)$.

   a Find in terms of **i** and **j** the velocity vector of the liner.

   b Find the position vector of the liner at time t hours after it has sailed from $(6, -6)$.

   c Find when the liner is due East of the fishing boat.

   d Find the time and position of the liner when it is nearest to the fishing boat.

4 A fishing trawler is moving with constant speed of $3\sqrt{2}$ km/h in the direction $\begin{bmatrix} 1 \\ 1 \end{bmatrix}$.
Initially it is at the point $(-8, -5)$.

  A lighthouse L on an island is at point $(0, 0)$.

   a Find in terms of **i** and **j**:

     i the initial position vector of the trawler

     ii the direction vector of the trawler

     iii the position vector of the trawler at any time t hours $(t \geqslant 0)$.

   b Find the time at which the trawler is closest to the island.

   c Find whether the trawler will be breaking the law, given that it is not allowed within 4 km of the island.

5 Let $\begin{bmatrix} 1 \\ 0 \end{bmatrix}$ represent a 1 km due East displacement

and $\begin{bmatrix} 0 \\ 1 \end{bmatrix}$ represent a 1 km due North displacement.

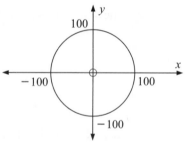

The control tower of an airport is at $(0, 0)$. Aircraft within 100 km of $(0, 0)$ will become visible on the radar screen at the control tower. At 12:00 noon an aircraft is at A which is 200 km East and 100 km North of the control tower.

It is flying parallel to the vector $\mathbf{b} = \begin{bmatrix} -3 \\ -1 \end{bmatrix}$ with a speed of $40\sqrt{10}$ km/h.

   a Write down the velocity vector of the aircraft.

   b Write a vector equation for the path of the aircraft (using t to represent the time in hours that have elapsed since 12:00 noon).

   c Find the position of the aircraft at 1:00 pm.

   d Show that at 1:00 pm the aircraft first becomes visible on the radar screen.

   e Find the time when the aircraft will be closest to the control tower and find the distance between the aircraft and the control tower at this time.

   f At what time will the aircraft disappear from the radar screen?

6 The diagram shows a railway track that has equation $2x + 3y = 36$.

The axes represent two long country roads. All distances are in kilometres.

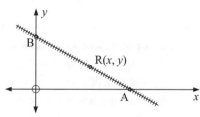

   a Find the coordinates of A and B.

   b $R(x, y)$ is any point on the railway track.
     Express the coordinates of point R in terms of x only.

   c Some railway workers have set up a base camp at P(4, 0). Find $\overrightarrow{PR}$ and $\overrightarrow{AB}$.

   d Hence, find the coordinates of the point on the railway track that would be closest to P. Find this distance.

7 Point $P(x(t),\ y(t))$ moves such that $x(t) = 10 + at$ and $y(t) = 12 - 3t$, $t \geqslant 0$ where t is the time in seconds and distance units are centimetres.

   a Find the initial position of P.

   b The speed of P is constant at 13 cm/s. Find a.

   c In the case where $a < 0$, plot the motion of P over the first 4 seconds.

8 Boat A's position is given by $x(t) = 3 - t$, $y(t) = 2t - 4$ where the distance units are kilometres and the time units are hours. Boat B's position is given by $x(t) = 4 - 3t$, $y(t) = 3 - 2t$.

   a Find the initial position of each boat.

   b Find the velocity vector of each boat.

   c What is the angle between the paths of the boats?

   d At what time are the boats closest to each other?

GEOMETRIC APPLICATIONS OF $\mathbf{r} = \mathbf{a} + t\mathbf{b}$

Vector equations of two intersecting lines can be **solved simultaneously** to find the point where the lines meet.

Example 12

Line 1 has vector equation $\begin{bmatrix} x \\ y \end{bmatrix} = \begin{bmatrix} -2 \\ 1 \end{bmatrix} + s \begin{bmatrix} 3 \\ 2 \end{bmatrix}$ and

line 2 has vector equation $\begin{bmatrix} x \\ y \end{bmatrix} = \begin{bmatrix} 15 \\ 5 \end{bmatrix} + t \begin{bmatrix} -4 \\ 1 \end{bmatrix}$, s and t are scalars.

The two lines meet at E. Use vector methods to find the coordinates of E.

The lines meet where $\begin{bmatrix} -2 \\ 1 \end{bmatrix} + s \begin{bmatrix} 3 \\ 2 \end{bmatrix} = \begin{bmatrix} 15 \\ 5 \end{bmatrix} + t \begin{bmatrix} -4 \\ 1 \end{bmatrix}$

$\therefore \quad -2 + 3s = 15 - 4t \qquad$ and $\quad 1 + 2s = 5 + t$

$\therefore \quad 3s + 4t = 17 \ \ ...... \ (1) \qquad$ and $\quad 2s - t = 4 \ \ ...... \ (2)$

$\qquad 3s + 4t = 17$

$\qquad 8s - 4t = 16 \qquad\qquad$ {when (2) is multiplied by 4}

$\overline{}$

$\therefore \quad 11s \qquad = 33$

So, $s = 3$ and in (2) $\quad 2(3) - t = 4$, i.e., $t = 2$

Thus, using line 1, $\quad \begin{bmatrix} x \\ y \end{bmatrix} = \begin{bmatrix} -2 \\ 1 \end{bmatrix} + 3 \begin{bmatrix} 3 \\ 2 \end{bmatrix} = \begin{bmatrix} 7 \\ 7 \end{bmatrix}$

Checking in line 2, $\quad \begin{bmatrix} x \\ y \end{bmatrix} = \begin{bmatrix} 15 \\ 5 \end{bmatrix} + 2 \begin{bmatrix} -4 \\ 1 \end{bmatrix} = \begin{bmatrix} 7 \\ 7 \end{bmatrix} \qquad \therefore$ they meet at (7, 7)

Is this the best way to find the point of intersection of the two lines?

EXERCISE 17B.4

1 The triangle formed by the three lines is ABC.

Line 1 (AB) is $\begin{bmatrix} x \\ y \end{bmatrix} = \begin{bmatrix} -1 \\ 6 \end{bmatrix} + r \begin{bmatrix} 3 \\ -2 \end{bmatrix}$,   line 2 (AC) is $\begin{bmatrix} x \\ y \end{bmatrix} = \begin{bmatrix} 0 \\ 2 \end{bmatrix} + s \begin{bmatrix} 1 \\ 1 \end{bmatrix}$ and

line 3 (BC) is $\begin{bmatrix} x \\ y \end{bmatrix} = \begin{bmatrix} 10 \\ -3 \end{bmatrix} + t \begin{bmatrix} -2 \\ 3 \end{bmatrix}$ where r, s and t are scalars.

   a   Accurately, on a grid, draw the three lines.
   b   Hence, find the coordinates of A, B and C.   **c**   Prove that $\triangle$ABC is isosceles.
   d   Use vector methods to *check* your answers to **b**.

2 A parallelogram is defined by four lines with equations:

Line 1 (AB) is $\begin{bmatrix} x \\ y \end{bmatrix} = \begin{bmatrix} -4 \\ 6 \end{bmatrix} + r \begin{bmatrix} 7 \\ 3 \end{bmatrix}$,   line 2 (AD) is $\begin{bmatrix} x \\ y \end{bmatrix} = \begin{bmatrix} -4 \\ 6 \end{bmatrix} + s \begin{bmatrix} 1 \\ 2 \end{bmatrix}$,

line 3 (CD) is $\begin{bmatrix} x \\ y \end{bmatrix} = \begin{bmatrix} 22 \\ 25 \end{bmatrix} + t \begin{bmatrix} -7 \\ -3 \end{bmatrix}$,   line 4 (CB) is $\begin{bmatrix} x \\ y \end{bmatrix} = \begin{bmatrix} 22 \\ 25 \end{bmatrix} + u \begin{bmatrix} -1 \\ -2 \end{bmatrix}$,

where r, s, t and u are scalars.

Lines 1 and 2 intersect at point A$(-4, 6)$,   lines 1 and 4 meet at B,   lines 3 and 4 meet at C   and   lines 2 and 3 meet at D.

   a   Draw an accurate sketch of the four lines and the parallelogram formed by them. Label the vertices.
   b   From your diagram find the coordinates of B, C and D.
   c   Use vector methods to confirm your answers to **b**.

3 An isosceles triangle ABC is formed by these lines:

Line 1 (AB) is $\begin{bmatrix} x \\ y \end{bmatrix} = \begin{bmatrix} 0 \\ 2 \end{bmatrix} + r \begin{bmatrix} 2 \\ 1 \end{bmatrix}$,   line 2 (BC) is $\begin{bmatrix} x \\ y \end{bmatrix} = \begin{bmatrix} 8 \\ 6 \end{bmatrix} + s \begin{bmatrix} -1 \\ -2 \end{bmatrix}$ and

line 3 (AC) is $\begin{bmatrix} x \\ y \end{bmatrix} = \begin{bmatrix} 0 \\ 5 \end{bmatrix} + t \begin{bmatrix} 1 \\ -1 \end{bmatrix}$ where r, s and t are scalars.

   a   Use vector methods to find the coordinates of A, B and C.
   b   Which two sides of the triangle are equal in length? Find their lengths.

4 Line QP has vector equation $\begin{bmatrix} x \\ y \end{bmatrix} = \begin{bmatrix} 3 \\ -1 \end{bmatrix} + r \begin{bmatrix} 14 \\ 10 \end{bmatrix}$. Line QR: $\begin{bmatrix} x \\ y \end{bmatrix} = \begin{bmatrix} 3 \\ -1 \end{bmatrix} + s \begin{bmatrix} 17 \\ -9 \end{bmatrix}$.

Line PR has vector equation $\begin{bmatrix} x \\ y \end{bmatrix} = \begin{bmatrix} 0 \\ 18 \end{bmatrix} + t \begin{bmatrix} 5 \\ -7 \end{bmatrix}$.

Triangle PQR is formed by these lines. r, s and t are scalars.

   a   Use vector methods to find the coordinates of P, Q and R.
   b   Find vectors $\overrightarrow{PQ}$ and $\overrightarrow{PR}$ and evaluate $\overrightarrow{PQ} \bullet \overrightarrow{PR}$.
   c   Hence, find the size of $\angle$QPR.   **d**   Find the area of $\triangle$PQR.

5 Quadrilateral ABCD is formed by these lines:

Line 1 (AB) is $\begin{bmatrix} x \\ y \end{bmatrix} = \begin{bmatrix} 2 \\ 5 \end{bmatrix} + r \begin{bmatrix} 4 \\ 1 \end{bmatrix}$,   line 2 (BC) is $\begin{bmatrix} x \\ y \end{bmatrix} = \begin{bmatrix} 18 \\ 9 \end{bmatrix} + s \begin{bmatrix} -8 \\ 32 \end{bmatrix}$,

line 3 (CD) is $\begin{bmatrix} x \\ y \end{bmatrix} = \begin{bmatrix} 14 \\ 25 \end{bmatrix} + t \begin{bmatrix} -8 \\ -2 \end{bmatrix}$ and   line 4 (AD) is $\begin{bmatrix} x \\ y \end{bmatrix} = \begin{bmatrix} 3 \\ 1 \end{bmatrix} + u \begin{bmatrix} -3 \\ 12 \end{bmatrix}$

where r, s, t and u are scalars.

Lines 1 and 2 meet at B, lines 2 and 3 at C, lines 3 and 4 at D, lines 1 and 4 at A(2, 5).

a Use vector methods to find the coordinates of B, C and D.

b Write down vectors $\overrightarrow{AC}$ and $\overrightarrow{DB}$ and hence find:

     i $|\overrightarrow{AC}|$ **ii** $|\overrightarrow{DB}|$ **iii** $\overrightarrow{AC} \bullet \overrightarrow{DB}$

c What do the answers to **b** tell you about quadrilateral ABCD?

C   RELATIONSHIP BETWEEN LINES

LINE CLASSIFICATION

In 2-D, lines are either:

- intersecting   (meet at a point, with a unique solution)

- parallel   (do not meet at all, i.e., no solution)

- coincident   (i.e., the same line, all points satisfy both equations)

In 3-D, lines are either

- intersecting, parallel or coincident (coplanar, i.e., in the same plane)
- skew lines (not coplanar and can only occur in 3-D.)

i.e.,   or

 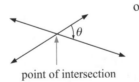 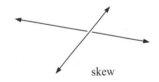

point of intersection   skew

> **Skew lines** are any lines which are neither parallel nor intersecting.

- If the lines are **parallel**, the angle between them is 0°.
- If the lines are **intersecting**, the angle between them is θ^o, as shown.
- If the lines are **skew**, there is still an angle that one line makes with the other and if we translate one line to intersect the other, the angle between the original lines is defined as the angle between the intersecting lines,

     i.e.,

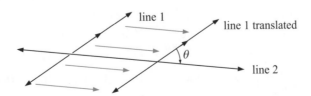

Example 13

Line 1 has equations $x = -1 + 2s$, $y = 1 - 2s$ and $z = 1 + 4s$.
Line 2 has equations $x = 1 - t$, $y = t$ and $z = 3 - 2t$.
Show that line 1 and line 2 are parallel.

Line 1 is $\begin{bmatrix} x \\ y \\ z \end{bmatrix} = \begin{bmatrix} -1 \\ 1 \\ 1 \end{bmatrix} + s \begin{bmatrix} 2 \\ -2 \\ 4 \end{bmatrix}$ with direction vector $\begin{bmatrix} 2 \\ -2 \\ 4 \end{bmatrix}$.

Likewise, line 2 has direction vector $\begin{bmatrix} -1 \\ 1 \\ -2 \end{bmatrix}$,

and as $\begin{bmatrix} 2 \\ -2 \\ 4 \end{bmatrix} = -2 \begin{bmatrix} -1 \\ 1 \\ -2 \end{bmatrix}$, then lines 1 and 2 are parallel.

{If $\mathbf{a} = k\mathbf{b}$ for some scalar k, then $\mathbf{a} \parallel \mathbf{b}$.}

Example 14

Line 1 has equations $x = -1 + 2s$, $y = 1 - 2s$ and $z = 1 + 4s$.
Line 2 has equations $x = 1 - t$, $y = t$ and $z = 3 - 2t$.
Line 3 has equations $x = 1 + 2u$, $y = -1 - u$, $z = 4 + 3u$.
a Show that line 2 and line 3 intersect and find the angle between them.
b Show that line 1 and line 3 are skew.

a   Equating x, y and z values in lines 2 and 3 gives

$$1 - t = 1 + 2u \qquad t = -1 - u \qquad \text{and} \qquad 3 - 2t = 4 + 3u$$
$$\therefore \quad t = -2u, \qquad \therefore \quad t = -1 - u, \qquad \text{and} \quad 3u + 2t = -1 \quad \dots \dots \text{(1)}$$

Solving these we get $\quad -2u = -1 - u \quad \therefore \quad -u = -1$
$$\therefore \quad u = 1 \quad \text{and so} \quad t = -2$$

Checking in (1) $\quad 3u + 2t = 3(1) + 2(-2) = 3 - 4 = -1 \quad \checkmark$

$\therefore \quad u = 1$, $t = -2$ satisfies all three equations, a *common solution*.

Using $u = 1$, they meet at $(1 + 2(1), -1 - (1), 4 + 3(1))$ i.e., $(3, -2, 7)$

The direction of line 2 could be defined by $\mathbf{a} = \begin{bmatrix} -1 \\ 1 \\ -2 \end{bmatrix}$.

The direction of line 3 could be defined by $\mathbf{b} = \begin{bmatrix} 2 \\ -1 \\ 3 \end{bmatrix}$.

Now $\mathbf{a} \bullet \mathbf{b} = |\mathbf{a}|\,|\mathbf{b}| \cos\theta$, where θ is the angle between $\mathbf{a}$ and $\mathbf{b}$

$$\therefore \quad -2 - 1 - 6 = \sqrt{1 + 1 + 4}\,\sqrt{4 + 1 + 9}\cos\theta$$
$$\therefore \quad -9 = \sqrt{6}\sqrt{14}\cos\theta$$
$$\therefore \quad \cos\theta = \frac{-9}{\sqrt{84}}$$

So, $\theta \doteqdot 169.11^o$ i.e., 169° (to 3 s.f.)

b   Equating x, y and z values in lines 1 and 3 gives

$$-1 + 2s = 1 + 2u \qquad 1 - 2s = -1 - u \quad \text{and} \quad 1 + 4s = 4 + 3u$$
$$\therefore \; 2s - 2u = 2, \qquad \therefore \; -2s + u = -2, \qquad \text{and} \quad 4s - 3u = 3 \; \; \ldots \; (1)$$

Solving these we get
$$2s - 2u = 2$$
$$\therefore \; \frac{-2s + u = -2}{}$$
$$\therefore \; -u = 0 \qquad \{\text{adding them}\}$$
$$\therefore \quad u = 0 \quad \text{and so} \quad 2s = 2 \quad \text{i.e.,} \quad s = 1$$

Checking in (1), $4s - 3u = 4(1) - 3(0) = 4 \neq 3$

So, there is no simultaneous solution to all 3 equations.

$\therefore$ the lines cannot meet, and as they are not parallel they must be skew.

Note: Even though lines 1 and 3 in **Example 14** were skew we could still find the angle one makes with the other using the same method as in **b**.

PERPENDICULAR AND PARALLEL TESTS (FOR 2-D AND 3-D)

Non-zero vectors $\mathbf{v}$ and $\mathbf{w}$ are
- perpendicular if $\mathbf{v} \bullet \mathbf{w} = 0$
- parallel if $\mathbf{v} \bullet \mathbf{w} = \pm |\mathbf{v}| \, |\mathbf{w}|$

Proof: If perpendicular, $\theta = 90°$

then $\mathbf{v} \bullet \mathbf{w} = |\mathbf{v}| \, |\mathbf{w}| \cos 90°$
$$= |\mathbf{v}| \, |\mathbf{w}| \, 0$$
$$= 0$$

If parallel, $\theta = 0°$ or $180°$

where $\cos \theta = 1$ or -1
$$\therefore \quad \mathbf{v} \bullet \mathbf{w} = |\mathbf{v}| \, |\mathbf{w}| \times \pm 1$$
$$\text{i.e.,} \quad \mathbf{v} \bullet \mathbf{w} = \pm |\mathbf{v}| \, |\mathbf{w}|$$

EXERCISE 17C

1   Classify the following line pairs as either parallel, intersecting or skew and in each case find the measure of the acute angle between them:

a $x = 1 + 2t$, $y = 2 - t$, $z = 3 + t$ and $x = -2 + 3s$, $y = 3 - s$, $z = 1 + 2s$

b $x = -1 + 2\lambda$, $y = 2 - 12\lambda$, $z = 4 + 12\lambda$
and $x = 4\mu - 3$, $y = 3\mu + 2$, $z = -\mu - 1$

c $x = 6t$, $y = 3 + 8t$, $z = -1 + 2t$ and $x = 2 + 3s$, $y = 4s$, $z = 1 + s$

d $x = 2 - y = z + 2$ and $x = 1 + 3s$, $y = -2 - 2s$, $z = 2s + \frac{1}{2}$

e $x = 1 + \lambda$, $y = 2 - \lambda$, $z = 3 + 2\lambda$ and $x = 2 + 3\mu$, $y = 3 - 2\mu$, $z = \mu - 5$

f $x = 1 - 2t$, $y = 8 + t$, $z = 5$ and $x = 2 + 4s$, $y = -1 - 2s$, $z = 3$

Example 15

Discuss the solutions to $\begin{cases} 3x - y = 2 \\ 6x - 2y = k \end{cases}$ $k \in \mathcal{R}$, giving a geometric interpretation.

In augmented matrix form $\begin{bmatrix} 3 & -1 & | & 2 \\ 6 & -2 & | & k \end{bmatrix} \sim \begin{bmatrix} 3 & -1 & | & 2 \\ 0 & 0 & | & k - 4 \end{bmatrix}$ $R_2 - 2R_1$

If $\underline{k - 4 = 0}$, the system is consistent, i.e., the lines $3x - y = 2$ and $6x - 2y = 4$ are coincident.

Let $x = t$, then $y = -2 + 3t$.

There are infinitely many solutions $x = t$, $y = -2 + 3t$, $t \in \mathcal{R}$.

This line has direction vector $\begin{bmatrix} 1 \\ 3 \end{bmatrix}$ or slope 3 and passes through the point $(0, -2)$.

If $k - 4 \neq 0$ i.e., $k \neq 4$ the system is inconsistent, i.e., the lines
$$3x - y = 2 \quad \text{and}$$
$$6x - 2y = 4 \quad \text{are parallel and have no points of intersection.}$$

2 Consider the two lines whose equations are $3x - y = 8$ and $6x - 2y = k$ where k is some real number. Discuss the nature of the intersection of these lines for different values of k.

3 Discuss for the different values of a, the geometric solutions of the equations
$$4x + 8y = 1 \qquad \text{In general, we need to discuss the cases for a unique solution,}$$
$$2x - ay = 11. \qquad \text{infinite solutions and no solutions.}$$

SHORTEST DISTANCE FROM A POINT TO A LINE (2-D AND 3-D)

The coordinates of any point P, on the line can be expressed in terms of one variable, the parameter t, say.

Hence we can find the vector $\overrightarrow{AP}$ in terms of t, where A is a point which is not on the line.

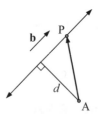

But the shortest distance d occurs when $\overrightarrow{AP}$ is perpendicular to **b**, so find t for which $\overrightarrow{AP} \bullet \mathbf{b} = 0$.

Hence find $|\overrightarrow{AP}|$ find this value of t and $\mathbf{d} = |\overrightarrow{AP}|$.

Example 16

Find the shortest distance from P$(-1, 2, 3)$ to the line $\dfrac{x - 1}{2} = \dfrac{y + 4}{3} = z - 3$.

The equation of the line in parametric form is $x = 1 + 2\lambda$, $y = -4 + 3\lambda$, $z = 3 + \lambda$

$\therefore$ any point A on this line has coordinates $(1 + 2\lambda, -4 + 3\lambda, 3 + \lambda)$

$\therefore$ $\overrightarrow{PA} = \begin{bmatrix} 2 + 2\lambda \\ -6 + 3\lambda \\ \lambda \end{bmatrix}$ and the direction vector of the line is $\mathbf{b} = \begin{bmatrix} 2 \\ 3 \\ 1 \end{bmatrix}$

Now for the shortest distance $\overrightarrow{PA} \bullet \mathbf{b} = 0$ {perpendicular distance}

$\therefore$ $4 + 4\lambda - 18 + 9\lambda + \lambda = 0$

$\therefore$ $14\lambda = 14$

$\therefore$ $\lambda = 1$

$\therefore$ $\overrightarrow{PA} = \begin{bmatrix} 4 \\ -3 \\ 1 \end{bmatrix}$

$\therefore$ $d = |\overrightarrow{PA}| = \sqrt{26}$ units

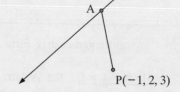

4 Find the distance from the point $(2, -3)$ to the line $3x - y = 4$.

5 Find the distance from the point $(3, 0, -1)$ to the line with equation
   $\mathbf{r} = 2\mathbf{i} - \mathbf{j} + 4\mathbf{k} + \lambda(3\mathbf{i} + 2\mathbf{j} + \mathbf{k})$.

6 Find the distance from $(1, 1, 3)$ to the line $\mathbf{r} = \begin{bmatrix} 1 \\ -1 \\ 2 \end{bmatrix} + \lambda \begin{bmatrix} 2 \\ 3 \\ 1 \end{bmatrix}$.

THE SHORTEST DISTANCE BETWEEN SKEW LINES (EXTENSION)

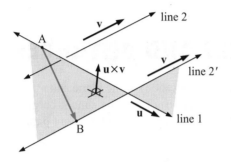

Suppose line 1 contains point A and has direction vector $\mathbf{u}$ and line 2 contains point B and has direction vector $\mathbf{v}$.

Line 2 is translated to line $2'$ so that line $2'$ and line 1 intersect.

$\mathbf{u} \times \mathbf{v}$ is a vector which is perpendicular to both $\mathbf{u}$ and $\mathbf{v}$ and line 2 is parallel to the shaded plane containing lines 1 and $2'$.

So, the shortest distance d is the length of the projection vector of $\overrightarrow{AB}$ on $\mathbf{u} \times \mathbf{v}$

i.e., $$d = \frac{|\, \overrightarrow{AB} \bullet (\mathbf{u} \times \mathbf{v})\,|}{|\,\mathbf{u} \times \mathbf{v}\,|}.$$

Example 17

Find the shortest distance between the skew lines $x = t$, $y = 1 - t$, $z = 2 + t$ and $x = 3 - s$, $y = -1 + 2s$, $z = 4 - s$.

line 1 contains A$(0, 1, 2)$ and has direction $\mathbf{u} = \begin{bmatrix} 1 \\ -1 \\ 1 \end{bmatrix}$

line 2 contains B$(3, -1, 4)$ and has direction $\mathbf{v} = \begin{bmatrix} -1 \\ 2 \\ -1 \end{bmatrix}$

So $\overrightarrow{AB} = \begin{bmatrix} 3 - 0 \\ -1 - 1 \\ 4 - 2 \end{bmatrix} = \begin{bmatrix} 3 \\ -2 \\ 2 \end{bmatrix}$

and $\mathbf{u} \times \mathbf{v} = \begin{vmatrix} -1 & 1 \\ 2 & -1 \end{vmatrix} \mathbf{i} + \begin{vmatrix} 1 & 1 \\ -1 & -1 \end{vmatrix} \mathbf{j} + \begin{vmatrix} 1 & -1 \\ -1 & 2 \end{vmatrix} \mathbf{k}$

$= -\mathbf{i} + \mathbf{k}$

Now $d = \dfrac{|\, \overrightarrow{AB} \bullet (\mathbf{u} \times \mathbf{v})\,|}{|\,\mathbf{u} \times \mathbf{v}\,|}$ i.e., d is the projection of $\overrightarrow{AB}$ on $\mathbf{u} \times \mathbf{v}$

$= \dfrac{|(3)(-1) + (-2)(0) + (2)(1)|}{\sqrt{(-1)^2 + 0^2 + 1^2}}$

$= \dfrac{|-1|}{\sqrt{2}}$

$= \tfrac{1}{\sqrt{2}}$ units

7 Find the shortest distance between the skew lines:

   a $\;x = 1 + 2t, \quad y = -t, \quad z = 2 + 3t \quad$ and $\quad x = y = z$

   b $\;x = 1 - t, \quad y = 1 + t, \quad z = 3 - t \quad$ and $\quad x = 2 + s, \quad y = 1 - 2s, \quad z = s$

8 Find the shortest distance between the lines given in question **1**, **Exercise 17C**.

   Note: •   To find the distance between parallel lines, find the distance from a point on one line to the other line.

          •   What is the shortest distance between intersecting/coincident lines?

D   PLANES AND DISTANCES

To find the equation of a plane, you require the direction (orientation) of the plane and a fixed (known) point on the plane. However, the direction (orientation) of a plane cannot be given by a single parallel vector because infinitely many planes of different orientation are parallel to a single direction vector.

Thus planes (which are 2-D) require **two** non-parallel vectors to define their orientation uniquely.

Any point R(x, y, z) on the plane with a known point A(a_1, a_2, a_3) and two non-parallel

vectors $\;\mathbf{b} = \begin{bmatrix} b_1 \\ b_2 \\ b_3 \end{bmatrix}\;$ and $\;\mathbf{c} = \begin{bmatrix} c_1 \\ c_2 \\ c_3 \end{bmatrix}\;$ must satisfy the vector equation

$$\overrightarrow{AR} = \lambda \mathbf{b} + \mu \mathbf{c} \quad \text{for some scalars } \lambda \text{ and } \mu.$$

i.e., $\quad \overrightarrow{OR} - \overrightarrow{OA} = \lambda \mathbf{b} + \mu \mathbf{c}$

$\therefore \quad \overrightarrow{OR} = \overrightarrow{OA} + \lambda \mathbf{b} + \mu \mathbf{c}$

i.e., $\qquad$ **$\mathbf{r} = \mathbf{a} + \lambda \mathbf{b} + \mu \mathbf{c}\;$ is the vector equation of the plane**

where $\quad \mathbf{r} = \begin{bmatrix} x \\ y \\ z \end{bmatrix}\;$ is the position vector of any point on the plane,

$\qquad \mathbf{a} = \begin{bmatrix} a_1 \\ a_2 \\ a_3 \end{bmatrix}\;$ is the position vector of the known point A(a_1, a_2, a_3) on the plane

and **b** and **c** are any two non-parallel vectors that are parallel to the plane.

Note: $\quad \lambda, \mu \in \mathcal{R}\;$ are two independent parameters for the plane (2-D).

Another way of defining the direction of a plane is to consider the vector (cross) product of the two parallel vectors **b** and **c** to the plane given above.

n is the **normal vector** to the plane where $\mathbf{n} = \mathbf{b} \times \mathbf{c}$.

n is perpendicular to **b** and **c** and consequently is perpendicular to any vector or line in the plane or parallel to the plane.

This is because any vector parallel to the plane can be written as $\lambda \mathbf{b} + \mu \mathbf{c}$.

Challenge: Show $\;\mathbf{n} \perp \lambda \mathbf{b} + \mu \mathbf{c}$.

Suppose a plane in space has normal vector $\mathbf{n} = \begin{bmatrix} a \\ b \\ c \end{bmatrix}$

and that it passes through the fixed point $A(x_1, y_1, z_1)$.

$R(x, y, z)$ moves anywhere in the plane.

Now $\overrightarrow{AR}$ is perpendicular to $\mathbf{n}$

$$\therefore \quad \mathbf{n} \bullet \overrightarrow{AR} = 0$$

$$\therefore \quad \begin{bmatrix} a \\ b \\ c \end{bmatrix} \bullet \begin{bmatrix} x - x_1 \\ y - y_1 \\ z - z_1 \end{bmatrix} = 0$$

$$\therefore \quad a(x - x_1) + b(y - y_1) + c(z - z_1) = 0$$

$$\therefore \quad ax + by + cz = ax_1 + by_1 + cz_1$$

Note:
- $\mathbf{n} \bullet \overrightarrow{AR} = 0$ is the **vector equation of the plane**. It could also be written as $\mathbf{n} \bullet (\mathbf{r} - \mathbf{a}) = 0$,   which implies $\mathbf{r} \bullet \mathbf{n} = \mathbf{a} \bullet \mathbf{n}$ Why?

- So,   if a plane has normal vector $\begin{bmatrix} a \\ b \\ c \end{bmatrix}$, and passes through (x_1, y_1, z_1)
  then it has equation
  $ax + by + cz = ax_1 + by_1 + cz_1 = d$,   say,   where d is a constant.

- $ax + by + cz = d$ is the **Cartesian equation of the plane** where $\mathbf{n} = \begin{bmatrix} a \\ b \\ c \end{bmatrix}$
  is a normal vector of the plane.

Example 18

Find the equation of the plane with normal vector $\begin{bmatrix} 1 \\ 2 \\ 3 \end{bmatrix}$ and containing $(-1, 2, 4)$.

Since $\mathbf{n} = \begin{bmatrix} 1 \\ 2 \\ 3 \end{bmatrix}$ and $(-1, 2, 4)$ lies on the plane, the equation is
$$x + 2y + 3z = (-1) + 2(2) + 3(4)$$
i.e., $x + 2y + 3z = 15$

EXERCISE 17D

1 Find the equation of the plane:

  a with normal vector $\begin{bmatrix} 2 \\ -1 \\ 3 \end{bmatrix}$ and through $(-1, 2, 4)$

  b perpendicular to the line through $A(2, 3, 1)$ and $B(5, 7, 2)$ and through A

  c perpendicular to the line connecting $A(1, 4, 2)$ and $B(4, 1, -4)$ and containing P such that $AP : PB = 1 : 2$

  d containing $A(3, 2, 1)$ and the line $x = 1 + t, \; y = 2 - t, \; z = 3 + 2t$.

2 State the normal vector to the plane with equation:

  a $2x + 3y - z = 8$ **b** $3x - y = 11$ **c** $z = 2$ **d** $x = 0$

3 Find the equation of the:

  a XOZ-plane   **b** plane perpendicular to the Z-axis and through $(2, -1, 4)$.

Example 19

Find the equation of the plane through A$(-1, 2, 0)$, B$(3, 1, 1)$ and C$(1, 0, 3)$:

a   in vector form   **b**   in normal form

a $\overrightarrow{AB} = \begin{bmatrix} 4 \\ -1 \\ 1 \end{bmatrix}$ and $\overrightarrow{BC} = \begin{bmatrix} -2 \\ -1 \\ 2 \end{bmatrix}$, choose $\overrightarrow{CB} = \begin{bmatrix} 2 \\ 1 \\ -2 \end{bmatrix}$

Now $\overrightarrow{AB}$ and $\overrightarrow{CB}$ are two non-parallel vectors both parallel to the plane.

Thus the equation of the plane is $\mathbf{r} = \begin{bmatrix} 1 \\ 0 \\ 3 \end{bmatrix} + \lambda \begin{bmatrix} 4 \\ -1 \\ 1 \end{bmatrix} + \mu \begin{bmatrix} 2 \\ 1 \\ -2 \end{bmatrix}$, $\lambda, \mu \in \mathcal{R}$.

Note: $\mathbf{r} = \begin{bmatrix} x \\ y \\ z \end{bmatrix}$ and I chose C as the known (fixed) point on the plane.

b   If **n** is the normal vector,

then $\mathbf{n} = \overrightarrow{AB} \times \overrightarrow{AC} = \begin{bmatrix} 4 \\ -1 \\ 1 \end{bmatrix} \times \begin{bmatrix} 2 \\ -2 \\ 3 \end{bmatrix}$

$\therefore \ \mathbf{n} = \begin{vmatrix} \mathbf{i} & \mathbf{j} & \mathbf{k} \\ 4 & -1 & 1 \\ 2 & -2 & 3 \end{vmatrix} = \mathbf{i}(-3+2) + \mathbf{j}(2-12) + \mathbf{k}(-8+4) = \begin{bmatrix} -1 \\ -10 \\ -6 \end{bmatrix} = -\begin{bmatrix} 1 \\ 10 \\ 6 \end{bmatrix}$

Thus the plane has equation $x + 10y + 6z = (-1) + 10(2) + 6(0)$

i.e., $x + 10y + 6z = 19$

[**Note:**   Check that all 3 points satisfy this equation.]

4   Find the equation of the plane in   **i**   vector form   **ii**   normal vector form,   through:

a   A$(0, 2, 6)$,   B$(1, 3, 2)$ and   C$(-1, 2, 4)$

b   A$(3, 1, 2)$,   B$(0, 4, 0)$ and   C$(0, 0, 1)$

c   A$(2, 0, 3)$,   B$(0, -1, 2)$ and   C$(4, -3, 0)$.

5   Find the equations of the following *lines*:

a   through $(1, -2, 0)$ and normal to the plane $x - 3y + 4z = 8$

b   through $(3, 4, -1)$ and normal to the plane $x - y - 2z = 11$.

Example 20

Find the parametric equations of the line through A$(-1, 2, 3)$ and B$(2, 0, -3)$ and hence find where this line meets the plane with equation $x - 2y + 3z = 26$.

$\overrightarrow{AB} = \begin{bmatrix} 3 \\ -2 \\ -6 \end{bmatrix}$ $\therefore$ line AB has parametric equations

$x = -1 + 3t, \quad y = 2 - 2t, \quad z = 3 - 6t$ ..... (∗)

and this line meets the plane $x - 2y + 3z = 26$ where

$-1 + 3t - 2(2 - 2t) + 3(3 - 6t) = 26$

$\therefore \quad 4 - 11t = 26$

$\therefore \quad -11t = 22$ and so $t = -2$

$\therefore$ meets plane at $(-7, 6, 15)$ {substitute $t = -2$ into ∗}

6 Find the parametric equations of the line through A(2, −1, 3) and B(1, 2, 0) and hence find where this line meets the plane with equation $x + 2y − z = 5$.

7 Find the parametric equations of the line through P(1, −2, 4) and Q(2, 0, −1) and hence find where this line meets:

    a the YOZ-plane   **b** the plane with equation $y + z = 2$

    c the line with equations $\dfrac{x − 3}{2} = \dfrac{y + 2}{3} = \dfrac{z − 30}{−1}$.

Example 21

Find the coordinates of the foot of the normal from A(2, −1, 3) to the plane $x − y + 2z = 27$. Hence find the shortest distance from A to the plane.

$x − y + 2z = 27$ has normal vector $\begin{bmatrix} 1 \\ −1 \\ 2 \end{bmatrix}$

∴ the parametric equations of AN are

$$x = 2 + t, \quad y = −1 − t, \quad z = 3 + 2t$$

and this line meets the plane $x − y + 2z = 27$ where

$$2 + t − (−1 − t) + 2(3 + 2t) = 27$$
$$\text{i.e.,} \quad 2 + t + 1 + t + 6 + 4t = 27$$
$$\text{i.e.,} \quad 6t + 9 = 27$$
$$\therefore \quad 6t = 18$$
$$\therefore \quad t = 3 \qquad \therefore \text{ N is } (5, −4, 9).$$

The shortest distance $\text{AN} = \sqrt{(5 − 2)^2 + (−4 − −1)^2 + (9 − 3)^2}$
$$= \sqrt{9 + 9 + 36} = \sqrt{54} \text{ units.}$$

---

8 In the following, find the foot of the normal from A to the given plane and hence find the shortest distance from A to the plane:

    a A(1, 0, 2); $2x + y − 2z + 11 = 0$ **b** A(2, −1, 3); $x − y + 3z = −10$
    c A(1, −4, −3); $4x − y − 2z = 8$

9 Find the coordinates of the mirror image of A(3, 1, 2) when reflected in the plane $x + 2y + z = 1$.

10 Does the line through (3, 4, −1) and normal to $x + 4y − z = −2$ intersect any of the coordinate axes?

11 Find the equations of the plane through A(1, 2, 3) and B(0, −1, 2) which is parallel to: **a** the X-axis   **b** the Y-axis   **c** the Z-axis.

12 Show that the lines $x − 1 = \dfrac{y − 2}{2} = z + 3$ and $x + 1 = y − 3 = 2z + 5$ are coplanar and find the equation of the plane which contains them.

13 $A(1, 2, k)$ lies on the plane $x + 2y - 2z = 8$. Find:

  a the value of k

  b the coordinates of B such that AB is normal to the plane and 6 units from it.

Example 22

Find the coordinates of the foot of the normal N from $A(2, -1, 3)$ to the plane
with equation $\mathbf{r} = \mathbf{i} + 3\mathbf{k} + \lambda(4\mathbf{i} - \mathbf{j} + \mathbf{k}) + \mu(2\mathbf{i} + \mathbf{j} - 2\mathbf{k})\lambda, \ \lambda, \mu \in \mathcal{R}$.

The normal through A to the plane has direction vector given by

$$(4\mathbf{i} - \mathbf{j} + \mathbf{k}) \times (2\mathbf{i} + \mathbf{j} - 2\mathbf{k}) = \begin{vmatrix} \mathbf{i} & \mathbf{j} & \mathbf{k} \\ 4 & -1 & 1 \\ 2 & 1 & -2 \end{vmatrix} = \begin{bmatrix} 1 \\ 10 \\ 6 \end{bmatrix}.$$

Hence $\begin{bmatrix} 1 \\ 10 \\ 6 \end{bmatrix}$ is a direction vector of a normal line through point A.

This equation of the line AN is $\begin{bmatrix} x \\ y \\ z \end{bmatrix} = \begin{bmatrix} 2 \\ -1 \\ 3 \end{bmatrix} + t \begin{bmatrix} 1 \\ 10 \\ 6 \end{bmatrix}$

so that N must have coordinates of the form $(2 + t, \ -1 + 10t, \ 3 + 6t)$.

But N lies in the plane $\therefore \ \begin{bmatrix} 2 + t \\ -1 + 10t \\ 3 + 6t \end{bmatrix} = \begin{bmatrix} 1 \\ 0 \\ 3 \end{bmatrix} + \lambda \begin{bmatrix} 4 \\ -1 \\ 1 \end{bmatrix} + \mu \begin{bmatrix} 2 \\ 1 \\ -2 \end{bmatrix}$

$$\Rightarrow \qquad \begin{aligned} 2 + t &= 1 + 4\lambda + 2\mu \\ -1 + 10t &= -\lambda + \mu \\ 3 + 6t &= 3 + \lambda - 2\mu \end{aligned} \qquad \Rightarrow \qquad \begin{aligned} 4\lambda + 2\mu - t &= 1 \\ -\lambda + \mu - 10t &= -1 \\ \lambda - 2\mu - 6t &= 0 \end{aligned}$$

Solving simultaneously with technology gives $\ \lambda = \frac{40}{137}, \ \mu = \frac{-7}{137}, \ t = \frac{9}{137}$

$\therefore$ N is the point $\left(2\frac{9}{137}, \ -\frac{47}{137}, 3\frac{54}{137}\right)$

Check by substituting for λ and μ in the equation of the plane.
Here a calculator is virtually essential.

---

14 In the following, find the foot of the normal from A to the given plane and hence find
the shortest distance from A to the plane:

  a $A(3, 2, 1)$ to the plane $\ \mathbf{r} = 3\mathbf{i} + \mathbf{j} + 2\mathbf{k} + \lambda(2\mathbf{i} + \mathbf{j} + \mathbf{k}) + \mu(4\mathbf{i} + 2\mathbf{j} - 2\mathbf{k})$

  b $A(1, 0, -2)$ to the plane $\ \mathbf{r} = \mathbf{i} - \mathbf{j} + \mathbf{k} + \lambda(3\mathbf{i} - \mathbf{j} + 2\mathbf{k}) + \mu(-\mathbf{i} + \mathbf{j} - \mathbf{k})$

15 Q is any point in the plane
$Ax + By + Cz + D = 0$.

d is the distance from $P(x_1, y_1, z_1)$
to the given plane.

  a Explain why $d = \dfrac{|\overrightarrow{QP} \bullet \mathbf{n}|}{|\mathbf{n}|}$.

  b Hence, show that $d = \dfrac{|Ax_1 + By_1 + Cz_1 + D|}{\sqrt{A^2 + B^2 + C^2}}$.

  c Check your answers to question **8** using the formula of **b**.

16 Find the distance from:

 a $(0, 0, 0)$ to $x + 2y - z = 10$ **b** $(1, -3, 2)$ to $x + y - z = 2$.

Note: •   To find the distance between two parallel planes, find a point on one of the planes and use the method in **Example 22**.

   •   To find the distance between a line and a plane, both of which are parallel, find a point on the line and use the method in **Example 22**.

17 Find the distance between the parallel planes:

 a $x + y + 2z = 4$ and $2x + 2y + 4z + 11 = 0$

 b $ax + by + cz + d_1 = 0$ and $ax + by + cz + d_2 = 0$.

18 Show that the line $x = 2 + t$, $y = -1 + 2t$, $z = -3t$ is parallel to the plane $11x - 4y + z = 0$,   and find its distance from the plane.

19 Find the equations of the two planes which are parallel to $2x - y + 2z = 5$ and 2 units from it.

E   ANGLES IN SPACE

THE ANGLE BETWEEN A LINE AND A PLANE

Suppose a line has direction vector **d** and a plane has normal vector **n** and allow **n** to intersect the line making an angle of θ^o with it. The required angle is ϕ^o and

$$\sin \phi = \cos \theta = \frac{|\, \mathbf{n} \bullet \mathbf{d} \,|}{|\, \mathbf{n} \,||\, \mathbf{d} \,|}$$

$$\therefore \quad \phi = \sin^{-1} \left(\frac{|\, \mathbf{n} \bullet \mathbf{d} \,|}{|\, \mathbf{n} \,||\, \mathbf{d} \,|} \right)$$

Example 23

Find the acute angle between the plane $x + 2y - z = 8$ and the line with equations $x = t$, $y = 1 - t$, $z = 3 + 2t$.

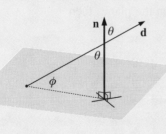

$$\mathbf{n} = \begin{bmatrix} 1 \\ 2 \\ -1 \end{bmatrix} \quad \text{and} \quad \mathbf{d} = \begin{bmatrix} 1 \\ -1 \\ 2 \end{bmatrix}$$

$$\phi = \sin^{-1} \left(\frac{|1 - 2 - 2|}{\sqrt{1 + 4 + 1}\sqrt{1 + 1 + 4}} \right)$$

$$= \sin^{-1} \left(\frac{3}{\sqrt{6}\sqrt{6}} \right)$$

$$= \sin^{-1} \left(\tfrac{1}{2} \right)$$

$$= 30^o$$

EXERCISE 17E

1 Find the acute angle between:

  a the plane $x - y + z = 5$ and the line $\dfrac{x-1}{4} = \dfrac{y+1}{3} = z + 2$

  b the plane $2x - y + z = 8$ and the line $x = t + 1, \quad y = -1 + 3t, \quad z = t$

  c the plane $3x + 4y - z = -4$ and the line $x - 4 = 3 - y = 2(z + 1)$

  d the plane $\mathbf{r}_p = 2\mathbf{i} - \mathbf{j} + \mathbf{k} + \lambda(3\mathbf{i} - 4\mathbf{j} - \mathbf{k}) + \mu(\mathbf{i} + \mathbf{j} - 2\mathbf{k})$ and
      the line $\mathbf{r}_l = 3\mathbf{i} + 2\mathbf{j} - \mathbf{k} + t(\mathbf{i} - \mathbf{j} + \mathbf{k})$.

THE ANGLE BETWEEN TWO PLANES

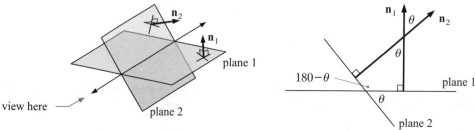

$\cos \theta = \dfrac{|\mathbf{n}_1 \bullet \mathbf{n}_2|}{|\mathbf{n}_1|\,|\mathbf{n}_2|}$ is the cosine of the acute angle between two planes.

So,   if two planes have normal vectors $\mathbf{n}_1$ and $\mathbf{n}_2$ and θ is the
            acute angle between them then $\theta = \cos^{-1}\left(\dfrac{|\mathbf{n}_1 \bullet \mathbf{n}_2|}{|\mathbf{n}_1|\,|\mathbf{n}_2|}\right)$.

Example 24

Find the acute angle between the planes with equations $x + y - z = 8$
and $2x - y + 3z = -1$.

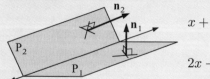

$x + y - z = 8$ has normal vector $\mathbf{n}_1 = \begin{bmatrix} 1 \\ 1 \\ -1 \end{bmatrix}$ and

$2x - y + 3z = -1$ has normal vector $\mathbf{n}_2 = \begin{bmatrix} 2 \\ -1 \\ 3 \end{bmatrix}$

If θ is the acute angle between the planes then

$\theta = \cos^{-1}\left(\dfrac{|\mathbf{n}_1 \bullet \mathbf{n}_2|}{|\mathbf{n}_1|\,|\mathbf{n}_2|}\right)$

$= \cos^{-1}\left(\dfrac{|2 + -1 + -3|}{\sqrt{1+1+1}\sqrt{4+1+9}}\right)$

$= \cos^{-1}\left(\dfrac{2}{\sqrt{42}}\right)$

$\doteqdot 72.02^{o}$

2 Find the acute angle between the planes with equations:

a $2x - y + z = 3$
   $x + 3y + 2z = 8$

b $x - y + 3z = 2$
   $3x + y - z = -5$

c $3x - y + z = -11$
   $2x + 4y - z = 2.$

d $\mathbf{r}_1 = 3\mathbf{i} + 2\mathbf{j} - \mathbf{k} - \lambda(\mathbf{i} - \mathbf{j} + \mathbf{k}) + \mu(2\mathbf{i} - 4\mathbf{j} + 3\mathbf{k})$
   and $\mathbf{r}_2 = \mathbf{i} + \mathbf{j} - \mathbf{k} - \lambda(2\mathbf{i} + \mathbf{j} + \mathbf{k}) + \mu(\mathbf{i} + \mathbf{j} + \mathbf{k})$

e $3x - 4y + z = -2$ and $\mathbf{r} = \begin{bmatrix} 2 \\ -1 \\ 1 \end{bmatrix} + \lambda \begin{bmatrix} 3 \\ -1 \\ 0 \end{bmatrix} + \mu \begin{bmatrix} 2 \\ 1 \\ 1 \end{bmatrix}$

F   THE INTERSECTION OF TWO OR MORE PLANES

- **Two planes** in space could be

   (1)   intersecting

   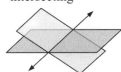

   (2)   parallel

   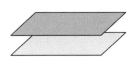

   (3)   coincident

   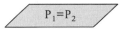

- **Three planes** in space could be

   (1)   all coincident

   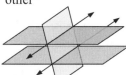

   (2)   two coincident and one other

   (3)   two coincident and one parallel

   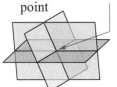

   (4)   two parallel and one other

   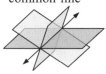

   (5)   all 3 parallel

   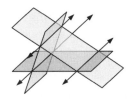

   (6)   all meet at the one point

   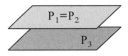

   (7)   all 3 meet in a common line

   (8)

   the line of intersection of any 2 is parallel to the third plane.

Peanuts software (winplot) displays these cases and should be visited.

This work should be linked to **Chapter 14** Matrices, and solutions can be found by using inverse matrices (where there is a unique solution) and/or row operations on the augmented matrix.

The use of row operations on the augmented matrix is essential when the solution is not unique, i.e., the matrix of coefficients is singular (determinant $= 0$) and this matrix is not invertible.

Example 25

a Use elementary row operations to solve the system: $x + 3y - z = 0$
$$3x + 5y - z = 0$$
$$x - 5y + (2 - m)z = 9 - m^2$$
for a real number m. Give geometric interpretations of your results.

b Hence solve $x + 3y - z = 0$,   giving a geometric interpretation.
$$3x + 5y - z = 0$$
$$x - 5y + z = 8$$

a Augmented matrix

$$\begin{bmatrix} 1 & 3 & -1 & | & 0 \\ 3 & 5 & -1 & | & 0 \\ 1 & -5 & 2-m & | & 9-m^2 \end{bmatrix}$$

$$\sim \begin{bmatrix} 1 & 3 & -1 & | & 0 \\ 0 & -4 & 2 & | & 0 \\ 0 & -8 & 3-m & | & 9-m^2 \end{bmatrix} \begin{matrix} R_2 \to R_2 - 3R_1 \\ R_3 \to R_3 - R_1 \end{matrix}$$

$$\sim \begin{bmatrix} 1 & 3 & -1 & | & 0 \\ 0 & 2 & -1 & | & 0 \\ 0 & 0 & -m-1 & | & 9-m^2 \end{bmatrix} \begin{matrix} R_2 \to R_2 \times -\frac{1}{2} \\ R_3 \to R_3 - 2R_2 \end{matrix}$$

Case (1) If $m = -1$, the augmented matrix becomes $\begin{bmatrix} 1 & 3 & -1 & | & 0 \\ 0 & 2 & -1 & | & 0 \\ 0 & 0 & 0 & | & 8 \end{bmatrix}$.

The system is inconsistent, $\therefore$ no solutions.

$\therefore$ the three planes do not have a common point of intersection

The normals are $\mathbf{n}_1 = \begin{bmatrix} 1 \\ 3 \\ -1 \end{bmatrix}$, $\mathbf{n}_2 = \begin{bmatrix} 3 \\ 5 \\ -1 \end{bmatrix}$, $\mathbf{n}_3 = \begin{bmatrix} 1 \\ -5 \\ 3 \end{bmatrix}$

None of the planes are parallel.

$\therefore$ the line of intersection of any two is parallel to the third plane.

Case (2) If $m \neq -1$ there is a unique solution as $(-m-1)z = 9 - m^2$
$$(m+1)z = m^2 - 9$$
$$\therefore \quad z = \frac{m^2 - 9}{m + 1}$$

From row 2, $2y - z = 0$ $\therefore$ $y = \frac{1}{2}z = \frac{m^2 - 9}{2(m+1)}$

From row 1, $x = -3y + z = \frac{-3(m^2-9)}{2(m+1)} + \frac{2(m^2-9)}{2(m+1)} = \frac{9-m^2}{2(m+1)}$

So the three planes meet at a (unique) point,

$$\left(\frac{9-m^2}{2(m+1)}, \frac{m^2-9}{2(m+1)}, \frac{m^2-9}{m+1} \right), \quad \text{provided} \quad m \neq -1$$

b Comparing with **a**, $2 - m = 1$ $\therefore$ $m = 1$

$\therefore$ the three planes meet at the point $\left(\frac{8}{4}, \frac{-8}{4}, \frac{-8}{2} \right)$, i.e., $(2, -2, -4)$.

Example 26

a   Find the intersection of the planes $x + y + 2z = 2$
$\qquad\qquad\qquad\qquad\qquad\qquad\qquad\quad\; 2x + y - z = 4$

b   Hence solve $x + y + 2z = 2$
$\qquad\qquad\qquad 2x + y - z = 4$ Give a geometric interpretation
$\qquad\qquad\qquad\; x - y - z = 5$ of your result

---

a   The augmented matrix $\begin{bmatrix} 1 & 1 & 2 & | & 2 \\ 2 & 1 & -1 & | & 4 \end{bmatrix} \sim \begin{bmatrix} 1 & 1 & 2 & | & 2 \\ 0 & 1 & 5 & | & 0 \end{bmatrix}$

The system is consistent with infinite solutions.

Let $z = t, \quad y = -5t, \quad x = 2 + 3t, \quad t \in \mathcal{R}$ are the solutions,
∴   the two planes whose equations are given meet in the line
$\qquad x = 2 + 3t, \quad y = -5t, \quad z = t, \quad t \in \mathcal{R}.$

Note: This line passes through $(2, 0, 0)$ has direction vector $\begin{bmatrix} 3 \\ -5 \\ 1 \end{bmatrix}$.   Why?

b   The solutions of the first 2 equations are $x = 2 + 3t, \; y = -5t, \; z = t$

Substitute into the third equation gives $2 + 3t + 5t - t = 5 \quad \therefore \quad 7t = 3$
$\qquad\qquad\qquad\qquad\qquad\qquad\qquad\qquad\qquad\qquad\qquad\qquad \therefore \quad t = \tfrac{3}{7}$

$\qquad\qquad \therefore \quad x = \tfrac{23}{7}, \quad y = -\tfrac{15}{7}, \quad z = \tfrac{3}{7}$

∴   the three planes meet at the point $\left(\tfrac{23}{7}, \, -\tfrac{15}{7}, \, \tfrac{3}{7}\right)$ (unique solution)

or   the line of intersection of the first two planes meets the third plane at the
point $\left(\tfrac{23}{7}, \, -\tfrac{15}{7}, \, \tfrac{3}{7}\right)$.

EXERCISE 17F

1   **a**   How many solutions are possible $a_1 x + b_1 y + c_1 z = d_1$
  when solving simultaneously $a_2 x + b_2 y + c_2 z = d_2$?

  b   Under what conditions will the planes in **a** be: **i**   parallel   **ii**   coincident?

  c   Solve the following using elementary row operations and interpret each system of
  equations geometrically:

  i $x - 3y + 2z = 8$ **ii** $2x + y + z = 5$ **iii** $x + 2y - 3z = 6$
  $\quad\; 3x - 9y + 2z = 4$ $\quad\; x - y + z = 3$ $\quad\; 3x + 6y - 9z = 18$

2   Discuss the possible solution of the following systems where k is a real number, interpreting geometrically:

  a $x + 2y - z = 6$ **b** $x - y + 3z = 8$
  $\quad\; 2x + 4y + kz = 12$ $\quad\; 2x - 2y + 6z = k$

3   For the eight possible geometric solutions of three planes in space, comment on the possible solutions in each case.

For example,   has infinitely many solutions where x, y and z
$P_1 = P_2 = P_3$ are in terms of two parameters, s and t, say.

4 Solve the following systems using elementary row operations and in each case state the geometric meaning of your solution:

a
$$x + y - z = -5$$
$$x - y + 2z = 11$$
$$4x + y - 5z = -18$$

b
$$x - y + 2z = 1$$
$$2x + y - z = 8$$
$$5x - 2y + 5z = 11$$

c
$$x + 2y - z = 8$$
$$2x - y - z = 5$$
$$3x - 4y - z = 2$$

d
$$x - y + z = 8$$
$$2x - 2y + 2z = 11$$
$$x + 3y - z = -2$$

e
$$x + y - 2z = 1$$
$$x - y + z = 4$$
$$3x + 3y - 6z = 3$$

f
$$x - y - z = 5$$
$$x + y + z = 1$$
$$5x - y + 2z = 17$$

5 Solve the system of equations
$$x - y + 3z = 1$$
$$2x - 3y - z = 3$$
$$3x - 5y - 5z = k \quad \text{where } k \text{ takes all real values.}$$

State the geometrical meaning of the solution in each case assuming that the equations represent planes in space.

6 Find all values of m for which
$$x + 2y + mz = -1$$
$$2x + y - z = 3$$
$$mx - 2y + z = 1 \quad \text{has a unique solution.}$$

In the cases where there is no unique solution, solve the system. Give geometrical meaning to all possible solutions. Illustrate each case.

7 Find if and where the following planes meet:

$P_1 : \mathbf{r}_1 = 2\mathbf{i} - \mathbf{j} + \lambda(3\mathbf{i} + \mathbf{k}) + \mu(\mathbf{i} + \mathbf{j} - \mathbf{k})$
$\qquad P_3 : \mathbf{r}_3 = \begin{bmatrix} 2 \\ -1 \\ 2 \end{bmatrix} + t \begin{bmatrix} 1 \\ -1 \\ 0 \end{bmatrix} - u \begin{bmatrix} 0 \\ -1 \\ 2 \end{bmatrix}$

$P_2 : \mathbf{r}_2 = 3\mathbf{i} - \mathbf{j} + 3\mathbf{k} + r(2\mathbf{i} - \mathbf{k}) + s(\mathbf{i} + \mathbf{j})$

REVIEW SET 17A (2-D)

1 Find   **a**   the vector equation   **b**   the parametric equations

of the line that passes through $(-6, 3)$, with direction $\begin{bmatrix} 4 \\ -3 \end{bmatrix}$.

2 Find the vector equation of the line which cuts the y-axis at $(0, 8)$ and has direction $5\mathbf{i} + 4\mathbf{j}$.

3 $(-3, m)$ lies on the line with vector equation $\begin{bmatrix} x \\ y \end{bmatrix} = \begin{bmatrix} 18 \\ -2 \end{bmatrix} + t \begin{bmatrix} -7 \\ 4 \end{bmatrix}$.   Find m.

4 A particle at $P(x(t), y(t))$ moves such that $x(t) = -4 + 8t$ and $y(t) = 3 + 6t$, $t \geqslant 0$, t in seconds. Distance units are metres. Find the:

   a   initial position of P   **b**   position of P after 4 seconds
   c   speed of P   **d**   velocity vector of P.

5 Find the velocity vector of an object that is moving in the direction $3\mathbf{i} - \mathbf{j}$ with a speed of 20 km/h.

6 A yacht is sailing at a constant speed of $5\sqrt{10}$ km/h in the direction $-\mathbf{i} - 3\mathbf{j}$. Initially it is at point $(-6, 10)$. A beacon is at $(0, 0)$ at the centre of a tiny atoll.

  a Find in terms of $\mathbf{i}$ and $\mathbf{j}$:

  i   the initial position vector of the yacht

  ii the direction vector of the yacht

  iii the position vector of the yacht at any time t hours $(t \geqslant 0)$.

  b Find the time when the yacht is closest to the beacon.

  c Find whether there is a possibility that the yacht could hit the reef around the atoll given that the atoll has a radius of 8 km.

7 Submarine X23 is at $(2, 4)$ and fires a torpedo with velocity vector $\begin{bmatrix} 1 \\ -3 \end{bmatrix}$ at exactly 2.17 pm.   Submarine Y18 is at $(11, 3)$ and has velocity vector $\begin{bmatrix} -1 \\ a \end{bmatrix}$.   It fires a torpedo 2 minutes later to intercept the torpedo from X23. Given that the interception occurs:

  a find $x_1(t)$ and $y_1(t)$ for submarine X23

  b find $x_2(t)$ and $y_2(t)$ for submarine Y18.

  c At what time does the interception occur?

  d What was the direction and speed of the interception torpedo?

8 Trapezoid (trapezium) KLMN is formed by these lines:

  Line 1 (KL) is $\begin{bmatrix} x \\ y \end{bmatrix} = \begin{bmatrix} 2 \\ 19 \end{bmatrix} + p \begin{bmatrix} 5 \\ -2 \end{bmatrix}$,   line 2 (ML) is $\begin{bmatrix} x \\ y \end{bmatrix} = \begin{bmatrix} 33 \\ -5 \end{bmatrix} + q \begin{bmatrix} -11 \\ 16 \end{bmatrix}$

  line 3 (NK) is $\begin{bmatrix} x \\ y \end{bmatrix} = \begin{bmatrix} 3 \\ 7 \end{bmatrix} + r \begin{bmatrix} 4 \\ 10 \end{bmatrix}$ and   line 4 (MN) is $\begin{bmatrix} x \\ y \end{bmatrix} = \begin{bmatrix} 43 \\ -9 \end{bmatrix} + s \begin{bmatrix} -5 \\ 2 \end{bmatrix}$

  where p, q, r and s are scalars. Lines 1 and 2 meet at L$(22, 11)$.

  Lines 1 and 3 meet at K,   lines 2 and 4 at M,   lines 3 and 4 at N.

  a Which two lines are parallel? Why?

  b Which lines are perpendicular? Why?

  c Use vector methods to find the coordinates of K, M and N.

  d Calculate the area of trapezium KLMN.

REVIEW SET 17B (3-D)

1 Show that A$(1, 0, 4)$, B$(3, 1, 12)$, C$(-1, 2, 2)$ and D$(-2, 0, -5)$ are coplanar. Find:

  a the equation of the plane

  b the coordinates of the nearest point on the plane to E$(3, 3, 2)$.

2 A is $(3, 2, -1)$ and B$(-1, 2, 4)$.

  a Write down the vector equation of the line through A and B.

  b Find the equation of the plane through B with normal AB.

  c Find *two* points on the line AB which are $2\sqrt{41}$ units from A.

3 P_1 is the plane $2x - y - 2z = 9$ and P_2 is the plane $x + y + 2z = 1$.

  L is the line with parametric equations $x = t$, $y = 2t - 1$, $z = 3 - t$.

  Find the acute angle: **a**   that L makes with P_1 **b**   between P_1 and P_2.

4 For A$(3, -1, 1)$ and B$(0, 2, -1)$, find the:

   a vector equation of the line passing through A and B

   b the coordinates of P which divides BA in the ratio $2 : 5$.

5 For C$(-3, 2, -1)$ and D$(0, 1, -4)$ find the coordinates of the point(s) where the line passing through C and D meets the plane with equation $2x - y + z = 3$.

6 Given the lines $\dfrac{x - 8}{3} = \dfrac{y + 9}{-16} = \dfrac{z - 10}{7}$ and $x = 15 + 3t, \ y = 29 + 8t, \ z = 5 - 5t$:

   a show that they are skew   **b** find the acute angle between them

   c find the shortest distance between them.

7 **a** How far is X$(-1, 1, 3)$ from the plane $x - 2y - 2z = 8$?

   b Find the coordinates of the foot of the perpendicular from Q$(-1, 2, 3)$ to the line $2 - x = y - 3 = -\frac{1}{2}z$.

8 P$(2, 0, 1)$, Q$(3, 4, -2)$ and R$(-1, 3, 2)$ are three points in space. Find:

   a $\overrightarrow{PQ}, \ | \overrightarrow{PQ} |$ and $\overrightarrow{QR}$ **b** the parametric equations of line $\overleftrightarrow{PQ}$

   c Use **a** to find the vector equation of the plane PQR.

9 Given the point A$(-1, 3, 2)$, the plane $2x - y + 2z = 8$ and the line defined by $x = 7 - 2t, \ \ y = -6 + t, \ \ z = 1 + 5t, \ \ $ find:

   a the distance from A to the plane

   b the coordinates of the point on the plane nearest to A

   c the shortest distance from A to the line.

10 **a** Find the equation of the plane through A$(-1, 0, 2)$, B$(0, -1, 1)$ and C$(1, 2, -1)$:

   b Find the equation of the line, in parametric form, which passes through the origin and is normal to the plane in **a**.

   c Find the point where the line of **b** intersects the plane of **a**.

11 Solve the system
$$x - y + z = 5$$
$$2x + y - z = -1$$
$$7x + 2y + kz = -k \quad \text{for any real number } k,$$

using elementary row operations. Give geometric interpretations of your results.

REVIEW SET 17C

Click on the icon to obtain printable review sets and answers

Chapter 18

Descriptive statistics

BACKGROUND KNOWLEDGE IN STATISTICS

Before starting this course you should make sure that you have a good understanding of the necessary background knowledge.

Click on the icon alongside to obtain a printable set of exercises and answers on this background knowledge.

BACKGROUND KNOWLEDGE

THE PEA PROBLEM

A farmer wishes to investigate the effect of a new organic fertiliser on his crops of peas. He is hoping to improve the crop yield by using the fertiliser. He set up a small garden which was subdivided into two equal plots and planted many peas. Both plots were treated the same except for the use of the fertiliser on one, but not the other. All other factors such as watering were as normal.

A random sample of 150 pods was harvested from each plot at the same time and the number of peas in each pod counted. The results were:

Without fertiliser

4 6 5 6 5 6 4 6 4 9 5 3 6 8 5 4 6 8 6 5 6 7 4 6 5 2 8 6 5 6 5 5 5 4 4 4 6 7 5 6
7 5 5 6 4 8 5 3 7 5 3 6 4 7 5 6 5 7 5 7 6 7 5 4 7 5 5 5 6 6 5 6 7 5 8 6 8 6 7 6
6 3 7 6 8 3 3 4 4 7 6 5 6 4 5 7 3 7 7 6 7 7 4 6 6 5 6 7 6 3 4 6 6 3 7 6 7 6 8 6
6 6 6 4 7 6 6 5 3 8 6 7 6 8 6 7 6 6 6 8 4 4 8 6 6 2 6 5 7 3

With fertiliser

6 7 7 4 9 5 5 5 8 9 8 9 7 7 5 8 7 6 6 7 9 7 7 7 8 9 3 7 4 8 5 10 8 6 7 6 7 5 6 8
7 9 4 4 9 6 8 5 8 7 7 4 7 8 10 6 10 7 7 7 9 7 7 8 6 8 6 8 7 4 8 6 8 7 3 8 7 6 9 7
6 9 7 6 8 3 9 5 7 6 8 7 9 7 8 4 8 7 7 7 6 6 8 6 6 3 8 5 8 7 6 7 4 9 6 6 6 8 4 7 8
9 7 7 4 7 5 7 4 7 6 4 6 7 7 6 7 8 7 6 6 7 8 6 7 10 5 13 4 7 7

For you to consider:

- Can you state clearly the problem that the farmer wants to solve?
- How has the farmer tried to make a fair comparison?
- How could the farmer make sure that his selection is at random?
- What is the best way of organising this data?
- What are suitable methods of display?
- Are there any abnormally high or low results and how should they be treated?
- How can we best indicate the most typical pod size?
- How can we best indicate the spread of possible pod sizes?
- What is the best way to show 'typical pod size' and the spread?
- Can a satisfactory conclusion be made?

CONTINUOUS NUMERICAL DATA AND HISTOGRAMS

A **continuous numerical variable** can theoretically take any value on part of the number line. A continuous variable often has to be **measured** so that data can be recorded.

Examples of continuous numerical variables are:

The height of Year 10 students: the variable can take any value from about 140 cm to 200 cm.

The speed of cars on a stretch of highway: the variable can take any value from 0 km/h to the fastest speed that a car can travel, but is most likely to be in the range 30 km/h to 120 km/h.

ORGANISATION AND DISPLAY OF CONTINUOUS DATA

When data is recorded for a continuous variable there are likely to be many different values so this data is organised by grouping into **class intervals**. A special type of graph, called a **histogram**, is used to display the data.

A histogram is similar to a column graph but, to account for the continuous nature of the variable, a number line is used for the horizontal axis and the 'columns' are joined together.

An example is given alongside:

Note: The **modal class** (the class of values that appears most often) is easy to identify from a histogram.

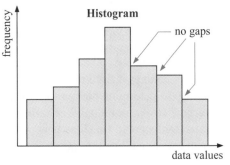

If the class intervals are the same size then the frequency is represented by the height of the 'columns'.

SUMMARY (COLUMN GRAPHS AND HISTOGRAMS)

Column graphs and histograms both have the following features:

- on the **vertical axis** we have the **frequency** of occurrence
- on the **horizontal axis** we have the range of scores
- **column widths are equal** and the height varies according to frequency.

Histograms are used whenever the data is **continuous** and have **no gaps between the columns**.

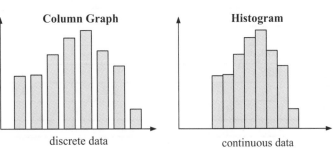

CASE STUDY   DRIVING A GOLF BALL

While Norm Gregory was here for the golf championship, I decided to ask for his cooperation in a data gathering exercise. He agreed and so I asked him to hit 30 balls in succession with his driver. I then measured how far each ball travelled in metres. The data was as follows:

244.6	245.1	248.0	248.8	250.0
251.1	251.2	253.9	254.5	254.6
255.9	257.0	260.6	262.8	262.9
263.1	263.2	264.3	264.4	265.0
265.5	265.6	266.5	267.4	269.7
270.5	270.7	272.9	275.6	277.5

This type of data must be **grouped** before a histogram can be drawn.

In forming groups, find the lowest and highest values, and then make the group width such that you achieve about 6 to 12 groups. In this case the lowest value is 244.6 m while the largest is 277.5 m. This gives a range of approximately 35 m, hence a group width of 5 will give eight groups.

We will use the following method of grouping. The group '240 - ' actually means that any data value 240 but < 245 can fit in this group. Similarly the group '260 - ' will contain data 260 but < 265. This technique creates a home for every number $\geqslant 240$ but < 280. Groups should all be of the same width.

A tally column is used to count the data that falls in a given group in an efficient way. Do not try to determine the number of data values in the 240- group first off. Simply place a vertical stroke in the tally column to register an entry as you work your way through the data from start to finish as it is presented to you. Every fifth entry in a group is marked with a diagonal line through the previous four so groups of five can be counted quickly.

A frequency column summarises the number of data values in each group. The relative frequency column measures the percentage of the total number of data values in each group. Here, percentages offer an easier way to compare the number of balls Norm hit 'over 270 m but under 275 m' to the number he hit 'under 245 m'.

Norm Gregory's 30 drives

Distance (m)	Tally	Frequency (f)	% Relative frequ. (rf)
240 -		1	3.3
245 -	|||	3	10.0
250 -	⊬††	6	20.0
255 -	||	2	6.7
260 -	⊬†† ||	7	23.3
265 -	⊬††	6	20.0
270 -	|||	3	10.0
275 - (but < 280)	||	2	6.7
	Totals	30	100.0

From this table two histograms can be drawn, firstly a **frequency histogram**, and secondly a **relative frequency histogram**. They look as follows. Note, all histograms require a title.

A **frequency histogram** displaying the distribution of 30 of Norm Gregory's drives.

A **relative frequency histogram** displaying the distribution of 30 of Norm Gregory's drives.

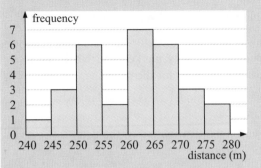

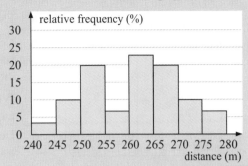

The advantage of the relative frequency histogram is best seen when you wish to compare distributions with different numbers of data values. Using percentages allows for a fair comparison.

Notice how the horizontal axis is labelled. The left edge of each bar is the first possible entry for that group.

Example 1

The weight of parcels sent on a particular day from a post office is recorded, in kilograms:

　　2.1, 3.0, 0.6, 1.5, 1.9, 2.4, 3.2, 4.2, 2.6, 3.1, 1.8, 1.7, 3.9, 2.4, 0.3, 1.5, 1.2

Organise the data using a frequency table and graph the data.

The data is *continuous* because the weight could be any value from 0.1 kg up to 5 kg.

The lowest weight recorded is 0.3 kg and the heaviest is 4.2 kg so we will use class intervals of 1 kg. The class interval 1- would include all weights from 1 kg up to, but not including 2 kg.

A histogram is used to graph this continuous data.

Weight (kg)	Frequency
0 -	2
1 -	6
2 -	4
3 -	4
4 - < 5	1

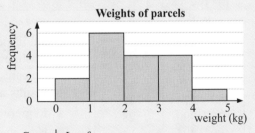

A stemplot could also be used to organise the data:

Note: The modal class is (1-< 2) kg as this occurred most frequently.

Stem	Leaf
0	3 6
1	2 5 5 7 8 9
2	1 4 4 6
3	0 1 2 9
4	2

Scale: 1 | 2 means 1.2 kg.

EXERCISE 18A

1 A frequency table for the heights of a basketball squad is given below.

Height (cm)	Frequency
170 -	1
175 -	8
180 -	9
185 -	11
190 -	9
195 -	3
200 - < 205	3

a Explain why 'height' is a continuous variable.

b Construct a histogram for the data. The axes should be carefully marked and labelled and include a heading for the graph.

c What is the modal class? Explain what this means.

d Describe the distribution of the data.

2 A school has conducted a survey of 60 students to investigate the time it takes for students to travel to school. The following data gives the travel time to the nearest minute:

12	15	16	8	10	17	25	34	42	18	24	18	45	33	38
45	40	3	20	12	10	10	27	16	37	45	15	16	26	32
35	8	14	18	15	27	19	32	6	12	14	20	10	16	14
28	31	21	25	8	32	46	14	15	20	18	8	10	25	22

a Is travel time a discrete or continuous variable?

b Construct an ordered stemplot for the data using stems 0, 1, 2, ...

c Describe the distribution of the data.

d What is the modal travelling time?

3 For the following data, state whether a histogram or a column graph should be used and draw the appropriate graph.

a The number of matches in 30 match boxes data.

Number of matches per box	47	49	50	51	52	53	55
Frequency	1	1	9	12	4	2	1

b The heights of 25 hockey players (to the nearest cm) data.

Height (cm)	120 - 129	130 - 139	140 - 149	150 - 159	160 - 169
Frequency	1	2	7	14	1

4

height (mm)	frequency
300 - 324	12
325 - 349	18
350 - 374	42
375 - 399	28
400 - 424	14
425 - 449	6

A plant inspector takes a random sample of two week old seedlings from a nursery and measures their height to the nearest mm.

The results are shown in the table alongside.

a Represent the data on a histogram.

b How many of the seedlings are 400 mm or more?

c What percentage of the seedlings are between 349 and 400 mm?

d The total number of seedlings in the nursery is 1462. Estimate the number of seedlings which measure

    i less than 400 mm   **ii** between 374 and 425 mm.

B — MEASURING THE CENTRE OF DATA

A better picture of the data in a data set can be seen if we can locate the **middle (centre)** of the data and have an indication of its **spread**. Knowing one of these without the other is often of little use.

There are *three statistics* that are used to measure the **centre** of a data set. These are: the **mean**, the **median** and the **mode**.

THE MEAN

> The **mean** of a data set is the statistical name for the arithmetic average and can be found by dividing the sum of the data by the number of data,
>
> i.e., $\text{mean} = \dfrac{\textbf{sum of all data values}}{\textbf{the number of data values}}$.

The mean gives us a single number which indicates a centre of the data set.

For example, a mean test mark of 73% tells us that there are several marks below 73% and several above it with 73% at the centre. 73% does not have to be one of the data set values.

'μ' reads 'mu'

If we let x be a data value

n be the number of data values in the sample, or population

$\sum$ mean "the sum of"

$\overline{x}$ represent the mean of a **sample** and

μ represent the mean of a **population**

then we have: $\mu = \dfrac{\sum x}{n}$ or $\overline{x} = \dfrac{\sum x}{n}$.

THE MEDIAN

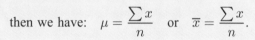

The **median** is the *middle value* of an ordered data set.

An ordered data set is obtained by listing the data, usually from smallest to largest. The median splits the data in two halves. Half the data are less than or equal to the median and half are greater than or equal to it.

For example, if the median mark for a test is 73% then you know that half the class scored less than or equal to 73% and half scored greater than or equal to 73%.

Note: For an **odd number** of data, the median is one of the data.

For an **even number** of data, the median is the average of the two middle values and may not be one of the original data.

Here is a **rule for finding the median** data values:

> If there are n data values, find $\dfrac{n+1}{2}$. The median is the $\left(\dfrac{n+1}{2}\right)$th data value.

For example:

When $n = 13$, $\dfrac{13+1}{2} = 7$, $\therefore$ median = 7th ordered data value.

DEMO

When $n = 14$, $\dfrac{14+1}{2} = 7.5$, $\therefore$ median = average of 7th and 8th ordered data values.

THE MERITS OF THE MEAN AND MEDIAN USED AS A MEASURE OF CENTRE

- Because of the way that the mean is calculated, for some data sets it is a very **poor** measure of a distribution's centre.
- All measures of centre are useless to support an argument if only they are quoted.
- The median is the only measure of centre that will locate the true centre regardless of the data set's features. It is unaffected by the presence of extreme values. It is called a resistant measure of centre.
- The mean is an accurate measure of centre if the distribution is symmetrical or approximately symmetrical. If it is not, then unbalanced high or low values will *drag* the mean toward them and hence cause the mean to be an inaccurate measure of centre. It is called a non-resistant measure of centre. *If it is considered inaccurate, it should not be used in discussion.*
- The following diagrams show the approximate relative postions of the mean and median for the more common shaped distributions.

THE RELATIONSHIP BETWEEN THE MEAN AND THE MEDIAN FOR DIFFERENT DISTRIBUTIONS

First of all consider a distribution that is **symmetric**.

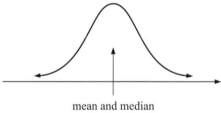

mean and median

Note: Other symmetrical shapes exist other than this '**bell**' type shape. Any symmetrical distribution will have a mean and median that are approximately equal.

positively skewed distribution

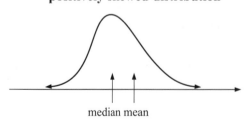

median mean

negatively skewed distribution

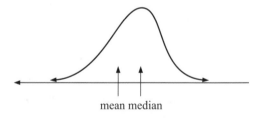

mean median

Hence if the data set has symmetry, both the mean and the median should accurately measure the centre of the distribution.

Note: The mean is influenced by all data values in the data set whereas the median is not.

INVESTIGATION   MERITS OF THE MEAN AND MEDIAN

Recall the data gained from Norm Gregory while he was here for the golf championship. The data was as follows:

STATISTICS
PACKAGE

244.6	245.1	248.0	248.8	250.0	270.5	251.1	251.2
253.9	254.5	254.6	270.7	255.9	257.0	260.6	262.8
262.9	272.9	263.1	263.2	264.3	264.4	265.0	275.6
265.5	265.6	266.5	267.4	269.7	277.5		

What to do:

1 Enter the data as a List into a **graphics calculator** or use the **Statistics package** supplied.

    a Produce a histogram of the data. Set the X values from 240 to 280 with an increment of 5. Set the Y values from 0 to 30.

    b Comment on the shape of the distribution.

    c Find **i** the median   **ii** the mean

    d Compare the mean and the median. Is the mean an accurate measure of the centre?

2 The mode is meaningless because no value occurs more than once.

    a Verify from the histogram above that the mode appears to be the category [260-265].

    b What would the mode be if our intervals were 2 m, starting at 240 m?

3 Now what would have happened if Norm had hit a few very bad drives? Let us say that his three shortest drives were very short!

    a Change the three shortest drives to 82.1 m, 103.2 m and 111.1 m.

    b Repeat **1 a, b, c** and **d** but set the X values from 75 to 300 with an increment of 25 for the histogram.

4 What would have happened if Norm had hit a few super long balls in addition to the very bad ones? Let us imagine that the longest balls he hit were very long.

    a Change the three longest drives to 403.9 m, 415.5 m and 420.0 m.

    b Repeat **1 a, b, c** and **d** but set the X values from 50 to 450 with an increment of 50 for the histogram.

While collecting the data from Norm, I decided to have a hit as well. I hit 30 golf balls with my driver. The relative frequency histogram reveals the results below.

This distribution is clearly positively skewed. This suggests that most of my hits were around the 140 to 170 metres but a few were around the 170 to 210 metres.

The mean would not be an accurate measure of the centre of this distribution due to the few higher scores. Indeed the mean is 163.66 m compared to the median of 157.50 m. Note that you have not been supplied with the data in this case. The idea is for you to get a feel for the data set from the histogram.

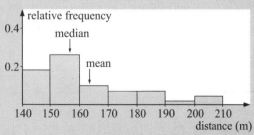

THE MODE

The **mode** is the most frequently occurring value in the data set.

UNGROUPED DATA

Example 2

The number of trucks using a road over a 13-day period is : 4 6 3 2 7 8 3 5 5 7 6 6 4.
For this data set, find: **a**   the mean   **b**   the median   **c**   the mode.

a   mean $= \dfrac{4+6+3+2+7+8+3+5+5+7+6+6+4}{13}$ $\longleftarrow$ sum of the data

$\longleftarrow$ 13 data values

$\doteqdot 5.08$ trucks

b   The ordered data set is: 2 3 3 4 4 5 5 6 6 6 7 7 8   {as $n = 13$, $\frac{n+1}{2} = 7$}

$\therefore$ median $= 5$ trucks

c   6 is the score which occurs the most often $\therefore$ mode $= 6$ trucks

For the truck data of **Example 2**, how are the measures of the middle affected if on the 14th
day the number of trucks was 7?

We expect the mean to rise as the new data value is greater than the old mean.

In fact,   new mean $= \dfrac{66 + 7}{14} = \dfrac{73}{14} \doteqdot 5.21$ trucks

The new ordered data set would be: 2 3 3 4 4 5   5 6   6 6 7 7 7 8

two middle scores

$\therefore$ median $= \dfrac{5 + 6}{2} = 5.5$ trucks

This new data set has two modes. The modes are 6 and 7 trucks and we say that the data set
is **bimodal**.

Note: • If a data set has three or more modes, we do not use the mode as a measure of
the middle.

• Consider the data: 4 2 5 6 7 4 5 3 5 4 7 6 3 5 8 6 5.
The dot plot of this data is:

For this data the mean, median and mode are all 5.

Equal values (or approximately equal values) of the mean, mode and median
can indicate a *symmetrical distribution* of data.

EXERCISE 18B.1

1   Find the   **i**   mean   **ii**   median   **iii**   mode   for each of the following data sets:

a   2, 3, 3, 3, 4, 4, 4, 5, 5, 5, 5, 6, 6, 6, 6, 6, 7, 7, 8, 8, 8, 9, 9

b   10, 12, 12, 15, 15, 16, 16, 17, 18, 18, 18, 18, 19, 20, 21

c   22.4, 24.6, 21.8, 26.4, 24.9, 25.0, 23.5, 26.1, 25.3, 29.5, 23.5

2 Consider the following two data sets:

Data set A: 3, 4, 4, 5, 6, 6, 7, 7, 7, 8, 8, 9, 10
Data set B: 3, 4, 4, 5, 6, 6, 7, 7, 7, 8, 8, 9, 15

  a Find the mean for both Data set A and Data set B.
  b Find the median of both Data set A and Data set B.
  c Explain why the mean of Data set A is less than the mean of Data set B.
  d Explain why the median of Data set A is the same as the median of Data set B.

3 The annual salaries of ten office workers are:

$23 000, $46 000, $23 000, $38 000, $24 000,
$23 000, $23 000, $38 000, $23 000, $32 000

  a Find the mean, median and modal salaries of this group.
  b Explain why the mode is an unsatisfactory measure of the middle in this case.
  c Is the median a satisfactory measure of the middle of this data set?

4 The following raw data is the daily rainfall (to the nearest millimetre) for the month of July 2001 in the desert:

3, 1, 0, 0, 0, 0, 0, 2, 0, 0, 3, 0, 0, 0, 7, 1, 1, 0, 3, 8, 0, 0, 0, 42, 21, 3, 0, 3, 1, 0, 0

  a Find the mean, median and mode for the data.
  b Give a reason why the median is not the most suitable measure of centre for this set of data.
  c Give a reason why the mode is not the most suitable measure of centre for this set of data.
  d Are there any outliers in this data set?
  e On some occasions outliers are removed because they are not typical of the rest of the data and are often due to errors in observation and/or calculation. If the outliers in the data set were accurately found, should they be removed before finding the measures of the middle?

5 A basketball team scored 43, 55, 41 and 37 goals in their first four matches.

  a What is the mean number of goals scored for the first four matches?
  b What score will the team need to shoot in the next match so that they maintain the same mean score?
  c The team shoots only 25 goals in the fifth match. What is the mean number of goals scored for the five matches?
  d The team shoots 41 goals in their sixth and final match. Will this increase or decrease their previous mean score? What is the mean score for all six matches?

Example 3	
The mean of five scores is 12.2. What is the sum of the scores?	$\dfrac{\text{sum of scores}}{5} = 12.2$ $\therefore$ sum of scores $= 12.2 \times 5 = 61$ i.e., the sum of scores is 61.

6 The mean of 10 scores is 11.6. What is the sum of the scores?

7 While on an outback safari, Bill drove, on average, 262 km per day for a period of 12 days. How far did Bill drive in total while on safari?

8 The mean monthly sales for a clothing store are $15 467. Calculate the total sales for the store for the year.

9 Find x if 5, 9, 11, 12, 13, 14, 17 and x have a mean of 12.

10 Find a, given that 3, 0, a, a, 4, a, 6, a and 3 have a mean of 4.

11 Over the complete assessment period, Gitta averaged 35 out of a possible 40 marks for her maths tests. However, when checking her files, she could only find 7 of the 8 tests. For these she scored 29, 36, 32, 38, 35, 34 and 39. Determine how many marks out of 40 she scored for the eighth test.

12 A sample of 10 measurements has a mean of 15.7 and a sample of 20 measurements has a mean of 14.3. Find the mean of all 30 measurements.

13 Jana had seven spelling tests, each with twelve words, but could only find the results of five of them. These were: 9, 5, 7, 9 and 10. She asked her teacher for the other two results and the teacher said that the mode of her scores was 9 and the mean was 8. What are the two missing results, given that Jana knows that her worst result was a 5?

DISCUSSION

Which of the measures of the middle is more affected by the presence of an outlier? Develop at least two examples to show how the measures of the middle can be altered by outliers.

MEASURES OF THE CENTRE FROM OTHER SOURCES

When the same data appear several times we often summarise the data in table form. Consider the data of the **given table**:

We can find the measures of the centre directly from the table.

Data value	Frequency	Product
3	1	$3 \times 1 = 3$
4	1	$4 \times 1 = 4$
5	3	$5 \times 3 = 15$
6	7	$6 \times 7 = 42$
7	15	$7 \times 15 = 105$
8	8	$8 \times 8 = 64$
9	5	$9 \times 5 = 45$
Total	40	278

The mode

The mode is 7. There are 15 of data value 7 which is more than any other data value.

The mean

Adding a **'Product' column** to the table helps to add all scores. For example, there are 15 data of value 7 and these add to $15 \times 7 = 105$.

So,   mean $= \dfrac{278}{40} = 6.95$

The median

There are 40 data values, an even number, so there are *two middle* data values. What are they? How do we find them from the table?

As the sample size $n = 40$,

$$\frac{n+1}{2} = \frac{41}{2} = 20.5$$

So, the median is the average of the 20th and 21st data values.

In the table, the blue numbers show us accumulated values.

We can see that the 20th and 21st data values (in order) are both 7's,

$$\therefore \quad \text{median} = \frac{7+7}{2} = 7$$

Data value	Frequency		
3	1	1 ◄	one number is 3
4	1	2 ◄	two numbers are 4 or less
5	3	5 ◄	five numbers are 5 or less
6	7	12 ◄	12 numbers are 6 or less
7	15	27 ◄	27 numbers are 7 or less
8	8		
9	5		
Total	40		

Notice that in this example the distribution is clearly skewed even though the mean, median and mode are nearly equal. So, we must be careful in saying that equal values of these measures of the middle enable us to say with certainty that the distribution is symmetric.

Example 4

The table alongside shows the number of aces served by tennis players in their first set of a tournament.

Number of aces	1	2	3	4	5	6
Frequency	4	11	18	13	7	2

Determine the mean number of aces in the first set.

No. of aces (x)	Freq. (f)	Product ($f\,x$)
1	4	4
2	11	22
3	18	54
4	13	52
5	7	35
6	2	12
Total	55	179

2 aces occurred 11 times. Instead of adding $2 + 2 + ... + 2$, 11 times we simply calculate 11×2.

$$\bar{x} = = \frac{\sum fx}{\sum f}$$

$$= \frac{179}{55}$$

$$\doteqdot 3.25 \text{ aces}$$

Note: $\bar{x} = \dfrac{\sum\limits_{i=1}^{6} f_i x_i}{\sum\limits_{i=1}^{6} f_i}$ has been abbreviated to $\bar{x} = \dfrac{\sum fx}{\sum f}$.

Example 5

In a class of 20 students the results of a spelling test out of 10 are shown in the table.

Calculate the:

a mean

b median

c mode

Score	Number of students
5	1
6	2
7	4
8	7
9	4
10	2
Total	20

a $\sum f = 20$

and $\sum fx = 1 \times 5 + 2 \times 6 + 4 \times 7 + 7 \times 8 + 4 \times 9 + 2 \times 10 = 157$

$\therefore \quad \overline{x} = \dfrac{\sum fx}{\sum f} = \dfrac{157}{20} = 7.85$

b   There are 20 scores, and so the median is the average of the 10th and the 11th

Score	Number of students	
5	1	← 1st student
6	2	← 2nd and 3rd student
7	4	← 4th, 5th, 6th and 7th student
8	7	← 8th, 9th, **10th, 11th**, 12th, 13th, 14th student
9	4	
10	2	

The 10th and 11th students both scored 8

$\therefore$ median $= 8$.

c   Looking down the 'number of students' column, the highest frequency is 7. This corresponds to a score of 8, $\therefore$ mode $= 8$.

POTTS

© Jim Russell, General Features Pty Ltd.

The publishers acknowledge the late Mr Jim Russell, General Features for the reproduction of this cartoon

EXERCISE 18B.2

1   The table alongside shows the results when 3 coins were tossed simultaneously 30 times. The number of heads appearing was recorded. Calculate the:

a   mode   **b**   median   **c**   mean.

Number of heads	Number of times occurred
0	4
1	12
2	11
3	3
Total	30

2   The following frequency table records the number of phone calls made in a day by 50 fifteen-year-olds.

No. of phone calls	Frequency
0	5
1	8
2	13
3	8
4	6
5	3
6	3
7	2
8	1
11	1

a   For this data, find the:
   i mean **ii** median **iii** mode.

b   Construct a column graph for the data and show the position of the measures of centre (mean, median and mode) on the horizontal axis.

c   Describe the distribution of the data.

d   Why is the mean larger than the median for this data?

e   Which measure of centre would be the most suitable for this data set?

3   A company claims that their match boxes contain, on average, 50 matches per box. On doing a survey, the Consumer Protection Society recorded the following results:

Number in a box	Frequency
47	5
48	4
49	11
50	6
51	3
52	1
Total	30

a   For the data calculate the:
   i mode **ii** median **iii** mean.

b   Do the results of this survey support the company's claim?

c   In court for 'false advertising', the company won their case against the Consumer Protection Society. Suggest why and how they did this.

4   Families at a school were surveyed. The number of children in each family was recorded. The results of the survey are shown alongside.

Number of Children	Frequencies
1	5
2	28
3	15
4	8
5	2
6	1
Total	59

   a   Calculate the:
      i mean **ii** mode **iii** median.
   b   The average Australian family has 2.2 children. How does this school compare to the national average?

c   The data set is skewed. Is the skewness positive or negative?

d   How has the skewness of the data affected the measures of this middle?

5   For the data displayed in the following stem-and-leaf plots find the:
   i mean   **ii** median   **iii** mode.

a

Stem	Leaf
5	3 5 6
6	0 1 2 4 6 7 9
7	3 3 6 8
8	4 7
9	1 where 5	3 means 53

b

Stem	Leaf
3	7
4	0 4 8 8
5	0 0 1 3 6 7 8 9
6	0 3 6 7 7 7
7	0 6 9
8	1 where 3	7 means 3.7

6 Revisit **The Pea Problem** on page **458**.

   a Use a frequency table for the *Without fertiliser* data to find the:
     i mean   **ii** mode   **iii** median   number of peas per pod.

   b Use a frequency table for the *With fertiliser* data to find the:
     i mean   **ii** mode   **iii** median   number of peas per pod.

   c Which of the measures of 'the centre' is appropriate to use in a report on this data?

   d Has the application of fertiliser significantly improved the number of peas per pod?

7 The selling prices of the last 10 houses sold in a certain district were as follows:

$146 400, $127 600, $211 000, $192 500,
$256 400, $132 400, $148 000, $129 500,
$131 400, $162 500

   a Calculate the mean and median selling prices and comment on the results.

   b Which measure would you use if you were:
     i a vendor wanting to sell your house
     ii looking to buy a house in the district?

8 The table alongside compares the mass at birth of some guinea pigs with their mass when they were two weeks old.

   a What was the mean birth mass?

   b What was the mean mass after two weeks?

   c What was the mean increase over the two weeks?

Guinea Pig	Mass (g) at birth	Mass (g) at 2 weeks
A	75	210
B	70	200
C	80	200
D	70	220
E	74	215
F	60	200
G	55	206
H	83	230

9 15 of 31 measurements are below 10 cm and 12 measurements are above 11 cm. Find the median if the other 4 measurements are 10.1 cm, 10.4 cm, 10.7 cm and 10.9 cm.

10 Two brands of matches claim that their boxes contain, on average, 50 matches per box. On doing a survey the Consumer Protection Society (C.P.S.) recorded the following results:

Brand A

number in a box	46	47	48	49	50	51	52	53	55
frequency	1	1	2	7	10	20	15	3	1

Brand B

number in a box	48	49	50	51	52	53	54
frequency	3	17	30	7	2	1	1

   a Find the average contents of Brands A and B.

   b Would it be 'fair' of the C.P.S. to prosecute the manufacturers of either brand, based on these statistics?

11 Towards the end of season, a netballer had played 14 matches and had an average of 16.5 goals per game. In the final two matches of the season the netballer threw 21 goals and 24 goals. Find the netballer's new average.

12 The mean and median of a set of 9 measurements are both 12. If 7 of the measurements are   7, 9, 11, 13, 14, 17 and 19,   find the other two measurements.

13 In an office of 20 people there are only 4 salary levels paid:

$50 000 (1 person), $42 000 (3 people), $35 000 (6 people), $28 000 (10 people).

   a Calculate: **i** the median salary **ii** the modal salary **iii** the mean salary.

   b Which measure of central tendency would be used by a top salary earner if she is the boss and is against a pay rise for the other employees?

GROUPED DATA

When information has been gathered in classes we use the **midpoint** of the class to represent all scores within that interval.

We are assuming that the scores within each class are evenly distributed throughout that interval. The mean calculated will therefore be an **approximation** to the true value.

Example 6

Find the approximate mean of the *ages of bus drivers* data, to the nearest year:

age (yrs)	21-25	26-30	31-35	36-40	41-45	46-50	51-55
frequency	11	14	32	27	29	17	7

age (yrs)	frequency (f)	midpoint (x)	f x
21-25	11	23	253
26-30	14	28	392
31-35	32	33	1056
36-40	27	38	1026
41-45	29	43	1247
46-50	17	48	816
51-55	7	53	371
Total	137		5161

$$\bar{x} = \frac{\sum f x}{\sum f}$$

$$\doteqdot \frac{5161}{137}$$

$$\doteqdot 37.7$$

EXERCISE 18B.3

1 50 students sit a mathematics test and the results are as follows:

Score	0-9	10-19	20-29	30-39	40-49
Frequency	2	5	7	27	9

Find an estimate of the mean score.

2 The table shows the petrol sales in one day by a number of city service stations.

   a How many service stations were involved in the survey?

   b Estimate the total amount of petrol sold for the day by the service stations.

   c Find the approximate mean sales of petrol for the day.

Thousands of litres (l)	frequency
2000 to 2999	4
3000 to 3999	4
4000 to 4999	9
5000 to 5999	14
6000 to 6999	23
7000 to 7999	16

3 This histogram illustrates the results of an aptitude test given to a group of people seeking positions in a company.

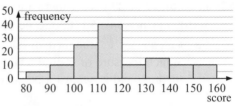

   a How many people sat for the test?

   b Find an estimate of the mean score for the test.

   c What fraction of the people scored less than 100 for the test?

   d If the top 20% of the people are offered positions in the company, estimate the minimum mark required.

C   CUMULATIVE DATA

Sometimes it is useful to know the number of scores that lie above or below a particular value. In such situations it is convenient to construct a **cumulative frequency distribution table** and use a graph called an **ogive (cumulative frequency polygon)** to represent the data.

Example 7

The data shown gives the weights of 120 male footballers.

   a Construct a cumulative frequency distribution table.

   b Represent the data on an ogive.

   c Use your graph to estimate the:

     i median weight

     ii number of men weighing less than 73 kg

     iii number of men weighing more than 92 kg.

Weight (w kg)	frequency
$55 \leqslant w < 60$	2
$60 \leqslant w < 65$	3
$65 \leqslant w < 70$	12
$70 \leqslant w < 75$	14
$75 \leqslant w < 80$	19
$80 \leqslant w < 85$	37
$85 \leqslant w < 90$	22
$90 \leqslant w < 95$	8
$95 \leqslant w < 100$	2
$100 \leqslant w < 105$	1

a

Weight (w kg)	frequency	cumulative frequency
$55 \leqslant w < 60$	2	2
$60 \leqslant w < 65$	3	5
$65 \leqslant w < 70$	12	17
$70 \leqslant w < 75$	14	31
$75 \leqslant w < 80$	19	50
$80 \leqslant w < 85$	37	87
$85 \leqslant w < 90$	22	109
$90 \leqslant w < 95$	8	117
$95 \leqslant w < 100$	2	119
$100 \leqslant w < 105$	1	120

this is $2 + 3$

this is $2 + 3 + 12$, etc.

this 50 means that there are 50 players who weigh less than 80 kg

Note: The cumulative frequency gives a *running total* of the number of players up to certain weights.

b   **Ogive of footballers' weights**

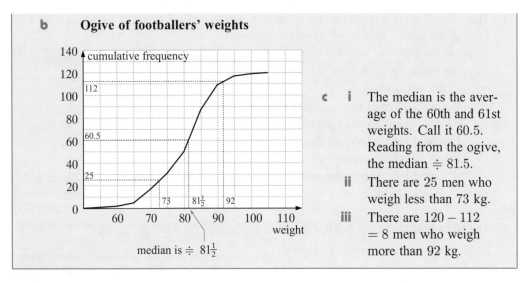

median is $\doteqdot 81\frac{1}{2}$

c **i** The median is the average of the 60th and 61st weights. Call it 60.5. Reading from the ogive, the median $\doteqdot 81.5$.

ii There are 25 men who weigh less than 73 kg.

iii There are $120 - 112 = 8$ men who weigh more than 92 kg.

EXERCISE 18C

1   The following frequency distribution was obtained by asking 50 randomly selected people the size of their shoes.

Shoe size	5	$5\frac{1}{2}$	6	$6\frac{1}{2}$	7	$7\frac{1}{2}$	8	$8\frac{1}{2}$	9	$9\frac{1}{2}$	10
frequency	1	1	0	3	5	13	17	7	2	0	1

Draw a cumulative frequency graph of the data and use it to find:

a   the median shoe size

b   how many people had a shoe size of: **i** $7\frac{1}{2}$ or more   **ii**   8 or less.

2   The following data shows the lengths of 30 trout caught in a lake during a fishing competition. Measurements are to the nearest centimetre.

31 38 34 40 24 33 30 36 38 32 35 32 36 27 35
40 34 37 44 38 36 34 33 31 38 35 36 33 33 28

a   Construct a cumulative frequency table for trout lengths, x cm, using the following intervals $24 \leqslant x < 27, \ 27 \leqslant x < 30, \ ....$ etc.

b   Draw a cumulative frequency graph.   **c**   Use **b** to find the median length.

d   Use the original data to find its median and compare your answer with **c**. Comment!

3   In an examination the following scores were achieved by a group of students:

Draw a cumulative frequency graph of the data and use it to find:

a   the median examination mark

b   how many students scored less than 65 marks

c   how many students scored between 50 and 70 marks

d   how many students failed, given that the pass mark was 45

e   the credit mark, given that the top 16% of students were awarded credits.

Score	frequency
$10 \leqslant x < 20$	2
$20 \leqslant x < 30$	5
$30 \leqslant x < 40$	7
$40 \leqslant x < 50$	21
$50 \leqslant x < 60$	36
$60 \leqslant x < 70$	40
$70 \leqslant x < 80$	27
$80 \leqslant x < 90$	9
$90 \leqslant x < 100$	3

4   The following table gives the age groups of car drivers involved in an accident in a city
    for a given year. Draw a cumulative frequency
    graph of the data and use it to find:

Age (in years)	No. of accidents
$16 \leqslant x < 20$	59
$20 \leqslant x < 25$	82
$25 \leqslant x < 30$	43
$30 \leqslant x < 35$	21
$35 \leqslant x < 40$	19
$40 \leqslant x < 50$	11
$50 \leqslant x < 60$	24
$60 \leqslant x < 80$	41

   a   the median age of the drivers involved
       in the accidents
   b   the percentage of drivers, with ages of
       23 or less, involved in accidents.
   c   Estimate the probability that a driver
       involved in an accident is:
       i   aged less than or equal to 27 years
       ii aged 27 years.

5   The table below gives the distribution of the life of electric light globes.

    Draw a cumulative frequency graph of
    the data and use it to estimate:

Life (hours)	Number of globes
$0 \leqslant l < 500$	5
$500 \leqslant l < 1000$	17
$1000 \leqslant l < 2000$	46
$2000 \leqslant l < 3000$	79
$3000 \leqslant l < 4000$	27
$4000 \leqslant l < 5000$	4

   a   the median life of a globe
   b   the percentage of globes which
       have a life of 2700 hours or less
   c   the number of globes which have a
       life between 1500 and 2500 hours.

D   MEASURING THE SPREAD OF DATA

We use two measures to describe a distribution.
These are its **centre** and its **variability** (or **spread**).

The given distributions have the same mean, but
clearly they have a different spread. For example,
the A distribution has most scores close to the mean
whereas the C distribution has greater spread.

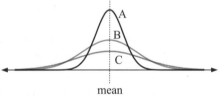

Consequently, we need to consider measures of variability (spread), and we will examine three
of these measures: the **range**, the **interquartile range** (**IQR**) and the **standard deviation**.

THE RANGE

For a given set of data the **range** is the difference between the maximum (largest) and the
minimum (smallest) data values.

Example 8

A greengrocer chain is to purchase apples from two different wholesalers. They take
six random samples of 50 apples to examine them for skin blemishes. The counts for
the number of blemished apples are: *Wholesaler Redapp*   5   17   15   3   9   11
                                       Wholesaler Pureapp   10   13   12   11   12   11
What is the range from each wholesaler?

Redapp   Range $= 17 - 3 = 14$ *Pureapp*   Range $= 13 - 10 = 3$

Note: The **range** is not considered to be a particularly reliable measure of spread as it uses only two data values.

THE UPPER AND LOWER QUARTILES AND THE INTERQUARTILE RANGE

The median divides the ordered data set into two halves and these halves are divided in half again by the **quartiles**.

The middle value of the lower half is called the **lower quartile**. One-quarter, or 25%, of the data have a value less than or equal to the lower quartile. 75% of the data have values greater than or equal to the lower quartile.

The middle value of the upper half is called the **upper quartile**. One-quarter, or 25%, of the data have a value greater than or equal to the upper quartile. 75% of the data have values less than or equal to the upper quartile.

interquartile range = upper quartile − lower quartile

The interquartile range is the range of the middle half (50%) of the data.

The data set has been divided into quarters by the lower quartile (Q_1), the median (Q_2) and the upper quartile (Q_3).

So, the **interquartile range**, $\mathbf{IQR = Q_3 - Q_1}$.

Example 9

For the data set: 6, 4, 7, 5, 3, 4, 2, 6, 5, 7, 5, 3, 8, 9, 3, 6, 5   find the
a median **b** lower quartile **c** upper quartile **d** interquartile range

The ordered data set is:
   2 3 3 3 4 4 5 5 5 5 6 6 6 7 7 8 9 (17 of them)

a   The median $= \left(\frac{17+1}{2}\right)$th score $=$ 9th score $= 5$

b/c   As the median is a data value we now ignore it and split the remaining data into two

   lower   upper $Q_1 =$ median of lower half $= \dfrac{3+4}{2} = 3.5$
   2 3 3 3 4 4 5 5   5 6 6 6 7 7 8 9
                                 $Q_3 =$ median of upper half $= \dfrac{6+7}{2} = 6.5$

d   IQR $= Q_3 - Q_1 = 6.5 - 3.5 = 3$

Example 10

For the data set: 11, 6, 7, 8, 13, 10, 8, 7, 5, 2, 9, 4, 4, 5, 8, 2, 3, 6 find
   a   the median   **b** Q_1 **c** Q_3 **d**   the interquartile range

The ordered data set is:
   2 2 3 4 4 5 5 6 6 7 7 8 8 8 9 10 11 13   (18 of them)

a   As $n = 18$, $\dfrac{n+1}{2} = 9.5$

   $\therefore$ median $= \dfrac{\text{9th value} + \text{10th value}}{2} = \dfrac{6+7}{2} = 6.5$

b/c   As the median is not a data value we split the data into two

lower   upper

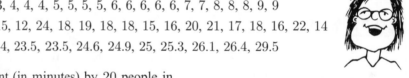

$\overbrace{2\ 2\ 3\ 4\ \boxed{4}\ 5\ 5\ 6\ 6}\ \ \overbrace{7\ 7\ 8\ 8\ \boxed{8}\ 9\ 10\ 11\ 13}$

   $\therefore$ $Q_1 = 4$, $Q_3 = 8$

Note: Some computer packages calculate quartiles in a different way to this example.

d   IQR $= Q_3 - Q_1$
   $= 8 - 4$
   $= 4$

EXERCISE 18D.1

Small sample, rounded continuous data, can often be treated in the same way as discrete data for the purpose of analysis.

1 For each of the following data sets, find:
- **i**   the median (make sure the data is ordered)
- **ii**   the upper and lower quartiles
- **iii**   the range   **iv**   the interquartile range.

a   2, 3, 3, 3, 4, 4, 4, 5, 5, 5, 5, 6, 6, 6, 6, 6, 7, 7, 8, 8, 8, 9, 9

b   10, 12, 15, 12, 24, 18, 19, 18, 18, 15, 16, 20, 21, 17, 18, 16, 22, 14

c   21.8, 22.4, 23.5, 23.5, 24.6, 24.9, 25, 25.3, 26.1, 26.4, 29.5

2 The time spent (in minutes) by 20 people in a queue at a bank waiting to be attended by a teller, has been recorded as follows:

3.4	2.1	3.8	2.2	4.5	1.4	0
0	1.6	4.8	1.5	1.9	0	3.6
5.2	2.7	3.0	0.8	3.8	5.2	

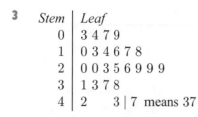

a Find the median waiting time and the upper and lower quartiles.

b Find the range and interquartile range of the waiting time.

c Copy and complete the following statements:
- **i**   "50% of the waiting times were greater than .... minutes."
- **ii**   "75% of the waiting times were less than ...... minutes."
- **iii**   "The minimum waiting time was .... minutes and the maximum waiting time was ..... minutes. The waiting times were spread over ...... minutes."

3

Stem	Leaf
0	3 4 7 9
1	0 3 4 6 7 8
2	0 0 3 5 6 9 9 9
3	1 3 7 8
4	2

$3 \mid 7$ means 37

For the data set given, find:
- **a**   the minimum value
- **b**   the maximum value
- **c**   the median
- **d**   the lower quartile
- **e**   the upper quartile
- **f**   the range
- **g**   the interquartile range.

4   The heights of 20 six-year-olds are recorded in the following stem-and-leaf plot:

Stem	Leaf
10	9
11	1 3 4 4 8 9
12	2 2 4 4 6 8 9 9
13	1 2 5 8 8

10 | 9   reads 109 cm

  a Find:

      i the median height

      ii the upper and lower quartiles of the data.

  b Copy and complete the following statements:

      i "Half of the children are no more than ..... cm tall."

      ii "75% of the children are no more than ......cm tall."

  c Find the: **i** range **ii** interquartile range for the height of six year olds.

  d Copy and complete:

    "The middle 50% of the children have heights spread over ..... cm."

5   Revisit **The Pea Problem** on page **458**.

  a For the *Without fertiliser* data, find:

      i the range   **ii** the median

      iii the lower quartile   **iv** the upper quartile

      v the interquartile range

  b Repeat **a** for the *With fertiliser* data.

  c Reconsider the questions posed. Amend your solutions where appropriate.

BOX-AND-WHISKER PLOTS

A **box-and-whisker plot** (or simply a **boxplot**) is a visual display of some of the descriptive statistics of a data set. It shows:

> - the minimum value (Min_x)
> - the lower quartile (Q_1)
> - the median (Q_2) These five numbers form what is known
> - the upper quartile (Q_3) as the **five-number summary** of a data set.
> - the maximum value (Max_x)

In **Example 10** on page **477** the **five-number summary** is

minimum $= 2$ and the corresponding boxplot is:

$Q_1 = 4$

median $= 6.5$

$Q_3 = 8$

maximum $= 13$

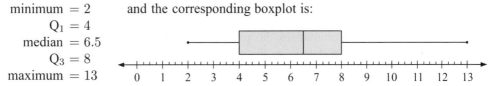

Note:
- The rectangular box represents the 'middle' half of the data set.
- The lower whisker represents the 25% of the data with smallest values.
- The upper whisker represents the 25% of the data with greatest values.

Example 11

For the data set: 4 5 9 5 1 7 8 7 3 5 6 3 4 3 2 5

a   construct the five-number summary
b   draw a boxplot
c   find the   i   range   ii   interquartile range
d   the percentage of data values above 3.

a   The ordered data set is

$$1 \quad 2 \quad 3 \quad \boxed{3 \quad 3} \quad 4 \quad 4 \quad \boxed{5 \; 5} \quad 5 \quad 5 \quad \boxed{6 \quad 7} \quad 7 \quad 8 \quad 9 \quad \text{(16 of them)}$$

$$Q_1 = 3 \qquad \text{median} = 5 \qquad Q_3 = 6.5$$

So the **5-number summary** is:
$$\begin{cases} \text{min. value} = 1 & Q_1 = 3 \\ \text{median} = 5 & Q_3 = 6.5 \\ \text{max. value} = 9 \end{cases}$$

b
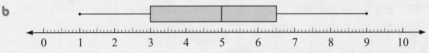

c   i   range = max. value $-$ min. value   ii   IQR = $Q_3 - Q_1$
$\qquad\qquad\quad = 9 - 1$ $\qquad\qquad\qquad\qquad\qquad\qquad\quad = 6.5 - 3$
$\qquad\qquad\quad = 8$ $\qquad\qquad\qquad\qquad\qquad\qquad\qquad = 3.5$

d   75% of the data values are above 3.

EXERCISE 18D.2

1
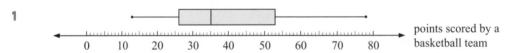
points scored by a basketball team

a   The boxplot given summarises the goals scored by a basketball team. Locate:
     i   the median   ii   the maximum value   iii   the minimum value
     iv   the upper quartile   v   the lower quartile
b   Calculate: i   the range   ii   the interquartile range

2
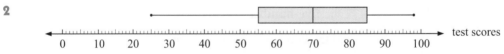
test scores

The boxplot shown summarises the results of a test (out of 100 marks). Copy and complete the following statements about the test results:

a   The highest mark scored for the test was ...... , the lowest mark was ......
b   Half of the class scored a mark greater than or equal to .....
c   The top 25% of the class scored at least ..... marks for the test.
d   The middle half of the class had scores between .... and .... for this test.
e   Find the range of the data set.
f   Find the interquartile range of the data set.

3 For the following data sets:

      i construct a 5-number summary   **ii** draw a boxplot

      iii find the range   **iv** find the interquartile range

a 3, 5, 5, 7, 10, 9, 4,   **b** 3, 7, 0, 1, 4, 6, 8,   **c**

Stem	Leaf
11	7
12	0 3 6 6 8
13	0 1 1 1 3 5 5 7
14	4 7 7 9 9
15	1

     7, 8, 6, 6, 5, 8, 6   8, 8, 9, 7, 5, 6, 8,

                       7, 8, 8, 2, 9

                                              11 | 7 reps 117

4 The following boxplots compare the time students in years 9 and 12 spend on homework over a one week period.

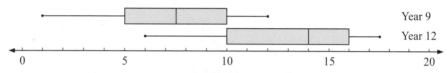

a Copy and complete:

Statistic	Year 9	Year 12
min. value		
Q_1		
median		
Q_3		
max. value		

b Determine the: **i** range **ii** interquartile range   for each group.

c True or false:

    i On average, Year 12 students spend about twice as much time on homework as Year 9 students.

    ii Over 25% of Year 9 students spend less time on homework than all Year 12 students.

5 Chorn examines a new variety of bean and does a count on the number of beans in 33 pods. Her results were:

5, 8, 10, 4, 2, 12, 6, 5, 7, 7, 5, 5, 5, 13, 9, 3, 4, 4, 7, 8, 9, 5, 5, 4, 3, 6, 6, 6, 6, 9, 8, 7, 6

    a Find the median, lower quartile and upper quartile of the data set.

    b Find the interquartile range of the data set.

    c Draw a boxplot of the data set.

6 Ranji counts the number of bolts in several boxes and tabulates the data as shown below:

Number of bolts	33	34	35	36	37	38	39	40
Frequency	1	5	7	13	12	8	0	1

    a Find the five-number summary for this data set.

    b Find the **i** range   **ii** IQR   for this data set.

    c Construct a boxplot for the data set.

PERCENTILES

> A **percentile** is the score, below which a certain percentage of the data lies.

For example, the 85th percentile is the score below which 85% of the data lies.

> Notice that: • the **lower quartile** (Q_1) is the 25th percentile
> • the **median** (Q_2) is the 50th percentile
> • the **upper quartile** (Q_3) is the 75th percentile.

If your score in a test is the 95th percentile, then 95% of the class have scored less than you.

Note:

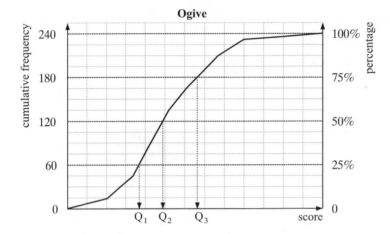

7 A botanist has measured the heights of 60 seedlings and has presented her findings on the ogive below.

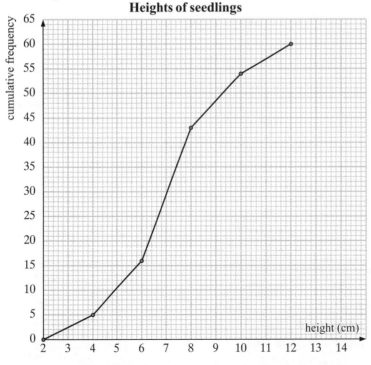

Heights of seedlings

a How many seedlings have heights of 5 cm or less?

b What percentage of seedlings are taller than 8 cm?

c What is the median height?

d What is the interquartile range for the heights?

e Find the 90th percentile for the data and explain what your answer means.

8   The following ogive displays the performance of 80 competitors in a cross-country race.

Cross-country race times

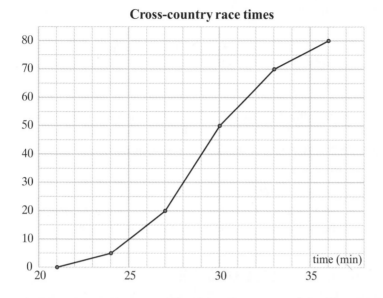

Find:

a   the lower quartile time

b   the median

c   the upper quartile

d   the interquartile range

e   an estimate of the 40th percentile.

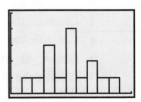

E   STATISTICS USING TECHNOLOGY

GRAPHICS CALCULATOR

A **graphics calculator** can be used to find descriptive statistics and to draw some types of graphs. (You will need to change the **viewing window** as appropriate.)

Consider the data set: 5 2 3 3 6 4 5 3 7 5 7 1 8 9 5

No matter what brand of calculator you use you should be able to:

- Enter the data as a **list**.

- Enter the **statistics calculation** part of the menu and obtain the descriptive statistics like these shown.

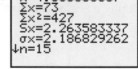

$\overline{x}$ is the mean

5-number summary

- Obtain a box-and-whisker plot such as:

(These screen dumps are from a TI-83.)

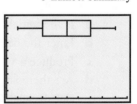

- Obtain a vertical barchart if required.

- Enter a second data set into another
  list and obtain a side-by-side boxplot
  for comparison with the first one.

  Use: 9 6 2 3 5 5 7 5 6 7 6 3 4 4 5 8 4

Now you should be able to create these by yourself.

EXERCISE 18E.1

1 **a** For your calculator enter the data set: 5 2 3 3 6 4 5 3 7 5 7 1 8 9 5 and obtain
the mean and the 5-number summary. This is the first graphics calculator example
shown on page **483** and you should check your results from it.

   b Obtain the boxplot for part **a**.

   c Obtain the vertical bar chart for part **a**.

   d Enter this data set: 9 6 2 3 5 5 7 5 6 7 6 3 4 4 5 8 4 into a second list. Find
the mean and 5-number summary. Now create a side-by-side boxplot for both sets
of data.

STATISTICS FROM A COMPUTER PACKAGE

Click on the icon to enter the **statistics package** on the CD.

Enter data set 1:   5 2 3 3 6 4 5 3 7 5 7 1 8 9 5
Enter data set 2:   9 6 2 3 5 5 7 5 6 7 6 3 4 4 5 8 4

Examine the side-by-side column graphs.

Click on the Box-and-Whisker spot to view the side-by-side boxplots.

Click on the Statistics spot to obtain the descriptive statistics.

Click on Print to obtain a print-out of all of these on one sheet of paper.

STATISTICS
PACKAGE

EXERCISE 18E.2 (Computer package and/or graphics calculator)

1 Shane and Brett play in the same cricket team and are fierce but friendly rivals when
it comes to bowling. During a season the number of wickets per innings taken by each
bowler was recorded as:

Shane: 1   6   2   0   3   4   1   4   2   3   0   3   2   4   3   4   3   3
         3   4   2   4   3   2   3   3   0   5   3   5   3   2   4   3   4   3

Brett: 7   2   4   8   1   3   4   2   3   0   5   3   5   2   3   1   2   0
         4   3   4   0   3   3   0   2   5   1   1   2   2   5   1   4   0   1

   a Is the variable discrete or continuous?

   b Enter the data into a graphics calculator or statistics package.

   c Produce a vertical column graph for each data set.

   d Are there any outliers? Should they be deleted before we
start to analyse the data?

   e Describe the shape of each distribution.

   f Compare the measures of the centre of each distribution.

   g Compare the spreads of each distribution.

   h Obtain side-by-side boxplots.

   i If using the statistics package, print out the graphs, boxplots and relevant statistics.

   j What conclusions, if any, can be drawn from the data?

2   A manufacturer of light globes claims that the newly invented type has a life 20% longer than the current globe type. Forty of each globe type are randomly selected and tested. Here are the results to the nearest hour.

Old type:	103	96	113	111	126	100	122	110	84	117
	111	87	90	121	99	114	105	121	93	109
	87	127	117	131	115	116	82	130	113	95
	103	113	104	104	87	118	75	111	108	112

New type:	146	131	132	160	128	119	133	117	139	123
	191	117	132	107	141	136	146	142	123	144
	133	124	153	129	118	130	134	151	145	131
	109	129	109	131	145	125	164	125	133	135

a   Is the variable discrete or continuous?

b   Enter the data into a graphics calculator or statistics package.

c   Are there any outliers? Should they be deleted before we start to analyse the data?

d   Compare the measures of centre and spread.

e   Obtain side-by-side boxplots.

f   Describe the shape of each distribution.

g   What conclusions, if any, can be drawn from the data?

F   VARIANCE AND STANDARD DEVIATION

The problem with the range and the IQR as a measure of spread is that both only use two values in their calculation. Some data sets can have their characteristics hidden when the IQR is quoted. It would be helpful if we could have a measure of spread that used all of the data values in its calculation. One such statistic is the **variance** (s^2).

Variance measures the average of the squared deviations of each data value from the mean.

The **deviation** of a data value x from the mean $\overline{x}$ is given by $x - \overline{x}$.

For a **sample**:

- the **variance** is $s_n^2 = \dfrac{\sum(x - \overline{x})^2}{n}$ where n is the sample size.

- the **standard deviation** is $s_n = \sqrt{\dfrac{\sum(x - \overline{x})^2}{n}}$.

For a **population**, the mean μ and the standard deviation σ are generally unknown and so we use:

- $\overline{x}$ to estimate the value of μ

- $s_{n-1}^2 = \dfrac{n}{n-1} s_n^2$ as an unbiased estimate of σ^2

    (So, $s_{n-1} = \sqrt{\dfrac{n}{n-1}} s_n$ is an unbiased estimate of σ)

Note: σ is the Greek letter *sigma* (lower case).

Another point to note is that the standard deviation is a **non-resistant** measure of spread. This is due to its dependence on the mean of the sample and that extreme values will give large values for $(x - \overline{x})^2$. It is only a useful measure if the distribution is approximately symmetrical. It does however have a powerful use when the data from which it came is **normally distributed**. This will be discussed later. Clearly the IQR and percentiles are more appropriate tools for measuring spread if the distribution is considerably skewed.

Example 12

Find the means and standard deviations for the apple samples of **Example 8**.
What do these statistics tell us?

Wholesaler Redapp

x	$x - \overline{x}$	$(x - \overline{x})^2$
5	−5	25
17	7	49
15	5	25
3	−7	49
9	−1	1
11	1	1
60	*Total*	150

$$\therefore \quad \overline{x} = \frac{60}{6} \qquad s = \sqrt{\frac{\sum(x - \overline{x})^2}{n}}$$
$$= 10 \qquad\qquad = \sqrt{\frac{150}{6}}$$
$$= 5$$

Wholesaler Pureapp

x	$x - \overline{x}$	$(x - \overline{x})^2$
10	−1.5	2.25
13	1.5	2.25
12	0.5	0.25
11	−0.5	0.25
12	0.5	0.25
11	−0.5	0.25
69	*Total*	5.5

$$\therefore \quad \overline{x} = \frac{69}{6} \qquad s = \sqrt{\frac{\sum(x - \overline{x})^2}{n}}$$
$$= 11.5 \qquad\qquad = \sqrt{\frac{5.5}{6}}$$
$$\doteqdot 0.957$$

Clearly, Wholesaler Purapp supplied apples with more blemishes on average but with less variability (smaller standard deviation) than for those supplied by Redapp.

Note: The sum of the deviations should always be 0.

EXERCISE 18F

1 Netballers Sally and Joanne compare their goal throwing scores for the last 8 matches.

Goals by Sally	23	17	31	25	25	19	28	32
Goals by Joanne	9	29	41	26	14	44	38	43

a Find the mean and standard deviation for the number of goals thrown by each goal shooter for these matches.

b Which measure is used to determine which of the goal shooters is more consistent?

2 Two test cricketers compare their bowling performances for the ten test matches for 2002. The number of wickets per match was recorded as:

Glen	0	10	1	9	11	0	8	5	6	7
Shane	4	3	4	1	4	11	7	6	12	5

a Show that each bowler has the same mean and range.

b Which performance do you suspect is more variable, Glen's bowling over the period or Shane's?

c Check your answer to **b** by finding the standard deviation for each distribution.

d Does the range or the standard deviation give a better indication of variability?

3 A manufacturer of softdrinks employs a statistician for quality control. Suppose that he needs to check that 375 mL of drink goes into each can. The machine which fills the cans may malfunction or slightly change its delivery due to constant vibration or other factors.

a Would you expect the standard deviation for the whole production run to be the same for one day as it is for one week? Explain.

b If samples of 125 cans are taken each day, what measure would be used to:

i check that 375 mL of drink goes into each can

ii check the variability of the volume of drink going into each can?

c What is the significance of a low standard deviation in this case?

4 The weights, in kg, of a sample of seven footballers are: 79, 64, 59, 71, 68, 68 and 74.

a Find the sample mean and standard deviation.

b Surprisingly, each footballer's weight had increased by exactly 10 kg when measured five years later. Find the new sample mean and standard deviation.

c Comment on your findings from **a** and **b** in general terms.

5 The weights of a sample of ten young turkeys to the nearest 0.1 kg are:

0.8,   1.1,   1.2,   0.9,   1.2,   1.2,   0.9,   0.7,   1.0,   1.1

a Find the sample mean and standard deviation.

b After being fed a special diet for one month, the weights of the turkeys doubled. Find the new sample mean and standard deviation.

c Comment, in general terms, on your findings from **a** and **b**.

Example 13

A random sample of 48 sheep was taken from a flock of over 2000 of them. The sample mean of their weights is 23.6 kg with variance 4.34 kg.

a Find the standard deviation of the sample.

b Find an unbiased estimation of the mean weight of sheep in the flock.

c Find an unbiased estimation of the standard deviation of the population from which the sample was taken

---

a $s_n = \sqrt{\text{variance}} = \sqrt{4.34} \doteqdot 2.08$ kg

b μ is estimated by $\bar{x} = 23.6$ kg

c σ is estimated by $s_{n-1} = \sqrt{\dfrac{n}{n-1}} s_n = \sqrt{\dfrac{48}{47}} \times 2.08 \doteqdot 2.11$ kg

6 A random sample of 87 deer from a huge herd had a mean weight of 93.8 kg with a variance of 45.9 kg.

  a Find the standard deviation of the sample.

  b Find an unbiased estimation of the mean and standard deviation of the entire herd from which the sample was taken.

7 The weights (in grams) of a random sample of sparrows are as follows:

  87 75 68 69 81 89 73 66 91 77 84 83 77 74 80 76 67

  a Find the mean and standard deviation of the sample.

  b Find unbiased estimates of the mean and standard deviation of the population from which the sample was taken.

8 A sample of 8 integers has a mean of 5 and a variance of 5.25 .
The integers are: 1, 3, 5, 7, 4, 5, p, q. Find p and q given that $p < q$.

9 A sample of 10 integers has a mean of 6 and a variance of 3.2 .
The integers are: 3, 9, 5, 5, 6, 4, a, 6, b, 8. Find a and b given that $a > b$.

10 **a** Show that $\displaystyle\sum_{i=1}^{3}(x_i - \bar{x})^2 = \sum_{i=1}^{3}(x_i^2) - 3\bar{x}^2$ and state the generalisation of this result.

  b When Jacko drives to the beach 16 times, he records his travel time x_i, in minutes.

  He finds that $\displaystyle\sum_{i=1}^{16} x_i = 519$ and $\displaystyle\sum_{i=1}^{16}(x_i^2) = 16\,983$.

  Calculate unbiased estimates of **i** the mean and **ii** the variance   driving times.

Note: In general, $\displaystyle\sum_{i=1}^{n}(x_i - \bar{x})^2 = \sum_{i=1}^{n}(x_i^2) - n\bar{x}^2.$

STANDARD DEVIATION FOR GROUPED DATA

For grouped data $s = \sqrt{\dfrac{\sum f(x - \bar{x})^2}{\sum f}}$ where

s is the **standard deviation**
x is **any score**, $\bar{x}$ is the **mean**
f is the **frequency** of each score

Example 14

Find the standard deviation of the distribution:

score	1	2	3	4	5
frequency	1	2	4	2	1

x	f	fx	$x - \bar{x}$	$(x - \bar{x})^2$	$f(x - \bar{x})^2$
1	1	1	-2	4	4
2	2	4	-1	1	2
3	4	12	0	0	0
4	2	8	1	1	2
5	1	5	2	4	4
Total	10	30			12

$\bar{x} = \dfrac{\sum fx}{\sum f} = \dfrac{30}{10} = 3$

$s = \sqrt{\dfrac{\sum f(x - \bar{x})^2}{\sum f}}$

$= \sqrt{\dfrac{12}{10}}$

$\doteqdot 1.10$

11 Below is a sample of *family size*.

Number of children, x	0	1	2	3	4	5	6	7
Frequency, f	14	18	13	5	3	2	2	1

  a Find the sample mean and standard deviation.

  b Find unbiased estimates of the mean and standard deviation of the population from which the sample was taken.

12 Below is a random sample of the ages of squash players at the Junior National Squash Championship.

Age	11	12	13	14	15	16	17	18
Frequency	2	1	4	5	6	4	2	1

  a Find the mean and standard deviation of the ages.

  b Find unbiased estimates of the mean and standard deviation of the population from which the sample was taken.

13 The number of toothpicks in a random sample of 48 boxes was counted and the results tabulated.

Number of toothpicks	33	35	36	37	38	39	40
Frequency	1	5	7	13	12	8	2

  a Find the mean and standard deviation of the age distribution.

  b Find unbiased estimates of the mean and standard deviation of the population from which the sample was taken.

14 The lengths of 30 randomly selected 12-day old babies were measured to the nearest cm and the following data obtained:

  a Find estimates of the mean length and the standard deviation of the lengths.

  b Find unbiased estimates of the mean and standard deviation of the population from which the sample was taken.

Length (cm)	Frequency
40 - 41	1
42 - 43	1
44 - 45	3
46 - 47	7
48 - 49	11
50 - 51	5
52 - 53	2

15 The weekly wages (in dollars) of 200 workers in a steel yard are given below:

  a Find estimates of the mean and the standard deviation of the wages.

  b Find unbiased estimates of the mean and standard deviation of the population from which the sample was taken.

Wage ($)	Number of Workers
360 - 369.99	17
370 - 379.99	38
380 - 389.99	47
390 - 399.99	57
400 - 409.99	18
410 - 419.99	10
420 - 429.99	10
430 - 439.99	3

G | THE SIGNIFICANCE OF STANDARD DEVIATION

If a large sample from a typical bell-shaped data distribution is taken, what percentage of the data values would lie between $\bar{x} - s$ and $\bar{x} + s$?

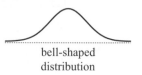

bell-shaped distribution

Click on the icon and try to answer this question. Repeat the sampling many times.

DEMO

Now try to determine the percentage of data values which would lie between $\bar{x} - 2s$ and $\bar{x} + 2s$ and between $\bar{x} - 3s$ and $\bar{x} + 3s$.

It can be shown that for any measured variable from any population that is normally distributed, no matter the values of the mean and standard deviation:

- approximately **68%** of the population will have a measure that falls between **1** standard deviation either side of the mean

- approximately **95%** of the population will have a measure that falls between **2** standard deviations either side of the mean

- approximately **99.7%** of the population will have a measure that falls between **3** standard deviations either side of the mean.

Example 15

A sample of 200 cans of peaches was taken from a warehouse and the contents of each can measured for net weight. The sample mean was 486 g with standard deviation 6.2 g. What proportion of the cans might lie within:

a 1 standard deviation from the mean   **b** 3 standard deviations from the mean?

a About 68% of the cans would be expected to have contents between 486 ± 6.2 g   i.e.,   479.8 g and 492.2 g.

b Nearly all of the cans would be expected to have contents between $486 \pm 3 \times 6.2$ g   i.e.,   467.4 and 504.6 g.

THE NORMAL CURVE

The smooth curve that models normal population data is asymptotic to the horizontal axis, so in theory the measurement limits within which all the members of the population will fall, do not exist.

Note also that the position of 1 standard deviation either side of the mean corresponds to the point where the normal curve changes from a concave to a convex curve.

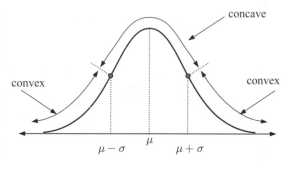

EXERCISE 18G

1 The mean height of players in a basketball competition is 184 cm. If the standard deviation is 5 cm, what percentage of them are likely to be:

    a taller than 189 cm
    b taller than 179 cm

    c between 174 cm and 199 cm
    d over 199 cm tall?

2 The mean average rainfall of Claudona for August is 48 mm with a standard deviation of 6 mm. Over a 20 year period, how many times would you expect there to be less than 42 mm of rainfall during August in Claudona?

3 Two hundred lifesavers competed in a swimming race. The mean time was 10 minutes 30 seconds. The standard deviation was 15 seconds. Find the number of competitors who probably:

    a took longer than 11 minutes
    b took less than 10 minutes 15 seconds

    c completed the race in a time between 10 min 15 sec and 10 min 45 sec.

4 The weights of babies born at Prince Louis Maternity Hospital last year averaged 3.0 kg with a standard deviation of 200 grams. If there were 545 babies born at this hospital last year, estimate the number that weighed:

    a less than 3.2 kg
    b between 2.8 kg and 3.4 kg.

REVIEW SET 18A

1 The data supplied below is the diameter (in cm) of a number of bacteria colonies as measured by a microbiologist 12 hours after seeding.

| 0.4 | 2.1 | 3.4 | 3.9 | 4.7 | 3.7 | 0.8 | 3.6 | 4.1 | 4.9 | 2.5 | 3.1 | 1.5 | 2.6 | 4.0 |
| 1.3 | 3.5 | 0.9 | 1.5 | 4.2 | 3.5 | 2.1 | 3.0 | 1.7 | 3.6 | 2.8 | 3.7 | 2.8 | 3.2 | 3.3 |

    a Produce a stemplot for this data. **b** Find the **i** median **ii** range of the data.

    c Comment on the skewness of the data.

2 The data below shows the distance, in metres, Thabiso threw a baseball.

71.2	65.1	68.0	71.1	74.6	68.8	83.2	85.0	74.5	87.4
84.3	77.0	82.8	84.4	80.6	75.9	89.7	83.2	97.5	82.9
90.5	85.5	90.7	92.9	95.6	85.5	64.6	73.9	80.0	86.5

    a Determine the highest and lowest value for the data set.

    b Produce between 6 and 12 groups in which to place all the data values.

    c Prepare a frequency distribution table.

    d For this data, draw a frequency histogram.

    e Determine: **i** the mean **ii** the median.

3 $5, 6, 8, a, 3, b$, have a mean of 6 and a variance of 3. Find the values of a and b.

4 For the following distribution of continuous grouped data:

Scores	0 to 9.9	10 to 19.9	20 to 29.9	30 to 39.9	40 to 49.9
Frequency	1	13	27	17	2

    a Construct a 'less than' ogive.
    b Find the median of the data.

    c Find the interquartile range.
    d Find the mean and standard deviation.

5 The back-to-back stemplot alongside represents the times for the 100 metre freestyle recorded by members of a swimming squad.

   a Copy and complete the following table:

	Girls	Boys
shape		
centre (median)		
spread (range)		

Girls		Boys
	32	1
4	33	0 2 2 7
7 6 3	34	1 3 4 4 8
8 7 4 3 0	35	0 2 4 7 9 9
8 8 3 3	36	7 8 8
7 6 6 6	37	0
6	38	
0	39	
	40	*leaf unit:*
1	41	0.1 sec

   b Write an argument that supports the conclusion you may make about the girls' and boys' swimming times.

6 The given parallel boxplots represent the 100-metre sprint times for the members of two athletics squads.

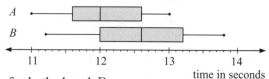

   a Determine the 5 number summaries for both A and B.

   b Determine the **i** range **ii** interquartile range for each group.

   c Copy and complete: **i** The members of squad ...... generally ran faster times.

                    ii The times in squad ...... were more varied.

7 Katja's golf scores for her last 20 rounds were:

   90   106   84   103   112   100   105   81   104   98

   107   95   104   108   99   101   106   102   98   101

   a Find the **i** median **ii** lower quartile **iii** upper quartile

   b Find the interquartile range of the data set.

   c Find the mean and standard deviation of her scores.

8 The number of litres of petrol purchased by a random sample of motor vehicle drivers is shown alongside:

   a Find the mean and standard deviation of the number of litres purchased.

   b Find unbiased estimates of the mean and standard deviation of the population this sample comes from.

Litres	Number of Vehicles
15 - 19	5
20 - 24	13
25 - 29	17
30 - 34	29
35 - 39	27
40 - 44	18
45 - 49	7

9 The average height of 17-year old boys was found to be normally distributed with a mean of 179 cm and a standard deviation of 8 cm. Calculate the percentage of 17-year old boys whose heights are:

   a more than 195 cm

   b between 163 cm and 195 cm

   c between 171 cm and 187 cm

Chapter 19

Probability

In the study of chance, we need a mathematical method to describe the likelihood of an event happening. We do this by carefully assigning a number which lies between 0 and 1 (inclusive).

> An event which has a 0% chance of happening (i.e., is impossible) is assigned a probability of 0.
>
> An event which has a 100% chance of happening (i.e., is certain) is assigned a probability of 1.
>
> All other events can then be assigned a probability between 0 and 1.

The number line below shows how we could interpret different probabilities:

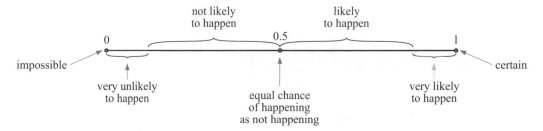

The assigning of probabilities is usually based on either:

- observing the results of an experiment (experimental probability),   or
- using arguments of symmetry (theoretical probability).

Probability theory is the study of the *chance* (or likelihood) of events happening.

The study of the theory of chance has vitally important applications in physical and biological sciences, economics, politics, sport, life insurance, quality control, production planning in industry and a host of other areas.

HISTORICAL NOTE

The development of modern probability theory began in 1653 when gambler Chevalier de Mere contacted mathematician **Blaise Pascal** with a problem on how to divide the stakes when a gambling game is interrupted during play. Pascal involved **Pierre de Fermat**, a lawyer and amateur mathematician, and together they solved the problem. While think-

Blaise Pascal

Pierre de Fermat

ing about it they laid the foundations upon which the laws of probability were formed.

In the late 17th century, English mathematicians compiled and analysed mortality tables. These tables showed how many people died at different ages. From these tables they could estimate the probability that a person would be alive at a future date. This led to the establishment of the first life-insurance company in 1699.

OPENING PROBLEM

Life Insurance Companies use statistics on **life expectancy** and **death rates** in order to work out the premiums to charge people who insure with them.

The table shows *expected numbers surviving at a given age* and the *expected remaining life at a given age.*

Life table					
Male			Female		
Age	Number surviving	Expected remaining life	Age	Number surviving	Expected remaining life
0	100 000	73.03	0	100 000	79.46
5	98 809	68.90	5	99 307	75.15
10	98 698	63.97	10	99 125	70.22
15	98 555	59.06	15	98 956	65.27
20	98 052	54.35	20	98 758	60.40
25	97 325	49.74	25	98 516	55.54
30	96 688	45.05	30	98 278	50.67
35	96 080	40.32	35	98 002	45.80
40	95 366	35.60	40	97 615	40.97
45	94 323	30.95	45	96 997	36.22
50	92 709	26.45	50	95 945	31.59
55	89 891	22.20	55	94 285	27.10
60	85 198	18.27	60	91 774	22.76
65	78 123	14.69	65	87 923	18.64
70	67 798	11.52	70	81 924	14.81
75	53 942	8.82	75	72 656	11.36
80	37 532	6.56	80	58 966	8.38
85	20 998	4.79	85	40 842	5.97
90	8416	3.49	90	21 404	4.12
95	2098	2.68	95	7004	3.00
99	482	2.23	99	1953	2.36

Notice that out of 100 000 births, 98 052 males are expected to survive to the age of 20 and at that age the survivors are expected to live a further 54.35 years.

Things to think about:

- Can you use the life table to estimate how many years you can expect to live?

- What is the estimated probability of a new born boy (or girl) reaching the age of 15?

- Can the table be used to estimate the probability that
    a 15 year old boy *will* reach the age of 75
    a 15 year old girl *will not* reach the age of 75?

- An insurance company sells policies to people to insure them against death over a 30-year period. If the person dies during this period the beneficiaries receive the agreed payout figure. Why are such policies cheaper to take out for say a 20 year old, than a 50 year old?

- How many of your classmates would you expect to be alive and able to attend a 30 year class reunion?

A   EXPERIMENTAL PROBABILITY

In experiments involving chance we agree to use appropriate language to accurately describe what we are doing and the results we are obtaining.

- The number of **trials** is the total number of times the experiment is repeated.
- The **outcomes** are the different results possible for one trial of the experiment.
- The **frequency** of a particular outcome is the number of times that this outcome is observed.
- The **relative frequency** of an outcome is the frequency of that outcome expressed as a fraction or percentage of the total number of trials.

When a small plastic cone was tossed into the air 279 times it fell on its *side* 183 times and on its *base* 96 times.

The relative frequencies of *side* and *base* are $\frac{183}{279} \doteqdot 0.656$ and $\frac{96}{279} \doteqdot 0.344$ respectively.

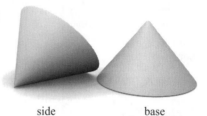

side   base

In the absence of any further data we say that the relative frequency of each event is our best estimate of the probability of each event occurring.

That is,   Experimental probability = relative frequency.

We write   Experimental P(side) = 0.656,   Experimental P(base) = 0.344

INVESTIGATION 1   TOSSING DRAWING PINS

If a drawing pin finishes we say it has finished on its *back*

and if we say it has finished on its *side*.

If two drawing pins are tossed simultaneously the possible results are:

two backs   back and side   two sides

What to do:

1 Obtain two drawing pins of the same shape and size. Toss the pair 80 times and record the outcomes in a table.

2 Obtain relative frequencies (experimental probabilities) for each of the three events.

3 Pool your results with four other people and so obtain experimental probabilities from 400 tosses.   **Note:** The others must have pins from the same batch, i.e., the same shape.

4 Which gives the more reliable estimates, your results or the groups'? Why?

5 Keep your results as they may be useful later in this chapter.

Note: In some cases, such as in the investigation above, experimentation is the only way of obtaining probabilities.

EXERCISE 19A

1 When a batch of 145 paper clips were dropped onto 6 cm by 6 cm squared paper it was observed that 113 fell completely inside squares and 32 finished up on the grid lines. Find, to 2 decimal places, the estimated probability of a clip falling:

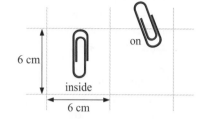

a inside a square   **b** on a line.

2

Length	Frequency
0 - 19	17
20 - 39	38
40 - 59	19
60+	4

Jose surveyed the length of TV commercials (in seconds). Find to 3 decimal places the estimated probability that a randomly chosen TV commercial will last:

a   20 to 39 seconds   **b**   more than a minute

c   between 20 and 59 seconds (inclusive)

3 Betul keeps records of the number of phone calls she receives over a period of consecutive days.

a For how many days did the survey last?

b Estimate Betul's chance of receiving:

　i no phone calls on one day

　ii 5 or more phone calls on a day

　iii less than 3 phone calls on a day.

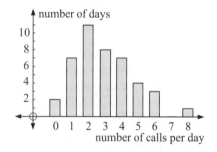

4 Pat does a lot of travelling in her car and she keeps records on how often she fills her car with petrol. The table alongside shows the frequencies of the *number of days between refills*. Estimate the likelihood that:

a there is a four day gap between refills

b there is at least a four day gap between refills.

Days between refills	Frequency
1	37
2	81
3	48
4	17
5	6
6	1

INVESTIGATION 2   COIN TOSSING EXPERIMENTS

In this investigation we will find experimental results when tossing:

- one coin 40 times
- two coins 60 times
- three coins 80 times

The coins do not have to be all the same type.

What to do:

1 Toss *one coin* 40 times. Record the number of heads resulting in a table.

Result	Tally	Frequency	Relative frequency
1 head			
0 head			

2 Toss *two coins* 60 times. Record the number of heads resulting in a table.

Result	Tally	Frequency	Relative frequency
2 heads			
1 head			
0 head			

3 Toss *three coins* 80 times. Record the number of heads resulting in a table.

Result	Tally	Frequency	Relative frequency
3 heads			
2 heads			
1 head			
0 head			

4 Share your results to **1**, **2** and **3** with several others. Comment on any similarities and differences.

5 Pool your results and find new relative frequencies for tossing one coin, two coins, tossing three coins.

6 Click on the icon to examine a coin tossing simulation.

COIN TOSSING

In   Number of coins   type   1 .

In   Number of flips   type   10 000 .

Click │ START │ and click │ START │ 9 more times, each time recording the % Frequency for each possible result. Comment on these results. Do your results agree with what you expected?

7 Repeat **6** but this time with *two coins* and then repeat **6** but this time with *three coins*.

From the previous investigation you should have observed that there are roughly twice as many 'one head' results as there are 'no heads' or 'two heads'.

The explanation for this is best seen using two different coins where you could get:

two heads	one head	one head	no heads

This shows that we should expect two heads : one head : no heads to be 1 : 2 : 1. However, due to chance, there will be variations from this when we look at experimental results.

INVESTIGATION 3   DICE ROLLING EXPERIMENTS

You will need: At least one normal six-sided die with numbers   **WORKSHEET** 1 to 6 on its faces. Several dice would be useful to speed up the experimentation.

What to do:

1 Examine a die. List the possible outcomes for the uppermost face when the die is rolled.

2 Consider the possible outcomes when the die is rolled 60 times.

Copy and complete the following table of your **expected results:**

Outcomes	Expected frequency	Expected relative frequency
⋮		

3 Roll the die 60 times and record the result on the uppermost face in a table like the one following:

Outcome	Tally	Frequency	Relative frequency
1			
2			
⋮			
6			
	Total	60	

4 Pool as much data as you can with other students.
  - Look at similarities and differences from one set to another.
  - Look at the overall pooled data added into one table.

5 How close to your expectation were your results?

6 Use the die rolling simulation from the computer package on the CD to roll the die 10 000 times and repeat this 10 times. On each occasion, record your results in a table like that in **3**. Do your results further confirm your expected results?

7 These are the different possible results when a pair of dice is rolled.

The illustration given shows that when two dice are rolled there are 36 possible outcomes. Of these, {1, 3}, {2, 2} and {3, 1} give a sum of 4.

Using the illustration above, copy and complete the following table of expected (theoretical) results:

Sum	2	3	4	5	⋯	12
Fraction of total			$\frac{3}{36}$			
Fraction as decimal			0.083			

8 If a pair of dice is rolled 360 times, how many of each result (2, 3, 4, ..., 12) would you expect to get? Extend your table of **7** by adding another row and write your **expected frequencies** within it.

9 Toss two dice 360 times and record in a table the *sum of the two numbers* for each toss.

WORKSHEET

Sum	Tally	Frequency	Rel. Frequency
2			
3			
4			
⋮			
12			
Total		360	1

10 Pool as much data as you can with other students and find the overall relative frequency of each *sum*.

11 Use the two dice simulation from the computer package on the CD to roll the pair of dice 10 000 times. Repeat this 10 times and on each occasion record your results in a table like that of **9**. Are your results consistent with your expectations?

SIMULATION

B   SAMPLE SPACE

A **sample space** is the set of all possible outcomes of an experiment.

There are a variety of ways of representing or illustrating sample spaces.

LISTING OUTCOMES

Example 1

List the sample space of possible outcomes for:
a   tossing a coin
b   rolling a die.

a   When a coin is tossed, there   **b**   When a die is rolled, there are 6
        are two possible outcomes.   possible outcomes.
        ∴   sample space = {H, T}   ∴   sample space = {1, 2, 3, 4, 5, 6}

2-DIMENSIONAL GRIDS

When an experiment involves more than one operation we can still use listing to illustrate the sample space. However, a grid can often be a better way of achieving this.

Example 2

Illustrate the possible outcomes when 2 coins are tossed by using a 2-dimensional grid.

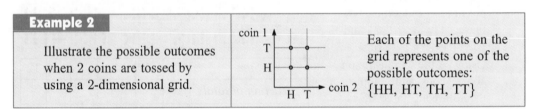

Each of the points on the grid represents one of the possible outcomes:
{HH, HT, TH, TT}

TREE DIAGRAMS

The sample space in **Example 2** could also be represented by a tree diagram. The advantage of tree diagrams is that they can be used when more than two operations are involved.

Example 3

Illustrate, using a tree diagram, the possible outcomes when:
a   tossing two coins
b   drawing two marbles from a bag containing many red, green and yellow marbles.

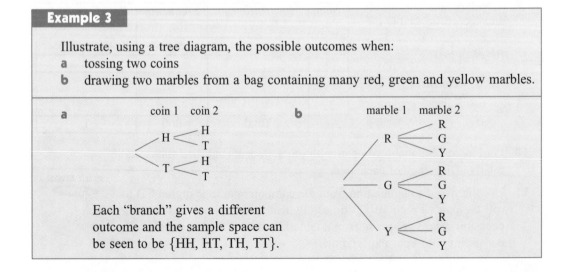

Each "branch" gives a different outcome and the sample space can be seen to be {HH, HT, TH, TT}.

EXERCISE 19B

1 List the sample space for the following:

    a twirling a square spinner labelled A, B, C, D

    b the sexes of a 2-child family

    c the order in which 4 blocks A, B, C and D can be lined up

    d the 8 different 3-child families.

2 Illustrate on a 2-dimensional grid the sample space for:

    a rolling a die and tossing a coin simultaneously

    b rolling two dice

    c rolling a die and spinning a spinner with sides A, B, C, D

    d twirling two square spinners; one labelled A, B, C, D and the other 1, 2, 3, 4.

3 Illustrate on a tree diagram the sample space for:

    a tossing a 5-cent and 10-cent coin simultaneously

    b tossing a coin and twirling an equilateral triangular spinner labelled A, B and C

    c twirling two equilateral triangular spinners labelled 1, 2 and 3 and X, Y and Z

    d drawing two tickets from a hat containing a number of pink, blue and white tickets.

C | THEORETICAL PROBABILITY

Consider the **octagonal spinner** alongside.

Since the spinner is symmetrical, when it is spun the arrowed marker could finish with **equal likelihood** on each of the sections marked 1 to 8.

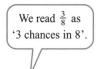

Therefore, we would say that the likelihood of obtaining a particular number, for example, 4, would be

$$1 \text{ chance in } 8, \qquad \tfrac{1}{8}, \qquad 12\tfrac{1}{2}\% \qquad \text{or} \qquad 0.125$$

This is a **mathematical** (or **theoretical**) probability and is based on what we theoretically expect to occur.

> The **theoretical probability** of a particular event is a measure of the chance of that event occurring in any trial of the experiment.

If we are interested in the event of getting a result of *6 or more* from one spin of the octagonal spinner, there are three favourable results (6, 7 or 8) out of the eight possible results, and each of these is equally likely to occur and so   P(6 or more) $= \tfrac{3}{8}$.

> We read $\tfrac{3}{8}$ as '3 chances in 8'.

In general, for an event E containing **equally likely** possible results:

$$P(E) = \frac{\textbf{the number of members of the event E}}{\textbf{the total number of possible outcomes}}.$$

Example 4

A ticket is *randomly selected* from a basket containing 3 green, 4 yellow and 5 blue tickets. Determine the probability of getting:

a a green ticket   **b** a green or yellow ticket
c an orange ticket   **d** a green, yellow or blue ticket

The sample space is   {G, G, G, Y, Y, Y, Y, B, B, B, B, B}
which has $3 + 4 + 5 = 12$ outcomes.

a   P(G)   **b**   P(a G or a Y)   **c**   P(O)   **d**   P(G, Y or B)

$= \frac{3}{12}$ $= \frac{3+4}{12}$ $= \frac{0}{12}$ $= \frac{3+4+5}{12}$

$= \frac{1}{4}$ $= \frac{7}{12}$ $= 0$ $= 1$

Note: In **Example 4** notice that in **c** an orange result cannot occur and the calculated probability is 0, which fits the fact that it has *no chance* of occurring.

Also notice in **d**, a green, yellow or blue result is certain to occur. It is 100% likely which is perfectly described using a 1.

The two events of   *no chance of occurring* with probability 0 and
                    certain to occur with probability 1 are two extremes.

Consequently, for any event E, $0 \leqslant P(E) \leqslant 1$.

COMPLEMENTARY EVENTS

Example 5

An ordinary 6-sided die is rolled once. Determine the chance of:
a getting a 6   **b** not getting a 6
c getting a 1 or 2   **d** not getting a 1 or 2

The sample space of possible outcomes is   {1, 2, 3, 4, 5, 6}

a   P(6)   **b**   P(not a 6)   **c**   P(1 or 2)   **d**   P(not a 1 or 2)

$= \frac{1}{6}$ $= $ P(1, 2, 3, 4 or 5) $= \frac{2}{6}$ $= $ P(3, 4, 5, or 6)

                 $= \frac{5}{6}$ $= \frac{4}{6}$

In **Example 5**, did you notice that   P(6) + P(not getting a 6) = 1   and that
                        P(1 or 2) + P(not getting a 1 or 2) = 1?

This is no surprise as *getting a 6* and *not getting a 6* are **complementary events** where one of them **must occur**.

NOTATION

If E is an event, then E′ is the **complementary event** of E.

So, **P(E) + P(E′) = 1**   A useful rearrangement is: P(E **not** occurring) = 1 − P(E occurring)

EXERCISE 19C

1 A marble is randomly selected from a box containing 5 green, 3 red and 7 blue marbles. Determine the probability that the marble is:

   a red   **b** green   **c** blue

   d not red   **e** neither green nor blue **f** green or red

2 A carton of a dozen eggs contains eight brown eggs. The rest are white.

   a How many white eggs are there in the carton?

   b What is the probability that an egg selected at random is: **i** brown **ii** white?

3 A dart board has 36 sectors, labelled 1 to 36. Determine the probability that a dart thrown at the board hits: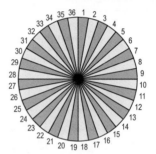

   a a multiple of 4

   b a number between 6 and 9 inclusive

   c a number greater than 20

   d 9

   e a multiple of 13

   f an odd number that is a multiple of 3.

4 What is the probability that a randomly chosen person has his/her next birthday on:

   a on a Tuesday   **b** on a week-end   **c** in July   **d** in January or February?

5 List the six different orders in which Antti, Kai and Neda may sit in a row. If the three of them sit randomly in a row, determine the probability that:

   a Antti sits in the middle   **b** Antti sits at the left end

   c Antti sits at the right end   **d** Kai and Neda are seated together

6 **a** List the 8 possible 3-child families, according to the gender of the children. For example, GGB means *"the first is a girl, the second is a girl, the third is a boy"*.

   b Assuming that each of these is equally likely to occur, determine the probability that a randomly selected 3-child family consists of:

      i all boys   **ii** all girls

      iii boy, then girl, then girl   **iv** two girls and a boy

      v a girl for the eldest   **vi** at least one boy.

7 **a** List, in systematic order, the 24 different orders in which four people A, B, C and D may sit in a row.

   b Hence, determine the probability that when the four people sit at random in a row:

      i A sits on one end   **ii** B sits on one of the two middle seats

     iii A and B are seated together

     iv A, B and C are seated together, not necessarily in that order.

8 Abdul hits the target of radius 30 cm with one shot from his rifle. What is the probability that he hits the bulls-eye (centre circle) of radius 20 cm?

D   USING GRIDS TO FIND PROBABILITIES

Two dimensional grids give us excellent visual displays of sample spaces. From these we can count favourable outcomes and so calculate probabilities.

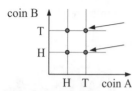

This point represents 'a tail from coin A' and 'a tail from coin B'.
This point represents 'a tail from coin A' and 'a head from coin B'.
There are four members of the sample space.

Example 6

Use a two-dimensional grid to illustrate the sample space for tossing a coin and rolling a die simultaneously. From this grid determine the probability of:

a tossing a head   **b** getting a tail and a 5   **c** getting a tail or a 5

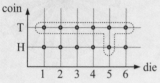

There are 12 members in the sample space.

a $P(\text{head}) = \frac{6}{12} = \frac{1}{2}$ **b** $P(\text{tail and a '5'}) = \frac{1}{12}$

c $P(\text{tail or a '5'}) = \frac{7}{12}$ {the enclosed points}

EXERCISE 19D

1 Draw the grid of the sample space when a 5-cent and a 10-cent coin are tossed simultaneously. Hence determine the probability of getting:

   a two heads   **b** two tails
   c exactly one head   **d** at least one head

2 A coin and a pentagonal spinner with sectors 1, 2, 3, 4 and 5 are rolled and spun respectively.

   a Draw a grid to illustrate the sample space of possible outcomes.
   b How many outcomes are possible?
   c Use your grid to determine the chance of getting:

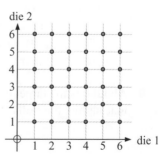

   i   a tail and a 3   **ii**   a head and an even number
   iii an odd number   **iv**   a head or a 5

3 A pair of dice is rolled. The 36 different possible 'pair of dice' results are illustrated below on a 2-dimensional grid.

Use the 2-dimensional grid of the 36 possible outcomes to determine the probability of getting:

   a two 3's   **b** a 5 and a 6
   c a 5 or a 6   **d** at least one 6
   e exactly one 6   **f** no sixes
   g a sum of 7   **h** a sum greater than 8
   i a sum of 7 or 11   **j** a sum of no more than 8.

DISCUSSION

Read and discuss: Three children have been experimenting with a coin, tossing it in the air and recording the outcomes. They have done this 10 times and have recorded 10 tails. Before the next toss they make the following statements:

Jackson: "It's got to be a head next time!"

Sally: "No, it always has an equal chance of being a head or a tail. The coin cannot remember what the outcomes have been."

Amy: "Actually, I think it will probably be a tail again, because I think the coin must be biased - it might be weighted somehow so that it is more likely to give a tail."

E   COMPOUND EVENTS

Consider the following problem:

Box X contains 2 blue and 2 green balls and Box Y contains 3 red and 1 white ball. A ball is randomly selected from each of the boxes. Determine the probability of getting "a blue ball from X and a red ball from Y."

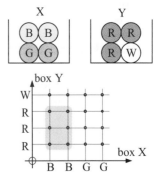

By illustrating the sample space on a two-dimensional grid as shown alongside, it can be seen that as 6 of the 16 possibilities are blue from X and red from Y and each outcome is equally likely,

P(blue from X **and** red from Y) $= \frac{6}{16}$

The question arises, "Is there a quicker, easier way to find this probability?"

INVESTIGATION 4   PROBABILITIES OF COMPOUND EVENTS

The purpose of this investigation is to find, if possible, a rule for finding P(A *and* B) for events A and B.

A coin is tossed and at the same time, a die is rolled. The result of the coin toss will be called outcome A, and likewise for the die, outcome B.

What to do:

a Copy and complete:

b What is the connection between P(A and B) and P(A), P(B)?

P(A *and* B)	P(A)	P(B)
P(a head and a 4)		
P(a head and an odd number)		
P(a tail and a number larger than 1)		
P(a tail and a number less than 3)		

INVESTIGATION 5   REVISITING DRAWING PINS

Since we cannot find by theoretical argument the probability that a drawing pin will land on its back ⊥ , the question arises for tossing two drawing pins, does

P(back *and* back) = P(back) × P(back)?

What to do:

1 From **Investigation 1** on page **496**, what is your estimate of P(back *and* back)?

2 **a** Count the number of drawing pins in a full packet. They must be identical to each other and the same ones that you used in **Investigation 1**.

   b Drop the whole packet onto a solid surface and count the number of *backs* and *sides*. Repeat this several times. Pool results with others and finally estimate P(back).

3 Find   P(back) × P(back)   using **2 b**.

4 Is   P(back *and* back) ≐ P(back) × P(back)?

From **Investigation 4 and 5**, it seems that:

If A and B are two events, where the occurrence of one of them does not affect the occurrence of the other, then $P(A \text{ and } B) = P(A) \times P(B)$.

Before we can formulate a rule, we need to distinguish between **independent** and **dependent** events.

INDEPENDENT EVENTS

> **Independent events** are events where the occurrence of one of the events **does not** affect the occurrence of the other event.

Consider again the example on the previous page. Suppose we happen to choose a blue ball from box X. This in no way affects the outcome when we choose a ball from box Y. The two events "a blue ball from X" and "a red ball from Y" are **independent events**.

In general: If A and B are **independent events** then $P(A \text{ and } B) = P(A) \times P(B)$.

This rule can be extended for any number of independent events.

For example: If A, B and C are all **independent events**, then
$$P(A \text{ and } B \text{ and } C) = P(A) \times P(B) \times P(C).$$

Example 7

A coin and a die are tossed simultaneously. Determine the probability of getting a head and a 3 without using a grid.

P(head and 3) = P(H) × P(3)   {as events are clearly physically independent}

$= \frac{1}{2} \times \frac{1}{6}$

$= \frac{1}{12}$

EXERCISE 19E.1

1 At a mountain village in New Guinea it rains on average 6 days a week. Determine the probability that it rains on:

   a any one day   **b** two successive days   **c** three successive days.

2   A coin is tossed 3 times. Determine the probability of getting the following sequences of results: **a**   head, then head, then head   **b**   tail, then head, then tail

3   A school has two photocopiers. On any one day, machine A has an 8% chance of malfunctioning and machine B has a 12% chance of malfunctioning. Determine the probability that on any one day both machines will: **a**   malfunction   **b**   work effectively.

4   A couple decide that they want 4 children, none of whom will be adopted. They will be disappointed if the children are not born in the order boy, girl, boy, girl. Determine the probability that they will be:

    a   happy with the order of arrival   **b**   unhappy with the order of arrival.

5   Two marksmen fire at a target simultaneously. Jiri hits the target 70% of the time and Benita hits it 80% of the time. Determine the probability that:

    a   they both hit the target

    b   they both miss the target

    c   Jiri hits it but Benita misses

    d   Benita hits it but Jiri misses.

6   An archer always hits a circular target with each arrow shot, and hits the bullseye 2 out of every 5 shots on average. If 3 arrows are shot at the target, determine the probability that the bullseye is hit:

    a   every time

    b   the first two times, but not on the third shot

    c   on no occasion.

DEPENDENT EVENTS

Suppose a hat contains 5 red and 3 blue tickets. One ticket is randomly chosen, its colour is noted and it is thrown in a bin. A second ticket is randomly selected. What is the chance that it is red?

If the first ticket was red,   P(second is red) $= \frac{4}{7}$ 4 reds remaining / 7 to choose from

If the first ticket was blue,   P(second is red) $= \frac{5}{7}$ 5 reds remaining / 7 to choose from

So, the probability of the second ticket being red **depends** on what colour the first ticket was. Here we have **dependent events**.

> Two or more events are **dependent** if they are **not independent**.
>
> **Dependent** events are events where the occurrence of one of the events *does affect* the occurrence of the other event.

For compound events which are dependent, a similar product rule applies as to that for independent events:

> If A and B are dependent events then
>   P(A then B) = P(A) $\times$ P(B given that A has occurred).

Example 8

A box contains 4 red and 2 yellow tickets. Two tickets are randomly selected, one by one from the box, *without* replacement. Find the probability that:

a   both are red   b   the first is red and the second is yellow.

a   P(both red)

= P(first selected is red *and* second is red)

= P(first selected is red) × P(second is red given that the first is red)

= $\frac{4}{6} \times \frac{3}{5}$ ← 3 reds remain out of a total of 5 after a red first draw

= $\frac{2}{5}$ 4 reds out of a total of 6 tickets

b   P(first is red *and* second is yellow)

= P(first is red) × P(second is yellow given that the first is red)

= $\frac{4}{6} \times \frac{2}{5}$ ← 2 yellows remain out of a total of 5 after a red first draw

= $\frac{4}{15}$ 4 reds out of a total of 6 tickets

EXERCISE 19E.2

1   A box contains 7 red and 3 green balls. Two balls are randomly selected from the box without replacement. Determine the probability that:

a   both are red

b   the first is green and the second is red

c   a green and a red are obtained.

Drawing two balls simultaneously is the same as selecting one ball after another with no replacement.

Example 9

A hat contains tickets with numbers 1, 2, 3, ..., 19, 20 printed on them. If 3 tickets are drawn from the hat, without replacement, determine the probability that all are prime numbers.

In each fraction the bottom number is the total from which the selection is made and the top number is *"how many of the particular event we want"*.

There are 20 numbers of which 8 are primes:
{2, 3, 5, 7, 11, 13, 17, 19} are primes.

∴ P(3 primes)

= P(1st drawn is prime *and* 2nd is prime *and* 3rd is prime)

= $\frac{8}{20} \times \frac{7}{19} \times \frac{6}{18}$

8 primes out of 20 numbers

7 primes out of 19 numbers after a successful first draw

≑ 0.049 12   6 primes out of 18 numbers after two successful draws

2   A bin contains 12 identically shaped chocolates of which 8 are strawberry-creams. If 3 chocolates are selected at random from the bin, determine the probability that:

a   they are all strawberry-creams   b   none of them are strawberry-creams.

3   A lottery has 100 tickets which are placed in a barrel. Three tickets are drawn at random from the barrel to decide 3 prizes. If John has 3 tickets in the lottery, determine his probability of winning:

    a first prize **b** first and second prize **c** all 3 prizes **d** none of the prizes

4   A hat contains 7 names of players in a tennis squad including the captain and the vice captain. If a team of 3 is chosen at random by drawing the names from the hat, determine the probability that it does not:

    a contain the captain **b** contain the captain or the vice captain.

F   USING TREE DIAGRAMS

Tree diagrams can be used to illustrate sample spaces provided that the alternatives are not too numerous. Once the sample space is illustrated, the tree diagram can be used for determining probabilities. Consider two archers:

Li with probability $\frac{3}{4}$ of hitting a target and Yuka with probability $\frac{4}{5}$.

They both shoot simultaneously.

The tree diagram for this information is:

H = hit   M = miss

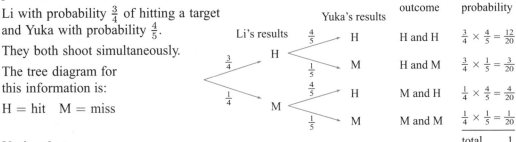

	outcome	probability
H and H		$\frac{3}{4} \times \frac{4}{5} = \frac{12}{20}$
H and M		$\frac{3}{4} \times \frac{1}{5} = \frac{3}{20}$
M and H		$\frac{1}{4} \times \frac{4}{5} = \frac{4}{20}$
M and M		$\frac{1}{4} \times \frac{1}{5} = \frac{1}{20}$
	total	1

Notice that:

- The probabilities for hitting and missing are marked on the branches.
- There are *four* alternative paths and each branch shows a particular outcome.
- All outcomes are represented and the probabilities are obtained by **multiplying**.

Example 10

Carl is not having much luck lately. His car will only start 80% of the time and his motorbike will only start 60% of the time.

  a Draw a tree diagram to illustrate this situation.

  b Use the tree diagram to determine the chance that:

    i both will start   **ii** Carl has no choice but to use his car.

  a C = car starts

      M = motorbike starts

	motorbike	outcome	probability
car C	0.6 → M	C and M	0.8×0.6=0.48
(0.8)	0.4 → M'	C and M'	0.8×0.4=0.32
C' (0.2)	0.6 → M	C' and M	0.2×0.6=0.12
	0.4 → M'	C' and M'	0.2×0.4=0.08
		total	1.00

  b **i** P(both start)

        = P(C and M)

        = 0.8 × 0.6

        = 0.48

      ii P(car starts, but motorbike does not)

          = P(C and M′)

          = 0.8 × 0.4

          = 0.32

EXERCISE 19F

1 Suppose this spinner is spun twice.

a Copy and complete the branches on the tree diagram shown.

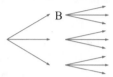

b What is the probability that black appears on both spins?

c What is the probability that yellow appears on both spins?

d What is the probability that different colours appear on both spins?

e What is the probability that black appears on either spin?

2 The probability of rain tomorrow is estimated to be $\frac{1}{5}$. If it does rain, Mudlark will start favourite with probability $\frac{1}{2}$ of winning. If it is fine he has a 1 in 20 chance of winning. Display the sample space of possible results of the horse race on a tree diagram. Determine the probability that Mudlark will win tomorrow.

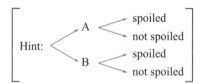

3 Machine A makes 40% of the bottles produced at a factory. Machine B makes the rest. Machine A spoils 5% of its product, while Machine B spoils only 2%. Determine the probability that the next bottle inspected at this factory is spoiled.

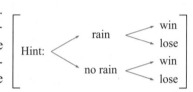

Example 11

Bag A contains 3 red and 2 yellow tickets. Bag B contains 1 red and 4 yellow tickets. A bag is randomly selected by tossing a coin and one ticket is removed from it. Determine the probability that it is yellow.

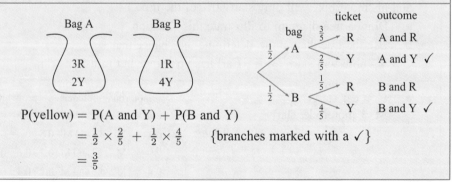

$P(\text{yellow}) = P(A \text{ and } Y) + P(B \text{ and } Y)$

$\qquad\quad = \frac{1}{2} \times \frac{2}{5} + \frac{1}{2} \times \frac{4}{5}$ {branches marked with a $\checkmark$}

$\qquad\quad = \frac{3}{5}$

---

4 Jar A contains 2 white and 3 red discs and Jar B contains 3 white and 1 red disc. A jar is chosen at random (by the flip of a coin) and one disc is taken at random from it. Determine the probability that the disc is red.

5 Three bags contain different numbers of blue and red marbles. A bag is selected using a die which has three A faces and two B faces and one C face.

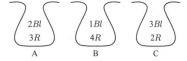

One marble is then selected randomly from the bag. Determine the probability that it is:

a blue   **b** red.

G   SAMPLING WITH AND WITHOUT REPLACEMENT

SAMPLING

Sampling is the process of selecting an object from a large group of objects and inspecting it, noting some feature(s). The object is then either **put back** (sampling **with replacement**) or **put to one side** (sampling **without replacement**).

Sometimes the inspection process makes it impossible to return the object to the large group.

Such processes include:

- Is the chocolate hard- or soft-centred? Bite it or squeeze it to see.
- Does the egg contain one or two yolks? Break it open and see.
- Is the object correctly made? Pull it apart to see.

This sampling process is used to maintain Quality Control in industrial processes.

Consider a box containing 3 red, 2 blue and 1 yellow marble. Suppose we wish to sample two marbles:

- by **replacement** of the first before the second is drawn
- by **not replacing** the first before the second is drawn.

Examine how the tree diagrams differ:

With replacement

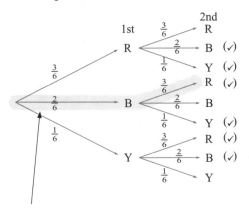

Without replacement

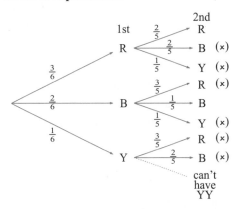

This branch represents Blue with the 1st draw and Red with the second draw and this is written as BR.

Notice that:
- with replacement

$$P(\text{two reds}) = \tfrac{3}{6} \times \tfrac{3}{6} = \tfrac{1}{4}$$

- without replacement

$$P(\text{two reds}) = \tfrac{3}{6} \times \tfrac{2}{5} = \tfrac{1}{5}$$

Example 12

For the example of the box containing 3 red, 2 blue and 1 yellow marble find the probability of getting two different colours:

a   if replacement occurs   **b**   if replacement does not occur.

a   P (two different colours)

$= $ P (RB or RY or BR or BY or YR or YB) {ticked ones}

$= \frac{3}{6} \times \frac{2}{6} + \frac{3}{6} \times \frac{1}{6} + \frac{2}{6} \times \frac{3}{6} + \frac{2}{6} \times \frac{1}{6} + \frac{1}{6} \times \frac{3}{6} + \frac{1}{6} \times \frac{2}{6}$

$= \frac{22}{36}$ which is $\frac{11}{18}$

b   P (two different colours)

$=$ P(RB or RY or BR or BY or YR or YB)   {crossed ones}

$= \frac{3}{6} \times \frac{2}{5} + \frac{3}{6} \times \frac{1}{5} + \frac{2}{6} \times \frac{3}{5} + \frac{2}{6} \times \frac{1}{5} + \frac{1}{6} \times \frac{3}{5} + \frac{1}{6} \times \frac{2}{5}$

$= \frac{22}{30}$ which is $\frac{11}{15}$

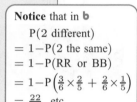

Notice that in **b**

P(2 different)

$= 1 - $ P(2 the same)

$= 1 - $ P(RR or BB)

$= 1 - $ P$\left(\frac{3}{6} \times \frac{2}{5} + \frac{2}{6} \times \frac{1}{5} \right)$

$= \frac{22}{30}$ etc

EXERCISE 19G   A tree diagram may be useful to help answer the following:

1   Two marbles are drawn in succession from a box containing 2 purple and 5 green marbles. Determine the probability that the two marbles are different colours if:

a   the first is replaced   **b**   the first is *not* replaced.

2   5 tickets numbered 1, 2, 3, 4 and 5, are placed in a bag. Two are taken from the bag without replacement. Determine the probability of getting:

a   both odd   **b**   both even   **c**   one odd and the other even.

3   Jar A contains 3 red and 2 green tickets. Jar B contains 3 red and 7 green tickets. A die has 4 faces with A's and 2 faces with B's, and when rolled it is used to select either jar A or jar B.

When a jar has been selected, two tickets are randomly selected without replacement from it. Determine the probability that:

a   both are green   **b**   they are different in colour.

4   Marie has a bag of sweets which are all identical in shape. The bag contains 6 orange drops and 4 lemon drops. She selects one sweet at random, eats it and then takes another, also at random. Determine the probability that:

a   both sweets were orange drops   **b**   both sweets were lemon drops

c   the first was an orange drop and the second was a lemon drop

d   the first was a lemon drop and the second was an orange drop

Add your answers to **a**, **b**, **c** and **d**. Explain why the answer must be 1.

Example 13

A bag contains 5 red and 3 blue marbles. Two marbles are drawn simultaneously from the bag. Determine the probability that at least one is red.

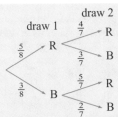

$$P(\text{at least one red}) = P(RR \text{ or } RB \text{ or } BR)$$

$$= \tfrac{5}{8} \times \tfrac{4}{7} + \tfrac{5}{8} \times \tfrac{3}{7} + \tfrac{3}{8} \times \tfrac{5}{7}$$

$$= \tfrac{20+15+15}{56}$$

$$= \tfrac{25}{28}$$

Note: *Alternatively,* $P(\text{at least one red}) = 1 - P(\text{no reds})$ {complementary events}

$$= 1 - P(BB), \quad \text{etc}$$

5 A bag contains four red and two blue marbles. Three marbles are selected simultaneously. Determine the probablity that:

   a   all are red   **b**   only two are red   **c**   at least two are red.

6 Bag A contains 3 red and 2 white marbles. Bag B contains 4 red and 3 white marbles. One marble is randomly selected from A and its colour noted. If it is red, 2 reds are added to B. If it is white, 2 whites are added to B. A marble is then selected from B. What are the chances that the marble selected from B is white?

7 A man holds two tickets in a 100-ticket lottery in which there are two winning tickets. If no replacement occurs, determine the probability that he will win:

   a   both prizes   **b**   neither prize   **c**   at least one prize.

INVESTIGATION 6   SAMPLING SIMULATION

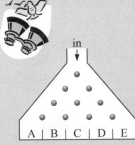

When balls enter the 'sorting' chamber they hit a metal rod and may go left or right with *equal chance*. This movement continues as the balls fall from one level of rods to the next. The balls finally come to rest in collection chambers at the bottom of the sorter. This sorter looks very much like a tree diagram rotated through $90°$.

Click on the icon to open the simulation. Notice that we can use the sliding bar to alter the probabilities of balls going to the left or right at each rod.

What to do:

1 To simulate the results of tossing *two coins*, set the bar to 50% **SIMULATION**

   and the sorter to show

   Run the simulation 200 times and repeat this four more times. Record each set of results.

2 A bag contains 7 blue and 3 red marbles and *two marbles* are randomly selected from it, the first being *replaced* before the second is drawn.

   The sorter should show   and set the bar to 70%

   as $P(\text{blue}) = \tfrac{7}{10} = 0.7 = 70\%$.

   Run the simulation a large number of times and use the results to estimate the probabilities of getting: **a**   two blues   **b**   one blue   **c**   no blues.

3 The tree diagram representation
of the marble selection in **2** is:

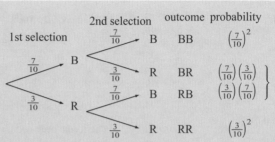

  a The tree diagram gives us
expected, theoretical probabilities for the different
outcomes. Do they agree
with the experimental results
obtained in **2**?

  b Write down the algebraic expansion of $(a+b)^2$.

  c Substitute $a = \frac{7}{10}$ and $b = \frac{3}{10}$ in the $(a+b)^2$ expansion. What do you notice?

4 From the bag of 7 blue and 3 red marbles, *three* marbles are randomly selected *with replacement*. Set the sorter to 3 levels and the bar to 70%.

Run the simulation a large number of times to obtain experimental estimates of the probabilities of getting:

  a three blues   **b** two blues   **c** one blue   **d** no blues.

5 **a** Use a tree diagram showing 1st selection, 2nd selection and 3rd selection to find theoretical probabilities of getting the results of **4**.

  b Show that $(a+b)^3 = a^3 + 3a^2b + 3ab^2 + b^3$ and use this expansion with $a = \frac{7}{10}$ and $b = \frac{3}{10}$ to also check the results of **4** and **5a**.

H   BINOMIAL PROBABILITIES

Consider rolling a die 3 times. The die has 2 faces of the same colour and the other 4 faces are black. If C represents "the result is coloured" and B represents "the result is black", the possible outcomes are as shown alongside:

$$\begin{array}{ccc} & \text{BCC} & \text{CBB} \\ & \text{CBC} & \text{BCB} \\ \text{CCC} & \text{CCB} \quad \text{BBC} & \text{BBB} \end{array}$$

Notice that the ratio of possible outcomes is $1 : 3 : 3 : 1$,   i.e.,

  one outcome is *all coloured*,   three outcomes are *two coloured and one black*,
  three outcomes are *one coloured and two black*, and   one outcome is *all black*.

Now for each die,

$P[C] = \frac{1}{3}$ and

$P[B] = \frac{2}{3}$. So,

for rolling the die 3
times we have the
following events
and probabilities:

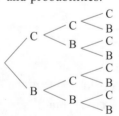

Event	Outcome	Probabilities	Total Probability
all coloured	CCC	$\left(\frac{1}{3}\right)\left(\frac{1}{3}\right)\left(\frac{1}{3}\right)$	$\left(\frac{1}{3}\right)^3 = \frac{1}{27}$
2 coloured and 1 black	BCC	$\left(\frac{2}{3}\right)\left(\frac{1}{3}\right)\left(\frac{1}{3}\right)$	$3\left(\frac{1}{3}\right)^2\left(\frac{2}{3}\right) = \frac{6}{27}$
	CBC	$\left(\frac{1}{3}\right)\left(\frac{2}{3}\right)\left(\frac{1}{3}\right)$	
	CCB	$\left(\frac{1}{3}\right)\left(\frac{1}{3}\right)\left(\frac{2}{3}\right)$	
1 coloured and 2 black	CBB	$\left(\frac{1}{3}\right)\left(\frac{2}{3}\right)\left(\frac{2}{3}\right)$	$3\left(\frac{1}{3}\right)\left(\frac{2}{3}\right)^2 = \frac{12}{27}$
	BCB	$\left(\frac{2}{3}\right)\left(\frac{1}{3}\right)\left(\frac{2}{3}\right)$	
	BBC	$\left(\frac{2}{3}\right)\left(\frac{2}{3}\right)\left(\frac{1}{3}\right)$	
all black	BBB	$\left(\frac{2}{3}\right)\left(\frac{2}{3}\right)\left(\frac{2}{3}\right)$	$\left(\frac{2}{3}\right)^3 = \frac{8}{27}$

Notice that $\left(\frac{1}{3}\right)^3 + 3\left(\frac{1}{3}\right)^2\left(\frac{2}{3}\right) + 3\left(\frac{1}{3}\right)\left(\frac{2}{3}\right)^2 + \left(\frac{2}{3}\right)^3$ is the binomial expansion for $\left(\frac{1}{3} + \frac{2}{3}\right)^3$.

In general,

> If E is an event with probability p of occurring and E′ (its complement, i.e., E not occurring) has probability q where clearly $p + q = 1$ then the **probability generator** for the various outcomes over n **independent trials** is $(p + q)^n$.

So, for example,   if E is the event of a randomly chosen light globe being faulty and
$$P(E) = p = 0.03, \quad \text{then} \quad P(E') = q = 0.97 .$$

Now if four independent samples are taken, the probability generator is $(0.03 + 0.97)^4$

$$= (0.03)^4 + 4(0.03)^3(0.97) + 6(0.03)^2(0.97)^2 + 4(0.03)(0.97)^3 + (0.97)^4$$

4 Es	3 Es and 1 E′	2 Es and 2 E′s	1 E and 3 E′s	4 E′s

Notice that $P(\text{E occurs } x \text{ times } \textbf{and} \text{ E' occurs } n - x \text{ times}) = \binom{n}{x} p^x q^{n-x}.$

Example 14

An archer has a 90% chance of hitting the target with each arrow and if 5 arrows are used, determine the probability generator and hence the chance of hitting the target
a   twice only   b   at most 3 times.

Let H be the event of 'hitting the target' $\therefore$ $P(H) = 0.9$ and $P(H') = 0.1$

So, the probability generator is $(0.9 + 0.1)^5$
$$= (0.9)^5 + 5(0.9)^4(0.1) + 10(0.9)^3(0.1)^2 + 10(0.9)^2(0.1)^3 + 5(0.9)(0.1)^4 + (0.1)^5$$

5 hits	4 hits and 1 miss	3 hits and 2 misses	2 hits and 3 misses	1 hit and 4 misses	5 misses

a   P(hits twice only)   b   P(hits at most 3 times)
   $= P(X = 2)$ $= P(X = 0, 1, 2 \text{ or } 3)$
   $= 10(0.9)^2(0.1)^3$ $= (0.1)^5 + 5(0.9)(0.1)^4 + 10(0.9)^2(0.1)^3 + 10(0.9)^3(0.1)^2$
   $= 0.0081$ $\doteqdot 0.0815$

EXERCISE 19H

1   **a**   Expand $(p + q)^4$.

   b   If a coin is tossed *four* times, what is the probability of getting 3 heads?

2   **a**   Expand $(p + q)^5$.

   b   If *five* coins are tossed simultaneously, what is the probability of getting:

   i   4 heads and 1 tail   **ii**   2 heads and 3 tails?

3   **a**   Expand $\left(\frac{2}{3} + \frac{1}{3}\right)^4$.

   b   Four chocolates are randomly taken (with replacement) from a box containing strawberry creams and almond centres in the ratio 2 : 1.   What is the probability of

getting: **i**   all strawberry creams   **ii**   two of each type
            iii   at least 2 strawberry creams?

4   **a**   Expand $(\frac{3}{4} + \frac{1}{4})^5$.

   b   In New Zealand in 1946, coins of value two shillings were of two types: normal kiwis and 'flat back' kiwis in the ratio 3 : 1. From a batch of 1946 two shilling coins, five were selected at random with replacement. What is the probability that:
   i   two were 'flat backs'   **ii**   at least 3 were 'flat backs'?

A graphics calculator can be used to find **binomial probabilities**.
For example, to find the probabilities in **Example 14** use:

in **a** $P(X = 2) = \text{binompdf}(5, 0.9, 2)$ in **b** $P(X \leqslant 3) = \text{binomcdf}(5, 0.9, 3)$
                    ↑ ↑ ↑   ↑ ↑ ↑
                    n p x n p x

5   When rifle shooter Huy fires a shot, the target is hit 80% of the time. If 4 shots are fired at the target, determine the probability that Huy has:
   a   2 hits and 2 misses   **b**   at least 2 hits.

6 5% of electric light bulbs are defective at manufacture. If 6 bulbs are tested at random with each one being replaced before the next is chosen, determine the probability that:
   a   two are defective   **b**   at least one is defective.

7   In a multiple choice test there are 10 questions and each question has 5 choices, one of which is correct. If 70% is the pass mark and Raj (who knows nothing) guesses at each answer, determine the probability that he will pass.

8   Martina beats Jelena in 2 games out of 3 at tennis. What is the probability that Jelena wins a set of tennis 6 games to 4?

   [**Hint:**   What is the score after 9 games?]

I   SETS AND VENN DIAGRAMS

A **Venn Diagram** usually consists of a rectangle which represents the sample space, and circles within it representing particular events.

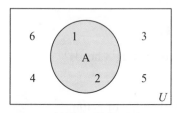

Venn diagrams are particularly useful for solving certain types of probability questions.

A number of probability laws can also be established using Venn diagrams.

This Venn diagram shows the event A = $\{1, 2\}$ when rolling a die. The sample space $U = \{1, 2, 3, 4, 5, 6\}$.

SET NOTATION

•

U, the **sample space** is represented by a rectangle and A, an **event**, is represented by a circle.

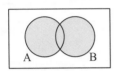   U

A′ is the **complement** of A.

It represents the non-occurrence of A.

Note: $P(A) + P(A') = 1$

If $U = \{1, 2, 3, 4, 5, 6, 7\}$ and $A = \{2, 4, 6\}$ then $A' = \{1, 3, 5, 7\}$

- $x \in A$ reads   'x is in A'   i.e., x is an element of set A.

- $n(A)$ reads 'the number of elements in set A'.

- $A \cup B$ denotes the **union** of sets A and B. This set contains all elements belonging to A **or** B **or both** A and B.

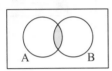

$A \cup B$ is shaded.

Note: $A \cup B = \{x : \ x \in A \ \textbf{or} \ x \in B\}$

- $A \cap B$ denotes the **intersection** of sets A and B. This is the set of all elements common to both sets.

$A \cap B$ is shaded.

Note: $A \cap B = \{x : \ x \in A \ \textbf{and} \ x \in B\}$

- **Disjoint sets** are sets which do not have elements in common.

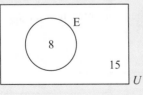

These two sets are disjoint.

$A \cap B = \phi$ where ϕ represents an **empty set**.

A and B are said to be **mutually exclusive**.

Note: It is not possible to represent independent events on a Venn diagram.

Example 15

The Venn diagram alongside represents a sample space, U, of all children in a class. Each dot represents a student. The event, E, shows all those students with blue eyes.

Determine the probability that a randomly selected child:

a   has blue eyes   **b**   does not have blue eyes.

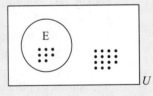

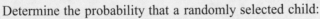

$n(U) = 23, \quad n(E) = 8$

a   P(blue eyes) $= \dfrac{n(E)}{n(U)} = \frac{8}{23}$

b   P(not blue eyes) $= \frac{15}{23}$

   {as 15 of the 23 are not in E}

or   P(not blue) $= 1 - $ P(blue eyes)   {complementary events}

   $= 1 - \frac{8}{23}$

   $= \frac{15}{23}$

Example 16

If A is the set of all factors of 36 and B is the set of all factors of 54,
find: **a** $A \cup B$ **b** $A \cap B$

> $A = \{1, 2, 3, 4, 6, 9, 12, 18, 36\}$ and $B = \{1, 2, 3, 6, 9, 18, 27, 54\}$
>
> **a** $A \cup B$ = the set of factors of 36 **or** 54
> $= \{1, 2, 3, 4, 6, 9, 12, 18, 27, 36, 54\}$
>
> **b** $A \cap B$ = the set of factors of both 36 **and** 54 $= \{1, 2, 3, 6, 9, 18\}$

Example 17

On separate Venn diagrams, using
two events A and B that intersect,
shade the region representing:
a in A but not in B
b neither in A nor B.

a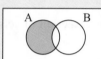

b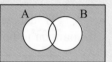

EXERCISE 19I

1 On separate Venn diagrams, using two events A and B that intersect, shade the region
representing:

a in A	**b** in B	**c** in both A and B
d in A or B	**e** in B but not in A	**f** in exactly one of A or B

Example 18

If the Venn diagram alongside illustrates the number
of people in a sporting club who play tennis (T) and
hockey (H), determine the number of people:
a in the club
b who play hockey
c who play both sports
d who play neither sport
e who play at least one sport

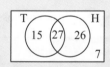

a Number in the club
     $= 15 + 27 + 26 + 7 = 75$

b Number who play hockey
     $= 27 + 26 = 53$

c Number who play both sports $= 27$

d Number who play neither sport
     $= 7$

e Number who play at least one sport
     $= 15 + 27 + 26 = 68$

2 The Venn diagram alongside illustrates the number of
students in a particular class who study Chemistry (C)
and History (H). Determine the number of students:
a in the class   **b** who study both subjects
c who study at least one of the subjects   **d** who only study Chemistry.

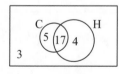

3 In a survey at an alpine resort, people were asked whether they liked skiing (S) or snowboarding (B). Use the Venn diagram to determine the number of people:

    a in the survey

    b who liked both activities

    c who liked neither activity

    d who liked exactly one activity.

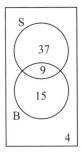

Example 19

In a class of 30 students, 19 study Physics, 17 study Chemistry and 15 study both of these subjects. Display this information on a Venn diagram and hence determine the probability that a randomly selected class member studies:

a both subjects   **b** at least one of the subjects

c Physics, but not Chemistry   **d** exactly one of the subjects

e neither subject   **f** Chemistry if it is known that the student studies Physics

---

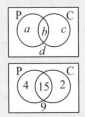

Let P represent the event of 'studying Physics', and C represent the event of 'studying Chemistry'.

Now $a + b = 19$ {as 19 study Physics}

            $b + c = 17$ {as 17 study Chemistry}

                 $b = 15$ {as 15 study both}

    $a + b + c + d = 30$ {as there are 30 in the class}

$\therefore$ $b = 15$, $a = 4$, $c = 2$, $d = 9$.

a P(studies both)

$= \frac{15}{30}$ or $\frac{1}{2}$

b P(studies at least one subject)

$= \frac{4+15+2}{30}$

$= \frac{7}{10}$

c P(studies P, but not C)

$= \frac{4}{30}$

$= \frac{2}{15}$

d P(studies exactly one)

$= \frac{4+2}{30}$

$= \frac{1}{5}$

e P(studies neither)

$= \frac{9}{30}$

$= \frac{3}{10}$

f P(studies C if it is known studies P)

$= \frac{15}{15+4}$

$= \frac{15}{19}$

---

4 In a class of 40 students, 19 play tennis, 20 play netball and 8 play neither of these sports. A student is randomly chosen from the class. Determine the probability that the student:

    a plays tennis   **b** does not play netball

    c plays at least one of the sports   **d** plays one and only one of the sports

    e plays netball, but not tennis   **f** plays tennis knowing he/she plays netball.

5 50 married men were asked whether they gave their wife flowers or chocolates for their last birthday. The results were: 31 gave chocolates, 12 gave flowers and 5 gave both chocolates and flowers. If one of the married men was chosen at random, determine the probability that he gave his wife:

    a   chocolates or flowers   **b**   chocolates but not flowers

    c   neither chocolates nor flowers

    d   flowers if it is known that he did not give her chocolates.

6 The medical records for a class of 30 children showed whether they had previously had measles or mumps. The records showed 24 had had measles, 12 had had measles and mumps, and 26 had had measles or mumps. If one child from the class is selected randomly from the group, determine the probability that he/she has had:

    a   mumps   **b**   mumps but not measles   **c**   neither mumps nor measles

    d   measles if it is known that the child has had mumps.

7 If A and B are two non-disjoint sets, shade the region of a Venn diagram representing

    a A' **b** $A' \cap B$ **c** $A \cup B'$ **d** $A' \cap B'$

8 The diagram alongside is the most general case for three events in the same sample space U.

On separate Venn diagram sketches, shade:

    a A **b** B' **c** $B \cap C$

    d $A \cup C$ **e** $A \cap B \cap C$ **f** $(A \cup B) \cap C$?

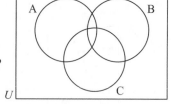

Set identities can be verified using Venn diagrams.

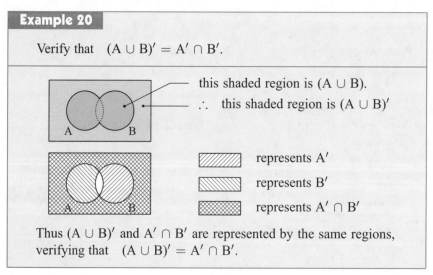

Example 20

Verify that $(A \cup B)' = A' \cap B'$.

this shaded region is $(A \cup B)$.

$\therefore$ this shaded region is $(A \cup B)'$

    ⬜ represents A'

    ⬜ represents B'

    ⬜ represents $A' \cap B'$

Thus $(A \cup B)'$ and $A' \cap B'$ are represented by the same regions, verifying that $(A \cup B)' = A' \cap B'$.

9 Verify that

    a $(A \cap B)' = A' \cup B'$ **b** $A \cup (B \cap C) = (A \cup B) \cap (A \cup C)$

    c $A \cap (B \cup C) = (A \cap B) \cup (A \cap C)$

10 Suppose $S = \{x: x \text{ is a positive integer} < 100\}$.

    Let $A = \{\text{multiples of 7 in S}\}$ and $B = \{\text{multiples of 5 in S}\}$.

    a How many elements are there in: **i** A **ii** B **iii** $A \cap B$ **iv** $A \cup B$?

b If $n(E)$ represents the number of elements in set E, verify that
$n(A \cup B) = n(A) + n(B) - n(A \cap B)$.

11

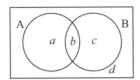

From the Venn diagram $P(A) = \dfrac{a+b}{a+b+c+d}$

a Use the Venn diagram to find:
  i P(B)   **ii** P(A and B)   **iii** P(A or B)   **iv** P(A) + P(B) − P(A and B)

b What is the connection between P(A or B) and P(A) + P(B) − P(A and B)?

J · LAWS OF PROBABILITY

THE ADDITION LAW

From question **11** of the previous exercise we showed that

> for two events A and B, $P(A \cup B) = P(A) + P(B) - P(A \cap B)$.

This is known as the **addition law of probability**, and can be written as

> P(**either** A **or** B) = P(A) + P(B) − P(**both** A **and** B)

Example 21

If $P(A) = 0.6$, $P(A \cup B) = 0.7$
and $P(A \cap B) = 0.3$,   find P(B).

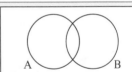

Since $P(A \cup B) = P(A) + P(B) - P(A \cap B)$,
  then $0.7 = 0.6 + P(B) - 0.3$
  $\therefore$ $P(B) = 0.4$

or

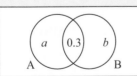

Using a Venn diagram with the probabilities on it,
  $a + 0.3 = 0.6$ $\therefore$ $a = 0.3$
  $a + b + 0.3 = 0.7$
  $\therefore$ $a + b = 0.4$
  $\therefore$ $0.3 + b = 0.4$
  $\therefore$ $b = 0.1$
  $\therefore$ $P(B) = 0.3 + b = 0.4$

MUTUALLY EXCLUSIVE EVENTS

> If A and B are **mutually exclusive** events then $P(A \cap B) = 0$
> and so the addition law becomes $P(A \cup B) = P(A) + P(B)$.

Example 22

A box of chocolates contains 6 with hard centres (H) and 12 with soft centres (S).
a   Are the events H and S mutually exclusive?
b   Find   i P(H)   ii P(S)   iii P(H ∩ S)   iv P(H ∪ S).

a   Chocolates cannot have both a hard and a soft centre.
     ∴ H and S are mutually exclusive.

b i P(H) $= \frac{6}{18}$ ii P(S) $= \frac{12}{18}$ iii   P(H ∩ S)   iv   P(H ∪ S)
       $= \frac{1}{3}$ $= \frac{2}{3}$ $= 0$ $= \frac{18}{18}$
                                                                                    $= 1$

CONDITIONAL PROBABILITY

Suppose we have two events A and B, then

A|B is used to represent that 'A occurs knowing that B has occurred'.

Example 23

In a class of 25 students, 14 like Pizza and 16 like coffee. One student likes neither
and 6 students like both. One student is randomly selected from the class.
What is the probability that the student:
a   likes Pizza   b   likes Pizza given that he/she likes coffee?

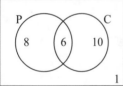

The Venn diagram of the situation is shown.
a   P(Pizza) $= \frac{14}{25}$ {of the 25 students 14 like Pizza}

b   P(Pizza|coffee) $= \frac{6}{16}$
    {of the 16 who like coffee, 6 like Pizza}

If A and B are events then

$$P(A|B) = \frac{P(A \cap B)}{P(B)}.$$

Proof:

P(A|B)

$$= \frac{b}{b+c}$$ {Venn diagram}

$$= \frac{b/(a+b+c+d)}{(b+c)/(a+b+c+d)}$$

$$= \frac{P(A \cap B)}{P(B)}$$

It follows that   P(A ∩ B) = P(A|B)P(B)   or   P(A ∩ B) = P(B|A)P(A)

Example 24

In a class of 40, 34 like bananas, 22 like pineapples and 2 dislike both fruits.
If a student is randomly selected, find the probability that the student:

a   likes both fruits   **b**   likes at least one fruit

c   likes bananas given that he/she likes pineapples

d   dislikes pineapples given that he/she likes bananas.

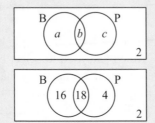

B represents students who like bananas
P represents students who like pineapples

We are given that $a + b = 34$
$$b + c = 22$$
$$a + b + c = 38$$

$$\therefore \quad c = 38 - 34 \quad \text{and so} \quad b = 18$$
$$= 4 \quad\quad\quad \text{and} \quad a = 16$$

a   P(likes both)   **b**   P(likes at least one)   **c**   P(B|P)   **d**   P(P'|B)

$$= \frac{18}{40} \quad\quad\quad = \frac{38}{40} \quad\quad\quad\quad\quad = \frac{18}{22} \quad\quad\quad = \frac{16}{34}$$

$$= \frac{9}{20} \quad\quad\quad = \frac{19}{20} \quad\quad\quad\quad\quad = \frac{9}{11} \quad\quad\quad = \frac{8}{17}$$

EXERCISE 19J

1   In a group of 50 students, 40 study Mathematics, 32 study Physics and each student
studies at least one of these subjects.

    a   From a Venn diagram find how many students study both subjects.

    b   If a student from this group is randomly selected, find the probability that he/she:

        i   studies Mathematics but not Physics

        ii   studies Physics given that he/she studies Mathematics.

2   In a class of 40 students, 23 have dark hair, 18 have brown eyes, and 26 have dark hair,
brown eyes or both. A child is selected at random. Determine the probability that the
child has:

    a   dark hair and brown eyes   **b**   neither dark hair nor brown eyes

    c   dark hair but not brown eyes   **d**   brown eyes given that the child has dark hair.

3   50 students go bushwalking. 23 get sunburnt, 22 get bitten by ants and 5 are both
sunburnt and bitten by ants. Determine the probability that a randomly selected student:

    a   escaped being bitten   **b**   was either bitten or sunburnt

    c   was neither bitten nor sunburnt

    d   was bitten, given that the student was sunburnt

    e   was sunburnt, given that the student was not bitten.

4   400 families were surveyed. It was found that 90% had a TV set and 60% had a
computer. Every family had at least one of these items. If one of these families is
randomly selected, find the probability it has a TV set given that it has a computer.

5 In a certain town 3 newspapers are published. 20% of the population read A, 16% read B, 14% read C, 8% read A and B, 5% read A and C, 4% read B and C and 2% read all 3 newspapers. A person is selected at random. Determine the probability that the person reads:

   a none of the papers   **b** at least one of the papers   **c** exactly one of the papers

   d either A or B   **e** A, given that the person reads at least one paper

   f C, given that the person reads either A or B or both.

Example 25

Bin A contains 3 red and 2 white tickets. Bin B contains 4 red and 1 white. A die with 4 faces marked A and two faces marked B is rolled and used to select bin A or B. A ticket is then selected from this bin. Determine the probability that:

   a the ticket is red   **b** the ticket was chosen from B given it is red.

bin   ticket

$\frac{4}{6}$ — A — $\frac{3}{5}$ R ✓ ①

A — $\frac{2}{5}$ W

$\frac{2}{6}$ — B — $\frac{4}{5}$ R ✓ ②

B — $\frac{1}{5}$ W

a $P(R)$

$= \frac{4}{6} \times \frac{3}{5} + \frac{2}{6} \times \frac{4}{5}$ {the ✓ paths}

$= \frac{2}{3}$

b $P(B|R) = \dfrac{P(B \cap R)}{P(R)}$

$= \dfrac{\frac{2}{6} \times \frac{4}{5}}{\frac{2}{3}}$ ⟵ path ②

$= \frac{2}{5}$

---

6 Urn A contains 2 red and 3 blue marbles, and urn B contains 4 red and 1 blue marble. Peter selects an urn by tossing a coin, and takes a marble from that urn.

   a Determine the probability that it is red.

   b Given that the marble is red, what is the probability it came from B?

7 The probability that Greta's mother takes her shopping is $\frac{2}{5}$. When Greta goes shopping with her mother she gets an icecream 70% of the time. When Greta does not go shopping with her mother she gets an icecream 30% of the time.

   Determine the probability that:

   a Greta's mother buys her an icecream when shopping.

   b Greta went shopping with her mother, given that her mother buys her an icecream.

8 On a given day, photocopier A has a 10% chance of a malfunction and machine B has a 7% chance of the same. Given that at least one of the machines has malfunctioned, what is the chance that it was machine B?

9 On any day, the probability that a boy eats his prepared lunch is 0.5 and the probability that his sister does likewise is 0.6. The probability that the girl eats her lunch given that the boy eats his is 0.9. Determine the probability that:

   a both eat their lunch   **b** the boy eats his lunch given that the girl eats hers

   c at least one of them eats lunch.

10 The probability that a randomly selected person has cancer is 0.02. The probability that he reacts positively to a test which detects cancer is 0.95 if he has cancer, and 0.03 if he does not. Determine the probability that a randomly selected person when tested:

    a reacts positively   **b** has cancer given that he reacts positively.

11 A double-headed, a double-tailed and an ordinary coin are placed in a tin can. One of the coins is randomly chosen without idenfitying it. The coin is tossed and falls "heads". Determine the probability that the coin is the "double-header".

K   INDEPENDENT EVENTS REVISITED

A and B are **independent events** if the occurrence (or non-occurrence) of one event does not affect the occurrence of the other,

$$\text{i.e.,}\quad P(A|B) = P(A)\quad\text{and}\quad P(B|A) = P(B).$$

So, as $P(A \cap B) = P(A|B)\,P(B),$

A and B are **independent events** $\Leftrightarrow$ $P(A \cap B) = P(A)\,P(B).$

Example 26

When two coins are tossed, A is the event of getting 2 heads. When a die is rolled, B is the event of getting a 5 or 6. Prove that A and B are independent events.

$P(A) = \frac{1}{4}$ and $P(B) = \frac{2}{6}$. Therefore, $P(A)\,P(B) = \frac{1}{4} \times \frac{2}{6} = \frac{1}{12}$

$P(A \cap B)$

$= P(2 \text{ heads } \textbf{and } \text{a 5 or a 6})$

$= \frac{2}{24}$

$= \frac{1}{12}$

So, as $P(A \cap B) = P(A)\,P(B)$, the events A and B are independent.

Example 27

$P(A) = \frac{1}{2},\quad P(B) = \frac{1}{3}$ and $P(A \cup B) = p.$ Find p if:

    a A and B are mutually exclusive   **b** A and B are independent.

  a If A and B are mutually exclusive, $A \cap B = \phi$

        and so $P(A \cap B) = 0$

        But $P(A \cup B) = P(A) + P(B) - P(A \cap B)$

        $\therefore\ p = \frac{1}{2} + \frac{1}{3} - 0 = \frac{5}{6}$

  b If A and B are independent, $P(A \cap B) = P(A)\,P(B) = \frac{1}{2} \times \frac{1}{3} = \frac{1}{6}$

    $\therefore\ P(A \cup B) = \frac{1}{2} + \frac{1}{3} - \frac{1}{6}$ i.e., $p = \frac{2}{3}$

EXERCISE 19K

1   If $P(R) = 0.4$, $P(S) = 0.5$ and $P(R \cup S) = 0.7$, are R and S independent events?

2   If $P(A) = \frac{2}{5}$, $P(B) = \frac{1}{3}$ and $P(A \cup B) = \frac{1}{2}$, find:

   a $P(A \cap B)$ **b** $P(B|A)$ **c** $P(A|B)$

   Are A and B independent events?

3   If $P(X) = 0.5$, $P(Y) = 0.7$, and X and Y are independent events, determine the probability of the occurrence of:

   a   both X and Y   **b**   X or Y   **c**   neither X nor Y

   d   X but not Y   **e**   X given that Y occurs.

4   The probability that A, B and C solve a particular problem is $\frac{3}{5}$, $\frac{2}{3}$, $\frac{1}{2}$, respectively.

   If they all try, determine the probability that the group solves the problem.

5   **a**   Find the probability of getting at least one six when a die is rolled 3 times.

   b   If a die is rolled n times, find the smallest n such that
      P(at least one 6 in n throws) > 99%.

6   A and B are independent events. Prove that A and B$'$ are also independent events.

L | PROBABILITIES USING PERMUTATIONS AND COMBINATIONS

Permutations and **combinations** can sometimes be used to find probabilities of various events particularly when large sample sizes occur. It is useful to remember that:

$$\text{P[an event]} = \frac{\text{number with the required properties of the event}}{\text{total number of unrestricted possibilities}}.$$

For example,   if we select at random a team of 4 boys and 3 girls from a squad of 8 boys and 7 girls, the total number of unrestricted possibilities is $_{15}C_7$ since we want any 7 of the 15 available for selection.

The number with the required property of '4 boys **and** 3 girls' is $_8C_4 \times {}_7C_3$ as from the 8 boys we want any 4 of them **and** from the 7 girls we want any 3 of them.

$$\therefore \quad \text{P[4 boys and 3 girls]} = \frac{_8C_4 \ \times \ {}_7C_3}{_{15}C_7}.$$

The biggest hurdle in probability problems involving permutations or combinations seems to be in sorting out which to use.

Remember: •   **permutations** involve **orderings** of objects or things, whereas

                 •   **combinations** involve **selections** (such as committees or teams).

Example 28

From a squad of 13 which includes 4 brothers, a team of 7 is randomly selected by drawing names from a hat. Determine the probability that the team contains
  a all the brothers **b** at least 2 of the brothers.

There are $_{13}C_7$ different teams of 7 that can be chosen from 13.

a Of these teams contain all 4 brothers and any 3 others.

$$\therefore \quad P[\text{contains all the brothers}] = \frac{_4C_4 \times _9C_3}{_{13}C_7} \doteqdot 0.048\,95$$

b P[at least 2 brothers] = P[2 brothers or 3 brothers or 4 brothers]

$$= \frac{_4C_2 \times _9C_5}{_{13}C_7} + \frac{_4C_3 \times _9C_4}{_{13}C_7} + \frac{_4C_4 \times _9C_3}{_{13}C_7}$$

$$\doteqdot 0.7832$$

Example 29

5 letters U, S, T, I, N are placed at random in a row.
What is the probability that the word UNITS is spelled out?

There are 5! different permutations of the letters, one of which spells UNITS.

$$\therefore \quad P(\text{UNITS is spelled}) = \tfrac{1}{5!} = \tfrac{1}{120}$$

Notice that counting permutations is not essential here. We could have used:

$$P(\text{UNITS}) = \tfrac{1}{5} \times \tfrac{1}{4} \times \tfrac{1}{3} \times \tfrac{1}{2} \times \tfrac{1}{1} = \tfrac{1}{120}$$

5 to choose from
and we want only U
now 4 are left
and we want N
etc.

EXERCISE 19L

1 A committee of 4 is chosen from 11 people by random selection. What is the chance that sisters X and Y are on the committee?

2 4 alphabet blocks; D, A, I and S are placed at random in a row. What is the likelihood that they spell out either AIDS or SAID?

3 A team of 7 is randomly chosen from a squad of 12. Determine the probability that both the captain and vice-captain are chosen.

4 4 people are killed in an air crash and 3 professional golfers were aboard. Determine the chance that none of the golfers was killed if 22 people were aboard.

5 5 boys sit at random on 5 seats in a row. Determine the probability that two of them (Keong and Uwe, say) **a** sit at the ends of the row **b** sit together.

6 A committee of 5 is randomly selected from 9 men and 7 women. Determine the likelihood that it consists of

    a all men   **b** at least 3 men   **c** at least one of each sex.

7 6 people including friends A, B and C are randomly seated on a row of 6 chairs. Determine the likelihood that A, B and C are seated together.

M   BAYES' THEOREM

We have actually been using **Bayes' theorem** when finding some probabilities from tree diagrams.

Bayes' theorem is:

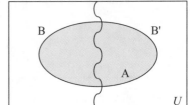

If A is an event in the sample space $B \cup B'$ then,

$$P(A|B) = \frac{P(A)\,P(B|A)}{P(A)\,P(B|A) + P(A')\,P(B|A')}$$

Note: Bayes' theorem can be extended to 3 or more mutually exclusive events, e.g., sample space $B_1 \cup B_2 \cup B$.

Example 30

A can contains 4 blue and 2 non-blue marbles. One marble is randomly drawn without replacement from the can and its colour is noted. A second marble is then drawn. What is the probability that:

a the second marble is blue

b the first was non-blue given that the second was blue?

	compare		product
$\frac{4}{6}$ B_1 $\frac{3}{5}$ B_2		B_1 $B_2\mid B_1$	$P(B_1 \cap B_2)$
$\frac{2}{5}$ B'_2		$B'_2\mid B_1$	$P(B_1 \cap B'_2)$
$\frac{2}{6}$ B'_1 $\frac{4}{5}$ B_2		B'_1 $B_2\mid B'_1$	$P(B'_1 \cap B_2)$
$\frac{1}{5}$ B'_2		$B'_2\mid B'_1$	$P(B'_1 \cap B'_2)$

a $P(B_2)$

$$= \frac{4}{6} \times \frac{3}{5} + \frac{2}{6} \times \frac{4}{5} \quad \longleftarrow \quad P(B_1)\,P(B_2|B_1) + P(B'_1)\,P(B_2|B'_1)$$

$$= \frac{2}{3}$$

b $P(B'_1|B_2)$

$$= \frac{P(B'_1 \cap B_2)}{P(B_2)}$$

$$= \frac{\frac{2}{6} \times \frac{4}{5}}{\frac{4}{6} \times \frac{3}{5} + \frac{2}{6} \times \frac{4}{5}} \quad \longleftarrow \quad \frac{P(B'_1)\,P(B_2|B'_1)}{P(B_1)\,P(B_2|B_1) + P(B'_1)\,P(B_2|B'_1)}$$

$$= \frac{2}{5}$$

Proof: (of Bayes' theorem)

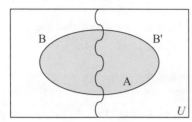

$$P(A|B)$$

$$= \frac{P(A \cap B)}{P(B)}$$

$$= \frac{P(B|A) \, P(A)}{P(B \cap A) + P(B \cap A')}$$

$$= \frac{P(B|A) \, P(A)}{P(B|A) \, P(A) + P(B|A') \, P(A')}$$

EXERCISE 19M

1 Coffee making machines, Alpha and Beta, produce 65% and 35% of coffee sold each day in identically shaped plastic cups. Alpha underfills a cup 4% of the time and machine Beta underfills 5% of the time.

  a If a cup of coffee is chosen at random, what is the probability it is underfilled?

  b A cup of coffee is randomly chosen and is found to be underfilled. What is the probability it came from Alpha?

2 54% of the students at a University are females. Of the male students 8% are colour-blind and of the female students 2% are colour-blind. If a randomly chosen student:

  a is colour-blind, find the probability that the student is male

  b is not colour-blind, find the probability that the student is female.

3 A marble is randomly chosen from a can containing 3 red and 5 blue marbles. It is re-placed by two marbles of the other colour. Another marble is then randomly chosen from the can. If the marbles that were chosen were the same colour, what is the probability that they were both blue?

4 35% of the animals in a deer herd carry the TPC gene. 58% of these deer also carry the SD gene, while 23% of the deer without the TPC gene carry the SD gene. If a deer is randomly chosen and is found to carry the SD gene, what is the probability it does not carry the TPC gene?

5 **a** 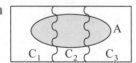 A sample space is made up of disjoint (mutually exclusive), and exhaustive events C_1, C_2 and C_3. Show that:

$$P(A) = P(C_1) \, P(A|C_1) + P(C_2) \, P(A|C_2) + P(C_3) \, P(A|C_3)$$

  b A printer has three presses A, B and C which print 30%, 40% and 30% of daily production. Due to the age and other problems the presses cannot be used 3%, 5% and 7% of the day, respectively.

    i What is the probability that a randomly chosen press is in use?

    ii If a machine is in use, what is the probability it is press A?

    iii If a machine is not in use, what is the probability it is A or C?

6 12% of the over-60 population of Agento were found to have lung cancer. For those with lung cancer, 50% were heavy smokers, 40% were moderate smokers and 10% were non-smokers. For those without lung cancer 5% were heavy smokers, 15% were moderate smokers and 80% were non-smokers.

  a What is the probability that a randomly selected person was a heavy smoker?

b What is the probability that a person has lung cancer given that the person was a moderate smoker?

c What is the probability that a person has lung cancer given that the person was a non-smoker?

REVIEW SET 19A

1 List the different orderings in which 4 people A, B, C and D could line up. If they line up at random, determine the probability that:

    a   A is next to C   **b**   there is exactly one person between A and C.

2 A coin is tossed and a square spinner, labelled A, B, C, D, is twirled. Determine the probability of obtaining:

    a   a head and consonant   **b**   a tail and C   **c**   a tail or a vowel.

3 A class contains 25 students. 13 play tennis, 14 play volleyball and 1 plays neither of these two sports. A student is randomly selected from the class. Determine the probability that the student:

    a   plays both tennis and volleyball   **b**   plays at least one of these two sports.

    c   plays volleyball given that he/she does not play tennis.

4 Niklas and Rolf play tennis and the winner is the first to win two sets. Niklas has a 40% chance of beating Rolf in any set. Draw a tree diagram showing the possible outcomes and hence determine the probability that Niklas will win the match.

5 The probability that a man will be alive in 25 years is $\frac{3}{5}$, and the probability that his wife will be alive is $\frac{2}{3}$. Determine the probability that in 25 years:

    a both will be alive   **b** at least one will be alive   **c** only the wife will be alive.

6 Each time Mae and Ravi play chess, Mae has a probability of $\frac{4}{5}$ that she wins. If they play 5 games, determine the probability that:

    a   Mae wins 3 games   **b**   Mae wins either 4 or 5 of the games.

7 If I buy 4 tickets in a 500 ticket lottery, determine the probability that I win:

    a   the first 3 prizes   **b**   at least one of the first 3 prizes.

8 A school photocopier has a 95% chance of working on any particular day. Find the probability that it will be working on at least one of the next two days.

9 A team of five is randomly chosen from six doctors and four dentists. Determine the likelihood that it consists of: **a** all doctors   **b** at least two doctors.

10 3 girls and 3 boys sit at random on 6 seats in a row. Determine the probability that:

    a   they alternate with girls sitting between boys   **b**   the girls are seated together.

11 All students in a school are vaccinated against measles. 48% of the students are males, of whom 16% have an allergic reaction to the vaccine. 35% of the girls also have a reaction. If a student is randomly chosen from the school, what is the probability that the student **a** has an allergic reaction **b** is female, given that a reaction occurred.

REVIEW SET 19B
Click on the icon to obtain printable review sets and answers

REVIEW SET 19B

Chapter 20

Introduction to calculus

Contents:

INTRODUCTION

Calculus is a branch of mathematics which deals with **rate of change**.

Speed is a rate of change; it is the rate of change in distance per unit of time.

We say that $\qquad$ average speed $= \dfrac{\text{distance travelled}}{\text{time taken}}$.

An average speed of 60 km/h means that in 1 hour, 60 km are travelled.

Calculus developed from these questions:

- What is speed?
- How is instantaneous speed calculated?

Calculus has been used in many branches of science and engineering since 1600 AD.

INVESTIGATION 1 $\qquad$ THE SPEED OF FALLING OBJECTS

 Secret agent James Speed has fallen from a plane. The problem he faces is to calculate his speed at any particular moment. If only he had brought his personal speedometer!

He knows that the distance fallen (d metres) by a falling object (from rest) is given by $d(t) = 5t^2$ and the average speed in the time interval $t_1 \leqslant t \leqslant t_2$ is given by $\dfrac{d(t_2) - d(t_1)}{t_2 - t_1}$ metres/second.

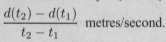

What to do:

a Copy and complete:

Time interval	Average speed in this interval
$1 \leqslant t \leqslant 2$	
$1 \leqslant t \leqslant 1.5$	
$1 \leqslant t \leqslant 1.1$	
$1 \leqslant t \leqslant 1.01$	
$1 \leqslant t \leqslant 1.001$	

b Using **a**, predict James' speed at the precise moment when $t = 1$. Explain your reasoning.

c Find the average speed between 1 and $1 + h$ seconds where h represents a small increment of time (which can be made as small as we like). Show how this answer supports your answer to **b**.

d Repeat steps **a**, **b** and **c** in order to find James' instantaneous speed at:
$\quad$ **i** $\quad t = 2$ seconds $\qquad$ **ii** $\quad t = 3$ seconds $\qquad$ **iii** $\quad t = 4$ seconds

e Copy and complete:

t	Instantaneous speed at this time
1	
2	
3	
4	

f Use **e** to predict a formula for instantaneous speed when $d = 5t^2$
i.e.,   complete: "if $d = 5t^2$, then instantaneous speed = ..."

g Calculate James' average speed between t and $t + h$ seconds and use this result
to explain why your answer in **f** is correct.

A   RATE OF CHANGE

Often we judge sporting performances by using rates. For example:

* Sir Donald Bradman's batting rate at Test cricket level was 99.94 *runs per innings*
* Dasha's basketball goal scoring rate was 17.25 *goals per game*
* Rangi's typing speed is 63 *words per minute* with an error rate of 2.3 *errors per page*

A **rate** is a comparison between two quantities of different kinds.

AVERAGE RATE OF CHANGE

Consider a trip from Adelaide to Melbourne in Australia.

The following table gives towns along the way, distances travelled and time taken.

We plot the *distance travelled* against the *time taken* to obtain a graph of the situation.

Even though there would be variable speed between each place we will join points with straight line segments.

We can find the average speed between any two places.

For example, the average speed from Bordertown to Nhill is:

Place	Time taken (min)	Distance travelled (km)
Adelaide tollgate	0	0
Tailem Bend	63	98
Bordertown	157	237
Nhill	204	324
Horsham	261	431
Ararat	317	527
Midland H/W Junction	386	616
Melbourne	534	729

$$\frac{\text{distance travelled}}{\text{time taken}} = \frac{(324 - 237) \text{ km}}{(204 - 157) \text{ min}}$$

$$= \frac{87 \text{ km}}{\frac{47}{60} \text{ h}}$$

$$\doteqdot 111 \text{ km/h}$$

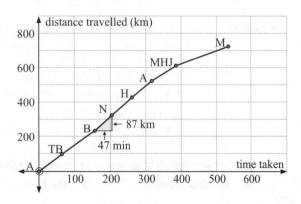

We notice that the average speed is the $\dfrac{y\text{-step}}{x\text{-step}}$ on the graph.

So, the average speed is the **slope of the line segment** joining the two points, which means that the faster the trip between two places, the greater the slope of the graph.

If $s(t)$ is the distance travelled function then the **average speed** over the time interval from $t = t_1$ to $t = t_2$ is given by:

$$\text{Average speed} = \dfrac{s(t_2) - s(t_1)}{t_2 - t_1}.$$

EXERCISE 20A.1

1 For the Adelaide to Melbourne data on page **533**, find the average speed from:

    a   Tailem Bend to Nhill   **b**   Horsham to Melbourne.

2 Tian walks to the newsagent to get a paper each morning. The travel graph alongside shows Tian's distance from home. Use the graph to answer the following questions.

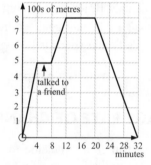

    a   How far is the newsagent from Tian's house?

    b   What is the slope of the line segment for the first 4 minutes of the walk?

    c   What was Tian's average walking speed for the first 4 minutes (m/min)?

    d   What is the physical representation of the slope in this problem?

    e   How many minutes did Tian stay at the newsagent's store?

    f   What was Tian's average speed on the return journey?

    g   What total distance did Tian walk?

3 During December a reservoir in Peru was losing water at a constant rate due to usage and evaporation. On December 12 the estimated water in the reservoir was 53.8 million kL and on December 23 the estimate was 48.2 million kL. No water entered the reservoir. What was the average rate of water loss during this period?

4 Kolya's water consumption invoices for a one year period show:

Period	Consumption
First quarter (Jan 01 to Mar 31)	106.8 kL
Second quarter (Apr 01 to Jun 30)	79.4 kL
Third quarter (Jul 01 to Sep 30)	81.8 kL
Fourth quarter (Oct 01 to Dec 31)	115.8 kL

Find the average rate of water consumption per day for:

    a   the first quarter   **b**   the first six months   **c**   the whole year.

CONSTANT AND VARIABLE RATES OF CHANGE

Once again let us visit the water filling demonstration. Water flows from a tap at a constant rate into vessels of various shapes. We see the water level change over time. A corresponding *height* against *time* graph shows what is happening to the height as time increases. Click on the icon to investigate the rate of change in height over time for the different shaped vessels given.

DEMO

AVERAGE RATES FROM CURVED GRAPHS

Consider the following example where we are to find average rates over a given time interval.

Example 1

The number of mice in a colony was recorded on a weekly basis.

a Estimate the average rate of increase in population for:
   i the period from week 3 to week 6
   ii the seven week period.

b What is the overall trend with regard to population increase over this period?

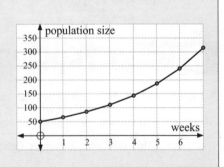

a i population rate

$$= \frac{\text{increase in population}}{\text{increase in time}}$$

$$= \frac{(240 - 110) \text{ mice}}{(6 - 3) \text{ weeks}}$$

$$\doteqdot 43 \quad \text{mice/week}$$

ii population rate

$$= \frac{(315 - 50) \text{ mice}}{(7 - 0) \text{ weeks}}$$

$$\doteqdot 38 \quad \text{mice/week}$$

b The population rate is increasing over the seven week period as shown by the increasing y-steps on the graph for equal x-steps.

You should notice that:

> The **average rate of change** between two points on the graph is the **slope of the chord** (or **secant**) connecting these two points.

EXERCISE 20A.2

1 For the travel graph given alongside find estimates of the average speed:

   a in the first 4 seconds

   b in the last 4 seconds

   c in the 8 second interval.

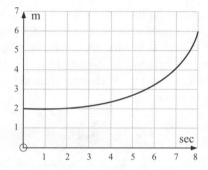

2 The number of lawn beetles per m^2 surviving in a lawn for various doses of poison is given in the graph.

   a Estimate the rate of beetle decrease when:

   i the dose increases from 0 to 10 g

   ii the dose increases from 4 to 8 g.

   b Describe the effect on the rate of beetle decline as the dose goes from 0 to 14 g.

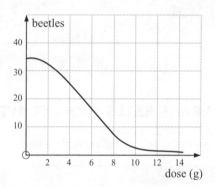

B   INSTANTANEOUS RATES OF CHANGE

A moving object such as a motor car, an aeroplane or a runner has variable speed.

At a particular instant in time, the speed of the object is called its **instantaneous speed**.

To examine this concept in greater detail consider the following investigation.

INVESTIGATION 2   INSTANTANEOUS SPEED

Earlier we noticed that:

"The average rate of change between two points on a graph is the slope of the chord connecting them."

But, what happens if these two points are extremely close together or in fact coincide?

To discover what will happen consider the following problem:

A ball bearing is dropped from the top of a tall building. The distance fallen after t seconds is recorded and the following graph of distance against time is obtained.

The question is, "What is the speed of the ball bearing at $t = 2$ seconds?

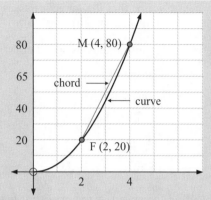

Notice that the average speed in the time interval $2 \leqslant t \leqslant 4$ is

$$= \frac{\text{distance travelled}}{\text{time taken}}$$

$$= \frac{(80 - 20) \text{ m}}{(4 - 2) \text{ s}}$$

$$= \frac{60}{2} \text{ m/s}$$

$$= 30 \text{ m/s}$$

What to do:

1 Click on the icon to start the demonstration. The slope box gives the starting slope of chord MF where F is the fixed point at which we require the speed of the ball bearing. Check that the slope of MF is that which is given in the slope box when the moving point M is at (4, 80).

2 Click on M and drag it slowly towards F. Write down the slope of the chord when M is at the point where t is:

    a 3   **b** 2.5   **c** 2.1   **d** 2.01

3 When M reaches F observe and record what happens. Why is this so?

4 What do you suspect is the speed of the ball bearing at $t = 2$? This speed is the *instantaneous speed* of the ball bearing at this instant.

5 Move M to the origin and then move it towards F from the other direction. Do you get the same result?

From the investigation you should have discovered that:

> The **instantaneous rate of change** (speed in this case) at a particular point is given by the **slope of the tangent** to the graph at that point.

VARIABLE RATES OF CHANGE

THE GRAPHICAL METHOD

Consider a cyclist who is stationary at an intersection. The graph alongside shows how the cyclist accelerates away from the intersection.

Notice that the average speed over the first 8 seconds is $\dfrac{100 \text{ m}}{8 \text{ sec}} = 12.5$ m/s.

Notice also that the cyclist's early speed is quite small, but is increasing as time goes by.

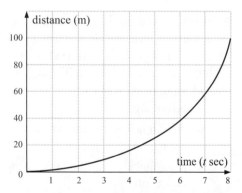

To find the instantaneous speed at any time instant, for example, $t = 4$ we simply draw the tangent at that point and find its slope.

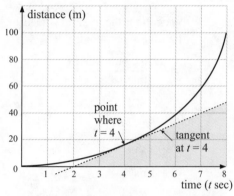

Notice that the tangent passes through $(2, 0)$ and $(7, 40)$

$\therefore$ instantaneous speed at $t = 4$

$=$ slope of tangent

$= \dfrac{(40 - 0) \text{ m}}{(7 - 2) \text{ s}}$

$= \frac{40}{5}$ m/s

$= 8$ m/s

At any point in time we can use this method to find the speed of the cyclist at that instant.

EXERCISE 20B.1

1 For each of the following graphs, find the approximate rate of change at the point shown by the arrow. Make sure your answer contains the correct units.

a
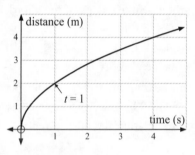

b
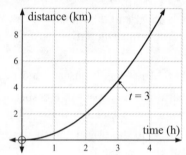

PRINTABLE
GRAPHS

c
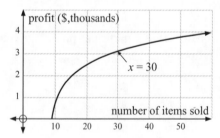

d
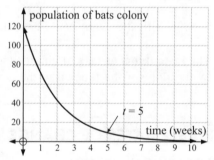

2 Water is leaking from a tank. The amount of water left in the tank (measured in thousands of litres) after x hours is given in the graph alongside.

   a How much water was in the tank originally?

   b How much water was in the tank after 1 hour?

   c How quickly was the tank losing water initially?

   d How quickly was the tank losing water after 1 hour?

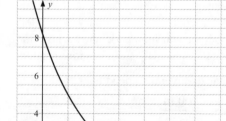

THE 'ZOOMING-IN' METHOD

Consider the graph of $y = x^2$ and its tangent at $(1, 1)$.

Screen dumps, showing the zooming-in technique, are given below.

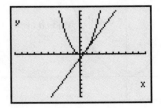 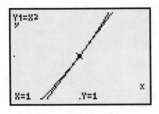 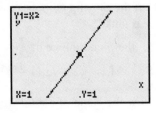

Each successive dump shows zooming in to the point $(1, 1)$.

The more we zoom-in, the closer the graph gets to a straight line. In fact the graph of $y = x^2$ and the tangent become indistinguishable over successively smaller x-intervals.

So we could choose two points on $y = x^2$ which are extremely close to $(1, 1)$, perhaps one on each side of $(1, 1)$, find the slope between these points and use this slope to estimate the slope of the tangent.

THE TABLE METHOD

We should have noticed in earlier exercises that drawing an accurate tangent to a curve at a given point is difficult. Three different people may produce three different results. So we need better methods for performing this procedure.

Consider the curve $y = x^2$ and the tangent at the point $(1, 1)$.

A table of values could be used to find the slope of the tangent at $(1, 1)$. We consider a point not at $(1, 1)$, find the slope to $(1, 1)$, and do the same for points closer and closer to $(1, 1)$.

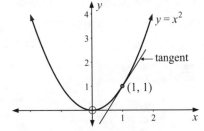

Consider this table:

x-coordinate	y-coordinate	slope of chord
2	4	$\frac{4-1}{2-1} = \frac{3}{1} = 3$
1.5	2.25	$\frac{2.25-1}{1.5-1} = \frac{1.25}{0.5} = 2.5$
1.1	1.21	$\frac{1.21-1}{1.1-1} = \frac{0.21}{0.1} = 2.1$
1.01	1.0201	$\frac{1.0201-1}{1.01-1} = \frac{0.201}{0.01} = 2.01$
1.001	1.002\,001	$\frac{1.002\,001-1}{1.001-1} = \frac{0.002\,001}{0.001} = 2.001$

It is fairly clear that:

- the slope of the tangent at $(1, 1)$ would be exactly 2
- the table method is tedious, but it does help to understand the ideas behind finding slopes at a given point.

THE ALGEBRAIC METHOD

To illustrate the algebraic method once again we will consider the curve $y = x^2$ and the tangent at F(1, 1).

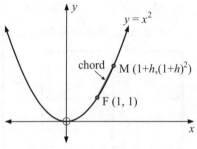

Let the moving point have x-coordinate $1 + h$ where h is small.

$\therefore$ the y-coordinate of $M = (1 + h)^2$. $\{$as $y = x^2\}$

So, M is $(1 + h, (1 + h)^2)$.

Now the slope of chord MF is $\dfrac{y\text{-step}}{x\text{-step}}$

$$= \frac{(1 + h)^2 - 1}{1 + h - 1}$$

$$= \frac{1 + 2h + h^2 - 1}{h}$$

$$= \frac{2h + h^2}{h}$$

$$= \frac{h(2 + h)}{h}$$

$$= 2 + h \quad \{\text{if } h \neq 0\}$$

Now as M approaches F, h approaches 0.

Consequently, $2 + h$ approaches 2.

So, we conclude that the tangent at (1, 1) has slope 2.

Example 2

Use the algebraic method to find the slope of the tangent to $y = x^2$ at the point where $x = 2$.

Let $M(2 + h, (2 + h)^2)$ be a point on $y = x^2$ which is close to F(2, 4).

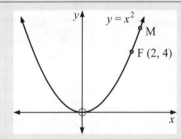

Slope of MF $= \dfrac{y\text{-step}}{x\text{-step}}$

$$= \frac{(2 + h)^2 - 4}{2 + h - 2}$$

$$= \frac{4 + 4h + h^2 - 4}{h} \qquad \{\text{using } (a + b)^2 = a^2 + 2ab + b^2\}$$

$$= \frac{h(4 + h)}{h}$$

$$= 4 + h \quad \{\text{as } h \neq 0\}$$

Now as M approaches F, h approaches 0, $4 + h$ approaches 4,

$\therefore$ the tangent at (2, 4) has slope 4.

EXERCISE 20B.2

1 Use the algebraic method to find the slope of the tangent to $y = x^2$ at the point where $x = 1.5$.

2 **a** Using $(x+h)^3 = (x+h)^2(x+h)$, show that $(x+h)^3 = x^3 + 3x^2h + 3xh^2 + h^3$.

  b Find $(1 + h)^3$ in expanded form using **a**.

  c Consider finding the slope of the tangent to $y = x^3$ at the point F(1, 1). If the x-coordinate of a moving point M, which is close to F, has value $1 + h$, state the coordinates of M.

  d Find the slope of the chord MF in simplest form $(h \neq 0)$.

  e What is the slope of the tangent to $y = x^3$ at the point (1, 1)?

3 Repeat **2** but this time find the slope of the tangent to $y = x^3$ at the point (2, 8).

4 Consider the graph of $y = \dfrac{1}{x}$.

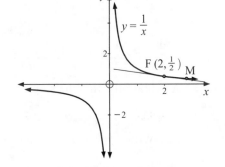

  a Write $\dfrac{1}{x+h} - \dfrac{1}{x}$ as a single fraction.

  b If point M has x-coordinate $2 + h$ state its y-coordinate and find the slope of MF in terms of h.

  c What is the slope of the tangent at the point where $x = 2$?

  d What is the slope of the tangent to $y = \dfrac{1}{x}$ at the point where $x = 3$?

5 **a** Show that $\dfrac{1}{(x+h)^2} - \dfrac{1}{x^2} = \dfrac{-2xh - h^2}{x^2(x+h)^2}$.

  b What does the identity in **a** become when $x = 2$?

  c Sketch the graph of $y = \dfrac{1}{x^2}$ for $x > 0$ only.

  d Find the slope of the tangent to $y = \dfrac{1}{x^2}$ at the point where $x = 2$.

6 **a** Copy and complete:
$$\frac{\sqrt{x+h} - \sqrt{x}}{h} = \left(\frac{\sqrt{x+h} - \sqrt{x}}{h}\right)\left(\frac{\sqrt{x+h} + \sqrt{x}}{\sqrt{x+h} + \sqrt{x}}\right) = \ldots\ldots$$

  b What identity results when $x = 9$ in part **a**?

  c Sketch the graph of $y = \sqrt{x}$.

  d Find the slope of the tangent to $y = \sqrt{x}$ at the point where $x = 9$.

  e The number of insects (in thousands) in a colony at time t days is modelled by $N = \sqrt{t}$ for $t \geqslant 4$. At what rate is the colony increasing in size after 9 days?

REVIEW SET 20

1 For the travel graph alongside, estimate the average speed for:

a the time interval $1 \leqslant t \leqslant 4$ seconds

b the time interval $1 \leqslant t \leqslant 10$ seconds.

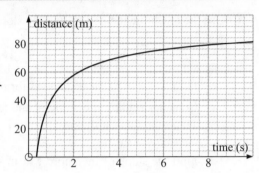

2

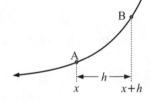

a Carefully draw a tangent to touch the curve at the point where $x = 4$.

b Hence, estimate the slope of $y = f(x)$ at $x = 4$.

3 Algebraically, find the slope of the tangent to $y = x^2$ at the point when $x = 4$.

4 Consider $f(x) = (2x + 3)^2$.

a Write $f(x + h)$ in simplest form.

b Find, in simplest form $\dfrac{f(x + h) - f(x)}{h}$.

c Interpret $\dfrac{f(x + h) - f(x)}{h}$ (see the diagram)

d Now let h approach 0. What does

i $\dfrac{f(x + h) - f(x)}{h}$ approach   **ii** $\dfrac{f(1 + h) - f(1)}{h}$ approach?

e What information is obtained in **d i** and **d ii**?

5 A particle moves in a straight line with displacement from O given by $s(t) = t^2 + 4t$ metres at time t seconds, $t \geqslant 0$. Find:

a the average velocity in the time interval $2 \leqslant t \leqslant 5$ seconds

b the average velocity in the time interval $2 \leqslant t \leqslant 2 + h$ seconds

c Find the number that $\dfrac{s(2 + h) - s(2)}{h}$ approaches as h approaches 0.

Comment on the significance of this value.

Note: If as h approaches 0, $\dfrac{s(2 + h) - s(2)}{h}$ approaches some number A, we

write $\displaystyle\lim_{h \to 0} \dfrac{s(2 + h) - s(2)}{h} = A$ where $\displaystyle\lim_{h \to 0}$ is read "the limit as h approaches 0 of"

Chapter 21

Differential calculus

HISTORICAL NOTE

Differential Calculus is a branch of Mathematics which originated in the 17th Century. **Sir Isaac Newton** and **Gottfried Wilhelm Leibnitz** are credited with the vital breakthrough in thinking necessary for the development of calculus. Both mathematicians were attempting to find an algebraic method for solving problems dealing with

- **slopes of tangents** to curves at any point on the curve, and
- finding the **rate of change** in one variable with respect to another.

Note:

Calculus is a Latin word meaning pebble. Ancient Romans used stones to count with.

Isaac Newton 1642 – 1727   **Gottfried Leibnitz 1646 – 1716**

Calculus has applications in a wide variety of fields including engineering, biology, chemistry, physics, economics and geography.

A   THE IDEA OF A LIMIT

We now investigate the slopes of chords (secants) from a fixed point on a curve over successively smaller intervals.

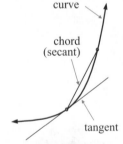

curve

chord
(secant)

tangent

Note: • A chord (secant) of a curve is a straight line segment which joins any two points on the curve.

• A tangent is a straight line which touches a curve at a point.

INVESTIGATION 1   THE SLOPE OF A TANGENT

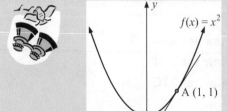

$f(x) = x^2$

A (1, 1)

Given a curve, how can we find the slope of a tangent at any point on it?

For example, the point A(1, 1) lies on the curve $f(x) = x^2$. What is the slope of the tangent at A.

DEMO

What to do:

1

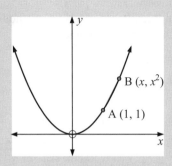

Suppose B lies on $f(x) = x^2$ and B has coordinates (x, x^2).

a   Show that the chord AB has slope

$$\frac{f(x) - f(1)}{x - 1} \quad \text{or} \quad \frac{x^2 - 1}{x - 1}.$$

b   Copy and complete:

x	Point B	Slope of AB
5	(5, 25)	6
3		
2		
1.5		
1.1		
1.01		
1.001		

2   Comment on the slope of AB as x gets closer to 1.

3   Repeat the process as x gets closer to 1, but from the left of A.

4   Click on the icon to view a demonstration of the process.

5   What do you suspect is the slope of the tangent at A?

The above investigation shows us that as x approaches 1, the slope of the chord approaches the slope of the tangent at $x = 1$.

Notation: We use a horizontal arrow, $\rightarrow$, to represent the word '*approaches*' or the phrase '*tends to*'.

So, $x \rightarrow 1$ is read as 'x approaches 1'   or   'x tends to 1'.

In the investigation we noticed that the slope of AB approached a limiting value of 2 as x approached 1, from either side of 1.

Consequently we can write,   as $x \rightarrow 1$, $\dfrac{x^2 - 1}{x - 1} \rightarrow 2$.

This idea is written simply as

$$\lim_{x \to 1} \frac{x^2 - 1}{x - 1} = 2$$

and is read as: the limit as x approaches 1   of $\dfrac{x^2 - 1}{x - 1}$ is   2.

In general,

if $\dfrac{f(x) - f(a)}{x - a}$ can be made as close as we like to some real number L by making x sufficiently close to a, we say that $\dfrac{f(x) - f(a)}{x - a}$ approaches a limit of L as x approaches a and write

$$\lim_{x \to a} \frac{f(x) - f(a)}{x - a} = L.$$

ALGEBRAIC/GEOMETRIC APPROACH

Fortunately we do not have to go through the graphical/table of values method (as illustrated in the investigation) each time we wish to find the slope of a tangent.

Recall that the   slope of AB $= \dfrac{x^2 - 1}{x - 1}$

$\therefore$ slope of AB $= \dfrac{(x+1)(x-1)}{x-1} = x + 1$ provided that $x \neq 1$

Now as B approaches A, $x \to 1$

$\therefore$ slope of AB $\to 2$ ...... (1)

> We say that the slope of AB approaches the value of 2 or **converges** to 2

From a geometric point of view:

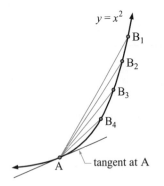

as B moves towards A,

the slope of AB $\to$ the slope of the tangent at A .... (2)

Thus, from (1) and (2), we conclude that as both limits must be the same, the slope of the tangent at A is 2.

LIMIT RULES

The following are useful limit rules:

- $\lim\limits_{x \to a} c = c$ c is a constant

- $\lim\limits_{x \to a} c \times u(x) = c \times \lim\limits_{x \to a} u(x)$ c is a constant, $u(x)$ is a function of x

- $\lim\limits_{x \to a} [u(x) + v(x)] = \lim\limits_{x \to a} u(x) + \lim\limits_{x \to a} v(x)$ $u(x)$ and $v(x)$ are functions of x

- $\lim\limits_{x \to a} [u(x)v(x)] = \left[\lim\limits_{x \to a} u(x)\right]\left[\lim\limits_{x \to a} v(x)\right]$ $u(x)$ and $v(x)$ are functions of x

We make no attempt to prove these rules at this stage. However, all can be readily verified.

For example: as $x \to 2$, $x^2 \to 4$ and $5x \to 10$ and $x^2 + 5x \to 14$ clearly verifies the third rule.

Before proceeding to a more formal method we will reinforce the algebraic/geometric method of finding slopes of tangents.

Example 1

Use the algebraic/geometric method to find the slope of the tangent to
$y = x^2$ at the point (2, 4).

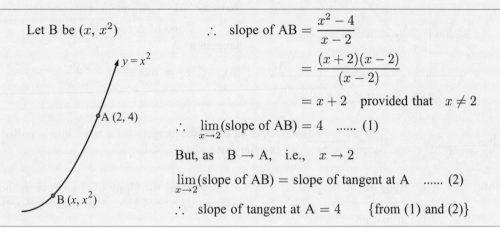

Let B be (x, x^2)

$\therefore$ slope of AB $= \dfrac{x^2 - 4}{x - 2}$

$= \dfrac{(x + 2)(x - 2)}{(x - 2)}$

$= x + 2$ provided that $x \neq 2$

$\therefore$ $\lim\limits_{x \to 2}$(slope of AB) $= 4$ ...... (1)

But, as   B $\to$ A,   i.e., $x \to 2$

$\lim\limits_{x \to 2}$(slope of AB) $=$ slope of tangent at A   ...... (2)

$\therefore$ slope of tangent at A $= 4$ {from (1) and (2)}

EXERCISE 21A

1   Use the algebraic/geometric method to find the slope of the tangent to:

a $y = x^2$ at the point where $x = 3$,   i.e.,   (3, 9)

b $y = \dfrac{1}{x}$ at the point where $x = 2$.

2   a   Show that $(x - a)(x^2 + ax + a^2) = x^3 - a^3$.

b   Use the algebraic/geometric method and **a** to find the slope of the tangent to $y = x^3$
at the point where $x = 2$.

3   a   Show that $\dfrac{\sqrt{x} - \sqrt{a}}{x - a} = \dfrac{1}{\sqrt{x} + \sqrt{a}}$.

b   Use the algebraic/geometric method and **a** to find the slope of the tangent to
$y = \sqrt{x}$ at the point where $x = 9$.

B ┃ DERIVATIVES AT A GIVEN x-VALUE

We are now at the stage where we can find slopes
of tangents at any point on a simple curve using a
limit method.

Notation: The slope of the tangent to a curve
$y = f(x)$ at $x = a$ is $f'(a)$,

read as. '*eff dashed a*'.

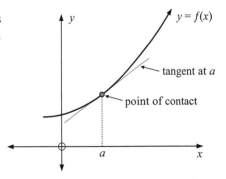

Consider a general function $y = f(x)$, a fixed point $A(a, f(a))$ and a variable point $B(x, f(x))$.

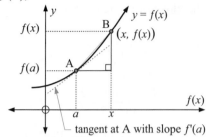

The slope of chord $AB = \dfrac{f(x) - f(a)}{x - a}$.

Now as $B \to A$, $x \to a$

and the slope of chord $AB \to$ slope of tangent at A

So, $f'(a) = \lim\limits_{x \to a} \dfrac{f(x) - f(a)}{x - a}$.

Thus $f'(a) = \lim\limits_{x \to a} \dfrac{f(x) - f(a)}{x - a}$ is the slope of the tangent at $x = a$ and is called **the derivative** at $x = a$.

Note:
- The slope of the tangent at $x = a$ is defined as the **slope of the curve** at the point where $x = a$, and is the instantaneous rate of change in y with respect to x at that point.
- Finding the slope using the limit method is said to be using **first principles**.

Example 2

Find, from first principles, the slope of the tangent to:

a $y = 2x^2 + 3$ at $x = 2$ **b** $y = 3 - x - x^2$ at $x = -1$

a $f'(2) = \lim\limits_{x \to 2} \dfrac{f(x) - f(2)}{x - 2}$ where $f(2) = 2(2)^2 + 3 = 11$

$\therefore \ f'(2) = \lim\limits_{x \to 2} \dfrac{2x^2 + 3 - 11}{x - 2}$

$= \lim\limits_{x \to 2} \dfrac{2x^2 - 8}{x - 2}$

$= \lim\limits_{x \to 2} \dfrac{2(x + 2)(x - 2)^{\,1}}{x - 2_{\,1}}$ {as $x \neq 2$}

$= 2 \times 4$

$= 8$

b $f'(-1) = \lim\limits_{x \to -1} \dfrac{f(x) - f(-1)}{x - (-1)}$ where $f(-1) = 3 - (-1) - (-1)^2$

$\qquad\qquad\qquad\qquad\qquad\qquad\qquad\qquad = 3 + 1 - 1$

$\qquad\qquad\qquad\qquad\qquad\qquad\qquad\qquad = 3$

$= \lim\limits_{x \to -1} \dfrac{3 - x - x^2 - 3}{x + 1}$

Note: $-f(-1) \neq f(1)$

$= \lim\limits_{x \to -1} \dfrac{-x - x^2}{x + 1}$

$= \lim\limits_{x \to -1} \dfrac{-x(1 + x)^{\,1}}{x + 1_{\,1}}$ {as $x \neq -1$}

$= 1$

Note: We only drop off $\lim\limits_{x \to -1}$ when we take that limit.

EXERCISE 21B

1 Find, from first principles, the slope of the tangent to:

   a $f(x) = 1 - x^2$ at $x = 2$ **b** $f(x) = 2x^2 + 5x$ at $x = -1$

   c $f(x) = 5 - 2x^2$ at $x = 3$ **d** $f(x) = 3x + 5$ at $x = -2$

Example 3

Find, from first principles, the derivative of:

   a $f(x) = \dfrac{9}{x}$ at $x = 2$ **b** $f(x) = \dfrac{2x - 1}{x + 3}$ at $x = -1$

---

a $f'(2) = \lim\limits_{x \to 2} \dfrac{f(x) - f(2)}{x - 2}$

$\qquad\qquad = \lim\limits_{x \to 2} \left(\dfrac{\frac{9}{x} - \frac{9}{2}}{x - 2} \right)$

$\qquad\qquad = \lim\limits_{x \to 2} \left(\dfrac{\frac{9}{x} - \frac{9}{2}}{x - 2} \right) \dfrac{2x}{2x}$ $\{2x$ is the LCD of $\frac{9}{x}$ and $\frac{9}{2}\}$

$\qquad\qquad = \lim\limits_{x \to 2} \dfrac{18 - 9x}{2x(x - 2)}$ $\{$Do not 'multiply out' the denominator.$\}$

$\qquad\qquad = \lim\limits_{x \to 2} \dfrac{-9\cancel{(x - 2)}^{\,1}}{2x\cancel{(x - 2)}_{\,1}}$ $\{$as $x \neq 2\}$

$\qquad\qquad = -\dfrac{9}{4}$

b $f'(-1) = \lim\limits_{x \to -1} \dfrac{f(x) - f(-1)}{x - (-1)}$ where $f(-1) = \dfrac{2(-1) - 1}{(-1) + 3}$

$\qquad\qquad = \lim\limits_{x \to -1} \left(\dfrac{\frac{2x-1}{x+3} + \frac{3}{2}}{x + 1} \right)$ $= -\dfrac{3}{2}$

$\qquad\qquad = \lim\limits_{x \to -1} \left(\dfrac{\frac{2x-1}{x+3} + \frac{3}{2}}{x + 1} \right) \times \dfrac{2(x + 3)}{2(x + 3)}$

$\qquad\qquad = \lim\limits_{x \to -1} \dfrac{2(2x - 1) + 3(x + 3)}{2(x + 1)(x + 3)}$

$\qquad\qquad = \lim\limits_{x \to -1} \dfrac{4x - 2 + 3x + 9}{2(x + 1)(x + 3)}$

$\qquad\qquad = \lim\limits_{x \to -1} \dfrac{7x + 7}{2(x + 1)(x + 3)}$

$\qquad\qquad = \lim\limits_{x \to -1} \dfrac{7\cancel{(x + 1)}^{\,1}}{2\cancel{(x + 1)}_{\,1}(x + 3)}$ ⟵ **Note:** There should always be cancelling of the original divisor at this step. Why?

$\qquad\qquad = \dfrac{7}{2(2)}$

$\qquad\qquad = \dfrac{7}{4}$

2 Find, from first principles, the derivative of:

a $f(x) = \dfrac{4}{x}$ at $x = 2$

b $f(x) = -\dfrac{3}{x}$ at $x = -2$

c $f(x) = \dfrac{1}{x^2}$ at $x = 4$

d $f(x) = \dfrac{4x}{x-3}$ at $x = 2$

e $f(x) = \dfrac{4x+1}{x-2}$ at $x = 5$

f $f(x) = \dfrac{3x}{x^2+1}$ at $x = -4$

Example 4

Find, using first principles, the instantaneous rate of change in $y = \sqrt{x}$ at $x = 9$.

$f(x) = \sqrt{x}$ and $f(9) = \sqrt{9} = 3$

Now $f'(9) = \lim\limits_{x \to 9} \dfrac{f(x) - f(9)}{x - 9}$

$= \lim\limits_{x \to 9} \dfrac{\sqrt{x} - 3}{x - 9}$

$= \lim\limits_{x \to 9} \dfrac{\sqrt{x} - 3}{(\sqrt{x} + 3)(\sqrt{x} - 3)}$ {treating $x - 9$ as the difference of two squares, $x \neq 9$}

$= \dfrac{1}{\sqrt{9} + 3}$

$= \tfrac{1}{6}$

---

3 Find, from first principles, the instantaneous rate of change in:

a $\sqrt{x}$ at $x = 4$

b $\sqrt{x}$ at $x = \tfrac{1}{4}$

c $\dfrac{2}{\sqrt{x}}$ at $x = 9$

d $\sqrt{x-6}$ at $x = 10$

An alternative formula for finding $f'(a)$ is

$$f'(a) = \lim\limits_{h \to 0} \frac{f(a+h) - f(a)}{h}$$

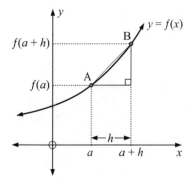

slope of AB $= \dfrac{f(a+h) - f(a)}{h}$

Note that as   B $\to$ A, $h \to 0$

and $f'(a) = \lim\limits_{h \to 0}$ (slope of AB)

which justifies the alternative formula.

Example 5

Use the first principles formula $f'(a) = \lim\limits_{h \to 0} \dfrac{f(a+h) - f(a)}{h}$ to find:

a the slope of the tangent to $f(x) = x^2 + 2x$ at $x = 5$

b the instantaneous rate of change of $f(x) = \dfrac{4}{x}$ at $x = -3$

a $f'(5) = \lim\limits_{h \to 0} \dfrac{f(5+h) - f(5)}{h}$ where $f(5) = 5^2 + 2(5) = 35$

$ = \lim\limits_{h \to 0} \dfrac{(5+h)^2 + 2(5+h) - 35}{h}$

$ = \lim\limits_{h \to 0} \dfrac{25 + 10h + h^2 + 10 + 2h - 35}{h}$

$ = \lim\limits_{h \to 0} \dfrac{h^2 + 12h}{h}$

$ = \lim\limits_{h \to 0} \dfrac{\overset{1}{\cancel{h}}(h+12)}{\underset{1}{\cancel{h}}}$ \quad \{as $h \neq 0$\}

$ = 12$

and so the slope of the tangent at $x = 5$ is 12.

b $f'(-3) = \lim\limits_{h \to 0} \dfrac{f(-3+h) - f(-3)}{h}$ where $f(-3) = \dfrac{4}{-3} = -\dfrac{4}{3}$

$ = \lim\limits_{h \to 0} \left(\dfrac{\frac{4}{-3+h} + \frac{4}{3}}{h} \right)$

$ = \lim\limits_{h \to 0} \left(\dfrac{\frac{4}{h-3} + \frac{4}{3}}{h} \right) \times \dfrac{3(h-3)}{3(h-3)}$

$ = \lim\limits_{h \to 0} \dfrac{12 + 4(h-3)}{3h(h-3)}$

$ = \lim\limits_{h \to 0} \dfrac{4\overset{1}{\cancel{h}}}{3\underset{1}{\cancel{h}}(h-3)}$ \quad \{as $h \neq 0$\}

$ = -\dfrac{4}{9}$

$\therefore$ the instantaneous rate of change in $f(x)$ at $x = -3$ is $-\dfrac{4}{9}$.

4 Use the first principles formula $f'(a) = \lim\limits_{h \to 0} \dfrac{f(a+h) - f(a)}{h}$ to find:

a the slope of the tangent to $f(x) = x^2 + 3x - 4$ at $x = 3$

b the slope of the tangent to $f(x) = 5 - 2x - 3x^2$ at $x = -2$

c the instantaneous rate of change in $f(x) = \dfrac{1}{2x - 1}$ at $x = -2$

d the slope of the tangent to $f(x) = \dfrac{1}{x^2}$ at $x = 3$

e the instantaneous rate of change in $f(x) = \sqrt{x}$ at $x = 4$

f the instantaneous rate of change in $f(x) = \dfrac{1}{\sqrt{x}}$ at $x = 1$

5 Using $f'(a) = \lim\limits_{h \to a} \dfrac{f(a + h) - f(a)}{h}$ find:

    a $f'(2)$ for $f(x) = x^3$

    b $f'(3)$ for $f(x) = x^4$

Reminder: $(a + b)^3 = a^3 + 3a^2b + 3ab^2 + b^3$ Binomial theorem

                $(a + b)^4 = a^4 + 4a^3b + 6a^2b^2 + 4ab^3 + b^4$ of **Chapter 9**.

C   THE DERIVATIVE FUNCTION

For a non-linear function with equation $y = f(x)$, slopes of tangents at various points continually change.

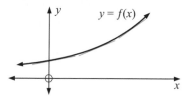

Our task is to determine a **slope function** so that when we replace x by a, say, we will be able to find the slope of the tangent at $x = a$.

Consider a general function $y = f(x)$ where A is $(x, f(x))$ and B is $(x + h, f(x + h))$.

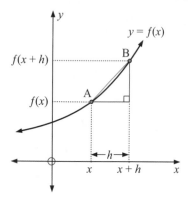

The chord AB has slope $= \dfrac{f(x + h) - f(x)}{x + h - x}$

$\qquad\qquad\qquad\qquad\qquad = \dfrac{f(x + h) - f(x)}{h}.$

If we now let B move closer to A, the slope of AB approaches the slope of the tangent at A.

So, the slope of the tangent at the variable point $(x, f(x))$ is the limiting value of

$\dfrac{f(x + h) - f(x)}{h}$ as h approaches 0.

Since this slope contains the variable x it is called a **slope function.**

DERIVATIVE FUNCTION

The **slope function**, also known as the **derived function**, or **derivative function** or simply the **derivative** is defined as

$$f'(x) = \lim_{h \to 0} \frac{f(x + h) - f(x)}{h}.$$

(**Note:** $\lim\limits_{h \to 0} \dfrac{f(x + h) - f(x)}{h}$ is the shorthand way of writing

"the limiting value of $\dfrac{f(x + h) - f(x)}{h}$ as h gets as close as we like to zero.")

INVESTIGATION 2   FINDING SLOPES OF FUNCTIONS WITH TECHNOLOGY

This investigation can be done by **graphics calculator** or by clicking on the icon to open the **demonstration**. The idea is to find slopes at various points on a simple curve in order to find and table x-coordinates of points and the slopes of the tangents at those points. From this table you should be able to predict or find the slope function for the curve.

What to do:

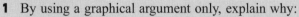

1 By using a graphical argument only, explain why:

   a for $f(x) = c$ where c is a constant, $f'(x) = 0$

   b for $f(x) = mx + c$ where m and c are constants, $f'(x) = m$.

2 Consider $f(x) = x^2$. Find $f'(x)$ for $x = 1, 2, 3, 4, 5, 6$ using technology. Predict $f'(x)$ from your results.

3 Use technology and modelling techniques to find $f'(x)$ for:

   a $f(x) = x^3$ **b** $f(x) = x^4$ **c** $f(x) = x^5$

   d $f(x) = \dfrac{1}{x}$ **e** $f(x) = \dfrac{1}{x^2}$ **f** $f(x) = \sqrt{x} = x^{\frac{1}{2}}$

4 Use the results of **3** to complete the following:

   "if $f(x) = x^n$, then $f'(x) = \ldots\ldots$"

Unfortunately the way of finding slope functions by the method shown in the investigation is insufficient for more complicated functions. Consequently, we need to use the **slope function** definition, but even this method is limited to relatively simple functions.

Example 6

Find, from first principles, the slope function of $f(x) = x^2$.

$$f'(x) = \lim_{h \to 0} \frac{f(x+h) - f(x)}{h}$$

$$= \lim_{h \to 0} \frac{(x+h)^2 - x^2}{h}$$

$$= \lim_{h \to 0} \frac{x^2 + 2hx + h^2 - x^2}{h}$$

$$= \lim_{h \to 0} \frac{h(2x+h)}{h} \quad \{\text{as } h \neq 0\}$$

$$= 2x$$

EXERCISE 21C

1 Find, from first principles, the slope function of $f(x)$ where $f(x)$ is:

   a x **b** 5 **c** x^3 **d** x^4

   Reminder: $(a + b)^3 = a^3 + 3a^2b + 3ab^2 + b^3$, etc.

2 Find, from first principles, $f'(x)$ given that $f(x)$ is:

   a $2x + 5$ **b** $x^2 - 3x$ **c** $x^3 - 2x^2 + 3$

Example 7

Find, from first principles, $f'(x)$ if $f(x) = \dfrac{1}{x}$.

$$\text{If } f(x) = \frac{1}{x}, \quad f'(x) = \lim_{h \to 0} \frac{f(x+h) - f(x)}{h}$$

$$= \lim_{h \to 0} \left[\frac{\frac{1}{x+h} - \frac{1}{x}}{h} \right] \times \frac{(x+h)x}{(x+h)x}$$

$$= \lim_{h \to 0} \frac{x - (x+h)}{hx(x+h)}$$

$$= \lim_{h \to 0} \frac{\cancel{h}^{-1}}{\cancel{h}x(x+h)_1} \qquad \{\text{as } h \neq 0\}$$

$$= -\frac{1}{x^2} \qquad \{\text{as } h \to 0, \; x + h \to x\}$$

Example 8

Find, from first principles, the slope function of $f(x) = \sqrt{x}$.

$$\text{If } f(x) = \sqrt{x}, \quad f'(x) = \lim_{h \to 0} \frac{f(x+h) - f(x)}{h}$$

$$= \lim_{h \to 0} \frac{\sqrt{x+h} - \sqrt{x}}{h}$$

$$= \lim_{h \to 0} \left(\frac{\sqrt{x+h} - \sqrt{x}}{h} \right) \left(\frac{\sqrt{x+h} + \sqrt{x}}{\sqrt{x+h} + \sqrt{x}} \right)$$

$$= \lim_{h \to 0} \frac{x + h - x}{h(\sqrt{x+h} + \sqrt{x})}$$

$$= \lim_{h \to 0} \frac{\cancel{h}^1}{\cancel{h}_1(\sqrt{x+h} + \sqrt{x})} \qquad \{\text{as } h \neq 0\}$$

$$= \frac{1}{\sqrt{x} + \sqrt{x}}$$

$$= \frac{1}{2\sqrt{x}}$$

3 Find, from first principles, the derivative of $f(x)$ when $f(x)$ is:

   a $\quad \dfrac{1}{x+2}$ **b** $\quad \dfrac{1}{2x-1}$ **c** $\quad \dfrac{1}{x^2}$ **d** $\quad \dfrac{1}{x^3}$

4 Find, from first principles, the derivative of $f(x)$ equal to:

   a $\quad \sqrt{x+2}$ **b** $\quad \dfrac{1}{\sqrt{x}}$ **c** $\quad \sqrt{2x+1}$

5 Using the results of derivatives in this exercise, copy and complete:

Use your table to predict a formula for $f'(x)$ given that $f(x) = x^n$ where n is rational.

6 Prove the rule "if $f(x) = x^n$ then $f'(x) = nx^{n-1}$ for $n \in Z^+$."

Function	Derivative (in form kx^n)
x	
x^2	$2x = 2x^1$
x^3	
x^4	
x^{-1}	
x^{-2}	
x^{-3}	
$x^{\frac{1}{2}}$	$\frac{1}{2\sqrt{x}} = \frac{1}{2}x^{-\frac{1}{2}}$
$x^{-\frac{1}{2}}$	

D   SIMPLE RULES OF DIFFERENTIATION

Differentiation is the process of finding the derivative (i.e., slope function).

Notation: If we are given a function $f(x)$ then $f'(x)$ represents the derivative function.

However, if we are given y in terms of x then y' or $\dfrac{dy}{dx}$ are commonly used to represent the derivative.

Note:
- $\dfrac{dy}{dx}$ reads "dee y by dee x", or " the derivative of y with respect to x".

- $\dfrac{dy}{dx}$ is **not a fraction**.   • $\dfrac{d(.....)}{dx}$ reads "the derivative of (....) with respect to x.

From question **5** of the previous exercise you should have discovered that if $f(x) = x^n$ then $f'(x) = nx^{n-1}$.

Are there other rules like this one which can be used to differentiate more complicated functions without having to resort to the tedious limit method? In the following investigation we may discover some additional rules.

INVESTIGATION 3   SIMPLE RULES OF DIFFERENTIATION

In this investigation we attempt to differentiate functions of the form cx^n where c is a constant, and functions which are a sum (or difference) of terms of the form cx^n.

What to do:

1 Find, from first principles, the derivatives of:
   a $4x^2$ **b** $2x^3$ **c** $5\sqrt{x}$

2 Compare your results with the derivatives of x^2, x^3 and $\sqrt{x}$ obtained earlier.
   Copy and complete: "If $f(x) = cx^n$, then $f'(x) = ...$"

3 Use first principles to find $f'(x)$ for:

    a $f(x) = x^2 + 3x$ **b** $f(x) = x^3 - 2x^2$

4 Use **3** to copy and complete: "If $f(x) = u(x) + v(x)$ then $f'(x) = \ldots\ldots$"

You should have discovered the following rules for differentiating functions.

Rules

$f(x)$	$f'(x)$	Name of rule
c (a constant)	0	**differentiating a constant**
x^n	nx^{n-1}	**differentiating x^n**
$c\,u(x)$	$c\,u'(x)$	**constant times a function**
$u(x) + v(x)$	$u'(x) + v'(x)$	**sum rule**

Each of these rules can be proved using the first principles definition of $f'(x)$.

The following proofs are worth examining.

- If $f(x) = cu(x)$ where c is a constant then $f'(x) = cu'(x)$.

    Proof: $\begin{aligned} f'(x) &= \lim_{h \to 0} \frac{f(x+h) - f(x)}{h} \\[2mm] &= \lim_{h \to 0} \frac{cu(x+h) - cu(x)}{h} \\[2mm] &= \lim_{h \to 0} c\left[\frac{u(x+h) - u(x)}{h}\right] \\[2mm] &= c \lim_{h \to 0} \frac{u(x+h) - u(x)}{h} \\[2mm] &= cu'(x) \end{aligned}$

- If $f(x) = u(x) + v(x)$ then $f'(x) = u'(x) + v'(x)$

    Proof: $\begin{aligned} f'(x) &= \lim_{h \to 0} \frac{f(x+h) - f(x)}{h} \\[2mm] &= \lim_{h \to 0} \left(\frac{u(x+h) + v(x+h) - [u(x) + v(x)]}{h}\right) \\[2mm] &= \lim_{h \to 0} \left(\frac{u(x+h) - u(x) + v(x+h) - v(x)}{h}\right) \\[2mm] &= \lim_{h \to 0} \frac{u(x+h) - u(x)}{h} + \lim_{h \to 0} \frac{v(x+h) - v(x)}{h} \\[2mm] &= u'(x) + v'(x) \end{aligned}$

Using the rules we have now developed we can differentiate sums of powers of x.

For example,   if $f(x) = 3x^4 + 2x^3 - 5x^2 + 7x + 6$ then

$$f'(x) = 3(4x^3) + 2(3x^2) - 5(2x) + 7(1) + 0$$
$$= 12x^3 + 6x^2 - 10x + 7$$

Example 9

Find $f'(x)$ for $f(x)$ equal to: **a** $5x^3 + 6x^2 - 3x + 2$ **b** $7x - \dfrac{4}{x} + \dfrac{3}{x^3}$

a $f(x) = 5x^3 + 6x^2 - 3x + 2$
$\therefore$ $f'(x) = 5(3x^2) + 6(2x) - 3(1) + 0$
$\qquad = 15x^2 + 12x - 3$

b $f(x) = 7x - \dfrac{4}{x} + \dfrac{3}{x^3}$
$\qquad = 7x - 4x^{-1} + 3x^{-3}$ {each term is in the form cx^n}
$\therefore$ $f'(x) = 7(1) - 4(-1x^{-2}) + 3(-3x^{-4})$
$\qquad = 7 + 4x^{-2} - 9x^{-4}$
$\qquad = 7 + \dfrac{4}{x^2} - \dfrac{9}{x^4}$

EXERCISE 21D

1 Find $f'(x)$ given that $f(x)$ is:

  a x^3 **b** $2x^3$ **c** $7x^2$

  d $x^2 + x$ **e** $4 - 2x^2$ **f** $x^2 + 3x - 5$

  g $x^3 + 3x^2 + 4x - 1$ **h** $5x^4 - 6x^2$ **i** $\dfrac{3x - 6}{x}$

  j $\dfrac{2x - 3}{x^2}$ **k** $\dfrac{x^3 + 5}{x}$ **l** $\dfrac{x^3 + x - 3}{x}$

  m $\dfrac{1}{\sqrt{x}}$ **n** $(2x - 1)^2$ **o** $(x + 2)^3$

2 Find $\dfrac{dy}{dx}$ for:

  a $y = 2x^3 - 7x^2 - 1$ **b** $y = \pi x^2$ **c** $y = \dfrac{1}{5x^2}$

  d $y = 100x$ **e** $y = 10(x + 1)$ **f** $y = 4\pi x^3$

3 Differentiate with respect to x:

  a $6x + 2$ **b** $x\sqrt{x}$ **c** $(5 - x)^2$

  d $\dfrac{6x^2 - 9x^4}{3x}$ **e** $4x - \dfrac{1}{4x}$ **f** $x(x + 1)(2x - 5)$

Example 10

Find the slope function of $f(x) = x^2 - \dfrac{4}{x}$ and hence find the slope of the tangent to the function at the point where $x = 2$.

$$f(x) = x^2 - \frac{4}{x} \qquad \therefore \quad f'(x) = 2x - 4(-1x^{-2}) \qquad \text{Now } f'(2) = 4 + 1 = 5,$$
$$= x^2 - 4x^{-1} \qquad \qquad = 2x + 4x^{-2} \qquad \text{So, the tangent has slope}$$
$$\qquad \qquad \qquad = 2x + \frac{4}{x^2} \qquad \text{of } 5.$$

4 Find the slope of the tangent to:

a $y = x^2$ at $x = 2$

b $y = \dfrac{8}{x^2}$ at $x = 9$

c $y = 2x^2 - 3x + 7$ at $x = -1$

d $y = \dfrac{2x^2 - 5}{x}$ at $x = 2$

e $y = \dfrac{x^2 - 4}{x^2}$ at $x = 4$

f $y = \dfrac{x^3 - 4x - 8}{x^2}$ at $x = -1$

Example 11

Find the slope function of $f(x)$ where $f(x)$ is: **a** $3\sqrt{x} + \dfrac{2}{x}$ **b** $x^2 - \dfrac{4}{\sqrt{x}}$

a $\quad f(x) = 3\sqrt{x} + \dfrac{2}{x} = 3x^{\frac{1}{2}} + 2x^{-1}$

$\therefore \quad f'(x) = 3(\tfrac{1}{2}x^{-\frac{1}{2}}) + 2(-1x^{-2})$

$\qquad = \tfrac{3}{2}x^{-\frac{1}{2}} - 2x^{-2}$

$\qquad = \dfrac{3}{2\sqrt{x}} - \dfrac{2}{x^2}$

b $\quad f(x) = x^2 - \dfrac{4}{\sqrt{x}} = x^2 - 4x^{-\frac{1}{2}}$

$\therefore \quad f'(x) = 2x - 4(-\tfrac{1}{2}x^{-\frac{3}{2}})$

$\qquad = 2x + 2x^{-\frac{3}{2}}$

$\qquad = 2x + \dfrac{2}{x\sqrt{x}}$

5 Find the slope function of $f(x)$ where $f(x)$ is:

a $4\sqrt{x} + x$

b $\sqrt[3]{x}$

c $-\dfrac{2}{\sqrt{x}}$

d $2x - \sqrt{x}$

e $\dfrac{4}{\sqrt{x}} - 5$

f $3x^2 - x\sqrt{x}$

g $\dfrac{5}{x^2\sqrt{x}}$

h $2x - \dfrac{3}{x\sqrt{x}}$

Example 12

If $y = 3x^2 - 4x$, find $\dfrac{dy}{dx}$ and interpret its meaning.

As $y = 3x^2 - 4x$, $\dfrac{dy}{dx} = 6x - 4$. $\dfrac{dy}{dx}$ is

- the slope function or derivative of $y = 3x^2 - 4x$ from which the slope at any point can be found
- the instantaneous rate of change in y as x changes.

6 **a** If $y = 4x - \dfrac{3}{x}$, find $\dfrac{dy}{dx}$ and interpret its meaning.

 b The position of a car moving along a straight road is given by $S = 2t^2 + 4t$ metres where t is the time in seconds. Find $\dfrac{dS}{dt}$ and interpret its meaning.

 c The cost of producing and selling x toasters each week is given by $C = 1785 + 3x + 0.002x^2$ dollars. Find $\dfrac{dC}{dx}$ and interpret its meaning.

E ⬛ THE CHAIN RULE

Composite functions are functions like $(x^2 + 3x)^4$, $\sqrt{2 - 3x}$ or $\dfrac{1}{x - x^2}$.

These functions are made up of two simpler functions.

- $y = (x^2 + 3x)^4$ is $y = u^4$ where $u = x^2 + 3x$
- $y = \sqrt{2 - 3x}$ is $y = \sqrt{u}$ where $u = 2 - 3x$
- $y = \dfrac{1}{x - x^2}$ is $y = \dfrac{1}{u}$ where $u = x - x^2$

Notice that in the example $(x^2 + 3x)^4$, if $f(x) = x^4$ and $g(x) = x^2 + 3x$ then

$$f(g(x)) = f(x^2 + 3x) = (x^2 + 3x)^4$$

All of these functions can be made up in this way where we compose a function of a function. Consequently, these functions are called **composite functions**.

EXERCISE 21E.1

1 Find $f(g(x))$ if:

 a $f(x) = x^2$ and $g(x) = 2x + 7$ **b** $f(x) = 2x + 7$ and $g(x) = x^2$
 c $f(x) = \sqrt{x}$ and $g(x) = 3 - 4x$ **d** $f(x) = 3 - 4x$ and $g(x) = \sqrt{x}$
 e $f(x) = \dfrac{2}{x}$ and $g(x) = x^2 + 3$ **f** $f(x) = x^2 + 3$ and $g(x) = \dfrac{2}{x}$

2 Find $f(x)$ and $g(x)$ given that $f(g(x))$ is:

 a $(3x + 10)^3$ **b** $\dfrac{1}{2x + 4}$ **c** $\sqrt{x^2 - 3x}$ **d** $\dfrac{10}{(3x - x^2)^3}$

DERIVATIVES OF COMPOSITE FUNCTIONS

INVESTIGATION 4   **DIFFERENTIATING COMPOSITES**

The purpose of this investigation is to gain insight into how we can differentiate composite functions.

We might suspect that if $y = (2x + 1)^2$ then $\dfrac{dy}{dx} = 2(2x + 1)^1 = 2(2x + 1)$

based on our previous rule "if $y = x^n$ then $\dfrac{dy}{dx} = nx^{n-1}$". But is this so?

What to do:

1 Consider $y = (2x+1)^2$. Expand the brackets and then find $\dfrac{dy}{dx}$. Is $\dfrac{dy}{dx} = 2(2x+1)$?

2 Consider $y = (3x+1)^2$. Expand the brackets and then find $\dfrac{dy}{dx}$. Is $\dfrac{dy}{dx} = 2(3x+1)^1$?

3 Consider $y = (ax+1)^2$. Expand the brackets and find $\dfrac{dy}{dx}$. Is $\dfrac{dy}{dx} = 2(ax+1)^1$?

4 If $y = u^2$ where u is a function of x, what do you suspect $\dfrac{dy}{dx}$ will be equal to?

5 Consider $y = (x^2 + 3x)^2$. Expand it and find $\dfrac{dy}{dx}$.

Does your answer agree with your suspected rule in **4**?

From the previous investigation you probably formulated the rule that:

$$\text{If } y = u^2 \text{ then } \frac{dy}{dx} = 2u \times \frac{du}{dx} = \frac{dy}{du}\frac{du}{dx}.$$

Now consider $y = (2x+1)^3$ which is really $y = u^3$ where $u = 2x+1$.

Expanding we have $y = (2x+1)^3$

$$= (2x)^3 + 3(2x)^2 1 + 3(2x)1^2 + 1^3 \quad \{\text{binomial expansion}\}$$

$$= 8x^3 + 12x^2 + 6x + 1$$

$$\therefore \quad \frac{dy}{dx} = 24x^2 + 24x + 6$$

$$= 6(4x^2 + 4x + 1)$$

$$= 6(2x+1)^2$$

$$= 3(2x+1)^2 \times 2$$

$$= 3u^2 \times \frac{du}{dx} \quad \text{which is again} \quad \frac{dy}{du}\frac{du}{dx}.$$

From the investigation and from the above example we formulate the **chain rule**.

$$\text{If } y = f(u) \text{ where } u = u(x) \text{ then } \frac{dy}{dx} = \frac{dy}{du}\frac{du}{dx}.$$

A non-examinable proof of this rule is included for completeness.

Proof: Consider $y = f(u)$ where $u = u(x)$.

For a small change of Δx in x, there is a small change of $u(x+h) - u(x) = \Delta u$ in u and a small change of Δy in y.

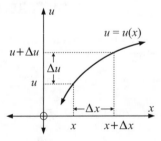
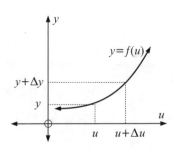

Now $\quad \dfrac{\Delta y}{\Delta x} = \dfrac{\Delta y}{\Delta u} \times \dfrac{\Delta u}{\Delta x} \qquad$ {fraction multiplication}

Now as $\quad \Delta x \to 0, \quad \Delta u \to 0 \quad$ also.

$$\therefore \quad \lim_{\Delta x \to 0} \frac{\Delta y}{\Delta x} = \lim_{\Delta u \to 0} \frac{\Delta y}{\Delta u} \times \lim_{\Delta x \to 0} \frac{\Delta u}{\Delta x} \qquad \{\text{limit rule}\}$$

$$\therefore \quad \frac{dy}{dx} = \frac{dy}{du}\frac{du}{dx}$$

{If in $\quad f'(x) = \lim\limits_{h \to 0} \dfrac{f(x+h) - f(x)}{h}, \quad$ we replace h by Δx and $\quad f(x+h) - f(x)$

by Δy, we have $\quad f'(x) = \dfrac{dy}{dx} = \lim\limits_{\Delta x \to 0} \dfrac{\Delta y}{\Delta x}.$}

Example 13

Find $\dfrac{dy}{dx}$ if: **a** $y = (x^2 - 2x)^4$ **b** $y = \dfrac{4}{\sqrt{1 - 2x}}$

a $\qquad\qquad y = (x^2 - 2x)^4$

$\qquad \therefore \quad y = u^4 \quad$ where $\quad u = x^2 - 2x$

$\qquad$ Now $\quad \dfrac{dy}{dx} = \dfrac{dy}{du}\dfrac{du}{dx} \qquad$ {chain rule}

$\qquad\qquad\qquad = 4u^3(2x - 2)$

$\qquad\qquad\qquad = 4(x^2 - 2x)^3(2x - 2)$

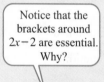

Notice that the brackets around $2x - 2$ are essential. Why?

b $\qquad\qquad y = \dfrac{4}{\sqrt{1 - 2x}}$

$\qquad \therefore \quad y = \dfrac{4}{\sqrt{u}} \quad$ where $\quad u = 1 - 2x$

$\qquad$ i.e., $\quad y = 4u^{-\frac{1}{2}} \quad$ where $\quad u = 1 - 2x$

$\qquad$ Now $\quad \dfrac{dy}{dx} = \dfrac{dy}{du}\dfrac{du}{dx} \qquad$ {chain rule}

$\qquad\qquad\qquad = 4 \times (-\tfrac{1}{2}u^{-\frac{3}{2}}) \times (-2)$

$\qquad\qquad\qquad = 4u^{-\frac{3}{2}} = 4(1 - 2x)^{-\frac{3}{2}}$

Note: If $y = [f(x)]^n$
then
$\dfrac{dy}{dx} = n[f(x)]^{n-1} \times f'(x)$

EXERCISE 21E.2

1 Write in the form au^n, clearly stating what u is:

   a $\dfrac{1}{(2x - 1)^2}$ **b** $\sqrt{x^2 - 3x}$ **c** $\dfrac{2}{\sqrt{2 - x^2}}$

   d $\sqrt[3]{x^3 - x^2}$ **e** $\dfrac{4}{(3 - x)^3}$ **f** $\dfrac{10}{x^2 - 3}$

2 Find the slope function $\dfrac{dy}{dx}$ for:

a $y = (4x - 5)^2$

b $y = \dfrac{1}{5 - 2x}$

c $y = \sqrt{3x - x^2}$

d $y = (1 - 3x)^4$

e $y = 6(5 - x)^3$

f $y = \sqrt[3]{2x^3 - x^2}$

g $y = \dfrac{6}{(5x - 4)^2}$

h $y = \dfrac{4}{3x - x^2}$

i $y = 2\left(x^2 - \dfrac{2}{x}\right)^3$

3 Find the slope of the tangent to:

a $y = \sqrt{1 - x^2}$ at $x = \frac{1}{2}$

b $y = (3x + 2)^6$ at $x = -1$

c $y = \dfrac{1}{(2x - 1)^4}$ at $x = 1$

d $y = 6 \times \sqrt[3]{1 - 2x}$ at $x = 0$

e $y = \dfrac{4}{x + 2\sqrt{x}}$ at $x = 4$

f $y = \left(x + \dfrac{1}{x}\right)^3$ at $x = 1$

4 If $y = x^3$ then $x = y^{\frac{1}{3}}$.

a Find $\dfrac{dy}{dx}$ and $\dfrac{dx}{dy}$ and hence show that $\dfrac{dy}{dx} \times \dfrac{dx}{dy} = 1$.

b Explain why $\dfrac{dy}{dx} \times \dfrac{dx}{dy} = 1$ whenever these derivatives exist for any general function $y = f(x)$.

F ■ PRODUCT AND QUOTIENT RULES

If $f(x) = u(x) + v(x)$ then $f'(x) = u'(x) + v'(x)$.

That is, the derivative of a sum of two functions is the sum of the derivatives.

But, what if $f(x) = u(x)v(x)$? Is $f'(x) = u'(x)v'(x)$?

That is, is the derivative of a product of two functions equal to the product of the derivatives of the two functions?

The following example shows that this cannot be true:

If $f(x) = x\sqrt{x}$ we could say $f(x) = u(x)v(x)$ where $u(x) = x$ and $v(x) = \sqrt{x}$.

Now $f(x) = x^{\frac{3}{2}}$ $\therefore$ $f'(x) = \frac{3}{2}x^{\frac{1}{2}}$.

But $u'(x)v'(x) = 1 \times \frac{1}{2}x^{-\frac{1}{2}} = \frac{1}{2}x^{-\frac{1}{2}} \neq f'(x)$

THE PRODUCT RULE

If $u(x)$ and $v(x)$ are two functions of x and $y = uv$ then

$$\frac{dy}{dx} = \frac{du}{dx}v + u\frac{dv}{dx} \quad \text{or} \quad y' = u'(v)\,v(x) + u(x)\,v'(x).$$

Consider the example $f(x) = x\sqrt{x}$ again.

This is a product $u(x)v(x)$ where $u(x) = x$ and $v(x) = x^{\frac{1}{2}}$

$$\therefore \quad u'(x) = 1 \quad \text{and} \quad v'(x) = \tfrac{1}{2}x^{-\frac{1}{2}}.$$

According to the product rule

$$\begin{aligned} f'(x) &= u'v + uv' \\ &= 1 \times x^{\frac{1}{2}} + x \times \tfrac{1}{2}x^{-\frac{1}{2}}. \\ &= x^{\frac{1}{2}} + \tfrac{1}{2}x^{\frac{1}{2}} \\ &= \tfrac{3}{2}x^{\frac{1}{2}} \quad \text{which is correct } \checkmark \end{aligned}$$

For completeness we now prove the product rule.

Proof: Let $y = u(x)v(x)$ and consider the effect of a small change in x of Δx.

Corresponding changes of Δu in u, Δv in v and Δy in y occur and as $y = uv$,

$$y + \Delta y = (u + \Delta u)(v + \Delta v)$$
$$\therefore \quad y + \Delta y = uv + (\Delta u)v + u(\Delta v) + \Delta u \Delta v$$
$$\Delta y = (\Delta u)v + u(\Delta v) + \Delta u \Delta v$$
$$\therefore \quad \frac{\Delta y}{\Delta x} = \left(\frac{\Delta u}{\Delta x}\right)v + u\left(\frac{\Delta v}{\Delta x}\right) + \left(\frac{\Delta u}{\Delta x}\right)\Delta v \quad \{\text{dividing each term by } \Delta x\}$$
$$\therefore \quad \lim_{\Delta x \to 0}\frac{\Delta y}{\Delta x} = \left(\lim_{\Delta x \to 0}\frac{\Delta u}{\Delta x}\right)v + u\left(\lim_{\Delta x \to 0}\frac{\Delta v}{\Delta x}\right) + 0 \quad \{\text{as } \Delta x \to 0, \Delta v \to 0 \text{ also}\}$$
$$\therefore \quad \frac{dy}{dx} = \frac{du}{dx}v + u\frac{dv}{dx}$$

Example 14

Find $\dfrac{dy}{dx}$ if: **a** $y = \sqrt{x}(2x+1)^3$ **b** $y = x^2(x^2 - 2x)^4$

a $y = \sqrt{x}(2x+1)^3$ is the product of $u = x^{\frac{1}{2}}$ and $v = (2x+1)^3$

$$\therefore \quad u' = \tfrac{1}{2}x^{-\frac{1}{2}} \quad \text{and} \quad \begin{aligned} v' &= 3(2x+1)^2 \times 2 \\ &= 6(2x+1)^2 \end{aligned}$$

Now $\dfrac{dy}{dx} = u'v + uv' \quad \{\text{product rule}\}$

$$= \tfrac{1}{2}x^{-\frac{1}{2}}(2x+1)^3 + x^{\frac{1}{2}} \times 6(2x+1)^2$$
$$= \tfrac{1}{2}x^{-\frac{1}{2}}(2x+1)^3 + 6x^{\frac{1}{2}}(2x+1)^2$$

b $y = x^2(x^2 - 2x)^4$ is the product of $u = x^2$ and $v = (x^2 - 2x)^4$

$$\therefore \quad u' = 2x \quad \text{and} \quad v' = 4(x^2 - 2x)^3(2x - 2)$$

Now $\dfrac{dy}{dx} = u'v + uv' \quad \{\text{product rule}\}$

$$= 2x(x^2 - 2x)^4 + x^2 \times 4(x^2 - 2x)^3(2x - 2)$$
$$= 2x(x^2 - 2x)^4 + 4x^2(x^2 - 2x)^3(2x - 2)$$

EXERCISE 21F.1

1 Find $\dfrac{dy}{dx}$ using the product rule:

   a $y = x^2(2x - 1)$ **b** $y = 4x(2x + 1)^3$ **c** $y = x^2\sqrt{3 - x}$

   d $y = \sqrt{x}(x - 3)^2$ **e** $y = 5x^2(3x^2 - 1)^2$ **f** $y = \sqrt{x}(x - x^2)^3$

2 Find the slope of the tangent to:

   a $y = x^4(1 - 2x)^2$ at $x = -1$ **b** $y = \sqrt{x}(x^2 - x + 1)^2$ at $x = 4$

   c $y = x\sqrt{1 - 2x}$ at $x = -4$ **d** $y = x^3\sqrt{5 - x^2}$ at $x = 1$

3 If $y = \sqrt{x}(3 - x)^2$ show that $\dfrac{dy}{dx} = \dfrac{(3 - x)(3 - 5x)}{2\sqrt{x}}$.

Find the x-coordinates of all points on $y = \sqrt{x}(3 - x)^2$ where the tangent is horizontal.

THE QUOTIENT RULE

Expressions like $\dfrac{x^2 + 1}{2x - 5}$, $\dfrac{\sqrt{x}}{1 - 3x}$ and $\dfrac{x^3}{(x - x^2)^4}$ are called **quotients**.

Quotient functions have form $Q(x) = \dfrac{u(x)}{v(x)}$.

    Notice that $u(x) = Q(x)v(x)$ and by the product rule,

$$u'(x) = Q'(x)v(x) + Q(x)v'(x)$$

$$\therefore \quad u'(x) - Q(x)v'(x) = Q'(x)v(x)$$

$$\text{i.e.,} \quad Q'(x)v(x) = u'(x) - \dfrac{u(x)}{v(x)}v'(x)$$

$$\therefore \quad Q'(x)v(x) = \dfrac{u'(x)v(x) - u(x)v'(x)}{v(x)}$$

$$\therefore \quad Q'(x) = \dfrac{u'(x)v(x) - u(x)v'(x)}{[v(x)]^2} \qquad \text{and this formula is}$$
$$\text{called the } \textbf{quotient rule}.$$

So, if $Q(x) = \dfrac{u(x)}{v(x)}$ then $Q'(x) = \dfrac{u'(x)v(x) - u(x)v'(x)}{[v(x)]^2}$

or   if $y = \dfrac{u}{v}$ where u and v are functions of x then $\dfrac{dy}{dx} = \dfrac{\dfrac{du}{dx}v - u\dfrac{dv}{dx}}{v^2}$.

Example 15

Use the quotient rule to find $\dfrac{dy}{dx}$ if: **a** $y = \dfrac{1 + 3x}{x^2 + 1}$ **b** $y = \dfrac{\sqrt{x}}{(1 - 2x)^2}$

   a $y = \dfrac{1 + 3x}{x^2 + 1}$ is a quotient with $u = 1 + 3x$ and $v = x^2 + 1$

$$\therefore \quad u' = 3 \qquad \text{and} \quad v' = 2x$$

Now $\dfrac{dy}{dx} = \dfrac{u'v - uv'}{v^2}$ {quotient rule}

$$= \frac{3(x^2 + 1) - (1 + 3x)2x}{(x^2 + 1)^2}$$

$$= \frac{3x^2 + 3 - 2x - 6x^2}{(x^2 + 1)^2}$$

$$= \frac{3 - 2x - 3x^2}{(x^2 + 1)^2}$$

b $y = \dfrac{\sqrt{x}}{(1 - 2x)^2}$ is a quotient where $u = x^{\frac{1}{2}}$ and $v = (1 - 2x)^2$

$\therefore$ $u' = \frac{1}{2}x^{-\frac{1}{2}}$ and $v' = 2(1 - 2x)^1 \times -2$
$$= -4(1 - 2x)$$

Now $\dfrac{dy}{dx} = \dfrac{u'v - uv'}{v^2}$

$$= \frac{\frac{1}{2}x^{-\frac{1}{2}}(1 - 2x)^2 - x^{\frac{1}{2}} \times -4(1 - 2x)}{(1 - 2x)^4}$$

$$= \frac{\frac{1}{2}x^{-\frac{1}{2}}(1 - 2x)^2 + 4x^{\frac{1}{2}}(1 - 2x)}{(1 - 2x)^4}$$

$$= \frac{(1 - 2x)\left[\dfrac{1 - 2x}{2\sqrt{x}} + 4\sqrt{x}\left(\dfrac{2\sqrt{x}}{2\sqrt{x}}\right)\right]}{(1 - 2x)^{4\ 3}}$$ {look for common factors}

$$= \frac{1 - 2x + 8x}{2\sqrt{x}(1 - 2x)^3}$$

$$= \frac{6x + 1}{2\sqrt{x}(1 - 2x)^3}$$

Note: Most of the time, simplification of $\dfrac{dy}{dx}$ as in the above example is unnecessary, especially if you want to find the slope of a tangent at a given point because you can substitute a value for x without simplifying. However, it is good to practice algebraic skills.

EXERCISE 21F.2

1 Use the quotient rule to find $\dfrac{dy}{dx}$ if:

a $y = \dfrac{1 + 3x}{2 - x}$ **b** $y = \dfrac{x^2}{2x + 1}$ **c** $y = \dfrac{x}{x^2 - 3}$

d $y = \dfrac{\sqrt{x}}{1 - 2x}$ **e** $y = \dfrac{x^2 - 3}{3x - x^2}$ **f** $y = \dfrac{x}{\sqrt{1 - 3x}}$

2 Find the slope of the tangent to:

a $y = \dfrac{x}{1 - 2x}$ at $x = 1$ **b** $y = \dfrac{x^3}{x^2 + 1}$ at $x = -1$

c $y = \dfrac{\sqrt{x}}{2x + 1}$ at $x = 4$ **d** $y = \dfrac{x^2}{\sqrt{x^2 + 5}}$ at $x = -2$

3   **a**   If $y = \dfrac{2\sqrt{x}}{1 - x}$,   show that $\dfrac{dy}{dx} = \dfrac{x + 1}{\sqrt{x}(1 - x)^2}$.

For what values of x is $\dfrac{dy}{dx}$ **i** zero   **ii** undefined?

b   If $y = \dfrac{x^2 - 3x + 1}{x + 2}$,   show that $\dfrac{dy}{dx} = \dfrac{x^2 + 4x - 7}{(x + 2)^2}$.

For what values of x is $\dfrac{dy}{dx}$ **i** zero   **ii** undefined?

G TANGENTS AND NORMALS

TANGENTS

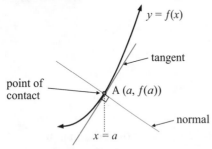
y = f(x)

tangent

point of contact

A $(a, f(a))$

normal

$x = a$

Consider a curve $y = f(x)$.

If A is the point with x-coordinate a, then the slope of the tangent at this point is $f'(a)$.

The equation of the tangent is

$$\dfrac{y - f(a)}{x - a} = f'(a) \quad \{\text{equating slopes}\}$$

$$or \quad y - f(a) = f'(a)(x - a)$$

NORMALS

A **normal** to a curve is a line which is perpendicular to the tangent at the point of contact.

Thus,   the slope of a normal at $x = a$ is $-\dfrac{1}{f'(a)}$.

For example, if $f(x) = x^2$ then $f'(x) = 2x$.

At $x = 2$, $f'(2) = 4$ and $-\dfrac{1}{f'(2)} = -\tfrac{1}{4}$.

So, at $x = 2$ the tangent has slope 4 and the normal has slope $-\tfrac{1}{4}$.

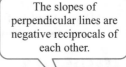
The slopes of perpendicular lines are negative reciprocals of each other.

Note: •   If a tangent touches $y = f(x)$ at (a, b) then it has equation

$$\dfrac{y - b}{x - a} = f'(a) \quad or \quad y - b = f'(a)(x - a).$$

•   Vertical and horizontal lines have equations $x = k$ and $y = c$ respectively.

Example 16

Find the equation of the tangent to $f(x) = x^2 + 1$ at the point where $x = 1$.

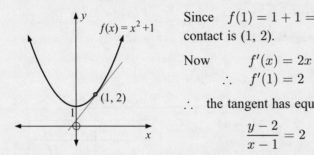

Since $f(1) = 1 + 1 = 2$, the point of contact is (1, 2).

Now $f'(x) = 2x$

$\therefore \quad f'(1) = 2$

$\therefore$ the tangent has equation

$$\frac{y - 2}{x - 1} = 2$$

i.e., $y - 2 = 2x - 2$

or $y = 2x$

Example 17

Find the equation of the normal to $y = \dfrac{8}{\sqrt{x}}$ at the point where $x = 4$.

When $x = 4$, $y = \frac{8}{\sqrt{4}} = \frac{8}{2} = 4$, $\therefore$ the point of contact is (4, 4).

Now as $y = 8x^{-\frac{1}{2}}$

$$\frac{dy}{dx} = -4x^{-\frac{3}{2}}$$

and when $x = 4$, $\dfrac{dy}{dx} = -4 \times 4^{-\frac{3}{2}} = -\frac{1}{2}$

$\therefore$ the normal at (4, 4) has slope $\frac{2}{1}$.

So, the equation of the normal is

$$\frac{y - 4}{x - 4} = 2 \quad \text{i.e.,} \quad y - 4 = 2x - 8$$

i.e., $y = 2x - 4$.

EXERCISE 21G

1 Find the equation of the tangent to:

   a $y = x - 2x^2 + 3$ at $x = 2$
   b $y = \sqrt{x} + 1$ at $x = 4$

   c $y = x^3 - 5x$ at $x = 1$
   d $y = \dfrac{4}{\sqrt{x}}$ at (1, 4)

2 Find the equation of the normal to:

   a $y = x^2$ at the point (3, 9)
   b $y = x^3 - 5x + 2$ at $x = -2$

   c $y = \dfrac{5}{\sqrt{x}} - \sqrt{x}$ at the point (1, 4)
   d $y = 8\sqrt{x} - \dfrac{1}{x^2}$ at $x = 1$

Example 18

Find the equations of any horizontal tangents to $y = x^3 - 12x + 2$.

$$\text{Let} \quad f(x) = x^3 - 12x + 2 \quad \therefore \quad f'(x) = 3x^2 - 12$$

Horizontal tangents have gradient 0 $\qquad \therefore \quad 3x^2 - 12 = 0$

$$\therefore \quad 3(x^2 - 4) = 0$$

$$\therefore \quad 3(x + 2)(x - 2) = 0$$

$$\therefore \quad x = -2 \text{ or } 2$$

Now $f(2) = 8 - 24 + 2 = -14$ and

$f(-2) = -8 + 24 + 2 = 18$

i.e.,   points of contact are

$(2, -14)$ and $(-2, 18)$

$\therefore$ tangents are $y = -14$ and $y = 18$.

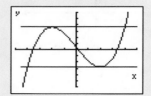

---

3 **a** Find the equations of the horizontal tangents to $y = 2x^3 + 3x^2 - 12x + 1$.

b Find all points of contact of horizontal tangents to the curve $y = 2\sqrt{x} + \dfrac{1}{\sqrt{x}}$.

c Find k if the tangent to $y = 2x^3 + kx^2 - 3$ at the point where $x = 2$ has slope 4.

d Find the equation of the tangent to $y = 1 - 3x + 12x^2 - 8x^3$ which is parallel to the tangent at $(1, 2)$.

4 **a** The tangent to the curve $y = x^2 + ax + b$,   where a and b are constants, is $2x + y = 6$ at the point where $x = 1$.   Find the values of a and b.

b The normal to the curve $y = a\sqrt{x} + \dfrac{b}{\sqrt{x}}$,   where a and b are constants, has equation $4x + y = 22$ at the point where $x = 4$.   Find the values of a and b.

Example 19

Find the equation of the tangent to $y = \sqrt{10 - 3x}$ at the point where $x = 3$.

Let $f(x) = (10 - 3x)^{\frac{1}{2}}$ $\qquad\qquad$ When $x = 3$, $y = \sqrt{10 - 9} = 1$

$\therefore \quad f'(x) = \frac{1}{2}(10 - 3x)^{-\frac{1}{2}} \times (-3)$ $\qquad \therefore$ point of contact is $(3, 1)$.

$\therefore \quad f'(3) = \frac{1}{2}(1)^{-\frac{1}{2}} \times (-3)$

$\qquad\quad = -\frac{3}{2}$

So, the tangent has equation $\dfrac{y - 1}{x - 3} = -\dfrac{3}{2}$ $\quad$ i.e., $2y - 2 = -3x + 9$

$\qquad\qquad\qquad\qquad\qquad\qquad\qquad\qquad$ or $3x + 2y = 11$

5 Find the equation of the tangent to:

a $y = \sqrt{2x + 1}$ at $x = 4$

b $y = \dfrac{1}{2 - x}$ at $x = -1$

c $f(x) = \dfrac{x}{1 - 3x}$ at $(-1, -\frac{1}{4})$

d $f(x) = \dfrac{x^2}{1 - x}$ at $(2, -4)$

6 Find the equation of the normal to:

a $y = \dfrac{1}{(x^2 + 1)^2}$ at $(1, \frac{1}{4})$

b $y = \dfrac{1}{\sqrt{3 - 2x}}$ at $x = -3$

c $f(x) = \sqrt{x}(1 - x)^2$ at $x = 4$

d $f(x) = \dfrac{x^2 - 1}{2x + 3}$ at $x = -1$.

7 $y = a\sqrt{1 - bx}$ where a and b are constants, has a tangent with equation $3x + y = 5$ at the point where $x = -1$. Find a and b.

Example 20

Find the coordinates of the point(s) where the tangent to $y = x^3 + x + 2$ at $(1, 4)$ meets the curve again.

$$f(x) = x^3 + x + 2$$
$$\therefore \quad f'(x) = 3x^2 + 1$$
$$\therefore \quad f'(1) = 3 + 1 = 4$$

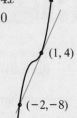

$\therefore$ the tangent at $(1, 4)$ has slope 4

and therefore its equation is $\dfrac{y - 4}{x - 1} = 4$

i.e., $y - 4 = 4x - 4$

or $y = 4x$

Now $y = 4x$ meets $y = x^3 + x + 2$ where $\qquad x^3 + x + 2 = 4x$

$$\therefore \quad x^3 - 3x + 2 = 0$$

and this cubic must have a repeated zero of $x = 1$ because of the tangent at $x = 1$

$$\therefore \quad (x - 1)^2(x + 2) = 0$$

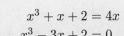

$$x^2 \times x = x^3 \quad (-1)^2 \times 2 = 2$$

$\therefore \quad x = 1$ or -2 and when $x = -2$, $y = (-2)^3 + (-2) + 2 = -8$

$\therefore$ tangent meets the curve again at $(-2, -8)$.

---

8 **a** Find where the tangent to the curve $y = x^3$, at the point where $x = 2$, meets the curve again.

b Find where the tangent to the curve $y = -x^3 + 2x^2 + 1$, at the point where $x = -1$, meets the curve again.

c Find where the tangent to the curve $y = x^3 + \dfrac{4}{x}$, at the point where $x = 1$, meets the curve again.

Example 21

Find the equations of the tangents to $y = x^2$ from the external point $(2, 3)$.

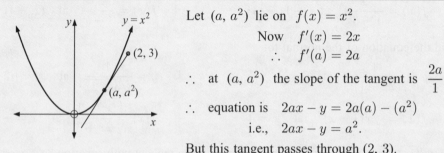

Let (a, a^2) lie on $f(x) = x^2$.

Now $f'(x) = 2x$

$\therefore \quad f'(a) = 2a$

$\therefore$ at (a, a^2) the slope of the tangent is $\dfrac{2a}{1}$

$\therefore$ equation is $2ax - y = 2a(a) - (a^2)$

i.e., $2ax - y = a^2$.

But this tangent passes through $(2, 3)$.

$\therefore \quad 2a(2) - 3 = a^2$

$\therefore \quad 4a - 3 = a^2$

i.e., $\quad a^2 - 4a + 3 = 0$

$(a - 1)(a - 3) = 0$

$\therefore \quad a = 1$ or 3

If $a = 1$, the tangent equation is $2x - y = 1$, with point of contact $(1, 1)$.

If $a = 3$, the tangent equation is $6x - y = 9$, with point of contact $(3, 9)$.

9   **a** Find the equation of the tangent to $y = x^2 - x + 9$ at the point where $x = a$. Hence, find the equations of the two tangents from $(0, 0)$ to the curve. State the coordinates of the points of contact.

b Find the equations of the tangents to $y = x^3$ from the external point $(-2, 0)$.

c Find the equation(s) of the normal(s) to $y = \sqrt{x}$ from the external point $(4, 0)$.

H   THE SECOND DERIVATIVE

The **second derivative** of a function $f(x)$ is the derivative of $f'(x)$, i.e., **the derivative of the first derivative**.

Notation: We use $f''(x)$, or y'' or $\dfrac{d^2y}{dx^2}$ to represent the second derivative.

Note that: • $\dfrac{d^2y}{dx^2} = \dfrac{d}{dx}\left(\dfrac{dy}{dx}\right)$ • $\dfrac{d^2y}{dx^2}$ reads "*dee two y by dee x squared*".

THE SECOND DERIVATIVE IN CONTEXT

Michael rides up a hill and down the other side to his friend's house. The dots on the graph show Michael's position at various times t.

$t = 0 \qquad t = 5 \quad t = 15 \qquad\qquad t = 17 \qquad\quad t = 19$

$t = 10$

Michael's place   friend's house

The distance travelled by Michael from his place is given at various times in the following table:

Time of ride (t min)	0	2.5	5	7.5	10	12.5	15	17	19
Distance travelled (s m)	0	498	782	908	989	1096	1350	1792	2500

A cubic model seems to fit this data well.

The model is $s \doteqdot 1.18t^3 - 30.47t^2 + 284.52t - 16.08$ metres.

Notice that the model gives $s(0) = -16.08$ m whereas the actual data gives $s(0) = 0$. This sort of problem often occurs when modelling from data.

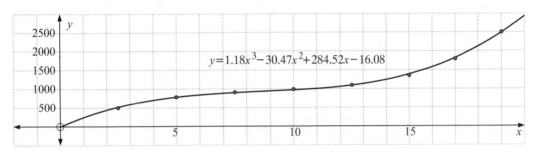

Now $\dfrac{ds}{dt} \doteqdot 3.54t^2 - 60.94t + 284.52$ metres/minute is the instantaneous rate of change in displacement per unit of time, i.e., instantaneous velocity.

The instantaneous rate of change in velocity at any point in time is the acceleration of the moving object and so,

$$\frac{d}{dt}\left(\frac{ds}{dt}\right) = \frac{d^2s}{dt^2} \quad \text{is the instantaneous acceleration,}$$

$$\text{i.e.,} \quad \frac{d^2s}{dt^2} = 7.08t - 60.94 \quad \text{metres/minute per minute.}$$

Notice that, when $t = 12$, $s \doteqdot 1050$ m

$$\frac{ds}{dt} \doteqdot 63 \quad \text{metres/minute} \quad \text{and} \quad \frac{d^2s}{dt^2} \doteqdot 24 \quad \text{metres/minute/minute}$$

We will examine displacement, velocity and acceleration in greater detail in the next chapter.

Example 22

Find $f''(x)$ given that

$$f(x) = x^3 - \frac{3}{x}.$$

Now $f(x) = x^3 - 3x^{-1}$

$\therefore \quad f'(x) = 3x^2 + 3x^{-2}$

$\therefore \quad f''(x) = 6x - 6x^{-3}$

$$= 6x - \frac{6}{x^3}$$

EXERCISE 21H

1 Find $f''(x)$ given that:

a $f(x) = 3x^2 - 6x + 2$

b $f(x) = 2x^3 - 3x^2 - x + 5$

c $f(x) = \dfrac{2}{\sqrt{x}} - 1$

d $f(x) = \dfrac{2 - 3x}{x^2}$

e $f(x) = (1 - 2x)^3$

f $f(x) = \dfrac{x + 2}{2x - 1}$

2 Find $\dfrac{d^2y}{dx^2}$ given that:

a $y = x - x^3$

b $y = x^2 - \dfrac{5}{x^2}$

c $y = 2 - \dfrac{3}{\sqrt{x}}$

d $y = \dfrac{4 - x}{x}$

e $y = (x^2 - 3x)^3$

f $y = x^2 - x + \dfrac{1}{1 - x}$

3 Find x when $f''(x) = 0$ for:

a $f(x) = 2x^3 - 6x^2 + 5x + 1$

b $f(x) = \dfrac{x}{x^2 + 2}.$

REVIEW SET 21A

1 Find the equation of the tangent to $y = -2x^2$ at the point where $x = -1$.

2 Find $\dfrac{dy}{dx}$ for: **a** $y = 3x^2 - x^4$ **b** $y = \dfrac{x^3 - x}{x^2}$

3 Find, from first principles, the derivative of $f(x) = x^2 + 2x$.

4 Find the equation of the normal to $y = \dfrac{1 - 2x}{x^2}$ at the point where $x = 1$.

5 Find where the tangent to $y = 2x^3 + 4x - 1$ at (1, 5) cuts the curve again.

6 The tangent to $y = \dfrac{ax + b}{\sqrt{x}}$ at $x = 1$ is $2x - y = 1$.   Find a and b.

7 Find a given that the tangent to $y = \dfrac{4}{(ax + 1)^2}$ at $x = 0$ passes through (1, 0).

8 Find the equation of the normal to $y = \dfrac{1}{\sqrt{x}}$ at the point where $x = 4$.

9 Determine the derivative   **a** $M = (t^2 + 3)^4$ **b** $A = \dfrac{\sqrt{t + 5}}{t^2}$
with respect to t of:

10 Use the rules of differentiation to find $\dfrac{dy}{dx}$ for:

a $y = \dfrac{4}{\sqrt{x}} - 3x$

b $y = (x - \dfrac{1}{x})^4$

c $y = \sqrt{x^2 - 3x}$

REVIEW SET 21B, 21C
Click on the icon to obtain printable review sets and answers

REVIEW SET 21B, 21C

Chapter 22

Applications of differential calculus

Contents:

One application of differential calculus is the finding of equations of tangents and normals to curves. There are many other uses, but in this chapter we consider only:

- **functions of time**
- **rates of change**
- **motion on a straight line**
- **curve properties**
- **optimisation**
- **applications in economics**

FUNCTIONS OF TIME

Earlier, we observed circular motion through a Ferris wheel.

We will revisit this demonstration and observe how far a particular point on the wheel is above the axle line and plot this height against the time of motion t.

Click on the icon to observe the motion.

The height function $h(t)$ metres is sinusoidal and its graph is:

DEMO

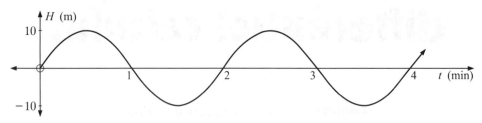

The graph has time units on the horizontal axis.

DISCUSSION

From the graph, how do we determine the diameter of the wheel?

How long does it take for the wheel to complete one revolution?

Does the graph have any feature(s) which enable us to deduce that the wheel is rotating with constant angular velocity?

In this section we consider functions and quantities which vary with time. The height function for the Ferris wheel is one such function.

Functions of time may be determined in cases where a particular motion is regular or approximately so.

For example, the Ferris wheel's height above the axle line is

$$H(t) = 10\sin(\pi t) \text{ metres}, \quad t \geqslant 0 \quad \text{and in seconds.}$$

This function can then be used to solve problems. If we could differentiate this function then we could find the rate of increase or decrease in height at any instant. However, not all functions of time can be fitted to a functional equation.

A   TIME RATE OF CHANGE

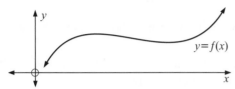

If we are given a function of x, $y = f(x)$ we know that $f'(x)$ or $\dfrac{dy}{dx}$ is the slope of the tangent at any value of x.

$\dfrac{dy}{dx}$ is also the rate of change in y with respect to x.

If we change the variable x to t which represents time, and the variable y to s which represents displacement, then $\dfrac{ds}{dt}$ would represent instantaneous velocity.

If y is changed to C where C represents the capacity of a person's lungs, then as time changes $\dfrac{dC}{dt}$ represents the instantaneous rate of change in lung capacity per unit of time.

$\dfrac{ds \;\longleftarrow\; \text{metres}}{dt \;\longleftarrow\; \text{minute}}$ has units metres/minute $\qquad$ $\dfrac{dC \;\longleftarrow\; \text{litres}}{dt \;\longleftarrow\; \text{second}}$ has units litres/second

EXERCISE 22A

1 The estimated future profits of a small business are given by $P(t) = 2t^2 - 12t + 118$ thousand dollars, where t is the time in years from now.

   a What is the current annual profit?   b Find $\dfrac{dP}{dt}$ and state its units.

   c What is the significance of $\dfrac{dP}{dt}$?

   d When will the profit i decrease ii increase?

   e What is the minimum profit and when does it occur?

   f Find $\dfrac{dP}{dt}$ at $t = 4$, 10 and 25. What do these figures represent?

2 If water is draining from a swimming pool such that the volume of water after t minutes is $V = 200(50 - t)^2$ m^3 find:

   a the average rate at which the water leaves the pool in the first 5 minutes

   b the instantaneous rate of draining at $t = 5$ minutes.

3 A ball is thrown vertically upwards and its height above the ground is given by $s(t) = 1.2 + 28.1t - 4.9t^2$ metres.

   a At what distance above the ground was the throw released?

   b Find $s'(t)$ (i.e., $\dfrac{ds}{dt}$) and state what it represents.

   c Find t when $s'(t) = 0$. What is the significance of this result?

   d What is the maximum height reached by the ball?

   e Find the ball's speed: i when released ii at $t = 2$ sec iii at $t = 5$ sec
     State the significance of the sign of the derivative.

   f How long will it take for the ball to hit the ground?

   g What is the significance of $\dfrac{d^2 s}{dt^2}$?

4 A shell is accidentally fired vertically upwards from ground level from a mortar and reaches the ground again after 14.2 seconds.

   a Given that its height above the ground at any time t is given by $s(t) = bt - 4.9t^2$ metres, show that the initial velocity of the shell is b m/s.

   b Find the initial velocity of the shell.

B   GENERAL RATES OF CHANGE

Earlier we discovered that: if $s(t)$ is a displacement function then $s'(t)$ or $\dfrac{ds}{dt}$ is the instantaneous rate of change in displacement with respect to time, which is of course the velocity function.

> In general, $\dfrac{dy}{dx}$ gives the **rate of change in y with respect to** x.

Note: If as x increases, y also increases, then $\dfrac{dy}{dx}$ will be positive,   whereas

if, as x increases, y decreases, then $\dfrac{dy}{dx}$ will be negative.

Example 1

According to a psychologist the ability of a person to understand spatial concepts is given by $A = \frac{1}{3}\sqrt{t}$ where t is the age in years, $t \in [5,\ 18]$.

  a Find the rate of improvement in ability to understand spatial concepts when the person is: **i** 9 years old   **ii** 16 years old.

  b Explain why $\dfrac{dA}{dt} > 0$, $t \in [5,\ 18]$ and comment on the significance of this result.

---

  a $A = \frac{1}{3}\sqrt{t} = \frac{1}{3}t^{\frac{1}{2}}$ $\therefore$ $\dfrac{dA}{dt} = \frac{1}{6}t^{-\frac{1}{2}} = \dfrac{1}{6\sqrt{t}}$

    i When $t = 9$, $\dfrac{dA}{dt} = \frac{1}{18}$ $\therefore$ rate of improvement is $\frac{1}{18}$ units per year for a 9 year old.

    ii When $t = 16$, $\dfrac{dA}{dt} = \frac{1}{24}$ $\therefore$ rate of improvement is $\frac{1}{24}$ units per year for a 16 year old.

  b   As $\sqrt{t}$ is never negative, $\dfrac{1}{6\sqrt{t}}$ is never negative,   Note that the rate of increase actually slows down as t increases.

    i.e., $\dfrac{dA}{dt} > 0$ for all t in $5 \leqslant t \leqslant 18$.

This means that the ability to understand spatial concepts increases with age but at a decreasing rate. This is clearly shown by the graph.

EXERCISE 22B

You are encouraged to **use technology to graph** the function for each question.

1   The quantity of a chemical which is responsible for 'elasticity' in human skin is given by $Q = 100 - 10\sqrt{t}$ where t is the age of a person.

    a   Find Q at: **i** $t = 0$ **ii** $t = 25$ **iii** $t = 100$ years.

    b   At what rate is the quantity of the chemical changing at the ages of:

       i   25 years   **ii**   50 years?

    c   Show that the rate at which the skin loses the chemical is decreasing for all $t > 0$.

2   The height of *pinus radiata*, grown in ideal conditions, is given by $H = 20 - \dfrac{9}{t+5}$

    metres, where t is the number of years after the tree was planted from an established juvenile tree.

    a   How high is the tree at planting?

    b   Find the height of the tree at $t = 4$, $t = 8$ and $t = 12$ years.

    c   Find the rate at which the tree is growing at $t = 0, 5$ and 10 years.

    d   Show that $\dfrac{dH}{dt} > 0$ for all $t \geqslant 0$.   What is the significance of this result?

3   The total cost of running a train is given by $C(v) = 200v + \dfrac{10\,000}{v}$ dollars   where v is the average speed of the train in kmph.

    a   Find the total cost of running the train at: **i**   20 kmph   **ii**   40 kmph.

    b   Find the rate of change in the cost of running the train at speeds of:

       i   10 kmph   **ii**   30 kmph.

    c   At what speed will the cost be a minimum?

4

Alongside is a land and sea profile where the x-axis is sea level and y-values give the height of the land or sea bed above (or below) sea level and

$$y = \tfrac{1}{10}x(x-2)(x-3) \text{ km.}$$

    a   Find where the lake is located relative to the shore line of the sea.

    b   Find $\dfrac{dy}{dx}$ and interpret its value when $x = \tfrac{1}{2}$ and when $x = 1\tfrac{1}{2}$ km.

    c   Find the deepest point of the lake and the depth at this point.

5   A tank contains 50 000 litres of water. The tap is left fully on and all the water drains from the tank in 80 minutes. The volume of water remaining in the tank after t minutes is given by $V = 50\,000\left(1 - \dfrac{t}{80}\right)^2$ where $0 \leqslant t \leqslant 80$.

    a   Find $\dfrac{dV}{dt}$ and draw the graph of $\dfrac{dV}{dt}$ against t.

    b   At what time was the outflow fastest?

    c   Find $\dfrac{d^2V}{dt^2}$ and interpret the fact that it is always constant and positive.

6 A fish farm grows and harvests barramundi in a large dam. The population P of fish at time t is of interest and the rate of change in the population $\dfrac{dP}{dt}$ is modelled by

$$\frac{dP}{dt} = aP\left(1 - \frac{P}{b}\right) - \left(\frac{c}{100}\right)P \quad \text{where } a, b \text{ and } c \text{ are}$$

known constants. a is the birth rate of the barramundi, b is the maximum carrying capacity of the dam and c is the percentage that is harvested.

a Explain why the fish population is stable when $\dfrac{dP}{dt} = 0$.

b If the birth rate is 6%, the maximum carrying capacity is 24 000 and 5% is harvested, find the stable population.

c If the harvest changes to 4%, what will the stable population increase to?

COST MODELS

Most often cost functions are polynomial models.

For example, the cost of producing x items per day may be given by

$$C(x) = \underline{0.000\,13x^3} + 0.002x^2 + 5x + 2200$$

cost of labour (including   raw material   fixed or overhead costs such as heating,
overtime) and other factors   costs   cooling, maintenance, rent, etc.

Example 2

For the cost model $C(x) = 0.000\,13x^3 + 0.002x^2 + 5x + 2200$:
a find $C'(x)$, which is called the marginal cost function
b find the marginal cost when 150 are produced. Interpret this result.
c Show that $C(151) - C(150)$ gives the approximate answer to **b**.

a The marginal cost function is
$C'(x) = 0.000\,39x^2 + 0.004x + 5$

b $C'(150) = \$14.38$ and is the rate at which the costs are increasing with respect to the production level x. It gives an estimated cost for making the 151st shirt.

c $C(151) - C(150) \doteq \$3448.19 - \$3433.75$
$\doteq \$14.44$

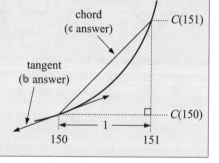

---

7 Seablue make jeans and the cost model for making x of them each day is
$$C(x) = 0.0003x^3 + 0.02x^2 + 4x + 2250 \text{ dollars.}$$

a Find the marginal cost function $C'(x)$.
b Find $C'(220)$. What does it estimate?
c Find $C(221) - C(220)$. What does this represent?
d Find $C''(x)$ and the value of x when $C''(x) = 0$. What is the significance of this point?

C   MOTION IN A STRAIGHT LINE

Suppose an object P moves along a straight line so that its position from an origin s, is given as some function of time t,

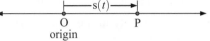

i.e., $s = s(t)$ where $t \geqslant 0$.

$s(t)$ is a **displacement function** and for any value of t it gives the displacement from O.

It is clear that   if $s(t) > 0,$ P is located to the **right of O**
if $s(t) = 0,$ P is located **at O**
if $s(t) < 0,$ P is located to the **left of O**.

MOTION GRAPHS

Consider $s(t) = t^2 + 2t - 3$ cm,   say,   then

$s(0) = -3$ cm, $s(1) = 0$ cm, $s(2) = 5$ cm, $s(3) = 12$ cm, $s(4) = 21$ cm.

To appreciate the motion of P we draw a **motion graph**.

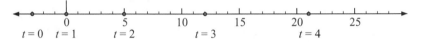

Click on the demo icon to get a better idea of the motion.

Fully animated, we not only get a good idea of the position of P but also of what is happening with regard to velocity and acceleration.

Note:
The straight line does not have to be horizontal.

VELOCITY AND ACCELERATION

AVERAGE VELOCITY

Recall that:

> The **average velocity** of an object moving in a straight line, in the time interval from $t = t_1$ to $t = t_2$ is the ratio of the change in displacement to the time taken,
>
> i.e.,   **average velocity** $= \dfrac{s(t_2) - s(t_1)}{t_2 - t_1}$,   where $s(t)$ is the displacement function.

INSTANTANEOUS VELOCITY

In **Chapter 20** we established that $\dfrac{s(1 + h) - s(1)}{h}$ approached a fixed value as h approached 0 and this value must be the instantaneous velocity at $t = 1$.

In general:

> If $s(t)$ is a displacement function of an object moving in a straight line, then
>
> $v(t) = s'(t) = \lim\limits_{h \to 0} \dfrac{s(t + h) - s(t)}{h}$ is the **instantaneous velocity** of the object at time t.

Example 3

A particle moves in a straight line with displacement from O given by
$s(t) = 3t - t^2$ metres at time t seconds. Find:

a the average velocity in the time interval from $t = 2$ to $t = 5$ seconds

b the average velocity in the time interval from $t = 2$ to $t = 2 + h$ seconds

c $\lim\limits_{h \to 0} \dfrac{s(2 + h) - s(2)}{h}$ and comment on its significance.

a average velocity

$$= \frac{s(5) - s(2)}{5 - 2} \text{ m/s}$$

$$= \frac{(15 - 25) - (6 - 4)}{3} \text{ m/s}$$

$$= \frac{-10 - 2}{3} \text{ m/s}$$

$$= -4 \text{ m/s}$$

b average velocity

$$= \frac{s(2 + h) - s(2)}{2 + h - 2}$$

$$= \frac{3(2 + h) - (2 + h)^2 - 2}{h}$$

$$= \frac{6 + 3h - 4 - 4h - h^2 - 2}{h}$$

$$= \frac{-h - h^2}{h}$$

$$= -1 - h \text{ m/s as } h \neq 0$$

c $\lim\limits_{h \to 0} \dfrac{s(2 + h) - s(2)}{h} = \lim\limits_{h \to 0} (-1 - h)$

$$= -1 \text{ m/s}$$

and this is the instantaneous velocity at time $t = 2$ seconds.

EXERCISE 22C.1

1 A particle P moves in a straight line with a displacement function of $s(t) = t^2 + 3t - 2$ metres, where $t \geqslant 0$, t in seconds.

  a Find the average velocity from $t = 1$ to $t = 3$ seconds.

  b Find the average velocity from $t = 1$ to $t = 1 + h$ seconds.

  c Find the value of $\lim\limits_{h \to 0} \dfrac{s(1 + h) - s(1)}{h}$ and comment on its significance.

  d Find the average velocity from time t to time $t + h$ seconds and interpret

$$\lim\limits_{h \to 0} \frac{s(t + h) - s(t)}{h}.$$

2 A particle P moves in a straight line with a displacement function of
$s(t) = 5 - 2t^2$ cm, where $t \geqslant 0$, t in seconds.

  a Find the average velocity from $t = 2$ to $t = 5$ seconds.

  b Find the average velocity from $t = 2$ to $t = 2 + h$ seconds.

  c Find the value of $\lim\limits_{h \to 0} \dfrac{s(2 + h) - s(2)}{h}$ and state the meaning of this value.

  d Interpret $\lim\limits_{h \to 0} \dfrac{s(t + h) - s(t)}{h}.$

AVERAGE ACCELERATION

If an object moves in a straight line with velocity function $v(t)$ then its **average acceleration** on the time interval from $t = t_1$ to $t = t_2$ is the ratio of its *change in velocity* to the time taken,

$$\text{i.e.,} \quad \textbf{average acceleration} = \frac{v(t_2) - v(t_1)}{t_2 - t_1}.$$

INSTANTANEOUS ACCELERATION

If a particle moves in a straight line with velocity function $v(t)$, then

the **instantaneous acceleration** at time t is $a(t) = v'(t) = \lim\limits_{h \to 0} \dfrac{v(t + h) - v(t)}{h}$

3 A particle moves in a straight line with velocity function $v(t) = 2\sqrt{t} + 3$ cm/s. where $t \geqslant 0$.

a Find the average acceleration from $t = 1$ to $t = 4$ seconds.

b Find the average acceleration from $t = 1$ to $t = 1 + h$ seconds.

c Find the value of $\lim\limits_{h \to 0} \dfrac{v(1 + h) - v(1)}{h}$. Interpret this value.

d Interpret $\lim\limits_{h \to 0} \dfrac{v(t + h) - v(t)}{h}$.

4 An object moves in a straight line with displacement function $s(t)$, and velocity function $v(t)$, $t \geqslant 0$. State the meaning of:

a $\lim\limits_{h \to 0} \dfrac{s(4 + h) - s(4)}{h}$

b $\lim\limits_{h \to 0} \dfrac{v(4 + h) - v(4)}{h}$

VELOCITY AND ACCELERATION FUNCTIONS

If a particle P, moves in a straight line and its position is given by the displacement function $s(t)$, $t \geqslant 0$, then:

- the **velocity** of P, at time t, is given by

  $v(t) = s'(t)$ {the derivative of the displacement function}

- the **acceleration** of P, at time t, is given by

  $a(t) = v'(t) = s''(t)$ {the derivative of the velocity function}

Note: $s(0)$, $v(0)$ and $a(0)$ give us the position, velocity and acceleration of the particle at time $t = 0$, and these are called the **initial conditions**.

SIGN INTERPRETATION

Suppose a particle P, moves in a straight line with displacement function $s(t)$ for locating the particle relative to an origin O, and has velocity function $v(t)$ and acceleration function $a(t)$.

We can use **sign diagrams** to interpret:

- where the particle is located relative to O
- the direction of motion and where a change of direction occurs
- when the particle's velocity is increasing/decreasing.

SIGNS OF $s(t)$:

$s(t)$	Interpretation
$= 0$	P is at O
> 0	P is located to the right of O
< 0	P is located to the left of O

SIGNS OF $v(t)$:

$v(t)$	Interpretation
$= 0$	P is instantaneously at rest
> 0	P is moving to the right
< 0	P is moving to the left

Note:

$$v(t) = \lim_{h \to 0} \frac{s(t+h) - s(t)}{h}. \quad \text{If } h > 0, \text{ so that } t + h > t,$$

then $v(t) > 0$ implies that $s(t+h) - s(t) > 0$

$$\therefore \quad s(t+h) > s(t)$$

i.e.,

$\therefore$ P is moving to the right.

SIGNS OF $a(t)$:

$a(t)$	Interpretation
> 0	velocity is increasing
< 0	velocity is decreasing
$= 0$	velocity may be a maximum or minimum

A useful table:

Phrase used in a question	t	s	v	a
initial conditions	0			
at the origin		0		
stationary			0	
reverses			0	
maximum height			0	
constant velocity				0
max. / min. velocity				0

SPEED

As we have seen, velocities have size (magnitude) and sign (direction). The speed of a particle is a measure of how fast it is travelling regardless of the direction of travel.

Thus   the speed at any instant is the modulus of the particle's velocity,

i.e.,   if S represents speed then $S = |v|$.

The question arises: "How can we determine when the speed of a particle is increasing or decreasing?"

We employ a **sign test**. This is:

- If the signs of $v(t)$ and $a(t)$ are the same, (i.e., both positive or both negative), then the **speed** of P is **increasing**.

- If the signs of $v(t)$ and $a(t)$ are opposite, then the **speed** of P is decreasing.

We prove *the first* of these as follows:

Proof: Let $S = |v|$,   be the speed of P at any instant

$$\therefore \quad S = \left\{ \begin{array}{ll} v & \text{if} \quad v \geqslant 0 \\ -v & \text{if} \quad v < 0 \end{array} \right. \quad \text{\{definition of modulus\}}$$

Case 1:   If $v > 0$, $S = v$ and $\therefore$ $\dfrac{dS}{dt} = \dfrac{dv}{dt} = a(t)$

and if $a(t) > 0$, $\dfrac{dS}{dt} > 0$ which implies that S is increasing.

Case 2:   If $v < 0$, $S = -v$ and $\therefore$ $\dfrac{dS}{dt} = -\dfrac{dv}{dt} = -a(t)$

and if $a(t) < 0$, $\dfrac{dS}{dt} > 0$ which also implies that S is increasing.

Thus if $v(t)$ and $a(t)$ have the same sign, the speed of P is increasing.

INVESTIGATION   DISPLACEMENT, VELOCITY AND ACCELERATION GRAPHS

In this investigation we examine the motion of a projec- MOTION DEMO
tile which is fired in a vertical direction under gravity.
Other functions of a different kind will be examined.

What to do:

1 Click on the icon to examine vertical projectile motion in a straight line. Observe first the displacement along the line, then look at the velocity or rate of change in displacement.

2 Examine the three graphs   • *displacement* v *time*   • *velocity* v *time*
                                    • *acceleration* v *time*

3 Pick from the menu or construct functions of your own choosing to investigate their displacement, velocity and acceleration functions.

Note: You can graph s, v, a and $|v|$ on your calculator then calculate values and make important conclusions.

You are encouraged to use the motion demo in the questions of the following exercise.

Example 4

A particle moves in a straight line with position, relative to some origin O, given by
$s(t) = t^3 - 3t + 1$ cm, where t is the time in seconds ($t \geqslant 0$).

a Find expressions for the particle's velocity and acceleration, and draw sign diagrams for each of them.

b Find the initial conditions and hence describe the motion at this instant.

c Describe the motion of the particle at $t = 2$ seconds.

d Find the position of the particle when changes in direction occur.

e Draw a motion diagram for the particle.

f For what time interval(s) is the particle's speed increasing?

g What is the total distance travelled for $t \in [0, 2]$?

a Since $s(t) = t^3 - 3t + 1$ cm

$$\therefore \quad v(t) = 3t^2 - 3 \text{ cm/s} \qquad \{\text{as } v(t) = s'(t)\}$$
$$= 3(t^2 - 1)$$
$$= 3(t + 1)(t - 1) \quad \text{which has sign diagram}$$

Note: $t \geqslant 0$
$\therefore$ critical value $t = -1$ is not required.

Also $a(t) = 6t$ cm/s^2 $\{\text{as } a(t) = v'(t)\}$

which has sign diagram

b When $t = 0$, $s(0) = 1$ cm
$$v(0) = -3 \text{ cm/s}$$
$$a(0) = 0 \text{ cm/s}^2$$

$\therefore$ particle is 1 cm to the right of O, moving to the left at a speed of 3 cm/s.
$$\{\text{speed} = |v|\}$$

c When $t = 2$, $s(2) = 8 - 6 + 1 = 3$ cm
$$v(2) = 12 - 3 = 9 \text{ cm/s}$$
$$a(2) = 12 \text{ cm/s}^2$$

$\therefore$ particle is 3 cm right of O, moving to the right at a speed of 9 cm/s and the speed is increasing. $\{\text{as } a \text{ and } v \text{ have the same sign}\}$

d Since $v(t)$ changes sign when $t = 1$, a change of direction occurs at this instant and $s(1) = 1 - 3 + 1 = -1$
$\therefore$ changes direction when $t = 1$ and is 1 cm left of O.

e

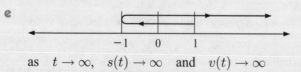

Note: The motion is actually **on the line**, not above it as shown.

as $t \to \infty$, $s(t) \to \infty$ and $v(t) \to \infty$

f Speed is increasing when $v(t)$ and $a(t)$ have the same sign   i.e., $t \geqslant 1$.

g Total distance travelled $= 2 + 4 = 6$ cm.

EXERCISE 22C.2 (Use a graphics calculator to check sign diagrams.)

1 An object moves in a straight line with position given by $s(t) = t^2 - 4t + 3$ cm from an origin O, $t \geqslant 0$, t in seconds.

   a Find expressions for its velocity and acceleration at any instant and draw sign diagrams for each function.

   b Find the initial conditions and explain what is happening to the object at that instant.

   c Describe the motion of the object at time $t = 2$ seconds.

   d At what time(s) does the object reverse direction? Find the position of the object at these instants.

   e Draw a motion diagram of the object.

   f For what time intervals is the speed of the object decreasing?

2 A stone is projected vertically upwards so that its position above ground level after t seconds is given by $s(t) = 98t - 4.9t^2$ metres, $t \geqslant 0$.

   a Find the velocity and acceleration functions for the stone and draw sign diagrams for each function.

   b Find the initial position and velocity of the stone.

   c Describe the stone's motion at times $t = 5$ and $t = 12$ seconds.

   d Find the maximum height reached by the stone.

   e Find the time taken for the stone to hit the ground.

3 A particle moves in a straight line with displacement function

$$s(t) = 12t - 2t^3 - 1 \text{ centimetres}, \quad t \geqslant 0, \quad t \text{ in seconds.}$$

   a Find velocity and acceleration functions for the particle's motion.

   b Find the initial conditions and interpret their meaning.

   c Find the times and positions when the particle reverses direction.

   d At what times is the particle's: **i** speed increasing   **ii** velocity increasing?

4 The position of a particle moving along the x-axis is given by $x(t) = t^3 - 9t^2 + 24t$ metres, $t \geqslant 0$, t in seconds.

   a Draw sign diagrams for the particle's velocity and acceleration functions.

   b Find the position of the particle at the times when it reverses direction, and hence draw a motion diagram for the particle.

   c At what times is the particle's: **i** speed decreasing   **ii** velocity decreasing?

   d Find the total distance travelled by the particle in the first 5 seconds of motion.

5 An experiment to determine the position of an object fired vertically upwards from the earth's surface was performed. From the results, a two dimensional graph of position above the earth's surface $s(t)$ metres, against time t seconds, was plotted.

It was noted that the graph was *parabolic.* Assuming a constant gravitational acceleration g, show that if the initial velocity is $v(0)$ then:

   a $v(t) = v(0) + gt$, and   **b** $s(t) = v(0) \times t + \frac{1}{2}gt^2$.

[Hint: Assume $s(t) = at^2 + bt + c$.]

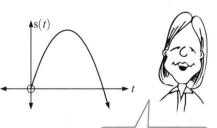

When finding total distance travelled, do not forget to look for dierction reversal first.

D   SOME CURVE PROPERTIES

Recall that $f'(x)$ or $\dfrac{dy}{dx}$ is the **slope function** of a curve.

The derivative of a function is another function which enables us to find the slope of a tangent to the curve at any point on it.

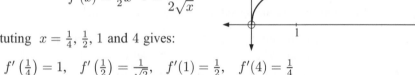

For example, if $f(x) = \sqrt{x}$ then

$$f(x) = x^{\frac{1}{2}} \quad \text{and}$$

$$f'(x) = \tfrac{1}{2}x^{-\frac{1}{2}} = \dfrac{1}{2\sqrt{x}}$$

Substituting $x = \frac{1}{4}, \frac{1}{2}, 1$ and 4 gives:

$$f'\left(\tfrac{1}{4}\right) = 1, \quad f'\left(\tfrac{1}{2}\right) = \tfrac{1}{\sqrt{2}}, \quad f'(1) = \tfrac{1}{2}, \quad f'(4) = \tfrac{1}{4}$$

i.e., the slopes are $1, \frac{1}{\sqrt{2}}, \frac{1}{2}$ and $\frac{1}{4}$ respectively.

Notice also that a tangent to the graph at any point, provided that $x > 0$, has a positive slope.

This fact is also observed from $f'(x) = \dfrac{1}{2\sqrt{x}}$ as $\sqrt{x}$ is never negative and $x > 0$.

MONOTONICITY

Many functions are **increasing** *for all* x whereas others are **decreasing** *for all* x.

For example,

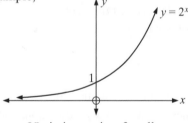

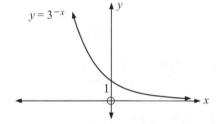

$y = 2^x$ is increasing for all x. $y = 3^{-x}$ is decreasing for all x.

Notice that:

- for an increasing function an increase in x produces an increase in y
- for a decreasing function an increase in x produces a decrease in y.

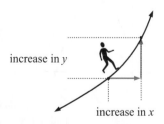

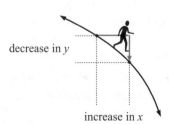

The majority of other functions have intervals where the function is increasing and intervals where it is decreasing.

For example:

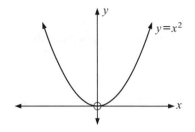

$y = x^2$ decreasing for $x \leqslant 0$ and increasing for $x \geqslant 0$.

Note: $x \leqslant 0$ is an interval of x values. So is $x \geqslant 0$.

INTERVALS

Some examples of intervals and their graphical representations are:

Algebraic form	Means	Alternative notation
$x \geqslant 4$		$[4, \infty[$
$x > 4$		$]4, \infty[$
$x \leqslant 2$		$]-\infty, 2]$
$x < 2$		$]-\infty, 2[$
$2 \leqslant x \leqslant 4$		$[2, 4]$
$2 \leqslant x < 4$		$[2, 4[$

INCREASING / DECREASING INTERVALS

Definition

> If S is an interval of real numbers and $f(x)$ is defined for all x in S, then:
> - $f(x)$ is **increasing** on S $\Leftrightarrow$ $f'(x) \geqslant 0$ for all x in S,   and
> - $f(x)$ is **decreasing** on S $\Leftrightarrow$ $f'(x) \leqslant 0$ for all x in S.

Note: $\Leftrightarrow$ is read as 'if and only if'

Example 5

Find intervals where $f(x)$ is:
a   increasing
b   decreasing.

a $f(x)$ is increasing for $x \leqslant -1$ and for $x \geqslant 2$.
{since tangents have slopes $\geqslant 0$ on these intervals}

b $f(x)$ is decreasing for $-1 \leqslant x \leqslant 2$.

EXERCISE 22D.1

1 Find intervals where $f(x)$ is   **i** increasing   **ii** decreasing:

a
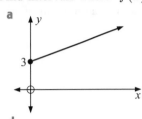

b
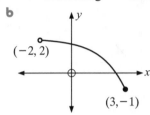

c
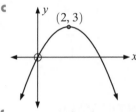

d
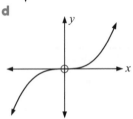

e
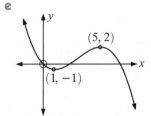

f
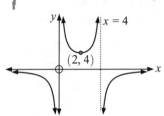

Sign diagrams for the derivative are extremely useful for determining intervals where a function is increasing/decreasing. Consider the following examples:

- $f(x) = x^2$

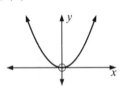

DEMO $f'(x) = 2x$ which has sign diagram

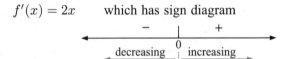

So $f(x) = x^2$ is   decreasing for $x \leqslant 0$
and   increasing for $x \geqslant 0$.

- $f(x) = -x^2$

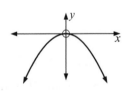

DEMO $f'(x) = -2x$ which has sign diagram

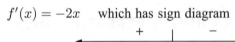

- $f(x) = x^3$

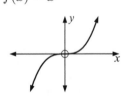

DEMO $f'(x) = 3x^2$ which has sign diagram

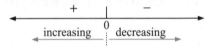

- $f(x) = x^3 - 3x + 4$

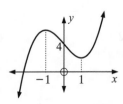

DEMO
$$f'(x) = 3x^2 - 3$$
$$= 3(x^2 - 1)$$
$$= 3(x + 1)(x - 1)$$
which has sign diagram

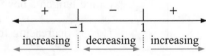

Example 6

Find the intervals where the following functions are increasing/deceasing:

a $f(x) = -x^3 + 3x^2 + 5$ **b** $f(x) = 3x^4 - 8x^3 + 2$

a $f(x) = -x^3 + 3x^2 + 5$

∴ $f'(x) = -3x^2 + 6x$

∴ $f'(x) = -3x(x - 2)$

which has sign diagram

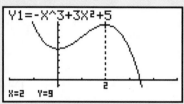

$$\begin{array}{c} - \quad | \quad + \quad | \quad - \\ \hline \quad 0 \quad\quad 2 \quad \end{array}$$

So, $f(x)$ is decreasing for
$x \leqslant 0$ and for $x \geqslant 2$ and
is increasing for $0 \leqslant x \leqslant 2$.

b $f(x) = 3x^4 - 8x^3 + 2$

∴ $f'(x) = 12x^3 - 24x^2$

$= 12x^2(x - 2)$

which has sign diagram

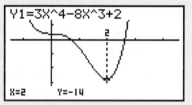

$$\begin{array}{c} - \quad | \quad - \quad | \quad + \\ \hline \quad 0 \quad\quad 2 \quad \end{array}$$

So, $f(x)$ is decreasing for
$x \leqslant 2$ and is increasing
for $x \geqslant 2$.

EXERCISE 22D.2

1   Find intervals where $f(x)$ is increasing/decreasing:

a $f(x) = x^2$

b $f(x) = -x^3$

c $f(x) = 2x^2 + 3x - 4$

d $f(x) = \sqrt{x}$

e $f(x) = \dfrac{2}{\sqrt{x}}$

f $f(x) = x^3 - 6x^2$

g $f(x) = -2x^3 + 4x$

h $f(x) = -4x^3 + 15x^2 + 18x + 3$

i $f(x) = 3x^4 - 16x^3 + 24x^2 - 2$

j $f(x) = 2x^3 + 9x^2 + 6x - 7$

k $f(x) = x^3 - 6x^2 + 3x - 1$

l $f(x) = x - 2\sqrt{x}$

m $f(x) = 3x^4 - 8x^3 - 6x^2 + 24x + 11$

n $f(x) = x^4 - 4x^3 + 2x^2 + 4x + 1$

Example 7

Consider $f(x) = \dfrac{3x - 9}{x^2 - x - 2}$.

a   Show that $f'(x) = \dfrac{-3(x - 5)(x - 1)}{(x - 2)^2(x + 1)^2}$ and draw its sign diagram.

b   Hence, find intervals where $y = f(x)$ is increasing/decreasing.

a $f(x) = \dfrac{3x - 9}{x^2 - x - 2}$

$$f'(x) = \dfrac{3(x^2 - x - 2) - (3x - 9)(2x - 1)}{(x - 2)^2(x + 1)^2} \qquad \{\text{quotient rule}\}$$

$$= \dfrac{3x^2 - 3x - 6 - [6x^2 - 21x + 9]}{(x - 2)^2(x + 1)^2}$$

$$= \dfrac{-3x^2 + 18x - 15}{(x - 2)^2(x + 1)^2}$$

$$= \dfrac{-3(x^2 - 6x + 5)}{(x - 2)^2(x + 1)^2}$$

$$= \dfrac{-3(x - 5)(x - 1)}{(x - 2)^2(x + 1)^2} \quad \text{which has sign diagram}$$

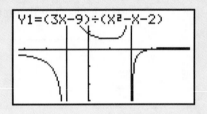

b $f(x)$ is increasing for $1 \leqslant x < 2$

and for $2 < x \leqslant 5$

$f(x)$ is decreasing for $x < -1$ and
for $-1 < x \leqslant 1$ and for $x \geqslant 5$.

Note: A screen dump of $y = f(x)$ is:

Y1=(3X-9)÷(X²-X-2)

---

2 **a** Consider $f(x) = \dfrac{4x}{x^2 + 1}$.

   i Show that $f'(x) = \dfrac{-4(x + 1)(x - 1)}{(x^2 + 1)^2}$ and draw its sign diagram.

   ii Hence, find intervals where $y = f(x)$ is increasing/decreasing.

b Consider $f(x) = \dfrac{4x}{(x - 1)^2}$.

   i Show that $f'(x) = \dfrac{-4(x + 1)}{(x - 1)^3}$ and draw its sign diagram.

   ii Hence, find intervals where $y = f(x)$ is increasing/decreasing.

c Consider $f(x) = \dfrac{-x^2 + 4x - 7}{x - 1}$.

   i Show that $f'(x) = \dfrac{-(x + 1)(x - 3)}{(x - 1)^2}$ and draw its sign diagram.

   ii Hence, find intervals where $y = f(x)$ is increasing/decreasing.

3 Find intervals where $f(x)$ is increasing/decreasing if:

   a $f(x) = \dfrac{x^3}{x^2 - 1}$ **b** $f(x) = x^2 + \dfrac{4}{x - 1}$

MAXIMA/MINIMA

Consider the following graph which has a restricted domain of $-5 \leqslant x \leqslant 6$.

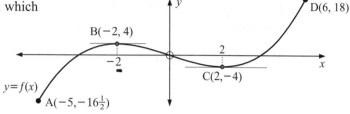

A is a **global minimum** as it is the minimum value of y and occurs at an endpoint.

B is a **local maximum** as it is a turning point where the curve has shape $\bigcap$ and $f'(x) = 0$ at that point.

C is a **local minimum** as it is a turning point where the curve has shape $\bigcup$ and $f'(x) = 0$ at that point.

D is a **global maximum** as it is the maximum value of y and occurs at the endpoint of the domain.

Note: For local maxima/minima, tangents at these points are **horizontal** and thus have a slope of 0,   i.e., $f'(x) = 0$.

HORIZONTAL INFLECTIONS (OR STATIONARY INFLECTIONS)

It is not true that whenever we find a value of x where $f'(x) = 0$ we have a local maximum or minimum.

For example, $f(x) = x^3$ has $f'(x) = 3x^2$
and $f'(x) = 0$ when $x = 0$.

Notice that the x-axis is a tangent to the curve which actually crosses over the curve at O(0, 0).

This tangent is horizontal and O(0, 0) is not a local maximum or minimum.

It is called a **horizontal inflection** (or **inflexion**) as the curve changes its curvature (shape).

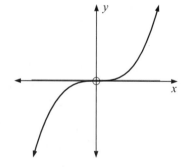

STATIONARY POINTS

A **stationary point** is a point where $f'(x) = 0$. It could be a local maximum, local minimum or a horizontal inflection.

Consider the following graph:

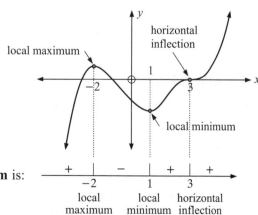

Its **slope sign diagram** is:

Summary:

Stationary point	Sign diagram of $f'(x)$ near $x = a$	Shape of curve near $x = a$
local maximum	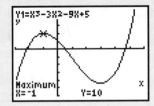	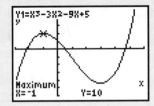
local minimum		
horizontal inflection or stationary inflection		

Find and classify all stationary points of $f(x) = x^3 - 3x^2 - 9x + 5$.

$f(x) = x^3 - 3x^2 - 9x + 5$

$\therefore \quad f'(x) = 3x^2 - 6x - 9$

$\quad = 3(x^2 - 2x - 3)$

$\quad = 3(x - 3)(x + 1)$,   which has sign diagram:

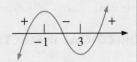

So, we have a local maximum at $x = -1$ and a local minimum at $x = 3$.

$f(-1) = (-1)^3 - 3(-1)^2 - 9(-1) + 5$

$\quad = -1 - 3 + 9 + 5$

$\quad = 10$ $\therefore$ local maximum at $(-1, 10)$

$f(3) = 3^3 - 3 \times 3^2 - 9 \times 3 + 5$

$\quad = 27 - 27 - 27 + 5$

$\quad = -22$ $\therefore$ local minimum at $(3, -22)$

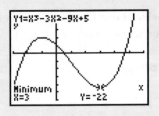

EXERCISE 22D.3

1 A, B and C are points where tangents are horizontal.

   a Classify points A, B and C.

   b Draw a sign diagram for the slope of $f(x)$ for all x.

   c State intervals where $y = f(x)$ is:

   i increasing   **ii** decreasing.

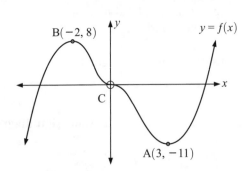

2 For each of the following functions, find and classify the stationary points and hence sketch the function showing all important features.

a $f(x) = x^2 - 2$
b $f(x) = x^3 + 1$
c $f(x) = x^3 - 3x + 2$
d $f(x) = x^4 - 2x^2$
e $f(x) = x^3 - 6x^2 + 12x + 1$
f $f(x) = \sqrt{x} + 2$
g $f(x) = x - \sqrt{x}$
h $f(x) = x^4 - 6x^2 + 8x - 3$
i $f(x) = 1 - x\sqrt{x}$
j $f(x) = x^4 - 2x^2 - 8$

3 At what value of x does the quadratic function, $f(x) = ax^2 + bx + c$, $a \neq 0$, have a stationary point? Under what conditions is the stationary point a local maximum or a local minimum?

4 $f(x) = 2x^3 + ax^2 - 24x + 1$ has a local maximum at $x = -4$. Find a.

5 $f(x) = x^3 + ax + b$ has a stationary point at $(-2, 3)$.

a   Find the values of a and b.

b   Find the position and nature of all stationary points.

6 A cubic polynomial $P(x)$, touches the line with equation $y = 9x + 2$ at the point $(0, 2)$ and has a stationary point at $(-1, -7)$. Find $P(x)$.

Example 9

Find the greatest and least value of $x^3 - 6x^2 + 5$ on the interval $-2 \leqslant x \leqslant 5$.

First we graph $y = x^3 - 6x^2 + 5$ on $[-2, 5]$.

The greatest value is clearly when $\dfrac{dy}{dx} = 0$.

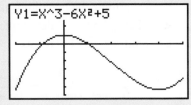

Now $\dfrac{dy}{dx} = 3x^2 - 12x$

$= 3x(x - 4)$

$= 0$ when $x = 0$ or 4.

So, the greatest value is $f(0) = 5$ when $x = 0$.

The least value is either $f(-2)$ or $f(4)$, whichever is smaller.

Now $f(-2) = -27$ and $f(4) = -27$

$\therefore$ least value is -27 when $x = -2$ and $x = 4$.

---

7 Find the greatest and least value of:

a $x^3 - 12x - 2$ for $-3 \leqslant x \leqslant 5$
b $4 - 3x^2 + x^3$ for $-2 \leqslant x \leqslant 3$

8 A manufacturing company makes door hinges. The cost function for making x hinges per hour is $C(x) = 0.0007x^3 - 0.1796x^2 + 14.663x + 160$ dollars where $50 \leqslant x \leqslant 150$. The condition $50 \leqslant x \leqslant 150$ applies as the company has a standing order filled by producing 50 each hour, but knows that production of more than 150 an hour is useless as they will not sell. Find the minimum and maximum hourly costs and the production levels when each occurs.

E   RATIONAL FUNCTIONS

Rational functions are functions of the form $f(x) = \dfrac{g(x)}{h(x)}$ where $g(x)$ and $h(x)$ are polynomials.

For example, $f(x) = \dfrac{2x - 1}{x^2 + 2}$ and $f(x) = \dfrac{x^2 - 4}{x^2 - 3x + 2}$ are rational functions.

One feature of a rational function is the presence of **asymptotes**.

These are lines (or curves) that a function's graph approaches when x or y takes large values.

> **Vertical asymptotes** are vertical lines which the graph of a function approaches.
>
> These can be found by solving $h(x) = 0$ in the case where $f(x) = \dfrac{g(x)}{h(x)}$.
>
> **Horizontal asymptotes** are horizontal lines which the graph of a function approaches.
> These can be found by finding what value $f(x)$ approaches as $|x| \to \infty$.

Functions of the form $y = \dfrac{\text{linear}}{\text{linear}}$ were covered in **Chapter 6**.

FUNCTIONS OF THE FORM $f(x) = \dfrac{\text{linear}}{\text{quadratic}}$

Example 10

Consider $f(x) = \dfrac{3x - 9}{x^2 - x - 2}$.

a Determine the equations of any asymptotes.
b Find $f'(x)$ and determine the position and nature of any stationary points.
c Find the axis intercepts.   **d** Sketch the graph of the function.

a $f(x) = \dfrac{3x - 9}{x^2 - x - 2} = \dfrac{3x - 9}{(x - 2)(x + 1)}$

Vertical asymptotes are $x = 2$ and $x = -1$ {when the denominator is 0}

Horizontal asymptote is $y = 0$ {as $|x| \to \infty$, $f(x) \to 0$}

b $f'(x) = \dfrac{3(x^2 - x - 2) - (3x - 9)(2x - 1)}{(x - 2)^2(x + 1)^2}$

$= \dfrac{3x^2 - 3x - 6 - [6x^2 - 21x + 9]}{(x - 2)^2(x + 1)^2}$ So, $f'(x)$ has sign diagram:

$= \dfrac{-3x^2 + 18x - 15}{(x - 2)^2(x + 1)^2}$

$= \dfrac{-3(x^2 - 6x + 5)}{(x - 2)^2(x + 1)^2}$ $\therefore$ a local maximum when $x = 5$ and a local minimum when $x = 1$

$= \dfrac{-3(x - 5)(x - 1)}{(x - 2)^2(x + 1)^2}$ local max. $(5, \frac{1}{3})$

local min. $(1, 3)$

c   Cuts the x-axis when $y = 0$

$\therefore \quad 3x - 9 = 0,$ i.e., $x = 3$

So, the x-intercept is 3.

Cuts the y-intercept when $x = 0$

$\therefore \quad y = \frac{-9}{-2} = 4\frac{1}{2}$

So, the y-intercept is $4\frac{1}{2}$.

d

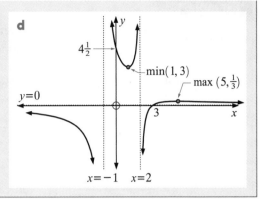

EXERCISE 22E.1

1 Determine the equations of the asymptotes of:

a $y = \dfrac{2x}{x^2 - 4}$

b $y = \dfrac{1 - x}{(x + 2)^2}$

c $y = \dfrac{3x + 2}{x^2 + 1}$

2 For each of the following functions:

   i   determine the equation(s) of the asymptotes

   ii   find $f'(x)$ and hence determine the position and nature of any stationary points

   iii   find the axis intercepts

   iv   sketch the graph of the function, showing all information in **a**, **b** and **c**.

a $f(x) = \dfrac{4x}{x^2 + 1}$

b $f(x) = \dfrac{4x}{x^2 - 4x - 5}$

c $f(x) = \dfrac{4x}{(x - 1)^2}$

d $f(x) = \dfrac{3x - 3}{(x + 2)^2}$

FUNCTIONS OF THE FORM $y = \dfrac{\text{quadratic}}{\text{quadratic}}$

Functions such as $y = \dfrac{2x^2 - x + 3}{x^2 + x - 2}$ have a **horizontal asymptote** which can be found by dividing every term by x^2.

Notice that $y = \dfrac{2 - \dfrac{1}{x} + \dfrac{3}{x^2}}{1 + \dfrac{1}{x} - \dfrac{2}{x^2}}$ and as $|x| \to \infty$, $y \to \dfrac{2}{1}$ i.e., $y \to 2$.

EXERCISE 22E.2

1 Determine the equations of the asymptotes of:

a $y = \dfrac{2x^2 - x + 2}{x^2 - 1}$

b $y = \dfrac{-x^2 + 2x - 1}{x^2 + x + 1}$

c $y = \dfrac{3x^2 - x + 2}{(x + 2)^2}$

Example 11

For $f(x) = \dfrac{x^2 - 3x + 2}{x^2 + 3x + 2}$.

a Determine the equations of its asymptotes.

b Find $f'(x)$ and determine the position and nature of any turning points.

c Find the axis intercepts.

d Sketch the graph of the function.

---

a $f(x) = \dfrac{x^2 - 3x + 2}{x^2 + 3x + 2} = \dfrac{1 - \dfrac{3}{x} + \dfrac{2}{x^2}}{1 + \dfrac{3}{x} + \dfrac{2}{x^2}}$ $\therefore$ HA is $y = \dfrac{1}{1}$ i.e., $y = 1$

{as $|x| \to \infty$, $y \to 1$}

$f(x) = \dfrac{x^2 - 3x + 2}{(x+1)(x+2)}$ $\therefore$ vertical asymptotes are $x = -1$ and $x = -2$

b $f'(x) = \dfrac{(2x - 3)(x^2 + 3x + 2) - (x^2 - 3x + 2)(2x + 3)}{(x+1)^2(x+2)^2}$

$= \dfrac{6x^2 - 12}{(x+1)^2(x+2)^2}$ {on simplifying}

$= \dfrac{6(x + \sqrt{2})(x - \sqrt{2})}{(x+1)^2(x+2)^2}$ and has sign diagram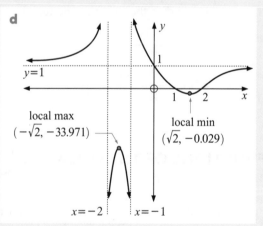

So, we have a local maximum at $x = -\sqrt{2}$ and a local minimum at $x = \sqrt{2}$.
The local max. is $(-\sqrt{2}, -33.971)$.   The local min. is $(\sqrt{2}, -0.029)$.

c Cuts the x-axis when $y = 0$

$\therefore$ $x^2 - 3x + 2 = 0$

$\therefore$ $(x - 1)(x - 2) = 0$

i.e.,   at $x = 1$ or 2

Cuts the y-axis when $x = 0$

$\therefore$ $y = \frac{2}{2} = 1$

d

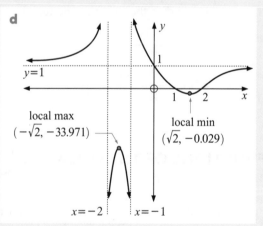

local max
$(-\sqrt{2}, -33.971)$

local min
$(\sqrt{2}, -0.029)$

$x = -2$ $x = -1$

---

2 For each of the following functions:

   i   determine the equation(s) of the asymptotes

  ii   find $f'(x)$ and hence determine the position and nature of any turning points

 iii   find the axis intercepts

  iv   sketch the function, showing all information obtained in **i**, **ii** and **iii**.

a $y = \dfrac{x^2 - x}{x^2 - x - 6}$

b $y = \dfrac{x^2 - 1}{x^2 + 1}$

c $y = \dfrac{x^2 - 5x + 4}{x^2 + 5x + 4}$

d $y = \dfrac{x^2 - 6x + 5}{(x + 1)^2}$

FUNCTIONS OF THE FORM $\quad y = \dfrac{\textbf{quadratic}}{\textbf{linear}}$

Functions such as $\quad y = \dfrac{x^2 + 2x - 1}{x + 3}, \quad y = \dfrac{2x^2 - x + 4}{x - 2}, \quad$ etc., have an **oblique asymptote** which can be found using the division process.

For example, $\quad y = \dfrac{x^2 + 2x - 1}{x + 3} = x - 1 + \dfrac{2}{x + 3} \quad$ on division.

If $|x| \to \infty$, $\dfrac{2}{x + 3} \to 0$ and so $y \doteqdot x - 1$. Thus $y = x - 1$ is an oblique asymptote.

Example 12

For $f(x) = \dfrac{-x^2 + 4x - 7}{x - 1}$

  a Determine the equation of its asymptotes.

  b Find $f'(x)$ and determine the position and nature of any turning points.

c Find the axis intercepts.   **d** Sketch the graph of the function.

---

a $f(x) = \dfrac{-x^2 + 4x - 7}{x - 1} = -x + 3 - \dfrac{4}{x - 1}$

$$
\begin{array}{r|rrr}
1 & -1 & 4 & -7 \\
  & 0 & -1 & 3 \\
\hline
  & -1 & 3 & -4 \\
\end{array}
$$

which has a **vertical asymptote** of $x = 1$ {as $x \to 1$, $|f(x)| \to \infty$}

and an **oblique asymptote** of $y = -x + 3$ {as $|x| \to \infty$, $y \to -x + 3$}

b $f'(x) = \dfrac{(-2x + 4)(x - 1) - (-x^2 + 4x - 7) \times 1}{(x - 1)^2}$

$\qquad = \dfrac{-2x^2 + 6x - 4 + x^2 - 4x + 7}{(x - 1)^2} \qquad$ which has sign diagram:

$\qquad = \dfrac{-x^2 + 2x + 3}{(x - 1)^2}$

$\qquad = \dfrac{-(x^2 - 2x - 3)}{(x - 1)^2}$

$\qquad = -\dfrac{(x + 1)(x - 3)}{(x - 1)^2}$

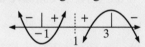

$\therefore$ a **local maximum** at $(3, -2)$

$\{f(3) = \frac{-9 + 12 - 7}{2} = -2\}$

and a **local minimum** at $(-1, 6)$

$\{f(-1) = \frac{-1 - 4 - 7}{-2} = 6\}$

c Cuts the x-axis when $y = 0$,

$\qquad \therefore \quad -x^2 + 4x - 7 = 0$

$\qquad \therefore \quad\;\; x^2 - 4x + 7 = 0$

$\qquad \therefore \quad \Delta = 16 - 4 \times 1 \times 7 < 0$

$\therefore$ no real roots

$\therefore$ does not cut the x-axis

Cuts the y-axis when $x = 0$.

$\therefore \quad y = \frac{-7}{-1} = 7 \quad \therefore \quad y$-intercept is 7.

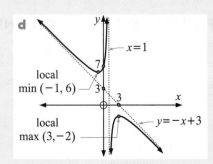

EXERCISE 22.E.3

1 For each of the following functions:
    i   determine the equations of the asymptotes
    ii   find $f'(x)$ and determine the position and nature of any turning points
    iii   find the axes intercepts   **iv**   sketch the graph of the function

    a $y = \dfrac{x^2 + 4x + 5}{x + 2}$ **b** $y = \dfrac{x^2 + 3x}{x + 1}$ **c** $y = -2x + 1 - \dfrac{2}{x - 2}$

F   INFLECTIONS AND SHAPE TYPE

When a curve, or part of a curve, has shape we say that the shape is **concave downwards**.

If a curve, or part of a curve, has shape   we say that the shape is **concave upwards**.

TEST FOR SHAPE

Consider the **concave downwards** curve:

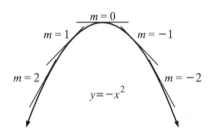

Notice that as x increases for all points on the curve the slope is decreasing,

i.e., $f'(x)$ is decreasing,

∴   its derivative is negative,

i.e., $f''(x) < 0$.

Likewise, if the curve is **concave upwards**:

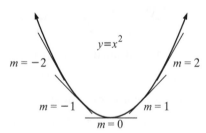

As the values of x increase for all points on the curve the slope is increasing,

i.e., $f'(x)$ is increasing,

∴   its derivative is positive,

i.e., $f''(x) > 0$.

POINTS OF INFLECTION (INFLEXION)

A **point of inflection** is a point on a curve at which a change of curvature (shape) occurs,

i.e.,   or

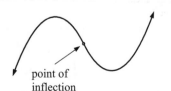

point of inflection

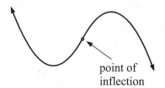

point of inflection

DEMO

Notes:
- If the tangent at a point of inflection is horizontal we say that we have a **horizontal** or **stationary inflection**.

  For example,

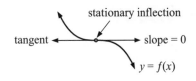

- If the tangent at a point of inflection is not horizontal we say that we have a **non-horizontal** or **non-stationary inflection**.

  For example,

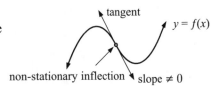

- Notice that the tangent at the point of inflection (the **inflecting tangent**) crosses the curve at that point.

Consequently,

> we have a **point of inflection** at $x = a$ if $f''(a) = 0$ **and** the sign of $f''(x)$ changes on either side of $x = a$,
>
> i.e., $f''(x)$ has **sign diagram**, in the vicinity of a, of either $\xleftarrow{\quad + \;\big|\; - \quad}_{\;\;a}$ or $\xleftarrow{\quad - \;\big|\; + \quad}_{\;\;a}$

Observe that if $f(x) = x^4$ then $f'(x) = 4x^3$ and $f''(x) = 12x^2$ and $f''(x)$ has sign

diagram $\xleftarrow{\qquad + \quad\big|\quad + \qquad}_{\qquad\; 0}$

Although $f''(0) = 0$ we do not have a point of inflection at $(0, 0)$ since the sign of $f''(x)$ does not change on either side of $x = 0$. In fact the graph of $f(x) = x^4$ is:

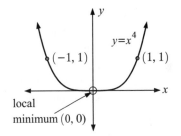

Summary:

concave downwards	For a curve (or part curve) which is **concave downwards** in an interval S, $f''(x) < 0$ for all x in S.
concave upwards	For a curve (or part curve) which is **concave upwards** in an interval S, $f''(x) > 0$ for all x in S.
If $f''(x)$ has a sign change on either side of $x = a$, and $f''(a) = 0$, then • we have a **horizontal inflection** if $f'(a) = 0$ also, • we have a **non-horizontal inflection** if $f'(a) \neq 0$.	

Click on the demo icon to examine some standard functions for turning points, points of inflection and intervals where the function is increasing, decreasing, concave up/down.

Example 13

Find and classify all points of inflection of $f(x) = x^4 - 4x^3 + 5$.

$$f(x) = x^4 - 4x^3 + 5$$
$$\therefore \quad f'(x) = 4x^3 - 12x^2$$
$$\therefore \quad f''(x) = 12x^2 - 24x$$
$$\qquad = 12x(x - 2) \quad \text{which has sign diagram}$$
$$f''(x) = 0 \quad \text{when} \quad x = 0 \text{ or } 2$$

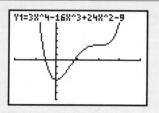

and since the signs of $f''(x)$ change about $x = 0$ and $x = 2$, we have points of inflection at these two points.

Also $f'(0) = 0$ and $f'(2) = 32 - 48 \neq 0$
and $f(0) = 5$, $f(2) = 16 - 32 + 5 = -11$

Thus $(0, 5)$ is a horizontal inflection and $(2, -11)$ is a non-horizontal inflection.

EXERCISE 22F

1 Find and classify, if they exist, all points of inflection of:

   a $f(x) = x^2 + 3$
   b $f(x) = 2 - x^3$
   c $f(x) = x^3 - 6x^2 + 9x + 1$
   d $f(x) = x^3 + 6x^2 + 12x + 5$
   e $f(x) = -3x^4 - 8x^3 + 2$
   f $f(x) = 3 - \dfrac{1}{\sqrt{x}}$

Example 14

For $f(x) = 3x^4 - 16x^3 + 24x^2 - 9$:
a find and classify all points where $f'(x) = 0$
b find and classify all points of inflection
c find intervals where the function is increasing/decreasing
d find intervals where the function is concave up/down.
e Hence, sketch the graph showing *all* important features.

$f(x) = 3x^4 - 16x^3 + 24x^2 - 9$
a $\quad \therefore \quad f'(x) = 12x^3 - 48x^2 + 48x$
$$\qquad\qquad = 12x(x^2 - 4x + 4)$$
$$\qquad\qquad = 12x(x - 2)^2$$
which has sign diagram

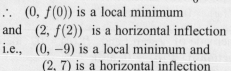

$\therefore \quad (0, f(0))$ is a local minimum
and $(2, f(2))$ is a horizontal inflection
i.e., $(0, -9)$ is a local minimum and
$\qquad (2, 7)$ is a horizontal inflection

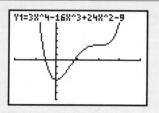

b $\quad f''(x) = 36x^2 - 96x + 48$
$$\qquad = 12(3x^2 - 8x + 4)$$
$$\qquad = 12(x - 2)(3x - 2)$$
which has sign diagram

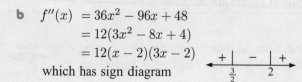

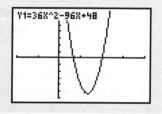

∴   (2, 7) is a horizontal inflection

and $\left(\frac{2}{3}, f\left(\frac{2}{3}\right)\right)$ i.e., $\left(\frac{2}{3}, -2.48\right)$ is a non-horizontal inflection.

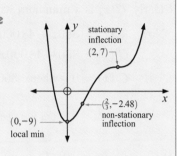

c $f(x)$ is decreasing for $x \leqslant 0$

$f(x)$ is increasing for $x \geqslant 0$.

d $f(x)$ is concave up for $x \leqslant \frac{2}{3}$ and for $x \geqslant 2$

$f(x)$ is concave down for $\frac{2}{3} \leqslant x \leqslant 2$.

2   For each of the following functions:

   i   find and classify all points where $f'(x) = 0$

   ii   find and classify all points of inflection

   iii   find intervals where the function is increasing/decreasing

   iv   find intervals where the function is concave up/down.

   v   Sketch the graph showing *all* important features.

a $f(x) = x^2$ **b** $f(x) = x^3$ **c** $f(x) = \sqrt{x}$

d $f(x) = x^3 - 3x^2 - 24x + 1$ **e** $f(x) = 3x^4 + 4x^3 - 2$ **f** $f(x) = (x - 1)^4$

g $f(x) = x^4 - 4x^2 + 3$ **h** $f(x) = 3 - \dfrac{4}{\sqrt{x}}$

G   OPTIMISATION

Many problems where we try to find the **maximum** or **minimum** value of a variable can be solved using differential calculus techniques. The solution is often referred to as the **optimum** solution. Consider the following problem.

An industrial shed is to have a total floor space of 600 m² and is to be divided into 3 rectangular rooms of equal size. The walls, internal and external, will cost $60 per metre to build. What dimensions should the shed have to minimise the cost of the walls?

We let one room be x m by y m as shown.

The total length of wall material is L where $L = 6x + 4y$ metres.

However we do know that the total area is 600 m²,

∴ $3x \times y = 600$ and so $y = \dfrac{200}{x}$

Knowing this relationship enables us to write

L in terms of one variable (x in this case),

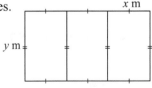

Note: $x > 0$ and $y > 0$

i.e., $L = 6x + 4\left(\dfrac{200}{x}\right)$ m,   i.e., $L = \left(6x + \dfrac{800}{x}\right)$ m

and at $60/metre, the total cost is $C(x) = 60\left(6x + \dfrac{800}{x}\right)$ dollars.

When graphed we have:

Clearly, $C(x)$ is a minimum when $C'(x) = 0$.

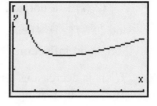

Now $C(x) = 360x + 48\,000x^{-1}$

$\therefore$ $C'(x) = 360 - 48\,000x^{-2}$

$\therefore$ $C'(x) = 0$ when $360 = \dfrac{48\,000}{x^2}$

i.e., $x^2 = \dfrac{48\,000}{360} \doteqdot 133.333$ and so $x \doteqdot 11.547$

Now when $x \doteqdot 11.547$, $y \doteqdot \dfrac{200}{11.547} \doteqdot 17.321$ and $C(11.547) \doteqdot 8313.84$ dollars.

So, the minimum cost is about \$8310 when the shed is 34.6 m by 17.3 m.

WARNING

The maximum/minimum value does not always occur when the first derivative is zero.

It is essential to also examine the values of the function at the end point(s) of the domain for global maxima/minima, i.e., given $a \leqslant x \leqslant b$, you should also consider $f(a)$ and $f(b)$.

Example:

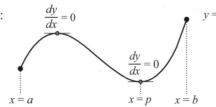

In the illustrated example, the maximum value of y occurs at $x = b$ and the minimum value of y occurs at $x = p$.

TESTING OPTIMAL SOLUTIONS

If one is trying to optimise a function $f(x)$ and we find values of x such that $f'(x) = 0$, how do we know whether we have a maximum or a minimum solution? The following are acceptable evidence.

SIGN DIAGRAM TEST

If near to $x = a$ where $f'(a) = 0$ the sign diagram is:

- we have a **local maximum**
- we have a **local minimum**.

SECOND DERIVATIVE TEST

If near $x = a$ where $f'(a) = 0$ and:

- $\dfrac{d^2y}{dx^2} < 0$ we have $\bigcap$ shape,

  i.e.,   a **local maximum**

- $\dfrac{d^2y}{dx^2} > 0$ we have $\bigcup$ shape,

  i.e.,   a **local minimum**.

GRAPHICAL TEST

If we have a graph of $y = f(x)$ showing $\bigcap$ we have a **local maximum** and $\bigcup$ we have a **local minimum**.

OPTIMISATION PROBLEM SOLVING METHOD

The following steps should be followed:

Step 1: Draw a large, clear diagram(s) of the situation.

Step 2: Find an equation with the variable to be **optimised** (**maximised** or **minimised**) as the subject of the formula in terms of **one** convenient **variable**, x say. Also find what restrictions there may be on x.

Step 3: Find the **first derivative** and find the value(s) of x when it is **zero**.

Step 4: If there is a restricted domain such as $a \leqslant x \leqslant b$, the maximum/minimum value of the function may occur either when the derivative is zero or at $x = a$ or at $x = b$. Show by the **sign diagram test**, the **second derivative test** or the **graphical test**, that you have a maximum or a minimum situation.

To illustrate the method we consider the following example.

Example 15

A rectangular cake dish is made by cutting out squares from the corners of a 25 cm by 40 cm rectangle of tin-plate and folding the metal to form the container.
What size squares must be cut out in order to produce the cake dish of maximum volume?

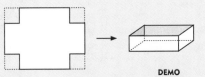

DEMO

Step 1: Let x cm be the lengths of the sides of the squares cut out.

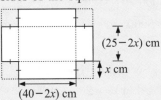

$(25-2x)$ cm
x cm
$(40-2x)$ cm

Step 2:

Volume = length × width × depth
$$= (40 - 2x)(25 - 2x)x \text{ cm}^3$$
i.e., $V = (40 - 2x)(25x - 2x^2) \text{ cm}^3$

Notice that $x > 0$ and $25 - 2x > 0$
$\therefore \quad 0 < x < 12.5$

Step 3: Now $\dfrac{dV}{dx} = -2(25x - 2x^2) + (40 - 2x)(25 - 4x)$ {product rule}
$$= -50x + 4x^2 + 1000 - 50x - 160x + 8x^2$$
$$= 12x^2 - 260x + 1000$$
$$= 4(3x^2 - 65x + 250)$$
$$= 4(3x - 50)(x - 5) \quad \text{which is 0 when} \quad x = \tfrac{50}{3} = 16\tfrac{2}{3} \text{ or } x = 5$$

Step 4: **Sign diagram test** $\dfrac{dV}{dx}$ has sign diagram:

```
       +   -
   |--/‾‾\----|....J
   0   5    \  16⅔
           12.5
```

or **Second derivative test**

$\dfrac{d^2V}{dx^2} = 24x - 260$ and at $x = 5$, $\dfrac{d^2V}{dx^2} = -140$ which is < 0

$\therefore$ shape is $\bigcap$ and we have a local maximum.

So, the maximum volume is obtained when $x = 5$,

i.e., 5 cm squares are cut from the corners.

Example 16

Find the most economical shape (minimum surface area) for a box with a square base, vertical sides and an open top, given that it must contain 4 litres.

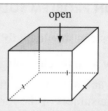

open

Step 1: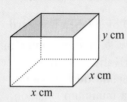

y cm

x cm

x cm

Let the base lengths be x cm and the depth be y cm. Now the volume

$$V = \text{length} \times \text{width} \times \text{depth}$$
$$\therefore \quad V = x^2 y$$
$$\therefore \quad 4000 = x^2 y \quad .... \text{(1)} \quad \{\text{as 1 litre} \equiv 1000 \text{ cm}^3\}$$

Step 2:   Now total surface area,

$$A = \text{area of base} + 4 \text{ (area of one side)}$$
$$\therefore \quad A(x) = x^2 + 4xy$$
$$\therefore \quad A(x) = x^2 + 4x \left(\frac{4000}{x^2} \right) \quad \{\text{using (1)}\}$$
$$\therefore \quad A(x) = x^2 + 16\,000 x^{-1}$$

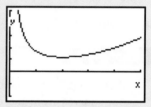

Notice:
$x > 0$ as x is a length.

Step 3:   Thus $A'(x) = 2x - 16\,000 x^{-2}$

and $A'(x) = 0$ when $2x = \dfrac{16\,000}{x^2}$

i.e., $2x^3 = 16\,000$

$x^3 = 8000$

$x = \sqrt[3]{8000}$

$x = 20$

Step 4:   **Sign diagram test**   *or*   **Second derivative test**

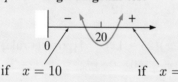

$$A''(x) = 2 + 32\,000 x^{-3}$$
$$= 2 + \frac{32\,000}{x^3}$$

if $x = 10$ if $x = 30$

$A'(10) = 20 - \frac{16\,000}{100}$ $A'(30) = 60 - \frac{16\,000}{900}$

$= 20 - 160$ $\doteqdot 60 - 17.8$

$= -140$ $\doteqdot 42.2$

which is always positive as $x^3 > 0$ for all $x > 0$.

Each of these tests establishes that minimum material is used to make the container when $x = 20$, and $y = \dfrac{4000}{20^2} = 10$,

i.e.,

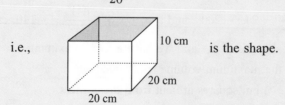

10 cm

20 cm

20 cm

is the shape.

EXERCISE 22G

Use **calculus techniques** in the following problems.

1 A duck farmer wishes to build a rectangular enclosure of area 100 m². The farmer must purchase wire netting for three of the sides as the fourth side is an existing fence of another duck yard. Naturally the farmer wishes to minimise the length (and therefore the cost) of the fencing required to complete the job.

   a If the shorter sides are of length x m, show that the required length of wire netting to be purchased is $L = 2x + \dfrac{100}{x}$.

   b Use **technology** to help you sketch the graph of $y = 2x + \dfrac{100}{x}$.

   c Find the minimum value of L and the corresponding value of x when this occurs.

   d Sketch the optimum situation with its dimensions.

2 Radioactive waste is to be disposed of in fully enclosed lead boxes of inner volume 200 cm³. The base of the box has dimensions in the ratio $2 : 1$.

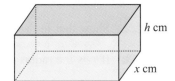

   a What is the inner length of the box?

   b Explain why $x^2 h = 100$.

   c Explain why the inner surface area of the box is given by $A(x) = 4x^2 + \dfrac{600}{x}$ cm².

   d Use technology to help sketch the graph of $y = 4x^2 + \dfrac{600}{x}$.

   e Find the minimum inner surface area of the box and the corresponding value of x.

   f Draw a sketch of the optimum box shape with dimensions shown.

3 Consider the manufacture of 1 L capacity tin cans where the cost of the metal used to manufacture them is to be minimised. This means that the surface area is to be as small as possible but still must hold a litre.

   a Explain why the height h, is given by $h = \dfrac{1000}{\pi r^2}$ cm.

   b Show that the total surface area A, is given by $A = 2\pi r^2 + \dfrac{2000}{r}$ cm².

   c Use technology to help you sketch the graph of A against r.

   d Find the value of r which makes A as small as possible.

   e Draw a sketch of the dimensions of the can of smallest surface area.

4 Sam has sheets of metal which are 36 cm by 36 cm square and wishes to use them. He cuts out identical squares which are x cm by x cm from the corners of each sheet. The remaining shape is then bent along the dashed lines to form an open container.

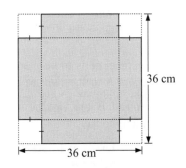

   a Show that the capacity of the container is given by $V(x) = x(36 - 2x)^2$ cm³.

   b What sized squares should be cut out to produce the container of greatest capacity?

5 An athletics track has two 'straights' of length l m and two semi-circular ends of radius x m. The perimeter of the track is 400 m.

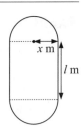

   a Show that $l = 200 - \pi x$, and hence write down the possible values that x may have.

   b Show that the area inside the track is $A = 400x - \pi x^2$.

   c What values of l and x produce the largest area inside the track?

6 A sector of radius 10 cm is bent to form a conical cup as shown.

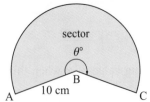   becomes   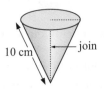   — join   when edges AB and CB are joined with tape

Suppose the resulting cone has base radius r cm and height h cm.

   a Show that in the sector, arc $AC = \dfrac{\theta \pi}{18}$.

   b If r is the radius of the cone, explain why $r = \dfrac{\theta}{36}$.

   c If h is the height of the cone show that $h = \sqrt{100 - \left(\frac{\theta}{36}\right)^2}$.

   d If $V(\theta)$ is the cone's capacity, find $V(\theta)$ in terms of θ only.

   e Use technology to sketch the graph of $V(\theta)$.

   f Find θ when $V(\theta)$ is a maximum.

7 B is a row boat 5 km out at sea from A. AC is a straight sandy beach, 6 km long. Peter can row the boat at 8 kmph and run along the beach at 17 kmph. Suppose Peter rows directly from B to X, where X is some point on AC and $AX = x$ km.

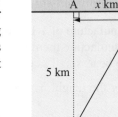

   a Explain why $0 \leqslant x \leqslant 6$.

   b If $T(x)$ is the *total time* Peter takes to row to X and then run along the beach

   to C, show that $T(x) = \dfrac{\sqrt{x^2 + 25}}{8} + \dfrac{6 - x}{17}$ hrs.

   c Find x when $\dfrac{dT}{dx} = 0$. What is the significance of this value of x? Prove your statement.

8 A pipeline is to be placed so that it connects point A to the river to point B.

A and B are two homesteads and X is the pumphouse.

How far from M should point X be so that the pipeline is as short as possible?

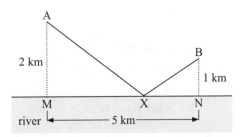

9

Open cylindrical bins are to contain 100 litres. Find the radius and the height of the bin made from the least amount of material (i.e., minimise the surface area).

10 Two lamps are of intensities 40 and 5 candle-power respectively and are 6 m apart. If the intensity of illumination I, at any point is directly proportional to the power of the source and inversely proportional to the square of the distance from the source, find the darkest point on the line joining the two lamps.

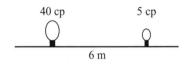

Sometimes the variable to be optimised is in the form of a single square root function. In these situations it is convenient to square the function and use the fact that "if $A > 0$, the optimum value of $A(x)$ occurs at the same value of x as the optimum value of $[A(x)]^2$."

Example 17

An animal enclosure is a right angled triangle with one leg being a drain. The farmer has 300 m of fencing available for the other two sides, AB and BC.

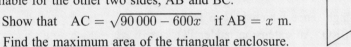

a Show that $AC = \sqrt{90\,000 - 600x}$ if $AB = x$ m.

b Find the maximum area of the triangular enclosure.
(**Hint:** If the area is A m^2, find A^2 in terms of x.
Notice that A is a maximum when A^2 takes its maximum value.)

---

a $(AC)^2 + x^2 = (300 - x)^2$ {Pythagoras}

   $\therefore$ $(AC)^2 = 90\,000 - 600x + x^2 - x^2$

   $\qquad\qquad = 90\,000 - 600x$

   $\therefore$ $AC = \sqrt{90\,000 - 600x}$

b The area of triangle ABC is

$$A(x) = \tfrac{1}{2}(\text{base} \times \text{altitude})$$

$$= \tfrac{1}{2}(AC \times x)$$

$$= \tfrac{1}{2}x\sqrt{90\,000 - 600x}$$

So $[A(x)]^2 = \dfrac{x^2}{4}(90\,000 - 600x) = 22\,500x^2 - 150x^3$

$\therefore$ $\dfrac{d}{dx}[A(x)]^2 = 45\,000x - 450x^2$

$\qquad\qquad = 450x(100 - x)$

with sign diagram:

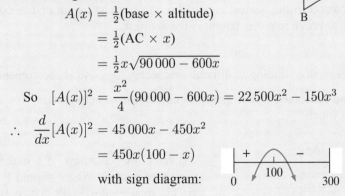

So $A(x)$ is maximised when $x = 100$

$A_{\max} = \tfrac{1}{2}(100)\sqrt{90\,000 - 60\,000}$

$\qquad \doteq 8660$ m^2

11 A right angled triangular pen is made from 24 m of fencing used for sides AB and BC. Side AC is an existing brick wall.

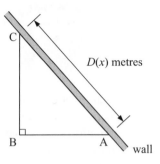

D(x) metres

wall

    a If AB $= x$ m, find $D(x)$, the distance AC, in terms of x.

    b Find $\dfrac{d[D(x)]^2}{dx}$ and hence draw a sign diagram for it.

    c Find the smallest and the greatest value of $D(x)$ and the design of the pen in each case.

12 At 1.00 pm a ship A leaves port P, and sails in the direction 30°T at 12 kmph. Also, at 1.00 pm ship B is 100 km due East of P and is sailing at 8 kmph towards P. Suppose t is the number of hours after 1.00 pm.

    a Show that the distance $D(t)$ km, between the two ships is given by
$$D(t) = \sqrt{304t^2 - 2800t + 10\,000} \text{ km}$$

    b Find the minimum value of $[D(t)]^2$ for all $t \geqslant 0$.

    c At what time, to the nearest minute, are the ships closest?

13 AB is a 1 m high fence which is 2 m from a vertical wall, RQ. An extension ladder PQ is placed on the fence so that it touches the ground at P and the wall at Q.

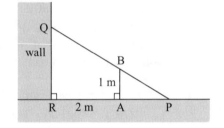

    a If AP $= x$ m, find QR in terms of x.

    b If the ladder has length $L(x)$ m show that $[L(x)]^2 = (x+2)^2 \left(1 + \dfrac{1}{x^2}\right)$.

    c Show that $\dfrac{d[L(x)]^2}{dx} = 0$ only when $x = \sqrt[3]{2}$.

    d Find, correct to the nearest centimetre, the shortest length of the extension ladder. You must prove that this length is the shortest.

Sometimes the derivative finding is difficult and technology use is recommended.

Use the **graphing package** or your **graphics calculator** to help solve the following problems.

GRAPHING PACKAGE

14

A, B and C are computers. A printer P is networked to each computer. Where should P be located so that the total cable length AP + BP + CP is a minimum?

15 Three towns and their grid references are marked on the diagram alongside. A pumping station is to be located at P on the pipeline, to pump water to the three towns. Grid units are kilometres.

Exactly where should P be located so that pipelines to Aden, Bracken and Caville in total are as short as possible?

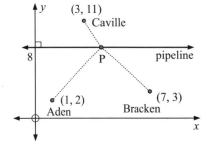

Sometimes technology does not provide easy solutions to problems where optimisation is required. This occurs when at least one quantity is unknown.

Example 18

A square sheet of metal has squares cut from its corners as shown.

What sized square should be cut out so that when bent into an open box shape the container holds maximum liquid?

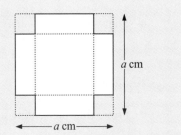

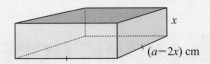

Let x cm by x cm squares be cut out.

Volume = length × width × depth
$$= (a - 2x) \times (a - 2x) \times x$$

i.e., $V(x) = x(a - 2x)^2$

Now $V'(x) = 1(a - 2x)^2 + x \times 2(a - 2x)^1 \times (-2)$ {product rule}
$$= (a - 2x)[a - 2x - 4x]$$
$$= (a - 2x)(a - 6x)$$

and $V'(x) = 0$ when $x = \dfrac{a}{2}$ or $\dfrac{a}{6}$

We notice that $a - 2x > 0$ i.e., $a > 2x$ or $x < \dfrac{a}{2}$, So, $0 < x < \dfrac{a}{2}$

Thus $x = \dfrac{a}{6}$ is the only value in $0 < x < \dfrac{a}{2}$ with $V'(x) = 0$.

Second derivative test:

Now $V''(x) = -2(a - 6x) + (a - 2x)(-6)$ {product rule}
$$= -2a + 12x - 6a + 12x$$
$$= 24x - 8a$$

∴ $V''(\dfrac{a}{6}) = 4a - 8a = -4a$ which is < 0

So, volume is maximised when $x = \dfrac{a}{6}$.

Conclusion: When $x = \dfrac{a}{6}$, the resulting container has maximum capacity.

16

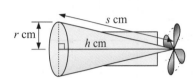

The trailing cone of a guided long range torpedo is to be conical with slant edge s cm where s is fixed, but unknown. The cone is hollow and must contain maximum volume of fuel.

Find the ratio of $s : r$ when maximum fuel carrying capacity occurs.

17 A company constructs rectangular seating plans and arranges seats for pop concerts on AFL grounds. All AFL grounds used are elliptical in shape and the equation of the ellipse illustrated is $\dfrac{x^2}{a^2} + \dfrac{y^2}{b^2} = 1$ where a and b are the lengths of its semi-major and semi-minor axes as shown.

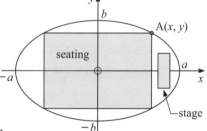

a Show that $y = \dfrac{b}{a}\sqrt{a^2 - x^2}$ for A as shown.

b Show that the seating area is given by $A(x) = \dfrac{4bx}{a}\sqrt{a^2 - x^2}$.

c Show that $A'(x) = 0$ when $x = \dfrac{a}{\sqrt{2}}$.

d Prove that the seating area is a maximum when $x = \dfrac{a}{\sqrt{2}}$.

e Given that the area of the ellipse is πab, what percentage of the ground is occupied by the seats in the optimum case?

H   ECONOMIC MODELS

Suppose we have a **cost function** $C(x)$ where $C(x)$ is the cost of producing x items of a product.

The **marginal cost** is the instantaneous rate of change in cost with respect to x, the number of items, i.e., $C'(x)$ and is the slope function of the cost function.

We saw that a typical cost function was modelled by a polynomial.

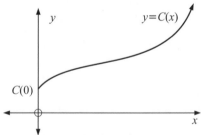

AVERAGE COST FUNCTIONS

Many manufacturers will be interested in gearing production so that the **average cost** of an item is minimised.

$A(x) = \dfrac{C(x)}{x}$ is the cost per item when x of them are made.

Notice that $\dfrac{C(x)}{x}$ is the slope of the line from $O(0,0)$ to $y = C(x)$.

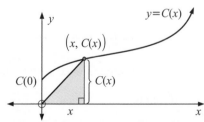

From the graph it appears that the average cost is a minimum when

average cost = marginal cost.

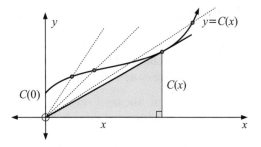

This is easily checked using calculus.

$$A(x) = \frac{C(x)}{x} \quad \therefore \quad A'(x) = \frac{C'(x)x - C(x) \times 1}{x^2} \quad \text{and}$$

$$A'(x) = 0 \quad \text{when} \qquad xC'(x) = C(x)$$

$$\text{i.e.,} \quad C'(x) = \frac{C(x)}{x}$$

$$\text{i.e.,} \quad C'(x) = A(x)$$

So,　　　　average cost is a minimum when　marginal cost = average cost

---

Example 19

For the cost model $C(x) = 0.000\,13x^3 + 0.002x^2 + 5x + 2200$:

a   find the average cost function and draw a sketch graph of it.

b   At what production level is average cost minimised?

---

a $A(x) = \dfrac{C(x)}{x} = 0.000\,13x^2 + 0.002x + 5 + \dfrac{2200}{x}$ dollars/item

```
A(x)
 40
 30
 20
 10
      0    100    200    300    400    500    x
```

b $C'(x) = 0.000\,39x^2 + 0.004x + 5$

Now $C'(x) = A(x)$ when

$$0.000\,39x^2 + 0.004x + 5 = 0.000\,13x^2 + 0.002x + 5 + \frac{2200}{x}$$

i.e., $0.000\,26x^2 + 0.002x - \dfrac{2200}{x} = 0$

i.e., $x \doteqdot 201$

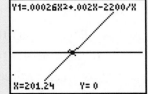

DEMAND, REVENUE AND PROFIT FUNCTIONS

Suppose $p(x)$ is the price per item that the business charges when selling x items. $p(x)$ is called the **demand function** (or **price function**) and is a decreasing function as cost of production reduces as volume increases.

If we sell x items the total revenue raised would be $R(x) = xp(x)$ where $R(x)$ is called the **revenue function** (or **sales function**).

Finally, if x items are sold, the total profit is $P(x) = R(x) - C(x)$ and $P(x)$ is called the **profit function**.

Note:
- The rate of change in revenue $R'(x)$ is the **marginal revenue function**.
- The rate of change in profit $P'(x)$ is the **marginal profit function**.

MAXIMISING PROFIT

Profit is maximised when $P'(x) = 0$.

Since $P(x) = R(x) - C(x)$ then $P'(x) = R'(x) - C'(x)$.

$\therefore$ $P'(x) = 0$ when $R'(x) = C'(x)$ i.e., marginal revenue = marginal cost

By the **second derivative test**,

as $P''(x) = R''(x) - C''(x)$

we require $P''(x) < 0$

i.e., $R''(x) - C''(x) < 0$

i.e., $R''(x) < C''(x)$

Example 20

For cost function $C(x) = 0.000\,13x^3 + 0.002x^2 + 5x + 2200$ dollars and demand function $p(x) = 36.5 - 0.008x$ dollars, $x \geqslant 0$:

a state the revenue function and find the marginal revenue function.
b What level of production will maximise profits?

a $R(x) = xp(x) = 36.5x - 0.008x^2$

and $R'(x) = 36.5 - 0.016x$

b If $C'(x) = R'(x)$ then

$0.000\,39x^2 + 0.004x + 5 = 36.5 - 0.016x$

$\therefore$ $0.000\,39x^2 + 0.02x - 31.5 = 0$

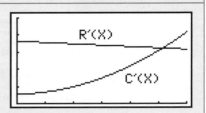

which has solutions $x \doteqdot -315.07$ or 259.71

But $x \geqslant 0$, so $C'(x) = R'(x)$ only when $x \doteqdot 260$

And as $R''(x) = -0.016$ and $C''(x) = 0.000\,78x + 0.004$

$R''(260) = -0.016$ and $C''(260) \doteqdot 0.207$

i.e., $R''(260) < C''(260)$

So maximum profit is made when 260 items are produced.

EXERCISE 22H

1 $C(x) = 38\,000 + 250x + x^2$ dollars is the cost function for producing x items. Find:

    a   the cost, average cost per item and marginal cost for producing 800 items

    b   the production level needed to minimise average cost and the corresponding average cost.

2   A cost function for producing x items is $C(x) = 295 + 24x - 0.08x^2 + 0.0008x^3$ dollars. Find:

    a   the average cost and marginal cost functions   **b**   the minimum average cost

    c   the minimum marginal cost.

3   A small manufacturer can produce x fittings per day where $0 \leqslant x \leqslant 10\,000$. The costs are:

    • $1000 per day for the workers   • $2 per day per fitting

    • $\$\dfrac{5000}{x}$ per day for running costs and maintenance.

    How many fittings should be produced daily to minimise costs?

4   For the cost function $C(x) = 720 + 4x + 0.02x^2$ dollars and price function $p(x) = 15 - 0.002x$ dollars, find the production level that will maximise profits.

5   The total cost of producing x blankets per day is $\frac{1}{4}x^2 + 8x + 20$ dollars and each blanket may be sold at $(23 - \frac{1}{2}x)$ dollars.

    How many blankets should be produced per day to maximise the total profit?

6   The cost of running a boat is $\dfrac{v^2}{10}$ dollars per hour where v is the speed of the boat.

    All other costs amount to $62.50 per hour. Find the speed which will minimise the total cost per kilometre.

I   IMPLICIT DIFFERENTIATION

For relations such as $y^3 + 3xy^2 - xy + 11 = 0$ it is often difficult or impossible to make y the subject of the formula. Such relationships between x and y are called **implicit relations**.

To gain insight into how such relations can be differentiated we will examine a familiar case.

Consider the circle with centre (0, 0) and radius 2.

The equation of the circle is $x^2 + y^2 = 4$.

Suppose A(x, y) lies on the circle.

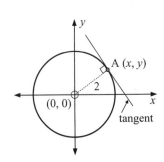

The radius OA has slope $= \dfrac{y\text{-step}}{x\text{-step}} = \dfrac{y - 0}{x - 0} = \dfrac{y}{x}$

$\therefore$ the tangent at A has slope $-\dfrac{x}{y}$ {the negative reciprocal}

Thus $\dfrac{dy}{dx} = -\dfrac{x}{y}$ for all points (x, y) on the circle.

This result was achievable because of a circle property.

In general implicit relations do not have a simple means of finding $\dfrac{dy}{dx}$ as in the case of a circle.

Another way of finding $\dfrac{dy}{dx}$ for a circle is to split the relation into two parts.

As $x^2 + y^2 = 4$, then $y^2 = 4 - x^2$ and so $y = \pm\sqrt{4 - x^2}$.

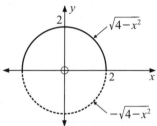

Case 1:

$y = \sqrt{4 - x^2} = (4 - x^2)^{\frac{1}{2}}$

$\therefore \quad \dfrac{dy}{dx} = \frac{1}{2}(4 - x^2)^{-\frac{1}{2}} \times (-2x)$

$\qquad = \dfrac{-x}{\sqrt{4 - x^2}}$

$\qquad = -\dfrac{x}{y}$

Case 2:

$y = -\sqrt{4 - x^2} = -(4 - x^2)^{\frac{1}{2}}$

$\therefore \quad \dfrac{dy}{dx} = -\frac{1}{2}(4 - x^2)^{-\frac{1}{2}} \times (-2x)$

$\qquad = \dfrac{x}{\sqrt{4 - x^2}}$

$\qquad = \dfrac{x}{-y}$

So, $\dfrac{dy}{dx} = -\dfrac{x}{y}$ (both cases).   The question is: *"Is there a better way of finding $\dfrac{dy}{dx}$?"*

IMPLICIT DIFFERENTIATION

The process by which we differentiate implicit functions is called **implicit differentiation**. We simply **differentiate term-by-term** across the equation.

For example,   if $x^2 + y^2 = 4$ then $\dfrac{d}{dx}(x^2) + \dfrac{d}{dx}(y^2) = \dfrac{d}{dx}(4)$

$$\therefore \quad 2x + 2y\dfrac{dy}{dx} = 0 \quad \text{and so,} \quad \dfrac{dy}{dx} = -\dfrac{x}{y}$$

Note: $\dfrac{d}{dx}(y^n) = ny^{n-1}\dfrac{dy}{dx}$ using the *chain rule*.

Example 21

If y is a function of x find: **a** $\dfrac{d}{dx}(y^3)$ **b** $\dfrac{d}{dx}\left(\dfrac{1}{y}\right)$ **c** $\dfrac{d}{dx}(xy^2)$

---

a $\dfrac{d}{dx}(y^3) = 3y^2\dfrac{dy}{dx}$ **b** $\dfrac{d}{dx}\left(\dfrac{1}{y}\right) = \dfrac{d}{dx}(y^{-1}) = -y^{-2}\dfrac{dy}{dx}$

c $\dfrac{d}{dx}(xy^2) = 1 \times y^2 + x \times 2y\dfrac{dy}{dx}$ {product rule}

$\qquad\qquad = y^2 + 2xy\dfrac{dy}{dx}$

EXERCISE 22I

1 If y is a function of x, find:

    a $\dfrac{d}{dx}(2y)$
    b $\dfrac{d}{dx}(-3y)$
    c $\dfrac{d}{dx}(y^3)$
    d $\dfrac{d}{dx}(\dfrac{1}{y})$
    e $\dfrac{d}{dx}(y^4)$

    f $\dfrac{d}{dx}(\sqrt{y})$
    g $\dfrac{d}{dx}\left(\dfrac{1}{y^2}\right)$
    h $\dfrac{d}{dx}(xy)$
    i $\dfrac{d}{dx}(x^2 y)$
    j $\dfrac{d}{dx}(xy^2)$

Example 22

Find $\dfrac{dy}{dx}$ if: **a** $x^2 + y^3 = 8$ **b** $x + x^2 y + y^3 = 100$

a $x^2 + y^3 = 8$

$\therefore \dfrac{d}{dx}(x^2) + \dfrac{d}{dx}(y^3) = \dfrac{d}{dx}(8)$

i.e., $2x + 3y^2 \dfrac{dy}{dx} = 0$

$\therefore \quad 3y^2 \dfrac{dy}{dx} = -2x$

$\therefore \quad \dfrac{dy}{dx} = \dfrac{-2x}{3y^2}$

b $x + x^2 y + y^3 = 100$

$\therefore \dfrac{d(x)}{dx} + \dfrac{d}{dx}(x^2 y) + \dfrac{d}{dx}(y^3) = \dfrac{d}{dx}(100)$

$\therefore \quad 1 + \left[2xy + x^2 \dfrac{dy}{dx}\right] + 3y^2 \dfrac{dy}{dx} = 0$

$\uparrow$ {product rule}

$\therefore \quad (x^2 + 3y^2)\dfrac{dy}{dx} = -1 - 2xy$

$\therefore \quad \dfrac{dy}{dx} = \dfrac{-1 - 2xy}{x^2 + 3y^2}$

---

2 Find $\dfrac{dy}{dx}$ if:
a $x^2 + y^2 = 25$
b $x^2 + 3y^2 = 9$
c $y^2 - x^2 = 8$

d $x^2 - y^3 = 10$
e $x^2 + xy = 4$
f $x^3 - 2xy = 5$

Example 23

Find the slope of the tangent to $x^2 + y^3 = 5$ at the point where $x = 2$.

First we find $\dfrac{dy}{dx}$,   i.e., $2x + 3y^2 \dfrac{dy}{dx} = 0$ {implicit differentiation}

$\therefore \quad 3y^2 \dfrac{dy}{dx} = -2x$ and so $\dfrac{dy}{dx} = \dfrac{-2x}{3y^2}$

But when $x = 2$, $4 + y^3 = 5$ and $\therefore$ $y = 1$

Consequently $\dfrac{dy}{dx} = \dfrac{-2(2)}{3(1)^2} = -\dfrac{4}{3}$

So, the slope of the tangent at $x = 2$ is $-\dfrac{4}{3}$.

---

3 Find the slope of the tangent to:

    a $x + y^3 = 4y$ at $y = 1$ **b** $x + y = 8xy$ at $x = \frac{1}{2}$

REVIEW SET 22A

1 A particle P, moves in a straight line with position relative to the origin O given by
$s(t) = 2t^3 - 9t^2 + 12t - 5$ cm,   where t is the time in seconds $(t \geqslant 0)$.

  a Find expressions for the particle's velocity and acceleration and draw sign diagrams for each of them.

  b Find the initial conditions.

  c Describe the motion of the particle at time $t = 2$ seconds.

  d Find the times and positions where the particle changes direction.

  e Draw a diagram to illustrate the motion of P.

  f Determine the time intervals when the particle's speed is increasing.

2 The cost per hour of running a freight train is given by $C(v) = 10v + \dfrac{90}{v}$ dollars where v is the average speed of the train.

  a Find the cost of running the train for:

    i two hours at 15 kmph   **ii** 5 hours at 24 kmph.

  b Find the rate of change in the cost of running the train at speeds of:

    i 10 kmph   **ii** 6 kmph.

  c At what speed will the cost be a minimum?

3 For the function $f(x) = 2x^3 - 3x^2 - 36x + 7$:

  a find and classify all stationary points and points of inflection

  b find intervals where the function is increasing and decreasing

  c find intervals where the function is concave up/down

  d sketch the graph of $y = f(x)$,   showing all important features.

4 Rectangle ABCD is inscribed within the parabola $y = k - x^2$ and the x-axis, as shown.

  a If OD $= x$,   show that the rectangle ABCD has area function $A(x) = 2kx - 2x^3$.

  b If the area of ABCD is a maximum when AD $= 2\sqrt{3}$,   find k.

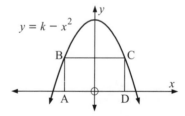

5 A manufacturer of open steel boxes has to make one with a square base and a volume of 1 m³. The steel costs \$2 per square metre.

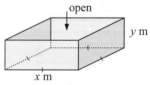

  a If the base measures x m by x m and the height is y m, find y in terms of x.

  b Hence, show that the total cost of the steel is $C(x) = 2x^2 + \dfrac{8}{x}$ dollars.

  c Find the dimensions of the box costing the manufacturer least to make.

6 **a** Find $\dfrac{dy}{dx}$ given that $x^2y + 2xy^3 = -18$.

  b Find the equation of the tangent to $x^2y + 2xy^3 = -18$ at the point $(1, -2)$.

REVIEW SET 22B

REVIEW SET 22B

Click on the icon to obtain printable review sets and answers

Chapter **23**

Derivatives of exponential and logarithmic functions

Contents:

The simplest **exponential functions** are of the form $f(x) = a^x$ where a is any positive constant, $a \neq 1$.

All members of the exponential family $f(x) = a^x$ have the properties that:

- their graphs pass through the point $(0, 1)$
- their graphs are asymptotic to the x-axis at one end
- their graphs are above the x-axis for all values of x
- their graphs are concave up for all x
- their graphs are increasing for $a > 1$ and decreasing for $0 < a < 1$.

For example,

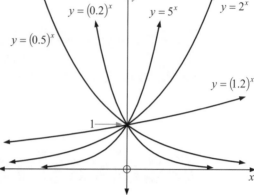

A | DERIVATIVES OF EXPONENTIAL FUNCTIONS

INVESTIGATION 1   THE DERIVATIVE OF $y = a^x$

This investigation could be done by using a **graphics calculator** or by clicking on the icon for a **computer** method.

The purpose of this investigation is to observe the nature of the derivative of $f(x) = a^x$ for $a = 2, 3, 4, 5, \frac{1}{2}$ and $\frac{1}{4}$.

CALCULUS DEMO

MODELLING SOFTWARE

What to do:

1 For $y = 2^x$ find the gradient of the tangent at $x = 0, 0.5, 1,$ 1.5, 2 and 2.5. Use modelling techniques from your graphics calculator or by clicking on the icon to show that

$$\frac{dy}{dx} \doteqdot 0.693 \times 2^x.$$

2 Repeat **1** for $y = 3^x$.
3 Repeat **1** for $y = 5^x$.
4 Repeat **1** for $y = (0.5)^x$.
5 Use **1, 2, 3** and **4** to help write a statement about the derivative of the general exponential $y = a^x$ for $a > 0, a \neq 1$.

From the previous investigation you should have discovered that:

- if $f(x) = a^x$ then $f'(x) = ka^x$ where k is a constant
- k is the derivative of $y = a^x$ at $x = 0$, i.e., $k = f'(0)$.

This result is easily proved algebraically.

If $f(x) = a^x$, then $f'(x) = \lim\limits_{h \to 0} \dfrac{f(x+h) - f(x)}{h}$ {first principles definition}

$$= \lim\limits_{h \to 0} \dfrac{a^{x+h} - a^x}{h}$$

$$= \lim\limits_{h \to 0} \dfrac{a^x(a^h - 1)}{h}$$

$$= a^x \times \left(\lim\limits_{h \to 0} \dfrac{a^h - 1}{h} \right)$$ {as a^x is independent of h}

But $f'(0) = \lim\limits_{h \to 0} \dfrac{f(0+h) - f(0)}{h}$

$$= \lim\limits_{h \to 0} \dfrac{a^h - 1}{h}$$

$$\therefore \quad f'(x) = a^x f'(0)$$

At this stage we realise that if we can find a value of a such that $f'(0) = 1$, then we have found *a function which is its own derivative*.

INVESTIGATION 2   **FINDING a WHEN $y = a^x$ AND $\dfrac{dy}{dx} = a^x$**

Click on the icon to graph $f(x) = a^x$ and its derivative function $y = f'(x)$.   **DEMO**

Experiment with different values of a until the graphs of $f(x) = a^x$ and $y = f'(x)$ are the same.

Because of the nature of this investigation only an approximate value of a (to 2 decimal places) can be found.

From **Investigation 2** you should have discovered that if $a \doteqdot 2.72$ and $f(x) = a^x$ then $f'(x) = a^x$ also.

To find this value of a more accurately we could return to the algebraic approach.

We showed that if $f(x) = a^x$ then $f'(x) = a^x \left(\lim\limits_{h \to 0} \dfrac{a^h - 1}{h} \right)$.

So if $f'(x) = a^x$ we require $\lim\limits_{h \to 0} \dfrac{a^h - 1}{h} = 1$.

Now if $\lim\limits_{h \to 0} \dfrac{a^h - 1}{h} = 1$ then roughly speaking,

$$\dfrac{a^h - 1}{h} \doteqdot 1 \quad \text{for values of } h \text{ which are close to } 0$$

$$\therefore \quad a^h \doteqdot 1 + h \quad \text{for } h \text{ close to } 0.$$

Thus $a^{\frac{1}{n}} \doteq 1 + \dfrac{1}{n}$ for large values of n $\{h = \dfrac{1}{n} \to 0$ as $n \to \infty\}$

$\therefore$ $a \doteq \left(1 + \dfrac{1}{n}\right)^{n}$ for large values of n.

We now examine $\left(1 + \dfrac{1}{n}\right)^{n}$ as $n \to \infty$.

Notice:

n	$\left(1+\dfrac{1}{n}\right)^{n}$	n	$\left(1+\dfrac{1}{n}\right)^{n}$
10	$2.593\,742\,460$	10^{7}	$2.718\,281\,693$
10^{2}	$2.704\,813\,829$	10^{8}	$2.718\,281\,815$
10^{3}	$2.716\,923\,932$	10^{9}	$2.718\,281\,827$
10^{4}	$2.718\,145\,927$	10^{10}	$2.718\,281\,828$
10^{5}	$2.718\,268\,237$	10^{11}	$2.718\,281\,828$
10^{6}	$2.718\,280\,469$	10^{12}	$2.718\,281\,828$

In fact as $n \to \infty$, $\left(1 + \dfrac{1}{n}\right)^{n} \to 2.718\,281\,828\,459\,045\,235 \ldots.$

and this irrational number is given the symbol e to represent it,

i.e., $e = 2.718\,281\,828\,459\,045\,235 \ldots.$ and is called **exponential** e.

Thus,   if $f(x) = e^{x}$ then $f'(x) = e^{x}$.

We have discussed $y = e^{x}$ near to the origin. But, what happens to the graph for large positive and negative x-values?

Notice that $\dfrac{dy}{dx} = e^{x} = y$.

For x large and positive, we write $x \to \infty$.

As $y = e^{x}$, $y \to \infty$ very rapidly.

So $\dfrac{dy}{dx} \to \infty$.

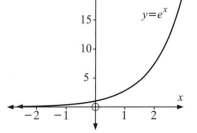

This means that the slope of the curve is very large for large x values.

For x large and negative, we write $x \to -\infty$.

As $y = e^{x}$, $y \to 0$ and so $\dfrac{dy}{dx} \to 0$.

This means for large negative x, the graph becomes flatter.

Observe that $e^{x} > 0$ for all x.

THE DERIVATIVE OF $e^{f(x)}$

Functions such as e^{-x}, e^{2x+3}, e^{-x^2}, $x^2 e^{2x}$, etc need to be differentiated in problem solving. How do we differentiate such functions?

Consider $y = e^{f(x)}$.

Now $y = e^u$ where $u = f(x)$.

But $\dfrac{dy}{dx} = \dfrac{dy}{du}\dfrac{du}{dx}$ {chain rule}

$\therefore \quad \dfrac{dy}{dx} = e^u \dfrac{du}{dx}$

$= e^{f(x)} \times f'(x)$

Add these additional rules to those found in **Chapter 21**.

Summary:

Function	Derivative
e^x	e^x
$e^{f(x)}$	$e^{f(x)} \times f'(x)$

Alternative notation: e^x is sometimes written as $\exp(x)$.

For example, $\exp(1-x) = e^{1-x}$.

Example 1

Find the slope function for y equal to:

a $2e^x + e^{-3x}$ **b** $x^2 e^{-x}$ **c** $\dfrac{e^{2x}}{x}$

a if $y = 2e^x + e^{-3x}$, then $\dfrac{dy}{dx} = 2e^x + e^{-3x}(-3)$

$= 2e^x - 3e^{-3x}$

b if $y = x^2 e^{-x}$, then $\dfrac{dy}{dx} = 2xe^{-x} + x^2 e^{-x}(-1)$ {product rule}

$= 2xe^{-x} - x^2 e^{-x}$

c if $y = \dfrac{e^{2x}}{x}$, then $\dfrac{dy}{dx} = \dfrac{e^{2x}(2)x - e^{2x}(1)}{x^2}$ {quotient rule}

$= \dfrac{e^{2x}(2x - 1)}{x^2}$

EXERCISE 23A

1 Find the slope function for $f(x)$ equal to:

a e^{4x} **b** $e^x + 3$ **c** $\exp(-2x)$ **d** $e^{\frac{x}{2}}$

e $2e^{-\frac{x}{2}}$ **f** $1 - 2e^{-x}$ **g** $4e^{\frac{x}{2}} - 3e^{-x}$ **h** $\dfrac{e^x + e^{-x}}{2}$

i e^{-x^2} **j** $e^{\frac{1}{x}}$ **k** $10(1 + e^{2x})$ **l** $20(1 - e^{-2x})$

m e^{2x+1} **n** $e^{\frac{x}{4}}$ **o** e^{1-2x^2} **p** $e^{-0.02x}$

2 Use the product or quotient rules to find the derivative of:

a xe^x

b $x^3 e^{-x}$

c $\dfrac{e^x}{x}$

d $\dfrac{x}{e^x}$

e $x^2 e^{3x}$

f $\dfrac{e^x}{\sqrt{x}}$

g $\sqrt{x}e^{-x}$

h $\dfrac{e^x + 2}{e^{-x} + 1}$

Example 2

Find the slope function of $f(x)$ equal to: **a** $(e^x - 1)^3$ **b** $\dfrac{1}{\sqrt{2e^{-x} + 1}}$

a $y = (e^x - 1)^3$

$\quad = u^3 \quad$ where $\quad u = e^x - 1$

$\dfrac{dy}{dx} = \dfrac{dy}{du}\dfrac{du}{dx}$

$\quad = 3u^2 \dfrac{du}{dx}$

$\quad = 3(e^x - 1)^2 \times e^x$

$\quad = 3e^x(e^x - 1)^2$

b $y = (2e^{-x} + 1)^{-\frac{1}{2}}$

$\quad = u^{-\frac{1}{2}} \quad$ where $\quad u = 2e^{-x} + 1$

$\dfrac{dy}{dx} = \dfrac{dy}{du}\dfrac{du}{dx}$

$\quad = -\tfrac{1}{2}u^{-\frac{3}{2}}\dfrac{du}{dx}$

$\quad = -\tfrac{1}{2}(2e^{-x} + 1)^{-\frac{3}{2}} \times 2e^{-x}(-1)$

$\quad = e^{-x}(2e^{-x} + 1)^{-\frac{3}{2}}$

---

3 Find the slope function of $f(x)$ equal to:

a $(e^x + 2)^4$

b $\dfrac{1}{1 - e^{-x}}$

c $\sqrt{e^{2x} + 10}$

d $\dfrac{1}{(1 - e^{3x})^2}$

e $\dfrac{1}{\sqrt{1 - e^{-x}}}$

f $x\sqrt{1 - 2e^{-x}}$

4 If $y = Ae^{kx}$, where A and k are constants:

a show that **i** $\dfrac{dy}{dx} = ky$ **ii** $\dfrac{d^2y}{dx^2} = k^2y$.

b Predict the connection between $\dfrac{d^n y}{dx^n}$ and y and prove your conjecture using the principle of mathematical induction.

5 If $y = 2e^{3x} + 5e^{4x}$, show that $\dfrac{d^2y}{dx^2} - 7\dfrac{dy}{dx} + 12y = 0$.

Example 3

Find the position and nature of any turning points of $y = (x - 2)e^{-x}$.

$\dfrac{dy}{dx} = (1)e^{-x} + (x - 2)e^{-x}(-1) \qquad$ {product rule}

$\quad = e^{-x}(1 - (x - 2))$

$\quad = \dfrac{3 - x}{e^x} \quad$ where $\quad e^x$ is positive for all x.

So, $\dfrac{dy}{dx} = 0$ when $x = 3$.

The sign diagram of $\dfrac{dy}{dx}$ is:

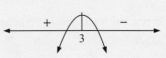

$\therefore$ at $x = 3$ we have a maximum turning point.

But when $x = 3$, $y = (1)e^{-3} = \dfrac{1}{e^3}$

$\therefore$ the maximum turning point is $(3, \dfrac{1}{e^3})$.

6 Find the position and nature of the turning point(s) of:

    a $y = xe^{-x}$ **b** $y = x^2 e^x$ **c** $y = \dfrac{e^x}{x}$ **d** $y = e^{-x}(x+2)$

B   USING NATURAL LOGARITHMS

Recall that:

- if $e^x = a$ then $x = \ln a$ and vice versa i.e., $e^x = a \iff x = \ln a$.

- The graph of $y = \ln x$ is the reflection of the graph of $y = e^x$ in the mirror line $y = x$.

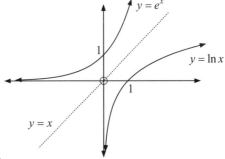

- $y = e^x$ and $y = \ln x$ are inverse functions.

- From the definition $\quad e^x = a \iff x = \ln a \quad$ we observe that $\quad e^{\ln a} = a$

    This means that: any positive real number can be written as a power of e,

    or alternatively,   the **natural logarithm** of any positive number is its power of e, i.e., $\ln e^n = n$.

Recall that the **laws of logarithms** in base e are identical to those for base 10.

These are: For $a > 0$, $b > 0$ • $\ln(ab) = \ln a + \ln b$

             • $\ln\left(\dfrac{a}{b}\right) = \ln a - \ln b$

             • $\ln(a^n) = n \ln a$ **Note:** $\ln e^n = n$

    Notice also that: • $\ln 1 = 0$ and $\ln e = 1$

             • $\ln\left(\dfrac{1}{a}\right) = -\ln a$

EXERCISE 23B (Mainly review)

1 Write as a natural logarithmic equation:

    a $N = 50e^{2t}$ **b** $P = 8.69e^{-0.0541t}$ **c** $S = a^2 e^{-kt}$

Example 4

Find, without a calculator, the exact values of: **a** $\ln e^3$ **b** $e^{3\ln 2}$

    a $\ln e^3$ **b** $e^{3\ln 2}$

       $= 3$ $= e^{\ln 2^3}$ {third log law}

                            $= e^{\ln 8}$ {as $2^3 = 8$}

                            $= 8$ {as $e^{\ln a} = a$}

---

2 Without using a calculator, evaluate:

    a $\ln e^2$ **b** $\ln \sqrt{e}$ **c** $\ln\left(\dfrac{1}{e}\right)$ **d** $\ln\left(\dfrac{1}{\sqrt{e}}\right)$

    e $e^{\ln 3}$ **f** $e^{2\ln 3}$ **g** $e^{-\ln 5}$ **h** $e^{-2\ln 2}$

3 Write as a power of e: **a** 2 **b** 10 **c** a **d** a^x

Example 5

Solve for x: **a** $e^x = 7$ **b** $e^x + 2 = 15e^{-x}$

    a $e^x = 7$ **b** $e^x + 2 = 15e^{-x}$

    $\therefore \quad \ln e^x = \ln 7$ $\therefore \quad e^x(e^x + 2) = 15e^{-x} \times e^x$

      $\therefore \quad x = \ln 7$ $\therefore \quad e^{2x} + 2e^x = 15$

                            $\therefore \quad e^{2x} + 2e^x - 15 = 0$

                       $\therefore \quad (e^x + 5)(e^x - 3) = 0$

                           $\therefore \quad e^x = -5$ or 3

                       $\therefore \quad x = \ln 3$ {as e^x cannot be -5}

---

4 Solve for x:

    a $e^x = 2$ **b** $e^x = -2$ **c** $e^x = 0$

    d $e^{2x} = 2e^x$ **e** $e^x = e^{-x}$ **f** $e^{2x} - 5e^x + 6 = 0$

    g $e^x + 2 = 3e^{-x}$ **h** $1 + 12e^{-x} = e^x$ **i** $e^x + e^{-x} = 3$

Notice that: $a^x = (e^{\ln a})^x = e^{(\ln a)x}$ $\therefore \quad \dfrac{d(a^x)}{dx} = e^{(\ln a)x} \times \ln a = a^x \ln a$

So,   if $y = a^x$ then $\dfrac{dy}{dx} = a^x \ln a$.

5 Find $\dfrac{dy}{dx}$ for   **a** $y = 2^x$ **b** $y = 5^x$ **c** $y = x2^x$

                      d $y = x^3 6^{-x}$ **e** $y = \dfrac{2^x}{x}$ **f** $y = \dfrac{x}{3^x}$

Example 6

Find algebraically, the points of intersection of $y = e^x - 3$ and $y = 1 - 3e^{-x}$.
Check your solution using technology.

The functions meet where

$$e^x - 3 = 1 - 3e^{-x}$$
$$\therefore \quad e^x - 4 + 3e^{-x} = 0$$
$$\therefore \quad e^{2x} - 4e^x + 3 = 0 \quad \{\text{multiplying each term by } e^x\}$$
$$\therefore \quad (e^x - 1)(e^x - 3) = 0$$
$$\therefore \quad e^x = 1 \text{ or } 3$$
$$\therefore \quad x = \ln 1 \text{ or } \ln 3$$
$$\therefore \quad x = 0 \text{ or } \ln 3$$

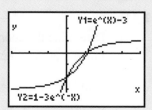

when $x = 0$, $y = e^0 - 3 = -2$
when $x = \ln 3$, $e^x = 3$ $\therefore$ $y = 3 - 3 = 0$
$\therefore$ functions meet at $(0, -2)$ and at $(\ln 3, 0)$.

6 Find algebraically, the point(s) of intersection of:

a $y = e^x$ and $y = e^{2x} - 6$ **b** $y = 2e^x + 1$ and $y = 7 - e^x$

c $y = 3 - e^x$ and $y = 5e^{-x} - 3$ Check your answers using technology.

Example 7

Consider the function $y = 2 - e^{-x}$.
a Find the x-intercept.   **b** Find the y-intercept.
c Show algebraically that the function is increasing for all x.
d Show algebraically that the function is concave down for all x.
e Use technology to help graph $y = 2 - e^{-x}$.
f Explain why $y = 2$ is a horizontal asymptote.

a Any graph cuts the x-axis when $y = 0$,   i.e., $0 = 2 - e^{-x}$
$$\therefore \quad e^{-x} = 2$$
$$\therefore \quad -x = \ln 2$$
$$\therefore \quad x = -\ln 2$$

The graph cuts the x-axis at $-\ln 2$ (or $\doteqdot -0.69$).

b The y-intercept occurs when $x = 0$ i.e., $y = 2 - e^0 = 2 - 1 = 1$.

c $\dfrac{dy}{dx} = 0 - e^{-x}(-1) = e^{-x} = \dfrac{1}{e^x}$

Now $e^x > 0$ for all x, $\therefore$ $\dfrac{dy}{dx} > 0$ for all x

$\therefore$ the function is increasing for all x.

d $\dfrac{d^2y}{dx^2} = e^{-x}(-1) = \dfrac{-1}{e^x}$ which is < 0 for all x

∴   the function is concave down for all x.

e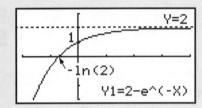

f   As $x \to \infty$, $e^x \to \infty$

and $e^{-x} \to 0$

∴ $2 - e^{-x} \to 2$

i.e., $y \to 2$ (below)

7   The function $y = e^x - 3e^{-x}$ cuts the x-axis at P and the y-axis at Q.

   a   Determine the coordinates of P and Q.

   b   Prove that the function is increasing for all x.

   c   Show that $\dfrac{d^2y}{dx^2} = y$.

      What can be deduced about the concavity of the function above and below the x-axis?

   d   Use technology to help graph $y = e^x - 3e^{-x}$.

      Show the features of **a**, **b** and **c** on the graph.

8 $f(x) = e^x - 3$ and $g(x) = 3 - 5e^{-x}$.

   a   Find the x and y-intercepts of both functions.

   b   Discuss $f(x)$ and $g(x)$ as $x \to \infty$ and as $x \to -\infty$.

   c   Find algebraically the point(s) of intersection of the functions.

   d   Sketch the graph of both functions on the same set of axes. Show all important features on your graph.

C   DERIVATIVES OF LOGARITHMIC FUNCTIONS

INVESTIGATION 3   THE DERIVATIVE OF $\ln x$

If $y = \ln x$,   what is the slope function?   CALCULUS GRAPHING PACKAGE

What to do:

1   Click on the icon to see the graph of $y = \ln x$

A tangent is drawn to a point on the graph and the slope of this tangent is given.

The graph of the slope of the tangent is displayed as the point on the graph of $y = \ln x$ is dragged.

2   What do you suspect the equation of the slope is?

3   Find the slope at $x = 0.25$, $x = 0.5$, $x = 1$, $x = 2$, $x = 3$, $x = 4$, $x = 5$.
Do your results confirm your suspicion from **2**?

From the investigation you should have observed that $\quad$ if $\;y = \ln x\;$ then $\;\dfrac{dy}{dx} = \dfrac{1}{x}.$

An algebraic proof of this fact is as follows.

Proof: $\quad$ As $\;y = \ln x\;$ then $\quad x = e^y\;$ and we differentiate with respect to x

$$\therefore \quad 1 = e^y\frac{dy}{dx} \quad \text{\{by the chain rule\}}$$

$$\therefore \quad 1 = x\frac{dy}{dx} \quad \text{\{as } e^y = x\text{\}}$$

$$\therefore \quad \frac{1}{x} = \frac{dy}{dx}$$

Also, if $\;y = \ln f(x)\;$ then $\;y = \ln u\;$ where $\;u = f(x).$

Now $\;\dfrac{dy}{dx} = \dfrac{dy}{du}\dfrac{du}{dx} = \dfrac{1}{u}f'(x) = \dfrac{f'(x)}{f(x)}$ $\qquad$ **Summary:**

Function	Derivative
$\ln x$	$\dfrac{1}{x}$
$\ln f(x)$	$\dfrac{f'(x)}{f(x)}$

Example 8

Find the slope function of: $\quad$ **a** $\;\; y = \ln(kx)\;\;$ where k is a constant
$\qquad\qquad\qquad\qquad\qquad$ **b** $\;\; y = \ln(1 - 3x) \qquad$ **c** $\;\; y = x^3 \ln x$

a $\quad$ If $\;y = \ln(kx),$

$\qquad$ then $\dfrac{dy}{dx} = \dfrac{k}{kx} \quad\begin{matrix}\longleftarrow f'(x)\\ \longleftarrow f(x)\end{matrix}$

$\qquad\qquad\qquad = \dfrac{1}{x}$

b $\quad$ If $\;y = \ln(1 - 3x),$

$\qquad$ then $\dfrac{dy}{dx} = \dfrac{-3}{1 - 3x} \quad\begin{matrix}\longleftarrow f'(x)\\ \longleftarrow f(x)\end{matrix}$

$\qquad\qquad\qquad = \dfrac{3}{3x - 1}$

c $\quad$ If $\;y = x^3 \ln x,\;$ then $\;\dfrac{dy}{dx} = 3x^2 \ln x + x^3\left(\dfrac{1}{x}\right) \quad$ {product rule}

$\qquad\qquad\qquad\qquad\qquad\qquad = 3x^2 \ln x + x^2$

$\qquad\qquad\qquad\qquad\qquad\qquad = x^2(3\ln x + 1)$

EXERCISE 23C

1 $\;$ Find the slope function of:

$\quad$ **a** $\;\; y = \ln(7x)$ $\qquad$ **b** $\;\; y = \ln(2x + 1)$ $\qquad$ **c** $\;\; y = \ln(x - x^2)$

$\quad$ **d** $\;\; y = 3 - 2\ln x$ $\qquad$ **e** $\;\; y = x^2 \ln x$ $\qquad$ **f** $\;\; y = \dfrac{\ln x}{2x}$

$\quad$ **g** $\;\; y = e^x \ln x$ $\qquad$ **h** $\;\; y = (\ln x)^2$ $\qquad$ **i** $\;\; y = \sqrt{\ln x}$

$\quad$ **j** $\;\; y = e^{-x} \ln x$ $\qquad$ **k** $\;\; y = \sqrt{x}\ln(2x)$ $\qquad$ **l** $\;\; y = \dfrac{2\sqrt{x}}{\ln x}$

2 Find $\dfrac{dy}{dx}$ for:

a $y = x \ln 5$

b $y = \ln(x^3)$

c $y = \ln(x^4 + x)$

d $y = \ln(10 - 5x)$

e $y = [\ln(2x + 1)]^3$

f $y = \dfrac{\ln(4x)}{x}$

g $y = \ln\left(\dfrac{1}{x}\right)$

h $y = \ln(\ln x)$

i $y = \dfrac{1}{\ln x}$

The laws of logarithms can help us to differentiate some logarithmic functions more easily.

Example 9

Differentiate with respect to x:

a $y = \ln(xe^{-x})$

b $y = \ln\left[\dfrac{x^2}{(x+2)(x-3)}\right]$

a As $y = \ln(xe^{-x})$, then
$$y = \ln x + \ln e^{-x} \quad \{\text{log of a product law}\}$$
$$\therefore \quad y = \ln x - x \quad \{\ln e^a = a\}$$

Differentiating with respect to x, we get $\dfrac{dy}{dx} = \dfrac{1}{x} - 1$

b As $y = \ln\left[\dfrac{x^2}{(x+2)(x-3)}\right]$ then $y = \ln x^2 - \ln[(x+2)(x-3)]$
$$= 2\ln x - [\ln(x+2) + \ln(x-3)]$$
$$= 2\ln x - \ln(x+2) - \ln(x-3)$$
$$\therefore \quad \dfrac{dy}{dx} = \dfrac{2}{x} - \dfrac{1}{x+2} - \dfrac{1}{x-3}$$

Note: Differentiating **b** using the rule $\dfrac{dy}{dx} = \dfrac{f'(x)}{f(x)}$ is extremely tedious and difficult.

3 After using logarithmic laws, differentiate with respect to x:

a $y = \ln\sqrt{1 - 2x}$

b $y = \ln\left(\dfrac{1}{2x+3}\right)$

c $y = \ln\left(e^x\sqrt{x}\right)$

d $y = \ln\left(x\sqrt{2 - x}\right)$

e $y = \ln\left(\dfrac{x+3}{x-1}\right)$

f $y = \ln\left(\dfrac{x^2}{3-x}\right)$

g $f(x) = \ln\left((3x-4)^3\right)$

h $f(x) = \ln\left(x(x^2+1)\right)$

i $f(x) = \ln\left(\dfrac{x^2 + 2x}{x - 5}\right)$

4 a Find $\dfrac{dy}{dx}$ for: i $y = \log_2 x$ ii $y = \log_{10} x$ iii $y = x\log_3 x$

b By substituting $e^{\ln 2}$ for 2 in $y = 2^x$ find $\dfrac{dy}{dx}$.

c Show that if $y = a^x$, then $\dfrac{dy}{dx} = a^x \times \ln a$

5 Consider $f(x) = \ln(2x - 1) - 3$.

   a Find the x-intercept.

   b Can $f(0)$ be found? What is the significance of this result?

   c Find the slope of the tangent to the curve at $x = 1$.

   d For what values of x does $f(x)$ have meaning?

   e Find $f''(x)$ and hence explain why $f(x)$ is concave down whenever $f(x)$ has meaning.

   f Graph the function.

6 Prove that $\dfrac{\ln x}{x} \leqslant \dfrac{1}{e}$ for all $x > 0$. (**Hint:** Let $f(x) = \dfrac{\ln x}{x}$ and find its greatest value.)

7 Consider the function $f(x) = x - \ln x$.

Show that the graph of $y = f(x)$ has a local minimum and that this is the only turning point. Hence prove that $\ln x \leqslant x - 1$ for all $x > 0$.

D   APPLICATIONS

The applications we consider here are:

- **tangents and normals**   • **rates of change**   • **curve properties**
- **displacement, velocity** and **acceleration**   • **optimisation (maxima/minima)**

EXERCISE 23D

1 Find the equation of the tangent to $y = e^{-x}$ at the point where $x = 1$.

2 Find the equation of the tangent to $y = \ln(2 - x)$ at the point where $x = -1$.

3 The tangent at $x = 1$ to $y = x^2 e^x$ cuts the x and y-axes at A and B respectively. Find the coordinates of A and B.

4 Find the equation of the normal to $y = \ln \sqrt{x}$ at the point where $y = -1$.

5 Find the equation of the tangent to $y = e^x$ at the point where $x = a$.

Hence, find the equation of the tangent to $y = e^x$ from the origin.

6 Consider $f(x) = \ln x$.

   a For what values of x is $f(x)$ defined?

   b Find the signs of $f'(x)$ and $f''(x)$ and comment on the geometrical significance of each.

   c Sketch the graph of $f(x) = \ln x$ and find the equation of the normal at the point where $y = 1$.

7 Find, correct to 2 decimal places, the angle between the tangents to $y = 3e^{-x}$ and $y = 2 + e^x$ at their point of intersection.

8 A radioactive substance decays according to the formula $W = 20e^{-kt}$ grams where t is the time in hours.

   a Find k given that the weight is 10 grams after 50 hours.

   b Find the weight of radioactive substance present at:

      i $t = 0$ hours   **ii** $t = 24$ hours   **iii** $t = 1$ week.

   c   How long will it take for the weight to reach 1 gram?

   d   Find the rate of radioactive decay at: i $t = 100$ hours   ii $t = 1000$ hours.

   e   Show that $\dfrac{dW}{dt}$ is proportional to the weight of substance remaining.

9 The temperature of a liquid after being placed in a refrigerator is given by
$T = 5 + 95e^{-kt}$ °C where k is a positive constant and t is the time in minutes.

   a   Find k if the temperature of the liquid is 20°C after 15 minutes.

   b   What was the temperature of the liquid when it was first placed in the refrigerator?

   c   Show that $\dfrac{dT}{dt}$ is directly proportional to $T - 5$.

   d   At what rate is the temperature changing at:

      i $t = 0$ mins   ii $t = 10$ mins   iii $t = 20$ mins?

10 The height of a certain species of shrub t years after it is planted is given by
$$H(t) = 20\ln(3t + 2) + 30 \text{ cm}, \ t \geqslant 0.$$

   a   How high was the shrub when it was planted?

   b   How long would it take for the shrub to reach a height of 1 m?

   c   At what rate is the shrub's height changing:

      i   3 years after being planted   ii   10 years after being planted?

11 In the conversion of sugar solution to alcohol, the chemical reaction obeys the law
$A = s(1 - e^{-kt})$, $t \geqslant 0$ where t is the number of hours after the reaction commenced,
s is the original sugar concentration (%) and A is the alcohol produced, in litres.

   a   Find A when $t = 0$.   b   If after 3 hours, $A = 5$ when $s = 10$, find k.

   c   Find the speed of the reaction at time 5 hours, when $s = 10$.

   d   Show that the speed of the reaction is proportional to $A - s$.

12 Consider the function $f(x) = \dfrac{e^x}{x}$.

   a   Does the graph of $y = f(x)$ have any x or y-intercepts?

   b   Discuss $f(x)$ as $x \to \infty$ and as $x \to -\infty$.

   c   Find and classify any stationary points of $y = f(x)$.

   d   Sketch the graph of $y = f(x)$ showing all important features.

   e   Find the equation of the tangent to $f(x) = \dfrac{e^x}{x}$ at the point where $x = -1$.

13 A particle P, moves in a straight line so that its displacement from the origin O, is given
by $s(t) = 100t + 200e^{-\frac{t}{5}}$ cm   where t is the time in seconds, $t \geqslant 0$.

   a   Find the velocity and acceleration functions.

   b   Find the initial position, velocity and acceleration of P.

   c   Discuss the velocity of P as $t \to \infty$.

   d   Sketch the graph of the velocity function.

   e   Find when the velocity of P is 80 cm per second.

14 A psychologist claims that the ability $A(t)$ to memorise simple facts during infancy
years can be calculated using the formula $A(t) = t\ln t + 1$ where $0 < t \leqslant 5$, t being

the age of the child in years.

   a At what age is the child's memorising ability a minimum?

   b Sketch the graph of $A(t)$ against t.

15 The most common function used in statistics is the *normal distribution function* given by $f(x) = \dfrac{1}{\sqrt{2\pi}} e^{-\frac{1}{2}x^2}$.

   a Find the stationary points of the function and find intervals where the function is increasing and decreasing.

   b Find all points of inflection.   **c** Discuss $f(x)$ as $x \to \infty$ and as $x \to -\infty$.

   d Sketch the graph of $y = f(x)$ showing all important features.

16 In making electric kettles, the manufacturer performs a cost control study and discovers that to produce x kettles the cost per kettle $C(x)$ is given by

$$C(x) = 4\ln x + \left(\frac{30 - x}{10}\right)^2 \quad \text{hundred dollars}$$

with a minimum production capacity per day of 10 kettles.

How many kettles should be manufactured to keep the cost per kettle a minimum?

17 Infinitely many rectangles which sit on the x-axis can be inscribed under the curve $y = e^{-x^2}$.

Determine the coordinates of C when rectangle ABCD has maximum area.

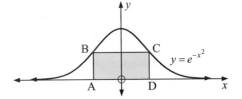

18 The revenue generated when a manufacturer sells x torches per day is given by $R(x) \doteqdot 1000\ln\left(1 + \dfrac{x}{400}\right) + 600$ dollars.

Each torch costs the manufacturer \$1.50 to produce plus fixed costs of \$300 per day. How many torches should be produced daily to maximise the profits made?

19 A quadratic of the form $y = ax^2$, $a > 0$, touches the logarithmic function $y = \ln x$.

   a If the x-coordinate of the point of contact is b, explain why $ab^2 = \ln b$ and $2ab = \dfrac{1}{b}$.

   b Deduce that the point of contact is $(\sqrt{e}, \frac{1}{2})$.

   c What is the value of a?

   d What is the equation of the common tangent?

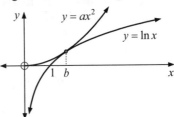

20 A small population of wasps is observed. After t weeks the population is modelled by

$$P(t) = \frac{50\,000}{1 + 1000e^{-0.5t}} \quad \text{wasps, where} \quad 0 \leqslant t \leqslant 25.$$

Find when the wasp population was growing fastest.

21 $f(t) = ate^{bt^2}$ has a maximum value of 1 when $t = 2$. Find constants a and b.

REVIEW SET 23A

1 Differentiate with respect to x:

    a $y = e^{x^3+2}$
    b $y = \dfrac{e^x}{x^2}$
    c $x^3 + xy^4 = xe^y$

2 Find the equation of the normal to $y = e^{-x^2}$ at the point where $x = 1$.

3 Sketch the graphs of $y = e^x + 3$ and $y = 9 - e^{-x}$ on the same set of axes.
Determine the coordinates of the points of intersection.

4 Consider the function $f(x) = \dfrac{e^x}{x-1}$.

    a Find the x and y-intercepts.
    b For what values of x is $f(x)$ defined?
    c Find the signs of $f'(x)$ and $f''(x)$ and comment on the geometrical significance of each.
    d Sketch the graph of $y = f(x)$ and find the equation of the tangent at the point where $x = 2$.

5 The height of a tree t years after it was planted is given by
$H(t) = 60 + 40\ln(2t + 1)$ cm, $t \geqslant 0$.

    a How high was the tree when it was planted?
    b How long would it take for the tree to reach: **i** 150 cm **ii** 300 cm?
    c At what rate is the tree's height increasing after: **i** 2 years **ii** 20 years?

6 A particle, P, moves in a straight line such that its position is given by
$s(t) = 80e^{-\frac{t}{10}} - 40t$ m where t is the time in seconds, $t \geqslant 0$.

    a Find the velocity and acceleration functions.
    b Find the initial position, velocity and acceleration of P.
    c Discuss the velocity of P as $t \to \infty$.
    d Sketch the graph of the velocity function.
    e Find when the velocity is -44 metres per second.

7 Infinitely many rectangles can be inscribed under the curve $y = e^{-x}$ as shown. Determine the coordinates of A when the rectangle OBAC has maximum area.

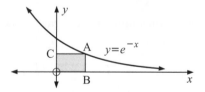

8 A shirt maker sells x shirts per day with revenue function

$$R(x) = 200\ln\left(1 + \frac{x}{100}\right) + 1000 \text{ dollars.}$$

The manufacturing costs are determined by the cost function
$C(x) = (x - 100)^2 + 200$ dollars. How many shirts should be sold daily to maximise profits? What is the maximum daily profit?

REVIEW SET 23B

REVIEW SET 23B

Click on the icon to obtain printable review sets and answers

Chapter 24

Derivatives of circular functions and related rates

Contents:

INTRODUCTION

Recall from **Chapter 13** that sine and cosine curves arise naturally from a consideration of motion in a circle.

Click on the icon to observe the motion of point P around the unit circle and observe the graphs of P's height relative to the x-axis and then P's displacement from the y-axis. The resulting graphs are those of $y = \cos t$ and $y = \sin t$.

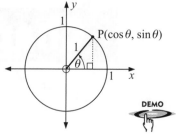

Suppose P moves anticlockwise around the unit circle with constant linear speed of 1 unit/second.

Then, after 2π seconds, P has covered 2π units which is one full revolution.

We therefore know that in t seconds P travels through t radians. Consequently at time t, P is at $(\cos t, \sin t)$.

Note: • The **angular velocity** of P is the time rate of change in $\angle AOP$,

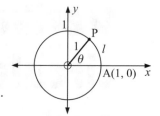

i.e., angular velocity of P is $\dfrac{d\theta}{dt}$ and

$\dfrac{d\theta}{dt} = 1$ radian/sec in the above circular motion.

 • If l is arc length AP, the **linear speed** of P is the time rate of change in l,

i.e., linear speed is $\dfrac{dl}{dt}$.

Notice that $l = r\theta = 1\theta = \theta$ and $\dfrac{dl}{dt} = \dfrac{d\theta}{dt} = 1$ radian/sec.

Angular velocity is only meaningful in motion along a circular or elliptical arc.

DERIVATIVES OF $\sin t$ AND $\cos t$

Click on the icon to observe the graph of $y = \sin t$ as a tangent of unit t-step moves across the curve. The y-step is translated onto the slope graph. Repeat for the graph of $y = \cos t$.

You should be able to guess what $(\sin t)'$ and $(\cos t)'$ are equal to.

From our observations from the previous computer demonstration we suspect that

$$(\sin t)' = \cos t \quad \text{and} \quad (\cos t)' = -\sin t.$$

$$\text{i.e.,} \quad \frac{d}{dt}(\sin t) = \cos t \quad \text{and} \quad \frac{d}{dt}(\cos t) = -\sin t$$

For completeness we will now look at a first principles argument to prove that

$$\frac{d}{dt}(\sin t) = \cos t.$$

Now consider the following algebraic argument as to why $\dfrac{d}{dx}(\sin x) = \cos x$.

A   DERIVATIVES OF CIRCULAR FUNCTIONS

We have already observed that in circular motion it appears that $\dfrac{d}{dt}(\sin t) = \cos t$ and

$\dfrac{d}{dt}(\cos t) = -\sin t$.

DERIVATIVES

Also we can use our moving tangent software to observe the same results.

Click on the icon to observe the result.

We will now look at the first principles argument to prove that $\dfrac{d}{dt}(\sin t) = \cos t$.

However, in order to differentiate trigonometric functions from first principles we require the following theorem.

Theorem: If θ is in radians, then $\displaystyle\lim_{\theta\to 0}\dfrac{\sin\theta}{\theta} = 1$.

INVESTIGATION   **EXAMINING $\dfrac{\sin\theta}{\theta}$ NEAR $\theta = 0$**

This investigation looks at $\dfrac{\sin\theta}{\theta}$ where θ is close to 0

graphically, numerically and geometrically. (θ is in radians).

DEMO

What to do:

1   Show that $f(\theta) = \dfrac{\sin\theta}{\theta}$ is an even function. What does this mean geometrically?

2   Since $\dfrac{\sin\theta}{\theta}$ is even we need only examine $\dfrac{\sin\theta}{\theta}$ for positive θ.

   a   What is the value of $\dfrac{\sin\theta}{\theta}$ when $\theta = 0$?

   b   Graph $y = \dfrac{\sin\theta}{\theta}$ for $-\dfrac{\pi}{2} \leqslant \theta \leqslant \dfrac{\pi}{2}$ using a graphics calculator or graphing package.

   c   Explain why the graph indicates that $\displaystyle\lim_{\theta\to 0}\dfrac{\sin\theta}{\theta} = 1$.

GRAPHING PACKAGE

3   Copy and complete, using your calculator:

   Extend your table to include negative values of θ which approach 0.

θ	$\sin\theta$	$\dfrac{\sin\theta}{\theta}$
1		
0.5		
0.1		
0.01		
0.001		
$\vdots$		

4   Explain why the area of the shaded segment is

$A = \tfrac{1}{2}r^2(\theta - \sin\theta)$.

Indicate how to use the given figure and the shaded area to show that, if θ is in radians and $\theta > 0$, then $\displaystyle\lim_{\theta\to 0}\dfrac{\sin\theta}{\theta} = 1$.

A more formal proof of the theorem follows.

Proof:

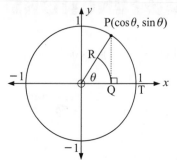

Suppose $P(\cos\theta, \sin\theta)$ lies on the unit circle in the first quadrant.

PQ is drawn perpendicular to the x-axis and arc QR, with centre O, is drawn.

Now, area of sector $OQR \leqslant$ area $\triangle OQP \leqslant$ area sector OTP

$$\therefore \quad \tfrac{1}{2}(OQ)^2 \times \theta \leqslant \tfrac{1}{2}(OQ)(PQ) \leqslant \tfrac{1}{2}(OT)^2 \times \theta$$

i.e., $\quad \tfrac{1}{2}\theta\cos^2\theta \leqslant \tfrac{1}{2}\cos\theta\sin\theta \leqslant \tfrac{1}{2}\theta$

$$\therefore \quad \cos\theta \leqslant \quad \frac{\sin\theta}{\theta} \quad \leqslant \frac{1}{\cos\theta}$$

{on dividing throughout by $\tfrac{1}{2}\theta\cos\theta$, which is positive}

Now as $\theta \to 0$, both $\cos\theta \to 1$ and $\dfrac{1}{\cos\theta} \to 1$ $\quad \therefore \quad \dfrac{\sin\theta}{\theta} \to 1$ also.

Thus, for $\theta > 0$ and in radians, $\displaystyle\lim_{\theta\to 0}\frac{\sin\theta}{\theta} = 1$.

Also, since $\dfrac{\sin\theta}{\theta}$ is an even function, as $f(-\theta) = f(\theta)$ for all θ,

then, for $\theta < 0$ and in radians, $\displaystyle\lim_{\theta\to 0}\frac{\sin\theta}{\theta} = 1$ also.

Thus $\qquad \displaystyle\lim_{\theta\to 0}\frac{\sin\theta}{\theta} = 1$.

THE DERIVATIVE OF $\sin x$

Consider $f(x) = \sin x$. $\quad$ Now $\quad f'(x) = \displaystyle\lim_{h\to 0}\frac{f(x+h) - f(x)}{h}$

$$= \lim_{h\to 0}\frac{\sin(x+h) - \sin x}{h}$$

$$= \lim_{h\to 0}\frac{2\cos\left(\frac{x+h+x}{2}\right)\sin\left(\frac{x+h-x}{2}\right)}{h}$$

$$= \lim_{h\to 0}\frac{2\cos\left(x+\frac{h}{2}\right)\sin\left(\frac{h}{2}\right)}{h}$$

$$= \lim_{h\to 0}\frac{2\cos\left(x+\frac{h}{2}\right)}{2} \times \frac{\sin\left(\frac{h}{2}\right)}{\frac{h}{2}}$$

$$= \cos x \times 1 \quad \left\{\text{as } h \to 0,\ \tfrac{h}{2} \to 0,\ \frac{\sin\frac{h}{2}}{\frac{h}{2}} \to 1\right\}$$

$$= \cos x$$

That is, $\qquad$ if $\ f(x) = \sin x\ $ then $\ f'(x) = \cos x$, $\ $ provided that x is in radians.

Note:
- At step (1) we have used $\ \sin S - \sin D = 2\cos\left(\frac{S+D}{2}\right)\sin\left(\frac{S-D}{2}\right)$

- At step (2) we have used $\ \displaystyle\lim_{\theta\to 0}\frac{\sin\theta}{\theta} = 1$; $\ $ as $\ h \to 0$, $\ \frac{h}{2} \to 0$ $\ $ also.

THE DERIVATIVE OF $\cos x$

Consider $y = \cos x = \sin\left(\frac{\pi}{2} - x\right)$ $\quad \{\sin(\frac{\pi}{2} - x) = \cos x\}$

$\therefore \quad y = \sin u \quad$ where $\quad u = \frac{\pi}{2} - x$

$\therefore \quad \dfrac{dy}{dx} = \dfrac{dy}{du}\dfrac{du}{dx} = \cos u \times (-1) \quad$ {chain rule}

$\qquad\qquad = -\cos u$

$\qquad\qquad = -\cos(\frac{\pi}{2} - x)$

$\qquad\qquad = -\sin x$

So, if $f(x) = \cos x$, then $f'(x) = -\sin x$. $\quad$ (x in radians)

THE DERIVATIVE OF $\tan x$

Consider $y = \tan x = \dfrac{\sin x}{\cos x}$ $\qquad u = \sin x, \quad v = \cos x$

Summary:

For x in radians

$\therefore \quad \dfrac{dy}{dx} = \dfrac{\cos x \cos x - \sin x(-\sin x)}{[\cos x]^2}$ {chain rule}

$\qquad = \dfrac{\cos^2 x + \sin^2 x}{\cos^2 x}$

$\qquad = \dfrac{1}{\cos^2 x}$ or $\sec^2 x$

DERIVATIVE DEMO

Function	Derivative
$\sin x$	$\cos x$
$\cos x$	$-\sin x$
$\tan x$	$\dfrac{1}{\cos^2 x} = \sec^2 x$

THE DERIVATIVES OF $\sin[f(x)]$, $\cos[f(x)]$ AND $\tan[f(x)]$

Consider $y = \sin[f(x)]$ where $f(x) = u$, say

i.e., $y = \sin u$

Now $\dfrac{dy}{dx} = \dfrac{dy}{du} \times \dfrac{du}{dx}$ $\quad$ {chain rule}

$\qquad = \cos u \times f'(x)$

$\qquad = \cos[f(x)] \times f'(x)$

Thus

Function	Derivative
$\sin[f(x)]$	$\cos[f(x)]f'(x)$
$\cos[f(x)]$	$-\sin[f(x)]f'(x)$
$\tan[f(x)]$	$\dfrac{f'(x)}{\cos^2[f(x)]}$

Example 1

Differentiate with respect to x: $\qquad$ **a** $\quad x\sin x$ $\qquad$ **b** $\quad 4\tan^2(3x)$

a If $y = x\sin x$,

then by the product rule

$\dfrac{dy}{dx} = (1)\sin x + (x)\cos x$

$\qquad = \sin x + x\cos x$

b If $y = 4\tan^2(3x) = 4[\tan(3x)]^2$

then by the chain rule

$\dfrac{dy}{dx} = 8[\tan(3x)]^1 \times \dfrac{d}{dx}[\tan(3x)]$

$\qquad = 8\tan(3x)\dfrac{3}{\cos^2(3x)}$

$\qquad = \dfrac{24\tan(3x)}{\cos^2(3x)}$

EXERCISE 24A

1 Find $\dfrac{dy}{dx}$ for:

    a $y = \sin(2x)$ **b** $y = \sin x + \cos x$ **c** $y = \cos(3x) - \sin x$

    d $y = \sin(x + 1)$ **e** $y = \cos(3 - 2x)$ **f** $y = \tan(5x)$

    g $y = \sin\left(\frac{x}{2}\right) - 3\cos x$ **h** $y = 3\tan(\pi x)$ **i** $y = 4\sin x - \cos(2x)$

2 Differentiate with respect to x:

    a $x^2 + \cos x$ **b** $\tan x - 3\sin x$ **c** $e^x \cos x$ **d** $e^{-x} \sin x$

    e $\ln(\sin x)$ **f** $e^{2x} \tan x$ **g** $\sin(3x)$ **h** $\cos\left(\dfrac{x}{2}\right)$

    i $3\tan(2x)$ **j** $x\cos x$ **k** $\dfrac{\sin x}{x}$ **l** $x\tan x$

3 Differentiate with respect to x:

    a $\sin(x^2)$ **b** $\cos(\sqrt{x})$ **c** $\sqrt{\cos x}$ **d** $\sin^2 x$

    e $\cos^3 x$ **f** $\cos x \sin(2x)$ **g** $\cos(\cos x)$ **h** $\cos^3(4x)$

    i $\dfrac{1}{\sin x}$ **j** $\dfrac{1}{\cos(2x)}$ **k** $\dfrac{2}{\sin^2(2x)}$ **l** $\dfrac{8}{\tan^3\left(\frac{x}{2}\right)}$

4 If $y = x^4$ then $\dfrac{dy}{dx} = 4x^3$, $\dfrac{d^2y}{dx^2} = 12x^2$, $\dfrac{d^3y}{dx^3} = 24x$, $\dfrac{d^4y}{dx^4} = 24$ and higher

    derivatives are all zero.   Consider $y = \sin x$.

    a Find $\dfrac{dy}{dx}, \dfrac{d^2y}{dx^2}, \dfrac{d^3y}{dx^3}, \dfrac{d^4y}{dx^4}$.   **b** Explain why $\dfrac{d^n y}{dx^n}$ can have four different values.

5   **a** If $y = \sin(2x + 3)$,   show that $\dfrac{d^2y}{dx^2} + 4y = 0$.

    b If $y = 2\sin x + 3\cos x$,   show that $y'' + y = 0$. $\left(y'' \text{ is } \dfrac{d^2y}{dx^2}\right)$

    c Show that the curve with equation $y = \dfrac{\cos x}{1 + \sin x}$ cannot have horizontal tangents.

Example 2

Find the equation of the tangent to $y = \tan x$ at the point where $x = \frac{\pi}{4}$.

    Let $f(x) = \tan x$ $f(\frac{\pi}{4}) = \tan\frac{\pi}{4} = 1$

    $\therefore \quad f'(x) = \dfrac{1}{\cos^2 x}$ $\therefore$ $f'(\frac{\pi}{4}) = \dfrac{1}{[\cos\left(\frac{\pi}{4}\right)]^2} = \dfrac{1}{\left(\frac{1}{\sqrt{2}}\right)^2} = 2$

So at $(\frac{\pi}{4}, 1)$, the tangent has slope 2

    $\therefore$ the equation is $\dfrac{y - 1}{x - \frac{\pi}{4}} = 2$ i.e., $y - 1 = 2x - \frac{\pi}{2}$

                                                     i.e., $y = 2x + \left(1 - \frac{\pi}{2}\right)$

6 Find the equation of:

   a the tangent to $y = \sin x$ at the origin

   b the tangent to $y = \tan x$ at the origin

   c the normal to $y = \cos x$ at the point where $x = \frac{\pi}{6}$

   d the normal to $y = \dfrac{1}{\sin(2x)}$ at the point where $x = \frac{\pi}{4}$.

Example 3

Find the rate of change in the area of triangle ABC when $\theta = 60°$ given that θ is a variable angle.

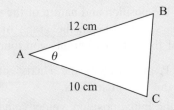

$$\text{Area} \quad A = \tfrac{1}{2} \times 10 \times 12 \times \sin\theta \qquad \{\text{Area} = \tfrac{1}{2}ab\sin C\}$$

$$\therefore \quad A = 60\sin\theta$$

$$\therefore \quad \frac{dA}{d\theta} = 60\cos\theta$$

and when $\theta = \frac{\pi}{3}$, $\cos\theta = \frac{1}{2}$ **Note:** θ is in radians

$$\therefore \quad \frac{dA}{d\theta} = 30 \text{ cm}^2 \text{ / radian}$$

---

7 In Indonesia large tides occur. The depth of water d metres at time t hours after midnight is given by $d = 9.3 + 6.8\cos(0.507t)$ metres.

   a Is the tide rising or falling at 8.00 am?

   b What is the rate of change in the depth of water at 8.00 am?

8 The voltage in a circuit is given by $V(t) = 340\sin(100\pi t)$ where t is the time in seconds. At what rate is the voltage changing:

   a when $t = 0.01$ **b** when $V(t)$ is a maximum?

(sin θ is a maximum when $\theta = \frac{\pi}{2}$)

9 A piston moves as a result of rod AP attached to a flywheel of radius 1 m. $AP = 2$ m. P has coordinates $(\cos t, \sin t)$.

   a Point A is $(-x, 0)$.

     Show that $x = \sqrt{4 - \sin^2 t} - \cos t$.

   b Find the rate at which x is changing at the instant when:

     i $t = 0$ **ii** $t = \frac{\pi}{2}$ **iii** $t = \frac{2\pi}{3}$

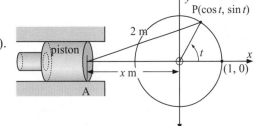

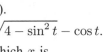

10 Determine the position and nature of the stationary points of $y = f(x)$ on the interval $0 \leqslant x \leqslant 2\pi$ and show them on a sketch graph of the function:

   a $y = \sin x$ **b** $y = \cos(2x)$ **c** $y = \sin^2 x$

11 Consider the function $f(x) = \dfrac{1}{\cos x}$ for $0 \leqslant x \leqslant 2\pi$.

    a For what values of x is $f(x)$ undefined in this interval?

    b Find the position and nature of any stationary points in this interval.

    c Prove that $f(x+2\pi) = f(x)$, $x \in \mathcal{R}$. What is the geometrical significance of this?

    d Sketch the graph of $y = \dfrac{1}{\cos x}$, $x \in [-\frac{\pi}{2}, \frac{5\pi}{2}]$ and show the stationary points on it.

12 Determine the position and nature of the stationary points of $y = \sin(2x) + 2\cos x$ on $0 \leqslant x \leqslant 2\pi$. Sketch the graph of the function on this interval, and show the positions of the stationary points you found on it.

13 A particle P, moves along the x-axis with position given by $x(t) = 1 - 2\cos t$ cm where t is the time in seconds.

    a State the initial position, velocity and acceleration of P.

    b Describe the motion when $t = \frac{\pi}{4}$ seconds.

    c Find the times when the particle reverses direction on $0 \leqslant t \leqslant 2\pi$ and find the position of the particle at these instances.

    d When is the particle's speed increasing on $0 \leqslant t \leqslant 2\pi$?

B   THE DERIVATIVES OF RECIPROCAL CIRCULAR FUNCTIONS

If $y = \csc x$, then $y = \dfrac{1}{\sin x} = u^{-1}$ $\therefore$ $\dfrac{dy}{dx} = -1u^{-2}\dfrac{du}{dx} = \dfrac{-1}{(\sin x)^2}\cos x$

    where $u = \sin x$

$$= -\frac{1}{\sin x}\frac{\cos x}{\sin x}$$

$$= -\csc x \cot x$$

Likewise, • if $y = \sec x$, then $\dfrac{dy}{dx} = \sec x \tan x$

    • if $y = \cot x$, then $\dfrac{dy}{dx} = -\csc^2 x$

Summary:

Function	Derivative
$\csc x$	$-\csc x \cot x$
$\sec x$	$\sec x \tan x$
$\cot x$	$-\csc^2 x$

Example 4

Find $\dfrac{dy}{dx}$ for: **a** $y = \csc(3x)$ **b** $y = \sqrt{\cot(\frac{x}{2})}$

a $y = \csc(3x)$

$\therefore$ $\dfrac{dy}{dx} = -\csc(3x)\cot(3x)\dfrac{d}{dx}(3x)$

$= -3\csc(3x)\cot(3x)$

b $y = \left(\cot(\frac{x}{2})\right)^{\frac{1}{2}}$

$\therefore$ $\dfrac{dy}{dx} = \frac{1}{2}\left(\cot(\frac{x}{2})\right)^{-\frac{1}{2}} \times -\csc^2(\frac{x}{2}) \times \frac{1}{2}$

$= \dfrac{-\csc^2(\frac{x}{2})}{4\sqrt{\cot(\frac{x}{2})}}$

EXERCISE 24B

1 a Prove using $y = (\cos x)^{-1}$, that $\dfrac{d}{dx}(\sec x) = \sec x \tan x$.

   b If $y = \cot x$, prove that $\dfrac{dy}{dx} = -\csc^2 x$ using the quotient rule.

2 Find $\dfrac{dy}{dx}$ for:

   a $y = x \sec x$ **b** $y = e^x \cot x$ **c** $y = 4 \sec(2x)$

   d $y = e^{-x} \cot(\frac{x}{2})$ **e** $y = x^2 \csc x$ **f** $y = x\sqrt{\csc x}$

   g $y = \ln(\sec x)$ **h** $y = x \csc(x^2)$ **i** $y = \dfrac{\cot x}{\sqrt{x}}$

3 Find the equation of the tangent to:

   a $y = \sec x$ at $x = \frac{\pi}{4}$ **b** $y = \cot(\frac{x}{2})$ at $x = \frac{\pi}{3}$

4 Find the equation of the normal to:

   a $y = \csc x$ at $x = \frac{\pi}{6}$ **b** $y = \sqrt{\sec(\frac{x}{3})}$ at $x = \pi$

C   THE DERIVATIVES OF INVERSE CIRCULAR FUNCTIONS

$y = \sin x$, $x \in [-\frac{\pi}{2}, \frac{\pi}{2}]$ is a 1-1 function and so has an inverse function f^{-1}.

This function is called

$$f^{-1}(x) = \arcsin x \quad \text{or} \quad \sin^{-1} x.$$

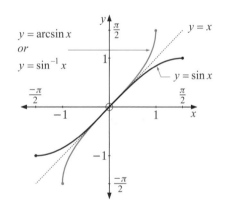

Likewise, $y = \cos x$, $x \in [0, \pi]$ has inverse function $f^{-1}(x) = \arccos x$ or $\cos^{-1} x$.

and $y = \tan x$, $x \in\,]-\frac{\pi}{2}, \frac{\pi}{2}[$ has inverse function $f^{-1}(x) = \arctan x$ or $\tan^{-1} x$.

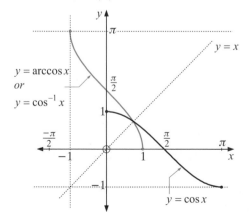

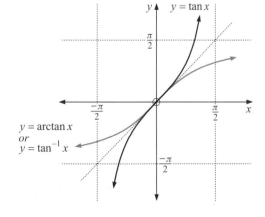

EXERCISE 24C.1

1 Use a calculator to check the graphs of $y = \arcsin x$, $y = \arccos x$ and $y = \arctan x$.

2 Find, giving your answer in radians:

  a $\arccos(1)$ **b** $\arcsin(-1)$ **c** $\arctan(1)$ **d** $\arctan(-1)$

  e $\arcsin(\frac{1}{2})$ **f** $\arccos(\frac{-\sqrt{3}}{2})$ **g** $\arctan(\sqrt{3})$ **h** $\arccos(-\frac{1}{\sqrt{2}})$

  i $\arctan(-\frac{1}{\sqrt{3}})$ **j** $\sin^{-1}(-0.767)$ **k** $\cos^{-1}(0.327)$ **l** $\tan^{-1}(-50)$

3 Find the exact solution of: **a** $\arcsin x = \frac{\pi}{3}$ **b** $\arctan(3x) = -\frac{\pi}{4}$

4 Use $\tan(\theta - \phi) = \dfrac{\tan\theta - \tan\phi}{1 + \tan\theta\tan\phi}$ to show that $\arctan(5) - \arctan(\frac{2}{3}) = \frac{\pi}{4}$.

DERIVATIVES OF INVERSE CIRCULAR FUNCTIONS

If $y = \arcsin x$ If $y = \arctan x$

then $x = \sin y$ then $x = \tan y$

$$\frac{dx}{dy} = \cos y = \sqrt{1 - \sin^2 y} \qquad\qquad \frac{dx}{dy} = \sec^2 y = 1 + \tan^2 y$$

$$\therefore \quad \frac{dx}{dy} = \sqrt{1 - x^2} \qquad\qquad\qquad \therefore \quad \frac{dx}{dy} = 1 + x^2$$

$$\therefore \quad \frac{dy}{dx} = \frac{1}{\sqrt{1 - x^2}}, \quad x \in\ ]-1, 1[\qquad \therefore \quad \frac{dy}{dx} = \frac{1}{1 + x^2}, \quad x \in \mathcal{R}$$

Note: From the chain rule, $\dfrac{dy}{dx}\dfrac{dx}{dy} = \dfrac{dy}{dy} = 1$.   So, $\dfrac{dy}{dx}$ and $\dfrac{dx}{dy}$ are reciprocals.

EXERCISE 24C.2

1 If $y = \arccos x$, show that $\dfrac{dy}{dx} = \dfrac{-1}{\sqrt{1 - x^2}}$, $x \in\ ]-1, 1[$

2 Find $\dfrac{dy}{dx}$ for:

  a $y = \arctan(2x)$ **b** $y = \arccos(3x)$ **c** $y = \arcsin(\frac{x}{4})$

  d $y = \arccos(\frac{x}{5})$ **e** $y = \arctan(x^2)$ **f** $y = \arccos(\sin x)$

3 Find $\dfrac{dy}{dx}$ for: **a** $y = x \arcsin x$ **b** $y = e^x \arccos x$ **c** $y = e^{-x} \arctan x$

4   **a** Prove that, if $y = \arcsin(\frac{x}{a})$, then $\dfrac{dy}{dx} = \dfrac{1}{\sqrt{a^2 - x^2}}$, for $x \in\ ]-a, a[$

  b Prove that, if $y = \arctan(\frac{x}{a})$, then $\dfrac{dy}{dx} = \dfrac{a}{a^2 + x^2}$, for $x \in \mathcal{R}$.

  c If $y = \arccos(\frac{x}{a})$, find $\dfrac{dy}{dx}$

5 Sonia approaches a painting which has its bottom edge 2 m above eye level and its top edge 3 m above eye level.

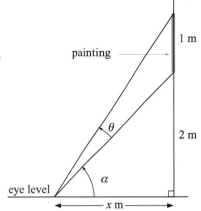

   a Given α and θ as in the diagram, find $\tan \alpha$ and $\tan(\alpha + \theta)$.

   b Find θ in terms of x only.
     Note: $\theta = (\alpha + \theta) - \alpha$.

   c Show that $\dfrac{d\theta}{dx} = \dfrac{2}{x^2 + 4} - \dfrac{3}{x^2 + 9}$ and

     hence find x when $\dfrac{d\theta}{dx} = 0$.

   d Interpret the result you have found in **c**.

D   MAXIMA/MINIMA WITH TRIGONOMETRY

Example 5

Two corridors meet at right angles and are 2 m and 3 m wide respectively. θ is the angle marked on the given figure and AB is a thin metal tube which must be kept horizontal as it moves around the corner from one corridor to the other without bending it.

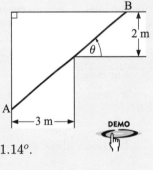

   a Show that the length AB, is given by $\quad L = \dfrac{3}{\cos \theta} + \dfrac{2}{\sin \theta}$

   b Show that $\dfrac{dL}{d\theta} = 0$ when $\theta = \arctan\left(\sqrt[3]{\tfrac{2}{3}}\right) \doteqdot 41.14^\circ$.

   c Find L when $\theta = \arctan\left(\sqrt[3]{\tfrac{2}{3}}\right)$ and comment on the significance of this value.

   a $\quad \cos \theta = \dfrac{3}{a}$ and $\sin \theta = \dfrac{2}{b}$ $\quad \therefore \quad a = \dfrac{3}{\cos \theta}$ and $b = \dfrac{2}{\sin \theta}$

     Now $\quad L = a + b = \dfrac{3}{\cos \theta} + \dfrac{2}{\sin \theta} = 3[\cos \theta]^{-1} + 2[\sin \theta]^{-1}$

   b $\quad \therefore \quad \dfrac{dL}{d\theta} = -3[\cos \theta]^{-2} \times (-\sin \theta) - 2[\sin \theta]^{-2} \times \cos \theta$

$$= \frac{3 \sin \theta}{\cos^2 \theta} - \frac{2 \cos \theta}{\sin^2 \theta}$$

$$= \frac{3 \sin^3 \theta - 2 \cos^3 \theta}{\cos^2 \theta \sin^2 \theta}$$

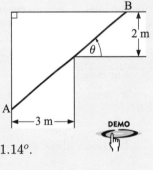

     Thus $\quad \dfrac{dL}{d\theta} = 0 \quad \Leftrightarrow \quad 3 \sin^3 \theta = 2 \cos^3 \theta$

                i.e., $\quad \tan^3 \theta = \tfrac{2}{3}$

                   $\therefore \quad \tan \theta = \sqrt[3]{\tfrac{2}{3}}$ and so $\theta = \arctan\left(\sqrt[3]{\tfrac{2}{3}}\right) \doteqdot 41.14^\circ$

c   *Sign diagram of* $\dfrac{dL}{d\theta}$:

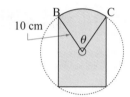

$$\frac{dL}{d\theta} \doteqdot -4.93 < 0, \quad \frac{dL}{d\theta} \doteqdot 9.06 > 0$$

Thus, AB is minimised when $\theta \doteqdot 41.14°$ and $L \doteqdot 7.023$ metres, and if we ignore the width of the rod, then the greatest length of rod able to be horizontally carried around the corner is of length 7.023 m.

EXERCISE 24D

1   A circular piece of tinplate of radius 10 cm has 3 segments removed (as illustrated). If θ is the measure of angle COB, show that the remaining area is given by $A = 50(\theta + 3\sin\theta)$.

   Hence, find θ to the nearest $\frac{1}{10}$ of a degree when the area A is a maximum.

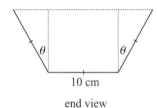

2   A symmetrical gutter is made from a sheet of metal 30 cm wide by bending it twice (as shown).

   For θ as indicated:

   a   deduce that the cross-sectional area is given by
   $$A = 100\cos\theta(1 + \sin\theta).$$

   b   Hence, show that $\dfrac{dA}{d\theta} = 0$ when $\sin\theta = \frac{1}{2}$ or -1.

   c   What value is θ if the gutter has maximum carrying capacity?

3   Hieu can row a boat across a circular lake of radius 2 km at 3 kmph. He can walk around the edge of the lake at 5 kmph.

   What is Hieu's longest possible time to get from P to R by rowing from P to Q and walking from Q to R?

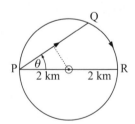

4   Fence AB is 2 m high and is 2 m from a house. XY is a ladder which touches the ground at X, the house at Y, and the fence at B.

   a   If L is the length of XY, show that
   $$L = \frac{2}{\cos\theta} + \frac{2}{\sin\theta}.$$

   b   Show that $\dfrac{dL}{d\theta} = \dfrac{2\sin^3\theta - 2\cos^3\theta}{\sin^2\theta\cos^2\theta}$

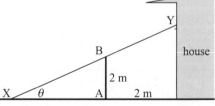

   c   What is the length of the shortest ladder XY which touches at X, B and Y?

5 In **Example 5**, suppose the corridors are those in a hospital and are 4 m wide and 3 m wide respectively. What is the maximum length of thin metal tube that can be moved around the corner? Remember it must be kept horizontal and must not be bent.

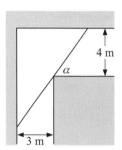

6 How far should X be from A if angle θ is to be a maximum?

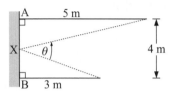

7 A and B are two homesteads. A pump house is to be located at P on the canal to pump water to both A and B.

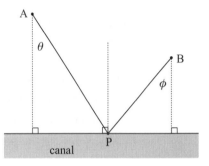

a If A and B are a km and b km from the canal respectively, show that:

$$AP + PB = \frac{a}{\cos \theta} + \frac{b}{\cos \phi} = L, \quad \text{say.}$$

b Show that $\dfrac{dL}{d\theta} = \dfrac{a \sin \theta}{\cos^2 \theta} + \dfrac{b \sin \phi}{\cos^2 \phi} \dfrac{d\phi}{d\theta}.$

c Explain why $a \tan \theta + b \tan \phi$ is a constant and hence show that $\dfrac{d\phi}{d\theta} = \dfrac{-a \cos^2 \phi}{b \cos^2 \theta}.$

d Hence, show that $\dfrac{dL}{d\theta} = 0 \quad \Leftrightarrow \quad \sin \theta = \sin \phi.$

e What can be deduced from **d**? (All reasoning must be given with an appropriate 'test'.)

E   RELATED RATES

If a 5 m ladder rests against a vertical wall with its feet on horizontal ground, and the ladder slips at A, the following diagram shows positions of the ladder at certain instances.

DEMO

Click on the icon to view the motion of the sliding ladder.

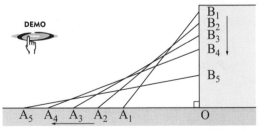

If $AO = x$ m and $OB = y$ m, then $x^2 + y^2 = 5^2$. {Pythagoras}

Differentiating this equation with respect to time, t,

gives $\qquad 2x \dfrac{dx}{dt} + 2y \dfrac{dy}{dt} = 0$

or $\qquad x \dfrac{dx}{dt} + y \dfrac{dy}{dt} = 0.$

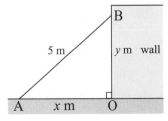

This equation is called a **differential equation** and describes the motion of the ladder at any instant.

Notice that $\dfrac{dx}{dt}$ is the rate of change in x with respect to time t, and is the velocity of A relative to point O.

Likewise, $\dfrac{dy}{dt}$ is the rate at which B moves downwards.

Observe that   • $\dfrac{dx}{dt}$ is *positive* as x is increasing   • $\dfrac{dy}{dt}$ is *negative* as y is decreasing.

Problems involving differential equations where one of the variables is t (time) are called **related rates** problems.

The method for solving such problems is:

Step 1:   Draw a large, clear diagram of the **general situation**. Sometimes two or more diagrams are necessary.

Step 2:   Write down the information, label the diagram(s) and make sure you distinguish between the **variables** and the **constants**.

Step 3:   Write down an **equation** connecting the variables.

Step 4:   **Differentiate** the equation with respect to t to obtain a **differential equation**.

Step 5:   Finally, solve for the **particular case** (some instant in time).

Example 6

A 5 m long ladder rests against a vertical wall with its feet on horizontal ground. The feet on the ground slip, and at the instant when they are 3 m from the wall, they are moving at 10 m/s. At what speed is the other end of the ladder moving at this instant?

We **must not** substitute the particular case values too early. The differential equation, in fully generalised form, must be established first.

Let OA $= x$ m and OB $= y$ m

$\therefore$ $x^2 + y^2 = 5^2$ {Pythagoras}

Differentiating with respect to t gives

$$2x\dfrac{dx}{dt} + 2y\dfrac{dy}{dt} = 0, \quad \text{i.e., } x\dfrac{dx}{dt} + y\dfrac{dy}{dt} = 0$$

Particular case: at the instant $\dfrac{dx}{dt} = 10$ m/s

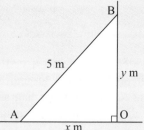

$\therefore$ $3(10) + 4\dfrac{dy}{dt} = 0$

$\therefore$ $\dfrac{dy}{dt} = -\dfrac{15}{2}$

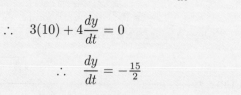

$\therefore$ y is decreasing at 7.5 m/s

Thus OB is decreasing at 7.5 m/s.

$\therefore$ B is moving down the wall at 7.5 m/s (at that instant).

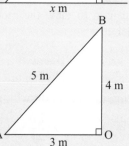

Checklist for finding relationships:	• Pythagoras' theorem.
	• Similar triangles, where corresponding sides are in proportion.
	• Right angled triangle trigonometry.
	• Sine and Cosine Rules.

EXERCISE 24E

1 a and b are variables related by the equation $ab^3 = 40$. At the instant when $a = 5$, b is increasing at 1 unit per second. What is happening to a at this instant?

2 The area of a variable rectangle remains constant at 100 cm^2. The length of the rectangle is decreasing at 1 cm per minute. At what rate is the breadth increasing at the instant when the rectangle is a square?

3 A stone is thrown into a lake and a circular ripple moves out at a constant speed of 1 m/s. Find the rate at which the circle's area is increasing at the instant when:

    a $t = 2$ seconds   **b** $t = 4$ seconds.

Example 7

The volume of a cube increases at a constant rate of 10 cm^3 per second. Find the rate of change in its total surface area at the instant when its sides are 20 cm long.

Let x cm be the lengths of the sides of the cube.

Now $A = 6x^2$ and $V = x^3$

$$\therefore \quad \frac{dA}{dt} = 12x\frac{dx}{dt} \quad \text{and} \quad \frac{dV}{dt} = 3x^2\frac{dx}{dt}$$

Particular case: at the instant when $x = 20$

$$\frac{dV}{dt} = 10 \qquad \therefore \quad 10 = 3 \times 20^2 \times \frac{dx}{dt}$$

$$\therefore \quad \frac{dx}{dt} = \tfrac{10}{1200} = \tfrac{1}{120} \text{ cm/s}$$

Thus $\dfrac{dA}{dt} = 12 \times 20 \times \tfrac{1}{120}$ cm^2/s $= 2$ cm^2/s

$\therefore$ the surface area is increasing at 2 cm^2 per second.

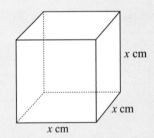

---

4 Air is being pumped into a spherical weather balloon at a constant rate of 6π m^3 per minute. Find the rate of change in its surface area at the instant when its radius is 2 m.

$[V = \tfrac{4}{3}\pi r^3 \quad \text{and} \quad A = 4\pi r^2.]$

5 For the given mass of gas in a cylinder $pv^{1.5} = 400$ where p is the pressure in N/m^2 and v is the volume in m^3.

If the pressure increases at 3 N/m^2 per minute, find the rate at which the volume is changing at the instant when the pressure is 50 N/m^2.

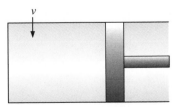

6 Wheat runs from a hole in a silo at a constant rate and forms a conical heap whose base radius is treble the height. If after 1 minute, the height of the heap is 20 cm, find the rate at which the height is rising at this instant. $[V_{cone} = \frac{1}{3}\pi r^2 h.]$

7 A trough of length 6 m has a uniform cross-section which is an equilateral triangle with sides 1 m. Water leaks from the bottom of the trough at a constant rate of 0.1 m³/min.

Find the rate at which the water level is falling at the instant when it is 20 cm deep.

end view

8 Two jet aeroplanes fly eastwards on a parallel course, 12 km apart, with air speeds of 200 m/s and 250 m/s respectively. How fast is their separation changing at the instant when the slower jet is 5 km ahead of the faster one?

9 A ground-level floodlight shines on a building and is located 40 m from the foot of the building. A 2 m tall person walks directly towards the building at 1 m/s. How fast is the person's shadow on the building shortening at the instant when the person is:

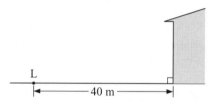

a 20 m from the building **b** 10 m from the building?

Example 8

Triangle ABC is right angled at A, and AB = 20 cm. The angle ABC increases at a constant rate of 1° per minute. At what rate is BC changing at the instant when angle ABC measures 30°?

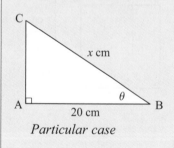

Particular case

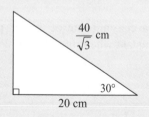

Let $\angle ABC = \theta$ and $BC = x$ cm

Now $\cos\theta = \dfrac{20}{x} = 20x^{-1}$

$\therefore \quad -\sin\theta \dfrac{d\theta}{dt} = -20x^{-2}\dfrac{dx}{dt}$

$\cos 30° = \dfrac{20}{x}$

$\therefore \quad \dfrac{\sqrt{3}}{2} = \dfrac{20}{x} \qquad \dfrac{d\theta}{dt} = 1° \text{ /min} = \frac{\pi}{180} \text{ radians/min}$

$\therefore \quad x = \frac{40}{\sqrt{3}}$

Thus $-\sin 30° \times \frac{\pi}{180} = -20 \times \dfrac{3}{1600} \times \dfrac{dx}{dt}$

$\therefore \quad -\frac{1}{2} \times \frac{\pi}{180} = -\frac{3}{80}\dfrac{dx}{dt}$

$\therefore \quad \dfrac{dx}{dt} = \frac{\pi}{360} \times \frac{80}{3} \text{ cm/min}$

$\doteqdot 0.2327 \text{ cm/min}$

$\therefore$ BC is increasing at 0.2327 cm/min.

10 A right angled triangle ABC has a fixed hypotenuse AC of length 10 cm, and side AB increases at 0.1 cm per second. At what rate is angle CAB increasing at the instant when the triangle is isosceles?

11 An aeroplane flies horizontally away from an observer at an altitude of 5000 m, with an air speed of 200 m/s. At what rate is its angle of elevation to the observer changing at the instant when the angle of elevation is: **a** 60° **b** 30°?

12 A rectangle PQRS has PQ of length 20 cm and QR increases at a constant rate of 2 cm/s. At what rate is the acute angle between the diagonals of the rectangle changing at the instant when QR is 15 cm long?

13 Triangle PQR is right angled at Q and PQ is 6 cm long. If QR increases at 2 cm per minute, find the rate of change in angle P at the instant when QR is 8 cm.

14 Two trains A and B leave X simultaneously at 120° to one another with constant speeds of 12 m/s and 16 m/s respectively. Find the rate at which the distance between them changes after 2 minutes.

15 AOB is a fixed diameter of a circle of radius 5 cm. A point P moves around the circle at a constant rate of 1 revolution in 10 seconds. Find the rate at which AP is changing at the instant when:

  a AP is 5 cm and increasing

  b P is at B.

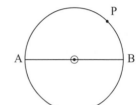

16 Shaft AB is 30 cm long and is attached to a flywheel at A. B is confined to motion along OX. The radius of the wheel is 15 cm, and the wheel rotates clockwise at 100 revolutions per second. Find the rate of change in angle ABO when angle AOX is:

  a 120° **b** 180°.

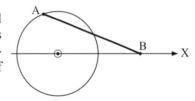

17 A farmer has a water trough of length 8 m which has a semi-circular cross-section of diameter 1 m. Water is pumped into the trough at a constant rate of 0.1 m^3 per minute.

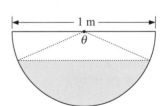

  a Show that the volume of water in the trough is given by $V = \theta - \sin\theta$ where θ is the angle as illustrated (in radians).

  b Find the rate at which the water level is rising at the instant when it is 25 cm deep.

  [Hint: First find $\dfrac{d\theta}{dt}$ and then find $\dfrac{dh}{dt}$ at the given instant.**]**

REVIEW SET 24A

1 Differentiate with respect to x:

  a $\sin(5x)\ln(x)$ **b** $\sin(x)\cos(2x)$ **c** $e^{-2x}\tan x$

2 Show that the equation of the tangent to $y = x\tan x$ at $x = \frac{\pi}{4}$ is $(2+\pi)x - 2y = \dfrac{\pi^2}{4}$.

3 Find $f'(x)$ and $f''(x)$ for:

    a $f(x) = 3\sin x - 4\cos(2x)$ **b** $f(x) = \sqrt{x}\cos(4x)$

4 A particle moves in a straight line along the x-axis in such a way that its position is given by $x(t) = 3 + \sin(2t)$ cm   after t seconds.

    a Find the initial position, velocity and acceleration of the particle.

    b Find the times when the particle changes direction during $0 \leqslant t \leqslant \pi$ secs.

    c Find the total distance travelled by the particle in the first π seconds.

5 Consider $f(x) = \sqrt{\cos x}$ for $0 \leqslant x \leqslant 2\pi$.

    a For what values of x is $f(x)$ meaningful?

    b Find $f'(x)$ and hence find intervals where $f(x)$ is increasing and decreasing.

    c Sketch the graph of $y = f(x)$ on $0 \leqslant x \leqslant 2\pi$.

6 A cork moves up and down in a bucket of water such that the distance from the centre of the cork to the bottom of the bucket is given by $s(t) = 30 + \cos(\pi t)$ cm where t is the time in seconds, $t \geqslant 0$.

    a Find the cork's velocity at time, $t = 0$, $\frac{1}{2}$, 1, $1\frac{1}{2}$, 2 sec.

    b Find the time intervals when the cork is falling.

7 Four straight sticks of fixed length a, b, c and d are hinged together at P, Q, R and S.

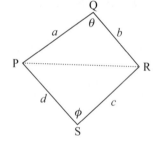

    a Use the cosine rule to find an equation which connects a, b, c, d, $\cos\theta$ and $\cos\phi$ and hence show that $\dfrac{d\theta}{d\phi} = \dfrac{cd\sin\phi}{ab\sin\theta}$

    b Hence, show that the area of quadrilateral PQRS is a maximum when it is a cyclic quadrilateral.

8 A light bulb hangs from the ceiling at a distance h metres above the floor directly above point N. At any point A on the floor, which is x metres from the light bulb, the illumination I is given by

$$I = \frac{\sqrt{8}\cos\theta}{x^2} \text{ units.}$$

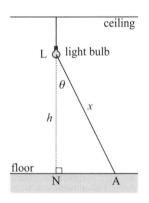

    a If $NA = 1$ metre, show that at A, $I = \sqrt{8}\cos\theta\sin^2\theta$.

    b The light bulb may be lifted or lowered to change the intensity at A. Assuming that $NA = 1$ metre, find the height the bulb has to be above the floor for greatest illumination at A.

REVIEW SET 24B

Click on the icon to obtain printable review sets and answers

REVIEW SET 24B

Chapter 25

Integration

Contents:

We have already seen the usefulness in problem solving when using Differential Calculus. The antiderivative has a large number of useful applications. These include:

- finding areas where curved boundaries are involved
- finding volumes of revolution
- finding distances travelled from velocity functions
- finding hydrostatic pressure
- finding work done by a force
- finding centres of mass and moments of inertia
- solving problems in economics and biology
- solving problems in statistics
- solving problems involving differential equations.

A   ANTIDIFFERENTIATION

In many problems in calculus we know the rate of change of one variable with respect to another,   i.e., $\dfrac{dy}{dx}$,   but we need to know y in terms of x.

For example,

- The slope function $f'(x)$, of a curve is $2x + 3$, and the curve passes through the origin. What is the function $y = f(x)$?

- The rate of change in temperature (in $^\circ$C) $\dfrac{dT}{dt} = 10e^{-t}$ where t is the time in minutes, $t \geqslant 0$. What is the temperature function given that initially the temperature was 11°C?

> The process of finding y from $\dfrac{dy}{dx}$ (or $f(x)$ from $f'(x)$) is the reverse process of differentiation and is called **antidifferentiation**.

Consider the following problem: If $\dfrac{dy}{dx} = x^2$, what is y in terms of x?

From our work on differentiation we know that y must involve x^3 as when we differentiate power functions the index reduces by 1.

If $y = x^3$ then $\dfrac{dy}{dx} = 3x^2$, so if we start with $y = \frac{1}{3}x^3$ then $\dfrac{dy}{dx} = x^2$.

> If $F(x)$ is a function where $F'(x) = f(x)$ we say that:
> - the **derivative** of $F(x)$ is $f(x)$ and
> - the **antiderivative** of $f(x)$ is $F(x)$.

However, if $y = \frac{1}{3}x^3 + 2$, $y = \frac{1}{3}x^3 + 100$ or $y = \frac{1}{3}x^3 - 7$ then $\dfrac{dy}{dx} = x^2$.

In fact, there are infinitely many such functions of the form $y = \frac{1}{3}x^3 + c$ where c is an arbitrary constant. Ignoring the arbitrary constant we say that: $\frac{1}{3}x^3$ is the antiderivative of x^2 as it is the simplest function which when differentiated gives x^2.

Example 1

Find the antiderivative of: **a** x^3 **b** e^{2x} **c** $\dfrac{1}{\sqrt{x}}$

a We know that the derivative of x^4 involves x^3

i.e., $\dfrac{d}{dx}(x^4) = 4x^3$ and $\therefore$ $\dfrac{d}{dx}(\frac{1}{4}x^4) = x^3$

So, the antiderivative of x^3 is $\frac{1}{4}x^4$.

b As $\dfrac{d}{dx}(e^{2x}) = e^{2x} \times 2$ then $\dfrac{d}{dx}(\frac{1}{2}e^{2x}) = \frac{1}{2} \times e^{2x} \times 2 = e^{2x}$

So, the antiderivative of e^{2x} is $\frac{1}{2}e^{2x}$.

c $\dfrac{1}{\sqrt{x}} = x^{-\frac{1}{2}}$ Now $\dfrac{d}{dx}(x^{\frac{1}{2}}) = \frac{1}{2}x^{-\frac{1}{2}}$ $\therefore$ $\dfrac{d}{dx}(2x^{\frac{1}{2}}) = 2(\frac{1}{2})x^{-\frac{1}{2}} = x^{-\frac{1}{2}}$

$\therefore$ the antiderivative of $\dfrac{1}{\sqrt{x}}$ is $2\sqrt{x}$.

EXERCISE 25A

1 **a** Find the antiderivative of:

     i x **ii** x^2 **iii** x^5 **iv** x^{-2} **v** x^{-4} **vi** $x^{\frac{1}{3}}$ **vii** $x^{-\frac{1}{2}}$

   b From your answers in **a**, predict a general rule for the antiderivative of x^n.

2 **a** Find the antiderivative of:

     i e^{2x} **ii** e^{5x} **iii** $e^{\frac{1}{2}x}$ **iv** $e^{0.01x}$ **v** $e^{\pi x}$ **vi** $e^{\frac{x}{3}}$

   b From your answers in **a**, predict a general rule for the antiderivative of e^{kx} where k is a constant.

3 Find the antiderivative of:

   a $6x^2 + 4x$ by differentiating $x^3 + x^2$ **b** e^{3x+1} by differentiating e^{3x+1}

   c $\sqrt{x}$ by differentiating $x\sqrt{x}$ **d** $(2x+1)^3$ by differentiating $(2x+1)^4$

B   INTEGRATION

Earlier we showed that the **antiderivative** of x^2 was $\frac{1}{3}x^3$

i.e., if $f(x) = x^2$ then $F(x) = \frac{1}{3}x^3$.

We also showed that $\frac{1}{3}x^3 + c$ where c is any constant, has derivative x^2.

We say that "the **integral** of x^2 is $\frac{1}{3}x^3 + c$" and write $\int x^2 dx = \frac{1}{3}x^3 + c$

this reads "the integral of x^2 with respect to x"

In general,   if $F'(x) = f(x)$ then $\int f(x)\,dx = F(x) + c$.

DISCOVERING INTEGRALS

Since integration or finding antiderivatives is the reverse process of differentiating we can discover integrals by differentiation. For example,

- if $F(x) = x^4$, then $F'(x) = 4x^3$ $\therefore$ $\int 4x^3 dx = x^4 + c$

- if $F(x) = \sqrt{x} = x^{\frac{1}{2}}$, then $F'(x) = \frac{1}{2}x^{-\frac{1}{2}} = \dfrac{1}{2\sqrt{x}}$

$$\therefore \quad \int \frac{1}{2\sqrt{x}} dx = \sqrt{x} + c$$

The rules
- $\int k\, f(x)\, dx = k \int f(x)\, dx$, k is a constant

and
- $\int [f(x) + g(x)] dx = \int f(x) dx + \int g(x) dx$ may prove useful.

The first tells us that a constant k may be written before the integral sign and the second tells us that the integral of a sum is the sum of the separate integrals. This rule enables us to **integrate term-by-term**.

To prove the first of these rules we consider differentiating $kF(x)$ where $F'(x) = f(x)$.

$$\text{Now} \quad \frac{d}{dx}(k\,F(x)) = k\,F'(x) = k\,f(x) \qquad \therefore \quad \int k\,f(x)\,dx = k\,F(x)$$
$$= k \int f(x)\,dx$$

Example 2	
If $y = x^4 + 2x^3$, find $\dfrac{dy}{dx}$ and hence find $\int (2x^3 + 3x^2)\,dx$.	If $y = x^4 + 2x^3$, then $\dfrac{dy}{dx} = 4x^3 + 6x^2$ $\therefore \int 4x^3 + 6x^2 \, dx = x^4 + 2x^3 + c_1$ $\therefore \int 2(2x^3 + 3x^2)\, dx = x^4 + 2x^3 + c_1$ $\therefore 2\int (2x^3 + 3x^2)\, dx = x^4 + 2x^3 + c_1$ $\therefore \int (2x^3 + 3x^2)\, dx = \frac{1}{2}x^4 + x^3 + c$

EXERCISE 25B.1

1 If $y = x^7$, find $\dfrac{dy}{dx}$ and hence find $\int x^6 \, dx$.

2 If $y = x^3 + x^2$, find $\dfrac{dy}{dx}$ and hence find $\int (3x^2 + 2x)\, dx$.

3 If $y = e^{2x+1}$, find $\dfrac{dy}{dx}$ and hence find $\int e^{2x+1}\, dx$.

4 If $y = (2x+1)^4$, find $\dfrac{dy}{dx}$ and hence find $\int (2x+1)^3 \, dx$.

5 If $y = x\sqrt{x}$, find $\dfrac{dy}{dx}$ and hence find $\int \sqrt{x}\, dx$.

6 If $y = \dfrac{1}{\sqrt{x}}$, find $\dfrac{dy}{dx}$ and hence find $\displaystyle\int \dfrac{1}{x\sqrt{x}}\,dx$.

7 Prove the rule $\displaystyle\int [f(x) + g(x)]\,dx = \int f(x)\,dx + \int g(x)\,dx$.

   [**Hint:** Suppose $F(x)$ is the antiderivative of $f(x)$ and $G(x)$ is the

   antiderivative of $g(x)$.   Find $\dfrac{d}{dx}[F(x) + G(x)]$.]

8 Find $\dfrac{dy}{dx}$ if $y = \sqrt{1 - 4x}$ and hence find $\displaystyle\int \dfrac{1}{\sqrt{1 - 4x}}\,dx$.

9 By considering $\dfrac{d}{dx}\ln(5 - 3x + x^2)$,   find $\displaystyle\int \dfrac{4x - 6}{5 - 3x + x^2}\,dx$.

10 By considering $\dfrac{d}{dx}(2^x)$,   find $\displaystyle\int 2^x\,dx$.   [**Hint:** $2^x = (e^{\ln 2})^x$.]

11 By considering $\dfrac{d}{dx}(x\ln x)$,   find $\displaystyle\int \ln x\,dx$.

In earlier chapters we developed rules to help us differentiate functions more efficiently. Following is a summary of these rules:

Function	Derivative	Name
c, a constant	0	
$mx + c$, m and c are constants	m	
x^n	nx^{n-1}	**power rule**
$cu(x)$	$cu'(x)$	
$u(x) + v(x)$	$u'(x) + v'(x)$	**sum rule**
$u(x)v(x)$	$u'(x)v(x) + u(x)v'(x)$	**product rule**
$\dfrac{u(x)}{v(x)}$	$\dfrac{u'(x)v(x) - u(x)v'(x)}{[v(x)]^2}$	**quotient rule**
$y = f(u)$ where $u = u(x)$	$\dfrac{dy}{dx} = \dfrac{dy}{du}\dfrac{du}{dx}$	**chain rule**
e^x	e^x	
$e^{f(x)}$	$e^{f(x)}f'(x)$	
$\ln x$	$\dfrac{1}{x}$	
$\ln f(x)$	$\dfrac{f'(x)}{f(x)}$	
$[f(x)]^n$	$n[f(x)]^{n-1}f'(x)$	

These rules or combinations of them can be used to differentiate almost all functions.

However, the task of finding **antiderivatives** is not so easy and cannot be contained by listing a set of rules as we did above. In fact huge books of different types of functions and their integrals have been written. Fortunately our course is restricted to a few special cases.

SIMPLE INTEGRALS

Notice that $\dfrac{d}{dx}(kx + c) = k$ $\qquad\qquad \therefore \quad \int k\,dx = kx + c$

if $n \neq -1$, $\quad \dfrac{d}{dx}\left(\dfrac{x^{n+1}}{n+1} + c\right) = \dfrac{(n+1)x^n}{n+1} = x^n$ $\quad \therefore \quad \int x^n\,dx = \dfrac{x^{n+1}}{n+1} + c$

$$\frac{d}{dx}(e^x + c) = e^x \qquad\qquad \therefore \quad \int e^x\,dx = e^x + c$$

if $x > 0$, $\qquad \dfrac{d}{dx}(\ln x + c) = \dfrac{1}{x}$

if $x < 0$, $\qquad \dfrac{d}{dx}(\ln(-x) + c) = \dfrac{-1}{-x} = \dfrac{1}{x}$ $\qquad \therefore \quad \int \dfrac{1}{x}\,dx = \ln|x| + c$

Summary:
- $\int k\,dx = kx + c$ {k is a constant}
- $\int x^n\,dx = \dfrac{x^{n+1}}{n+1} + c$
- $\int e^x\,dx = e^x + c$
- $\int \dfrac{1}{x}\,dx = \ln|x| + c$

c is always an arbitrary constant called "the **integrating constant**" or "the **constant of integration**".

Example 3

Find:

a $\int(x^3 - 2x^2 + 5)\,dx$

b $\int\left(\dfrac{1}{x^3} - \sqrt{x}\right)dx$

a $\int(x^3 - 2x^2 + 5)\,dx$
$$= \frac{x^4}{4} - \frac{2x^3}{3} + 5x + c$$

b $\int\left(\dfrac{1}{x^3} - \sqrt{x}\right)dx$
$$= \int(x^{-3} - x^{\frac{1}{2}})\,dx$$
$$= \frac{x^{-2}}{-2} - \frac{x^{\frac{3}{2}}}{\frac{3}{2}} + c$$
$$= -\frac{1}{2x^2} - \tfrac{2}{3}x^{\frac{3}{2}} + c$$

EXERCISE 25B.2

1 Find:

a $\int(x^4 - x^2 - x + 2)\,dx$ **b** $\int(\sqrt{x} + e^x)\,dx$ **c** $\int\left(3e^x - \dfrac{1}{x}\right)dx$

d $\int\left(x\sqrt{x} - \dfrac{2}{x}\right)dx$ **e** $\int\left(\dfrac{1}{x\sqrt{x}} + \dfrac{4}{x}\right)dx$ **f** $\int\left(\tfrac{1}{2}x^3 - x^4 + x^{\frac{1}{3}}\right)dx$

g $\int\left(x^2 + \dfrac{3}{x}\right)dx$ **h** $\int\left(\dfrac{1}{2x} + x^2 - e^x\right)dx$ **i** $\int\left(5e^x + \tfrac{1}{3}x^3 - \dfrac{4}{x}\right)dx$

Example 4

Find: **a** $\int \left(3x + \dfrac{2}{x}\right)^2 dx$ **b** $\int \left(\dfrac{x^2 - 2}{\sqrt{x}}\right) dx$

Notice that we expanded the brackets and simplified to a form that can be integrated.

a $\int \left(3x + \dfrac{2}{x}\right)^2 dx$

$= \int \left(9x^2 + 12 + \dfrac{4}{x^2}\right) dx$

$= \int (9x^2 + 12 + 4x^{-2}) \, dx$

$= \dfrac{9x^3}{3} + 12x + \dfrac{4x^{-1}}{-1} + c$

$= 3x^3 + 12x - \dfrac{4}{x} + c$

b $\int \left(\dfrac{x^2 - 2}{\sqrt{x}}\right) dx$

$= \int \left(\dfrac{x^2}{\sqrt{x}} - \dfrac{2}{\sqrt{x}}\right) dx$

$= \int (x^{\frac{3}{2}} - 2x^{-\frac{1}{2}}) \, dx$

$= \dfrac{x^{\frac{5}{2}}}{\frac{5}{2}} - \dfrac{2x^{\frac{1}{2}}}{\frac{1}{2}} + c$

$= \tfrac{2}{5}x^2 \sqrt{x} - 4\sqrt{x} + c$

Note: There is no product or quotient rule for integration. Consequently we often have to carry out multiplication or division before we integrate.

2 Find:

a $\int (x^2 + 3x - 2) \, dx$ **b** $\int \left(\sqrt{x} - \dfrac{1}{\sqrt{x}}\right) dx$ **c** $\int 2e^x - \dfrac{1}{x^2} \, dx$

d $\int \dfrac{1 - 4x}{x\sqrt{x}} \, dx$ **e** $\int (2x + 1)^2 \, dx$ **f** $\int \dfrac{x^2 + x - 3}{x} \, dx$

g $\int \dfrac{2x - 1}{\sqrt{x}} \, dx$ **h** $\int \dfrac{x^2 - 4x + 10}{x^2\sqrt{x}} \, dx$ **i** $\int (x + 1)^3 \, dx$

3 Find y if: (Do not forget the integrating constant c.)

a $\dfrac{dy}{dx} = 6$ **b** $\dfrac{dy}{dx} = 4x^2$ **c** $\dfrac{dy}{dx} = 5x - x^2$

d $\dfrac{dy}{dx} = \dfrac{1}{x^2}$ **e** $\dfrac{dy}{dx} = 2e^x - 5$ **f** $\dfrac{dy}{dx} = 4x^3 + 3x^2$

4 Find y if:

a $\dfrac{dy}{dx} = (1 - 2x)^2$ **b** $\dfrac{dy}{dx} = \sqrt{x} - \dfrac{2}{\sqrt{x}}$ **c** $\dfrac{dy}{dx} = \dfrac{x^2 + 2x - 5}{x^2}$

5 Find $f(x)$ if:

a $f'(x) = x^3 - 5x + 3$ **b** $f'(x) = 2\sqrt{x}(1 - 3x)$ **c** $f'(x) = 3e^x - \dfrac{4}{x}$

The constant of integration can be found if we are given a point on the curve.

Example 5

Find $f(x)$ given that $f'(x) = x^3 - 2x^2 + 3$ and $f(0) = 2$.

Since $f'(x) = x^3 - 2x^2 + 3$, then $f(x) = \int (x^3 - 2x^2 + 3)\, dx$

i.e., $f(x) = \dfrac{x^4}{4} - \dfrac{2x^3}{3} + 3x + c$

But $f(0) = 2$, $\therefore$ $0 - 0 + 0 + c = 2$ i.e., $c = 2$

Thus $f(x) = \dfrac{x^4}{4} - \dfrac{2x^3}{3} + 3x + 2$

6 Find $f(x)$ given that:

a $f'(x) = 2x - 1$ and $f(0) = 3$
b $f'(x) = 3x^2 + 2x$ and $f(2) = 5$

c $f'(x) = e^x + \dfrac{1}{\sqrt{x}}$ and $f(1) = 1$
d $f'(x) = x - \dfrac{2}{\sqrt{x}}$ and $f(1) = 2$.

If we are given the second derivative we need to integrate twice to find the function. This creates two integrating constants and so we need two facts in order to find them.

Example 6

Find $f(x)$ given that $f''(x) = 12x^2 - 4$, $f'(0) = -1$ and $f(1) = 4$.

If $f''(x) = 12x^2 - 4$

$f'(x) = \dfrac{12x^3}{3} - 4x + c$ {integrating with respect to x}

i.e., $f'(x) = 4x^3 - 4x + c$

But $f'(0) = -1$ $\therefore$ $0 - 0 + c = -1$ and so $c = -1$

Thus $f'(x) = 4x^3 - 4x - 1$

$\therefore$ $f(x) = \dfrac{4x^4}{4} - \dfrac{4x^2}{2} - x + d$ {integrating again}

i.e., $f(x) = x^4 - 2x^2 - x + d$

But $f(1) = 4$ $\therefore$ $1 - 2 - 1 + d = 4$ $\therefore$ $d = 6$

Thus $f(x) = x^4 - 2x^2 - x + 6$

7 Find $f(x)$ given that:

a $f''(x) = 2x + 1$, $f'(1) = 3$ and $f(2) = 7$

b $f''(x) = 15\sqrt{x} + \dfrac{3}{\sqrt{x}}$, $f'(1) = 12$ and $f(0) = 5$

c $f''(x) = 2x$ and the points $(1, 0)$ and $(0, 5)$ lie on the curve.

C   INTEGRATING e^{ax+b} AND $(ax+b)^n$

Since $\dfrac{d}{dx}\left(\dfrac{1}{a}e^{ax+b}\right) = \dfrac{1}{a}e^{ax+b} \times a = e^{ax+b}$

then $$\int e^{ax+b}\,dx = \dfrac{1}{a}e^{ax+b} + c$$

Likewise if $n \neq -1$,

since $\dfrac{d}{dx}\left(\dfrac{1}{a(n+1)}(ax+b)^{n+1}\right) = \dfrac{1}{a(n+1)}(n+1)(ax+b)^n \times a,$

$$= (ax+b)^n$$

then $$\int (ax+b)^n\,dx = \dfrac{1}{a}\dfrac{(ax+b)^{n+1}}{n+1} + c, \quad n \neq -1$$

Also, since $\dfrac{d}{dx}\left(\dfrac{1}{a}\ln(ax+b)\right) = \dfrac{1}{a}\left(\dfrac{a}{ax+b}\right) = \dfrac{1}{ax+b}$ for $ax+b > 0$

then $\displaystyle\int \dfrac{1}{ax+b}\,dx = \dfrac{1}{a}\ln(ax+b) + c$

In fact $$\int \dfrac{1}{ax+b}\,dx = \dfrac{1}{a}\ln|ax+b| + c$$

Example 7

Find:

a $\int (2x+3)^4\,dx$

b $\displaystyle\int \dfrac{1}{\sqrt{1-2x}}\,dx$

a $\int (2x+3)^4\,dx$

$= \tfrac{1}{2} \times \dfrac{(2x+3)^5}{5} + c$

$= \tfrac{1}{10}(2x+3)^5 + c$

b $\displaystyle\int \dfrac{1}{\sqrt{1-2x}}\,dx$

$= \int (1-2x)^{-\frac{1}{2}}\,dx$

$= \tfrac{1}{-2} \times \dfrac{(1-2x)^{\frac{1}{2}}}{\frac{1}{2}} + c$

$= -\sqrt{1-2x} + c$

EXERCISE 25C

1 Find:

a $\int (2x+5)^3\,dx$ b $\displaystyle\int \dfrac{1}{(3-2x)^2}\,dx$ c $\displaystyle\int \dfrac{4}{(2x-1)^4}\,dx$ d $\int (4x-3)^7\,dx$

e $\int \sqrt{3x-4}\,dx$ f $\displaystyle\int \dfrac{10}{\sqrt{1-5x}}$ g $\int 3(1-x)^4\,dx$ h $\displaystyle\int \dfrac{4}{\sqrt{3-4x}}\,dx$

2   **a**   If $\dfrac{dy}{dx} = \sqrt{2x - 7}$, find $y = f(x)$ given that $y = 11$ when $x = 8$.

    b   Function $f(x)$ has slope function $\dfrac{4}{\sqrt{1 - x}}$, and passes through the point $(-3, -11)$.

    Find the point on the graph of the function $y = f(x)$ with x-coordinate -8.

3   Find:

    a $\int 3(2x - 1)^2 \, dx$ **b** $\int (x^2 - x)^2 \, dx$ **c** $\int (1 - 3x)^3 \, dx$

    d $\int (1 - x^2)^2 \, dx$ **e** $\int 4\sqrt{5 - x} \, dx$ **f** $\int (x^2 + 1)^3 \, dx$

Example 8

Find: **a** $\int (2e^{2x} - e^{-3x}) \, dx$ **b** $\displaystyle\int \dfrac{4}{1 - 2x} \, dx$

    a $\int (2e^{2x} - e^{-3x}) \, dx$

        $= 2(\tfrac{1}{2})e^{2x} - (\tfrac{1}{-3})e^{-3x} + c$

        $= e^{2x} + \tfrac{1}{3}e^{-3x} + c$

    b $\displaystyle\int \dfrac{4}{1 - 2x} \, dx = 4\int \dfrac{1}{1 - 2x} \, dx$

                           $= 4\left(\dfrac{1}{-2}\right) \ln |1 - 2x| + c$

                           $= -2 \ln |1 - 2x| + c$

---

4   Find:

    a $\int \left(2e^x + 5e^{2x}\right) \, dx$ **b** $\int \left(x^2 - 2e^{-3x}\right) \, dx$ **c** $\displaystyle\int \left(\sqrt{x} + 4e^{2x} - e^{-x}\right) \, dx$

    d $\displaystyle\int \dfrac{1}{2x - 1} \, dx$ **e** $\displaystyle\int \dfrac{5}{1 - 3x} \, dx$ **f** $\displaystyle\int \left(e^{-x} - \dfrac{4}{2x + 1}\right) \, dx$

    g $\int (e^x + e^{-x})^2 \, dx$ **h** $\int (e^{-x} + 2)^2 \, dx$ **i** $\displaystyle\int \left(x - \dfrac{5}{1 - x}\right) \, dx$

5   Find y given that:

    a $\dfrac{dy}{dx} = (1 - e^x)^2$ **b** $\dfrac{dy}{dx} = 1 - 2x + \dfrac{3}{x + 2}$ **c** $\dfrac{dy}{dx} = e^{-2x} + \dfrac{4}{2x - 1}$

6   To find $\displaystyle\int \dfrac{1}{4x} \, dx$, Tracy's answer was $\displaystyle\int \dfrac{1}{4x} \, dx = \tfrac{1}{4} \ln |4x| + c$

    and Nadine's answer was $\displaystyle\int \dfrac{1}{4x} dx = \tfrac{1}{4} \int \dfrac{1}{x} \, dx = \tfrac{1}{4} \ln |x| + c$

    Which of them has found the correct answer?   Prove your statement.

7   **a**   If $f'(x) = 2e^{-2x}$ and $f(0) = 3$,   find $f(x)$.

    b   If $f'(x) = 2x - \dfrac{2}{1 - x}$ and $f(-1) = 3$,   find $f(x)$.

    c   If a curve has slope function $\sqrt{x} + \tfrac{1}{2}e^{-4x}$ and passes through $(1, 0)$, find the equation of the function.

8 Show that $\dfrac{3}{x+2} - \dfrac{1}{x-2} = \dfrac{2x-8}{x^2-4}$, and hence find $\displaystyle\int \dfrac{2x-8}{x^2-4}\,dx$.

9 Show that $\dfrac{1}{2x-1} - \dfrac{1}{2x+1} = \dfrac{2}{4x^2-1}$, and hence find $\displaystyle\int \dfrac{2}{4x^2-1}\,dx$.

D   INTEGRATING $f(u)u'(x)$ BY SUBSTITUTION

$\displaystyle\int (x^2+3x)^4(2x+3)\,dx$ is of the form $\displaystyle\int f(u)\,u'(x)\,dx$

where $f(u)=u^4$, $u=x^2+3x$ and $u'(x)=2x+3$

Likewise, $\displaystyle\int e^{x^2-x}(2x-1)\,dx$ is of the form $\displaystyle\int f(u)\,u'(x)\,dx$

where $f(u)=e^u$, $u=x^2-x$ and $u'(x)=2x-1$

Also, $\displaystyle\int \dfrac{3x^2+2}{x^3+2x}\,dx$ is of the form $\displaystyle\int f(u)\,u'(x)\,dx$

where $f(u)=\dfrac{1}{u}$, $u=x^3+2x$ and $u'(x)=3x^2+2$

How do we integrate such functions? It is clear that making a **substitution** involving u makes it easier to understand. Let us examine the first example more closely.

$\displaystyle\int (x^2+3x)^4(2x+3)\,dx = \int u^4\,\dfrac{du}{dx}\,dx$ {if $u=x^2+3x$ then $\dfrac{du}{dx}=2x+3$}

What do we do now? Fortunately we can apply the following **theorem** (special result):

$$\int f(u)\,\frac{du}{dx}\,dx = \int f(u)\,du$$

This theorem enables us to replace $\dfrac{du}{dx}\,dx$ by du.

Proof: Suppose $F(u)$ is the antiderivative of $f(u)$,   i.e., $F'(u)=f(u)$

$\therefore$ $\displaystyle\int f(u)\,du = F(u)+c$ ...... (1)

But $\dfrac{d}{dx}F(u) = \dfrac{d}{du}F(u)\,\dfrac{du}{dx}$ {chain rule}

$= F'(u)\,\dfrac{du}{dx}$

$= f(u)\,\dfrac{du}{dx}$

$\therefore$ $\displaystyle\int f(u)\,\dfrac{du}{dx}\,dx = F(u)+c$

$= \displaystyle\int f(u)\,du$ {from (1)}

So, $\int (x^2 + 3x)^4 (2x + 3)\, dx = \int u^4 \dfrac{du}{dx}\, dx$ $\{u = x^2 + 3x\}$

$\qquad\qquad\qquad\qquad\quad = \int u^4\, du$ $\{$replacing $\dfrac{du}{dx}\, dx$ by $du\}$

$\qquad\qquad\qquad\qquad\quad = \dfrac{u^5}{5} + c$

$\qquad\qquad\qquad\qquad\quad = \frac{1}{5}(x^2 + 3x)^5 + c$

Example 9

Use substitution to find:

$\int \sqrt{x^3 + 2x}\,(3x^2 + 2)\, dx$

$\int \sqrt{x^3 + 2x}\,(3x^2 + 2)\, dx$

$= \int \sqrt{u}\, \dfrac{du}{dx}\, dx$ where $u = x^3 + 2x$

$= \int \sqrt{u}\, du$ $\{$theorem$\}$

$= \int u^{\frac{1}{2}}\, du$

$= \dfrac{u^{\frac{3}{2}}}{\frac{3}{2}} + c$

$= \frac{2}{3}(x^3 + 2x)^{\frac{3}{2}} + c$ $\{$substituting $u = x^3 + 2x\}$

Example 10

Use substitution to find: **a** $\displaystyle\int \dfrac{3x^2 + 2}{x^3 + 2x}\, dx$ **b** $\int xe^{1-x^2}\, dx$

a $\displaystyle\int \dfrac{3x^2 + 2}{x^3 + 2x}\, dx$

$= \displaystyle\int \dfrac{1}{x^3 + 2x}(3x^2 + 2)\, dx$

$= \displaystyle\int \dfrac{1}{u}\dfrac{du}{dx}\, dx$ $\{u = x^3 + 2x\}$

$= \int \dfrac{1}{u}\, du$

$= \ln |u| + c$

$= \ln |x^3 + 2x| + c$

b $\displaystyle\int xe^{1-x^2}\, dx$

$= \displaystyle\int e^u \left(\dfrac{1}{-2}\dfrac{du}{dx}\right) dx$ $\{u = 1 - x^2$

$\qquad\qquad\qquad\qquad\qquad \therefore\ \dfrac{du}{dx} = -2x\}$

$= -\frac{1}{2}\int e^u\, du$

$= -\frac{1}{2}e^u + c$

$= -\frac{1}{2}e^{1-x^2} + c$

EXERCISE 25D

1 Integrate with respect to x:

a $3x^2(x^3 + 1)^4$

b $\dfrac{2x}{\sqrt{x^2 + 3}}$

c $\sqrt{x^3 + x}\,(3x^2 + 1)$

d $4x^3(2 + x^4)^3$

e $(x^3 + 2x + 1)^4(3x^2 + 2)$

f $\dfrac{x^2}{(3x^3 - 1)^4}$

g $\dfrac{x}{(1-x^2)^5}$

h $\dfrac{x+2}{(x^2+4x-3)^2}$

i $x^4(x+1)^4(2x+1)$

2 Find:

a $\displaystyle\int -2e^{1-2x}\,dx$

b $\displaystyle\int 2xe^{x^2}\,dx$

c $\displaystyle\int x^2e^{x^3+1}\,dx$

d $\displaystyle\int \dfrac{e^{\sqrt{x}}}{\sqrt{x}}\,dx$

e $\displaystyle\int (2x-1)e^{x-x^2}\,dx$

f $\displaystyle\int \dfrac{e^{\frac{x-1}{x}}}{x^2}\,dx$

3 Find:

a $\displaystyle\int \dfrac{2x}{x^2+1}\,dx$

b $\displaystyle\int \dfrac{x}{2-x^2}\,dx$

c $\displaystyle\int \dfrac{2x-3}{x^2-3x}\,dx$

d $\displaystyle\int \dfrac{6x^2-2}{x^3-x}\,dx$

e $\displaystyle\int \dfrac{4x-10}{5x-x^2}\,dx$

f $\displaystyle\int \dfrac{1-x^2}{x^3-3x}\,dx$

4 Find $f(x)$ if $f'(x)$ is:

a $x^2(3-x^3)^2$

b $\dfrac{4}{x\ln x}$

c $x\sqrt{1-x^2}$

d xe^{1-x^2}

e $\dfrac{1-3x^2}{x^3-x}$

f $\dfrac{(\ln x)^3}{x}$

E   DEFINITE INTEGRALS

If $F(x)$ is the antiderivative of $f(x)$ where $f(x)$ is continuous on the interval $a \leqslant x \leqslant b$ then the **definite integral** of $f(x)$ on this interval is

$$\int_a^b f(x)\,dx = F(b) - F(a)$$

Note: $\displaystyle\int_a^b f(x)\,dx$ reads "the integral of $f(x)$ from $x = a$ to $x = b$, with respect to x".

Notation: We write $F(b) - F(a) = [F(x)]_a^b$.

Example 11

Find $\int_1^3 (x^2+2)\,dx$

$\displaystyle\int_1^3 (x^2+2)\,dx$

$= \left[\dfrac{x^3}{3} + 2x\right]_1^3$

$= \left(\dfrac{3^3}{3} + 2(3)\right) - \left(\dfrac{1^3}{3} + 2(1)\right)$

$= (9+6) - (\tfrac{1}{3}+2)$

$= 12\tfrac{2}{3}$

Check:

```
fnInt(X²+2,X,1,3
)
          12.66666667
```

EXERCISE 25E.1

1   Evaluate the following and check with your graphics calculator:

a $\displaystyle\int_0^1 x^3\, dx$

b $\displaystyle\int_0^2 (x^2 - x)\, dx$

c $\displaystyle\int_0^1 e^x\, dx$

d $\displaystyle\int_1^4 \left(x - \frac{3}{\sqrt{x}}\right) dx$

e $\displaystyle\int_4^9 \frac{x-3}{\sqrt{x}}\, dx$

f $\displaystyle\int_1^3 \frac{1}{x}\, dx$

g $\displaystyle\int_1^2 (e^{-x} + 1)^2\, dx$

h $\displaystyle\int_2^6 \frac{1}{\sqrt{2x-3}}\, dx$

i $\displaystyle\int_0^1 e^{1-x}\, dx$

Example 12

Evaluate: a $\displaystyle\int_2^3 \frac{x}{x^2-1}\, dx$ b $\displaystyle\int_0^1 \frac{6x}{(x^2+1)^3}\, dx$

---

a   In $\displaystyle\int_2^3 \frac{x}{x^2-1}\, dx$,   we let $u = x^2 - 1$ $\therefore$ $du = \dfrac{du}{dx}\, dx = 2x\, dx$

and   when $x = 2$, $u = 2^2 - 1 = 3$

when $x = 3$, $u = 3^2 - 1 = 8$

$\therefore$ $\displaystyle\int_2^3 \frac{x}{x^2-1}\, dx = \int_3^8 \frac{1}{u}\left(\tfrac{1}{2}\, du\right)$

$= \dfrac{1}{2}\displaystyle\int_3^8 \frac{1}{u}\, du$

$= \dfrac{1}{2}\left[\ln|u|\right]_3^8$

$= \dfrac{1}{2}(\ln 8 - \ln 3)$

$= \dfrac{1}{2}\ln\!\left(\dfrac{8}{3}\right)$

```
.5ln (8÷3)
            0.4904146265
∫(X÷(X²-1),2,3,1E-4)
            0.4904146265



Solve d/dx d²/dx² ∫dx        ▷
```

b   In $\displaystyle\int_0^1 \frac{6x}{(x^2+1)^3}\, dx$,   we let $u = x^2 + 1$ $\therefore$ $du = \dfrac{du}{dx}\, dx = 2x\, dx$

So $\displaystyle\int_0^1 \frac{6x}{(x^2+1)^3}\, dx = \int_1^2 \frac{1}{u^3}(3\, du)$ and   when $x = 0$, $u = 1$

when $x = 1$, $u = 2$

$= 3\displaystyle\int_1^2 u^{-3}\, du$

$= 3\left[\dfrac{u^{-2}}{-2}\right]_1^2$

$= 3\left(\dfrac{2^{-2}}{-2} - \dfrac{1^{-2}}{-2}\right)$

$= \dfrac{9}{8}$

```
∫(6×X÷(X²+1)^3,0,1,1E
-4)
                   1.125



Solve d/dx d²/dx² ∫dx        ▷
```

2 Evaluate the following and check with your graphics calculator:

a $\displaystyle\int_1^2 \frac{x}{(x^2+2)^2}\,dx$

b $\displaystyle\int_0^1 x^2 e^{x^3+1}\,dx$

c $\displaystyle\int_0^3 x\sqrt{x^2+16}\,dx$

d $\displaystyle\int_1^2 xe^{-2x^2}\,dx$

e $\displaystyle\int_2^3 \frac{x}{2-x^2}\,dx$

f $\displaystyle\int_1^2 \frac{\ln x}{x}\,dx$

g $\displaystyle\int_0^1 \frac{1-3x^2}{1-x^3+x}\,dx$

h $\displaystyle\int_2^4 \frac{6x^2-4x+4}{x^3-x^2+2x}\,dx$

i $\displaystyle\int_0^1 (x^2+2x)^n(x+1)\,dx$

[Careful!]

PROPERTIES OF DEFINITE INTEGRALS

EXERCISE 25E.2

1 Use technology to find:

a $\displaystyle\int_1^4 \sqrt{x}\,dx$ and $\displaystyle\int_1^4 (-\sqrt{x})\,dx$

b $\displaystyle\int_0^1 x^7\,dx$ and $\displaystyle\int_0^1 (-x^7)\,dx$

2 Use technology to find:

a $\displaystyle\int_0^1 x^2\,dx$

b $\displaystyle\int_1^2 x^2\,dx$

c $\displaystyle\int_0^2 x^2\,dx$

d $\displaystyle\int_0^1 3x^2\,dx$

3 Use technology to find:

a $\displaystyle\int_0^2 (x^3-4x)\,dx$

b $\displaystyle\int_2^3 (x^3-4x)\,dx$

c $\displaystyle\int_0^3 (x^3-4x)\,dx$

4 What generalisation can be made from: a question **1**   b questions **2** and **3**?

5 Use technology to find:

a $\displaystyle\int_0^1 x^2\,dx$

b $\displaystyle\int_0^1 \sqrt{x}\,dx$

c $\displaystyle\int_0^1 (x^2+\sqrt{x})\,dx$

What do you notice?

From the previous exercise the following properties of definite integrals were observed:

- $\displaystyle\int_a^b [-f(x)]\,dx = -\int_a^b f(x)\,dx$

- $\displaystyle\int_a^b cf(x)\,dx = c\int_a^b f(x)\,dx, \quad c \text{ is any constant}$

- $\displaystyle\int_a^b f(x)\,dx + \int_b^c f(x)\,dx = \int_a^c f(x)\,dx$

- $\displaystyle\int_a^b [f(x)+g(x)]\,dx = \int_a^b f(x)\,dx + \int_a^b g(x)\,dx$

We will examine proofs of these facts later in the course.

EXERCISE 25E.3

1 The graph of $y = f(x)$ is illustrated:

Evaluate the following integrals using area interpretation:

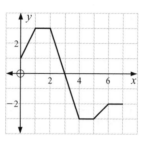

a $\displaystyle\int_0^3 f(x)\,dx$ **b** $\displaystyle\int_3^7 f(x)\,dx$

c $\displaystyle\int_2^4 f(x)\,dx$ **d** $\displaystyle\int_0^7 f(x)\,dx$

2 The graph of $y = f(x)$ is illustrated:

Evaluate the following using area interpretation:

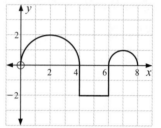

a $\displaystyle\int_0^4 f(x)\,dx$ **b** $\displaystyle\int_4^6 f(x)\,dx$

c $\displaystyle\int_6^8 f(x)\,dx$ **d** $\displaystyle\int_0^8 f(x)\,dx$

3 Write as a single integral:

a $\displaystyle\int_2^4 f(x)\,dx + \int_4^7 f(x)\,dx$ **b** $\displaystyle\int_1^3 g(x)\,dx + \int_3^8 g(x)\,dx + \int_8^9 g(x)\,dx$

4 **a** If $\displaystyle\int_1^3 f(x)\,dx = 2$ and $\displaystyle\int_1^6 f(x)\,dx = -3$, find $\displaystyle\int_3^6 f(x)\,dx$.

b If $\displaystyle\int_0^2 f(x)\,dx = 5$, $\displaystyle\int_4^6 f(x)\,dx = -2$ and $\displaystyle\int_0^6 f(x)\,dx = 7$,

find $\displaystyle\int_2^4 f(x)\,dx$.

REVIEW SET 25A

1 Integrate with respect to x: **a** $\dfrac{4}{\sqrt{x}}$ **b** $\dfrac{3}{1-2x}$ **c** xe^{1-x^2}

2 Find the exact value of: **a** $\displaystyle\int_{-5}^{-1} \sqrt{1-3x}\,dx$ **b** $\displaystyle\int_0^1 \dfrac{4x^2}{(x^3+2)^3}\,dx$

3 By differentiating $y = \sqrt{x^2-4}$, find $\displaystyle\int \dfrac{x}{\sqrt{x^2-4}}\,dx$.

4 A curve $y = f(x)$ has $f''(x) = 18x+10$. Find $f(x)$ if $f(0) = -1$ and $f(1) = 13$.

5 $\dfrac{4x-3}{2x+1}$ can be written in the form $A + \dfrac{B}{2x+1}$.

    a   Find the value of A and B.   **b**   Hence find $\displaystyle\int_0^2 \dfrac{4x-3}{2x+1}\,dx$.

6 Find the exact value of: **a** $\displaystyle\int_3^4 \dfrac{1}{\sqrt{2x+1}}\,dx$ **b** $\displaystyle\int_0^1 x^2 e^{x^3+1}\,dx$

    Check your answers using technology.

7 If $\displaystyle\int_0^a e^{1-2x}\,dx = \frac{e}{4}$,   find a in the form $\ln k$.

REVIEW SET 25B

1 Find: **a** $\displaystyle\int \left(2e^{-x} - \dfrac{1}{x} + 3\right) dx$ **b** $\displaystyle\int \left(\sqrt{x} - \dfrac{1}{\sqrt{x}}\right)^2 dx$

2 Evaluate: **a** $\displaystyle\int_1^2 (x^2-1)^2\,dx$ **b** $\displaystyle\int_1^2 x(x^2-1)^2\,dx$

3 By differentiating $(3x^2+x)^3$,   find $\displaystyle\int (3x^2+x)^2(6x+1)\,dx$.

4 Given that $f'(x) = x^2 - 3x + 2$ and $f(1) = 3$, find $f(x)$.

5 Find the exact value of $\displaystyle\int_2^3 \dfrac{1}{\sqrt{3x-4}}\,dx$.

6 $f''(x) = 3x^2 + 2x$ and $f(0) = f(2) = 3$.

    Find: **a** $f(x)$ **b** the equation of the normal to $y = f(x)$ at $x = 2$.

7 Find A, B, C and D using the division algorithms, if:

$$\dfrac{x^3 - 3x + 2}{x - 2} = Ax^2 + Bx + C + \dfrac{D}{x-2}. \quad \text{Hence find} \quad \int \dfrac{x^3 - 3x + 2}{x-2}\,dx.$$

8 **a** Find $\displaystyle\int \dfrac{1}{x+2}\,dx - \int \dfrac{2}{x-1}\,dx$.

    b Hence find $\displaystyle\int \dfrac{x+5}{(x+2)(x-1)}\,dx$.

REVIEW SET 25C

1 Find y if: **a** $\dfrac{dy}{dx} = (x^2 - 1)^2$ **b** $\dfrac{dy}{dx} = 400 - 20e^{-\frac{x}{2}}$

2 Evaluate: **a** $\displaystyle\int_{-2}^{0} \dfrac{4}{2x - 1}\, dx$ **b** $\displaystyle\int_{0}^{1} \dfrac{10x}{\sqrt{3x^2 + 1}}\, dx$

3 Find $\dfrac{d}{dx}(\ln x)^2$ and hence find $\displaystyle\int \dfrac{\ln x}{x}\, dx$.

4 Given that $f''(x) = 4x^2 - 3$, $f'(0) = 6$ and $f(2) = 3$, find $f(3)$.

5 Find $\displaystyle\int (2x + 3)^n\, dx$ for all integers n.

6 **a** Find $(e^x + 2)^3$ using the binomial expansion.

   b Hence find the exact value of $\displaystyle\int_{0}^{1} (e^x + 2)^3\, dx$.

   c Check **b** using technology.

7 A function has slope function $2\sqrt{x} + \dfrac{a}{\sqrt{x}}$ and passes through the points (0, 2) and (1, 4).   Find a and hence explain why the function $y = f(x)$ has no stationary points.

8 $\displaystyle\int_{a}^{2a} (x^2 + ax + 2)\, dx = \dfrac{73a}{2}$. Find a.

Chapter 26

Integration (areas and other applications)

Contents:

A   AREAS WHERE BOUNDARIES ARE CURVED

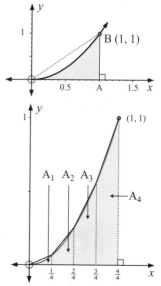

We will begin with trying to find the area between the x-axis and $y = x^2$ from $x = 0$ to $x = 1$. The function $y = x^2$ provides us with a curved boundary.

It is clear that the required area is less than the area of triangle OAB, i.e., area $< \frac{1}{2}$ unit^2.

We cannot exactly subdivide the region into triangles, rectangles, trapezia, etc. so existing area formulae cannot be used.

However, we could find better approximations to the exact area by using them.

For example, if the region is subdivided into strips of width $\frac{1}{4}$, an over-estimate of the required area could be made by joining the points on the curve with straight lines as shown.

Now   area $< A_1 + A_2 + A_3 + A_4$

i.e.,   area $< \left(\dfrac{\frac{0}{16} + \frac{1}{16}}{2}\right)\frac{1}{4} + \left(\dfrac{\frac{1}{16} + \frac{4}{16}}{2}\right)\frac{1}{4} + \left(\dfrac{\frac{4}{16} + \frac{9}{16}}{2}\right)\frac{1}{4} + \left(\dfrac{\frac{9}{16} + \frac{16}{16}}{2}\right)\frac{1}{4}$

$\{$using area of trapezium $= \left(\frac{a+b}{2}\right)h \qquad \}$

$\therefore$ area $< \frac{1}{4}[\frac{1}{32} + \frac{5}{32} + \frac{13}{32} + \frac{25}{32}]$

i.e.,   area $< \frac{11}{32}$ where $\frac{11}{32} = 0.343\,75$

An estimate of the area is $\doteq 0.34$ units^2, which is a better estimate than that which would have been obtained if we had used two strips.

DISCUSSION

How could the estimate of the area under $y = x^2$ be improved?

What factors must be considered when trying to improve area estimates?

EXERCISE 26A.1

1 Use the method outlined above to find an estimate of the area:

a between $y = x^2$ and the x-axis from $x = 0$ to $x = 1$ if five vertical strips of equal width are drawn

b between $y = \dfrac{1}{x}$ and the x-axis from $x = 1$ to $x = 2$ if five vertical strips of equal width are drawn.

2 Repeat **1** but this time use ten vertical strips.

UPPER AND LOWER RECTANGLES

Another way of finding areas it to use only rectangles and find lower and upper sums of their areas. This gives us a lower and an upper bound for the actual area.

For example, consider $y = x^2$ again with four vertical strips.

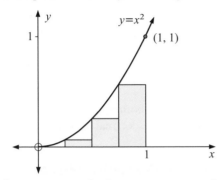
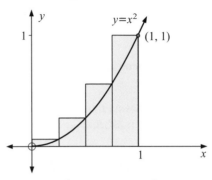

If A_L represents the lower area sum and A_U represents the upper sum, then

$$A_L = \tfrac{1}{4}(0)^2 + \tfrac{1}{4}\left(\tfrac{1}{4}\right)^2 + \tfrac{1}{4}\left(\tfrac{1}{2}\right)^2 + \tfrac{1}{4}\left(\tfrac{3}{4}\right)^2 = 0.218\,75$$

and $\quad A_U = \tfrac{1}{4}\left(\tfrac{1}{4}\right)^2 + \tfrac{1}{4}\left(\tfrac{1}{2}\right)^2 + \tfrac{1}{4}\left(\tfrac{3}{4}\right)^2 + \tfrac{1}{4}(1)^2 = 0.468\,75$

So, if A is the actual area then $\quad 0.218\,75 \quad < \quad A \quad < \quad 0.468\,75$

a lower
bound

an upper
bound

The following diagrams show lower and upper rectangles for n subdivisions where $n = 10$, 25 and 50.

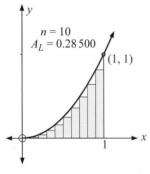
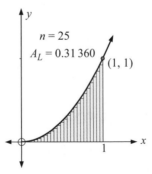
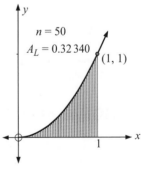

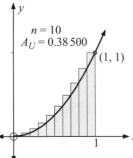
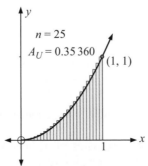
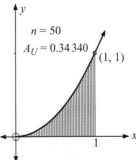

A summary of these results together with average of A_L and A_U are worth considering:

n	A_L	A_U	Average
4	0.218 75	0.468 75	0.343 75
10	0.285 00	0.385 00	0.335 00
25	0.313 60	0.353 60	0.333 60
50	0.323 40	0.343 40	0.333 40

Now click on the icon to examine cases $n = 4, 10, 25, 50, 100, 1000$ and $10\,000$.

AREA FINDER

From the table it seems that as n gets larger A_L and A_U both approach or converge to the same number $0.333\,333\,3.....$ which we recognise as the decimal expansion of $\frac{1}{3}$.

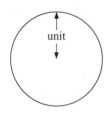

INVESTIGATION 1   FINDING AREAS USING RECTANGLES

This investigation is about finding estimates of areas under simple curves by finding upper and lower rectangle sums by direct calculation and by using technology. **Note:** $[a,\ b]$ is interval notation for $a \leqslant x \leqslant b$.

What to do:

1   Consider finding the area between $y = x^3$ and the x-axis from $x = 0$ to $x = 1$.

   a   First graph the curve and shade the required area.

   b   Subdivide the interval $[0,\ 1]$ into five equal intervals and construct upper and lower rectangles. This case is $n = 5$.   **AREA FINDER**

   c   Find the upper and lower area sums.

   d   Click on the icon and use the technology to find upper and lower area sums when $n = 5, 10, 50, 200, 1000$ and $10\,000$. Display your answers in table form.

   e   What do you suspect the actual area to be?

2   Repeat **1 a** to **d** for the function $y = \dfrac{1}{x}$ and the x-axis from $x = 1$ to $x = 2$.

RATIONAL APPROXIMATIONS FOR π

unit

A circle of radius 1 unit has area $A = \pi \times 1^2 = \pi$ units^2.

Notice in the figure that the length of PQ is $\sqrt{2}$.

We can see that

$$\text{area PQRS} < \pi < \text{area ABCD}$$

$$\therefore \quad \sqrt{2} \times \sqrt{2} < \pi < 2 \times 2$$

$$\therefore \quad 2 < \pi < 4$$

$$\uparrow \qquad\qquad \uparrow$$

lower bound   upper bound

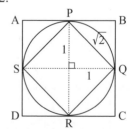

It is clear that 2 and 4 are not good estimates of π, however they do provide us with lower and upper bounds between which the true value of π lies.

Consider the quarter circle of centre $(0,\ 0)$
and radius 2 units as illustrated.

Its area is $\frac{1}{4}$ (full circle of radius 2)

$$= \frac{1}{4} \times \pi \times 2^2$$

$$= \pi$$

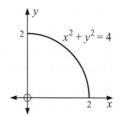

Recall that π is an irrational number whose decimal expansion neither terminates nor recurs.

We will now employ the lower and upper rectangle technique to find **rational bounds** for π.

Consider the case $n = 5$.

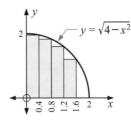 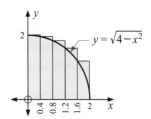

$$A_L = (0.4)\sqrt{4-(0.4)^2} + (0.4)\sqrt{4-(0.8)^2} + (0.4)\sqrt{4-(1.2)^2} + (0.4)\sqrt{4-(1.6)^2}$$

$$= 2.637\,04......$$

and $A_U = (0.4)\sqrt{4-0^2} + (0.4)\sqrt{4-(0.4)^2} + (0.4)\sqrt{4-(0.8)^2} + (0.4)\sqrt{4-(1.2)^2} +$

$$(0.4)\sqrt{4-(1.6)^2}$$

$$= 3.437\,04......$$

From this, $2.637 < \pi < 3.437$ provides us with rational bounds for π which are *better* than the earlier ones obtained geometrically.

As in the case of previous area finding, using lower and upper sums, we should be able to obtain even better bounds by increasing the number of vertical strips from $n = 5$ to 10 to 50 to 100, etc.

Click on the icon and experiment with increasing values of n to get better rational bounds for the actual value of π.

AREA FINDER

EXERCISE 26A.2

AREA FINDER

1 Alongside is the graph of $y = 2^x$. The tangent at $(1,\ 2)$ is drawn.

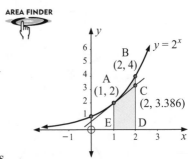

    a Use the figure to find rational lower and upper bounds for the shaded area.

    b Now consider the original graph without the tangent.

       Use five subdivisions of the interval $[1,\ 2]$ to obtain lower and upper sums of rectangular areas.

    c Click on the icon to check your answer to **b** ($n = 5$). Now obtain 'better' rational bounds for the area by considering $n = 10,\ 50,\ 100,\ 500,\ 5000$. Display your answers in table form.

2 Consider the graph of $y = 1 + e^x$ where
$e = 2.718\,281\,82.....$

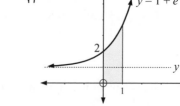

a Use five subdivisions of $[0, 1]$ and find the
lower and upper area sums.

b Now use the area finder to find the lower
and upper sums for $n = 100,\ 1000,\ 10\,000,$
$100\,000$.

c What do you notice about your answers to **b**?

3 **a** Sketch the region between the curve $y = \sqrt{1 + x^3}$ and the x-axis on the interval
$[0, 2]$.

   b Use technology to find the lower and upper rectangle sums for $n = 100$ and
$n = 10\,000$ subdivisions.

   c What is your best estimate of the exact area?

4 **a** Sketch the region between the curve $y = \dfrac{4}{1 + x^2}$ and the x-axis on $[0, 1]$.

   b Use technology to find the lower and upper rectangle sums for $n = 100,\ 1000,$
and $10\,000$.

   c What is your best estimate of the exact area? Comment on the result.

5 Find the area enclosed by the curve $y = \sqrt[3]{x^2 + 2}$ and the x-axis from $x = 0$ to
$x = 5$ to the best accuracy you can.

Example 1

Find, using graphical and other facts: **a** $\displaystyle\int_0^2 (2x + 1)\,dx$ **b** $\displaystyle\int_0^1 \sqrt{1 - x^2}\,dx$

Check your answers using technology.

a
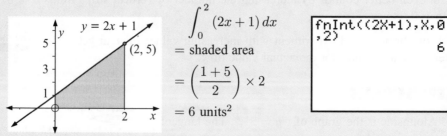

$\displaystyle\int_0^2 (2x + 1)\,dx$

$= $ shaded area

$= \left(\dfrac{1 + 5}{2}\right) \times 2$

$= 6$ units^2

```
fnInt((2X+1),X,0
,2)
                6
```

b As $y = \sqrt{1 - x^2}$, then $y^2 = 1 - x^2$ i.e., $x^2 + y^2 = 1$ which is the
equation of the unit circle. $y = \sqrt{1 - x^2}$ is the upper half.

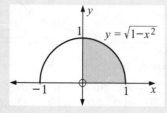

$\displaystyle\int_0^1 \sqrt{1 - x^2}\,dx$

$= $ shaded area

$= \frac{1}{4}(\pi r^2),\quad r = 1$

$= \dfrac{\pi}{4}$

```
fnInt(√(1-X²),X,
0,1)
         .7853984608
π/4
         .7853981634
```

6 Use graphical evidence and other area facts to find:

a $\displaystyle\int_1^3 (1 + 4x)\, dx$

b $\displaystyle\int_{-1}^2 (2 - x)\, dx$

c $\displaystyle\int_{-1}^1 |x|\, dx$

d $\displaystyle\int_0^2 |x - 1|\, dx$

e $\displaystyle\int_{-2}^2 \sqrt{4 - x^2}\, dx$

f $\displaystyle\int_{-2}^0 (1 + \sqrt{4 - x^2})\, dx$

Summary:

We can see from the examples in the previous exercise that:

> For a function $f(x)$ where $f(x) \geqslant 0$ on an interval $[\,a,\,b\,]$ the area between the x-axis and the function, between $x = a$ and $x = b$, is given by $A = \displaystyle\int_a^b f(x)\, dx$.

The following area calculations are worth noting:

Consider a constant function $f(t) = 5$, say.

the shaded area
$$= (x - a) \times 5 = 5x - 5a$$

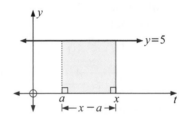

Now consider the simplest linear function, $f(t) = t$.

the shaded area
$$= \left(\frac{x + a}{2}\right)(x - a)$$
$$= \frac{x^2 - a^2}{2} = \frac{x^2}{2} - \frac{a^2}{2}$$

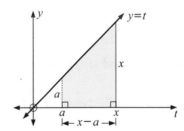

Can you see the relationship between the original functions and the shaded functions in the answers?

B   THE FUNDAMENTAL THEOREM OF CALCULUS

Isaac Newton showed the link between differential calculus and the definite integral (the limit of an area sum). This link is called the Fundamental theorem of calculus. The beauty of this theorem is that it enables us to evaluate complicated summations.

We have already established that:

"if $f(x)$ is a continuous positive function on an interval $[a, b]$ then the area under the curve between $x = a$ and $x = b$ is

$$\int_a^b f(x)\, dx \text{ ".}$$

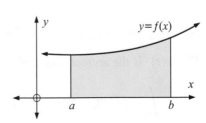

Consider a function $y = f(x)$ which has antiderivative $F(x)$ and an area function $A(t)$, where $A(t)$ is the area from $x = a$ to $x = t$,

i.e., $A(t) = \displaystyle\int_a^t f(x)\,dx.$

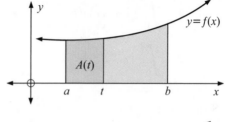

$A(t)$ is clearly an increasing function and

$A(a) = 0$ and $A(b) = \displaystyle\int_a^b f(x)\,dx$ ..... (1)

Now consider a narrow strip of the region between $x = t$ and $x = t + h$.

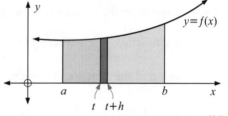

The area of this strip is $A(t + h) - A(t)$.

Since the narrow strip is contained within two rectangles then

area of smaller $\leqslant A(t + h) - A(t) \leqslant$ area of larger
       rectangle   rectangle

$\therefore \quad hf(t) \leqslant A(t + h) - A(t) \leqslant hf(t + h)$

$\therefore \quad f(t) \leqslant \dfrac{A(t + h) - A(t)}{h} \leqslant f(t + h)$

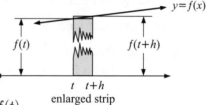

enlarged strip

Now taking limits as $h \to 0$ gives $f(t) \leqslant A'(t) \leqslant f(t)$

Consequently $A'(t) = f(t)$

i.e., $A(t)$, the area function, is an antiderivative of $f(t)$.

So, $A(t)$ and $F(t)$ differ by a constant,   i.e., $A(t) = F(t) + c$ ..... (2)

Now $\displaystyle\int_a^b f(x)\,dx = A(b)$ {from (1)}
$= F(b) + c$ {from (2)}

However $A(a) = F(a) + c$ on letting $t = a$ in (2)

$\therefore \quad 0 = F(a) + c$ and so $c = -F(a)$

Thus, $\displaystyle\int_a^b f(x)\,dx = F(b) - F(a)$

Hence,

The Fundamental theorem of calculus is:

For a continuous function $f(x)$ with antiderivative $F(x)$, $\displaystyle\int_a^b f(x)\,dx = F(b) - F(a)$.

Note: Considering a velocity-time function $v(t)$ we know that $\dfrac{ds}{dt} = v$.

So, $s(t)$ is the antiderivative of $v(t)$ and by the Fundamental theorem of calculus,

$\displaystyle\int_{t_1}^{t_2} v(t)\,dt = s(t_2) - s(t_1)$ gives the **displacement** over the time interval $[t_1, t_2]$.

The following properties of the definite integral can all be deduced from the Fundamental theorem of calculus and some can be easily demonstrated graphically.

$$\bullet \quad \int_a^a f(x)\, dx = 0$$

$$\bullet \quad \int_a^b c\, dx = c(b-a) \qquad \{c \text{ is a constant}\}$$

$$\bullet \quad \int_b^a f(x)\, dx = - \int_a^b f(x)\, dx$$

$$\bullet \quad \int_a^b f(x)\, dx + \int_b^c f(x)\, dx = \int_a^c f(x)\, dx$$

$$\bullet \quad \int_a^b c\, f(x)\, dx = c \int_a^b f(x)\, dx$$

$$\bullet \quad \int_a^b [f(x) \pm g(x)]\, dx = \int_a^b f(x)\, dx \pm \int_a^b g(x)\, dx$$

For example, consider $\displaystyle \int_a^b f(x)\, dx + \int_b^c f(x)\, dx = \int_a^c f(x)\, dx$

Proof:
$$\int_a^b f(x)\, dx + \int_b^c f(x)\, dx$$
$$= F(b) - F(a) + F(c) - F(b)$$
$$= F(c) - F(a)$$
$$= \int_a^c f(x)\, dx$$

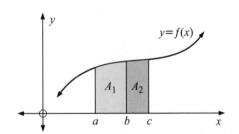

EXERCISE 26B

1 Use the Fundamental theorem of calculus to show that:

a $\displaystyle \int_a^a f(x)\, dx = 0$ and explain the result graphically

b $\displaystyle \int_a^b c\, dx = c(b-a)$, c is a constant

c $\displaystyle \int_b^a f(x)\, dx = - \int_a^b f(x)\, dx$

d $\displaystyle \int_a^b c\, f(x)\, dx = c \int_a^b f(x)\, dx$, c is a constant

e $\displaystyle \int_a^b [f(x) + g(x)]\, dx = \int_a^b f(x)\, dx + \int_a^b g(x)\, dx$

Example 2

Use the Fundamental theorem of calculus to find the area between the x-axis and:

a $y = x^2$ from $x = 0$ to $x = 1$ **b** $y = \sqrt{x}$ from $x = 1$ to $x = 9$

a

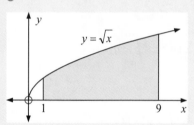

$f(x) = x^2$ has antiderivative $F(x) = \dfrac{x^3}{3}$

So the area $= \int_0^1 x^2 \, dx$

$= F(1) - F(0)$

$= \tfrac{1}{3} - 0$

$= \tfrac{1}{3}$ units^2

b

$f(x) = \sqrt{x} = x^{\frac{1}{2}}$ so, $F(x) = \dfrac{x^{\frac{3}{2}}}{\frac{3}{2}} = \tfrac{2}{3}x\sqrt{x}$

So the area $= \int_1^9 x^{\frac{1}{2}} \, dx$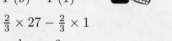

$= F(9) - F(1)$

$= \tfrac{2}{3} \times 27 - \tfrac{2}{3} \times 1$

$= 17\tfrac{1}{3}$ units^2

2 Use the Fundamental theorem of calculus to find the area between the x-axis and:

a $y = x^3$ from $x = 0$ to $x = 1$ **b** $y = x^3$ from $x = 1$ to $x = 2$

c $y = x^2 + 3x + 2$ on $[1, 3]$ **d** $y = \sqrt{x}$ from $x = 0$ to $x = 2$

e $y = e^x$ from $x = 0$ to $x = 1.5$ **f** $y = \dfrac{1}{\sqrt{x}}$ from $x = 1$ to $x = 4$

g $y = x^3 + 2x^2 + 7x + 4$ from $x = 1$ to $x = 1.25$

Check each answer using technology.

INVESTIGATION 2 $\int_a^b f(x)\,dx$ **AND AREAS**

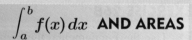

Does $\displaystyle\int_a^b f(x)\,dx$ always give us an area?

What to do:

1 Find $\displaystyle\int_0^1 x^3\,dx$ and $\displaystyle\int_{-1}^1 x^3\,dx$.

2 Explain why the first integral in **1** gives an area whereas the second integral does not. Graphical evidence is essential.

3 Find $\displaystyle\int_{-1}^0 x^3\,dx$ and explain why the answer is negative.

4 Check that $\displaystyle\int_{-1}^{0} x^3\,dx + \int_{0}^{1} x^3\,dx = \int_{-1}^{1} x^3\,dx.$

C | FINDING AREAS BETWEEN CURVES

We have already established that:

If $f(x)$ is positive and continuous on the interval $a \leqslant x \leqslant b$, then the area bounded by $y = f(x)$, the x-axis and the vertical lines $x = a$ and $x = b$

is given by $\displaystyle\int_{a}^{b} f(x)\,dx.$

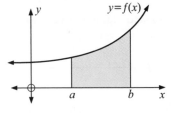

Notice also that the area bounded by $x = f(y)$, the y-axis and the horizontal lines $y = a$ and $y = b$

is given by $\displaystyle\int_{a}^{b} f(y)\,dy.$

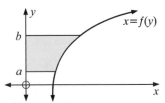

Example 3

Find the area of the region enclosed by $y = x^2 + 1$, the x-axis, $x = 1$ and $x = 2$.

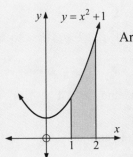

$$\begin{aligned}
\text{Area} &= \int_{1}^{2} (x^2 + 1)\,dx \\
&= \left[\frac{x^3}{3} + x\right]_{1}^{2} \\
&= \left(\tfrac{8}{3} + 2\right) - \left(\tfrac{1}{3} + 1\right) \\
&= 3\tfrac{1}{3} \text{ units}^2
\end{aligned}$$

To check your result on a graphics calculator (e.g., TI-83),

enter $y = x^2 + 1$ on $\boxed{\text{Y=}}$ then $\boxed{\text{GRAPH}}$, $\boxed{\text{CALC}}$ 7

asks for lower and upper limits 1 $\boxed{\text{ENTER}}$ 2 $\boxed{\text{ENTER}}$

or **fn** Int $(X^2 + 1, X, 1, 2)$

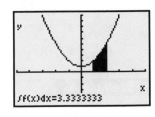

EXERCISE 26C

1 Find the area of the region bounded by: (Check answers using technology.)

   a $y = x^2$, the x-axis and $x = 1$ **b** $y = x^3$, the x-axis, $x = 1$ and $x = 4$

   c $y = e^x$, the x-axis, the y-axis and $x = 1$

   d the x-axis and the part of $y = 6 + x - x^2$ above the x-axis

   e $x = y^2 + 1$, the y-axis and the lines $y = 1$ and $y = 2$

   f $x = \sqrt{y + 5}$, the y-axis and the lines $y = -1$ and $y = 4$

AREA BETWEEN TWO FUNCTIONS

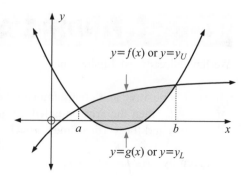

If two functions $f(x)$ and $g(x)$ intersect at $x = a$ and $x = b$ and $f(x) \geqslant g(x)$ for all x in the interval $a \leqslant x \leqslant b$, regardless of the position of the x-axis, then the area of the shaded region between their points of intersection is given by

$$\int_a^b [f(x) - g(x)]\, dx \quad or \quad \int_a^b [y_U - y_L]\, dx.$$

Proof: If we translate each curve vertically through $[0, k]$ until it is completely above the x-axis, the area is preserved (i.e., does not change).

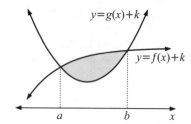

Area of shaded region

$= \int_a^b [f(x) + k]\, dx - \int_a^b [g(x) + k]\, dx$

$= \int_a^b [f(x) - g(x)]\, dx$

2   Use $\int_a^b [f(x) - g(x)]\, dx$ or $\int_a^b [y_U - y_L]\, dx$ to find the area between:

   a the axes and $y = \sqrt{9 - x}$

   b $y = \dfrac{1}{x}$, the x-axis, $x = 1$ and $x = 4$

   c $y = \dfrac{1}{x}$, the x-axis, $x = -1$ and $x = -3$

   d $y = 2 - \dfrac{1}{\sqrt{x}}$, the x-axis and $x = 4$

   e $y = e^x + e^{-x}$, the x-axis, $x = -1$ and $x = 1$.

   f $y = e^x$, the y-axis, the lines $y = 2$ and $y = 3$ using $\int \ln y\, dy = y \ln y - y + c$

Example 4

Use $\int_a^b [y_U - y_L]\, dx$ to find the area bounded by the x-axis and $y = x^2 - 2x$.

The curve cuts the x-axis when $y = 0$

$\therefore \quad x^2 - 2x = 0$

$\therefore \quad x(x - 2) = 0$

$\therefore \quad x = 0$ or 2

i.e., x intercepts are 0 and 2.

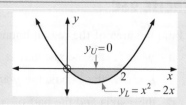

$$\text{Area} = \int_0^2 [y_U - y_L]\,dx$$

$$= \int_0^2 [0 - (x^2 - 2x)]\,dx$$

$$= \int_0^2 (2x - x^2)\,dx$$

$$= \left[x^2 - \frac{x^3}{3}\right]_0^2$$

$$= \left(4 - \tfrac{8}{3}\right) - (0)$$

$\therefore$ the area is $\tfrac{4}{3}$ units^2.

```
∫(2X-X²,0,2,1E-4)
              1.333333333




Solve d/dx d/dx ∫dx          ▷
```

3   Use $\int_a^b [y_U - y_L]\,dx$ to find the area bounded by:

a   the x-axis and $y = x^2 + x - 2$ **b**   the x-axis, $y = e^{-x} - 1$ and $x = 2$

c   the x-axis and the part of $y = 3x^2 - 8x + 4$ below the x-axis

d $y = x^3 - 4x$,   the x-axis, $x = 1$,   and $x = 2$.

Example 5

Find the area of the region enclosed by $y = x + 2$ and $y = x^2 + x - 2$.

$y = x + 2$ meets $y = x^2 + x - 2$ where
$$x^2 + x - 2 = x + 2$$
$$\therefore \quad x^2 - 4 = 0$$
$$\therefore \quad (x + 2)(x - 2) = 0$$
$$\therefore \quad x = \pm 2$$

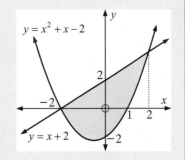

$$\text{Area} = \int_{-2}^2 [y_U - y_L]\,dx$$

$$= \int_{-2}^2 [(x + 2) - (x^2 + x - 2)]\,dx$$

$$= \int_{-2}^2 (4 - x^2)\,dx$$

$$= \left[4x - \frac{x^3}{3}\right]_{-2}^2$$

$$= \left(8 - \tfrac{8}{3}\right) - \left(-8 + \tfrac{8}{3}\right)$$

$$= 10\tfrac{2}{3} \text{ units}^2$$

```
∫(4-X²,-2,2,1E-4)
              10.66666667




Solve d/dx d/dx ∫dx          ▷
```

4   **a**   Find the area of the region enclosed by $y = x^2 - 2x$ and $y = 3$.

b   Consider the graphs of $y = x - 3$ and $y = x^2 - 3x$.

　　i   Sketch each graph on the same set of axes.

　　ii   Find the coordinates of the points where the graphs meet. Check algebraically.

　　iii   Find the area of the region enclosed by the two graphs.

c   Determine the area of the region enclosed by $y = \sqrt{x}$ and $y = x^2$.

d On the same set of axes, graph $y = e^x - 1$ and $y = 2 - 2e^{-x}$, showing axis intercepts and asymptotes.

Find algebraically, the points of intersection of $y = e^x - 1$ and $y = 2 - 2e^{-x}$.

Find the area of the region enclosed by the two curves.

e Determine the area of the region bounded by $y = 2e^x$, $y = e^{2x}$ and $x = 0$.

5 On the same set of axes, draw the graphs of the relations $y = 2x$ and $y^2 = 4x$. Determine the area of the region enclosed by these relations.

6 Sketch the circle with equation $x^2 + y^2 = 9$.

  a Explain why the 'upper half' of the circle has equation $y = \sqrt{9 - x^2}$.

  b Hence, determine $\int_0^3 \sqrt{9 - x^2}\, dx$ without actually integrating the function.

  c Check your answer using technology.

Example 6

Find the total area of the regions contained by $y = f(x)$ and the x-axis for $f(x) = x^3 + 2x^2 - 3x$.

$$\begin{aligned} f(x) &= x^3 + 2x^2 - 3x \\ &= x(x^2 + 2x - 3) \\ &= x(x - 1)(x + 3) \end{aligned}$$
$\therefore \quad y = f(x)$ cuts the x-axis at 0, 1, -3.

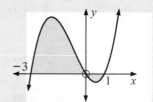

Total area

$= \int_{-3}^0 [(x^3 + 2x^2 - 3x) - 0]\, dx + \int_0^1 [0 - (x^3 + 2x^2 - 3x)]\, dx$

$= \int_{-3}^0 (x^3 + 2x^2 - 3x)\, dx - \int_0^1 (x^3 + 2x^2 - 3x)\, dx$

$= \left[\dfrac{x^4}{4} + \dfrac{2x^3}{3} - \dfrac{3x^2}{2} \right]_{-3}^0 - \left[\dfrac{x^4}{4} + \dfrac{2x^3}{3} - \dfrac{3x^2}{2} \right]_0^1$

$= (0 - -11\tfrac{1}{4}) - (-\tfrac{7}{12} - 0)$

$= 11\tfrac{5}{6}$ units^2

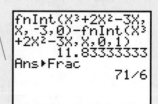

Note: The area in **Example 6** may be found using technology

as   total area $= \int_{-3}^1 |x^3 + 2x^2 - 3x|\, dx$.

Check this.

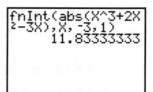

7 Find the area enclosed by the function $y = f(x)$ and the x-axis for:

  a $f(x) = x^3 - 9x$ **b** $f(x) = -x(x-2)(x-4)$ **c** $f(x) = x^4 - 5x^2 + 4$.

8 For the given graphs of $y = x^3 - 4x$ and $y = 3x + 6$:

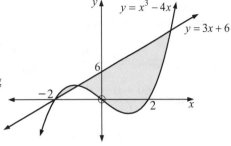

    a write the shaded area as

       i the sum of two definite integrals

       ii a single definite integral involving modulus.

    b Find the total shaded area.

9 Find the areas enclosed by:

    a $y = x^3 - 5x$ and $y = 2x^2 - 6$ **b** $y = -x^3 + 3x^2 + 6x - 8$ and $y = 5x - 5$

    c $y = 2x^3 - 3x^2 + 18$ and $y = x^3 + 10x - 6$

10 **a** Explain why the total area shaded is *not* equal to $\int_1^7 f(x)\,dx$.

    b What is the total shaded area equal to in terms of integrals?

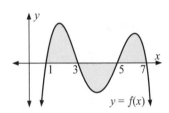

11 The shaded area is 0.2 units^2.

Find k, correct to 4 decimal places.

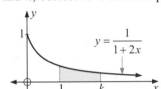

12 The shaded area is 1 unit^2.

Find b, correct to 4 decimal places.

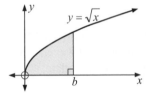

13 The shaded area is 2.4 units^2.

Find k, correct to 4 decimal places.

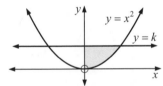

14 The shaded area is $6a$ units^2.

Find a.

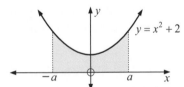

D | DISTANCES FROM VELOCITY FUNCTIONS

Suppose a car travels at a constant positive velocity of 60 km/h for 15 minutes.

Since the velocity is positive we can use speed instead of velocity.

The distance travelled is   60 km/h $\times \frac{1}{4}$ h $= 15$ km.

However, when we graph *speed* against *time*, the graph is a horizontal line and it is clear that the distance travelled is the area shaded.

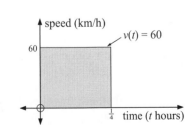

[As   average speed $= \dfrac{\text{distance travelled}}{\text{time taken}}$

then   distance = speed $\times$ time.]

Now suppose the speed decreases at a constant rate so that the car, initially travelling at 60 km/h, stops in 6 minutes.

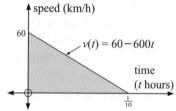

Now   average speed $= \dfrac{\text{distance travelled}}{\text{time taken}}$

then $\dfrac{60+0}{2} = \dfrac{\text{distance}}{\frac{1}{10}}$

$\therefore$ $30 \times \frac{1}{10} = \text{distance}$ i.e.,   distance $= 3$ km

But the triangle has area $= \frac{1}{2}$ base $\times$ altitude $= \frac{1}{2} \times \frac{1}{10} \times 60 = 3$

So, once again the shaded area gives us the distance travelled.

Using definite integral notation:

distance travelled $= \displaystyle\int_0^{\frac{1}{4}} 60 \, dt = 15$ {for the first example}

and distance travelled $= \displaystyle\int_0^{\frac{1}{10}} (60 - 600t) \, dt = 3$ {for the second example}

These results suggest that: distance travelled $= \displaystyle\int_{t_1}^{t_2} v(t) \, dt$ provided we do not change direction.

The area under the velocity-time graph gives distance travelled regardless of the shape of the velocity function. However, when the graph is made up of straight line segments the distance is usually easy to calculate.

Example 7

The velocity-time graph for a train journey is as illustrated in the graph alongside. Find the total distance travelled by the train.

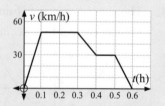

   Total distance travelled
$=$ total area under the graph
$=$ area A $+$ area B $+$ area C $+$ area D $+$ area E
$= \frac{1}{2}(0.1)50 + (0.2)50 + \left(\frac{50+30}{2}\right)(0.1) + (0.1)30$
$\quad + \frac{1}{2}(0.1)30$
$= 2.5 + 10 + 4 + 3 + 1.5$
$= 21$ km

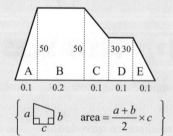

In general,   for a velocity-time function $v(t)$
where $v(t) \geqslant 0$,

distance travelled $= \displaystyle\int_{t_1}^{t_2} v(t) dt$

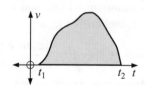

EXERCISE 26D.1

1 A runner has velocity-time graph as shown. Find the total distance travelled by the runner.

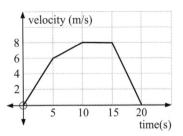

2

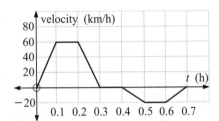

A car travels along a straight road and its velocity-time function is illustrated.

  a What is the significance of the graph:
    i above the t-axis
    ii below the t-axis?

  b Find the final displacement of the car.

3 A triathlete rides off from rest accelerating at a constant rate for 3 minutes until she reaches 40 km/h. She then maintains a constant speed for 4 minutes until reaching a section where she slows down at a constant rate to 30 km/h in one minute. She then continues at this rate for 10 minutes before reducing her speed uniformly and is stationary 2 minutes later. After drawing a graph, find how far she has travelled.

DISTANCE FROM VELOCITY

In this section we are concerned with **motion in a straight line**, i.e., **linear motion**.

Given a **velocity function** we can determine the **displacement function** by integration.

From the displacement function we can determine **total distances travelled** in some time interval $a \leqslant t \leqslant b$.

Recall that for some displacement function $s(t)$ the velocity function is $s'(t)$ and that $t \geqslant 0$ in all situations.

Consider the following example:

A particle moves in a straight line with velocity function $v(t) = t - 3$ cm/s.

How far does it travel in the first 4 seconds of motion?

We notice that $v(t) = s'(t) = t - 3$ which has sign diagram:

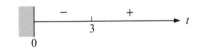

Since the velocity function changes sign at $t = 3$ seconds, the particle **reverses direction** at this time.

Now $s(t) = \int (t - 3) \, dt$

$\therefore \quad s(t) = \dfrac{t^2}{2} - 3t + c$ cm   and we are given no information to determine the value of c.

Also the total distance travelled is not $s(4) - s(0)$ because of the reversal of direction at $t = 3$ seconds.

We find the position of the particle at $t = 0$, $t = 3$ and $t = 4$.

$$s(0) = c, \qquad s(3) = c - 4\tfrac{1}{2}, \qquad s(4) = c - 4.$$

Hence, we can draw a diagram
of the motion:

$c-4\tfrac{1}{2}$ $c-4$ c

Thus the total distance travelled is $(4\tfrac{1}{2} + \tfrac{1}{2})$ cm $= 5$ cm.

Notice that $s(4) - s(0) = c - 4 - c = -4$ does not give the total distance travelled.

Summary

To find the total distance travelled given a velocity function $v(t) = s'(t)$ on $a \leqslant t \leqslant b$:

- Draw a sign diagram for $v(t)$ so that we can determine directional changes, if they exist.
- Determine $s(t)$ by integration, with integrating constant c, say.
- Find $s(a)$ and $s(b)$. Also find $s(t)$ at every point where there is a direction reversal.
- Draw a motion diagram.
- Determine the total distance travelled from the motion diagram.

Example 8

A particle P moves in a straight line with velocity function $v(t) = t^2 - 3t + 2$ m/s.
a How far does P travel in the first 4 seconds of motion?
b Find the displacement of P after 4 seconds

a $v(t) = s'(t) = t^2 - 3t + 2$ $\therefore$ sign diagram of v is:

$$= (t - 1)(t - 2)$$

Since the signs change, P reverses direction at $t = 1$ and $t = 2$ secs.

Now $s(t) = \int (t^2 - 3t + 2)\, dt = \dfrac{t^3}{3} - \dfrac{3t^2}{2} + 2t + c$

Now $s(0) = c$ $s(1) = \tfrac{1}{3} - \tfrac{3}{2} + 2 + c = c + \tfrac{5}{6}$

$s(2) = \tfrac{8}{3} - 6 + 4 + c = c + \tfrac{2}{3}$ $s(4) = \tfrac{64}{3} - 24 + 8 + c = c + 5\tfrac{1}{3}$

Motion diagram:

c $c+\tfrac{2}{3}$ $c+\tfrac{5}{6}$ $c+5\tfrac{1}{3}$

$\therefore$ total distance $= \left(c + \tfrac{5}{6} - c\right) + \left(c + \tfrac{5}{6} - [c + \tfrac{2}{3}]\right) + \left(c + 5\tfrac{1}{3} - [c + \tfrac{2}{3}]\right)$

$= \tfrac{5}{6} + \tfrac{5}{6} - \tfrac{2}{3} + 5\tfrac{1}{3} - \tfrac{2}{3}$

$= 5\tfrac{2}{3}$ m

b Displacement $=$ final position $-$ original position

$= s(4) - s(0)$

$= c + 5\tfrac{1}{3} - c$

$= 5\tfrac{1}{3}$ i.e., $5\tfrac{1}{3}$ m to the right.

Note: In practice we can use:

• total distance travelled $= \displaystyle\int_a^b |v(t)| \, dt$

• displacement $= \displaystyle\int_a^b v(t) \, dt$

Check the answers to **Example 8** using these formulae and your calculator.

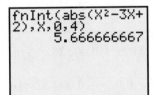

EXERCISE 26D.2

1 A particle has velocity function $v(t) = 1 - 2t$ cm/s as it moves in a straight line.

  a Find the total distance travelled in the first second of motion.

  b Find the displacement of the particle at the end of one second.

2 Particle P has velocity $v(t) = t^2 - t - 2$ cm/s.

  a Find the total distance travelled in the first 3 seconds of motion.

  b Find the displacement of the particle at the end of three seconds.

3 A particle moves along the x-axis with velocity function $x'(t) = 16t - 4t^3$ units/s. Find the total distance travelled in the time interval:

  a $0 \leqslant t \leqslant 3$ seconds   **b** $1 \leqslant t \leqslant 3$ seconds.

4 The velocity of a particle travelling in a straight line is given by $v(t) = 50 - 10e^{-0.5t}$ m/s, where $t \geqslant 0$, t in seconds.

  a State the initial velocity of the particle.

  b Find the velocity of the particle after 3 seconds.

  c How long would it take for the particle's velocity to increase to 45 m/s?

  d Discuss $v(t)$ as $t \to \infty$.

  e Show that the particle's acceleration is always positive.

  f Draw the graph of $v(t)$ against t.

  g Find the total distance travelled by the particle in the first 3 seconds of motion.

5 A train moves along a straight track with acceleration $\frac{t}{10} - 3$ m/s^2. If the initial velocity of the train is 45 m/s, determine the total distance travelled in the first minute.

6 A body has initial velocity 20 m/s as it moves in a straight line with acceleration function $4e^{-\frac{t}{20}}$ m/s^2.

  a Show that as t increases the body approaches a limiting velocity.

  b Find the total distance travelled in the first 10 seconds of motion.

E   PROBLEM SOLVING BY INTEGRATION

Example 9

The marginal cost of producing x urns per week is given by $2.15 - 0.02x + 0.000\,36x^2$ dollars per urn provided that $0 \leqslant x \leqslant 120$.

The set up costs before production starts are \$185. Find the total cost of producing 100 urns per day.

The marginal cost is $\dfrac{dC}{dx}$ and $\dfrac{dC}{dx} = 2.15 - 0.02x + 0.000\,36x^2$ \$/urn

$$\therefore \quad C(x) = \int(2.15 - 0.02x + 0.000\,36x^2)\,dx$$

$$= 2.15x - 0.02\frac{x^2}{2} + 0.000\,36\frac{x^3}{3} + c$$

$$= 2.15x - 0.01x^2 + 0.000\,12x^3 + c$$

But $C(0) = 185$ $\therefore \quad c = 185$

$$\therefore \quad C(x) = 2.15x - 0.01x^2 + 0.000\,12x^3 + 185$$

$$C(100) = 2.15(100) - 0.01(100)^2 + 0.000\,12(100)^3 + 185$$

$$= 420$$

$\therefore$ the total cost is \$420.

EXERCISE 26E

1   The marginal cost per day of producing x gadgets is $C'(x) = 3.15 + 0.004x$ dollars per gadget.   What is the total cost of daily production of 800 gadgets given that the fixed costs before production commences are \$450 a day?

2   The marginal profit for producing x dinner plates per week is given by $15 - 0.03x$ dollars per plate.   If no plates are made a loss of \$650 each week occurs.

    a   Find the profit function.

    b   What is the maximum profit and when does it occur?

    c   What production levels enable a profit to be made?

Example 10

A metal tube has an annulus cross-section as shown. The outer radius is 4 cm and the inner radius is 2 cm. Within the tube, water is maintained at a temperature of 100°C. Within the metal the temperature drops off from inside

to outside according to $\dfrac{dT}{dx} = -\dfrac{10}{x}$ where x is

the distance from the central axis O, and $2 \leqslant x \leqslant 4$. Find the temperature of the outer surface of the tube.

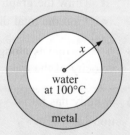

water at 100°C

metal

tube cross-section

$$\frac{dT}{dx} = \frac{-10}{x} \qquad \therefore \quad T = \int \frac{-10}{x}\, dx$$

$$\therefore \quad T = -10 \ln |x| + c$$

But when $\quad x = 2, \quad T = 100$

$$\therefore \quad 100 = -10 \ln 2 + c$$

$$\therefore \quad c = 100 + 10 \ln 2$$

Thus $T = -10 \ln x + 100 + 10 \ln 2$

i.e., $\quad T = 100 + 10 \ln \left(\frac{2}{x} \right)$

and when $\quad x = 4, \quad T = 100 + 10 \ln \left(\frac{1}{2} \right) \doteqdot 93.07$

$\therefore$ the outer surface temperature is 93.07°C.

3 Jon needs to bulk-up for the next AFL season. His energy needs t days after starting his weight gain program are given by $\quad E(t) = 350(80 + 0.15t)^{0.8} - 120(80 + 0.15t)$ calories/day. Find Jon's total energy needs over the first week of the program.

4 The tube cross-section shown has inner radius of 3 cm and outer radius 6 cm and within the tube water is maintained at a temperature of 100°C. Within the metal the temperature falls off at a rate according to $\quad \dfrac{dT}{dx} = \dfrac{-20}{x^{0.63}}$ where x is the distance from the central axis O and $3 \leqslant x \leqslant 6$.

Find the temperature of the outer surface of the tube.

5 A thin horizontal cantilever of length 1 metre has a deflection of y metres at a distance of x m from the fixed end.

It is known that $\quad \dfrac{d^2 y}{dx^2} = -\frac{1}{10}(1 - x)^2.$

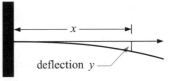

a Find the equation for measuring the deflection from the horizontal at any point on the beam. [**Hint:** When $x = 0$, what are y and $\dfrac{dy}{dx}$?]

b Determine the greatest deflection of the beam.

6

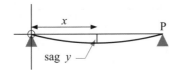

A plank of wood is supported only at its ends, O and P 4 metres from O. The plank sags under its own weight, a distance of y metres, x metres from end O.

The differential equation $\quad \dfrac{d^2 y}{dx^2} = 0.01 \left(2x - \dfrac{x^2}{2} \right) \quad$ relates the variables x and y.

a Find the equation for measuring the sag from the horizontal at any point along the plank.

b Find the maximum sag from the horizontal.

c Find the sag from the horizontal at a distance 1 m from P.

d Find the angle the plank makes with the horizontal 1 m from P.

7 A contractor digs roughly cylindrical wells to a depth of h metres and estimates that the cost of digging a well x metres deep is $\frac{1}{2}x^2 + 4$ dollars per m³.

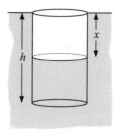

If a well is to have a radius r cm, show that the total cost of digging a well is given by

$$C(h) = \pi r^2 \left(\frac{h^3 + 24h}{6} \right) + C_0 \text{ dollars.}$$ $$\left[\textbf{Hint:}\ \frac{dC}{dx} = \frac{dC}{dV}\frac{dV}{dx} \right]$$

8 A farmer with a large property plans a rectangular fruit orchard with one boundary being an irrigation canal. He has 4 km of fencing to fence the orchard.

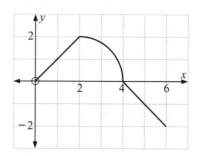

The farmer knows that the yield per unit of area changes the further you are away from the canal. This yield, Y per unit of area is proportional to

$\dfrac{1}{\sqrt{x+4}}$ where x is as shown in the figure.

a Explain why $\dfrac{dY}{dA} = \dfrac{k}{\sqrt{x+4}}$ where k is a constant.

b Show that $\dfrac{dY}{dx} = \dfrac{k(4-2p)}{\sqrt{x+4}}$ by using the chain rule.

c Explain why $Y = \displaystyle\int_0^p \dfrac{k(4-2p)}{\sqrt{x+4}}\,dx.$ **d** Show that $Y = 4k(2-p)[\sqrt{p+4}-2]$.

e What dimensions should the orchard be if yield is to be a maximum?

REVIEW SET 26A

1 **a** Sketch the graph of $y = \sqrt{x}$ from $x = 1$ to $x = 4$.

b By using a lower sum and rectangular strips of width 0.5, estimate the area between $y = \sqrt{x}$, the x-axis, $x = 1$ and $x = 4$.

2 The function $y = f(x)$ is graphed.
Find:

a $\displaystyle\int_0^4 f(x)\,dx$

b $\displaystyle\int_4^6 f(x)\,dx$

c $\displaystyle\int_0^6 f(x)\,dx$

3 Write the total shaded area:

a as the sum of three definite integrals

b as one definite integral involving modulus.

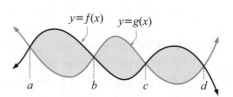

4   O is a point on a straight line. A particle moving on this straight line has a velocity of 27 cm/s as it passes through O. Its acceleration t seconds later is $6t - 30$ cm/s^2. Find the total distance (from O) that the particle has travelled when it momentarily comes to rest for the *second* time.

5   Draw the graphs of $y^2 = x - 1$ and $y = x - 3$.

   a   Find the coordinates where the graphs meet.   **b**   Find the enclosed area.

6   Determine k if the enclosed region has area $5\frac{1}{3}$ units^2.

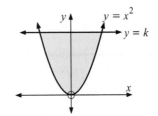

7   By appealing only to geometrical evidence, explain why: $\displaystyle\int_0^1 e^x \, dx + \int_1^e \ln x \, dx = e$.

8   A boat travelling in a straight line has its engine turned off at time $t = 0$. Its velocity in metres per second at time t seconds is then given by $v(t) = \dfrac{100}{(t+2)^2}$ m/s, $t \geqslant 0$.

   a   Find the initial velocity of the boat, and its velocity after 3 seconds.
   b   Discuss $v(t)$ as $t \to \infty$.   **c**   Sketch the graph of $v(t)$ against t.
   d   Find how long it takes for the boat to travel 30 metres.
   e   Find the acceleration of the boat at any time t.
   f   Show that $\dfrac{dv}{dt} = -kv^{\frac{3}{2}}$, and find the value of the constant k.

9   Find the total finite area enclosed by $y = x^3$ and $y = 7x^2 - 10x$.

10   Find a given that the area of the region between $y = e^x$ and the x-axis from $x = 0$ to $x = a$ is 2 units^2.

Hence determine b, given that the area of the region between $x = a$ and $x = b$ is also 2 units^2.

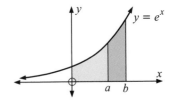

REVIEW SET 26B

1   A particle moves in a straight line with velocity $v(t) = 2t - 3t^2$ m/s. Find the distance travelled in the first second of motion.

2   Find the area of the region enclosed by $y = x^2 + 4x + 1$ and $y = 3x + 3$.

3   The current $I(t)$ amps, in a circuit falls off in accordance with $\dfrac{dI}{dt} = \dfrac{-100}{t^2}$ where t is the time in seconds, provided that $t \geqslant 0.2$ seconds.

It is known that when $t = 2$, the current is 150 amps. Find a formula for the current at any time $(t \geqslant 0.2)$, and hence find:

   a   the current after 20 seconds   **b**   what happens to the current as $t \to \infty$.

4 Determine $\int_0^2 \sqrt{4 - x^2}\, dx$ by considering the graph of $y = \sqrt{4 - x^2}$.

5 Is it true that $\int_{-1}^3 f(x)\, dx$ represents the area
of the shaded region?
Explain your answer briefly.

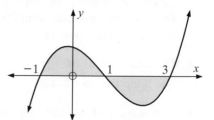

6 Consider $f(x) = \dfrac{x}{1 + x^2}$.

   a Find the position and nature of all turning points of $y = f(x)$.
   b Discuss $f(x)$ as $x \to \infty$ and as $x \to -\infty$.
   c Sketch the graph of $y = f(x)$.
   d Find the area enclosed by $y = f(x)$,
        the x-axis and the vertical line $x = -2$.

7 OABC is a rectangle and the two shaded
regions are equal in area. Find k.

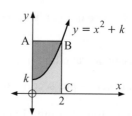

8 **a** Sketch the region bounded by $y = x^3 + 2$,   the y-axis and the horizontal lines
        $y = 3$ and $y = 6$.

   b Write x in the form $f(y)$.

   c Find the area of the region graphed in **a**.

9 Find the area enclosed by $y = 2x^3 - 9x$ and $y = 3x^2 - 10$.

Chapter **27**

Circular function integration

Contents:

A | BASIC CIRCULAR FUNCTION INTEGRALS

Earlier we discovered that integrals of functions can be found by appropriate differentiation. Observe the following:

$$\frac{d}{dx}(\sin x + c) \qquad \frac{d}{dx}(-\cos x + c) \qquad \frac{d}{dx}(\tan x + c)$$

$$= \cos x + 0 \qquad\qquad = -(-\sin x) + 0 \qquad\quad = \frac{1}{\cos^2 x}$$

$$= \cos x \qquad\qquad\quad = \sin x$$

$$\therefore \int \cos x \, dx = \sin x + c \quad \therefore \int \sin x \, dx = -\cos x + c \quad \therefore \int \frac{1}{\cos^2 x} \, dx = \tan x + c$$

We can now extend our basic list of integrals to include these discoveries.

Thus, the integrals of basic functions are:

Function	Integral	Function	Integral
k (a constant)	$kx + c$	e^x	$e^x + c$
x^n $(n \neq -1)$	$\dfrac{x^{n+1}}{n+1} + c$	$\cos x$	$\sin x + c$
		$\sin x$	$-\cos x + c$
$\dfrac{1}{x}$	$\ln|x| + c$	$\dfrac{1}{\cos^2 x}$ or $\sec^2 x$	$\tan x + c$

Reminder:

$$\int [f(x) \pm g(x)]dx = \int f(x)dx \pm \int g(x)dx$$

$$\int kf(x)dx = k\int f(x)dx \qquad (k \text{ is a constant})$$

Example 1

Integrate with respect to x:

a $2\sin x - \cos x$

b $\dfrac{3}{\cos^2 x} - \dfrac{2}{x} + \sqrt{x}$

a $\int [2\sin x - \cos x]dx$

$= 2(-\cos x) - \sin x + c$

$= -2\cos x - \sin x + c$

b $\int \left[\dfrac{3}{\cos^2 x} - \dfrac{2}{x} + x^{\frac{1}{2}} \right] dx$

$= 3\tan x - 2\ln|x| + \dfrac{x^{\frac{3}{2}}}{\frac{3}{2}} + c$

$= 3\tan x - 2\ln|x| + \frac{2}{3}x^{\frac{3}{2}} + c$

EXERCISE 27A

1   Integrate with respect to x:

a $3\sin x - 2$

b $4x - 2\cos x$

c $2\sqrt{x} + \dfrac{4}{\cos^2 x}$

d $\dfrac{1}{\cos^2 x} + 2\sin x$

e $\dfrac{x}{2} - \dfrac{1}{\cos^2 x}$

f $\sin x - 2\cos x + e^x$

2 Find:

a $\int \left(\sqrt{x} + \frac{1}{2} \cos x \right) dx$ **b** $\int (\theta - \sin \theta) \, d\theta$ **c** $\int \left(t\sqrt{t} + \frac{2}{\cos^2 t} \right) dt$

d $\int (2e^t - 4 \sin t) \, dt$ **e** $\int \left(3 \cos t - \frac{1}{t} \right) dt$ **f** $\int \left(3 - \frac{2}{\theta} + \frac{1}{\cos^2 \theta} \right) d\theta$

Example 2

Find $\dfrac{d}{dx}(x \sin x)$ and hence deduce $\int x \cos x \, dx$.

$\dfrac{d}{dx}(x \sin x) = (1) \sin x + (x) \cos x$ {product rule of differentiation}

$\qquad\qquad\quad = \sin x + x \cos x$

Thus $\int (\sin x + x \cos x) dx = x \sin x + c_1$ {antidifferentiation}

$\therefore \quad \int \sin x \, dx + \int x \cos x \, dx = x \sin x + c_1$

$\therefore \quad -\cos x + c_2 + \int x \cos x \, dx = x \sin x + c_1$

$\therefore \quad \int x \cos x \, dx = x \sin x + \cos x + c$

Example 3

By considering $\dfrac{d}{dx}\left(\dfrac{1}{\sin x} \right)$,

determine $\displaystyle\int \dfrac{\cos x}{\sin^2 x} \, dx$.

$\dfrac{d}{dx}\left(\dfrac{1}{\sin x} \right) = \dfrac{d}{dx}[\sin x]^{-1}$

$\qquad\qquad\quad = -[\sin x]^{-2} \times \dfrac{d}{dx}(\sin x)$

$\qquad\qquad\quad = -\dfrac{1}{\sin^2 x} \times \cos x$

$\qquad\qquad\quad = -\dfrac{\cos x}{\sin^2 x}$

Hence $\displaystyle\int -\dfrac{\cos x}{\sin^2 x} \, dx = \dfrac{1}{\sin x} + c_1$

$\therefore \quad \displaystyle\int \dfrac{\cos x}{\sin^2 x} \, dx = -\dfrac{1}{\sin x} + c$

---

3 **a** Find $\dfrac{d}{dx}(e^x \sin x)$ and hence find $\int e^x(\sin x + \cos x) dx$.

b By considering $\dfrac{d}{dx}(e^{-x} \sin x)$, deduce $\displaystyle\int \dfrac{\cos x - \sin x}{e^x} \, dx$.

c Find $\dfrac{d}{dx}(x \cos x)$ and hence deduce $\int x \sin x \, dx$.

d By considering $\dfrac{d}{dx}\left(\dfrac{1}{\cos x}\right)$, determine $\displaystyle\int \dfrac{\tan x}{\cos x} \, dx$.

Example 4

Find $f(x)$ given that $f'(x) = 2\sin x - \sqrt{x}$ and $f(0) = 4$.

Since $f'(x) = 2\sin x - \sqrt{x} = 2\sin x - x^{\frac{1}{2}}$

then $f(x) = \int \left[2\sin x - x^{\frac{1}{2}} \right] dx$

$\therefore \quad f(x) = 2 \times (-\cos x) - \dfrac{x^{\frac{3}{2}}}{\frac{3}{2}} + c$

$\therefore \quad f(x) = -2\cos x - \frac{2}{3} x^{\frac{3}{2}} + c$

But $f(0) = -2\cos 0 - 0 + c$

$\therefore \quad 4 = -2 + c$ and so $c = 6$

Thus $f(x) = -2\cos x - \frac{2}{3} x^{\frac{3}{2}} + 6$.

4 Find $f(x)$ given that:

   a $f'(x) = x^2 - 4\cos x$ and $f(0) = 3$ **b** $f'(x) = 2\cos x - 3\sin x$ and $f\left(\frac{\pi}{4}\right) = \frac{1}{\sqrt{2}}$

   c $f'(x) = \sqrt{x} - \dfrac{2}{\cos^2 x}$ and $f(\pi) = 0$.

B INTEGRALS OF $f(ax+b)$ CIRCULAR FUNCTIONS

Observe the following: As $\dfrac{d}{dx}(\sin(ax+b)) = \cos(ax+b) \times a$,

then $\int a\cos(ax+b)\,dx = \sin(ax+b) + c_1$

i.e., $a \int \cos(ax+b)\,dx = \sin(ax+b) + c_1$

$\therefore \quad \int \cos(ax+b)\,dx = \dfrac{1}{a}\sin(ax+b) + c$

Likewise we can show $\int \sin(ax+b)\,dx = -\dfrac{1}{a}\cos(ax+b) + c$ and

$$\int \frac{1}{\cos^2(ax+b)}\,dx = \frac{1}{a}\tan(ax+b) + c$$

Summary:

Function	Integral	Function	Integral
$\cos(ax+b)$	$\dfrac{1}{a}\sin(ax+b) + c$	$(ax+b)^n$	$\dfrac{1}{a}\dfrac{(ax+b)^{n+1}}{n+1} + c, \quad n \neq -1$
$\sin(ax+b)$	$-\dfrac{1}{a}\cos(ax+b) + c$	e^{ax+b}	$\dfrac{1}{a}e^{ax+b} + c$
$\dfrac{1}{\cos^2(ax+b)}$ or $\sec^2(ax+b)$	$\dfrac{1}{a}\tan(ax+b) + c$	$\dfrac{1}{ax+b}$	$\dfrac{1}{a}\ln|ax+b| + c$

Example 5

Integrate with respect to x: **a** $e^{-2x} - \dfrac{4}{\cos^2(2x)}$ **b** $2\sin(3x) + \cos(4x)$

a
$$\int \left(e^{-2x} - \frac{4}{\cos^2(2x)}\right) dx$$
$$= \frac{1}{-2} \times e^{-2x} - 4 \times \tfrac{1}{2}\tan(2x) + c$$
$$-\tfrac{1}{2}e^{-2x} - 2\tan(2x) + c$$

b
$$\int (2\sin(3x) + \cos(4x))\, dx$$
$$= 2 \times \tfrac{1}{3}(-\cos(3x)) + \tfrac{1}{4}\sin(4x) + c$$
$$= -\tfrac{2}{3}\cos(3x) + \tfrac{1}{4}\sin(4x) + c$$

EXERCISE 27B

1 Integrate with respect to x:

a $\sin(3x)$ **b** $2\cos(4x)$ **c** $\dfrac{1}{\cos^2(2x)}$

d $3\cos\left(\dfrac{x}{2}\right)$ **e** $3\sin(2x) - e^{-x}$ **f** $e^{2x} - \dfrac{2}{\cos^2\left(\frac{x}{2}\right)}$

g $2\sin\left(2x + \frac{\pi}{6}\right)$ **h** $-3\cos\left(\frac{\pi}{4} - x\right)$ **i** $\dfrac{4}{\cos^2\left(\frac{\pi}{3} - 2x\right)}$

j $\cos(2x) + \sin(2x)$ **k** $2\sin(3x) + 5\cos(4x)$ **l** $\tfrac{1}{2}\cos(8x) - 3\sin x$

Integrals involving $\sin^2(ax+b)$ and $\cos^2(ax+b)$ can be found by first using

$$\sin^2\theta = \tfrac{1}{2} - \tfrac{1}{2}\cos(2\theta) \quad \text{or} \quad \cos^2\theta = \tfrac{1}{2} + \tfrac{1}{2}\cos(2\theta).$$

These formulae are simply rearrangements of $\cos(2\theta)$ formulae.

For example,   • $\sin^2(3x)$ becomes $\tfrac{1}{2} - \tfrac{1}{2}\cos(6x)$

• $\cos^2(\tfrac{x}{2})$ becomes $\tfrac{1}{2} + \tfrac{1}{2}\cos 2(\tfrac{x}{2}) = \tfrac{1}{2} + \tfrac{1}{2}\cos x$

Example 6

Integrate $(2 - \sin x)^2$.

$$\int (2 - \sin x)^2 dx$$
$$= \int (4 - 4\sin x + \sin^2 x)\, dx$$
$$= \int \left(4 - 4\sin x + \tfrac{1}{2} - \tfrac{1}{2}\cos(2x)\right) dx$$
$$= \int \left(\tfrac{9}{2} - 4\sin x - \tfrac{1}{2}\cos(2x)\right) dx$$
$$= \tfrac{9}{2}x + 4\cos x - \tfrac{1}{2} \times \tfrac{1}{2}\sin(2x) + c$$
$$= \tfrac{9}{2}x + 4\cos x - \tfrac{1}{4}\sin(2x) + c$$

2 Integrate with respect to x:

a $\cos^2 x$ **b** $\sin^2 x$ **c** $1 + \cos^2(2x)$

d $3 - \sin^2(3x)$ **e** $\tfrac{1}{2}\cos^2(4x)$ **f** $(1 + \cos x)^2$

3 Use the identity $\cos^2 \theta = \frac{1}{2} + \frac{1}{2}\cos(2\theta)$ to show that

$$\cos^4 x = \tfrac{1}{8}\cos(4x) + \tfrac{1}{2}\cos(2x) + \tfrac{3}{8} \quad \text{and hence find} \quad \int \cos^4 x \, dx.$$

Example 7

Integrate with respect to x: **a** $\cos^3 x \sin x$ **b** $\dfrac{\cos x}{\sin x}$

a $\quad \int \cos^3 x \sin x \, dx$

$= \int [\cos x]^3 \sin x \, dx$

We let $u = \cos x$, $\therefore \dfrac{du}{dx} = -\sin x$

$= \int u^3 \left(-\dfrac{du}{dx}\right) dx$

$= -\int u^3 \, du$

$= -\dfrac{u^4}{4} + c$

$= -\tfrac{1}{4}[\cos x]^4 + c$

b $\quad \displaystyle\int \dfrac{\cos x}{\sin x} \, dx$

We let $u = \sin x$, $\therefore \dfrac{du}{dx} = \cos x$

$= \displaystyle\int \dfrac{1}{u}\dfrac{du}{dx} \, dx$

$= \displaystyle\int \dfrac{1}{u} \, du$

$= \ln|u| + c$

$= \ln|\sin x| + c$

Note: In **b** if we let $u = \cos x$, $\dfrac{du}{dx} = -\sin x$ and $\displaystyle\int \dfrac{\cos x}{\sin x} \, dx = \int \dfrac{u}{-\dfrac{du}{dx}} \, dx.$

However, this substitution leads nowhere as simplification to a form where the integration can be performed does not occur.

4 Integrate by substitution:

a $\sin^4 x \cos x$ **b** $\dfrac{\sin x}{\sqrt{\cos x}}$ **c** $\tan x$ **d** $\sqrt{\sin x}\cos x$

e $\dfrac{\cos x}{(2 + \sin x)^2}$ **f** $\dfrac{\sin x}{\cos^3 x}$ **g** $\dfrac{\sin x}{1 - \cos x}$ **h** $\dfrac{\cos(2x)}{\sin(2x) - 3}$

Example 8

Find $\int \sin^3 x \, dx$.

$\int \sin^3 x \, dx = \int \sin^2 x \sin x \, dx$

$\quad = \int (1 - \cos^2 x)\sin x \, dx \quad$ let $u = \cos x$

$\quad = \int (1 - u^2)\left(-\dfrac{du}{dx}\right) dx \quad \therefore \dfrac{du}{dx} = -\sin x$

$\quad = \int (u^2 - 1) \, du$

$\quad = \dfrac{u^3}{3} - u + c$

$\quad = \tfrac{1}{3}\cos^3 x - \cos x + c$

5 Find:

    a $\int \cos^3 x \, dx$ **b** $\int \sin^5 x \, dx$ **c** $\int \sin^4 x \cos^3 x \, dx$

    Hint: In **b** $\sin^5 x = \sin^4 x \sin x = (1 - \cos^2 x)^2 \sin x$, etc.

6 Find $f(x)$ if $f'(x)$ is:

    a $\sin x \, e^{\cos x}$ **b** $\sin^3(2x) \cos(2x)$ **c** $\dfrac{\sin x + \cos x}{\sin x - \cos x}$ **d** $\dfrac{e^{\tan x}}{\cos^2 x}$

7 Find:

    a $\int \cot x \, dx$ **b** $\int \cot(3x) \, dx$ **c** $\int \csc^2 x \, dx$

    d $\int \sec x \tan x \, dx$ **e** $\int \csc x \cot x \, dx$ **f** $\int \tan(3x) \sec(3x) \, dx$

    g $\int \csc\left(\frac{x}{2}\right) \cot\left(\frac{x}{2}\right) \, dx$ **h** $\int \sec^3 x \sin x \, dx$ **i** $\int \dfrac{\csc^2 x}{\sqrt{\cot x}} \, dx$

C   DEFINITE INTEGRALS

Recall that: the **Fundamental Theorem of Calculus** is:

If $F(x)$ is the integral of $f(x)$, then providing $f(x)$ is continuous on $a \leqslant x \leqslant b$,

$$\int_a^b f(x)dx = F(b) - F(a).$$

Example 9

Evaluate: **a** $\displaystyle\int_0^{\frac{\pi}{3}} \sin x \, dx$ **b** $\displaystyle\int_0^{\frac{\pi}{8}} \dfrac{1}{\cos^2(2x)} \, dx$

a $\displaystyle\int_0^{\frac{\pi}{3}} \sin x \, dx$

    $= [-\cos x]_0^{\frac{\pi}{3}}$

    $= (-\cos \frac{\pi}{3}) - (-\cos 0)$

    $= -\frac{1}{2} + 1$

    $= \frac{1}{2}$

```
fnInt(sin(X),X,0
,π/3)
          .50000
```

b $\displaystyle\int_0^{\frac{\pi}{8}} \dfrac{1}{\cos^2(2x)} \, dx$

    $= \left[\frac{1}{2} \tan(2x)\right]_0^{\frac{\pi}{8}}$

    $= \left(\frac{1}{2} \tan \frac{\pi}{4}\right) - \left(\frac{1}{2} \tan 0\right)$

    $= \frac{1}{2} \times 1 - \frac{1}{2} \times 0$

    $= \frac{1}{2}$

EXERCISE 27C

1 Evaluate:

    a $\displaystyle\int_0^{\frac{\pi}{6}} \cos x \, dx$ **b** $\displaystyle\int_{\frac{\pi}{3}}^{\frac{\pi}{2}} \sin x \, dx$ **c** $\displaystyle\int_{\frac{\pi}{4}}^{\frac{\pi}{3}} \dfrac{1}{\cos^2 x} \, dx$

    d $\displaystyle\int_0^{\frac{\pi}{6}} \sin(3x) \, dx$ **e** $\displaystyle\int_0^{\frac{\pi}{4}} \cos^2 x \, dx$ **f** $\displaystyle\int_0^{\frac{\pi}{2}} \sin^2 x \, dx$

Example 10

Evaluate: $\displaystyle\int_{\frac{\pi}{6}}^{\frac{\pi}{2}} \sqrt{\sin x}\,\cos x\,dx$

$\displaystyle\int_{\frac{\pi}{6}}^{\frac{\pi}{2}} \sqrt{\sin x}\,\cos x\,dx$

$= \displaystyle\int_{\frac{\pi}{6}}^{\frac{\pi}{2}} \sqrt{u}\,\frac{du}{dx}\,dx$

$= \displaystyle\int_{\frac{1}{2}}^{1} u^{\frac{1}{2}}\,du$

$= \left[\dfrac{u^{\frac{3}{2}}}{\frac{3}{2}}\right]_{\frac{1}{2}}^{1}$

$= \frac{2}{3}(1)^{\frac{3}{2}} - \frac{2}{3}\left(\frac{1}{2}\right)^{\frac{3}{2}}$

$= \frac{2}{3} - \frac{1}{3\sqrt{2}}$

Let $u = \sin x$ $\therefore$ $\dfrac{du}{dx} = \cos x$

when $x = \frac{\pi}{2}$, $u = \sin\frac{\pi}{2} = 1$

when $x = \frac{\pi}{6}$, $u = \sin\frac{\pi}{6} = \frac{1}{2}$

```
∫(√(sin X)×cos X,π÷6,
π÷2,1ε-6)
              0.43096
```

2 Evaluate:

a $\displaystyle\int_{0}^{\frac{\pi}{3}} \frac{\sin x}{\sqrt{\cos x}}\,dx$

b $\displaystyle\int_{0}^{\frac{\pi}{6}} \sin^2 x \cos x\,dx$

c $\displaystyle\int_{0}^{\frac{\pi}{4}} \tan x\,dx$

d $\displaystyle\int_{\frac{\pi}{6}}^{\frac{\pi}{2}} \frac{1}{\tan x}\,dx$

e $\displaystyle\int_{0}^{\frac{\pi}{6}} \frac{\cos x}{1 - \sin x}\,dx$

D   AREA DETERMINATION

Reminders:

- If $f(x)$ is **positive** and **continuous** on the interval $a \leqslant x \leqslant b$ then the shaded area is given by

$$\int_{a}^{b} f(x)\,dx.$$

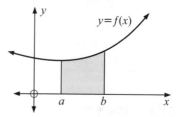

- If $f(x)$ and $g(x)$ are **continuous** functions on the interval $a \leqslant x \leqslant b$ then if $f(x) \geqslant g(x)$ on this interval the shaded area is given by

$$\int_{a}^{b} [f(x) - g(x)]\,dx.$$

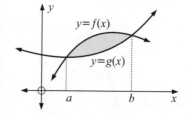

Examples:

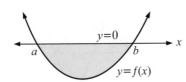

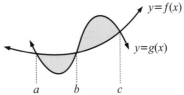

$$\text{Area} \quad = \int_a^b [0 - f(x)] \, dx$$

$$= -\int_a^b f(x) \, dx$$

$$\text{Area} = \int_a^b [f(x) - g(x)] \, dx + \int_b^c [g(x) - f(x)] \, dx$$

Example 11

Find the area enclosed by one arch of $y = \sin(2x)$.

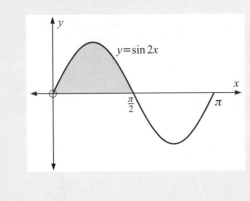

period is $\frac{2\pi}{2} = \pi$

$\therefore$ first positive x-intercept is $\frac{\pi}{2}$

required area

$$= \int_0^{\frac{\pi}{2}} \sin(2x) \, dx$$

$$= \left[\tfrac{1}{2}(-\cos(2x)) \right]_0^{\frac{\pi}{2}}$$

$$= -\tfrac{1}{2} \left[\cos(2x) \right]_0^{\frac{\pi}{2}}$$

$$= -\tfrac{1}{2}(\cos \pi - \cos 0)$$

$$= 1 \text{ unit}^2$$

EXERCISE 27D

1 **a** Show that the area enclosed by $y = \sin x$ and the x-axis from $x = 0$ to $x = \pi$ is 2 units^2.

  b Find the area enclosed by $y = \sin^2 x$ and the x-axis from $x = 0$ to $x = \pi$.

2 A region has boundaries defined by $y = \sin x$, $y = \cos x$ and the y-axis. Find the area of the region.

3 The graph alongside shows a small portion of the graph of $y = \tan x$.

A is a point on the graph with a y-coordinate of 1.

  a Find the coordinates of A.

  b Find the shaded area.

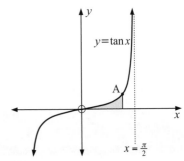

4 The illustrated curves are those of $y = \sin x$ and $y = \sin(2x)$.

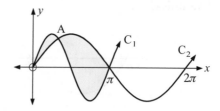

a   Identify each curve.

b   Find algebraically the coordinates of A.

c   Find the total area enclosed by C_1 and C_2 for $0 \leqslant x \leqslant \pi$.

5

The illustrated curves are those of $y = \cos(2x)$ and $y = \cos^2 x$.

a   Identify each curve.

b   Determine the coordinates of A, B, C, D and E.

c   Show that the area of the shaded region is $\frac{\pi}{2}$ units^2.

REVIEW SET 27A

1 Integrate with respect to x: a $\sin^7 x \cos x$ b $\tan(2x)$ c $e^{\sin x} \cos x$

2 Find the derivative of $x \tan x$ and hence determine $\displaystyle\int \frac{x}{\cos^2 x} dx$.

3 Determine the area enclosed by $y = \dfrac{2x}{\pi}$ and $y = \sin x$.

4 Evaluate: a $\displaystyle\int_0^{\frac{\pi}{3}} \cos^2\left(\frac{x}{2}\right) dx$ b $\displaystyle\int_0^{\frac{\pi}{4}} \tan x \, dx$

5 Differentiate $\ln \sec x$, given that $\sec x > 0$.
What integral can be deduced from this derivative?

6 Evaluate $\displaystyle\int_{\frac{\pi}{6}}^{\frac{\pi}{2}} \frac{\cos \theta}{\sin \theta} d\theta$

7 Determine the area of the region enclosed by $y = x$, $y = \sin x$ and $x = \pi$.

REVIEW SET 27B

REVIEW SET 27B

Click on the icon to obtain printable review sets and answers

Chapter 28

Volumes of revolution

Contents:

A   SOLIDS OF REVOLUTION

Consider the curve $y = f(x)$ for $a \leqslant x \leqslant b$.
If the shaded part is rotated about the x-axis a
3-dimensional solid will be formed.

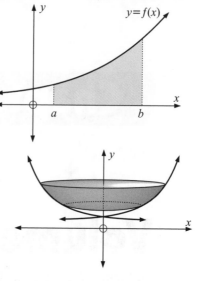

This solid is called a **solid of revolution**.

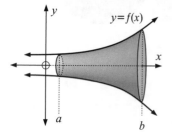

Similarly if the
part of the curve
is rotated about
the y-axis a
solid of revolu-
tion will also be
formed.

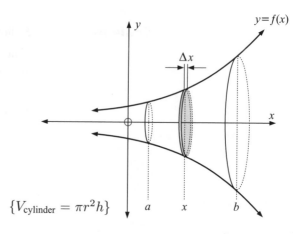

In this chapter we will mainly be concerned with volumes of solids formed by a **revolution about the x-axis**.

VOLUME OF REVOLUTION

We can use integration to find volumes
of revolution between $x = a$ and
$x = b$.

The solid can be thought to be made
up of an infinite number of thin cylindrical discs.

The left-most disc has approximate
volume $\pi[f(a)]^2 \Delta x$.

The right-most disc has approximate
volume $\pi[f(b)]^2 \Delta x$.

$\{V_{\text{cylinder}} = \pi r^2 h\}$

In general, $\pi[f(x)]^2 \Delta x$ is the approximate volume for the illustrated disc.

As there are infinitely many discs, $\Delta x \to 0$ and

$$\lim_{\Delta x \to 0} \sum_{x=a}^{x=b} \pi[f(x)]^2 \Delta x = \int_a^b \pi[f(x)]^2 dx = \int_a^b \pi y^2 dx$$

When the region enclosed by $y = f(x)$, the
x-axis and the vertical lines $x = a$, $x = b$ is
rotated about the x-axis to generate a solid, the
volume of the solid is given by $\pi \int_a^b y^2 \, dx$.

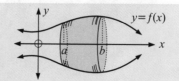

Example 1

Use integration to find the volume of the solid generated when the line $y = x$ for $1 \leqslant x \leqslant 4$ is revolved around the x-axis.

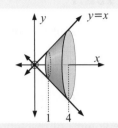

Volume of revolution $= \pi \displaystyle\int_a^b y^2 \, dx$

$\phantom{\text{Volume of revolution}} = \pi \displaystyle\int_1^4 x^2 \, dx$

$\phantom{\text{Volume of revolution}} = \pi \left[\dfrac{x^3}{3} \right]_1^4$

$\phantom{\text{Volume of revolution}} = \pi \left(\dfrac{64}{3} - \dfrac{1}{3} \right)$

$\phantom{\text{Volume of revolution}} = 21\pi \quad \text{cubic units}$

Note: The volume of a cone can be calculated using

$V_{\text{cone}} = \frac{1}{3} \pi r^2 h$

So, in this example

$V = \frac{1}{3} \pi 4^2 (4) - \frac{1}{3} \pi 1^2 (1)$

$ = \dfrac{64\pi}{3} - \dfrac{\pi}{3}$

$ = 21\pi \quad \text{which checks } \checkmark$

Example 2

Find the volume of the solid formed when the graph of the function $y = x^2$ for $0 \leqslant x \leqslant 5$ is revolved about the x-axis.

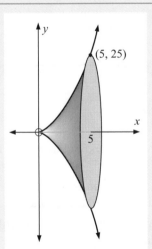

Volume of revolution

$= \pi \displaystyle\int_a^b y^2 \, dx$

$= \pi \displaystyle\int_0^5 (x^2)^2 \, dx$

$= \pi \displaystyle\int_0^5 x^4 \, dx$

$= \pi \left[\dfrac{x^5}{5} \right]_0^5$

$= \pi (625 - 0)$

$= 625\pi \quad \text{cubic units}$

Note:
enter $Y_1 = X^2$
$fnInt(\pi * Y_1^2, X, 0, 5)$
gives this volume.

Note: For the illustrated figure, where revolution about the y-axis has occurred, the volume of the solid formed is

$$V = \pi \int_a^b x^2 \, dy$$

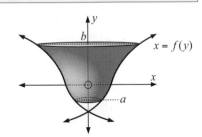

EXERCISE 28A.1

1   Find the volume of the solid formed when the following are revolved about the x-axis:

   a $y = 2x$ for $0 \leqslant x \leqslant 3$ **b** $y = \sqrt{x}$ for $0 \leqslant x \leqslant 4$

   c $y = x^3$ for $1 \leqslant x \leqslant 2$ **d** $y = x^{\frac{3}{2}}$ for $1 \leqslant x \leqslant 4$

   e $y = x^2$ for $2 \leqslant x \leqslant 4$ **f** $y = \sqrt{25 - x^2}$ for $0 \leqslant x \leqslant 5$

2   Find the volume of revolution when the shaded region is revolved about the x-axis.

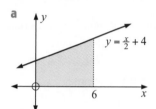 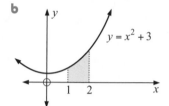 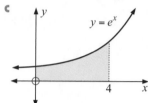

3

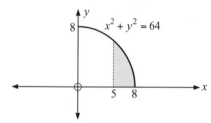

The shaded region is rotated about the x-axis.

   a   Find the volume of revolution.

   b   A hemispherical bowl of radius 8 cm contains water to a depth of 3 cm. What is the volume of water?

4   **a**   What is the name of the solid of revolution when the shaded region is revolved about the x-axis?

   b   Find in the form $y = ax + b$, the equation of the line segment AB.

   c   Find a formula for the volume of the solid using

$$\pi \int_a^b y^2 \, dx.$$

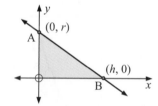

5

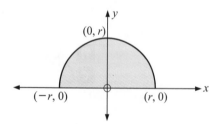

A circle, centre $(0, 0)$ and radius r units has equation $x^2 + y^2 = r^2$.

   a   If the shaded region is revolved about the x-axis, what solid is formed?

   b   Use integration to show that the volume of revolution is $\frac{4}{3}\pi r^3$.

6   Find the volume of the solid formed when:

   a $y = x^2$, between $y = 0$ and $y = 4$ is revolved about the y-axis

   b $y = \sqrt{x}$, between $y = 1$ and $y = 4$ is revolved about the y-axis

   c $y = \ln x$, between $y = 0$ and $y = 2$ is revolved about the y-axis.

Example 3

One arch of $y = \sin x$ is rotated about the x-axis.

What is the volume of revolution?

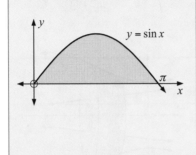

$y = \sin x$

$$\text{Volume} = \pi \int_a^b [f(x)]^2 \, dx$$

$$= \pi \int_0^\pi \sin^2 x \, dx$$

$$= \pi \int_0^\pi \left[\tfrac{1}{2} - \tfrac{1}{2}\cos(2x) \right] \, dx$$

$$= \pi \left[\tfrac{x}{2} - \tfrac{1}{2} \left(\tfrac{1}{2} \right) \sin(2x) \right]_0^\pi$$

$$= \pi \left[\left(\tfrac{\pi}{2} - \tfrac{1}{4}\sin(2\pi) \right) - \left(0 - \tfrac{1}{4}\sin 0 \right) \right]$$

$$= \pi \times \tfrac{\pi}{2}$$

$$= \frac{\pi^2}{2} \quad \text{cubic units}$$

EXERCISE 28A.2

1 Find the volume of revolution when these regions are rotated about the x-axis:

   a $y = \cos x$ for $0 \leqslant x \leqslant \frac{\pi}{2}$
        b $y = \cos(2x)$ for $0 \leqslant x \leqslant \frac{\pi}{4}$

   c $y = \sqrt{\sin x}$ for $0 \leqslant x \leqslant \pi$
        d $y = \dfrac{1}{\cos x}$ for $0 \leqslant x \leqslant \frac{\pi}{3}$

2 **a** Sketch the graph of $y = \sin x + \cos x$ for $0 \leqslant x \leqslant \frac{\pi}{2}$

   b Hence, find the volume of revolution of the shape bounded by $y = \sin x + \cos x$, the x-axis, $x = 0$ and $x = \frac{\pi}{4}$ when it is rotated about the x-axis.

3 **a** Sketch the graph of $y = 4\sin(2x)$ from $x = 0$ to $x = \frac{\pi}{4}$

   b Hence, find the volume of the revolution of the shape bounded by $y = 4\sin(2x)$, the x-axis, $x = 0$ and $x = \frac{\pi}{4}$ when it is rotated about the x-axis.

B VOLUMES FOR TWO DEFINING FUNCTIONS

Consider the circle, centre $(0, 3)$, radius 1 unit.

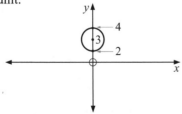

What solid of revolution will be obtained if this circle is revolved about the x-axis?

Yes, a doughnut is formed! (*Torus* is its proper mathematical name.) We can use integration to find its volume.

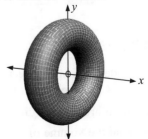

In general, if the region bounded by $y = f(x)$ (on top) and $y = g(x)$ and the lines $x = a$, $x = b$ is revolved about the x-axis, then its volume of revolution is given by:

$$V = \pi \int_a^b [f(x)]^2 \, dx - \pi \int_a^b [g(x)]^2 \, dx$$

So, $V = \pi \int_a^b \left([f(x)]^2 - [g(x)]^2 \right) dx \quad$ or $\quad \pi \int_a^b \left(y_U^2 - y_L^2 \right) dx$

Rotating

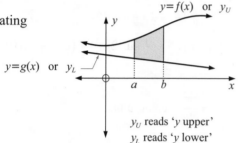

$y = f(x)$ or y_U

$y = g(x)$ or y_L

y_U reads 'y upper'
y_L reads 'y lower'

about the
x-axis
gives

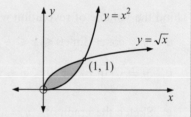

Example 4

Find the volume of revolution generated
by revolving the region between $y = x^2$
and $y = \sqrt{x}$ about the x-axis.

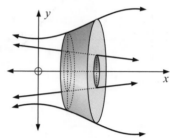

The required volume $= \pi \int_0^1 \left(y_U^2 - y_L^2 \right) dx$

$$= \pi \int_0^1 \left((\sqrt{x})^2 - (x^2)^2 \right) dx$$

$$= \pi \int_0^1 (x - x^4) \, dx$$

$$= \pi \left[\frac{x^2}{2} - \frac{x^5}{5} \right]_0^1$$

$$= \pi \left(\left(\tfrac{1}{2} - \tfrac{1}{5} \right) - (0) \right)$$

$$= \tfrac{3\pi}{10} \text{ units}^3$$

EXERCISE 28B

1   The shaded region (between $y = 4 - x^2$ and
$y = 3$) is revolved about the x-axis.

    a   What are the coordinates of A and B?

    b   Find the volume of revolution.

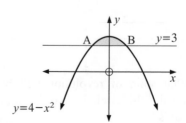

2

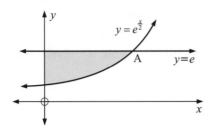

The shaded region is revolved about the x-axis.

  a Find the coordinates of A.

  b Find the volume of revolution.

3 The shaded region (between $y = x$, $y = \dfrac{1}{x}$ and $x = 2$) is revolved about the x-axis.

  a What are the coordinates of A?

  b Find the volume of revolution.

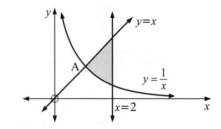

4

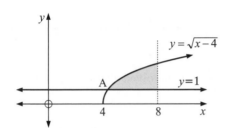

The shaded region (between $y = \sqrt{x - 4}$, $y = 1$ and $x = 8$) is revolved about the x-axis.

  a What are the coordinates of A?

  b Find the volume of revolution.

5 The illustrated circle has equation $x^2 + (y - 3)^2 = 4$.

  a Show that $y = 3 \pm \sqrt{4 - x^2}$.

  b Draw a diagram and show on it what part of the circle is represented by $y = 3 + \sqrt{4 - x^2}$ and what part by $y = 3 - \sqrt{4 - x^2}$.

  c Find the volume of revolution of the shaded region about the x-axis.

    Hint: Use your calculator to evaluate the integral.

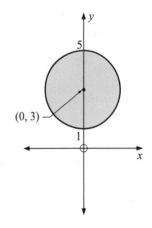

A REMARKABLE FACT

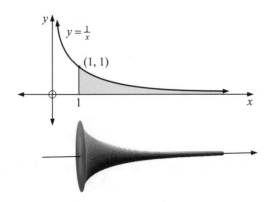

The shaded area from $x = 1$ to infinity is **infinite** whereas its volume of revolution is **finite**.

You can use integration to prove this fact. Try it!

REVIEW SET 28

1 Find the volume of the solid of revolution when the following are revolved about the x-axis:

   a $y = x$ between $x = 4$ and $x = 10$

   b $y = x + 1$ between $x = 4$ and $x = 10$

   c $y = \sin x$ between $x = 0$ and $x = \pi$

   d $y = \sqrt{9 - x^2}$ between $x = 0$ and $x = 3$.

2 Find the volume of the solid of revolution when the shaded region is revolved about the x-axis:

   a

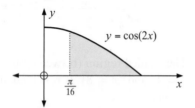

   b

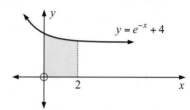

3 Find the volume of revolution when $y = \dfrac{1}{\sin x}$ is revolved about the x-axis for $\frac{\pi}{4} \leqslant x \leqslant \frac{3\pi}{4}$.

4 Find the volume of revolution generated by revolving the shaded region about the x-axis:

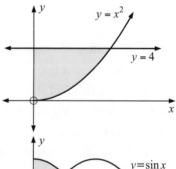

5 Find the volume of revolution if the shaded region is revolved about the x-axis:

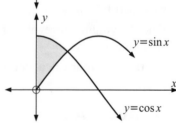

6

   a Use $V = \frac{1}{3}\pi r^2 h$ to find the volume of this cone.

   b Check your answer to **a** by using integration.

7 Find the volume enclosed when $y = x^3$ from the x-axis to $y = 8$, is revolved about the y-axis.

Chapter 29

Further integration and differential equations

Contents:

Various techniques for finding integrals exist. Some of these include:

- integrating **term-by-term**
- integrating by using the **reverse process of differentiation**
- integration by **substitution**
- integration by **parts**

The first three of these have been used in previous work.

A   THE INTEGRALS OF $\dfrac{1}{\sqrt{a^2 - x^2}}$ AND $\dfrac{1}{x^2 + a^2}$

The integrals of $\dfrac{1}{\sqrt{a^2 - x^2}}$ and $\dfrac{1}{x^2 + a^2}$ can be obtained by considering the derivatives

of $y = \arcsin\left(\frac{x}{a}\right)$ and $y = \arctan\left(\frac{x}{a}\right)$.

Consider $y = \arcsin\left(\frac{x}{a}\right)$

$\therefore \quad x = a\sin y$

and so $\dfrac{dx}{dy} = a\cos y = a\sqrt{1 - \sin^2 y}$

$\therefore \quad \dfrac{dx}{dy} = a\sqrt{1 - \dfrac{x^2}{a^2}}$

$\qquad = \sqrt{a^2 - x^2}$

$\therefore \quad \dfrac{dy}{dx} = \dfrac{1}{\sqrt{a^2 - x^2}}$

and if $y = \arctan\left(\frac{x}{a}\right)$,

$\therefore \quad x = a\tan y$

and so $\dfrac{dx}{dy} = a\sec^2 y = a(1 + \tan^2 y)$

$\therefore \quad \dfrac{dx}{dy} = a\left(1 + \dfrac{x^2}{a^2}\right)$

$\qquad = \dfrac{a^2 + x^2}{a}$

$\therefore \quad \dfrac{dy}{dx} = \dfrac{a}{x^2 + a^2}$

$\therefore \quad \displaystyle\int \dfrac{1}{\sqrt{a^2 - x^2}}\, dx = \arcsin\left(\frac{x}{a}\right) + c$

$\therefore \quad \displaystyle\int \dfrac{1}{x^2 + a^2}\, dx = \frac{1}{a}\arctan\left(\frac{x}{a}\right) + c$

Example 1

Find: **a** $\displaystyle\int \dfrac{1}{\sqrt{9 - x^2}}\, dx$ **b** $\displaystyle\int \dfrac{5}{4x^2 + 8}\, dx$

a $\displaystyle\int \dfrac{1}{\sqrt{9 - x^2}}\, dx$

$= \arcsin\left(\frac{x}{3}\right) + c$

b $\displaystyle\int \dfrac{5}{4x^2 + 8}\, dx$

$= \frac{5}{4}\displaystyle\int \dfrac{1}{x^2 + (\sqrt{2})^2}\, dx$

$= \frac{5}{4} \times \frac{1}{\sqrt{2}}\arctan\left(\frac{x}{\sqrt{2}}\right) + c$

$= \frac{5}{4\sqrt{2}}\arctan\left(\frac{x}{\sqrt{2}}\right) + c$

EXERCISE 29A

1 Find:

    a $\displaystyle\int \frac{4}{\sqrt{1-x^2}}\,dx$ **b** $\displaystyle\int \frac{3}{\sqrt{4-x^2}}\,dx$ **c** $\displaystyle\int \frac{1}{x^2+16}\,dx$ **d** $\displaystyle\int \frac{1}{4x^2+1}\,dx$

    e $\displaystyle\int \frac{1}{\sqrt{1-4x^2}}\,dx$ **f** $\displaystyle\int \frac{2}{\sqrt{4-9x^2}}\,dx$ **g** $\displaystyle\int \frac{1}{4+2x^2}\,dx$ **h** $\displaystyle\int \frac{5}{9+4x^2}\,dx$

2   **a** Sketch the graph of $\displaystyle y = \frac{1}{\sqrt{1-x^2}}$

     b Explain algebraically why the function
       i is symmetrical about the y-axis   **ii** has domain $x \in \,]-1,\,1[$

     c Find the exact area enclosed by the function and the x-axis, the y-axis and the line $x = \frac{1}{2}$.

B   FURTHER INTEGRATION BY SUBSTITUTION

Here are some suggestions of possible substitutions to help integrate more difficult functions.

Note that these substitutions may not lead to success, so, some other substitutions may be needed.

With practise you will develop a feeling for which substitution is best in a given situation.

When a function contains	*Try substituting*
$\sqrt{f(x)}$	$u = f(x)$
$\ln x$	$u = \ln x$
$\sqrt{a^2 - x^2}$	$x = a\sin\theta$
$x^2 + a^2$ *or* $\sqrt{x^2 + a^2}$	$x = a\tan\theta$
$\sqrt{x^2 - a^2}$	$x = a\sec\theta$

Example 2	Find $\int x\sqrt{x+2}\,dx$.

$$\int x\sqrt{x+2}\,dx \qquad\qquad \text{Let}\quad u = x+2$$
$$= \int (u-2)\sqrt{u}\,\frac{du}{dx}\,dx \qquad \therefore\quad \frac{du}{dx} = 1$$
$$= \int \left(u^{\frac{3}{2}} - 2u^{\frac{1}{2}}\right)du$$
$$= \frac{u^{\frac{5}{2}}}{\frac{5}{2}} - \frac{2u^{\frac{3}{2}}}{\frac{3}{2}} + c$$
$$= \tfrac{2}{5}(x+2)^{\frac{5}{2}} - \tfrac{4}{3}(x+2)^{\frac{3}{2}} + c$$

EXERCISE 29B

1 Find using a suitable substitution:

    a $\int x\sqrt{x-3}\,dx$ **b** $\int x^2\sqrt{x+1}\,dx$ **c** $\int x^3\sqrt{3-x^2}\,dx$

    d $\int t^3\sqrt{t^2+2}\,dt$ **e** $\displaystyle\int \frac{\sqrt{x-1}}{x}\,dx$ **Hint:** in **e**, let $u = \sqrt{x-1}$.

Example 3

Find the exact value of $\int_{-4}^{6} x\sqrt{x+4}\,dx$.

Let $u = x + 4$ $\therefore \dfrac{du}{dx} = 1$ $\therefore \int_{-4}^{6} x\sqrt{x+4}\,dx = \int_{0}^{10} (u-4)\sqrt{u}\,du$

when $x = -4$, $u = 0$

when $x = 6$, $u = 10$

$$= \int_{0}^{10} \left(u^{\frac{3}{2}} - 4u^{\frac{1}{2}}\right) du$$

```
Plot1 Plot2 Plot3
\Y1▄X√(X+4)
-----
fnInt(Y1,X,-4,6)
       42.16370172
-----
(40/3)√(10
       42.16370214
```

$$= \left[\tfrac{2}{5}u^{\frac{5}{2}} - \tfrac{8}{3}u^{\frac{3}{2}}\right]_{0}^{10}$$

$$= \tfrac{2}{5} \times 10^{\frac{5}{2}} - \tfrac{8}{3} \times 10^{\frac{3}{2}}$$

$$= 40\sqrt{10} - \tfrac{80}{3}\sqrt{10}$$

$$= \tfrac{40}{3}\sqrt{10}$$

2 Find the exact value of:

a $\int_{3}^{4} x\sqrt{x-1}\,dx$ **b** $\int_{0}^{3} x\sqrt{x+6}\,dx$ **c** $\int_{2}^{5} x^2\sqrt{x-2}\,dx$

Check each answer using technology.

Example 4

Find $\int \dfrac{\sqrt{x^2 - 9}}{x}\,dx$.

Try $x = 3\sec\theta$, $\therefore \dfrac{dx}{d\theta} = 3\sec\theta\tan\theta$

So, $\int \dfrac{\sqrt{x^2 - 9}}{x}\,dx = \int \dfrac{\sqrt{9\sec^2\theta - 9}}{3\sec\theta}\,3\sec\theta\tan\theta\,d\theta$ $\sec\theta = \dfrac{x}{3}$

$$= \int 3\sqrt{\sec^2\theta - 1}\,\tan\theta\,d\theta$$

$$= \int 3\tan^2\theta\,d\theta$$

$$= \int (3\sec^2\theta - 3)\,d\theta$$ $\therefore \cos\theta = \dfrac{3}{x}$

$$= 3\tan\theta - 3\theta + c$$

$$= \sqrt{x^2 - 9} - 3\arccos\left(\tfrac{3}{x}\right) + c$$ $\therefore \tan\theta = \dfrac{\sqrt{x^2 - 9}}{3}$

3 Integrate with respect to x:

a $\dfrac{x^2}{9 + x^2}$ **b** $\dfrac{x^2}{\sqrt{1 - x^2}}$ **c** $\dfrac{2x}{x^2 + 9}$ **d** $\dfrac{4\ln x}{x\left(1 + [\ln x]^2\right)}$

e $\dfrac{\sqrt{x^2 - 4}}{x}$ **f** $\sin x \cos 2x$ **g** $\dfrac{1}{\sqrt{9 - 4x^2}}$ **h** $\dfrac{x^3}{1 + x^2}$

i $\dfrac{1}{x\left(9 + 4\left[\ln x\right]^2\right)}$ **j** $\dfrac{1}{x(x^2 + 16)}$ **k** $\dfrac{1}{x^2\sqrt{16 - x^2}}$ **l** $x^2\sqrt{4 - x^2}$

C   INTEGRATION BY PARTS

Some functions can only be integrated using **integration by parts**.

Since $\dfrac{d}{dx}(uv) = u'v + uv'$ then $\int (u'v + uv')\,dx = uv$

$$\therefore \quad \int u'v\,dx + \int uv'\,dx = uv$$

$$\therefore \quad \int uv'\,dx = uv - \int u'v\,dx$$

So, providing $\int u'v\,dx$ can be easily found, we can find $\int uv'\,dx$ using

$$\int uv'\,dx = uv - \int u'v\,dx \quad \text{or} \quad \int u\,\frac{dv}{dx}\,dx = uv - \int v\,\frac{du}{dx}\,dx$$

Example 5

Find: **a** $\int xe^{-x}\,dx$ **b** $\int x\cos x\,dx$

a $u = x \qquad v' = e^{-x}$
  $u' = 1 \qquad v = -e^{-x}$

$\therefore \int xe^{-x}\,dx = -xe^{-x} - \int(-e^{-x})\,dx$
  $= -xe^{-x} + (-e^{-x}) + c$
  $= -e^{-x}(x + 1) + c$

Check:

$\dfrac{d}{dx}(-e^{-x}(x + 1) + c)$
$= e^{-x}(x + 1) + -e^{-x}(1) + 0$
$= xe^{-x} + e^{-x} - e^{-x}$
$= xe^{-x}$ ✓

b $u = x \qquad v' = \cos x$
  $u' = 1 \qquad v = \sin x$

$\therefore \int x\cos x\,dx = x\sin x - \int \sin x\,dx$
  $= x\sin x - (-\cos x) + c$
  $= x\sin x + \cos x + c$

Check:

$\dfrac{d}{dx}(x\sin x + \cos x + c)$
$= 1 \times \sin x + x\cos x - \sin x$
$= \cancel{\sin x} + x\cos x - \cancel{\sin x}$
$= x\cos x$ ✓

EXERCISE 29C

1 Use integration by parts to find the integral of:

  a xe^x **b** $x\sin x$ **c** $x^2\ln x$

  d $x\sin 3x$ **e** $x\cos 2x$ **f** $x\sec^2 x$

  g $\ln x$ **h** $(\ln x)^2$ **i** $\arctan x$

  [**Hint:** In **g** write $\ln x$ as $1\ln x$ and in **i** write $\arctan x$ as $1\arctan x$.]

Sometimes it is necessary to use integration by parts *twice* in order to find an integral.

Example 6

Find $\int e^x \sin x \, dx$.

$\int e^x \sin x \, dx$

$= e^x(-\cos x) - \int e^x(-\cos x) \, dx \longleftarrow$ $\quad \begin{cases} u = e^x & v' = \sin x \\ u' = e^x & v = -\cos x \end{cases}$

$= -e^x \cos x + \int e^x \cos x \, dx$

$= -e^x \cos x + e^x \sin x - \int e^x \sin x \, dx \longleftarrow$ $\quad \begin{cases} u = e^x & v' = \cos x \\ u' = e^x & v = \sin x \end{cases}$

$\therefore \quad 2 \int e^x \sin x \, dx = -e^x \cos x + e^x \sin x$

$\therefore \quad \int e^x \sin x \, dx = \frac{1}{2}e^x(\sin x - \cos x) + c$

2 Find these integrals:

   a $x^2 e^{-x}$ **b** $e^x \cos x$ **c** $e^{-x} \sin x$ **d** $x^2 \sin x$

3   **a** Use integration by parts to find $\int u^2 e^u \, du$.

    b Hence find $\int (\ln x)^2 \, dx$ using the substitution $u = \ln x$.

4   **a** Use integration by parts to find $\int u \sin u \, du$.

    b Hence find $\int \sin \sqrt{2x} \, dx$ using the substitution $u^2 = 2x$.

5 Find $\int \cos \sqrt{3x} \, dx$ using the substitution $u^2 = 3x$.

INVESTIGATION   **FUNCTIONS WHICH CANNOT BE INTEGRATED**

Some trigonometric functions do not have indefinite integrals. However definite integrals can still be determined by **numerical methods**.

For example, consider finding the area between $f(x) = \sin(x^2)$ and the x-axis from $x = 0$ to $x = 1$.

The graph of $f(x) = \sin(x^2)$ is:

$f(x)$ is an even function and does not have an indefinite integral.

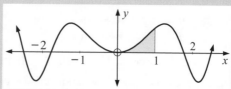

What to do:

1 We can obtain a good estimate of the shaded area using the 'midpoint' rule with $n = 10$. Since the integral is from 0 to 1, $a = 0$ and $b = 1$.

    The rule is: $\displaystyle\int_0^1 \sin(x^2) \, dx \doteqdot [f(0.05) + f(0.15) + f(0.25) + \ldots\ldots + f(0.95)] \, \Delta x$

    where $\Delta x = \dfrac{b-a}{n}$ to find an estimate of the integral to 3 decimal places.

2 Click on the area finder icon and find the area estimate for $n = 10, \, 100, \, 1000, \, 10\,000$.   **AREA FINDER**

3 Use your graphics calculator's definite integral function to find the area.

4 Now find $\int_0^2 \sin(x^2) \, dx$.

5 What is the area enclosed between $y = \sin(x^2)$, the x-axis and the vertical line $x = 2$?

D SEPARABLE DIFFERENTIAL EQUATIONS

The derivative of a function is the rate at which the function changes with respect to its independent variable.

> A **differential equation** is an equation which connects the derivative(s) of a function to the function itself and variables in which the function is defined.

Examples of differential equations are: $\dfrac{dy}{dx} = \dfrac{x^2}{y}$ and $\dfrac{d^2y}{dx^2} - 3\dfrac{dy}{dx} + 4y = 0$

SEPARABLE DIFFERENTIAL EQUATIONS

> Differential equations which can be written in the form $\dfrac{dy}{dx} = \dfrac{f(x)}{g(y)}$ are known as **separable differential equations**.

Notice that $g(y)\dfrac{dy}{dx} = f(x)$ and so $\displaystyle\int g(y)\dfrac{dy}{dx}\,dx = \int f(x)\,dx$ when we integrate both sides with respect to x.

Consequently, $\int g(y)\,dy = \int f(x)\,dx$ which enables us to solve the original differential equation.

When we integrate, the solution involves unknown constants, and this is called a **general solution** of the differential equation. The constants are evaluated using **initial conditions** to give a **particular solution**.

Example 7

Find the general solutions to the following separable differential equations:

a $\dfrac{dy}{dx} = ky$

b $\dfrac{dy}{dx} = k(A - y)$

a $\qquad \dfrac{dy}{dx} = ky$

$\therefore \quad \dfrac{1}{y}\dfrac{dy}{dx} = k$

$\displaystyle\int \dfrac{1}{y}\dfrac{dy}{dx}\,dx = \int k\,dx$

$\therefore \quad \displaystyle\int \dfrac{1}{y}\,dy = \int k\,dx$

$\therefore \quad \ln|y| = kx + c$

$\therefore \quad y = \pm e^{kx+c}$

$\therefore \quad y = \pm e^{c}e^{kx}$

$\therefore \quad y = Ae^{kx}$

$\{A \text{ is a constant}\}$

b $\qquad \dfrac{dy}{dx} = k(A - y) = -k(y - A)$

$\therefore \quad \dfrac{1}{y - A}\dfrac{dy}{dx} = -k$

$\therefore \quad \displaystyle\int \dfrac{1}{y - A}\dfrac{dy}{dx}\,dx = \int -k\,dx$

$\therefore \quad \displaystyle\int \dfrac{1}{y - A}\,dy = \int -k\,dx$

$\therefore \quad \ln|y - A| = -kx + c$

$\therefore \quad |y - A| = e^{-kx+c}$

$\therefore \quad y - A = \pm e^{c}e^{-kx}$

$\therefore \quad y - A = Be^{-kx} \quad \{B \text{ a constant}\}$

$\therefore \quad y = A + Be^{-kx}$

Example 8

Solve $\dfrac{dV}{dh} = k\sqrt{V}$ given that $V(9) = 1$ and $V(13) = 4$ $\{k$ a constant$\}$.

Since $\dfrac{dV}{dh} = k\sqrt{V}$ then

$$\frac{1}{\sqrt{V}} \frac{dV}{dh} = k$$

$$\therefore \quad \int V^{-\frac{1}{2}} \frac{dV}{dh}\, dh = \int k\, dh$$

$$\therefore \quad \int V^{-\frac{1}{2}}\, dV = \int k\, dh$$

$$\therefore \quad \frac{V^{\frac{1}{2}}}{\frac{1}{2}} = kh + c$$

This is the general solution

$$\therefore \quad 2\sqrt{V} = kh + c$$

These are the initial conditions

But $V(9) = 1$ and $V(13) = 4$

$$\therefore \quad 2\sqrt{1} = k(9) + c \quad \text{and} \quad 2\sqrt{4} = k(13) + c$$

i.e., $9k + c = 2$ and $13k + c = 4$

Solving these equations simultaneously gives $k = \frac{1}{2}$ and $c = -\frac{5}{2}$

$$\therefore \quad 2\sqrt{V} = \tfrac{1}{2}h - \tfrac{5}{2} = \frac{h-5}{2}$$

$$\therefore \quad \sqrt{V} = \frac{h-5}{4}$$

$$\therefore \quad V = \left(\frac{h-5}{4}\right)^2$$

This is the particular solution

Don't forget to check your solution.

These are some examples where differential equations are observed:

A falling object

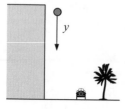

$$\frac{d^2y}{dt^2} = 9.8$$

A parachutist

$$m\frac{dv}{dt} = mg - av^2$$

Object on a spring

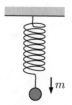

$$m\frac{d^2y}{dt^2} = -ky$$

EXERCISE 29D.1

1 Find the general solution of the following differential equations:

a $\dfrac{dy}{dx} = 5y$

b $\dfrac{dM}{dt} = -2M$

c $\dfrac{dy}{dx} = \dfrac{2}{y}$

d $\dfrac{dP}{dt} = 3\sqrt{P}$

e $\dfrac{dQ}{dt} = 2Q + 3$

f $\dfrac{dQ}{dt} = \dfrac{1}{2Q + 3}$

2 Find the particular solution of the following differential equations:

a $\dfrac{dy}{dx} = 4y$ and when $x = 0$, $y = 10$

b $\dfrac{dM}{dt} = -3M$ and $M(0) = 20$

c $\dfrac{dy}{dt} = \dfrac{\sqrt{y}}{3}$ and when $t = 24$, $y = 9$

d $\dfrac{dP}{dn} = 2P + 3$ and $P(0) = 2$

e $\dfrac{dy}{dx} = k\sqrt{y}$ where k is a constant, $y(4) = 1$ and $y(5) = 4$

3 If the slope of a curve at any point is equal to twice the y-coordinate at that point, show that the curve is an exponential function.

4 a If $\dfrac{dp}{dt} = -\frac{1}{2}p$, and when $t = 0$, $p = 10$, find p when $t = 2$.

  b If $\dfrac{dM}{dr} = 8 - 2M$ and $M = 2$ when $r = 0$, find r when $M = 3.5$.

5 $\dfrac{ds}{dt} + ks = 0$ where k is a constant, and when $t = 0$, $s = 50$.

  If it is also known that $s = 20$ when $t = 3$, show that $s = 50(0.4)^{\frac{t}{3}}$.

Example 9

The curve $y = f(x)$ has a y-intercept of 3 and the tangent to this curve at the point (x, y) has an x-intercept of $x + 2$.

Find the equation, $y = f(x)$, of this curve.

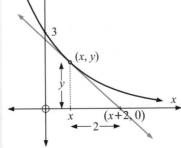

Slope of tangent at (x, y) is $\dfrac{dy}{dx} = \dfrac{y - 0}{x - (x + 2)} = -\dfrac{y}{2}$

$\therefore \dfrac{1}{y}\dfrac{dy}{dx} = -\dfrac{1}{2}$

$\therefore \displaystyle\int \dfrac{1}{y}\dfrac{dy}{dx}\,dx = \int -\tfrac{1}{2}\,dx$

$\therefore \displaystyle\int \dfrac{1}{y}\,dy = -\tfrac{1}{2}x + c$

$\therefore \ln|y| = -\tfrac{1}{2}x + c$

$\therefore y = Ae^{-\frac{1}{2}x}$

$x = 0$, $y = 3 \Rightarrow 3 = A$

$\therefore y = 3e^{-\frac{1}{2}x}$

Example 10

Find the particular solutions of the following separable differential equations with given initial conditions: **a** $y' = 3xy$, $y(0) = e$ **b** $y' = 6y^2x^3$, $y(0) = 1$

a
$$\frac{dy}{dx} = 3xy$$

$$\therefore \quad \frac{1}{y}\frac{dy}{dx} = 3x$$

$$\therefore \quad \int \frac{1}{y}\frac{dy}{dx}\,dx = \int 3x\,dx$$

$$\therefore \quad \int \frac{1}{y}\,dy = \int 3x\,dx$$

$$\therefore \quad \ln|y| = \frac{3x^2}{2} + c$$

$$\therefore \quad |y| = e^{\frac{3x^2}{2}+c}$$

$$\therefore \quad y = Ae^{1.5x^2}$$

But when $x = 0$, $y = e$

$$\therefore \quad e = A$$

$$\therefore \quad y = e^{1.5x^2+1}$$

b
$$\frac{dy}{dx} = 6y^2x^3$$

$$\therefore \quad y^{-2}\frac{dy}{dx} = 6x^3$$

$$\therefore \quad \int y^{-2}\frac{dy}{dx}\,dx = \int 6x^3\,dx$$

$$\therefore \quad \int y^{-2}\,dy = \int 6x^3\,dx$$

$$\therefore \quad \frac{y^{-1}}{-1} = \frac{6x^4}{4} + c$$

But $y(0) = 1$

$$\therefore \quad -1 = c$$

So, $-\dfrac{1}{y} = \dfrac{3x^4}{2} - 1$

$$\therefore \quad \frac{1}{y} = 1 - \frac{3x^4}{2}$$

$$\therefore \quad y = \frac{1}{1 - 1.5x^4}$$

EXERCISE 29D.2

1 Find the general solution of:

    a $xy' = 3y$ **b** $xy = 4y'$ **c** $y' = ye^x$ **d** $y' = xe^y$

2 Solve $\dfrac{dz}{dr} = z + zr^2$, $z(0) = 1$.

3 Solve $\dfrac{dy}{dx} = -2xy$ if $y = 1$ when $x = 0$.

4 The tangent to the curve $y = f(x)$ at the point $(x,\ y)$ has an x-intercept of $x + 3$. If the curve has an y-intercept of 2, find $f(x)$.

5 A curve is known to have $\dfrac{dy}{dx} = \dfrac{x}{y}$. Find the general solution to this differential equation and hence find the curve that passes through the point $(5,\ -4)$. Find a if $(a,\ 3)$ also lies on this curve.

6 A curve has $\dfrac{dy}{dx} = y^2(1 + x)$ and passes through the point $(1,\ 2)$.

    a Find the equation of this curve.

    b Find the equations for the curve's asymptotes.

7 Compare the differential equations: $\dfrac{dy}{dx} = -\dfrac{x}{y}$ with $\dfrac{dy}{dx} = \dfrac{y}{x}$.

a Prove that the solution curves for these differential equations intersect at right angles.

b Solve the differential equations analytically and give a geometrical interpretation of the situation.

Example 11

The number of bacteria present in a culture increases at a rate proportional to the number present. If the number increases by 10% in one hour, what percentage increase occurs after a further 5 hours?

If N is the number of bacteria present at time t hours,

then $\dfrac{dN}{dt} \propto N$, $\therefore$ $\dfrac{dN}{dt} = kN$, k is a constant

$\therefore \quad \dfrac{1}{N}\dfrac{dN}{dt} = k$

and $\displaystyle\int \dfrac{1}{N}\dfrac{dN}{dt}\,dt = \int k\,dt$

$\therefore \quad \displaystyle\int \dfrac{1}{N}dN = \int k\,dt$

$\therefore \quad \ln N = kt + c$ {$|N|$ is not necessary as $N > 0$}

Now when $t = 0$, $N = N_0$ say,

$\therefore \quad \ln N_0 = c$

$\therefore \quad \ln N = kt + \ln N_0$ ...... (1)

When $t = 1$, $N = 1.1N_0$ {110% of N_0 is $1.1N_0$}

$\therefore$ in (1) $\ln(1.1N_0) = k + \ln N_0$

$\therefore \quad k = \ln(1.1N_0) - \ln N_0$

$\therefore \quad k = \ln\left(\dfrac{1.1N_0}{N_0}\right) = \ln(1.1)$

So (1) becomes $\ln N = t\ln(1.1) + \ln N_0$

$\therefore \quad N = N_0 \times (1.1)^t$

After a further 5 hours, $t = 6$

$\therefore \quad N = N_0(1.1)^6$

$\doteqdot 1.7716 \times N_0$

$\doteqdot 177.16\%$ of N_0

$\therefore$ N has increased by 77.16%.

---

8 A body moves with velocity v metres per second and its acceleration is proportional to v. If $v = 4$ when $t = 0$ and $v = 6$ when $t = 4$, find the formula for v in terms of t. Hence, find v when $t = 5$ seconds.

9 In the 'inversion' of raw sugar, the rate of change in the weight w kg of raw sugar is directly proportional to w. If, after 10 hours, 80% reduction has occurred, how much raw sugar remains after 30 hours?

10 When a transistor ratio is switched off, the current falls away according to the differential equation $\dfrac{dI}{dt} = -kI$ where k is a constant. If the current drops to 10% in the first second, how long will it take to drop to 0.1% of its original value?

Example 12

A raindrop falls with acceleration $9.8 - \dfrac{v}{3}$ m/sec^2, where v is its velocity. Show that the raindrop's velocity is $v = 29.4(1 - e^{-\frac{t}{3}})$ m/s and it approaches a limiting value of 29.4 m/s.

Acceleration is $\dfrac{dv}{dt}$, so $\dfrac{dv}{dt} = 9.8 - \dfrac{v}{3}$ m/s^2

$\therefore \quad \dfrac{dv}{dt} = \dfrac{29.4 - v}{3}$

$\therefore \quad \left(\dfrac{1}{v - 29.4}\right)\dfrac{dv}{dt} = -\tfrac{1}{3}$

$\therefore \quad \displaystyle\int \left(\dfrac{1}{v - 29.4}\right)\dfrac{dv}{dt}\,dt = \int -\tfrac{1}{3}\,dt$

$\therefore \quad \displaystyle\int \left(\dfrac{1}{v - 29.4}\right) dv = \int -\tfrac{1}{3}\,dt$

$\therefore \quad \ln|v - 29.4| = -\tfrac{1}{3}t + c$

$\therefore \quad v - 29.4 = Ae^{-\frac{t}{3}}$

$\therefore \quad v = 29.4 + Ae^{-\frac{t}{3}}$

Now when $t = 0$, $v = 0$ and so $A = -29.4$

$\therefore \quad v = 29.4 - 29.4e^{-\frac{t}{3}}$

$\therefore \quad v = 29.4(1 - e^{-\frac{t}{3}})$

Now as $t \to \infty$, $e^{-\frac{t}{3}} \to 0$ $\therefore$ $v - 29.4 \to 0$ and so $v \to 29.4$ m/s

---

11 A lump of metal of mass 1 kg is released from rest in water. After t seconds its velocity is v m/s and the resistance due to the water is $4v$ Newtons.

The equation for the motion is $\dfrac{dv}{dt} = g - 4v$ where g is the gravitational constant.

a Prove that $v = \dfrac{g}{4}(1 - e^{-4t})$ and hence show that there is a limiting velocity.

b When is the metal falling at $\dfrac{g}{10}$ m/s?

12 Water evaporates from a lake at a rate proportional to the volume of water remaining.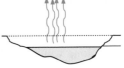

    a Explaining the symbols used, why does $\dfrac{dV}{dt} = k(V_0 - V)$ represent this situation?

    b If 50% of the water evaporates in 20 days, find the percentage of water remaining after 50 days without rain.

Example 13

Water flows out of a tap at the bottom of a large cylindrical tank of radius 2 m at a rate proportional to the square root of the depth of the water remaining in it. Initially the tank is full to a depth of 9 m. After 15 minutes the depth of water is 4 m. How long would it take for the tank to empty?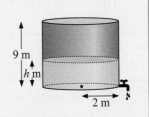

We are given that $\dfrac{dV}{dt} \propto \sqrt{h}$ where h is the depth of water

i.e., $\dfrac{dV}{dt} = k\sqrt{h}$ where k is a constant.

Now $\dfrac{dV}{dt} = \dfrac{dV}{dh}\dfrac{dh}{dt}$ {chain rule}

The volume of the tank is $V = \pi r^2 h = 4\pi h$ $\therefore$ $\dfrac{dV}{dh} = 4\pi$.

$\therefore$ $k\sqrt{h} = 4\pi\dfrac{dh}{dt}$

$\therefore$ $\dfrac{4\pi}{\sqrt{h}}\dfrac{dh}{dt} = k$

$\therefore$ $\int 4\pi h^{-\frac{1}{2}}\dfrac{dh}{dt}\,dt = \int k\,dt$

$\therefore$ $4\pi \int h^{-\frac{1}{2}}\,dh = \int k\,dt$

$\therefore$ $4\pi\dfrac{h^{\frac{1}{2}}}{\frac{1}{2}} = kt + c$ and so, $8\pi\sqrt{h} = kt + c$ ...... (1)

Now when $t = 0$, $h = 9$

$\therefore$ in (1) $8\pi\sqrt{9} = c$ $\therefore$ $c = 24\pi$

So, $8\pi\sqrt{h} = kt + 24\pi$ ...... (2)

And when $t = 15$, $h = 4$

$\therefore$ $16\pi = 15k + 24\pi$ and so $k = -\dfrac{8\pi}{15}$

$\therefore$ $8\pi\sqrt{h} = -\dfrac{8\pi}{15}t + 24\pi$

$\therefore$ $\sqrt{h} = -\dfrac{t}{15} + 3$

Now when it is empty $h = 0$ $\therefore$ $0 = -\dfrac{t}{15} + 3$

$\therefore$ $t = 45$ So, it empties in 45 minutes.

13 Water flows out of a tap at the bottom of a cylindrical tank of height 4 m and radius 2 m. The tank is initially full and the water escapes at a rate proportional to the square root of the depth of the water remaining. After 2 hours the depth of water is 1 m. How long would it take for the tank to empty?

14 Water evaporates from an r cm radius hemispherical bowl

such that $\dfrac{dV}{dt} = -r^2$, where t is the time in hours.

The volume of water, of depth h, in a hemispherical bowl of radius r is given by $V = \frac{1}{3}\pi h^2(3r - h)$.

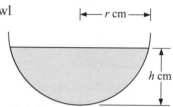

a Assuming r is a constant, use $\dfrac{dV}{dt} = \dfrac{dV}{dh}\dfrac{dh}{dt}$ to set up a differential equation between h and t.

b Suppose the bowl's radius is 10 cm and that initially it was full of water.

Show that $t = \frac{\pi}{300}(h^3 - 30h^2 + 2000)$ and hence find the time taken for the depth of water to reach the 5 cm mark.

Newton's law of cooling is:

"The rate at which an object changes temperature is proportional to the difference between its temperature and that of the surrounding medium,   i.e., $\dfrac{dT}{dt} \propto (T - T_m)$."

Use Newton's law of cooling to solve questions **15** and **16**.

15 The temperature inside a refrigerator is maintained at 5°C. An object at 100°C is placed in the refrigerator to cool. After 1 minute its temperature drops to 80°C. How long would it take for the temperature to drop to 10°C?

16 At 6 am the temperature of a corpse is 13°C and 3 hours later it falls to 9°C. Given that living body temperature is 37°C and the temperature of the surroundings is constant at 5°C, estimate the time of death.

17 a Given the complex number $z = r \operatorname{cis} \theta = r\cos\theta + ir\sin\theta$ where $r = |z|$ is a constant and $\theta = \arg z$ is variable, show that $\dfrac{dz}{d\theta} = iz$.

b Solve the differential equation $\dfrac{dz}{d\theta} = iz$, showing that $z = re^{i\theta}$ where r is a constant (**Euler's form**).

c From **a** and **b**, what can you say about $\operatorname{cis}\theta$ and $e^{i\theta}$?

d Show that

  i $|zw| = |z||w|$ and $\arg(zw) = \arg(z) + \arg(w)$ for complex numbers z, w.

  ii $\dfrac{\operatorname{cis}\theta}{\operatorname{cis}\phi} = \operatorname{cis}(\theta - \phi)$ **iii** $e^{i\pi} + 1 = 0$ {called **Euler's identity**}

DIFFERENTIAL EQUATIONS WITH UNUSUAL SUBSTITUTIONS

These differential equations can be solved using methods already observed.

Example 14

Solve $x\dfrac{dy}{dx} = x + y$ by letting $y = ux$.

$y = ux$ $\therefore$ $\dfrac{dy}{dx} = \dfrac{du}{dx}x + u$ {product rule}

So, $x\left(\dfrac{du}{dx}x + u\right) = x + ux$ $\therefore$ $x^2\dfrac{du}{dx} + ux = x + ux$

$\therefore$ $x^2\dfrac{du}{dx} = x$

$\therefore$ $\dfrac{du}{dx} = \dfrac{1}{x}$

$\therefore$ $\displaystyle\int \dfrac{du}{dx}\,dx = \int \dfrac{1}{x}\,dx$

$\therefore$ $u = \ln|x| + c$

But $y = ux$ $\therefore$ $y = x\ln|x| + cx$ is the general solution.

EXERCISE 29D.3

1 Solve $\dfrac{dy}{dx} - 2xe^x = y$ by letting $y = ue^x$.

2 Solve $\left(\dfrac{dy}{dx}\right)^2 = y^2 + 2e^x y + e^{2x}$ by letting $y = ue^x$.

3 Solve $4xy\dfrac{dy}{dx} = -x^2 - y^2$ for $x > 0$ by letting $y = ux$.

4 Solve $x\dfrac{dy}{dx} - y = 4x^2 y$ by letting $y = ux$ or otherwise.

REVIEW SET 29A

1 Find $\int x^2\sqrt{4 - x}\,dx$.

2 Use integration by parts to find $\int \arctan x\,dx$. Check your answer using differentiation.

3 Find integrals of: **a** $e^{-x}\cos x$ **b** $x^2 e^x$ **c** $\dfrac{x^3}{\sqrt{9 - x^2}}$

4 Find the solution to $y' = -\dfrac{2e^x}{y}$ given that $y(0) = 4$.

5 The current I which flows through an electrical circuit with resistance R and inductance L can be determined from the differential equation $L\dfrac{dI}{dt} = E - RI$. Both R and L are constants, and so is the electromotive force E.

Given that $R = 4$, $L = 0.2$ and $E = 20$, find how long it will take for the current, initially 0 amps, to reach 0.5 amps.

6 The graph of $y = f(x)$ has a y-intercept of 3 and the tangent at the point (x, y) has an x-intercept of $x - 3$. Find the function $f(x)$.

7 Solve the differential equation $2xy\dfrac{dy}{dx} = x^2 + y^2$ by letting $y = ux$.

Hence show that if $y = 2$ when $x = 1$, a particular solution is $y^2 = x^2 + 3x$.

8 Use $\operatorname{cis} \theta = e^{i\theta}$ to prove that:

   a $\operatorname{cis} \theta \operatorname{cis} \phi = \operatorname{cis}(\theta + \phi)$ **b** $(\operatorname{cis} \theta)^n = \operatorname{cis} n\theta$

REVIEW SET 29B

1 Find: **a** $\displaystyle\int \frac{5}{\sqrt{9 - x^2}}\, dx$ **b** $\displaystyle\int \frac{1}{9 + 4x^2}\, dx$ **c** the exact value of $\displaystyle\int_7^{10} x\sqrt{x - 5}\, dx$

2 Find: **a** $\displaystyle\int x \cos x\, dx$ **b** $\displaystyle\int \frac{\sqrt{x^2 - 4}}{x}\, dx$

3 Given $\dfrac{dy}{dx} = \dfrac{1}{y + 2}$ and $y(0) = 0$, deduce that $y = \sqrt{2x + 4} - 2$.

4 Given $\dfrac{dy}{dx} = \dfrac{2x}{\cos y}$, with initial condition $y(1) = \frac{\pi}{2}$, show that $y = \arcsin(x^2)$.

5 OBLH is a seal slide at the zoo and has a varying slope. At *any* point P the slope is equal to the slope of a uniformly inclined plane with highest point P and with a 5 m long horizontal base along OB.

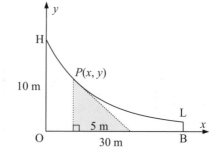

   a Show that $P(x, y)$ satisfies the equation $y = 10e^{-\frac{x}{5}}$.

   b Find the height of L above OB.

   c Find the slope at H and at L.

6 Bacteria grow in culture at a rate proportional to the number of bacteria present.

   a Write down a differential equation connecting the number of bacteria $N(t)$ at time t, to its growth rate.

   b If the population of bacteria doubles every 37 minutes and there were 10^5 bacteria initially, how many bacteria are present in the culture after 4 hours?

7 If a curve has $\dfrac{dy}{dx} = (y - 1)^2(2 + x)$ and passes through the point $(-1, 2)$:

   a find the equation of the curve   **b** find the equations of the asymptotes to the curve.

8 A cylindrical rainwater tank is initially full and the water runs out of it at a rate proportional to the volume of water left in it. If the tank is half full after 20 minutes, find the fraction of water remaining in the tank after one hour.

Chapter 30

Statistical distributions

Contents:

A   DISCRETE RANDOM VARIABLES

RANDOM VARIABLES

In previous work we have described events mainly using words. It is far more convenient where possible, to use numbers.

> A **random variable** represents in number form the possible outcomes, which could occur for some random experiment.

Note: A **discrete random variable** X has possible values $x_1, x_2, x_3, ...$

For example,   • the number of houses in your suburb which have a 'power safety switch'
   • the number of new bicycles sold each year by a bicycle store
   • the number of defective light bulbs in the purchase order of a city store.

A **continuous random variable** X has all possible values in some interval (on the number line).

For example,   • the heights of men could all lie in the interval $50 < x < 250$ cm
   • the volume of water in a rainwater tank during a given month.

Note: A discrete random variable involves a *count* whereas a continuous random variable involves *measurements*.

EXERCISE 30A

1   Classify the following random variables as continuous or discrete.
   a The quantity of fat in a lamb chop.
   b The mark out of 50 for a Geography test.
   c The weight of a seventeen year old student.
   d The volume of water in a cup of coffee.
   e The number of trout in a lake.
   f The number of hairs on a cat.
   g The length of hairs on a horse.
   h The height of a sky-scraper.

2   For each of the following:
   i   identify the random variable being considered
   ii give possible values for the random variable
   iii indicate whether the variable is continuous or discrete.

   a To measure the rainfall over a 24-hour period in Singapore, the height of water collected in a rain gauge (up to 200 mm) is used.
   b To investigate the stopping distance for a tyre with a new tread pattern a braking experiment is carried out.
   c To check the reliability of a new type of light switch, switches are repeatedly turned off and on until they fail.

3 A supermarket has four checkouts A, B, C and D. Management checks the weighing devices at each checkout. If a weighing device is accurate a yes (Y) is recorded; otherwise, no (N) is recorded. The random variable being considered is the number of weighing devices which are accurate.

    a Suppose X is the random variable. What values can x have?

    b Tabulate the possible outcomes and the corresponding values for x.

    c Describe, using x, the events of:

        i   2 being accurate   **ii**   at least two being accurate.

For any random variable there is a **probability distribution** associated with it.

For example,   when tossing two coins, the random variable could be 0 heads, 1 head or 2 heads, i.e., $x = 0$, 1 or 2. The associated probability distribution being $p_0 = \frac{1}{4}$, $p_1 = \frac{1}{2}$ and $p_2 = \frac{1}{4}$ and graph:

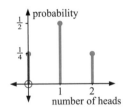 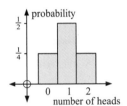

Note: We will write $P(X = x)$ as $P(x)$ or p_x .

Example 1

A supermarket has three checkout points A, B and C. Consumer affairs checks for accuracy of weighing scales at each checkout. If a weighing scale is accurate yes (Y) is recorded, and if not, no (N). Suppose the random variable is:

    X is the number of accurate weighing scales at the supermarket.

a   List the possible outcomes.

b   Describe using x the events of there being:

    i   one accurate scale   **ii**   at least one accurate scale.

a   Possible outcomes:

A	B	C	x
N	N	N	0
Y	N	N	1
N	Y	N	1
N	N	Y	1
N	Y	Y	2
Y	N	Y	2
Y	Y	N	2
Y	Y	Y	3

b **i** $x = 1$

    ii $x = 1$, 2 or 3

---

4 Consider tossing three coins simultaneously where the random variable under consideration is the number of heads that could result.

    a List the possible values of x.

    b Tabulate the possible outcomes and the corresponding values of x.

    c Find the values of $P(X = x)$, the probability of each x value occurring.

    d Graph the probability distribution $P(X = x)$ against x as a probability histogram.

B   DISCRETE PROBABILITY DISTRIBUTIONS

For each random variable there is a **probability distribution**. The probability of any given event

$$p_i \text{ lies between 0 and 1 (inclusive), i.e., } 0 \leqslant p_i \leqslant 1$$

$$\text{and } \sum_{i=1}^{n} p_i = 1 \text{ i.e., } p_1 + p_2 + p_3 + \ldots + p_n = 1.$$

The **probability distribution** of a **discrete random variable** can be given

- in table form
- in graphical form
- in functional form

and provides us with all possible values of the variable and the probability of the occurrence of each value.

Example 2

A magazine store recorded the number of magazines purchased by its customers in one day. 23% purchased one magazine, 38% purchased two, 21% purchased three, 13% purchased four and 5% purchased five.

a What is the random variable?   **b** Make a random variable probability table.

c Graph the probability distribution using a spike graph.

a The random variable X is the number of magazines sold.

So $x = 0, 1, 2, 3, 4$ or 5.

b

x_i	0	1	2	3	4	5
p_i	0.00	0.23	0.38	0.21	0.13	0.05

c
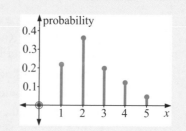

EXERCISE 30B

1 Find k in these probability distributions:

a

x	0	1	2
$P(x)$	0.3	k	0.5

b

x	0	1	2	3
$P(x)$	k	$2k$	$3k$	k

2 Jason's home run probabilities per game of baseball during his great career are given in the following table where X is the number of home runs per game:

x	0	1	2	3	4	5
$P(x)$	a	0.3333	0.1088	0.0084	0.0007	0.0000

a What is the value of a, i.e., $P(0)$? Explain what this figure means in real terms.

b What is the value of $P(2)$?

c What is the value of $P(1) + P(2) + P(3) + P(4) + P(5)$? Explain what this represents.

d Draw a probability distribution spike graph of $P(x)$ against x.

3 Explain why the following are not valid probability distributions:

a

x	0	1	2	3
$P(x)$	0.2	0.3	0.4	0.2

b

x	2	3	4	5
$P(x)$	0.3	0.4	0.5	-0.2

4 Sally's number of hits each softball match has the following probability distribution:

x	0	1	2	3	4	5
$P(x)$	0.07	0.14	k	0.46	0.08	0.02

    a State clearly what the random variable represents.

    b Find k.   **c** Find: **i** $P(x \geqslant 2)$ **ii** $P(1 \leqslant x \leqslant 3)$

5 A die is rolled twice.

    a Draw a grid which shows the sample space.

    b Suppose X denotes the sum of the dots uppermost on the die for the two rolls and find the probability distribution of X.

    c Draw a probability distribution histogram for this situation.

Consider the following example where a probability distribution is given in *functional form*.

Example 3

Show that the following are probability distribution functions:

a $P(x) = \dfrac{x^2 + 1}{34}$ $(x = 1, 2, 3, 4)$ **b** $P(x) = C_x^3 \, (0.6)^x (0.4)^{3-x}$ $(x = 0, 1, 2, 3)$

a $P(1) = \frac{2}{34}$ $P(2) = \frac{5}{34}$ $P(3) = \frac{10}{34}$ $P(4) = \frac{17}{34}$

all of which lie in $0 \leqslant P(i) \leqslant 1$ and $\sum P(i) = \frac{2}{34} + \frac{5}{34} + \frac{10}{34} + \frac{17}{34} = 1$

$\therefore$ $P(x)$ is a probability distribution function.

b For $P(x) = C_x^3 \, (0.6)^x (0.4)^{3-x}$

$P(0) = C_0^3 \, (0.6)^0 (0.4)^3$ $= 1 \times 1 \times (0.4)^3$ $= 0.064$

$P(1) = C_1^3 \, (0.6)^1 (0.4)^2$ $= 3 \times (0.6) \times (0.4)^2 = 0.288$

$P(2) = C_2^3 \, (0.6)^2 (0.4)^1$ $= 3 \times (0.6)^2 \times (0.4) = 0.432$

$P(3) = C_3^3 \, (0.6)^3 (0.4)^0$ $= 1 \times (0.6)^3 \times 1$ $= \underline{0.216}$

                                         Total   1.000

Since all probabilities lie between 0 and 1 and $\sum P(x_i) = 1$ then $P(x)$ is a probability distribution function.

---

6 Find k for the following probability distributions:

    a $P(x) = k(x + 2)$ for $x = 1, 2, 3$ **b** $P(x) = \dfrac{k}{x + 1}$ for $x = 0, 1, 2, 3$

7 A discrete random variable X has probability distribution given by:

$P(x) = k \left(\frac{1}{3}\right)^x \left(\frac{2}{3}\right)^{4-x}$ where $x = 0, 1, 2, 3, 4$.

    a Find $P(x)$ for $x = 0, 1, 2, 3$ and 4.   **b** Find k and hence find $P(x \geqslant 2)$.

8 Electrical components are produced and packed into boxes of 10. It is known that 4% of the components may be faulty. The random variable X denotes the number of faulty items in the box and has a probability distribution

$$P(x) = C_x^{10} (0.04)^x (0.96)^{10-x}, \quad x = 0, 1, 2, \ldots, 10.$$

   a Find the probability that a randomly selected box will contain no faulty component.

   b Find the probability that a randomly selected box will contain at least one faulty component.

Example 4

A bag contains 4 red and 2 blue marbles. Two marbles are randomly selected (without replacement). If X denotes the number of reds selected, find the probability distribution of X.

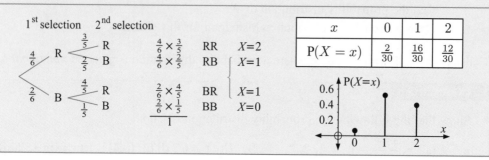

x	0	1	2
$P(X = x)$	$\frac{2}{30}$	$\frac{16}{30}$	$\frac{12}{30}$

---

9 A bag contains 5 blue and 3 green tickets. Two tickets are randomly selected (without replacement). X denotes the number of blue tickets selected.

   a Find the probability distribution of X.

   b If instead of two tickets, three tickets are randomly selected, find the probability distribution of X for $X = 0, 1, 2, 3$.

10 When a pair of dice is rolled, D denotes the sum of the top faces.

   a Display the possible results in a table.   **b** Find $P(D = 7)$.

   c Find the probability distribution of D.   **d** Find $P(D \geqslant 8 \mid D \geqslant 6)$.

11 The number of cars X, passing a shop during the period from 3.00 pm to 3.03 pm is given by $P(X = x) = \dfrac{(0.2)^x e^{-0.2}}{x!}$ where $x = 0, 1, 2, 3, \ldots$

   a Find **i** $P(X = 0)$ **ii** $P(X = 1)$ **iii** $P(X = 2)$.

   b Find the probability that at least three cars will pass the shop in the given period.

C   EXPECTATION

Consider the following problem: A die is to be rolled 120 times. On how many occasions would you expect the result to be a "six"?

In order to answer this question we must first consider all the possible outcomes of rolling the die. The possibilities are 1, 2, 3, 4, 5 and 6 and each of these is equally likely to occur.

Therefore, we would expect $\frac{1}{6}$ of them to be a "six" and $\frac{1}{6}$ of 120 is 20.

That is, we expect 20 of the 120 rolls of the die to yield a "six".

In general: If there are n members of a sample and the probability of an event occurring is p for each member, then the **expectation** of the occurrence of that event is $n \times p$.

Example 5

Each time a footballer kicks for goal he has a $\frac{3}{4}$ chance of being successful. If, in a particular game, he has 12 kicks for goal, how many goals would you expect him to kick?

$p = \mathrm{P(goal)} = \frac{3}{4}$ For a sample space of $n = 12$, the expected number of goals is $n \times p = 12 \times \frac{3}{4} = 9$

EXERCISE 30C

1 In a particular region, the probability that it will rain on any one day is 0.28. On how many days of the year would you expect it to rain?

2 **a** If 3 coins are tossed what is the chance that they all fall heads?

 b If the 3 coins are tossed 200 times, on how many occasions would you expect them all to fall heads?

3 If two dice are rolled simultaneously 180 times, on how many occasions would you expect to get a double?

4 A charity fundraiser gets a licence to run the following gambling game: A die is rolled and the returns to the player are given in the 'pay table' alongside. To play the game $4 is needed. A result of getting a 6 wins $10, so in fact you are ahead by $6 if you get a 6 on the first roll.

Result	Wins
6	$10
4, 5	$4
1, 2, 3	$1

 a What are your chances of playing one game and winning:
 i $10   **ii** $4   **iii** $1?

 b Your expected return from throwing a 6 is $\frac{1}{6} \times \$10$. What is your expected return from throwing:
 i a 4 or 5   **ii** a 1, 2 or 3   **iii** a 1, 2, 3, 4, 5 or 6?

 c What is your expected result at the end of one game?

 d What is your expected result at the end of 100 games?

5 During the snow season there is a $\frac{3}{7}$ probability of snow falling on any particular day. If Udo skis for five weeks, on how many days could he expect to see snow falling?

6 In a random survey of her electorate, a politician (A) discovered the residents' voting intentions in relation to herself and her two opponents B and C. The results are indicated alongside:

A	B	C
165	87	48

  a Estimate the probability that a randomly chosen voter in the electorate will vote for:
     i A **ii** B **iii** C.

  b If there are 7500 people in the electorate, how many of these would you expect to vote for: **i** A **ii** B **iii** C?

Example 6

In a game of chance, the player spins a square spinner labelled 1, 2, 3, 4, and wins the amount of money shown in the table alongside depending on which number comes up. Determine:

Number	1	2	3	4
Winnings	\$1	\$2	\$5	\$8

  a the expected return for one spin of the spinner

  b whether you would recommend a person to play this game if it costs \$5 to play one game.

  a As each number is equally likely, the probability for each number is $\frac{1}{4}$
     $\therefore$ expected return $= \frac{1}{4} \times 1 + \frac{1}{4} \times 2 + \frac{1}{4} \times 5 + \frac{1}{4} \times 8 = \$4$.

  b As the expected return is \$4 whereas it costs \$5 to play the game, you would not recommend that a person play the game.

EXPECTATION BY FORMULAE

For examples like **Example 6** part **a** we can define the expectation $\mathrm{E}(x)$ of a random

variable to be $\mathrm{E}(X) = \sum_{i=1}^{n} p_i x_i$ where

the x_i represents particular outcomes ($x_1 = \$1$, $x_2 = \$2$, etc.)
    p_i represents the probability of x_i occurring
    X is the random variable we are concerned about (in this case the 'return').

7 A person rolls a normal six-sided die and wins the number of dollars shown on the face.
  a How much does the person expect to win for one roll of the die?
  b If it costs \$4 to play the game, would you advise the person to play several games?

8 A single coin is tossed once. If a head appears you win \$2 and if a tail appears you lose \$1. How much would you expect to win when playing this game three times?

9 A person plays a game with a pair of coins. If a double head is spun, \$10 is won. If a head and a tail appear, \$3 is won. If a double tail appears \$5 is lost.
  a How much would a person expect to win playing this game once?
  b If the organiser of the game is allowed to make an average of \$1 per game, how much should be charged to play the game once?

D   THE MEAN AND STANDARD DEVIATION OF A DISCRETE RANDOM VARIABLE

Consider the table alongside:

x_i are the possible values of the random variable X, and f_i are the corresponding frequencies.

x_i	x_1	x_2	x_3	x_4	x_5	$\cdots$	x_n
f_i	f_1	f_2	f_3	f_4	f_5	$\cdots$	f_n

We define the **population mean** as $\mu = \dfrac{\sum f_i x_i}{\sum f_i}$,

the **population standard deviation** as $\sigma = \sqrt{\dfrac{\sum f_i (x_i - \mu)^2}{\sum f_i}}$,

and the **population variance** is σ^2.

Suppose we have 10 counters, one with a 1 written on it, four with 2 written on them, three with a 3 and two with a 4. One counter is to be randomly selected from a hat.

If the random variable is the number on a counter then it has

possible values, x_i	1	2	3	4
with frequencies, f_i	1	4	3	2
and probabilities, p_i	$\frac{1}{10}$	$\frac{4}{10}$	$\frac{3}{10}$	$\frac{2}{10}$

Now $\mu = \dfrac{\sum f_i x_i}{\sum f_i}$

$\therefore \quad \mu = \dfrac{1 \times 1 + 2 \times 4 + 3 \times 3 + 4 \times 2}{1 + 4 + 3 + 2}$

$\therefore \quad \mu = 1 \times \frac{1}{10} + 2 \times \frac{4}{10} + 3 \times \frac{3}{10} + 4 \times \frac{2}{10}$ which suggests, $\mu = \sum x_i p_i$.

Also $\sigma^2 = \dfrac{\sum f_i (x_i - \mu)^2}{\sum f_i}$

$\therefore \quad \sigma^2 = \dfrac{1(x_1 - \mu)^2}{10} + \dfrac{4(x_2 - \mu)^2}{10} + \dfrac{3(x_3 - \mu)^2}{10} + \dfrac{2(x_4 - \mu)^2}{10}$

$\therefore \quad \sigma^2 = \frac{1}{10}(x_1 - \mu)^2 + \frac{4}{10}(x_2 - \mu)^2 + \frac{3}{10}(x_3 - \mu)^2 + \frac{2}{10}(x_4 - \mu)^2$

So, $\sigma^2 = \sum (x_i - \mu)^2 p_i$

Now let us consider the **general case**.

For a random variable having possible values $x_1, x_2, x_3, \ldots., x_n$

with frequencies $f_1, f_2, f_3, \ldots., f_n$:

the population mean $\mu = \dfrac{\sum f_i x_i}{\sum f_i}$ {mean for tabled values}

$= \dfrac{f_1 x_1 + f_2 x_2 + f_3 x_3 + \ldots. + f_n x_n}{N}$ {if $\sum f_i = N$,   say}

$= x_1 \left(\dfrac{f_1}{N}\right) + x_2 \left(\dfrac{f_2}{N}\right) + x_3 \left(\dfrac{f_3}{N}\right) + \ldots. + x_n \left(\dfrac{f_n}{N}\right)$

$= x_1 p_1 + x_2 p_2 + x_3 p_3 + \ldots. + x_n p_n$

$= \sum x_i p_i$

Likewise $\sigma^2 = \dfrac{\sum f_i(x_i - \mu)^2}{\sum f_i}$

$$= \frac{f_1(x_1 - \mu)^2}{N} + \frac{f_2(x_2 - \mu)^2}{N} + \frac{f_3(x_3 - \mu)^2}{N} + \ldots + \frac{f_n(x_n - \mu)^2}{N}$$

$$= p_1(x_1 - \mu)^2 + p_2(x_2 - \mu)^2 + p_3(x_3 - \mu)^2 + \ldots + p_n(x_n - \mu)^2$$

$$= \sum (x_i - \mu)^2 p_i$$

We observe that:

> If a discrete random variable has possible values x_1, x_2, x_3, ..., x_n
> with probabilities p_1, p_2, p_3, ..., p_n of occurring,
>
> then   the population **mean** is $\mu = \sum x_i p_i$ and
>
> - the population **variance** is $\sigma^2 = \sum (x_i - \mu)^2 p_i$
> - the population **standard deviation** is $\sigma = \sqrt{\sum (x_i - \mu)^2 p_i}$.
>
> **Note:**   We can also show that $\sigma = \sqrt{\sum x_i^2 p_i - \mu^2}$
> This formula is easier to use than the first one.

Note that for a die: $\mu = \sum x_i p_i = 1(\frac{1}{6}) + 2(\frac{1}{6}) + 3(\frac{1}{6}) + 4(\frac{1}{6}) + 5(\frac{1}{6}) + 6(\frac{1}{6}) = 3.5$

and $\sigma^2 = \sum x_i^2 p_i - \mu^2 = 1^2(\frac{1}{6}) + 2^2(\frac{1}{6}) + 3^2(\frac{1}{6}) + 4^2(\frac{1}{6}) + 5^2(\frac{1}{6}) + 6^2(\frac{1}{6}) - (3.5)^2$

$$= 2.91666.....$$

Consequently, $\sigma \doteqdot 1.708$ and this can be checked from your calculator by generating 800 random digits from 1 to 6. Then find the mean and standard deviation. You should get a good approximation to the theoretical values obtained above.

Example 7

Find the mean and standard deviation of the data of **Example 2**.

The probability table is:

x_i	0	1	2	3	4	5
p_i	0.00	0.23	0.38	0.21	0.13	0.05

Now $\mu = \sum x_i p_i$

$$= 0(0.00) + (0.23) + 2(0.38) + 3(0.21) + 4(0.13) + 5(0.05)$$

$$= 2.39$$

i.e., in the long run, the average number of magazines purchased/customer is 2.39.

and $\sigma = \sqrt{(x_i - \mu)^2 p_i}$

$$= \sqrt{(1 - 2.39)^2 \times 0.23 + (2 - 2.39)^2 \times 0.38 + \ldots + (5 - 2.39)^2 \times 0.05}$$

$$\doteqdot 1.122$$

Note: The mean of a random variable is often referred to as '*the expected value of x*' or sometimes as '*the long run average value of x*'.

EXERCISE 30D

1 A country exports crayfish to overseas markets. The buyers are prepared to pay high prices when the crayfish arrive still alive. If X is the number of deaths per dozen crayfish, the probability distribution for X is given by:

x_i	0	1	2	3	4	5	>5
$P(x_i)$	0.54	0.26	0.15	k	0.01	0.01	0.00

   a Find k.

   b Over a long period, what is the mean number of deaths per dozen crayfish?

   c Find σ, the standard deviation for the probability distribution.

2 A random variable X has probability distribution given by

$$P(x) = \frac{x^2 + x}{20} \quad \text{for} \ x = 1, 2, 3. \quad \text{Calculate } \mu \text{ and } \sigma \text{ for this distribution.}$$

3 A random variable X has probability distribution given by
$$P(x) = C_x^3 (0.4)^x (0.6)^{3-x} \quad \text{for} \quad x = 0, 1, 2, 3.$$

   a Find $P(x)$ for $x = 0, 1, 2$ and 3 and display the results in table form.

   b Find the mean and standard deviation for the distribution.

4 Using $\sigma^2 = \sum(x_i - \mu)^2 p_i$ show that $\sigma^2 = \sum x_i^2 p_i - \mu^2$.

   (Hint: $\sigma^2 = \sum(x_i - \mu)^2 p_i = (x_1 - \mu)^2 p_1 + (x_2 - \mu)^2 p_2 + \ ...... \ + (x_n - \mu)^2 p_n$.
       Expand and regroup the terms.)

5 A random variable X has probability distribution shown alongside.

   a Copy and complete:

x_i	1	2	3	4	5
$P(x_i)$					

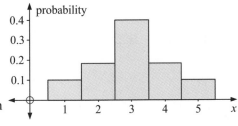

   b Find the mean μ and standard deviation of the X-distribution.

   c Determine **i** $P(\mu - \sigma < x < \mu + \sigma)$ **ii** $P(\mu - 2\sigma < x < \mu + 2\sigma)$

6 An insurance policy covers a \$20 000 sapphire ring against theft and loss. If it is stolen the insurance company will pay the policy owner in full. If it is lost they will pay the owner \$8000. From past experience the insurance company knows that the probability of theft is 0.0025 and of being lost is 0.03. How much should the company charge to cover the ring if they want a \$100 expected return?

7 A pair of dice is rolled and the random variable is M, the larger of the two numbers that are shown uppermost.

   a In table form obtain the probability distribution of M.

   b Find the mean and standard deviation of the M-distribution.

8 A uniform distribution has $P(x_1) = P(x_2) = P(x_3) = ...$ Give *two* examples of a uniform distribution.

E   EXPECTED VALUES (DISCRETE RV)

Recall that if X is a discrete random variable then its mean is $\mu = \sum x_i p_i$ and its variance $\sigma^2 = \sum (x_i - \mu)^2 p_i$. So, we define

- the **mean** as $E(X) = \mu = \sum x_i p_i$ and
- the **variance** as $Var(X) = \sigma^2 = \sum (x_i - \mu)^2 p_i = E(X - \mu)^2$.

PROPERTIES OF $E(X)$

If $E(X)$ is the expected value of random variable X then:

- $E(k) = k$ if k is a constant.
- $E(kX) = kE(X)$ if k is a constant.
- $E(A(X) + B(X)) = E(A(X)) + E(B(X))$ for functions A and B
  i.e.,   the expectation of a sum is the sum of the individual expectations.

These properties enable us to deduce that:

$$E(5) = 5, \qquad E(3X) = 3E(X) \qquad \text{and} \qquad E(X^2 + 2X + 3) = E(X^2) + 2E(X) + 3$$

The proofs of these properties, if required, are left to the reader.

Note: $E(X)$, the expected value of a discrete random variable, is a measure of the centre of the distribution of X. It is the **long-run mean** of the X-distribution, i.e., the mean we can expect for a very large sample from the population.

PROPERTY OF $Var(X)$

$$Var(X) = E(X^2) - \{E(X)\}^2 \qquad \text{i.e.,} \quad Var(X) = E(X^2) - \mu^2$$

Proof: $\begin{aligned} Var(X) &= E(X - \mu)^2 \\ &= E(X^2 - 2\mu X + \mu^2) \\ &= E(X^2) - 2\mu E(X) + \mu^2 \qquad \{\text{properties of } E(X)\} \\ &= E(X^2) - 2\mu^2 + \mu^2 \\ &= E(X^2) - \mu^2 \qquad\qquad\qquad \textbf{Note:} \quad \sigma = \sqrt{Var(X)} \end{aligned}$

Example 8

X has probability distribution

x	1	2	3	4
p_x	0.1	0.3	0.4	0.2

Find:

a   the mean of X **b**   the variance of X **c**   the standard deviation of X.

a $E(X) = \sum x p_x = 1(0.1) + 2(0.3) + 3(0.4) + 4(0.2)$

$\therefore$ $E(X) = 2.7$ so $\mu = 2.7$

b $E(X^2) = \sum x^2 p_x = 1^2(0.1) + 2^2(0.3) + 3^2(0.4) + 4^2(0.2) = 8.1$

But $\begin{aligned} Var(X) &= E(X^2) - \{E(X)\}^2 \\ &= 8.1 - 2.7^2 \\ &= 0.81 \end{aligned}$

c $\sigma = \sqrt{Var(X)} = 0.9$

EXERCISE 30E.1

1 X has probability distribution:

x	2	3	4	5	6
p_x	0.3	0.3	0.2	0.1	0.1

Find:

   a the mean of X **b** the variance of X **c** the standard deviation of X.

2 X has probability distribution:

x	5	6	7	8
p_x	0.2	k	0.4	0.1

Find:

   a the value of k **b** the mean of X **c** the variance of X.

3 X has probability distribution:

x	1	2	3	4
p_x	0.4	0.3	0.2	0.1

Find:

   a $E(X)$ **b** $E(X^2)$ **c** $Var(X)$ **d** σ

   e $E(X+1)$ **f** $Var(X+1)$ **g** $E(2X^2+3X-7)$

4 X has probability distribution:

x	1	2	3	4
p_x	0.2	a	0.3	b

Find a and b given that $E(X) = 2.8$ and $Var(X) = 1.26$.

5 The number of marsupials entering a park at night has random variable X where X suspected has probability distribution

$P(X = x) = a(x^2 - 8x)$ where $X = 0, 1, 2, 3, \ldots 8$.

   a Find constant a.   **b** Find the expected number of marsupials entering the park.

   c Find the standard deviation of X.

6 An unbiased coin is tossed four times. X is the number of heads which could appear.

   a Find the probability distribution of X.

   b Find: **i** the mean of X **ii** the standard deviation of X

7 A box contains 10 almonds, two of which are bitter and the remainder are normal. Brit randomly selects three almonds without replacement. Let X be the random variable for the number of bitter almonds Brit selects. Find:

   a the mean of X **b** the standard deviation of X.

INVESTIGATION 1 $E(aX + b)$ **AND** $Var(aX + b)$

The purpose of this investigation is to discover, if it exists, a relationship between $E(aX + b)$ and $E(X)$ and also $Var(aX + b)$ and $Var(X)$.

What to do:

1 Consider the X-distribution: 1, 2, 3, 4, 5

   a Find $E(X)$ and $Var(X)$.

   b If $Y = 2X + 3$, find the Y-distribution and hence find $E(2X+3)$ and $Var(2X+3)$.

   c Repeat **b** for $Y = 3X - 2$.   **d** Repeat **b** for $Y = -2X + 5$.

e Repeat **b** for $Y = \dfrac{X+1}{2}$.

2 Make up your own sample X distribution and repeat **1** for it.

3 Record all your results in table form for both distributions.

4 From **3**, what is the relationship between:
- $E(X)$ and $E(aX + b)$
- $Var(X)$ and $Var(aX + b)$?

From the investigation you should have discovered that

$$E(aX + b) = aE(X) + b \quad \text{and} \quad Var(aX + b) = a^2Var(X)$$

These results will be formally proved in the exercise which follows.

Example 9

X is distributed with mean 8.1 and standard deviation 2.37. If $Y = 4X - 7$, find the mean and standard deviation of the Y distribution.

$E(X) = 8.1$ and $Var(X) = 2.37^2$

$$\begin{aligned} E(4X - 7) &\qquad Var(4X - 7) \\ = 4E(X) - 7 &\qquad = 4^2Var(X) \\ = 4(8.1) - 7 &\qquad = 4^2 \times 2.37^2 \\ = 25.4 \end{aligned}$$

So, for the Y distribution,

the mean is 25.4 and the standard deviation is $4 \times 2.37 = 9.48$.

EXERCISE 30E.2

1 X is distributed with mean 6 and standard deviation 2 and $Y = 2X + 5$. Find the mean and standard deviation of the Y distribution.

2 **a** Use the properties of $E(X)$ to prove that $E(aX + b) = aE(X) + b$.

   b The mean of an X distribution is 3. Find the mean of the Y distribution where:

   i $Y = 3X + 4$ **ii** $Y = -2X + 1$ **iii** $Y = \dfrac{4X - 2}{3}$

3 X is a random variable with mean 5 and standard deviation 2.
   Find **i** $E(Y)$ **ii** $Var(Y)$ for:

   a $Y = 2X + 3$ **b** $Y = -2X + 3$ **c** $Y = \dfrac{X - 5}{2}$

4 Suppose $Y = 2X + 3$ where X is a random variable.
   Find in terms of $E(X)$ and $E(X^2)$:

   a $E(Y)$ **b** $E(Y^2)$ **c** $Var(Y)$

5 Using $Var(X) = E(X^2) - \{E(X)\}^2$, prove that $Var(aX + b) = a^2Var(X)$

   Note: $Var(aX + b) = E((aX + b)^2) - \{E(aX + b)\}^2$.

F   THE BINOMIAL DISTRIBUTION

In the previous section we considered the properties of discrete random variables.

We now examine a special discrete random variable which is applied to **sampling with replacement**. The probability distribution associated with this variable is known as the **binomial probability distribution**.

For **sampling without replacement** the **hypergeometric probability distribution** is the model used but is not appropriate in this course.

BINOMIAL EXPERIMENTS

When we have a repetition of a number of **independent trials** in which there are two possible results, **success** (the event occurs) or **failure** (the event does not occur), we have a **binomial experiment**.

The probability of a success p, must be constant for all trials.

Let q be the probability of a failure. So, $q = 1 - p$ (since $p + q = 1$).

The random variable X is the total number of successes in n trials.

THE BINOMIAL PROBABILITY DISTRIBUTION

Suppose a spinner has three blue edges and one white edge. Then, on each occasion it is spun, we will get a blue or a white.

The chance of finishing on blue is $\frac{3}{4}$ and on white is $\frac{1}{4}$.

If p is the probability of getting a blue, and q is the probability of getting a white then $p = \frac{3}{4}$ and $q = \frac{1}{4}$ (the chance of failing to get a blue).

Consider twirling the spinner $n = 3$ times. Let the random variable X be the number of blue results which could occur. Then $x = 0, 1, 2$ or 3.

Now $P(0) = P(\text{all 3 are white})$
$= \frac{1}{4} \times \frac{1}{4} \times \frac{1}{4}$
$= \left(\frac{1}{4}\right)^3$

$P(1) = P(\text{1 blue and 2 white})$
$= P(\text{BWW or WBW or WWB})$
$= \left(\frac{3}{4}\right)\left(\frac{1}{4}\right)^2 \times 3$ .....(1)

$P(2) = P(\text{2 blue and 1 white})$
$= P(\text{BBW or BWB or WBB})$
$= \left(\frac{3}{4}\right)^2 \left(\frac{1}{4}\right) \times 3$

$P(3) = P(\text{3 blues})$
$= \left(\frac{3}{4}\right)^3$

The coloured factor 3 in (1) is the number of ways of getting one success in three trials, which is combination C_1^3 (sometimes written as $\binom{3}{1}$).

We note that

$$P(0) = \left(\tfrac{1}{4}\right)^3 \qquad = C_0^3 \left(\tfrac{3}{4}\right)^0 \left(\tfrac{1}{4}\right)^3 \quad \doteqdot 0.0156$$

$$P(1) = 3\left(\tfrac{1}{4}\right)^2 \left(\tfrac{3}{4}\right)^1 = C_1^3 \left(\tfrac{3}{4}\right)^1 \left(\tfrac{1}{4}\right)^2 \quad \doteqdot 0.1406$$

$$P(2) = 3\left(\tfrac{1}{4}\right)^1 \left(\tfrac{3}{4}\right)^2 = C_2^3 \left(\tfrac{3}{4}\right)^2 \left(\tfrac{1}{4}\right)^1 \quad \doteqdot 0.4219$$

$$P(3) = \left(\tfrac{3}{4}\right)^3 \qquad = C_3^3 \left(\tfrac{3}{4}\right)^3 \left(\tfrac{1}{4}\right)^0 \quad \doteqdot 0.4219$$

This suggests that: $P(x) = C_x^3 \left(\tfrac{3}{4}\right)^x \left(\tfrac{1}{4}\right)^{3-x}$ where $x = 0, 1, 2, 3$

In general:

In the case of n trials where there are r *successes* and $n - r$ *failures*

$P(X = r) = C_r^n \, p^r q^{n-r}$ where $q = 1 - p$ and $r = 0, 1, 2, 3, 4, ..., n$.

p is the probability of a *success* and q is the probability of a *failure*.

$P(X = r)$ is the **binomial probability distribution function**.

Note:
- A binomial variable is often specified in the form B(n, p).
- $C_x^n = \binom{n}{x}$

Bin(n, p) is a useful notation. It indicates that the distribution is binomial and gives the values of n and p.

Example 10

72% of union members are in favour of a certain change to their conditions of employment. A random sample of five members is taken. Find the probability that:

a   three members are in favour of the change in conditions

b   at least three members are in favour of the changed conditions.

Let X denote the number of members in favour of the changes, then as $n = 5$, $X = 0, 1, 2, 3, 4$ or 5 and $p = 72\% = 0.72$

X is distributed as   B$(5, 0.72)$.

a $P(x = 3) = \text{binompdf}(5, 0.72, 3)$
$\doteqdot 0.2926$

b $P(x \geqslant 3) = 1 - P(x \leqslant 2)$
$= 1 - \text{binomcdf}(5, 0.72, 2)$
$\doteqdot 0.8623$

For binomial distributions:
- the probability distribution is discrete
- there are two outcomes, which we usually call *success* and *failure*
- the trials are **independent**, so the probability of success for a particular trial is not affected by the success or failure of previous trials. In other words, the probability of success is a constant in each trial for the experiment being considered.

EXERCISE 30F

1   For which of these probability experiments does the binomial distribution apply? Justify your answers, using a full sentence.

a   A coin is thrown 100 times. The variable is the number of heads.

    b One hundred coins are each thrown once. The variable is the number of heads.

    c A box contains 5 blue and 3 red marbles. I draw out 5 marbles, replacing the marble each time. The variable is the number of red marbles drawn.

    d A box contains 5 blue and 3 red marbles. I draw out 5 marbles. I do not replace the marbles that are drawn. The variable is the number of red marbles drawn.

    e A large bin contains ten thousand bolts, 1% of which are faulty. I draw a sample of 10 bolts from the bin. The variable is the number of faulty bolts.

2 At a manufacturing plant 35% of the employees worked night-shift. If 7 employees were selected at random, find the probability that:

    a exactly 3 of them worked night-shift   **b** less than 4 of them worked night-shift

    c at least 4 of them worked night-shift.

3 Records show that 6% of the items assembled on a production line are faulty. A random sample of 12 items is selected at random (with replacement). Find the probability that:

    a none will be faulty   **b** at most one will be faulty

    c at least two will be faulty   **d** less than 4 will be faulty.

4 The local bus service does not have a good reputation. It is known that the 8 am bus will run late on an average of two days out of every five. For any week of the year taken at random, find the probability of the 8 am bus being on time:

    a all 7 days   **b** only on Monday

    c on any 6 days   **d** on at least 4 days.

5 An infectious flu virus is spreading through a school. The probability of a randomly selected student having the flu next week is 0.3.

    a Calculate the probability that out of a class of 25 students, 2 or more will have the flu next week.

    b If more than 20% of the students are away with the flu next week, a class test will have to be cancelled. What is the probability that the test will be cancelled?

G MEAN AND STANDARD DEVIATION OF A BINOMIAL RANDOM VARIABLE

We toss a coin $n = 20$ times; as the probability of it falling '*a head*' is $p = \frac{1}{2}$, we expect it to fall '*heads*' $np = 10$ times.

Likewise, if we roll a die $n = 30$ times, as the probability of it falling 'a 4' is $p = \frac{1}{6}$, we expect it to obtain 'a 4' on $np = 5$ occasions.

So, in the general case:

> If a binomial experiment is repeated n times and a particular variable has probability p of occurring each time, then our expectation is that the mean μ will be $\mu = np$.

Finding the standard deviation is not so simple. Consider the following theoretical approach after which we verify the generalised result by simulation.

ONE TRIAL $(n=1)$

In the case of $n = 1$ where p is the probability of success and q is the probability of failure, the number of successes x could be 0 or 1.

The table of probabilities is

x_i	0	1
p_i	q	p

Now
$$\begin{aligned} \mu &= \sum p_i x_i \\ &= q(0) + p(1) \\ &= p \end{aligned}$$

and
$$\begin{aligned} \sigma^2 &= \sum x_i^2 p_i - \mu^2 \\ &= [(0)^2 q + (1)^2 p] - p^2 \\ &= p - p^2 \\ &= p(1 - p) \\ &= pq \quad \{\text{as} \quad q = 1 - p\} \end{aligned}$$

$$\therefore \quad \sigma = \sqrt{pq}$$

TWO TRIALS $(n=2)$

In the case where $n = 2$,
$$\left. \begin{aligned} P(0) &= C_0^2\, p^0 q^2 = q^2 \\ P(1) &= C_1^2\, p^1 q^1 = 2pq \\ P(2) &= C_2^2\, p^2 q^0 = p^2 \end{aligned} \right\} \quad \text{as} \quad x = 0, 1 \text{ or } 2$$

So, the table of probabilities is

x_i	0	1	2
p_i	q^2	$2pq$	p^2

with

$$\begin{aligned} \mu &= \sum p_i x_i \\ &= q^2(0) + 2pq(1) + p^2(2) \\ &= 2pq + 2p^2 \\ &= 2p(q + p) \\ &= 2p \quad \{\text{as} \quad p + q = 1\} \end{aligned}$$

and
$$\begin{aligned} \sigma^2 &= \sum x_i^2 p_i - \mu^2 \\ &= [0^2 \times q^2 + 1^2 \times 2pq + 2^2 \times p^2] - (2p)^2 \\ &= 2pq + 4p^2 - 4p^2 \\ &= 2pq \end{aligned}$$

$$\therefore \quad \sigma = \sqrt{2pq}$$

The case $n = 3$ produces $\mu = 3p$ and $\sigma = \sqrt{3pq}$ {in the following exercise}.

The case $n = 4$ produces $\mu = 4p$ and $\sigma = \sqrt{4pq}$.

These results suggest that in general:

> If x is a random variable which is binomial with parameters n and p i.e.,   B(n, p) then the mean of x is $\mu = np$ and the standard deviation of x is $\sigma = \sqrt{npq}$.

A general proof of this statement is beyond the scope of this course. However, the following investigation should help you appreciate the truth of the statement.

INVESTIGATION 2   **THE MEAN AND STANDARD DEVIATION OF A BINOMIAL RANDOM VARIABLE**

In this investigation we will examine binomial distributions randomly generated by the *sorting simulation* that you may have already used.

STATISTICS PACKAGE

What to do:

SIMULATION

1 Obtain experimental binomial distribution results for 1000 repetitions

    a $n = 4,\ p = 0.5$ **b** $n = 5,\ p = 0.6$ **c** $n = 6,\ p = 0.75$

2 For each of the distributions obtained in **1** find the mean μ and standard deviation σ from the statistics pack.

3 Use $\mu = np$ and $\sigma = \sqrt{npq}$ to see how your experimental values for μ and σ in **2** agree with the theoretical expectation.

4 Finally, comment on the shape of a binomial distribution for changes in the value of p. Go back to the sorting simulation and for $n = 50$, say, try $p = 0.2, 0.35, 0.5, 0.68, 0.85$.

Example 11

5% of a batch of batteries are defective. A random sample of 80 batteries is taken with replacement. Find the mean and standard deviation of the number of defectives in the sample.

This is a binomial sampling situation with $n = 80$, $p = 5\% = \frac{1}{20}$.

If X is the random variable for the number of defectives then X is $B(80, \frac{1}{20})$.

So, $\mu = np = 80 \times \frac{1}{20} = 4$ and $\sigma = \sqrt{npq} = \sqrt{80 \times \frac{1}{20} \times \frac{19}{20}} \doteqdot 1.95$

This means that we expect a defective battery 4 times, with standard deviation 1.95.

EXERCISE 30G

1 Suppose x is $B(6, p)$. For each of the following cases:

    i   find the mean and standard deviation of the X-distribution

    ii   graph the distribution using a histogram

    iii   comment on the shape of the distribution

  a   when $p = 0.5$ **b**   when $p = 0.2$ **c**   when $p = 0.8$

2 A coin is tossed 10 times and X is the number of heads which occur. Find the mean and standard deviation of the X-distribution.

3 Suppose X is $B(3, p)$.

  a   Find $P(0)$, $P(1)$, $P(2)$ and $P(3)$ using
$$P(x) = C_x^3 \, p^x \, q^{3-x}$$
     and display your results in a table:

x_i	0	1	2	3
p_i				

  b   Show that $\mu = 3p$ by using $\mu = \sum p_i x_i$.

  c   By using $\sigma^2 = \sum x_i^2 p_i - \mu^2$, show that $\sigma = \sqrt{3pq}$.

4 Bolts produced by a machine vary in quality. The probability that a given bolt is defective is 0.04. A random sample of 30 bolts is taken from the week's production. If X denotes the number of defectives in the sample, find the mean and standard deviation of the X-distribution.

5 A city restaurant knows that 13% of reservations are not honoured, i.e., the group does not come. Suppose the restaurant receives five reservations and X is the random variable on the number of groups that do not come. Find the mean and standard deviation of the X-distribution.

H   THE POISSON DISTRIBUTION

When Sandra proof read 80 pages of a text book she observed the following distribution of X, the number of errors per page:

X	0	1	2	3	4	5	6	7	8	9	10
frequency	3	11	16	18	15	9	5	1	1	0	1

The model describing this sort of distribution is the **Poisson model**. The **Poisson model** is defined as:

$$p_x = \mathrm{P}(X = x) = \frac{m^x e^{-m}}{x!} \quad \text{for} \quad x = 0, 1, 2, 3, 4, 5, \ldots .. \quad m \text{ is called the } \textbf{parameter}.$$

Whereas the **binomial distribution**, $\mathrm{B}(n, p)$ is used to determine the probability of obtaining a certain number of successes in a given number of trials, the **Poisson distribution** is used to determine the probability of obtaining a certain number of successes that can take place in a certain interval (of time or space).

Examples are:
- the number of incoming telephone calls to a given phone per hour
- the number of misprints on a typical page of a book
- the number of fish caught in a large lake per day
- the number of car accidents on a given road per month.

INVESTIGATION 3   POISSON MEAN AND VARIANCE

The **Poisson distribution** is defined as $\mathrm{P}(X = x) = \dfrac{m^x e^{-m}}{x!}$ for $x = 0, 1, 2, 3, \ldots ..$
This investigation enables you to discover the mean and variance of this distribution.

What to do:

1 Prove by solving the differential equation that: "There is only one solution of the differential equation $f'(x) = f(x)$ where $f(0) = 1$,   and it is $f(x) = e^x$ ".

2 Consider $f(x) = 1 + \dfrac{x}{1!} + \dfrac{x^2}{2!} + \dfrac{x^3}{3!} + \ldots + \dfrac{x^n}{n!} + \ldots$ which is an infinite power series.
   a Check that $f(0) = 1$ and find $f'(x)$. What do you notice?
   b From the result of question **1**, what can be deduced about $f(x)$?
   c Let $x = 1$ in your discovered result in **b**, and calculate the sum of the first 12 terms of the power series.

3 By observing that $\dfrac{2x}{1!} = \dfrac{x}{1!} + \dfrac{x}{1!}$, $\dfrac{3x^2}{2!} = \dfrac{x^2}{2!} + \dfrac{x^2}{1!}$, etc.,

   show that $1 + \dfrac{2x}{1!} + \dfrac{3x^2}{2!} + \dfrac{4x^3}{3!} + \ldots .. = e^x(1 + x)$.

4 If $p_x = \mathrm{P}(X = x) = \dfrac{m^x e^{-m}}{x!}$ $(x = 0, 1, 2, 3, \ldots ..)$ show that:

   a $\displaystyle\sum_{x=0}^{\infty} p_x = 1$ b $\mathrm{E}(X) = m$ c $\mathrm{Var}(X) = m$

From the investigation, you should have discovered that the Poisson distribution has mean m and variance m.

Conditions for a distribution to be Poisson:

1 The average number of occurrences (μ) is constant for each interval (i.e., it should be equally likely that the event occurs in one specific interval as in any other).

2 The probability of more than one occurrence in a given interval is very small (i.e., the typical number of occurrences in a given interval should be much less than is theoretically possible (say about 10%)).

3 The number of occurrences in disjoint intervals are independent of each other.

Notice that for *errors per page* example $m = \dfrac{\sum fx}{\sum f} = \dfrac{257}{80} \doteqdot 3.21$

The Poisson model, $p_x = \dfrac{(3.21)^x e^{-3.21}}{x!}$ gives

$p_0 \doteqdot 0.0404$	$80p_0 \doteqdot 3$	$p_4 \doteqdot 0.1785$	$80p_4 \doteqdot 14$	$p_8 = 0.0113$	$80p_8 \doteqdot 1$
$p_1 \doteqdot 0.1295$	$80p_1 \doteqdot 10$	$p_5 \doteqdot 0.1146$	$80p_5 \doteqdot 9$	$p_9 = 0.0040$	$80p_9 \doteqdot 0$
$p_2 \doteqdot 0.2079$	$80p_2 \doteqdot 17$	$p_6 \doteqdot 0.0613$	$80p_6 \doteqdot 5$	$p_{10} = 0.0013$	$80p_{10} \doteqdot 0$
$p_3 \doteqdot 0.2225$	$80p_3 \doteqdot 18$	$p_7 \doteqdot 0.0281$	$80p_7 \doteqdot 2$	$p_{11} = 0.0004$	$80p_{11} \doteqdot 0$

Notice that the agreement between the actual data and that obtained theoretically from the Poisson model is very close.

Note: $P_0(m)$ is the notation representing a Poisson distribution of mean m.

EXERCISE 30H

1 Sven's Florist Shop receives the following distribution of phone calls, X in number, between 9.00 am and 9.15 am on Fridays.

X	0	1	2	3	4	5	6
frequency	12	18	12	6	3	0	1

   a Find the mean of the X distribution.

   b Compare the actual data with that generated by the Poisson model.

2 a A Poisson distribution has a standard deviation of 2.67.

   i What is its mean?   **ii** What is its probability generating function?

   b For the distribution in **a**, find:

   i $P(X = 2)$ **ii** $P(X \leqslant 3)$ **iii** $P(X \geqslant 5)$ **iv** $P(X \geqslant 3)\,|\,X \geqslant 1)$

3 One gram of radioactive substance is positioned so that each emission of an alpha-particle will flash on a screen. The emissions over 500 periods of 10 second duration are given in the following table:

Number/period	0	1	2	3	4	5	6	7
Frequency	91	156	132	75	33	9	3	1

   a Find the mean of the distribution.

   b Fit a Poisson model to the data and compare the actual data to that from the model.

   c Find the standard deviation of the distribution. How close is it to $\sqrt{m}$ found in **a**?

4 Top cars rent cars to tourists. They have four cars which are hired out on a daily basis. The number of requests each day is distributed according to the Poisson model with a mean of 3. Determine the probability that:

    a none of its cars are rented   **b** at least 3 of its cars are rented

    c some requests will be refused   **d** all are hired out given that at least two are

5 A random variable X is distributed $P_0(m)$.

    a Find m given that $P(X = 1) + P(X = 2) = P(X = 3)$.

    b If $m = 2.7$, find   **i** $P(X \geqslant 3)$ **ii** $P(X \leqslant 4 \mid X \geqslant 2)$

I | CONTINUOUS PROBABILITY DENSITY FUNCTIONS

In previous sections we have looked at discrete random variables and have examined some probability distributions where the random variable X could take non-negative integer values i.e., $x = 0, 1, 2, 3, 4, \ldots$

However, for a **continuous random variable** X, x can take any real value. Consequently, a function is used to specify the probability distribution for a continuous random variable and that function is called the **probability density function**.

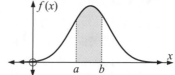

Probabilities are found by finding areas under the probability density function.

> A **continuous probability density function (pdf)**, $f(x)$, is a function where
>
> $f(x) \geqslant 0$ on a given interval, such as $[a, b]$ and $\displaystyle\int_a^b f(x)\,dx = 1$.

For a continuous pdf:

- The **mode** is the value of x, at the maximum value of $f(x)$ on $[a, b]$.

- The **median** m, is the solution for m of the equation $\displaystyle\int_a^m f(x)\,dx = \frac{1}{2}$.

- The **mean** μ or $E(X)$, is defined as $\displaystyle \mu = \int_a^b x f(x)\,dx$.

- **Var(X)** $= E(X^2) - \{E(X)\}^2 = \displaystyle\int_a^b x^2 f(x)\,dx - \mu^2$

Example 12

$$f(x) = \begin{cases} \frac{1}{2}x & \text{on } [0, 2] \\ 0 & \text{elsewhere} \end{cases} \quad \text{is a probability distribution function.}$$

    a Check that the above statement is true.

    b Find **i** the mode   **ii** the median   **iii** the mean of the distribution.

    c Find **i** Var(X)   **ii** σ

---

    a   Area $= \frac{1}{2} \times 2 \times 1 = 1$ ✓

                  or $\displaystyle\int_0^2 \frac{1}{2}x\,dx = \left[\frac{1}{4}x^2\right]_0^2 = 1$ ✓

b i mode $= 2$ **ii** The median is the solution of $\displaystyle\int_0^m \tfrac{1}{2}x\,dx = \tfrac{1}{2}$

i.e., $\left[\tfrac{1}{4}x^2\right]_0^m = \tfrac{1}{2}$

i.e., $\dfrac{m^2}{4} = \tfrac{1}{2}$

$m^2 = 2$

$m = \sqrt{2}$

iii $\mu = \displaystyle\int_0^2 x\,f(x)\,dx$ **c** $\displaystyle\int_0^2 x^2\,f(x)\,dx$ So, **i**   Var(X)

$= \displaystyle\int_0^2 \tfrac{1}{2}x^2\,dx$ $= \displaystyle\int_0^2 \tfrac{1}{2}x^3\,dx$ $= 2 - (1\tfrac{1}{3})^2$

$= 2 - (1\tfrac{1}{3})^2$

$= \tfrac{2}{9}$

$= \left[\tfrac{1}{6}x^3\right]_0^2$ $= \left[\tfrac{1}{8}x^4\right]_0^2$ **ii** σ

$= 1\tfrac{1}{3}$ $= 2$ $= \sqrt{\text{Var}(X)}$

$= \tfrac{\sqrt{2}}{3}$

EXERCISE 30I

1 $f(x) = \begin{cases} ax(x-4), & 0 \leqslant x \leqslant 4 \\ 0 \text{ elsewhere} \end{cases}$ is a continuous probability distribution function.

a Find a.   **b** Sketch the graph of $y = f(x)$.
c Find: **i** the mean   **ii** the mode   **iii** the median   **iv** the variance.

2 Given that $f(x) = \begin{cases} -0.2x(x-b) \\ 0 \text{ elsewhere} \end{cases}$ is a probability distribution function, $0 \leqslant x \leqslant b$.

a Find b.   **b** Find **i** the mean **ii** the variance of this distribution.

3 $f(x) = \begin{cases} ke^{-x}, & 0 \leqslant x \leqslant 3 \\ 0 \text{ elsewhere} \end{cases}$ is a probability distribution function.

a   Find k to 4 decimal places.   **b**   Find the median.

4 $f(x) = \begin{cases} kx^2(x-6), & 0 \leqslant x \leqslant 5 \\ 0 \text{ elsewhere} \end{cases}$ is a probability distribution function. Find:

a k **b** the mode   **c** the median   **d** the mean   **e** the variance.

Summary:

Discrete random variable	Continuous random variable
• $\mu = \text{E}(X) = \sum xp_x$	• $\mu = \text{E}(X) = \int xf(x)\,dx$
• $\sigma^2 = \text{Var}(X) \;\; = \text{E}(X-\mu)^2$	• $\sigma^2 = \text{Var}(X) \;\; = \text{E}(X-\mu)^2$
$= \sum(x-\mu)^2 p_x$	$= \int (x-\mu)^2\,f(x)\,dx$
$= \sum x^2 p_x - \mu^2$	$= \int x^2 f(x)\,dx - \mu^2$
$= \text{E}(X^2) - \{\text{E}(X)\}^2$	$= \text{E}(X^2) - \{\text{E}(X)\}^2$

J   NORMAL DISTRIBUTIONS

The normal distribution is the most important distribution for a continuous random variable. Many naturally occurring phenomena have a distribution that is normal, or approximately normal.   Some examples are:

- the chest sizes of English males
- yields of corn, wheat, etc.

- the lengths of adult female tiger sharks
- scores on tests taken by a large population

If X is **normally distributed** then its **probability density function** is given by

$$f(x) = \frac{1}{\sigma\sqrt{2\pi}}\, e^{-\frac{1}{2}\left(\frac{x-\mu}{\sigma}\right)^2} \quad \text{for} \quad -\infty < x < \infty.$$

This probability density function represents a **family of bell-shaped curves**.

These curves are all symmetrical about the vertical line $x = \mu$.

A typical **normal curve** is illustrated alongside.

Notice that $f(\mu) = \dfrac{1}{\sigma\sqrt{2\pi}}$.

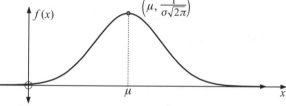

We say that: X is distributed normally with mean μ and variance σ^2
and write $X \sim N(\mu,\, \sigma^2)$

Each member of the family is specified by the **parameters** μ (the mean) and σ (the standard deviation).

NOTE ON PARAMETERS AND STATISTICS

A **parameter** is a numerical characteristic of a *population*.

A **statistic** is a numerical characteristic of a *sample*.

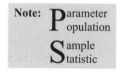

Note: **P**arameter
       Population

       Sample
       Statistic

For example, if we are examining the mean age of people in retirement villages throughout Canada the mean age found would be a *parameter*. If we take a random sample of 300 people from the population of all retirement village persons, then the mean age would be a *statistic*.

CHARACTERISTICS OF THE NORMAL PROBABILITY DENSITY FUNCTION

- The curve is symmetrical about the vertical line $x = \mu$.
- As $x \to \infty$ and as $x \to -\infty$ the normal curve approaches the x-axis.
- The area under the curve is one unit², and so $\displaystyle\int_{-\infty}^{\infty} f(x)\,dx = 1$.   Why is this?
- More scores are distributed closer to the mean than further away. Hence the typical **bell shape**.

A TYPICAL NORMAL DISTRIBUTION

A large sample of cockle shells were collected and the maximum distance across each shell was measured. Click on the video clip icon to see how a histogram of the data is built up. Now click on the demo icon to observe the effect of changing the class interval lengths for normally distributed data.

VIDEO CLIP

DEMO

THE GEOMETRICAL SIGNIFICANCE OF μ AND σ

For $\quad f(x) = \dfrac{1}{\sigma\sqrt{2\pi}} e^{-\frac{1}{2}\left(\frac{x-\mu}{\sigma}\right)^2} \quad$ we can obtain $\quad f'(x) = \dfrac{-1}{\sigma^2\sqrt{2\pi}} e^{-\frac{1}{2}\left(\frac{x-\mu}{\sigma}\right)^2} \times \left(\dfrac{x-\mu}{\sigma}\right)$

So $\quad f'(x) = 0 \quad$ only when $\quad x - \mu = 0 \quad$ i.e., when $\quad x = \mu$.

This result is as expected because at $\quad x = \mu, \quad f(x)$ is a maximum.

Also, on simplification, $\quad f''(x) = \dfrac{-1}{\sigma^2\sqrt{2\pi}} e^{-\frac{1}{2}\left(\frac{x-\mu}{\sigma}\right)^2} \left[\dfrac{1}{\sigma} - \dfrac{(x-\mu)^2}{\sigma^3}\right]$

So $\quad f''(x) = 0 \quad$ when $\quad \dfrac{(x-\mu)^2}{\sigma^3} = \dfrac{1}{\sigma}, \quad$ i.e., $\quad (x-\mu)^2 = \sigma^2$

$$\text{i.e.,} \quad x - \mu = \pm\sigma$$
$$x = \mu \pm \sigma$$

So at the points of inflection,
$x = \mu + \sigma \quad$ and $\quad x = \mu - \sigma$.

point of inflection → ← point of inflection

σ σ

$\mu - \sigma \quad \mu \quad \mu + \sigma$

x

Consequently:

> For a given normal curve the standard deviation is uniquely determined as the horizontal distance from the vertical line $x = \mu$ to a point of inflection.

HOW THE NORMAL DISTRIBUTION ARISES

Consider the oranges stripped from an orange tree. They do not all have the same weight. This variation may be due to several factors which could include:

- different genetic factors
- different times when the flowers were fertilised
- different amounts of sunlight reaching the leaves and fruit
- different weather conditions (some may be affected by the prevailing winds), etc.

The result is that much of the fruit could have weights centred about e.g., a mean weight of 214 grams and there are far fewer oranges that are much heavier or lighter.

Invariably, a bell-shaped distribution of weights would be observed and the normal distribution model fits the data fairly closely. Discuss why this is so.

Once a normal model has been established we can use it to make predictions about the distribution and to answer other relevant questions.

THE SIGNIFICANCE OF THE STANDARD DEVIATION σ

For a normal distribution with mean μ and standard deviation σ the proportional breakdown of where the random variable could lie is given below.

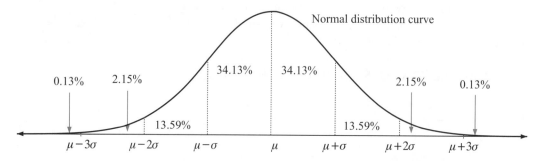

Notice that:

- Approximately $2 \times 34.13\% = 68.26\%$ of the values lie within one standard deviation of the mean.

- Approximately $2 \times (34.13\% + 13.59\%) = 95.44\%$ of the values lie within two standard deviations of the mean.

- Approximately 99.74% of the values lie within three standard deviations of the mean.

INVESTIGATION 4   STANDARD DEVIATION SIGNIFICANCE

The purpose of this investigation is to check whether normal distributions have about
- 68.3% of their values between $\overline{x} - s$ and $\overline{x} + s$
- 95.4% of their values between $\overline{x} - 2s$ and $\overline{x} + 2s$
- 99.7% of their values between $\overline{x} - 3s$ and $\overline{x} + 3s$.

DEMO

Click on the icon to start the demonstration in Microsoft® Excel.

Choose a random sample of size $n = 1000$ from a normal distribution and follow the procedure:
- find $\overline{x}$ and s
- find $\overline{x} - s$, $\overline{x} + s$; $\overline{x} - 2s$, $\overline{x} + 2s$; $\overline{x} - 3s$, $\overline{x} + 3s$
- count all values between $\overline{x} - s$ and $\overline{x} + s$ $\overline{x} - 2s$ and $\overline{x} + 2s$
  $\overline{x} - 3s$ and $\overline{x} + 3s$
- determine percentages in the intervals   • repeat several times.

Note: We are using $\overline{x}$ and s as we are taking samples from a normal distribution.

Example 13

The chest measurements of 18 year old male footballers is normally distributed with a mean of 95 cm and a standard deviation of 8 cm.

a Find the percentage of footballers with chest measurements between:
   i 87 cm and 103 cm   **ii** 103 cm and 111 cm

b Find the probability that the chest measurement of a randomly chosen footballer is between 87 cm and 111 cm.

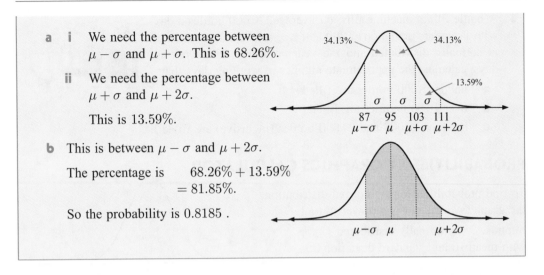

a i We need the percentage between $\mu - \sigma$ and $\mu + \sigma$. This is 68.26%.

ii We need the percentage between $\mu + \sigma$ and $\mu + 2\sigma$.

This is 13.59%.

b This is between $\mu - \sigma$ and $\mu + 2\sigma$.

The percentage is   68.26% + 13.59%
= 81.85%.

So the probability is 0.8185 .

EXERCISE 30J.1

1 Draw each of the following distributions accurately on one set of axes.

Distribution	form	mean (mL)	standard deviation (mL)
A	normal	25	5
B	normal	30	2
C	normal	21	10

2 Explain why it is likely that the distribution of each of the following variables is normal:
a the volume of soft drink in cans
b the diameter of bolts immediately after manufacture.

3 It is known that when a specific type of radish is grown in a certain manner without fertiliser the weights of the radishes produced are normally distributed with a mean of 40 g and a standard deviation of 10 g. When the same type of radish is grown in the same way except for the inclusion of fertiliser, it is known that the weights of the radishes produced are normally distributed with a mean of 140 g and a standard deviation of 40 g. Determine the proportion of radishes grown:
a without fertiliser with weights less than 50 grams
b with fertiliser with weights less than 60 grams
c with and without fertiliser with weights equal to or between 20 and 60 grams
d with and without fertiliser that will have weights greater than or equal to 60 grams.

4 The height of male students is normally distributed with a mean of 170 cm and a standard deviation of 8 cm.
a Find the percentage of male students whose height is:
i between 162 cm and 170 cm   **ii** between 170 cm and 186 cm.
b Find the probability that a randomly chosen student from this group has a height:
i between 178 cm and 186 cm   **ii** less than 162 cm
iii less than 154 cm   **iv** greater than 162 cm.

5 A bottle filling machine fills, on average, 20 000 bottles a day with a standard deviation of 2000. If we assume that production is normally distributed and the year comprises 260 working days, calculate the approximate number of working days that:

   a under 18 000 bottles are filled

   b over 16 000 bottles are filled

   c between 18 000 and 24 000 bottles (inclusive) are filled.

PROBABILITIES BY GRAPHICS CALCULATOR

To find probabilities for the normal distribution, the graphics calculator is a powerful tool.

Suppose X is normally distributed with mean 10 and standard deviation 2.

How do we find $P(8 \leqslant X \leqslant 11)$?

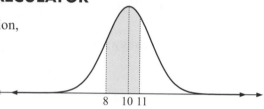

Click on the icon for your graphics calculator for instructions on how to obtain the normal distribution graph and determine probabilities.

EXERCISE 30J.2

Use a calculator to find these probabilities:

1 X is a random variable that is distributed normally with mean 70 and standard deviation 4. Find:
   a $P(70 \leqslant X \leqslant 74)$
   b $P(68 \leqslant X \leqslant 72)$
   c $P(X \leqslant 65)$

2 Given that X is a random variable that is distributed normally with mean 60 and standard deviation 5, find:

   a $P(60 \leqslant X \leqslant 65)$
   b $P(62 \leqslant X \leqslant 67)$
   c $P(X \geqslant 64)$

   d $P(X \leqslant 68)$
   e $P(X \leqslant 61)$
   f $P(57.5 \leqslant X \leqslant 62.5)$

INVESTIGATION 5   MEAN AND STANDARD DEVIATION OF $Z = \dfrac{x - \mu}{\sigma}$

Suppose a random variable X is **normally distributed** with mean μ and standard deviation σ.

For each value of X we can calculate a Z-**value** using the algebraic transformation $Z = \dfrac{X - \mu}{\sigma}$.

The question arises, "What is the mean and standard deviation of the Z-distribution?"

What to do:

Question **1** could be easily done on a **graphics calculator** or **spreadsheet**.

1 Consider the following X values: 1, 2, 2, 3, 3, 3, 3, 4, 4, 4, 4, 4, 5, 5, 5, 5, 6, 6, 7.

   a Draw a graph of the distribution to check that it is approximately normal.

   b Find the mean μ, and standard deviation σ, of the distribution of X values.

   c Use the transformation $Z = \dfrac{X - \mu}{\sigma}$ to convert each of the X values into Z values.

   d Find the mean and standard deviation of the distribution of Z values.

2 Click on the icon to bring up a large sample drawn from a normal population. By clicking appropriately we can repeat the four steps of question **1**.

3 Write a brief report of your findings.

K THE STANDARD NORMAL DISTRIBUTION (Z-DISTRIBUTION)

To obtain the **standard normal distribution** (sometimes called the Z-**distribution**) the transformation $Z = \dfrac{X - \mu}{\sigma}$ is applied to a normal X-distribution.

In **Investigation 5** we discovered that the mean of a Z-distribution is 0 and the standard deviation is 1.

The **probability density function** for the Z-distribution is $f(z) = \frac{1}{\sqrt{2\pi}} e^{-\frac{z^2}{2}}$, $-\infty < z < \infty$.

To get this, replace μ by 0, σ by 1 and x by z in the $f(x)$ function.

Note: The normal distribution function $f(x)$ has two parameters μ and σ whereas the **standard normal** distribution function $f(z)$ **has no parameters**.

This means that a table of values of $f(z)$ can be found and is unique, whereas a vast number of tables for many values of μ and σ would need to be constructed if they are to be useful.

Before graphics calculators and computer packages the standard normal distribution was used exclusively for normal probability calculations such as those which follow. However standard normal variables are essential for the following chapter on statistical inference.

CALCULATING PROBABILITIES USING THE Z-DISTRIBUTION

The table of values of $f(z)$ enables us to find $P(Z \leqslant a)$.

Note: $P(Z \leqslant a) = P(Z < a)$.

In fact, $P(Z \leqslant a) = \displaystyle\int_{-\infty}^{a} \frac{1}{\sqrt{2\pi}} e^{-\frac{1}{2}z^2}\, dz.$

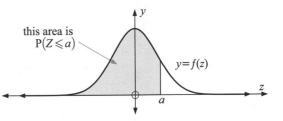

USING A GRAPHICS CALCULATOR TO FIND PROBABILITIES

For a TI-83:   To find $P(Z \leqslant a)$ or $P(Z < a)$ use   normalcdf($-$E99, a).

To find $P(Z \geqslant a)$ or $P(Z > a)$ use   normalcdf(a, E99).

To find $P(a \leqslant Z \leqslant b)$ or $P(a \leqslant Z \leqslant b)$ use   normalcdf(a, b).

STANDARD NORMAL CURVE AREAS ($Z \geq 0$)

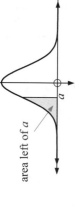

Each table value is the area to the left of the specified Z-value.

area left of a

z	.00	.01	.02	.03	.04	.05	.06	.07	.08	.09
				the second decimal digit of z						
0.0	0.5000	0.5040	0.5080	0.5120	0.5160	0.5199	0.5239	0.5279	0.5319	0.5359
0.1	0.5398	0.5438	0.5478	0.5517	0.5557	0.5596	0.5636	0.5675	0.5714	0.5753
0.2	0.5793	0.5832	0.5871	0.5910	0.5948	0.5987	0.6026	0.6064	0.6103	0.6141
0.3	0.6179	0.6217	0.6255	0.6293	0.6331	0.6368	0.6406	0.6443	0.6480	0.6517
0.4	0.6554	0.6591	0.6628	0.6664	0.6700	0.6736	0.6772	0.6808	0.6844	0.6879
0.5	0.6915	0.6950	0.6985	0.7019	0.7054	0.7088	0.7123	0.7157	0.7190	0.7224
0.6	0.7257	0.7291	0.7324	0.7357	0.7389	0.7422	0.7454	0.7486	0.7517	0.7549
0.7	0.7580	0.7611	0.7642	0.7673	0.7704	0.7734	0.7764	0.7794	0.7823	0.7852
0.8	0.7881	0.7910	0.7939	0.7967	0.7995	0.8023	0.8051	0.8078	0.8106	0.8133
0.9	0.8159	0.8186	0.8212	0.8238	0.8264	0.8289	0.8315	0.8340	0.8365	0.8389
1.0	0.8413	0.8438	0.8461	0.8485	0.8508	0.8531	0.8554	0.8577	0.8599	0.8621
1.1	0.8643	0.8665	0.8686	0.8708	0.8729	0.8749	0.8770	0.8790	0.8810	0.8830
1.2	0.8849	0.8869	0.8888	0.8907	0.8925	0.8944	0.8962	0.8980	0.8997	0.9015
1.3	0.9032	0.9049	0.9066	0.9082	0.9099	0.9115	0.9131	0.9147	0.9162	0.9177
1.4	0.9192	0.9207	0.9222	0.9236	0.9251	0.9265	0.9279	0.9292	0.9306	0.9319
1.5	0.9332	0.9345	0.9357	0.9370	0.9382	0.9394	0.9406	0.9418	0.9429	0.9441
1.6	0.9452	0.9463	0.9474	0.9484	0.9495	0.9505	0.9515	0.9525	0.9535	0.9545
1.7	0.9554	0.9564	0.9573	0.9582	0.9591	0.9599	0.9608	0.9616	0.9625	0.9633
1.8	0.9641	0.9649	0.9656	0.9664	0.9671	0.9678	0.9686	0.9693	0.9699	0.9706
1.9	0.9713	0.9719	0.9726	0.9732	0.9738	0.9744	0.9750	0.9756	0.9761	0.9767
2.0	0.9772	0.9778	0.9783	0.9788	0.9793	0.9798	0.9803	0.9808	0.9812	0.9817
2.1	0.9821	0.9826	0.9830	0.9834	0.9838	0.9842	0.9846	0.9850	0.9854	0.9857
2.2	0.9861	0.9864	0.9868	0.9871	0.9875	0.9878	0.9881	0.9884	0.9887	0.9890
2.3	0.9893	0.9896	0.9898	0.9901	0.9904	0.9906	0.9909	0.9911	0.9913	0.9916
2.4	0.9918	0.9920	0.9922	0.9925	0.9927	0.9929	0.9931	0.9932	0.9934	0.9936
2.5	0.9938	0.9940	0.9941	0.9943	0.9945	0.9946	0.9948	0.9949	0.9951	0.9952
2.6	0.9953	0.9955	0.9956	0.9957	0.9959	0.9960	0.9961	0.9962	0.9963	0.9964
2.7	0.9965	0.9966	0.9967	0.9968	0.9969	0.9970	0.9971	0.9972	0.9973	0.9974
2.8	0.9974	0.9975	0.9976	0.9977	0.9977	0.9978	0.9979	0.9979	0.9980	0.9981
2.9	0.9981	0.9982	0.9982	0.9983	0.9984	0.9984	0.9985	0.9985	0.9986	0.9986
3.0	0.9987	0.9987	0.9987	0.9988	0.9988	0.9989	0.9989	0.9989	0.9990	0.9990
3.1	0.9990	0.9991	0.9991	0.9991	0.9992	0.9992	0.9992	0.9992	0.9993	0.9993
3.2	0.9993	0.9993	0.9994	0.9994	0.9994	0.9994	0.9994	0.9995	0.9995	0.9995
3.3	0.9995	0.9995	0.9995	0.9996	0.9996	0.9996	0.9996	0.9996	0.9996	0.9997
3.4	0.9997	0.9997	0.9997	0.9997	0.9997	0.9997	0.9997	0.9997	0.9997	0.9998

STANDARD NORMAL CURVE AREAS ($Z \leq 0$)

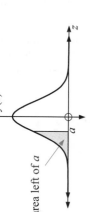

Each table value is the area to the left of the specified Z-value.

area left of a

z	.00	.01	.02	.03	.04	.05	.06	.07	.08	.09
				the second decimal digit of z						
-3.4	0.0003	0.0003	0.0003	0.0003	0.0003	0.0003	0.0003	0.0003	0.0003	0.0002
-3.3	0.0005	0.0005	0.0005	0.0004	0.0004	0.0004	0.0004	0.0004	0.0004	0.0003
-3.2	0.0007	0.0007	0.0006	0.0006	0.0006	0.0006	0.0006	0.0005	0.0005	0.0005
-3.1	0.0010	0.0009	0.0009	0.0009	0.0008	0.0008	0.0008	0.0008	0.0007	0.0007
-3.0	0.0013	0.0013	0.0013	0.0012	0.0012	0.0011	0.0011	0.0011	0.0010	0.0010
-2.9	0.0019	0.0018	0.0018	0.0017	0.0016	0.0016	0.0015	0.0015	0.0014	0.0014
-2.8	0.0026	0.0025	0.0024	0.0023	0.0023	0.0022	0.0021	0.0021	0.0020	0.0019
-2.7	0.0035	0.0034	0.0033	0.0032	0.0031	0.0030	0.0029	0.0028	0.0027	0.0026
-2.6	0.0047	0.0045	0.0044	0.0043	0.0041	0.0040	0.0039	0.0038	0.0037	0.0036
-2.5	0.0062	0.0060	0.0059	0.0057	0.0055	0.0054	0.0052	0.0051	0.0049	0.0048
-2.4	0.0082	0.0080	0.0078	0.0075	0.0073	0.0071	0.0069	0.0068	0.0066	0.0064
-2.3	0.0107	0.0104	0.0102	0.0099	0.0096	0.0094	0.0091	0.0089	0.0087	0.0084
-2.2	0.0139	0.0136	0.0132	0.0129	0.0125	0.0122	0.0119	0.0116	0.0113	0.0110
-2.1	0.0179	0.0174	0.0170	0.0166	0.0162	0.0158	0.0154	0.0150	0.0146	0.0143
-2.0	0.0228	0.0222	0.0217	0.0212	0.0207	0.0202	0.0197	0.0192	0.0188	0.0183
-1.9	0.0287	0.0281	0.0274	0.0268	0.0262	0.0256	0.0250	0.0244	0.0239	0.0233
-1.8	0.0359	0.0351	0.0344	0.0336	0.0329	0.0322	0.0314	0.0307	0.0301	0.0294
-1.7	0.0446	0.0436	0.0427	0.0418	0.0409	0.0401	0.0392	0.0384	0.0375	0.0367
-1.6	0.0548	0.0537	0.0526	0.0516	0.0505	0.0495	0.0485	0.0475	0.0465	0.0455
-1.5	0.0668	0.0655	0.0643	0.0630	0.0618	0.0606	0.0594	0.0582	0.0571	0.0559
-1.4	0.0808	0.0793	0.0778	0.0764	0.0749	0.0735	0.0721	0.0708	0.0694	0.0681
-1.3	0.0968	0.0951	0.0934	0.0918	0.0901	0.0885	0.0869	0.0853	0.0838	0.0823
-1.2	0.1151	0.1131	0.1112	0.1093	0.1075	0.1056	0.1038	0.1020	0.1003	0.0985
-1.1	0.1357	0.1335	0.1314	0.1292	0.1271	0.1251	0.1230	0.1210	0.1190	0.1170
-1.0	0.1587	0.1562	0.1539	0.1515	0.1492	0.1469	0.1446	0.1423	0.1401	0.1379
-0.9	0.1841	0.1814	0.1788	0.1762	0.1736	0.1711	0.1685	0.1660	0.1635	0.1611
-0.8	0.2119	0.2090	0.2061	0.2033	0.2005	0.1977	0.1949	0.1922	0.1894	0.1867
-0.7	0.2420	0.2389	0.2358	0.2327	0.2296	0.2266	0.2236	0.2206	0.2177	0.2148
-0.6	0.2743	0.2709	0.2676	0.2643	0.2611	0.2578	0.2546	0.2514	0.2483	0.2451
-0.5	0.3085	0.3050	0.3015	0.2981	0.2946	0.2912	0.2877	0.2843	0.2810	0.2776
-0.4	0.3446	0.3409	0.3372	0.3336	0.3300	0.3264	0.3228	0.3192	0.3156	0.3121
-0.3	0.3821	0.3783	0.3745	0.3707	0.3669	0.3632	0.3594	0.3557	0.3520	0.3483
-0.2	0.4207	0.4168	0.4129	0.4090	0.4052	0.4013	0.3974	0.3936	0.3897	0.3859
-0.1	0.4602	0.4562	0.4522	0.4483	0.4443	0.4404	0.4364	0.4325	0.4286	0.4247
-0.0	0.5000	0.4960	0.4920	0.4880	0.4840	0.4801	0.4761	0.4721	0.4681	0.4641

Example 14

If Z is a standard normal variable, find:

  a $P(Z \leqslant 1.5)$ **b** $P(Z > 0.84)$ **c** $P(-0.41 \leqslant Z \leqslant 0.67)$

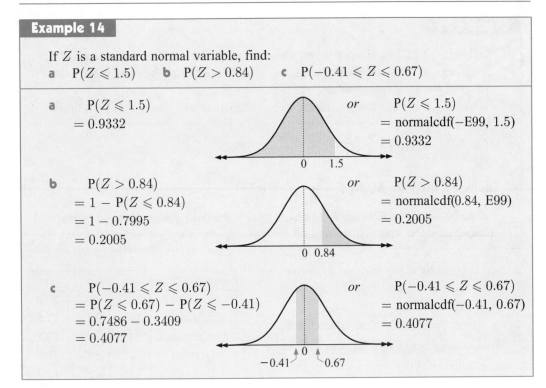

  a $P(Z \leqslant 1.5)$
     $= 0.9332$

or $P(Z \leqslant 1.5)$
     $= \text{normalcdf}(-\text{E99}, 1.5)$
     $= 0.9332$

  b $P(Z > 0.84)$
     $= 1 - P(Z \leqslant 0.84)$
     $= 1 - 0.7995$
     $= 0.2005$

or $P(Z > 0.84)$
     $= \text{normalcdf}(0.84, \text{E99})$
     $= 0.2005$

  c $P(-0.41 \leqslant Z \leqslant 0.67)$
     $= P(Z \leqslant 0.67) - P(Z \leqslant -0.41)$
     $= 0.7486 - 0.3409$
     $= 0.4077$

or $P(-0.41 \leqslant Z \leqslant 0.67)$
     $= \text{normalcdf}(-0.41, 0.67)$
     $= 0.4077$

EXERCISE 30K.1

1 For a random variable X the mean is μ and standard deviation is σ.

Using properties of $E(X)$ and $Var(X)$ find: **a** $E\left(\dfrac{X - \mu}{\sigma}\right)$ **b** $Var\left(\dfrac{X - \mu}{\sigma}\right)$

2 If Z has standard normal distribution, find *using tables* and a sketch:

  a $P(Z \leqslant 1.2)$ **b** $P(Z \geqslant 0.86)$ **c** $P(Z \leqslant -0.52)$

  d $P(Z \geqslant -1.62)$ **e** $P(-0.86 \leqslant Z \leqslant 0.32)$

3 If Z has standard normal distribution, find *using technology*:

  a $P(Z \geqslant 0.837)$ **b** $P(Z \leqslant 0.0614)$ **c** $P(Z \geqslant -0.876)$

  d $P(-0.3862 \leqslant Z \leqslant 0.2506)$ **e** $P(-2.367 \leqslant Z \leqslant -0.6503)$

4 If Z is standard normal distributed, find:

  a $P(-0.5 < Z < 0.5)$ **b** $P(-1.960 < Z < 1.960)$

5 Find a if Z has standard normal distribution and:

  a $P(Z \leqslant a) = 0.95$ **b** $P(Z \geqslant a) = 0.90$

WHAT DO Z-VALUES TELL US?

- If $Z_1 = 1.84$, then Z_1 is 1.84 standard deviations to the right of the mean.
- If $Z_2 = -0.273$, then Z_2 is 0.273 standard deviations to the left of the mean.

So, Z-values are useful when comparing results from two or more different distributions.

Example 15

Kelly scored 73% in History where the class mean was 68% and the standard deviation was 10.2. In Mathematics she scored 66% where the class mean was 62% and the standard deviation was 6.8.

In which subject did Kelly perform better, compared with the rest of her class?

Kelly's Z-score for History $= \dfrac{73 - 68}{10.2} \doteq 0.490$

Kelly's Z-score for Maths $= \dfrac{66 - 62}{6.8} \doteq 0.588$

So Kelly's result was better in Maths.   (0.588 standard deviations right of the mean compared with 0.490 standard deviations right of the mean for History.)

6 Sergio's results at the midyear examinations and subject mean and standard deviations were:

  a Find Sergio's Z-value for each subject.

  b Arrange Sergios performances in each subject in order from 'best' to 'worst'.

		μ	σ
Physics	83%	78%	10.8
Chemistry	77%	72%	11.6
Mathematics	84%	74%	10.1
German	91%	86%	9.6
Biology	72%	62%	12.2

7 Pedro is studying Algebra and Geometry and sits for the mid-year exams in each subject. He is told that his Algebra mark is 56% when the whole group's mean and standard deviation is 50.2% and 15.8% respectively. In Geometry he is told that the whole group's mean and standard deviation is 58.7% and 18.7% respectively. What percentage would he need to score in Geometry to have an equivalent result to his Algebra mark?

STANDARDISING ANY NORMAL DISTRIBUTION

To find probabilities for normally distributed random variable X we could follow these steps:

Step 1:   Convert X values to Z using $Z = \dfrac{X - \mu}{\sigma}$.

Step 2:   Sketch a standard normal curve and shade the required region.

Step 3:   Use the standard normal tables or a graphics calculator to find the probability.

Example 16

Given that X is a normal variable with mean 62 and standard deviation 7, find:
  a $P(X \leqslant 69)$ **b** $P(58.5 \leqslant X \leqslant 71.8)$

a $P(X \leqslant 69)$

$= P\left(\dfrac{X-62}{7} \leqslant \dfrac{69-62}{7}\right)$

$= P(Z \leqslant 1)$

$= 0.8413$ i.e., 84.13% chance that a randomly selected x-value is 69 or less.

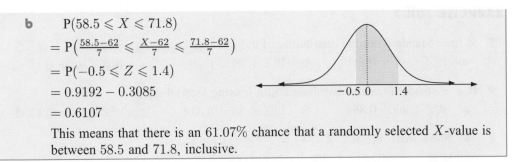

b $P(58.5 \leqslant X \leqslant 71.8)$

$= P\left(\frac{58.5-62}{7} \leqslant \frac{X-62}{7} \leqslant \frac{71.8-62}{7}\right)$

$= P(-0.5 \leqslant Z \leqslant 1.4)$

$= 0.9192 - 0.3085$

$= 0.6107$

This means that there is an 61.07% chance that a randomly selected X-value is between 58.5 and 71.8, inclusive.

These probabilities can be easily found using a graphics calculator without actually converting to standard normal Z-scores. Click on the icon for your calculator for instructions.

EXERCISE 30K.2

1 Given that a random variable X is normally distributed with a mean 70 and standard deviation 4, find the following probabilities by *first converting to the standard variable* Z, and then using the *tabled* probability values for Z:

    a $P(X \geqslant 74)$ **b** $P(X \leqslant 68)$ **c** $P(60.6 \leqslant X \leqslant 68.4)$

2 Given that the random variable X is normally distributed with mean 58.3 and standard deviation 8.96, find the following probabilities by *first converting to the standard variable* Z and then using your graphics calculator:

    a $P(X \geqslant 61.8)$ **b** $P(X \leqslant 54.2)$ **c** $P(50.67 \leqslant X \leqslant 68.92)$

3 The length of a nail L, is normally distributed with mean 50.2 mm and standard deviation 0.93 m. Find by first converting to Z values:

    a $P(L \geqslant 50)$ **b** $P(L \leqslant 51)$ **c** $P(49 \leqslant L \leqslant 50.5)$

FINDING QUANTILES (k values)

Suppose we have a population of adult snails where the length of a snail shell, X mm, is normally distributed with mean 23.6 mm and standard deviation 3.1 mm.

Consider the question: "What is, with 95% probability, the longest snail shell length?".

To answer this question we need to find the value of k such that $P(X \leqslant k) = 0.95$.

Example 17

Find k for which $P(X \leqslant k) = 0.95$ given that $X \sim N(70, 10^2)$

$P(X \leqslant k) = 0.95$ *or* Using technology: e.g., TI-83

$\therefore \; P\left(\frac{X-70}{10} \leqslant \frac{k-70}{10}\right) = 0.95$ $P(X \leqslant k) = 0.95$

$\therefore \; P\left(Z \leqslant \frac{k-70}{10}\right) = 0.95$ then $k = \text{invNorm}(0.95, 70, 10)$

$\therefore \;\; k \doteqdot 86.5$

Searching amongst the standard normal tables or from your graphics calculator:

$\frac{k-70}{10} \doteqdot 1.645$ and so $k \doteqdot 86.5$

This means that approximately 95% of the values are expected to be 86.5 or less.

EXERCISE 30K.3

1 Z has a standard normal distribution. Find k using the *tabled values* if:

   a $P(Z \leqslant k) = 0.81$ **b** $P(Z \leqslant k) = 0.58$ **c** $P(Z \leqslant k) = 0.17$

2 If Z is standard normal distributed, find k using technology if:

   a $P(Z \leqslant k) = 0.384$ **b** $P(Z \leqslant k) = 0.878$ **c** $P(Z \leqslant k) = 0.1384$

3 **a** Show that $P(-k \leqslant Z \leqslant k) = 2\,P(Z \leqslant k) - 1$.

   b If Z is standard normally distributed, find k if:

     i $P(-k \leqslant Z \leqslant k) = 0.238$ **ii** $P(-k \leqslant Z \leqslant k) = 0.7004$

4 **a** Find k if $P(X \leqslant k) = 0.9$ and $X \sim N(56, 18)$.

   b Find k if $P(X \geqslant k) = 0.8$ and $X \sim N(38.7, 8.8)$.

L   APPLICATIONS OF THE NORMAL DISTRIBUTION

Example 18

In 1972 the heights of rugby players was found to be normally distributed with mean 179 cm and standard deviation 7 cm. Find the probability that in 1972 a randomly selected player was: **a** at least 175 cm tall **b** between 170 cm and 190 cm.

If X is the height of a player then X is normally distributed , $\mu = 179$, $\sigma = 7$.

  a $P(X \geqslant 175)$ **b** $P(170 \leqslant X \leqslant 190)$

     $= \text{normalcdf}\,(175, \text{E99}, 179, 7)$ $= \text{normalcdf}\,(170, 190, 179, 7)$

     $= 0.716$ {graphics calculator} $= 0.843$ {graphics calculator}

Note: It is good practice to **always** verify your results using an alternative method (if possible).

Example 19

A University professor determines that 80% of this year's History candidates should pass the final examination. The examination results are expected to be normally distributed with mean 62 and standard deviation 13. Find the lowest score necessary to pass the examination.

Let the random variable X denote the final examination result, then $X \sim N(62, 13^2)$

We need to find k such that $P(X \geqslant k) = 0.8$

          $\therefore$ $P(X \leqslant k) = 0.2$

                $\therefore$ $k = \text{invNorm}(0.2, 62, 13) \doteqdot 51.1$

So, the minimum pass mark is 51.1.

EXERCISE 30L

1   A machine produces metal bolts. The lengths of these bolts have a normal distribution (mean of 19.8 cm and standard deviation of 0.3 cm). A bolt is selected at random from the machine. Find the probability that it will have a length between 19.7 cm and 20 cm.

2   Max's customers put money for charity in a collection box on the front counter of his shop. The average weekly collection is approximately normally distributed with a mean of $40 and a standard deviation of $6. What proportion of weeks would he expect to collect: a   between $30.00 and $50.00   b   at least $50.00?

3   The students of Class X sat a Physics test. From the results, the average score was 46 with a standard deviation of 25. The teacher decided to award an A to the top 7% of the students in the class. Assuming that the scores were normally distributed, find the lowest score that a student must obtain in order to achieve an A.

4   Eels are washed onto a beach after a storm. Their lengths are found to have a normal distribution with a mean of 41 cm and a variance of 11 cm^2.

   a   If an eel is randomly selected, find the probability that it is at least 50 cm.

   b   Find the proportion of eels measuring between 40 cm and 50 cm.

   c   How many eels from a sample of 200 would you expect to measure at least 45 cm?

Example 20

Find the mean and the standard deviation of a normally distributed random variable X, if $P(X \geqslant 50) = 0.2$ and $P(X \leqslant 20) = 0.3$.

$$P(X \leqslant 20) = 0.3$$
$$\therefore \ P(Z \leqslant \frac{20 - \mu}{\sigma}) = 0.3$$
$$\therefore \ \frac{20 - \mu}{\sigma} = \text{invNorm}(0.3)$$
$$\therefore \ 20 - \mu \doteqdot -0.5244\sigma \ ..... \ (1)$$

$$P(X \geqslant 50) = 0.2$$
$$\therefore \ P(X \leqslant 50) = 0.8$$
$$\therefore \ P(Z \leqslant \frac{50 - \mu}{\sigma}) = 0.8$$
$$\therefore \ \frac{50 - \mu}{\sigma} = 0.8416$$
$$\therefore \ 50 - \mu \doteqdot 0.8416\sigma \ ..... \ (2)$$

Solving (1) and (2) simultaneously we get $\mu \doteqdot 31.5$, $\sigma \doteqdot 22.0$ Check with a GC!

5   Find the mean and the standard deviation of a normally distributed random variable X, if $P(X \geqslant 35) = 0.32$ and $P(X \leqslant 8) = 0.26$.

6   a   A random variable, X, is normally distributed. Find the mean and the standard deviation of X, given that $P(X \geqslant 80) = 0.1$ and $P(X \leqslant 30) = 0.15$.

   b   It was found that 10% of the students scored at least 80 marks and no more than 15% scored less than 30 marks in the Mathematics examination at the end of the year. What proportion of students scored more than 50 marks?

7   Circular metal tokens are used to operate a washing machine in a laundromat. The diameters of the tokens are known to be normally distributed. Only tokens with diameters between 1.94 and 2.06 cm will operate the machine.

   a   Find the mean and the standard deviation of the distribution given that 2% of the tokens are too small, and 3% are too large.

   b   Find the probability that less than two tokens out of 20 will not operate the machine.

REVIEW SET 30A

1 $f(x) = \dfrac{a}{x^2 + 1}$ for $x = 0, 1, 2, 3$ is a probability distribution function.

   a Find a.   b Hence, find $P(x \geqslant 1)$.

2 A random variable X has probability distribution function $P(x) = C_x^4 \left(\frac{1}{2}\right)^x \left(\frac{1}{2}\right)^{4-x}$
   for $x = 0, 1, 2, 3, 4$.

   a Find $P(x)$ for $x = 0, 1, 2, 3, 4$.   b Find μ and σ for this distribution.

3 A manufacturer finds that 18% of the items produced from one of the assembly lines are
   defective. During a floor inspection, the manufacturer randomly selects ten items. Find
   the probability that the manufacturer finds:

   a   one defective   b   two defective   c   at least two defectives.

4 A random sample of 120 toothbrushes is made (with replacement) from a very large
   batch where 4% are known to be defective. Find:

   a   the mean   b   the standard deviation of the number of defectives in the sample.

5 At a social club function, a dice game is played where on a single roll of a six-sided die
   the following payouts are made:
   $2 for an odd number, $3 for a 2, $6 for a 4   and $9 for a 6.

   a   What is the expected return for a single roll of the die?
   b   If the club charges $5 for each roll, how much money would the club expect to
       make if 75 people played the game once each?

6 The arm lengths of 18 year old females are normally distributed with mean 64 cm and
   standard deviation 4 cm.

   a Find the percentage of 18 year old females whose arm lengths are:
      i   between 60 cm and 72 cm   ii   greater than 60 cm.
   b Find the probability that a randomly chosen 18 year old female has an arm length
      in the range 56 cm to 68 cm.

7 The length of steel rods produced by a machine is normally distributed with a standard
   deviation of 3 mm. It is found that 2% of all rods are less than 25 mm long. Find the
   mean length of rods produced by the machine.

8 $f(x) = \begin{cases} ax(x - 3), & 0 \leqslant x \leqslant 2 \\ 0 \text{ elsewhere} \end{cases}$ is a continuous probability distribution function.

   a Find a. b Sketch the graph of $y = f(x)$.
   c Find: i   the mean   ii   the mode   iii   the median   iv   the variance.
   d Find $P(1 \leqslant x \leqslant 2)$.

REVIEW SET 30B

Click on the icon to obtain printable review sets and answers

REVIEW SET 30B

ANSWERS

EXERCISE 1A

1 a, d, e **2** a, b, c, e, g **3** No, e.g., $x = 1$ **4** $y = \pm\sqrt{9 - x^2}$

EXERCISE 1B

1 a Domain $\{x: -1 < x \leqslant 5\}$, Range $\{y: 1 < y \leqslant 3\}$
  b Domain $\{x: x \neq 2\}$, Range $\{y: y \neq -1\}$
  c Domain $\{x: x \in \mathcal{R}\}$, Range $\{y: 0 < y \leqslant 2\}$
  d Domain $\{x: x \in \mathcal{R}\}$, Range $\{y: y \geqslant -1\}$
  e Domain $\{x: x \geqslant -4\}$, Range $\{y: y \geqslant -3\}$
  f Domain $\{x: x \neq \pm 2\}$, Range $\{y: y \leqslant -1$ or $y > 0\}$

2 a Domain $\{x: x \geqslant 0\}$, Range $\{y: y \geqslant 0\}$
  b Domain $\{x: x \neq 0\}$, Range $\{y: y > 0\}$
  c Domain $\{x: x \leqslant 4\}$, Range $\{y: y \geqslant 0\}$
  d Domain $\{x: x \in \mathcal{R}\}$, Range $\{y: y \geqslant -2\frac{1}{4}\}$
  e Domain $\{x: x \in \mathcal{R}\}$, Range $\{y: y \leqslant 2\frac{1}{12}\}$
  f Domain $\{x: x \neq 0\}$, Range $\{y: y \leqslant -2$ or $y \geqslant 2\}$
  g Domain $\{x: x \neq 2\}$, Range $\{y: y \neq 1\}$
  h Domain $\{x: x \in \mathcal{R}\}$, Range $\{y: y \in \mathcal{R}\}$
  i Domain $\{x: x \neq -1$ or $2\}$, Range $\{y: y \leqslant \frac{1}{3}$ or $y \geqslant 3\}$
  j Domain $\{x: x \neq 0\}$, Range $\{y: y \geqslant 2\}$
  k Domain $\{x: x \neq 0\}$, Range $\{y: y \leqslant -2$ or $y \geqslant 2\}$
  l Domain $\{x: x \in \mathcal{R}\}$, Range $\{y: y \geqslant -8\}$

EXERCISE 1C

1 a 2 b 8 c -1 d -13 e 1
2 a 2 b 2 c -16 d -68 e $\frac{17}{4}$
3 a $7-3a$ b $7+3a$ c $-3a-2$ d $10-3b$ e $1-3x$
4 a $2x^2 + 19x + 43$ b $2x^2 - 11x + 13$ c $2x^2 - 3x - 1$
  d $2x^4 + 3x^2 - 1$ e $2x^4 - x^2 - 2$
5 a i $-\frac{7}{2}$ ii $-\frac{3}{4}$ iii $-\frac{4}{9}$ b $x = 4$ c $\dfrac{2x+7}{x-2}$ d $x = \frac{9}{5}$

6 f is the function which converts x into $f(x)$ whereas $f(x)$ is the value of the function at any value of x.

7 a 6210 Yen value after 4 years b $t = 4.5$, the time for the photocopier to reach a value of 5780 Yen. c 9650 Yen

8

9 $f(x) = -2x + 5$
10 $a = 3$, $b = -1$, $c = -4$, $T(x) = 3x^2 - x - 4$

EXERCISE 1D

1 a $5 - 2x$ b $-2x - 2$ c 11
2 $f(g(x)) = (2 - x)^2$, Domain $\{x: x$ is in $\mathcal{R}\}$,
  Range $\{y: y \geqslant 0\}$
  $g(f(x)) = 2 - x^2$, Domain $\{x: x$ is in $\mathcal{R}\}$,
  Range $\{y: y \geqslant 2\}$
3 a $x^2 - 6x + 10$ b $2 - x^2$ c $x = \pm\frac{1}{\sqrt{2}}$

EXERCISE 4

4 a Let $x = 0$, $\therefore$ $b = d$ and so
  $$ax + b = cx + b$$
  $\therefore$ $ax = cx$ for all x
  Let $x = 1$, $\therefore$ $a = c$
  b $(f \circ g)(x) = [2a]x + [2b + 3] = 1x + 0$ for all x
  $\therefore$ $2a = 1$ and $2b + 3 = 0$
  $\therefore$ $a = \frac{1}{2}$ and $b = -\frac{3}{2}$
  c Yes, $\{(g \circ f)(x) = [2a]x + [3a + b]\}$

EXERCISE 1E

1
2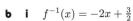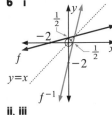

EXERCISE 1F

1 a i 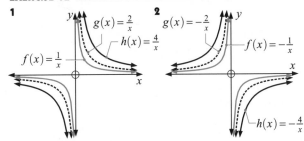 b i

  ii, iii
  $f^{-1}(x) = \dfrac{x - 1}{3}$

  ii, iii
  $f^{-1}(x) = 4x - 2$

2 a i $f^{-1}(x) = \dfrac{x - 5}{2}$ b i $f^{-1}(x) = -2x + \frac{3}{2}$
  ii 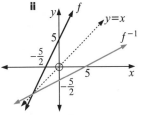 ii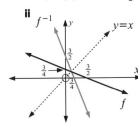

  c i $f^{-1}(x)$ ii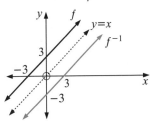
  $= x - 3$

3 a 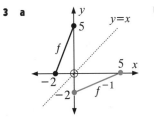 b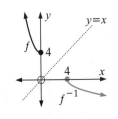

c

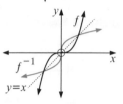

d

4 a

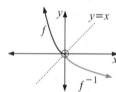

inverse

5

b No **c** Yes, it is $y = \sqrt{x+4}$

EXERCISE 1G

1 a $f : x \mapsto \dfrac{1}{x}$, $x \neq 0$ satisfies both the vertical and horizontal line tests and $\therefore$ has an inverse function.

b $f^{-1}(x) = \dfrac{1}{x}$ and $f(x) = \dfrac{1}{x}$ i.e., $f = f^{-1}$

$\therefore$ f is a self-inverse function

2 a $y = \dfrac{3x-8}{x-3}$ is symmetrical about $y = x$,

$\therefore$ f is a self-inverse function.

b $f^{-1}(x) = \dfrac{3x-8}{x-3}$ and $f(x) = \dfrac{3x-8}{x-3}$

i.e., $f = f^{-1}$ $\therefore$ f is a self-inverse function

3 b i is the only one

c ii Domain $\{x : x \geqslant 1\}$ **iii** Domain $\{x : x \geqslant 1\}$

4 a $f^{-1}(x) = -\sqrt{x}$ **b**

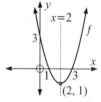

5 a

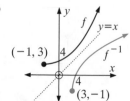

A horizontal line above the vertex cuts the graph **twice**. So, it does not have an inverse.

b For $x \geqslant 2$, all horizontal lines cut 0 or once only. $\therefore$ has an inverse

c Hint: Inverse is $x = y^2 - 4y + 3$ for $y \geqslant 2$

d i Domain is $\{x : x \geqslant 2\}$, Range is $\{y : y \geqslant -1\}$

ii Domain is $\{x : x \geqslant -1\}$, Range is $\{y : y \geqslant 2\}$

e Hint: Find $(f \circ f^{-1})(x)$ and $(f^{-1} \circ f)(x)$ and show that they both equal x.

6 a $f^{-1}(x) = \sqrt{x-3} - 1$, $x \geqslant 3$

b

c i Domain $\{x : x \geqslant -1\}$
Range $\{y : y \geqslant 3\}$

ii Domain $\{x : x \geqslant 3\}$
Range $\{y : y \geqslant -1\}$

7 a 10 **b** $x = 3$ **8 a i** 25 **ii** 16 **b** $x = 1$

9 $(f^{-1} \circ g^{-1})(x) = \dfrac{x+3}{8}$ and $(g \circ f)^{-1}(x) = \dfrac{x+3}{8}$

10 a Is not **b** Is **c** Is **d** Is **e** Is

12 a B is $(f(x), x)$ **b** $x = f^{-1}(f(x)) = (f^{-1} \circ f)(x)$

c Start with B first and repeat the process used in **a** and **b**.

REVIEW SET 1A

1 a 0 **b** -15 **c** $-\dfrac{5}{4}$

2 a i Range $= \{y : y \geqslant -5\}$, Domain $= \{x : x \text{ is in } \mathcal{R}\}$

ii x-int. -1, 5; y-int. $-\dfrac{25}{9}$ **iii** is a function **iv** no

b i Range $= \{y : y = 1 \text{ or } -3\}$ Domain $= \{x : x \text{ is in } \mathcal{R}\}$

ii no x-intercepts; y-intercept 1 **iii** is a function **iv** no

3 a Domain $= \{x : x \geqslant -2\}$, Range $= \{y : 1 \leqslant y < 3\}$

b Domain $= \{x \text{ is in } \mathcal{R}\}$, Range $= \{y : y = -1, 1 \text{ or } 2\}$

4 a $10 - 6x$ **b** $x = 2$ **5** $a = 1$, $b = -6$, $c = 5$

6 a $x = 0$

b

c Domain $= \{x : x \neq 0\}$,
Range $= \{y : y > 0\}$

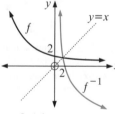

7 a $2x^2 + 1$ **b** $4x^2 - 12x + 11$

8 a i $1 - 2\sqrt{x}$ **ii** $\sqrt{1 - 2x}$

b For $f \circ g$, Domain $\{x : x \geqslant 0\}$, Range $\{y : y \leqslant 1\}$
For $g \circ f$, Domain $\{x : x \leqslant \frac{1}{2}\}$, Range $\{y : y \geqslant 0\}$

9 a $f(x) = \sqrt{x}$, $g(x) = 1 - x^2$ **b** $g(x) = x^2$, $f(x) = \dfrac{x-2}{x+1}$

REVIEW SET 1B

1 a $x^2 - x - 2$ **b** $x^4 - 7x^2 + 10$

2 a $f^{-1}(x) = \dfrac{7-x}{4}$ **b** $f^{-1}(x) = \dfrac{5x-3}{2}$

3 a Domain $\{x : x \in \mathcal{R}\}$, Range $\{y : y \geqslant -4\}$

b Domain $\{x : x \neq 0, 2\}$, Range $\{y : y \leqslant -1 \text{ or } y > 0\}$

4 a

b

5 a $f^{-1}(x) = \dfrac{x-2}{4}$ **b** $f^{-1}(x) = \dfrac{3-4x}{5}$

6 a

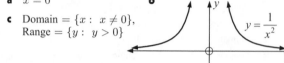

b $f^{-1}(x) = \dfrac{x+7}{2}$

7 a, d

b If $x \leqslant -3$, we have the graph to the left of $x = -3$ and any horizontal line cuts it at most once.

c $y = -3 - \sqrt{x+2}$

e Range of g $\{y: y \geqslant -2\}$, Domain of g^{-1} $\{x: x \geqslant -2\}$
   Range of g^{-1} $\{y: y \leqslant -3\}$

8 a $h^{-1}(x) = 4 + \sqrt{x-3}$

9 $(f^{-1} \circ h^{-1})(x) = x - 2$ and $(h \circ f)^{-1}(x) = x - 2$

EXERCISE 2A

1 a 4, 13, 22, 31, ...   **b** 45, 39, 33, 27, ...
  c 2, 6, 18, 54, ...   **d** 96, 48, 24, 12, ...

2 a Starts at 8 and each term is 8 more than the previous term. Next two terms 40, 48.

  b Starts at 2, each term is 3 more than the previous term; 14, 17.

  c Starts at 36, each term is 5 less than the previous term; 16, 11.

  d Starts at 96, each term is 7 less than the previous term; 68, 61.

  e Starts at 1, each term is 4 times the previous term; 256, 1024.

  f Starts at 2, each term is 3 times the previous term; 162, 486.

  g Starts at 480, each term is half the previous term; 30, 15.

  h Starts at 243, each term is $\frac{1}{3}$ of the previous term; 3, 1.

  i Starts at 50 000, each term is $\frac{1}{5}$ of the previous term; 80, 16.

3 a Each term is the square of the number of the term; 25, 36, 49.

  b Each term is the cube of the number of the term; 125, 216, 343.

  c Each term is $n \times (n+1)$ where n is the number of the term; 30, 42, 56.

EXERCISE 2B

1 a 2, 4, 6, 8, 10 **b** 4, 6, 8, 10, 12 **c** 1, 3, 5, 7, 9
   d -1, 1, 3, 5, 7 **e** 5, 7, 9, 11, 13 **f** 13, 15, 17, 19, 21
   g 4, 7, 10, 13, 16 **h** 1, 5, 9, 13, 17

2 a 2, 4, 8, 16, 32 **b** 6, 12, 24, 48, 96
   c 3, $1\frac{1}{2}$, $\frac{3}{4}$, $\frac{3}{8}$, $\frac{3}{16}$ **d** -2, 4, -8, 16, -32

3 17, 11, 23, -1, 47

EXERCISE 2C

1 a $u_1 = 6$, $d = 11$ **b** $u_n = 11n - 5$ **c** 545
   d yes, u_{30} **e** no

2 a $u_1 = 87$, $d = -4$, **b** $u_n = 91 - 4n$ **c** -69 **d** no

3 b $u_1 = 1$, $d = 3$ **c** 169 **d** $u_{151} = 451$

4 b $u_1 = 32$, $d = -\frac{7}{2}$ **c** -227 **d** $n \geqslant 68$

5 a $k = 17\frac{1}{2}$ **b** $k = 4$ **c** $k = 3$, $k = -1$

6 a $u_n = 6n - 1$ **b** $u_n = -\frac{3}{2}n + \frac{11}{2}$ **c** $u_n = -5n + 36$
   d $u_n = -\frac{3}{2}n + \frac{1}{2}$

7 a $6\frac{1}{4}$, $7\frac{1}{2}$, $8\frac{3}{4}$ **b** $3\frac{5}{7}$, $8\frac{3}{7}$, $13\frac{1}{7}$, $17\frac{6}{7}$, $22\frac{4}{7}$, $27\frac{2}{7}$

8 a $u_1 = 36$, $d = -\frac{2}{3}$ **b** 100 **9** 100 006

EXERCISE 2D

1 a $b = 18$, $c = 54$ **b** $b = 2\frac{1}{2}$, $c = 1\frac{1}{4}$ **c** $b = 3$, $c = -1\frac{1}{2}$

2 a $u_1 = 5$, $r = 2$ **b** $u_n = 5 \times 2^{n-1}$, $u_{15} = 81\,920$

3 a $u_1 = 12$, $r = -\frac{1}{2}$ **b** $u_n = 12 \times (-\frac{1}{2})^{n-1}$, $u_{13} = \frac{3}{1024}$

4 a $u_1 = 8$, $r = -\frac{3}{4}$, $u_{10} = -0.600\,677\,49$

5 a $u_1 = 8$, $r = \frac{1}{\sqrt{2}}$, $u_n = 2^{\frac{7}{2} - \frac{n}{2}}$

6 a $k = \pm 14$ **b** $k = 2$ **c** $k = -2$ or 4

7 a $u_n = 3 \times 2^{n-1}$ **b** $u_n = 32 \times (-\frac{1}{2})^{n-1}$
   c $u_n = 3 \times (\sqrt{2})^{n-1}$ **d** $u_n = 10 \times (\sqrt{2})^{1-n}$

8 a $u_9 = 13\,122$ **b** $u_{14} = 2916\sqrt{3} \doteqdot 5050.66$
   c $u_{18} \doteqdot 0.000\,091\,55$ **9 a** \$3993.00 **b** \$993.00

10 11 470.39 Euro **11 a** 43 923 Yen **b** 13 923 Yen

12 \$23 602.32 **13** 148 024.43 Yen **14** £51 249.06

15 \$14 976.01 **16** £11 477.02 **17** 19 712.33 Euro

18 19 522.47 Yen

19 a i 1550 ants **ii** 4820 ants **b** 12.2 weeks

20 a 278 animals **b** Year 2037

EXERCISE 2E.1

1 a i $S_n = 3 + 11 + 19 + 27 + \ldots + (8n - 5)$ **ii** 95
  b i $S_n = 42 + 37 + 32 + \ldots + (47 - 5n)$ **ii** 160
  c i $S_n = 12 + 6 + 3 + 1\frac{1}{2} + \ldots + 12(\frac{1}{2})^{n-1}$ **ii** $23\frac{1}{4}$
  d i $S_n = 2 + 3 + 4\frac{1}{2} + 6\frac{3}{4} + \ldots + 2(\frac{3}{2})^{n-1}$ **ii** $26\frac{3}{8}$
  e i $S_n = 1 + \frac{1}{2} + \frac{1}{4} + \frac{1}{8} + \ldots + \frac{1}{2^{n-1}}$ **ii** $1\frac{15}{16}$
  f i $S_n = 1 + 8 + 27 + 64 + \ldots + n^3$ **ii** 225

EXERCISE 2E.2

1 a 820 **b** 3087.5 **c** -1460 **d** -740

2 a 1749 **b** 2115 **c** $1410\frac{1}{2}$ **3** 203

4 -115.5 **5** 18 **6 a** 65 **b** 1914 **c** 47 850

7 a 14 025 **b** 71 071 **c** 3367

9 a $u_n = 2n - 1$ **c** $S_1 = 1$, $S_2 = 4$, $S_3 = 9$, $S_4 = 16$

10 56, 49 **11** 10, 4, -2 or -2, 4, 10

12 2, 5, 8, 11, 14 or 14, 11, 8, 5, 2

EXERCISE 2E.3

1 a 23.9766 $\doteqdot$ 24.0 **b** $\doteqdot$ 189 134 **c** $\doteqdot$ 4.000 **d** $\doteqdot$ 0.5852

2 a $S_n = \dfrac{3 + \sqrt{3}}{2}\left((\sqrt{3})^n - 1\right)$ **b** $S_n = 24(1 - (\frac{1}{2})^n)$
  c $S_n = 1 - (0.1)^n$ **d** $S_n = \frac{40}{3}(1 - (-\frac{1}{2})^n)$

3 c \$26 361.59

4 a $\frac{1}{2}$, $\frac{3}{4}$, $\frac{7}{8}$, $\frac{15}{16}$, $\frac{31}{32}$ **b** $S_n = \dfrac{2^n - 1}{2^n}$
  c $1 - (\frac{1}{2})^n = \dfrac{2^n - 1}{2^n}$ **d** as $n \to \infty$, $S_n \to 1$

5 b $S_n = 1 + 18(1 - (0.9)^{n-1})$ **c** 19 seconds

6 a i $u_1 = \frac{3}{10}$ **ii** $r = 0.1$ **b** $S_\infty = \frac{1}{3}$

7 a $\frac{4}{9}$ **b** $\frac{16}{99}$ **c** $\frac{104}{333}$

EXERCISE 2F

1 a 10 **b** 25 **c** 168 **d** 310

2 $2 + 5 + 8 + 11 + \ldots + 59 = 610$

3 a 160 **b** -630 **c** 135

4 a 3069 **b** $\frac{4095}{1024} \doteqdot 3.999$ **c** $-134\,217\,732$

5 a 420 **b** 2231.868 211 **6 a** $n = 37$ **b** $n = 11$

EXERCISE 2G

1 34th week (total sold = 2057)

2 After 85 months its value is \$501.88 and after 86 months its value is \$491.84, $\therefore$ during the 86th month its value is \$500.

3 54 or $\frac{2}{3}$ **4** 70 cm

5 The 20th terms are: arithmetic 39, geometric 3^{19}
   or arithmetic $7\frac{1}{3}$, geometric $(\frac{4}{3})^{19}$

6 $x = \frac{1}{2}$ **7 a** $u_1 = 7$, $u_2 = 10$, **b** 64

8 a $A_3 = \$8000(1.03)^3 - (1.03)^2 R - 1.03R - R$

b $A_8 = \$8000(1.03)^8 - (1.03)^7 R - (1.03)^6 R - (1.03)^5 R$
$\quad\quad - (1.03)^4 R - (1.03)^3 R - (1.03)^2 R - (1.03)R - R$
$\quad\quad = 0 \quad\quad R = \$1139.65$

REVIEW SET 2A

1 a $\frac{1}{3}, 1, 3, 9$ **b** $\frac{5}{4}, \frac{8}{5}, \frac{11}{6}, 2$ **c** $5, -5, 35, -65$

2 b $u_1 = 63$, $d = -5$ **c** -117 **d** $u_{54} = -202$

3 a $u_1 = 3$, $r = 4$ **b** $u_n = 3 \times 4^{n-1}$, $u_9 = 196\,608$

4 $k = -\frac{11}{2}$ **5** $u_n = 73 - 6n$, $u_{34} = -131$

6 b $u_1 = 6$, $r = \frac{1}{2}$ **c** $0.000\,183$

7 $u_n = 33 - 5n$, $S_n = \frac{n}{2}(61 - 5n)$ **8** $k = \pm\frac{2\sqrt{3}}{3}$

9 $u_n = \frac{1}{6} \times 2^{n-1}$ or $-\frac{1}{6} \times 2^{n-1}$

REVIEW SET 2B

1 a 81 **b** $-1\frac{1}{2}$ **c** -486 **2** $21, 19, 17, 15, 13, 11$

3 a $u_n = 89 - 3n$ **b** $u_n = \dfrac{2n+1}{n+3}$ **c** $u_n = 100(0.9)^{n-1}$

4 a $1 + 4 + 9 + 16 + 25 + 36 + 49$

b $\frac{4}{3} + \frac{5}{4} + \frac{6}{5} + \frac{7}{6} + \frac{8}{7} + \frac{9}{8} + \frac{10}{9} + \frac{11}{10}$

5 a $\sum\limits_{r=1}^{n}(7r-3)$ **b** $\sum\limits_{r=1}^{n}(\frac{1}{2})^{r+1}$ **6 a** 1587 **b** $47\frac{253}{256} \doteq 47.99$

7 a 70 **b** 241.2 **8** $u_{12} = 10\,240$

9 a 8415.31 Euro **b** 8488.67 Euro **c** 8505.75 Euro

REVIEW SET 2C

1 $u_n = (\frac{3}{4})2^{n-1}$ **a** $49\,152$ **b** $24\,575.25$ **2** 12

3 $u_{11} = \frac{8}{19\,683} \doteq 0.000\,406$ **4 a** 17 **b** $255\frac{511}{512} \doteq 256.0$

5 a $\$18\,726.65$ **b** $\$18\,885.74$

6 $\$13\,972.28$ **7 a** 3470 **b** Year 2008

8 18 metres **9 a** $0 < x < 1$ **b** $35\frac{5}{7}$

EXERCISE 3A

1 a $2^1 = 2$, $2^2 = 4$, $2^3 = 8$, $2^4 = 16$, $2^5 = 32$, $2^6 = 64$

b $3^1 = 3$, $3^2 = 9$, $3^3 = 27$, $3^4 = 81$

c $5^1 = 5$, $5^2 = 25$, $5^3 = 125$, $5^4 = 625$

d $7^1 = 7$, $7^2 = 49$, $7^3 = 343$

EXERCISE 3B

1 a -1 **b** 1 **c** 1 **d** -1 **e** 1 **f** -1 **g** -1
h -8 **i** -8 **j** 8 **k** -25 **l** 125

2 a 512 **b** -3125 **c** -243 **d** $16\,807$ **e** 512
f 6561 **g** -6561 **h** $5.117\,264\,691$
i $-0.764\,479\,956$ **j** $-20.361\,584\,96$

3 a $0.\overline{142857}$ **b** $0.\overline{142857}$ **c** $0.\overline{1}$ **d** $0.\overline{1}$ **e** $0.015\,625$
f $0.015\,625$ **g** 1 **h** 1 **4** 3 **5** 7

EXERCISE 3C

1 a 7^5 **b** 5^7 **c** a^9 **d** a^5 **e** b^{13} **f** a^{3+n}
g b^{7+m} **h** m^9

2 a 5^7 **b** 11^4 **c** 7^3 **d** a^4 **e** b^3 **f** p^{5-m}
g y^{a-5} **h** b^{2x-1}

3 a 3^8 **b** 5^{15} **c** 2^{28} **d** a^{10} **e** p^{20} **f** b^{5n}
g x^{3y} **h** a^{10x}

4 a 2^3 **b** 5^2 **c** 3^3 **d** 2^6 **e** 3^4 **f** 3^{a+2} **g** 5^{t-1}
h 3^{3n} **i** 2^{4-x} **j** 3^2 **k** 5^{4x-4} **l** 2^2 **m** 2^{y-2x}
n 2^{2y-3x} **o** 3^{2x} **p** 2^3

5 a a^3b^3 **b** a^4c^4 **c** b^5c^5 **d** $a^3b^3c^3$ **e** $16a^4$ **f** $25b^2$
g $81n^4$ **h** $8b^3c^3$ **i** $64a^3b^3$ **j** $\dfrac{a^3}{b^3}$ **k** $\dfrac{m^4}{n^4}$ **l** $\dfrac{32c^5}{d^5}$

6 a $8b^{12}$ **b** $\dfrac{9}{x^4y^2}$ **c** $25a^8b^2$ **d** $\dfrac{m^{12}}{16n^8}$ **e** $\dfrac{27a^9}{b^{15}}$
f $32m^{15}n^{10}$ **g** $\dfrac{16a^8}{b^4}$ **h** $125x^6y^9$ **i** $4a^2$ **j** $36b^4$
k $-8a^3$ **l** $-27m^6n^6$ **m** $16a^4b^{16}$ **n** $\dfrac{-8a^6}{b^6}$
o $\dfrac{16a^6}{b^2}$ **p** $\dfrac{9p^4}{q^6}$

7 a a^2 **b** $8b^5$ **c** m^3n **d** $7a^5$ **e** $4ab^2$ **f** $\dfrac{9m^3}{2}$
g $40h^5k^3$ **h** $\dfrac{1}{m^5}$ **i** p^3

8 a 1 **b** $\frac{1}{3}$ **c** $\frac{1}{6}$ **d** 1 **e** 4 **f** $\frac{1}{4}$ **g** 8 **h** $\frac{1}{8}$
i 25 **j** $\frac{1}{25}$ **k** 100 **l** $\frac{1}{100}$

9 a 1 **b** 1 **c** 3 **d** 1 **e** 2 **f** 1 **g** $\frac{1}{25}$ **h** $\frac{1}{32}$
i 3 **j** $\frac{5}{2}$ **k** $\frac{3}{4}$ **l** 12 **m** $2\frac{1}{4}$ **n** $\frac{4}{5}$ **o** $\frac{8}{7}$ **p** $\frac{7}{2}$

10 a $\dfrac{1}{2a}$ **b** $\dfrac{2}{a}$ **c** $\dfrac{3}{b}$ **d** $\dfrac{1}{3b}$ **e** $\dfrac{b^2}{4}$ **f** $\dfrac{1}{4b^2}$ **g** $\dfrac{1}{9n^2}$
h $\dfrac{n^2}{3}$ **i** $\dfrac{a}{b}$ **j** $\dfrac{1}{ab}$ **k** $\dfrac{a}{b^2}$ **l** $\dfrac{1}{a^2b^2}$ **m** $\dfrac{1}{2ab}$
n $\dfrac{2}{ab}$ **o** $\dfrac{2a}{b}$ **p** a^2b^3

11 a 3^{-1} **b** 2^{-1} **c** 5^{-1} **d** 2^{-2} **e** 3^{-3} **f** 5^{-2}
g 2^{-3x} **h** 2^{-4y} **i** 3^{-4a} **j** 3^{-2} **k** 5^{-2} **l** 5^{-3}
m 2^4 **n** $2^0 = 3^0 = 5^0$ **o** $2^{-3} \times 3^{-3}$ **p** $2^4 \times 5^2$

12 25 days **13 a** $5^3 = 21 + 23 + 25 + 27 + 29$
b $7^3 = 43 + 45 + 47 + 49 + 51 + 53 + 55$
c $12^3 = 133 + 135 + 137 + 139 + 141 + 143$
$\quad\quad + 145 + 147 + 149 + 151 + 153 + 155$

14 5^{75}

EXERCISE 3D

1 a $2^{\frac{1}{5}}$ **b** $2^{-\frac{1}{5}}$ **c** $2^{\frac{3}{2}}$ **d** $2^{\frac{5}{2}}$ **e** $2^{-\frac{1}{3}}$ **f** $2^{\frac{4}{3}}$
g $2^{\frac{3}{2}}$ **h** $2^{\frac{3}{2}}$ **i** $2^{-\frac{4}{3}}$ **j** $2^{-\frac{3}{2}}$

2 a $3^{\frac{1}{3}}$ **b** $3^{-\frac{1}{3}}$ **c** $3^{\frac{1}{4}}$ **d** $3^{\frac{3}{2}}$ **e** $3^{-\frac{5}{2}}$

3 a $7^{\frac{1}{3}}$ **b** $3^{\frac{3}{4}}$ **c** $2^{\frac{4}{5}}$ **d** $2^{\frac{5}{3}}$ **e** $7^{\frac{2}{7}}$ **f** $7^{-\frac{1}{3}}$
g $3^{-\frac{3}{4}}$ **h** $2^{-\frac{4}{5}}$ **i** $2^{-\frac{5}{3}}$ **j** $7^{-\frac{2}{7}}$

4 a 2.280 **b** 1.834 **c** 0.794 **d** 0.435

5 a 3 **b** 1.682 **c** 1.933 **d** 0.523

6 a 8 **b** 32 **c** 8 **d** 125 **e** 4 **f** $\frac{1}{2}$ **g** $\frac{1}{27}$
h $\frac{1}{16}$ **i** $\frac{1}{81}$ **j** $\frac{1}{25}$

EXERCISE 3E

1 a $x^5 + 2x^4 + x^2$ **b** $2^{2x} + 2^x$ **c** $x + 1$ **d** $e^{2x} + 2e^x$
e $2 \times 3^x - 1$ **f** $x^2 + 2x + 3$ **g** $1 + 5 \times 2^{-x}$ **h** $5^x + 1$
i $x^{\frac{3}{2}} + x^{\frac{1}{2}} + 1$

2 a $4^x + 2^{2+x} + 3$ **b** $9^x + 7 \times 3^x + 10$ **c** $25^x - 6 \times 5^x + 8$
d $4^x + 6 \times 2^x + 9$ **e** $9^x - 2 \times 3^x + 1$ **f** $16^x + 14 \times 4^x + 49$
g $x - 4$ **h** $4^x - 9$ **i** $x - x^{-1}$ **j** $x^2 + 4 + \dfrac{4}{x^2}$
k $e^{2x} - 2 + e^{-2x}$ **l** $25 - 10 \times 2^{-x} + 4^{-x}$

EXERCISE 3F

1 a $x = 1$ **b** $x = 2$ **c** $x = 3$ **d** $x = 0$ **e** $x = -1$
f $x = -1$ **g** $x = -3$ **h** $x = 2$ **i** $x = 0$
j $x = -4$ **k** $x = 5$ **l** $x = 1$

2 a $x = 2\frac{1}{2}$ **b** $x = -\frac{2}{3}$ **c** $x = -\frac{1}{2}$ **d** $x = -\frac{1}{2}$
e $x = -1\frac{1}{2}$ **f** $x = -\frac{1}{2}$ **g** $x = -\frac{1}{3}$ **h** $x = \frac{5}{3}$
i $x = \frac{1}{4}$ **j** $x = \frac{7}{2}$ **k** $x = -2$ **l** $x = -4$
m $x = 0$ **n** $x = \frac{5}{2}$ **o** $x = -2$ **p** $x = -6$

3 a $x = \frac{1}{7}$ **b** has no solutions **c** $x = 2\frac{1}{2}$

4 a $x = 3$ **b** $x = 3$ **c** $x = 2$ **d** $x = 2$ **e** $x = -2$
f $x = -2$

EXERCISE 3G

1 a 1.4 **b** 1.7 **c** 2.8 **d** 0.3
2 a
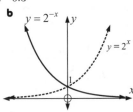

b
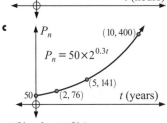

c
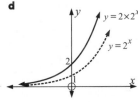

d
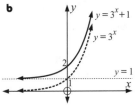

4 a
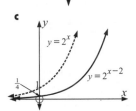

b
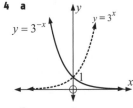

c
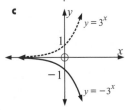

d
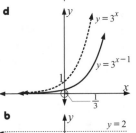

5 a
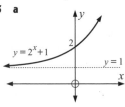

b
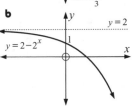

c
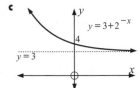

d
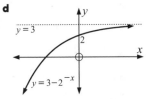

EXERCISE 3H

1 a 100 grams
b **i** 132 g
    ii 200 g
    iii 528 g

c
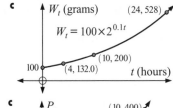

2 a 50
b **i** 76
    ii 141
    iii 400

c
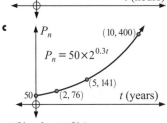

3 a V_0 **b** $2V_0$ **c** 100% **d** 183% increase, percentage increase at 50°C compared with 20°C

4 a 12 bears **b** 146 bears **c** 248% increase

EXERCISE 3I

1 a 250 g **b i** 112 g **ii** 50.4 g **iii** 22.6 g
c
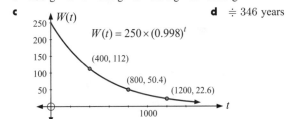
d $\doteqdot$ 346 years

2 1 8000 rabbits **3** $\doteqdot$ 26 weeks **4** yes
5
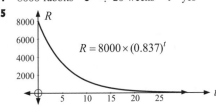

3 a 100°C
b **i** 81.2°C
    ii 75.8°C
    iii 33.9°C
c
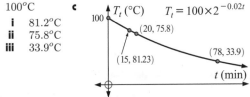

4 a 1000 g
b **i** 812 g
    ii 125 g
    iii 9.31×10^{-7} g
c
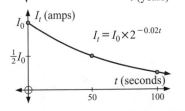

5 a W_0 **b** 12.9%
6 a I_0 **b** $0.986 I_0$
    c 1.38% decrease
    d $I_{50} = \frac{1}{2} I_0$
        $I_{100} = \frac{1}{4} I_0$

REVIEW SET 3A

1 a -1 **b** 27 **c** $\frac{2}{3}$ **2 a** $a^6 b^7$ **b** $\dfrac{2}{3x}$ **c** $\dfrac{y^2}{5}$

3 a 2^{-3} **b** 2^7 **c** 2^{12} **4 a** $\dfrac{1}{b^3}$ **b** $\dfrac{1}{ab}$ **c** $\dfrac{a}{b}$

5 a $x = -2$ **b** $x = \frac{3}{4}$ **6 a** 4 **b** $\frac{1}{9}$

7 a 2.28 **b** 0.517 **c** 3.16 **8 a** 3 **b** 24 **c** $\frac{3}{4}$

9

（graph showing $y = 2^x$ with y-intercept 1 and $y = 2^x - 4$ with y-intercept -3, asymptote $y = -4$）

a $y = 2^x$ has y-intercept 1 and horizontal asymptote $y = 0$

b $y = 2^x - 4$ has y-intercept -3 and horizontal asymptote $y = -4$

10 a $80^\circ C$

b i $26.8^\circ C$
  ii $9.00^\circ C$
  iii $3.02^\circ C$

d $\doteqdot 12.8$ min

c （graph of T ($^\circ$C) vs t (minutes), $T = 80 \times (0.913)^t$）

REVIEW SET 3B

1 a 8 **b** $-\frac{4}{5}$ **2 a** a^{21} **b** $p^4 q^6$ **c** $\dfrac{4b}{a^3}$

3 a 2^{-4} **b** 2^{x+2} **c** 2^{2x-3}

4 a $\dfrac{1}{x^5}$ **b** $\dfrac{2}{a^2 b^2}$ **c** $\dfrac{2a}{b^2}$ **5 a** $x = 4$ **b** $x = -\frac{2}{5}$

6 a 3^4 **b** 3^0 **c** 3^{-3} **d** 3^{-5} **7 a** 3^{3-2a} **b** $3^{\frac{5}{2} - \frac{3}{2}x}$

8 a

x	-2	-1	0	1	2
y	$-4\frac{8}{9}$	$-4\frac{2}{3}$	-4	-2	4

b as $x \to \infty$, $y \to \infty$; as $x \to -\infty$, $y \to -5$ (above)

c （graph of $y = 3^x - 5$, asymptote $y = -5$） **d** $y = -5$

9 a $x = \frac{1}{3}$ **b** $x = -\frac{4}{5}$ **10** $x = \frac{1}{2}$, $y = 3$

REVIEW SET 3C

1 a 2^{n+2} **b** $-\frac{6}{7}$ **c** $3\frac{3}{8}$ **d** $\dfrac{4}{a^2 b^4}$ **2 a** $288 = 2^5 \times 3^2$ **b** 2^{2x}

3 a 5^0 **b** $5^{\frac{3}{2}}$ **c** $5^{-\frac{1}{4}}$ **d** 5^{2a+6}

4 a -4 **b** $\dfrac{1}{4a^6}$ **c** $-\dfrac{b^3}{27}$

5 a $1 + e^{2x}$ **b** $2^{2x} + 10 \times 2^x + 25$ **c** $x - 49$

6 a $9 - 6 \times 2^a + 2^{2a}$ **b** $x - 4$ **c** $2^x + 1$

7 a $x = 5$ **b** $x = -4$

8 a 1500 g
b i 90.3 g
  ii 5.4 g
d 386 years

c （graph of W (grams) vs t (years), $W = 1500 \times (0.993)^t$）

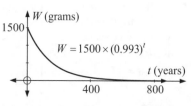

EXERCISE 4A

1 a $10^4 = 10\,000$ **b** $10^{-1} = 0.1$ **c** $10^{\frac{1}{2}} = \sqrt{10}$
  d $2^3 = 8$ **e** $2^{-2} = \frac{1}{4}$ **f** $3^{1.5} = \sqrt{27}$

2 a $\log_2 4 = 2$ **b** $\log_2(\frac{1}{8}) = -3$ **c** $\log_{10}(0.01) = -2$
  d $\log_7 49 = 2$ **e** $\log_2 64 = 6$ **f** $\log_3(\frac{1}{27}) = -3$

3 a 5 **b** -2 **c** $\frac{1}{2}$ **d** 3 **e** 6 **f** 7 **g** 2 **h** 3
  i -3 **j** $\frac{1}{2}$ **k** 2 **l** $\frac{1}{2}$ **m** 5 **n** $\frac{1}{3}$ **o** n **p** $\frac{1}{3}$
  q -1 **r** $\frac{3}{2}$ **s** 0 **t** 1

4 a $\doteqdot 2.18$ **b** $\doteqdot 1.40$ **c** $\doteqdot 1.87$ **d** $\doteqdot -0.0969$

5 a $x = 8$ **b** $x = 2$ **c** $x = 3$ **d** $x = 14$

6 a 2 **b** -1 **c** $\frac{5}{2}$ **d** $-\frac{1}{2}$

EXERCISE 4B

1 a 4 **b** -3 **c** 1 **d** 0 **e** $\frac{1}{2}$ **f** $\frac{1}{3}$ **g** $-\frac{1}{4}$ **h** $1\frac{1}{2}$ **i** $\frac{2}{3}$
  j $1\frac{1}{2}$ **k** $1\frac{1}{3}$ **l** $3\frac{1}{2}$ **m** n **n** $a+2$ **o** $1-m$ **p** $a-b$

2 a 〔log〕 $10\,000$ 〔ENTER〕, 4 **b** 〔log〕 0.001 〔ENTER〕, -3

c 〔log〕 〔2nd〕 〔$\sqrt{\ }$〕 10 〔)〕 〔)〕 〔ENTER〕, 0.5

d 〔log〕 10 〔^〕 〔(〕 1 〔÷〕 3 〔)〕 〔)〕 〔ENTER〕, $0.\overline{3}$

e 〔log〕 100 〔^〕 〔(〕 1 〔÷〕 3 〔)〕 〔ENTER〕, $0.\overline{6}$

f 〔log〕 10 〔×〕 〔2nd〕 〔$\sqrt{\ }$〕 10 〔)〕 〔)〕 〔ENTER〕, 1.5

g 〔log〕 1 〔÷〕 〔2nd〕 〔$\sqrt{\ }$〕 10 〔)〕 〔)〕 〔ENTER〕, -0.5

h 〔log〕 1 〔÷〕 10 〔^〕 0.25 〔)〕 〔ENTER〕, -0.25

3 a $10^{0.7782}$ **b** $10^{1.7782}$ **c** $10^{3.7782}$ **d** $10^{-0.2218}$
  e $10^{-2.2218}$ **f** $10^{1.1761}$ **g** $10^{3.1761}$ **h** $10^{0.1761}$
  i $10^{-0.8239}$ **j** $10^{-3.8239}$

4 a i 0.477 **ii** 2.477 **b** $\log 300 = \log(3 \times 10^2)$

5 a i 0.699 **ii** -1.301 **b** $\log 0.05 = \log(5 \times 10^{-2})$

6 a 100 **b** 10 **c** 1 **d** $\frac{1}{10}$ **e** $10^{\frac{1}{2}}$ **f** $10^{-\frac{1}{2}}$
  g 6.84 **h** $0.000\,631$

EXERCISE 4C

1 a $\log 16$ **b** $\log 4$ **c** $\log 8$ **d** $\log 20$ **e** $\log 2$
  f $\log 24$ **g** $\log 30$ **h** $\log 0.4$ **i** $\log 10$ **j** $\log 200$
  k $\log 0.4$ **l** $\log 1$ **m** $\log 0.005$ **n** $\log 20$ **o** $\log 28$

2 a $\log 96$ **b** $\log 72$ **c** $\log 8$ **d** $\log\left(\frac{25}{8}\right)$ **e** $\log 6$
  f $\log \frac{1}{2}$ **g** $\log 20$ **h** $\log 25$ **i** 1

3 a 2 **b** $\frac{3}{2}$ **c** 3 **d** $\frac{1}{2}$ **e** -2 **f** $-\frac{3}{2}$

5 a $\log y = x \log 2$ **b** $\log y \doteqdot 1.301 + 3 \log b$
  c $\log M = \log a + 4 \log d$ **d** $\log T \doteqdot 0.6990 + \frac{1}{2} \log d$
  e $\log R = \log b + \frac{1}{2} \log l$ **f** $\log Q = \log a - n \log b$
  g $\log y = \log a + x \log b$ **h** $\log F \doteqdot 1.301 - \frac{1}{2} \log n$
  i $\log L = \log a + \log b - \log c$ **j** $\log N = \frac{1}{2} \log a - \frac{1}{2} \log b$
  k $\log S \doteqdot 2.301 + 0.301 t$ **l** $\log y = m \log a - n \log b$

6 a $D = 2e$ **b** $F = \dfrac{5}{t}$ **c** $P = \sqrt{x}$ **d** $M = b^2 c$
  e $B = \dfrac{m^3}{n^2}$ **f** $N = \dfrac{1}{\sqrt[3]{p}}$ **g** $P = 10 x^3$ **h** $Q = \dfrac{100}{x}$

7 a $p + q$ **b** $2p + 3q$ **c** $2q + r$ **d** $r + \frac{1}{2} q - p$ **e** $r - 5p$
  f $p - 2q$

8 a $x + z$ **b** $z + 2y$ **c** $x + z - y$ **d** $2x + \frac{1}{2}y$
e $3y - \frac{1}{2}z$ **f** $2z + \frac{1}{2}y - 3x$

9 a 0.86 **b** 2.15 **c** 1.075

10 a $x = 9$ **b** $x = 2$ or 4 **c** $x = 25\sqrt{5}$ **d** $x = 200$
e $x = 5$ **f** $x = 3$

EXERCISE 4D

1 a $x \doteqdot 3.32$ **b** $x \doteqdot 2.73$ **c** $x \doteqdot 3.32$ **d** $x \doteqdot 37.9$
e $x \doteqdot -3.64$ **f** $x \doteqdot -7.55$ **g** $x \doteqdot 7.64$
h $x \doteqdot 32.0$ **i** $x \doteqdot 1150$

2 a $t \doteqdot 6.340$ **b** $t \doteqdot 74.86$ **c** $t \doteqdot 8.384$
d $t \doteqdot 132.9$ **e** $t \doteqdot 121.5$ **f** $t \doteqdot 347.4$

EXERCISE 4E

1 a 3.90 h **b** 15.5 h **2 a** 66.7 min **b** 221 min
3 a 25 years **b** 141 years **c** 166 years
4 a 10 000 years **b** 49 800 years **5** 15.8°C
6 166 seconds **7** 11.6 seconds

EXERCISE 4F

1 6.17 years, i.e., 6 years 62 days
2 8.65 years, i.e., 8 years 237 days

3 a $\dfrac{8.4\%}{12} = 0.7\% = 0.007 \quad r = 1 + 0.007 = 1.007$

b after 74 months

EXERCISE 4G

1 a $\doteqdot 2.26$ **b** $\doteqdot -10.3$ **c** $\doteqdot -2.46$ **d** $\doteqdot 5.42$
2 a $x \doteqdot -4.29$ **b** $x \doteqdot 3.87$ **c** $x \doteqdot 0.139$
3 a $x \doteqdot 0.683$ **b** $x \doteqdot -1.89$
4 a $x = 16$ **b** $x \doteqdot 1.71$ **5** $x = \dfrac{\log 8}{\log 25}$ or $\log_{25} 8$

EXERCISE 4H

1 a i $x \in\ ]-1, \infty\ [,$ **iii**
   $y \in \mathcal{R}$
ii VA is $x = -1$,
   x and y-intercepts 0
iv $x = -\frac{2}{3}$
v $f^{-1}(x) = 3^x - 1$

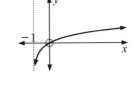

b i $x \in\ ]-1, \infty\ [,$ **iii**
   $y \in \mathcal{R}$
ii VA is $x = -1$,
   x-intercept 2,
   y-intercept 1
iv $x = 8$
v $f^{-1}(x) = 3^{1-x} - 1$

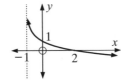

c i $x \in\ ]2, \infty\ [,$ **iii**
   $y \in \mathcal{R}$
ii VA is $x = 2$,
   x-intercept 27,
   no y-intercept
iv $x = 7$
v $f^{-1}(x) = 5^{2+x} + 2$

d i $x \in\ ]2, \infty\ [,$ **iii**
   $y \in \mathcal{R}$
ii VA is $x = 2$,
   x-intercept 7,
   no y-intercept
iv $x = 27$
v $f^{-1}(x) = 5^{1-x} + 2$

e i $x \in \mathcal{R}, x \neq 0$, **iii**
   $y \in \mathcal{R}$
ii VA is $x = 0$,
   x-intercepts $\pm\sqrt{2}$,
   no y-intercept
iv $x = \pm 2$
v if $x > 0$, $f^{-1}(x) = 2^{\frac{1-x}{2}}$
   if $x < 0$, $f^{-1}(x) = -2^{\frac{1-x}{2}}$

f i $x \in\ ]-\infty, -1\ [$ **iii**
   or $x \in\ ]4, \infty\ [$
   $y \in \mathcal{R}$
ii VA $x = -1$, $x = 4$
   x-ints. 4.19, -1.19,
   no y-intercept
iv $x = -1.10$ and 4.10
v if $f(x) = \log_2(x^2 - 3x - 4)$, $x > 4$,
   $f^{-1}(x) = \dfrac{3 + \sqrt{25 + 2^{x+2}}}{2}$
   if $f(x) = \log_2(x^2 - 3x - 4)$, $x < -1$,
   $f^{-1}(x) = \dfrac{3 - \sqrt{25 + 2^{x+2}}}{2}$

REVIEW SET 4A

1 a 3 **b** 8 **c** -2 **d** $\frac{1}{2}$ **e** 0 **f** 1 **g** $\frac{1}{4}$ **h** -1
i $\frac{1}{3}$ **j** $\frac{1}{2}$ **2 a** $\frac{1}{2}$ **b** $-\frac{1}{3}$ **c** $a + b + 1$

3 a $x = \frac{1}{8}$ **b** $x \doteqdot 82.7$ **c** $x \doteqdot 0.0316$

4 a $\log P = \log 3 + x \log b$ **b** $\log m = 3 \log n - 2 \log p$

5 a $k \doteqdot 3.25 \times 2^x$ **b** $Q = P^3 R$ **c** $A = \dfrac{B^5}{400}$

6 a $x \doteqdot 1.209$ **b** $x \doteqdot 1.822$

7 a 2500 g **d**
b 3290 years
c 42.3%

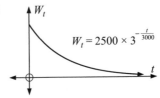

8 $x \doteqdot 2.32$

REVIEW SET 4B

1 a $\frac{3}{2}$ **b** $\frac{2}{3}$ **c** $a + b$
2 a $x = 1000$ **b** $x \doteqdot 4.70$ **c** $x \doteqdot 6.28$
3 a $\log 144$ **b** $\log_2\left(\frac{16}{9}\right)$ **c** $\log_4 80$

4 a $T = \dfrac{x^2}{y}$ **b** $K = n\sqrt{t}$

5 a $x \doteqdot 5.19$ **b** $x \doteqdot 4.29$ **c** $x \doteqdot -0.839$
6 a $2A + 2B$ **b** $A + 3B$ **c** $3A + \frac{1}{2}B$ **d** $4B - 2A$
e $3A - 2B$

7 a $x \in]-2, \infty [$,
$y \in \mathcal{R}$

b VA is $x = -2$,
x-intercept is 7,
y-intercept is -1.37

c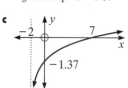

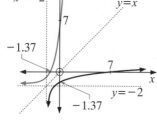

d $g^{-1}(x) = 3^{x+2} - 2$

8 $a = \sqrt[3]{5}$

EXERCISE 5A

1 $e^1 \doteqdot 2.718\,281\,828 \ldots$ **2**

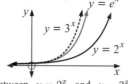

The graph of $y = e^x$ lies between $y = 2^x$ and $y = 3^x$.

3 One is the other
reflected in
the y-axis.

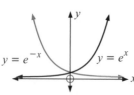

4 a

5 a $e^x > 0$ for all x **b i** $0.000\,000\,004\,12$ **ii** $970\,000\,000$

6 a $\doteqdot 7.39$ **b** $\doteqdot 20.1$ **c** $\doteqdot 2.01$ **d** $\doteqdot 1.65$ **e** $\doteqdot 0.368$

7 a $e^{\frac{1}{2}}$ **b** $e^{\frac{3}{2}}$ **c** $e^{-\frac{1}{2}}$ **d** e^{-2}

8 a $e^{0.18t}$ **b** $e^{0.004t}$ **c** $e^{-0.005t}$ **d** $\doteqdot e^{-0.167t}$

9 a 10.074 **b** $0.099\,261$ **c** 125.09 **d** $0.007\,994\,5$
e 41.914 **f** 42.429 **g** 3540.3 **h** $0.006\,342\,4$

10

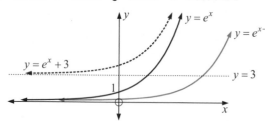

Domain of f, g and h is $\{x : x \in \mathcal{R}\}$
Range of f is $\{y : y > 0\}$ Range of g is $\{y : y > 0\}$
Range of h is $\{y : y > 3\}$

11

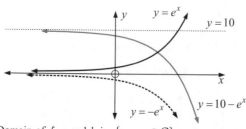

Domain of f, g and h is $\{x : x \in \mathcal{R}\}$

Range of f is $\{y : y > 0\}$ Range of g is $\{y : y < 0\}$
Range of h is $\{y : y < 10\}$

12 a i $2\,g$ **ii** $2.57\,g$ **iii** $4.23\,g$ **iv** $40.2\,g$
b

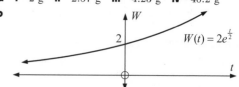

13 a i 64.6 amps
ii 16.7 amps

b

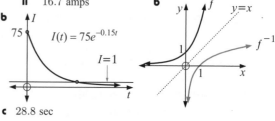

c 28.8 sec

14 a $f^{-1}(x) = \log_e x$
b

EXERCISE 5B

1 a 3 **b** 0 **c** $\frac{1}{3}$ **d** -2
3 x does not exist such that $e^x = -2$ or 0
4 a a **b** $a + 1$ **c** $a + b$ **d** ab **e** $a - b$
5 a $e^{1.7918}$ **b** $e^{4.0943}$ **c** $e^{8.6995}$ **d** $e^{-0.5108}$ **e** $e^{-5.1160}$
f $e^{2.7081}$ **g** $e^{7.3132}$ **h** $e^{0.4055}$ **i** $e^{-1.8971}$ **j** $e^{-8.8049}$
6 a $x \doteqdot 20.1$ **b** $x \doteqdot 2.72$ **c** $x = 1$ **d** $x \doteqdot 0.368$
e $x \doteqdot 0.006\,74$ **f** $x \doteqdot 2.30$ **g** $x \doteqdot 8.54$ **h** $x \doteqdot 0.0370$

EXERCISE 5C

1 a $\ln 16$ **b** $\ln 4$ **c** $\ln 8$ **d** $\ln 20$ **e** $\ln 2$ **f** $\ln 24$
g $\ln 3e$ **h** $\ln \dfrac{4}{e}$ **i** $\ln 10$ **j** $\ln 2e^2$ **k** $\ln \dfrac{40}{e^2}$ **l** $\ln 1$

2 a $\ln 96$ **b** $\ln 72$ **c** $\ln 8$ **d** $\ln \frac{25}{8}$ **e** $\ln 6$ **f** $\ln \frac{1}{2}$
g $\ln \frac{1}{2}$ **h** $\ln 3$ **i** $\ln 16$

3 a e.g., $\ln 9 = \ln 3^2 = 2\ln 3$

4 a $D = ex$ **b** $F = \dfrac{e^2}{p}$ **c** $P = \sqrt{x}$ **d** $M = e^3 y^2$

e $B = \dfrac{t^3}{e}$ **f** $N = \dfrac{1}{\sqrt[3]{g}}$ **g** $Q \doteqdot 8.66 x^3$ **h** $D \doteqdot 0.518 n^{0.4}$

EXERCISE 5D

1 a $x \doteqdot 2.303$ **b** $x \doteqdot 6.908$ **c** $x \doteqdot -4.754$
d $x \doteqdot 3.219$ **e** $x \doteqdot 15.18$ **f** $x \doteqdot -40.85$
g $x \doteqdot -14.63$ **h** $x \doteqdot 137.2$ **i** $x \doteqdot 4.868$

EXERCISE 5E

1 a $1.488\,h$ (1 h 29 min) **b** $10.730\,h$ (10 h 44 min)
2 a 17.329 years **b** 92.222 years **c** 115.129 years
3 8.047 sec **4** 21.320 min

EXERCISE 5F

1 a i $f^{-1}(x)$ **ii**
$= \ln(x - 5)$

iii domain of f is $\{x: \ x \in \mathcal{R}\}$, range is $\{y: \ y > 5\}$
domain of f^{-1} is $\{x: \ x > 5\}$, range is $\{y: y \in \mathcal{R}\}$

b i $f^{-1}(x)$ **ii**
$= \ln(x+3) - 1$

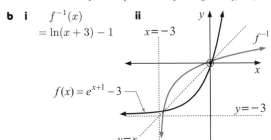

$x = -3$

f^{-1}

$f(x) = e^{x+1} - 3$

$y = -3$

$y = x$

iii domain of f is $\{x: \ x \in \mathcal{R}\}$, range is $\{y: \ y > -3\}$
domain of f^{-1} is $\{x: x > -3\}$, range is $\{y: y \in \mathcal{R}\}$

c i $f^{-1}(x)$ **ii**
$= e^{x+4}$

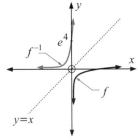

f^{-1}

e^4

f

$y = x$

iii domain of f is $\{x: x > 0\}$, range of f is $\{y: y \in \mathcal{R}\}$
domain of f^{-1} is $\{x: x \in \mathcal{R}\}$, range is $\{y: y > 0\}$

d i $f^{-1}(x)$ **ii**
$= 1 + e^{x-2}$

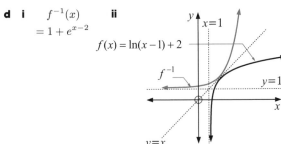

$x = 1$

$f(x) = \ln(x-1) + 2$

f^{-1}

$y = 1$

$y = x$

iii domain of f is $\{x: \ x > 1\}$, range is $\{y: \ y \in \mathcal{R}\}$
domain of f^{-1} is $\{x: \ x \in \mathcal{R}\}$, range is $\{y: \ y > 1\}$

2 $f^{-1}(x) = \frac{1}{2}\ln x$ **a** $\frac{1}{2}\ln(2x-1)$ **b** $\frac{1}{2}\ln\left(\frac{x+1}{2}\right)$

3 a A is $y = \ln x$ **b**
as its x-inter-
cept is 1

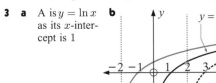

$y = \ln x$
$y = \ln(x+2)$

$-2 \ \ -1 \quad 1 \quad 2 \quad 3$

$y = \ln(x-2)$

c $y = \ln x$ has VA $x = 0$
$y = \ln(x-2)$ has VA $x = 2$
$y = \ln(x+2)$ has VA $x = -2$

4 $y = \ln(x^2) = 2\ln x$, so she is correct.
This is because the y-values are twice as large for $y = \ln(x^2)$
as they are for $y = \ln x$.

1 a $\doteqdot 54.6$ **b** $\doteqdot 22.2$ **c** $\doteqdot 0.0613$ **d** $\doteqdot 6.07$

2 a

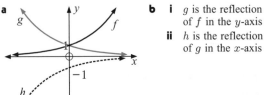

g f

-1

h

b i g is the reflection
of f in the y-axis
ii h is the reflection
of g in the x-axis

3

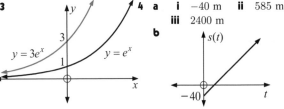

$y = 3e^x$ $y = e^x$

3
1

4 a i -40 m **ii** 585 m
iii 2400 m

b

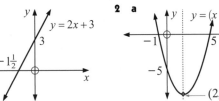

$s(t)$

-40 t

5 a 5 **b** $\frac{1}{2}$ **c** -1 **6 a** $2x$ **b** $2 + x$ **c** $1 - x$

7 a $x \doteqdot 148$ **b** $x \doteqdot 0.513$

8 a $\ln 24$ **b** $\ln 3$ **c** $\ln 4$ **d** $\ln 125$

9 a $5\ln 2$ **b** $3\ln 5$ **c** $6\ln 3$

10 a $x \doteqdot 5.99$ **b** $x \doteqdot 0.699$ **c** $x \doteqdot 6.80$
      d $x \doteqdot 1.10$ or 1.39

1 a $2x$ **b** $x + 2$ **c** $\dfrac{x}{2}$ **d** $2x + 3$

2 a $64x^3$ **b** $4x^3$ **c** $x^3 + 3x^2 + 3x + 1$
    d $2x^3 + 6x^2 + 6x - 1$

3 a 4^x **b** $2^{-x} + 1$ **c** $2^{x-2} + 3$ **d** $2^{x+1} + 3$

4 a $-\dfrac{1}{x}$ **b** $\dfrac{2}{x}$ **c** $\dfrac{2 + 3x}{x}$ **d** $\dfrac{2x + 1}{x - 1}$

1 a

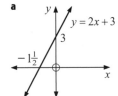

$y = 2x + 3$

3

$-1\frac{1}{2}$

2 a

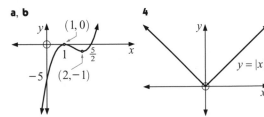

$y = (x-2)^2 - 9$

-1 5

-5

$(2, -9)$

b i $-1\frac{1}{2}$ **ii** 3
iii 2

b x-int's are -1 and 5
y-int is -5

3 a, b

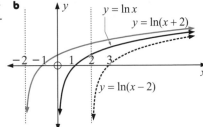

$(1, 0)$

1    $\frac{5}{2}$

-5 $(2, -1)$

4

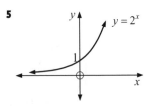

$y = |x|$

5

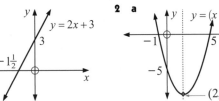

$y = 2^x$

1

When $x = 0$,
$y = 2^0 = 1$ ✓
$2^x > 0$ for all x as
the graph is always
above the y-axis. ✓

6

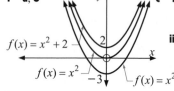

$y = \log_e x$

EXERCISE 6C.1

1 **a, b**

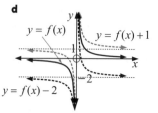

$f(x) = x^2 + 2$

$f(x) = x^2$

$f(x) = x^2 - 3$

c **i** If $b > 0$, the function is translated vertically upwards through b units.

ii If $b < 0$, the function is translated vertically downwards $|b|$ units.

2 **a**

$y = f(x)$

$y = f(x) + 1$

$y = f(x) - 2$

b

$y = f(x) + 1$

$y = f(x)$

$y = f(x) - 2$

c

$y = f(x) + 1$

$y = f(x)$

$y = f(x) - 2$

d

$y = f(x)$

$y = f(x) + 1$

$y = f(x) - 2$

3 **a**

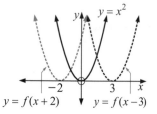

$y = x^2$

$y = f(x + 2)$

$y = f(x - 3)$

b **i** If $a > 0$, the graph is translated a units right.

ii If $a < 0$, the graph is translated $|a|$ units left.

4 **a**

$y = |x|$

$y = f(x + 2)$

$y = f(x - 1)$

b

$y = x^3$

$y = f(x + 2)$

$y = f(x - 1)$

c

$y = \ln x$

$y = f(x + 2)$

$y = f(x - 1)$

d

$x = -2$

$y = f(x + 2)$

$y = \frac{1}{x}$

$x = 1$

$y = f(x - 1)$

$y = f(x - a)$ is a horizontal translation of $y = f(x)$ through $\begin{bmatrix} a \\ 0 \end{bmatrix}$.

5 **a**

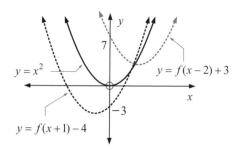

$y = x^2$

$y = f(x - 2) + 3$

$y = f(x + 1) - 4$

b

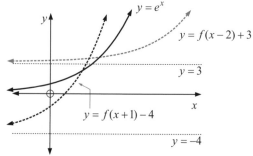

$y = e^x$

$y = f(x - 2) + 3$

$y = 3$

$y = f(x + 1) - 4$

$y = -4$

c

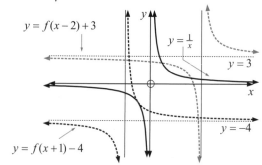

$y = f(x - 2) + 3$

$y = \frac{1}{x}$

$y = 3$

$y = -4$

$y = f(x + 1) - 4$

6 A translation of $\begin{bmatrix} 2 \\ -3 \end{bmatrix}$.

a

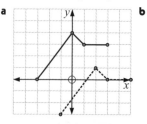

b

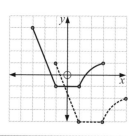

EXERCISE 6C.2

1 **a**

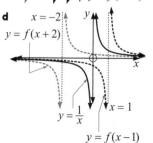

$y = f(x) = x^2$

$y = 3f(x)$

$y = 2f(x)$

b

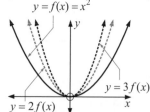

$y = f(x) = |x|$

$y = 2f(x)$

$y = 3f(x)$

c

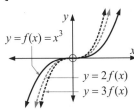

$y = f(x) = x^3$

$y = 2f(x)$

$y = 3f(x)$

d

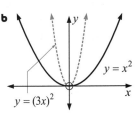

$y = f(x) = e^x$

$y = 3f(x)$

$y = 2f(x)$

5 a

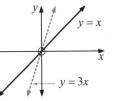

$y = x$

$y = 3x$

b

$y = x^2$

$y = (3x)^2$

e

$y = 3f(x)$

$y = 2f(x)$

$y = f(x) = \ln x$

f

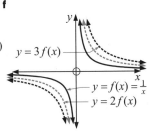

$y = 3f(x)$

$y = f(x) = \frac{1}{x}$

$y = 2f(x)$

c

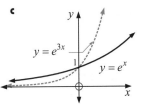

$y = e^{3x}$

$y = e^x$

2 a

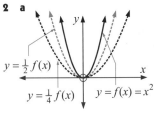

$y = \frac{1}{2}f(x)$

$y = \frac{1}{4}f(x)$ $y = f(x) = x^2$

b

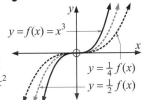

$y = f(x) = x^3$

$y = \frac{1}{4}f(x)$

$y = \frac{1}{2}f(x)$

6 a

$y = x^2$

$y = \left(\frac{x}{2}\right)^2$

b

$y = 2\left(\frac{x}{2}\right)$

$y = 2x$

c

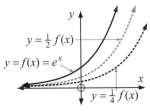

$y = \frac{1}{2}f(x)$

$y = f(x) = e^x$

$y = \frac{1}{4}f(x)$

c

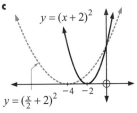

$y = (x+2)^2$

$y = \left(\frac{x}{2} + 2\right)^2$

3 p affects the vertical stretching or compressing of the graph of $y = f(x)$ by a factor of p. If $p > 1$ stretching occurs. If $0 < p < 1$ compression occurs.

7 k affects the horizontal stretching or compressing of $y = f(x)$ by a factor of $\frac{1}{k}$.

If $k > 1$ it moves closer to the y-axis.

If $0 < k < 1$ it moves further from the y-axis.

4 a

$y = x^2$

$y = (2x)^2$

b

$y = (x-1)^2$

$y = (2x-1)^2$

8 a

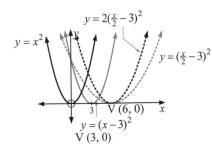

$x = -1$

$y = x^2$

$y = 3(x-2)^2 + 1$

$V(2, 1)$

$y = 2(x+1)^2 - 3$

$V(-1, -3)$

$x = 2$

c

$y = (2x+3)^2$

$y = (x+3)^2$

b

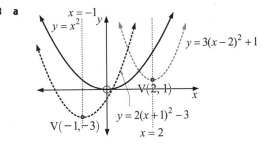

$y = x^2$

$y = 2\left(\frac{x}{2} - 3\right)^2$

$y = \left(\frac{x}{2} - 3\right)^2$

$y = (x-3)^2$

$V(3, 0)$ $V(6, 0)$

c

$y = \frac{1}{4}(2x+5)^2 + 1$

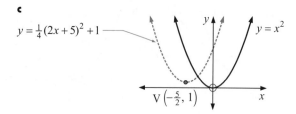

$V\left(-\frac{5}{2}, 1\right)$

EXERCISE 6D

1 a

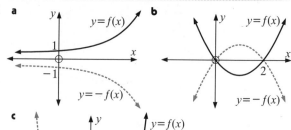

$y = f(x)$
$y = -f(x)$

b

$y = f(x)$
$y = -f(x)$

c

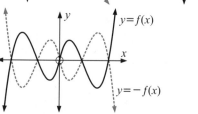

$y = f(x)$
$y = -f(x)$

EXERCISE 6C.3

1 a

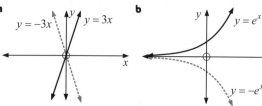

$y = -3x$ $y = 3x$

b

$y = e^x$
$y = -e^x$

c

$y = x^2$
$y = -x^2$

d

$y = \ln x$
$y = -\ln x$

e

$y = x^3 - 2$
$y = -x^3 + 2$

f

$y = 2(x+1)^2$
$y = -2(x+1)^2$

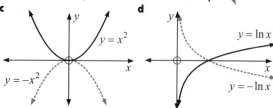

2 $y = -f(x)$ is the reflection of $y = f(x)$ in the x-axis.

3 a i $f(-x) = -2x + 1$ **ii** $f(-x) = x^2 - 2x + 1$
 iii $f(-x) = |-x - 3|$

b i

$y = 2x + 1$ $y = -2x + 1$

ii

$y = x^2 - 2x + 1$
$y = x^2 + 2x + 1$

iii

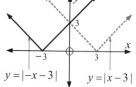

$y = |-x - 3|$ $y = |x - 3|$

4 $y = f(-x)$ is the reflection of $y = f(x)$ in the y-axis.

2 a

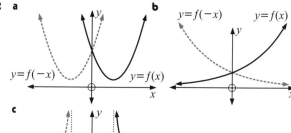

$y = f(-x)$ $y = f(x)$

b

$y = f(-x)$ $y = f(x)$

c

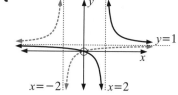

$y = 1$
$x = -2$ $x = 2$

3 a A **b** B **c** D **d** C

4

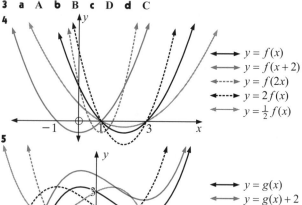

→ $y = f(x)$
→ $y = f(x+2)$
⇠ $y = f(2x)$
⇢ $y = 2f(x)$
⇢ $y = \frac{1}{2}f(x)$

5

→ $y = g(x)$
→ $y = g(x) + 2$
⇠ $y = -g(x)$
⇢ $y = g(x+1)$
→ $y = g(-x)$

6

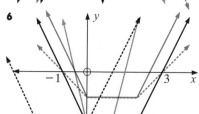

→ $y = h(x)$
→ $y = h(x) + 1$
⇢ $y = \frac{1}{2}h(x)$
⇢ $y = h(-x)$
→ $y = h(\frac{x}{2})$

EXERCISE 6E

1 a i $y = \dfrac{1}{2x}$ **ii** $y = \dfrac{3}{x}$ **iii** $y = \dfrac{1}{x+3}$

   iv $y = \dfrac{1}{x} + 4$ **v** $y = \dfrac{3}{2(x+3)} + 4$

b Domain is $\{x:\ x \in \mathcal{R},\ x \neq -3\}$
   Range is $\{y:\ y \in \mathcal{R},\ y \neq 4\}$

2 a VA is $x = 1$, HA is $y = 2$

b Vertically stretch, factor $\frac{1}{6}$ then translate by $\begin{bmatrix} -1 \\ -2 \end{bmatrix}$.

3 a i VA is $x = -1$, HA is $y = 2$

   ii x-intercept is $-\frac{3}{2}$, y-intercept is 3

   iii as $x \to -1$ (from left), $y \to -\infty$
      as $x \to -1$ (from right), $y \to \infty$
      as $x \to -\infty$, $y \to 2$ (from below)
      as $x \to \infty$, $y \to 2$ (from above)

   iv

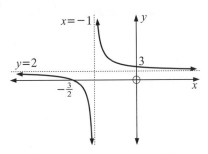

   v Translate $\begin{bmatrix} -1 \\ 2 \end{bmatrix}$.

b i VA is $x = 2$, HA is $y = 0$

   ii no x-intercept, y-intercept is $-1\frac{1}{2}$

   iii as $x \to 2$ (from left), $y \to -\infty$
      as $x \to 2$ (from right), $y \to \infty$
      as $x \to \infty$, $y \to 0$ (from above)
      as $x \to -\infty$, $y \to 0$ (from below)

   iv

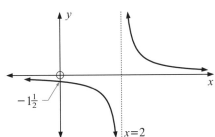

   v Vertically stretch with factor 3, then translate $\begin{bmatrix} 2 \\ 0 \end{bmatrix}$.

c i VA is $x = 3$, HA is $y = -2$

   ii x-intercept is $\frac{1}{2}$, y-intercept is $-\frac{1}{3}$

   iii as $x \to 3$ (from left), $y \to \infty$
      as $x \to 3$ (from right), $y \to -\infty$
      as $x \to -\infty$, $y \to -2$ (from above)
      as $x \to \infty$, $y \to -2$ (from below)

   iv

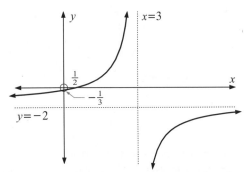

   v Vertically stretch, factor -5, then translate $\begin{bmatrix} 3 \\ -2 \end{bmatrix}$.

d i VA is $x = -\frac{1}{2}$, HA is $y = 2\frac{1}{2}$

   ii x-intercept is $\frac{1}{5}$, y-intercept is -1

   iii as $x \to -\frac{1}{2}$ (from left), $y \to \infty$
      as $x \to -\frac{1}{2}$ (from right), $y \to -\infty$
      as $x \to \infty$, $y \to 2\frac{1}{2}$ (from below)
      as $x \to -\infty$, $y \to 2\frac{1}{2}$ (from above)

   iv

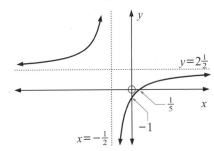

   v Vertically stretch, factor $-\frac{7}{4}$, then translate $\begin{bmatrix} -\frac{1}{2} \\ \frac{5}{2} \end{bmatrix}$.

4 a 70 weeds/ha **b** 30 weeds/ha **c** 3 days

   d

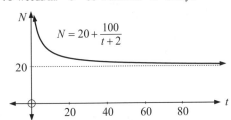

   e No, the number of weeds/ha will approach 20 (from above).

EXERCISE 6F

1 a

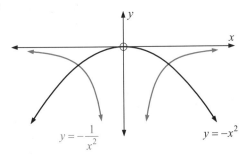

b

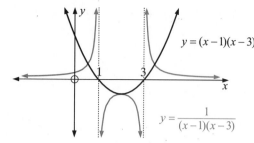

$y = (x-1)(x-3)$

$y = \dfrac{1}{(x-1)(x-3)}$

2 a invariant points are $(-1, -1)$ and $(1, -1)$
b invariant pts. are $(0.586, 1)$, $(2, -1)$ and $(3.414, 1)$

3 a

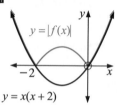

$y = |f(x)|$

$y = x(x+2)$

b

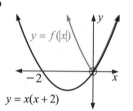

$y = f(|x|)$

$y = x(x+2)$

4 a

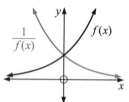

$\dfrac{1}{f(x)}$ $f(x)$

b

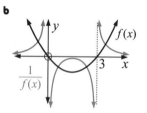

$f(x)$ $\dfrac{1}{f(x)}$

c

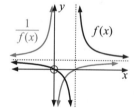

$\dfrac{1}{f(x)}$ $f(x)$

5 a

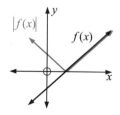

$|f(x)|$ $f(x)$

b

$|f(x)|$ $f(x)$

c

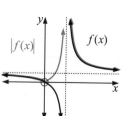

$|f(x)|$ $f(x)$

6 a

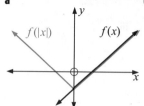

$f(|x|)$ $f(x)$

b

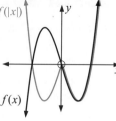

$f(|x|)$ $f(x)$

c

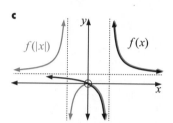

$f(|x|)$ $f(x)$

REVIEW SET 6A

1 a 3 **b** 8 **c** $4x^2 - 4x$ **d** $x^2 + 2x$ **e** $3x^2 - 6x - 2$
2 a -15 **b** 5 **c** $-x^2 + x + 5$ **d** $5 - \frac{1}{2}x - \frac{1}{4}x^2$
e $-x^2 - 3x + 5$

3 a -1 **b** $\dfrac{2}{x}$ **c** $\dfrac{8}{x}$ **d** $\dfrac{10 - 3x}{x + 2}$

4 a

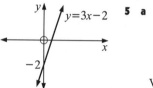

$y = 3x - 2$

5 a

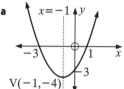

$x = -1$

$V(-1, -4)$

b i $\frac{2}{3}$ **ii** -2 **iii** 3
c i -1.1 **ii** 0.9

b i 1 and -3 **ii** -3
c $V(-1, -4)$
b i true **ii** false
iii false **iv** true

6 a

$y = 2^{-x}$

7

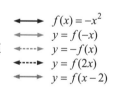

$f(x) = -x^2$
$y = f(-x)$
$y = -f(x)$
$y = f(2x)$
$y = f(x-2)$

8

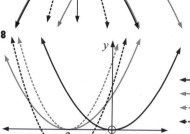

$f(x) = x^2$
$y = f(x+2)$
$y = 2f(x+2)$
$y = 2f(x+2) - 3$

EXERCISE 7A

1 a, c, d, e **2 a** $y = 20$ **b** $y = 27$ **c** $y = -4$ **d** $y = 37$
3 a 3 **b** -5 **c** -4 **d** 8
4 a no **b** no **c** no **d** no

EXERCISE 7B.1

1 a i ± 2
ii $x = 0$
iii $(0, -4)$
iv -4

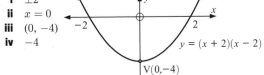

$y = (x + 2)(x - 2)$, V$(0, -4)$

b i 1, 3
ii $x = 2$
iii $(2, -2)$
iv 6

$y = 2(x - 1)(x - 3)$, $x = 2$, V$(2, -2)$

c i 1, 2
ii $x = \frac{3}{2}$
iii $(\frac{3}{2}, -\frac{3}{4})$
iv 6

$y = 3(x - 1)(x - 2)$, $x = 1\frac{1}{2}$, V$(\frac{3}{2}, -\frac{3}{4})$

d i 0, 4
ii $x = 2$
iii $(2, -2)$
iv 0

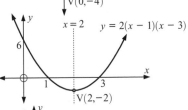

$y = \frac{1}{2}x(x - 4)$, $x = 2$, V$(2, -2)$

e i 0, -3
ii $x = -\frac{3}{2}$
iii $(-\frac{3}{2}, \frac{9}{2})$
iv 0

$y = -2x(x + 3)$, V$(-\frac{3}{2}, \frac{9}{2})$, $x = -\frac{3}{2}$

f i $-2, -3$
ii $x = -\frac{5}{2}$
iii $(-\frac{5}{2}, \frac{1}{8})$
iv -3

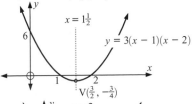

$y = -\frac{1}{2}(x + 2)(x + 3)$, V$(-\frac{5}{2}, \frac{1}{8})$, $x = -\frac{5}{2}$

2 a B **b** A **c** F **d** D **e** E **f** C

EXERCISE 7B.2

1 a i $x = 4$ **iv**
ii $(4, 3)$
iii 19

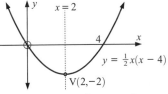

$y = (x - 4)^2 + 3$, $x = 4$, V$(4, 3)$

b i $x = -1$ **iv**
ii $(-1, 0)$
iii 2

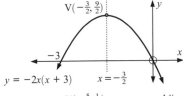

$y = 2(x + 1)^2$, V$(-1, 0)$, $x = -1$

c i $x = -3$ **iv**
ii $(-3, 2)$
iii -7

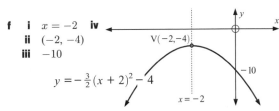

$y = -(x + 3)^2 + 2$, V$(-3, 2)$, $x = -3$, -7

d i $x = -2$ **iv**
ii $(-2, -4)$
iii 8

$y = 3(x + 2)^2 - 4$, $x = -2$, V$(-2, -4)$, 8

e i $x = 2$ **iv**
ii $(2, 0)$
iii 2

$y = \frac{1}{2}(x - 2)^2$, $x = 2$, V$(2, 0)$

f i $x = -2$ **iv**
ii $(-2, -4)$
iii -10

$y = -\frac{3}{2}(x + 2)^2 - 4$, V$(-2, -4)$, -10, $x = -2$

2 a G **b** A **c** E **d** B **e** I **f** C **g** D **h** F **i** H
3 a $x = 2$ **b** $x = -\frac{5}{2}$ **c** $x = 1$ **d** $x = 3$ **e** $x = -4$
f $x = -4$

4 a i

$y = x^2 + 4x$, $(-2, -4)$
ii $x = -2$
iii $(-2, -4)$

b i

$y = x(x - 4)$, $(2, -4)$
ii $x = 2$
iii $(2, -4)$

c i

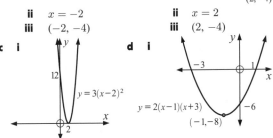

$y = 3(x - 2)^2$, 12
ii $x = 2$ **iii** $(2, 0)$

d i

$y = 2(x - 1)(x + 3)$, $(-1, -8)$, -6
ii $x = -1$ **iii** $(-1, -8)$

e i

$y = -2(x - 1)^2$, -2, 1
ii $x = 1$ **iii** $(1, 0)$

f i

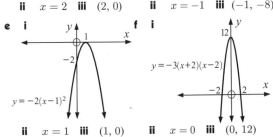

$y = -3(x + 2)(x - 2)$, 12
ii $x = 0$ **iii** $(0, 12)$

5 a i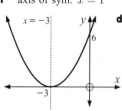

b i

ii axis of sym. $x = 1$

ii axis of sym. $x = 0$

c i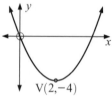

d i

ii axis of sym. $x = -3$

ii axis of sym. $x = 1$

6 a -1 and -5 **b** 3 (touching)

EXERCISE 7C

1 a $y = (x-1)^2 + 2$ **b** $y = (x+2)^2 - 6$

$V(1, 2)$ $V(-2, -6)$

c $y = (x-2)^2 - 4$ **d** $y = \left(x + \frac{3}{2}\right)^2 - \frac{9}{4}$

$V(2, -4)$ $V\left(-\frac{3}{2}, -\frac{9}{4}\right)$

e $y = \left(x + \frac{5}{2}\right)^2 - \frac{33}{4}$ **f** $y = \left(x - \frac{3}{2}\right)^2 - \frac{1}{4}$

$V\left(-\frac{5}{2}, -\frac{33}{4}\right)$ $V\left(\frac{3}{2}, -\frac{1}{4}\right)$

g $y = (x-3)^2 - 4$ **h** $y = (x+4)^2 - 18$

$V(3, -4)$ $V(-4, -18)$

i $y = \left(x - \frac{5}{2}\right)^2 - 5\frac{1}{4}$

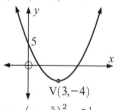

$V\left(\frac{5}{2}, -5\frac{1}{4}\right)$

2 a i $y = 2(x+1)^2 + 3$ **b i** $y = 2(x-2)^2 - 5$
ii $(-1, 3)$ **iii** 5 **ii** $(2, -5)$ **iii** 3
iv   **iv**

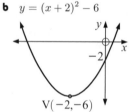

$y = 2x^2 + 4x + 5$ $V(-1, 3)$

$y = 2x^2 - 8x + 3$ $V(2, -5)$

c i $y = 2\left(x - \frac{3}{2}\right)^2 - \frac{7}{2}$ **d i** $y = 3(x-1)^2 + 2$
ii $\left(\frac{3}{2}, -\frac{7}{2}\right)$ **iii** 1 **ii** $(1, 2)$ **iii** 5
iv   **iv**

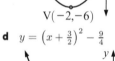

$y = 2x^2 - 6x + 1$ $V\left(\frac{3}{2}, -\frac{7}{2}\right)$

$y = 3x^2 - 6x + 5$ $V(1, 2)$

e i $y = -(x-2)^2 + 6$ **f i** $y = -2\left(x + \frac{5}{4}\right)^2 + \frac{49}{8}$
ii $(2, 6)$ **iii** 2 **ii** $\left(-\frac{5}{4}, \frac{49}{8}\right)$ **iii** 3
iv   **iv**

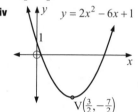

$V(2, 6)$ $y = -x^2 + 4x + 2$

$V\left(-\frac{5}{4}, \frac{49}{8}\right)$ $y = -2x^2 - 5x + 3$

3 a $y = (x-2)^2 + 3$ **b** $y = (x+3)^2 - 6$
c $y = -(x-2)^2 + 9$ **d** $y = 2\left(x + \frac{3}{2}\right)^2 - \frac{17}{2}$
e $y = -2\left(x + \frac{5}{2}\right)^2 + \frac{27}{2}$ **f** $y = 3\left(x - \frac{3}{2}\right)^2 - \frac{47}{4}$

EXERCISE 7D.1

1 a $x = 0, -\frac{7}{4}$ **b** $x = 0, -\frac{1}{3}$ **c** $x = 0, \frac{7}{3}$ **d** $x = 0, \frac{11}{2}$
e $x = 0, \frac{8}{3}$ **f** $x = 0, \frac{3}{2}$ **g** $x = 3, 2$ **h** $x = 4, -2$
i $x = 3, 7$ **j** $x = 3$ **k** $x = -4, 3$ **l** $x = -11, 3$

2 a $x = \frac{2}{3}$ **b** $x = -\frac{1}{2}, 7$ **c** $x = -\frac{2}{3}, 6$ **d** $x = \frac{1}{3}, -2$
e $x = \frac{3}{2}, 1$ **f** $x = -\frac{2}{3}, 2$ **g** $x = -\frac{2}{3}, 4$ **h** $x = \frac{1}{2}, -\frac{3}{2}$
i $x = -\frac{1}{4}, 3$ **j** $x = -\frac{3}{4}, \frac{5}{3}$ **k** $x = \frac{1}{7}, -1$ **l** $x = -2, \frac{28}{15}$

3 a $x = 2, 5$ **b** $x = -3, 2$ **c** $x = 0, -\frac{3}{2}$ **d** $x = 1, 2$
e $x = \frac{1}{2}, -1$ **f** $x = 3$

4 a $x = -3$ **b** $x = -3$ or -2 **c** $x = 1$ or 4 **d** no solution
5 a $x = 0$ or $\frac{2}{3}$ **b** $x = 3$ or -2 **c** $x = \frac{1}{2}$ or -7 **d** $x = 3$
6 a i 25 m   **ii** 25 m   **iii** 45 m
b i 2 secs and 4 secs   **ii** 0 secs and 6 secs
c once going up and once coming down
7 a i $-\$30$ **ii** $\$105$ **b** 6 or 58 cakes

EXERCISE 7D.2

1 a $x = -5 \pm \sqrt{2}$ **b** $x = -6 \pm \sqrt{11}$ **c** $x = 4 \pm 2\sqrt{2}$
d $x = 8 \pm \sqrt{7}$ **e** $x = -3 \pm \sqrt{5}$ **f** $x = 2 \pm \sqrt{6}$
g $x = -1 \pm \sqrt{10}$ **h** $x = -\frac{1}{2} \pm \frac{1}{2}\sqrt{3}$

2 a $x = 2 \pm \sqrt{3}$ **b** $x = -3 \pm \sqrt{7}$ **c** $x = 7 \pm \sqrt{3}$

d $x = 2 \pm \sqrt{7}$ **e** $x = -3 \pm \sqrt{2}$ **f** $x = 1 \pm \sqrt{7}$
g $x = -3 \pm \sqrt{11}$ **h** $x = 4 \pm \sqrt{6}$ **i** no real solns.

3 a $x = -1 \pm \frac{1}{\sqrt{2}}$ **b** $x = \frac{5}{2} \pm \frac{\sqrt{19}}{2}$ **c** $x = -2 \pm \sqrt{\frac{7}{3}}$

d $x = 1 \pm \sqrt{\frac{7}{3}}$ **e** $x = \frac{3}{2} \pm \sqrt{\frac{37}{20}}$ **f** $x = -\frac{1}{2} \pm \frac{\sqrt{6}}{2}$

EXERCISE 7E

1 a $x = 2 \pm \sqrt{7}$ **b** $x = -3 \pm \sqrt{2}$ **c** $x = 2 \pm \sqrt{3}$
d $x = -2 \pm \sqrt{5}$ **e** $x = 2 \pm \sqrt{2}$ **f** $x = \frac{1}{2} \pm \frac{1}{2}\sqrt{7}$
g $x = \sqrt{2}$ **h** $x = -\frac{4}{9} \pm \frac{\sqrt{7}}{9}$ **i** $x = -\frac{7}{4} \pm \frac{\sqrt{97}}{4}$

2 a $x = -2 \pm 2\sqrt{2}$ **b** $x = -\frac{5}{8} \pm \frac{\sqrt{57}}{8}$ **c** $x = \frac{5}{2} \pm \frac{\sqrt{13}}{2}$
d $x = \frac{1}{2} \pm \frac{1}{2}\sqrt{7}$ **e** $x = \frac{1}{2} \pm \frac{\sqrt{5}}{2}$ **f** $x = \frac{3}{4} \pm \frac{\sqrt{17}}{4}$

EXERCISE 7F

1 a $x = -3.414$ or -0.586 **b** $x = 0.317$ or -6.317
c $x = 2.77$ or -1.27 **d** $x = -1.08$ or 3.41
e $x = -0.892$ or 3.64 **f** $x = 1.34$ or -2.54

2 a $x = -4.83$ or 0.828 **b** $x = -1.57$ or 0.319
c $x = 0.697$ or 4.30 **d** $x = -0.823$ or 1.82
e $x = -0.618$ or 1.62 **f** $x = -0.281$ or 1.78

EXERCISE 7G

1 7 and -5 or -7 and 5 **2** 5 or $\frac{1}{5}$ **3** 14
4 18 and 20 or -18 and -20 **5** 15 and 17 or -15 and -17
6 15 sides **7** 3.48 cm **8 b** 6 cm by 6 cm by 7 cm
9 11.2 cm square **10** no **12** 221 ha **13** 2.03 m
14 52.1 km/h **15** 553 km/h **16** 51.1 km/h **17** 32

EXERCISE 7H

1 a $y = (x - 4)(x + 2)$ **b** $y = -(x - 4)(x + 2)$

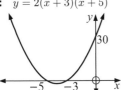

c $y = 2(x + 3)(x + 5)$ **d** $y = -3x(x + 4)$

e $y = 2(x + 3)^2$ **f** $y = -\frac{1}{4}(x + 2)^2$

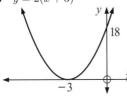

2 a $x = 1$ **b** $x = 1$ **c** $x = -4$ **d** $x = -2$ **e** $x = -3$ **f** $x = -2$

3 a $y = (x - 1)^2 + 3$ **b** $y = 2(x + 2)^2 + 1$

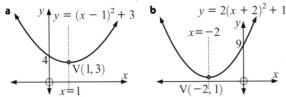

c

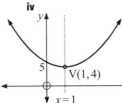
$y = -2(x - 1)^2 - 3$

d $y = \frac{1}{2}(x - 3)^2 + 2$

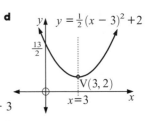

e $y = -\frac{1}{3}(x - 1)^2 + 4$

f $y = -\frac{1}{10}(x + 2)^2 - 3$

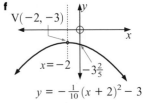

4 a $(2, -2)$ **b** $(-1, -4)$ **c** $(0, 4)$ **d** $(0, 1)$ **e** $(-2, -15)$
f $(-2, -5)$ **g** $(-\frac{3}{2}, -\frac{11}{2})$ **h** $(\frac{5}{2}, -\frac{19}{2})$ **i** $(1, -\frac{9}{2})$ **j** $(2, 6)$

5 a ± 3 **b** $\pm\sqrt{3}$ **c** -5 and -2 **d** 3 and -4 **e** 0 and 4
f -4 and -2 **g** -1 (touching) **h** 3 (touching)
i $2 \pm \sqrt{3}$ **j** $-2 \pm \sqrt{7}$ **k** $3 \pm \sqrt{11}$ **l** $-4 \pm \sqrt{5}$

6 a i $x = 1$ **b i** $x = -2$
ii $(1, 4)$ **ii** $(-2, -5)$
iii no x-intercept,   **iii** x-int. $-2 \pm \sqrt{5}$,
  y-intercept 5 y-intercept -1
iv   **iv**

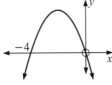

c i $x = \frac{5}{4}$ **d i** $x = \frac{3}{2}$
ii $(\frac{5}{4}, -\frac{9}{8})$ **ii** $(\frac{3}{2}, \frac{1}{4})$
iii x-intercepts $\frac{1}{2}$, 2,   **iii** x-intercepts 1, 2,
  y-intercept 2 y-intercept -2
iv   **iv**

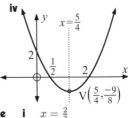

e i $x = \frac{2}{3}$ **f i** $x = \frac{1}{4}$
ii $(\frac{2}{3}, \frac{1}{3})$ **ii** $(\frac{1}{4}, \frac{9}{8})$
iii x-intercepts $\frac{1}{3}$, 1,   **iii** x-intercepts $-\frac{1}{2}$, 1,
  y-intercept -1 y-intercept 1
iv   **iv**

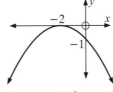

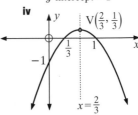

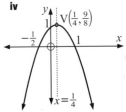

g **i** $x = 3$
 ii $(3, 9)$
 iii x-intercepts 0, 6, y-intercept 0
 iv

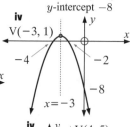

h **i** $x = -3$
 ii $(-3, 1)$
 iii x-int. -2, -4, y-intercept -8
 iv

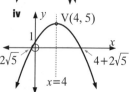

i **i** $x = 4$
 ii $(4, 5)$
 iii x-int. $4 \pm 2\sqrt{5}$, y-intercept 1

EXERCISE 7I.1

1 **a** 2 real distinct roots **b** a repeated root
 c 2 real distinct roots **d** 2 real distinct roots
 e no real roots **f** a repeated root

2 **a, b, d, f**

3 **a** $\Delta = 9 - 4m$ **i** $m = \frac{9}{4}$ **ii** $m < \frac{9}{4}$ **iii** $m > \frac{9}{4}$
 b $\Delta = 25 - 4m$ **i** $m = \frac{25}{4}$ **ii** $m < \frac{25}{4}$ **iii** $m > \frac{25}{4}$
 c $\Delta = 1 - 4m$ **i** $m = \frac{1}{4}$ **ii** $m < \frac{1}{4}$ **iii** $m > \frac{1}{4}$
 d $\Delta = 4 - 12m$ **i** $m = \frac{1}{3}$ **ii** $m < \frac{1}{3}$ **iii** $m > \frac{1}{3}$
 e $\Delta = 49 - 8m$ **i** $m = \frac{49}{8}$ **ii** $m < \frac{49}{8}$ **iii** $m > \frac{49}{8}$
 f $\Delta = 25 - 16m$ **i** $m = \frac{25}{16}$ **ii** $m < \frac{25}{16}$ **iii** $m > \frac{25}{16}$

EXERCISE 7I.2

1 **a** cuts x-axis twice **b** touches x-axis **c** cuts x-axis twice
 d cuts x-axis twice **e** cuts x-axis twice **f** touches x-axis

2 **a** $a = 1$ which is > 0 and $\Delta = -15$ which is < 0
 b $a = -1$ which is < 0 and $\Delta = -8$ which is < 0
 c $a = 2$ which is > 0 and $\Delta = -40$ which is < 0
 d $a = -2$ which is < 0 and $\Delta = -23$ which is < 0

3 $a = 3$ which is > 0 and $\Delta = k^2 + 12$ which is always > 0 {as $k^2 > 0$ for all k}

4 $a = 2$ which is > 0 and $\Delta = k^2 - 16$ ∴ positive definite when $k^2 < 16$ i.e., $-4 < k < 4$

EXERCISE 7J

1 **a** $y = 2(x - 1)(x - 2)$ **b** $y = 2(x - 2)^2$
 c $y = (x - 1)(x - 3)$ **d** $y = -(x - 3)(x + 1)$
 e $y = -3(x - 1)^2$ **f** $y = -2(x + 2)(x - 3)$

2 **a** C **b** E **c** B **d** F **e** G **f** H **g** A **h** D

3 **a** $y = \frac{3}{2}(x - 2)(x - 4)$ **b** $y = -\frac{1}{2}(x + 4)(x - 2)$
 c $y = -\frac{4}{3}(x + 3)^2$

4 **a** $y = 3x^2 - 18x + 15$ **b** $y = -4x^2 + 6x + 4$
 c $y = -x^2 + 6x - 9$ **d** $y = 4x^2 + 16x + 16$
 e $y = \frac{3}{2}x^2 - 6x + \frac{9}{2}$ **f** $y = -\frac{1}{3}x^2 + \frac{2}{3}x + 5$

5 **a** $y = -(x - 2)^2 + 4$ **b** $y = 2(x - 2)^2 - 1$
 c $y = -2(x - 3)^2 + 8$ **d** $y = \frac{2}{3}(x - 4)^2 - 6$
 e $y = -2(x - 2)^2 + 3$ **f** $y = 2(x - \frac{1}{2})^2 - \frac{3}{2}$

EXERCISE 7K

1 **a** $(1, 7)$ and $(2, 8)$ **b** $(4, 5)$ and $(-3, -9)$

c $(3, 0)$ (touching) **d** graphs do not meet

2 **a** $(0.59, 5.59)$ and $(3.41, 8.41)$ **b** $(3, -4)$ touching
 c graphs do not meet **d** $(-2.56, -18.81)$ and $(1.56, 1.81)$

3 **a** $(2, 4)$, $(-1, 1)$ **b** $(1, 0)$, $(-2, -3)$ **c** $(1, 4)$
 d $(1, 4)$, $(-4, -1)$

EXERCISE 7L

1 **a** 9 seconds **b** 162 m **c** 18 sec

2 **a** 12 **b** $100 **c** $244

3 **a** 15 m/s **b** $\frac{1}{2}$ sec; since the car was travelling downhill, it was accelerating. ∴ when the brake was applied, the speed of the vehicle still increased for a short time.
 c $15\frac{1}{8}$ m/s **d** 6 seconds

4 **a** 21 **b** $837 **c** $45 **5** **a** 30°C **b** 5.00 am **c** 5°C

6 **b** $x = 10$ **c** 200 m^2

7 **a** $y = -\frac{1}{100}x^2 + 70$ **b** supports are 21 m, 34 m, 45 m, 54 m, 61 m, 66 m, 69 m

REVIEW SET 7A

1 **a** -2, 1
 b $x = -\frac{1}{2}$
 c $(-\frac{1}{2}, \frac{9}{2})$
 d 4
 e

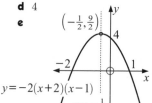

2 **a** $x = 2$
 b $(2, -4)$
 c -2
 d

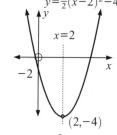

3 **a** $y = (x - 2)^2 - 5$
 b $(2, -5)$
 c -1
 d

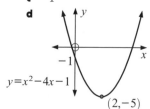

4 **a** $y = 2\left(x + \frac{3}{2}\right)^2 - \frac{15}{2}$
 b $(-\frac{3}{2}, -\frac{15}{2})$
 c -3
 d

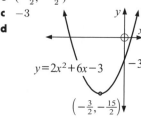

5 **a** $x = 15$ or -4 **b** $x = -\frac{5}{3}$ or 2 **c** $x = 0$ or 4

6 **a** $x = 5$ or 2 **b** $x = 3$ or 4 **c** $x = \frac{1}{2}$ or 3

7 $x = -\frac{7}{2} \pm \frac{\sqrt{65}}{2}$ **8** $x = -2 \pm \sqrt{3}$

9 **a** $x = \frac{7}{2} \pm \frac{\sqrt{37}}{2}$ **b** no real roots

REVIEW SET 7B

1

2 $x = \frac{4}{3}$, V($\frac{4}{3}$, $12\frac{1}{3}$)

3 $x = -1$, V(-1, -5)

4 **a** no real solutions
 b two real distinct solutions

5 $a = 3$ which is > 0 and $\Delta = -11$ which is < 0

6 $a = -2$ which is < 0 ∴ a max. max. $= 5$ when $x = 1$

7 $(4, 4)$ and $(-3, 18)$ **8** $k < -3\frac{1}{8}$ **9** **b** 15 m by 30 m

EXERCISE 8A

1 a $3i$ **b** $8i$ **c** $\frac{1}{2}i$ **d** $i\sqrt{5}$ **e** $i\sqrt{8}$

2 a $(x+3)(x-3)$ **b** $(x+3i)(x-3i)$

c $(x+\sqrt{7})(x-\sqrt{7})$ **d** $(x+i\sqrt{7})(x-i\sqrt{7})$

e $(2x+1)(2x-1)$ **f** $(2x+i)(2x-i)$

g $(\sqrt{2}x+3)(\sqrt{2}x-3)$ **h** $(\sqrt{2}x+3i)(\sqrt{2}x-3i)$

i $x(x+1)(x-1)$ **j** $x(x+i)(x-i)$

k $(x+1)(x-1)(x+i)(x-i)$

l $(x+2)(x-2)(x+2i)(x-2i)$

3 a $x=\pm5$ **b** $x=\pm5i$ **c** $x=\pm\sqrt{5}$ **d** $x=\pm i\sqrt{5}$

e $x=\pm\frac{3}{2}$ **f** $x=\pm\frac{3}{2}i$ **g** $x=0,\ x=\pm2$

h $x=0,\ x=\pm2i$ **i** $x=0,\ x=\pm\sqrt{3}$

j $x=0,\ x=\pm i\sqrt{3}$ **k** $x=\pm1,\ x=\pm i$

l $x=\pm3,\ x=\pm3i$

4 a $x=5\pm2i$ **b** $x=-3\pm4i$ **c** $x=-7\pm i$

d $x=\frac{3}{2}\pm\frac{1}{2}i$ **e** $x=\sqrt{3}\pm i$ **f** $x=\frac{1}{4}\pm\frac{i\sqrt{7}}{4}$

5 a $x=\pm i\sqrt{3}$ or ±1 **b** $x=\pm\sqrt{3}$ or $\pm i\sqrt{2}$

c $x=\pm3i$ or ±2 **d** $x=\pm i\sqrt{7}$ or $\pm i\sqrt{2}$

e $x=\pm1$ **f** $x=\pm i$

EXERCISE 8B.1

1

z	$\mathrm{Re}(z)$	$\mathrm{Im}(z)$		z	$\mathrm{Re}(z)$	$\mathrm{Im}(z)$
$3+2i$	3	2		$-3+4i$	-3	4
$5-i$	5	-1		$-7-2i$	-7	-2
3	3	0		$-11i$	0	-11
0	0	0		$i\sqrt{3}$	0	$\sqrt{3}$

2 a $7-i$ **b** $10-4i$ **c** $-1+2i$ **d** $3-3i$

e $4-7i$ **f** $12+i$ **g** $3+4i$ **h** $21-20i$

3 a $-3+7i$ **b** $2i$ **c** $-2+2i$ **d** $-1+i$

e $-5-12i$ **f** $-5+i$ **g** $-6-4i$ **h** $-1-5i$

4 a $i^0=1,\ i^1=i,\ i^2=-1,\ i^3=-i,\ i^4=1,\ i^5=i,$

$i^6=-1,\ i^7=-i,\ i^8=1,\ i^9=i,\ i^{-1}=-i,$

$i^{-2}=-1,\ i^{-3}=i,\ i^{-4}=1,\ i^{-5}=-i,\ i^{4n+3}=-i$

6 $(1+i)^4=-4,\ (1+i)^{101}=-2^{50}(1+i)$

7 $a=3,\ b=-5$

8 a $-\frac{1}{10}-\frac{7}{10}i$ **b** $-\frac{1}{5}+\frac{2}{5}i$ **c** $\frac{7}{5}+\frac{1}{5}i$ **d** $\frac{3}{25}+\frac{4}{25}i$

9 a $-\frac{2}{5}+\frac{1}{5}i$ **b** $-\frac{1}{13}+\frac{8}{13}i$ **c** $-\frac{2}{5}+\frac{3}{5}i$

10 a -2 **b** -4 **c** 3 **d** 0

EXERCISE 8B.2

1 a $x=0,\ y=-2$ **b** $x=-2$ **c** $x=3,\ y=2$

d $x=-\frac{2}{13},\ y=-\frac{3}{13}$

2 a $x=0,\ y=0$ **b** $x=3,\ y=-2$ or $x=4,\ y=-\frac{3}{2}$

c $x=2,\ y=-5$ or $x=-\frac{5}{3},\ y=6$ **d** $x=-1,\ y=0$

EXERCISE 8B.3

1 a $a(x^2-6x+10)=0\ \ a\neq0$

b $a(x^2-2x+10)=0,\ a\neq0$

c $a(x^2+4x+29),\ a\neq0$ **d** $a(x^2-2\sqrt{2}x+3)=0,\ a\neq0$

e $a(x^2-4x+1)=0,\ a\neq0$

f $a(3x^2+2x)=0,\ a\neq0$ **g** $a(x^2+2)=0,\ a\neq0$

h $a(x^2+12x+37)=0,\ a\neq0$

2 a $a=-6,\ b=10$ **b** $a=-2,\ b=-1$

c $a=-2,\ b=8$ or $a=0,\ b=0$

EXERCISE 8B.4

2 z^* **4 a** $\left[\dfrac{ac+bd}{c^2+d^2}\right]+\left[\dfrac{bc-ad}{c^2+d^2}\right]i$

7 a $[a^2-b^2]+[2ab]i$ **c** $z^3=[a^3-3ab^2]+[3a^2b-b^3]i$

8 a $a=0$ or $(b=0,\ a\neq-1)$

b $a^2-b^2=1$ and neither a nor b is 0

EXERCISE 8B.5

1 c $(z_1z_2z_3z_4....z_n)^*=z_1^*\,z_2^*\,z_3^*\,....\,z_n^*$ **d** $(z^n)^*=(z^*)^n$

EXERCISE 8C.1

1 a $3x^2+6x+9$ **b** $5x^2+7x+9$ **c** $-7x^2-8x-9$

d $4x^4+13x^3+28x^2+27x+18$

2 a x^3+x^2-4x+7 **b** x^3-x^2-2x+3

c $3x^3+2x^2-11x+19$ **d** $2x^3-x^2-x+5$

e $x^5-x^4-x^3+8x^2-11x+10$

f $x^4-2x^3+5x^2-4x+4$

3 a $2x^3-3x^2+4x+3$ **b** $x^4+x^3-7x^2+7x-2$

c $x^3+6x^2+12x+8$ **d** $4x^4-4x^3+13x^2-6x+9$

e $16x^4-32x^3+24x^2-8x+1$

f $18x^4-87x^3+56x^2+20x-16$

4 a $6x^3-11x^2+18x-5$ **b** $8x^3+18x^2-x+10$

c $-2x^3+7x^2+13x+10$ **d** $2x^3-7x^2+4x+4$

e $2x^4-2x^3-9x^2+11x-2$

f $15x^4+x^3-x^2+7x-6$ **g** $x^4-2x^3+7x^2-6x+9$

h $4x^4+4x^3-15x^2-8x+16$

i $8x^3+60x^2+150x+125$

j $x^6+2x^5+x^4-4x^3-4x^2+4$

EXERCISE 8C.2

1 a quotient is x, remainder is -3

b quotient is $x-4$, remainder is -3

c quotient is $2x^2+10x+16$, remainder is 35

2 a $x+1+\dfrac{10}{x-4}$ **b** $x+1-\dfrac{14}{x+3}$ **c** $2x-3-\dfrac{4}{x-2}$

d x^2+x-2 **e** $x^2+4x+4+\dfrac{11}{3x-1}$

f $x^3-2x^2+\frac{5}{2}x-\frac{1}{4}+\dfrac{\frac{19}{4}}{2x+3}$

3 a $x+2+\dfrac{9}{x-2}$ **b** $2x+1-\dfrac{1}{x+1}$ **c** $3x-4+\dfrac{3}{x+2}$

d x^2+3x-2 **e** $2x^2-8x+31-\dfrac{124}{x+4}$

f $x^2+3x+6+\dfrac{7}{x-2}$

EXERCISE 8C.3

1 a quotient is $x+1$, remainder is $-x-4$

b quotient is 3, remainder is $-x+3$

c quotient is $3x$, remainder is $-2x-1$

d quotient is 0, remainder is $x-4$

2 a $1-\dfrac{2x}{x^2+x+1}$ **b** $x-\dfrac{2x}{x^2+2}$

c $x^2 + x + 3 + \dfrac{3x-4}{x^2-x+1}$ **d** $2x + 4 + \dfrac{5x+2}{(x-1)^2}$

e $x^2 - 2x + 3 - \dfrac{4x+3}{(x+1)^2}$

f $x^2 - 3x + 5 + \dfrac{15-10x}{(x-1)(x+2)}$

3 quotient is $x^2 + 2x + 3$, remainder is 7

EXERCISE 8C.4

1 **a** $3x + 1 - \dfrac{2}{x-1}$ **b** $x^2 + 2x + \dfrac{5}{x+3}$

c $3z - 4 + \dfrac{6}{z+1}$ **d** $x^2 - 3x + 9$

e $z^3 + z^2 + 4z + 12 + \dfrac{32}{z-3}$ **f** $z^3 - z^2 + 2z - 3 + \dfrac{3}{z+1}$

2 **a** $P(x) = 3x^3 - 8x^2 + 5x + 2$
b $P(x) = x^3 - 4x^2 - 13x + 19$

EXERCISE 8D.1

1 **a** $4, -\frac{3}{2}$ **b** $-3 \pm i$ **c** $3 \pm \sqrt{3}$ **d** $0, \pm 2$

e $0, \pm i\sqrt{2}$ **f** $\pm 1, \pm i\sqrt{5}$

2 **a** $x = 1, -\frac{2}{5}$ **b** $x = -\frac{1}{2}, \pm i\sqrt{3}$ **c** $z = 0, 1 \pm i$

d $x = 0, \pm\sqrt{5}$ **e** $z = 0, \pm i\sqrt{5}$ **f** $z = \pm i\sqrt{2}, \pm\sqrt{5}$

3 **a** $(2x+3)(x-5)$ **b** $(z-3+i\sqrt{7})(z-3-i\sqrt{7})$

c $x(x+1+\sqrt{5})(x+1-\sqrt{5})$ **d** $z(3z-2)(2z+1)$

e $(z+1)(z-1)(z+\sqrt{5})(z-\sqrt{5})$

f $(z+i)(z-i)(z+\sqrt{2})(z-\sqrt{2})$

5 **a** $P(z) = a(z^2-4)(z-3)$ $a \neq 0$
b $P(z) = a(z+2)(z^2+1)$ $a \neq 0$
c $P(z) = a(z-3)(z^2+2z+2)$ $a \neq 0$
d $P(z) = a(z+1)(z^2+4z+2)$ $a \neq 0$

6 **a** $P(z) = a(z^2-1)(z^2-2)$ $a \neq 0$
b $P(z) = a(z-2)(z+1)(z^2+3)$ $a \neq 0$
c $P(z) = a(z^2-3)(z^2-2z+2)$ $a \neq 0$
d $P(z) = a(z^2-4z-1)(z^2+4z+13)$ $a \neq 0$

EXERCISE 8D.2

1 **a** $a = 2$, $b = 5$, $c = 5$ **b** $a = 3$, $b = 4$, $c = 3$
2 **a** $a = 2$, $b = -2$ or $a = -2$, $b = 2$ **b** $a = 3$, $b = -1$
4 $a = -2$, $b = 2$, $x = 1 \pm i$ or $-1 \pm \sqrt{3}$

5 **a** $a = -1$, zeros are $\frac{3}{2}$, $\dfrac{-1 \pm i\sqrt{3}}{2}$

b $a = 6$, zeros are $-\frac{2}{3}$, $\dfrac{1 \pm i\sqrt{11}}{2}$

6 **a** $a = -3$, $b = 6$ zeros are $-\frac{1}{2}$, 2, $\pm 2i$
b $a = 1$, $b = -15$ zeros are -3, $\frac{1}{2}$, $1 \pm \sqrt{2}$

7 **a** $P(x) = (x+3)^2(x-3)$ or $P(x) = (x-1)^2(x+5)$
b If $m = -2$, zeros are -1 (repeated) and $\frac{2}{3}$.
If $m = \frac{14}{243}$, zeros are $\frac{1}{9}$ (repeated) and $-\frac{14}{9}$.

EXERCISE 8D.3

1 **a** $P(x) = (x-2)Q(x) + 7$, $P(x)$ divided by $x - 2$
leaves a remainder of 7.

b $P(-3) = -8$, $P(x)$ divided by $x + 3$ leaves a
remainder of -8.

c $P(5) = 11$, $P(x) = (x-5)Q(x) + 11$

2 **a** 1 **b** 1 **3** **a** $a = 3$ **b** $a = 2$ **4** $a = -5$, $b = 6$
5 $a = -3$, $n = 4$ **6** **a** -3 **b** 1 **7** $3z - 5$

EXERCISE 8D.4

1 **a** $k = -8$, $P(x) = (x+2)(2x+1)(x-2)$
b $k = 2$, $P(x) = x(x-3)(x+\sqrt{2})(x-\sqrt{2})$

2 $a = 7$, $b = -14$

3 **a** If $k = 1$, zeros are 3, $-1 \pm i$.
If $k = -4$, zeros are ± 3, 1. **b** $m = -\frac{10}{7}$

4 **a i** $P(a) = 0$, $x - a$ is a factor **ii** $(x-a)(x^2+ax+a^2)$
b i $P(-a) = 0$, $x + a$ is a factor **ii** $(x+a)(x^2-ax+a^2)$
5 **b** $a = 2$

EXERCISE 8E.1

1 **a** cuts the x-axis at α **b** touches the x-axis at α
c cuts the x-axis at α with a change in shape

2 **a** $P(x) = 2(x+1)(x-2)(x-3)$
b $P(x) = -2(x+3)(2x+1)(2x-1)$
c $P(x) = \frac{1}{4}(x+4)^2(x-3)$
d $P(x) = \frac{1}{10}(x+5)(x+2)(x-5)$
e $P(x) = \frac{1}{4}(x+4)(x-3)^2$
f $P(x) = -2(x+3)(x+2)(2x+1)$

3 **a** $P(x) = (x-3)(x-1)(x+2)$
b $P(x) = x(x+2)(2x-1)$ **c** $P(x) = (x-1)^2(x+2)$
d $P(x) = (3x+2)^2(x-4)$

4 **a** F **b** C **c** A **d** E **e** D **f** B

5 **a** $P(x) = 5(2x-1)(x+3)(x-2)$
b $P(x) = -2(x+2)^2(x-1)$
c $P(x) = (x-2)(2x^2-3x+2)$

EXERCISE 8E.2

1 **a** $P(x) = 2(x+1)^2(x-1)^2$
b $P(x) = (x+3)(x+1)^2(3x-2)$
c $P(x) = -2(x+2)(x+1)(x-2)^2$
d $P(x) = -\frac{1}{3}(x+3)(x+1)(2x-3)(x-3)$
e $P(x) = \frac{1}{4}(x+1)(x-4)^3$ **f** $P(x) = x^2(x+2)(x-3)$

2 **a** C **b** F **c** A **d** E **e** B **f** D

3 **a** $P(x) = (x+4)(2x-1)(x-2)^2$
b $P(x) = \frac{1}{4}(3x-2)^2(x+3)^2$
c $P(x) = 2(x-2)(2x-1)(x+2)(2x+1)$
d $P(x) = (x-1)^2\left(\frac{8}{3}x^2 + \frac{8}{3}x - 1\right)$

EXERCISE 8E.3

1 **a** $-1, 2 \pm \sqrt{3}$ **b** $1, 1 \pm i$ **c** $\frac{7}{2}, -1 \pm 2i$
d $\frac{1}{2}, \pm i\sqrt{10}$ **e** $\pm\frac{1}{2}, 3, -2$ **f** $2, 1 \pm 3i$

2 **a** $x = -2, \pm i\sqrt{3}$ **b** $x = -2, -\frac{1}{2}, 1$
c $x = 2$ (treble root) **d** $x = -2, \frac{3}{2}, 3$
e $x = -3, 2, 1 \pm \sqrt{2}$ **f** $x = -\frac{1}{2}, 3, 2 \pm i$

3 a $(x-1)(x-1+i)(x-1-i)$
b $(x+3)(x+2i)(x-2i)$
c $(2x-1)(x-2-\sqrt{3})(x-2+\sqrt{3})$
d $(x-2)(x-1+2i)(x-1-2i)$
e $(x-1)(2x-3)(2x+1)$
f $(x+2)(3x-2)(x-i\sqrt{3})(x+i\sqrt{3})$
g $(x+1)(2x-1)(x-1-i\sqrt{3})(x-1+i\sqrt{3})$
h $(2x+5)(x+2i)(x-2i)$

4 a $-3.273, -0.860, 2.133$ **b** $-2.518, -1.178, 2.696$

EXERCISE 8F.1

1 $P(x) = a(2x+1)(x^2-2x+10)$ $a \neq 0$
2 $p(x) = 4x^3 - 20x^2 + 36x - 20$
3 $p = -3$, $q = 52$ other zeros are $2+3i$, -4
4 $a = -13$, $b = 34$ other zeros are $3-i$, $-2\pm\sqrt{3}$
5 $a = 3$, $P(z) = (z+3)(z+i\sqrt{3})(z-i\sqrt{3})$
6 $k = 2$, $P(x) = (x+i\sqrt{5})(x-i\sqrt{5})(3x+2)$

EXERCISE 8F.2

1 a $a = 700$, the time at which the barrier has returned to its original position
b $k = \frac{85}{36\,000\,000}$, $f(t) = \frac{85}{36\,000\,000}t(t-700)^2$
c 120 mm at 233 milliseconds

2 March

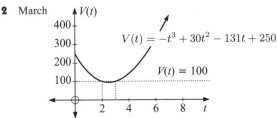

$V(t) = -t^3 + 30t^2 - 131t + 250$
$V(t) = 100$

3 9.938 m or 1.112 m

EXERCISE 8G.1

1 a $x \in \,]-\infty, -2\,[$ or $x \in \,]2, \infty\,[$
b $x \in \,]-\infty, 2-\sqrt{5}\,[$ or $x \in \,]2+\sqrt{5}, \infty\,[$ **c** $x \in R$
d $x \in \,]-\infty, 2\,]$ **e** $x \in [-4, -1\,[$
f $x \in \left[\frac{-3-\sqrt{17}}{2}, \frac{-3+\sqrt{17}}{2}\right]$ or $x \in \,]\frac{2}{3}, \infty\,[$

2 Domain is $x \in \,]0, \infty\,[$, $f(x) \leqslant 0$ for $x \in \,]0, 1]$

3 a

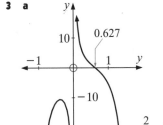

10
0.627
-1 1 y
-10

$y = \dfrac{2}{x} - e^{2x^2-x+1}$

b Domain is
$\{x:\ x \in \mathcal{R},\ x \neq 0\}$
Range is
$\{y:\ y \in \mathcal{R}\}$
c For $x \in \,]-\infty, 0\,[$
or $\,]0.627, \infty\,[$

4 a $x \in \,]-\infty, -\frac{1}{\sqrt{5}}\,]$ or $x \in [\frac{1}{\sqrt{5}}, \infty\,[$ **b** same as **a**

EXERCISE 8G.2

1 a

$\begin{array}{ccc} - & + & - \\ \hline & -2 & 2 \end{array}$

b

$\begin{array}{ccc} + & - & + \\ \hline & -\frac{1}{3} & 0 \end{array}$

c

$\begin{array}{ccc} + & - & + \\ \hline & -4 & 3 \end{array}$

d

$\begin{array}{ccc} + & - & + \\ \hline & -1-\sqrt{3} & -1+\sqrt{3} \end{array}$

e

$\begin{array}{ccc} - & + & - \\ \hline & 2-\sqrt{5} & 2+\sqrt{5} \end{array}$

f

$\begin{array}{c} - \\ \hline \end{array}$

g

$\begin{array}{cccc} - & + & - & + \\ \hline & -\frac{1}{2} & 0 & 1 \end{array}$

h

$\begin{array}{ccc} + & - & + \\ \hline & -3 & 2 \end{array}$

i

$\begin{array}{ccc} - & + & - \\ \hline & -\frac{1}{2} & 3 \end{array}$

j

$\begin{array}{cc} - & - \\ \hline & 2 \end{array}$

k

$\begin{array}{ccc} - & - & + \\ \hline & 0 & 2 \end{array}$

l

$\begin{array}{cccc} - & + & - & + \\ \hline & -2 & 0 & 1 \end{array}$

m

$\begin{array}{cc} - & + \\ \hline & 0 \end{array}$

n

$\begin{array}{cc} + & - \\ \hline & 3 \end{array}$

o

$\begin{array}{ccccc} + & - & + & - & + \\ \hline & -2 & -1 & 1 & 2 \end{array}$

p

$\begin{array}{ccc} - & + & + \\ \hline & -3 & 0 \end{array}$

q

$\begin{array}{ccc} + & - & + \\ \hline & -1 & \frac{1}{2} \end{array}$

r

$\begin{array}{cccc} + & - & + & - \\ \hline & \frac{2}{3} & 1 & 2 \end{array}$

EXERCISE 8G.3

1 a $x \in \,]-\infty, -3\,[$
b $x \in \,]-\infty, 2-\sqrt{11}]$ or $x \in [\,2+\sqrt{11}, \infty\,[$
c $x \in \,]2, 7\,[$ **d** $x \in \,]-\infty, \frac{1}{4}]$ or $x \in \,]2, \infty[$
e $x \in [-1, 0]$ or $x \in [1, \infty\,[$
f $x \in \,]-2, \frac{6}{11}\,[$ or $x \in \,]2, \infty\,[$
g $x \in [-1, 0\,[$ or $x \in [1, \infty\,[$ **h** $x \in \,]0, 2]$
i $x \in \,]-\infty, \frac{2}{3}\,[$ or $x \in [1, 2]$

2 $k \in \phi$, i.e., never true **3** $x \in [\ln 3, \infty\,[$

EXERCISE 8G.4

1 a $x \in [-1, 7]$ **b** $x \in [-1, 2]$
c $x \in \,]-\infty, -1\,[$ or $x \in [\frac{1}{3}, \infty\,[$
d $x \in \,]-\infty, -1]$ or $x \in [6, \infty\,[$ **e** $x \in [1, \infty\,[$
f $x \in [-1, \frac{1}{5}]$ **g** $x \in [\frac{3}{2}, 2\,[$ or $x \in \,]2, 3]$
h $x \in [-\frac{1}{4}, 1\,[$ or $x \in \,]1, \infty\,[$

2 a $x \in \,]1, 3\,[$ **b** $x \in \,]-\infty, 3\,[$
c $x \in \,]-\infty, -1\,[$ or $x \in \,]2, \infty\,[$ **d** $x \in [3, \infty\,[$

3

$f(x) = \dfrac{|x|}{x-2}$

$y = 1$
$y = -1$
$x = 2$

$x \in [-2, \frac{2}{3}]$ or $x \in \,]2, \infty\,[$

4 a

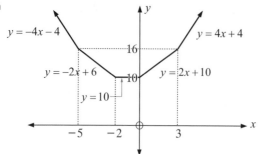

$y = -4x - 4$ $y = 4x + 4$
$y = -2x + 6$ $y = 2x + 10$
$y = 10$
16
10
-5 -2 3

b ii Anywhere between O and Q, minimum length of cable is 10 km.

iii At O, minimum length of cable is 17 km.

REVIEW SET 8A

1 a $a = 4, b = 0$ **b** $a = 3, b = -4$
c $a = 3, b = -7$ or $a = 14, b = -\frac{3}{2}$

2 a $12 + 5i$ **b** $-1 + i$ **c** $18 + 26i$

4 a $12x^4 - 9x^3 + 8x^2 - 26x + 15$
b $4x^4 - 4x^3 + 13x^2 - 6x + 9$

5 a $x^2 - 2x + 4 - \dfrac{8}{x+2}$ **b** $x - 5 + \dfrac{19x + 30}{(x+2)(x+3)}$

6 "If a polynomial $P(x)$ is divided by $x - k$ until a constant remainder R is obtained then $R = P(k)$."

7 $a = 7, b = 0$ or $a = 4, b = \pm\sqrt{3}$ **8** $1, -\frac{1}{2}, 1 \pm i\sqrt{5}$

9 $(z+2)^2(z-1+i)(z-1-i)$

10 $P(z) = z^4 - 6z^3 + 14z^2 - 10z - 7$

11 $k = 3, b = 27, x = 3, -3; k = -1, b = -5, x = -1, 5$

12 a $x \in \,]-\infty, -1-\sqrt{6}\,]$ or $x \in [-1+\sqrt{6}, \infty\,[$
b $x \in \,]-\infty, -3\,[$ or $x \in \,]\,0, 3\,[$
c $x \in \,]-\infty, \frac{16}{3}]$ or $x \in [16, \infty\,[$

13 $k \in \,]-\infty, \ 10-3\sqrt{10}\,[$ or $k \in \,]\,10 + 3\sqrt{10}, \infty\,[$

14 $k = -2, \ n = 36$

15 Another hint: Show that: $(\alpha\beta)^3 + (\alpha\beta)^2 - 1 = 0$

EXERCISE 9A

1 24 **2 a** 4 **b** 8 **c** 24 **3** 6 **4** 42 **5** 1680
6 a 125 **b** 60 **7** 17 576 000 **8 a** 4 **b** 9 **c** 81

EXERCISE 9B

1 a 13 **b** 20 **c** 19 **d** 32

EXERCISE 9C

1 1, 1, 2, 6, 24, 120, 720, 5040, 40 320, 362 880, 3 628 800
2 a 6 **b** 30 **c** $\frac{1}{7}$ **d** $\frac{1}{30}$ **e** 100 **f** 21
3 a n **b** $(n+2)(n+1)$ **c** $(n+1)n$
4 a $\frac{7!}{4!}$ **b** $\frac{10!}{8!}$ **c** $\frac{11!}{6!}$ **d** $\frac{13!}{10!3!}$ **e** $\frac{3!}{6!}$ **f** $\frac{4!16!}{20!}$
5 a $6 \times 4!$ **b** $10 \times 10!$ **c** $57 \times 6!$ **d** $131 \times 10!$
e $81 \times 7!$ **f** $62 \times 6!$ **g** $10 \times 11!$ **h** $32 \times 8!$
6 a 11! **b** 9! **c** 8! **d** 9 **e** 34 **f** $n+1$
g $(n-1)!$ **h** $(n+1)!$

EXERCISE 9D

1 a W, X, Y, Z
b WX, WY, WZ, XW, XY, XZ, YW, YX, YZ, ZW, ZX, ZY

c WXY, WXZ, WYX, WYZ, WZX, WZY, XWY, XWZ, XYW, XYZ, XZW, XZY, YWX, YWZ, YXW, YXZ, YZW, YZX, ZWX, ZWY, ZXW, ZXY, ZYW, ZYX

2 a AB, AC, AD, AE, BA, BC, BD, BE, CA, CB, CD, CE, DA, DB, DC, DE, EA, EB, EC, ED
b ABC, ABD, ABE, ACB, ACD, ACE, ADB, ADC, ADE, AEB, AEC, AED, BAC, BAD, BAE, BCA, BCD, BCE, BDA, BDC, BDE, BEA, BEC, BED, CAB, CAD, CAE, CBA, CBD, CBE, CDA, CDB, CDE, CEA, CEB, CED, DAB, DAC, DAE, DBA, DBC, DBE, DCA, DCB, DCE, DEA, DEB, DEC, EAB, EAC, EAD, EBA, EBC, EBD, ECA, ECB, ECD, EDA, EDB, EDC
2 at a time: 20   3 at a time: 60

3 a 120 **b** 336 **c** 5040 **4 a** 12 **b** 24 **c** 36
5 720 **a** 24 **b** 24 **c** 48 **6 a** 343 **b** 210 **c** 120
7 720, 72 **8 a** 648 **b** 64 **c** 72 **d** 136
9 a 120 **b** 48 **c** 72 **10 a** 3 628 800 **b** 241 920

EXERCISE 9E

1 a 8 **b** 28 **c** 56 **d** 28 **e** 1

3 ABC, ABD, ABE, ACD, ACE, ADE, BCD, BCE, BDE, CDE

4 $C_{11}^{17} = 12 376$ **5** $C_5^9 = 126$, $C_1^1 C_4^8 = 70$

6 $C_3^{13} = 286$, $C_1^1 C_2^{12} = 66$

7 $C_5^{12} = 792$ **a** $C_2^2 C_3^{10} = 120$ **b** $C_1^1 C_4^{10} = 420$

8 $C_3^3 C_0^1 C_6^{11} = 462$

9 a $C_1^1 C_3^9 = 84$ **b** $C_0^2 C_4^8 = 70$ **c** $C_0^2 C_1^1 C_3^7 = 35$

10 a $C_5^{16} = 4368$ **b** $C_3^{10} C_2^6 = 1800$ **c** $C_5^{10} C_0^6 = 252$
d $C_3^{10} C_2^6 + C_4^{10} C_1^6 + C_5^{10} C_0^6 = 3312$
e $C_5^{16} - C_5^{10} C_0^6 - C_0^{10} C_5^6 = 4110$

11 a $C_2^6 C_1^3 C_2^7 = 945$ **b** $C_2^6 C_3^{10} = 1800$
c $C_5^{16} - C_5^9 C_7^7 = 4347$

12 $C_2^{20} - 20 = 170$ **13 a** **i** $C_2^{12} = 66$ **ii** $C_1^{11} = 11$
b **i** $C_3^{12} = 220$ **ii** $C_2^{11} = 55$

14 $C_4^9 = 126$

15 a the different committees of 4 to be selected from 5 men and 6 women in all possible ways **b** C_r^{m+n}

16 a $\dfrac{C_6^{12}}{2} = 462$ **b** $\dfrac{C_4^{12} C_4^8 C_4^4}{3!} = 5775$

EXERCISE 9F

1 a $x^3 + 3x^2 + 3x + 1$ **b** $x^3 + 6x^2 + 12x + 8$
c $x^3 - 12x^2 + 48x - 64$ **d** $8x^3 + 12x^2 + 6x + 1$
e $8x^3 - 12x^2 + 6x - 1$ **f** $27x^3 - 27x^2 + 9x - 1$
g $8x^3 + 60x^2 + 150x + 125$ **h** $8x^3 + 12x + \frac{6}{x} + \frac{1}{x^3}$

2 a $x^4 + 8x^3 + 24x^2 + 32x + 16$
b $x^4 - 8x^3 + 24x^2 - 32x + 16$
c $16x^4 + 96x^3 + 216x^2 + 216x + 81$
d $81x^4 - 108x^3 + 54x^2 - 12x + 1$
e $x^4 + 4x^2 + 6 + \frac{4}{x^2} + \frac{1}{x^4}$
f $16x^4 - 32x^2 + 24 - \frac{8}{x^2} + \frac{1}{x^4}$

3 a $x^5 + 10x^4 + 40x^3 + 80x^2 + 80x + 32$
b $x^5 - 10x^4 + 40x^3 - 80x^2 + 80x - 32$
c $32x^5 + 80x^4 + 80x^3 + 40x^2 + 10x + 1$
d $32x^5 - 80x^3 + 80x - \frac{40}{x} + \frac{10}{x^3} - \frac{1}{x^5}$

4 a 1 6 15 20 15 6 1

b **i** $x^6 + 12x^5 + 60x^4 + 160x^3 + 240x^2 + 192x + 64$

    ii $64x^6 - 192x^5 + 240x^4 - 160x^3 + 60x^2 - 12x + 1$

    iii $x^6 + 6x^4 + 15x^2 + 20 + \frac{15}{x^2} + \frac{6}{x^4} + \frac{1}{x^6}$

5 **a** $7 + 5\sqrt{2}$ **b** $56 + 24\sqrt{5}$ **c** $232 - 164\sqrt{2}$

6 **a** $64 + 192x + 240x^2 + 160x^3 + 60x^4 + 12x^5 + x^6$

  b $65.944\,160\,601\,201$

7 $2x^5 + 11x^4 + 24x^3 + 26x^2 + 14x + 3$ **8 a** 270 **b** 4320

EXERCISE 9G

1 **a** $1^{11} + \binom{11}{1}(2x) + \binom{11}{2}(2x)^2 + \ldots + \binom{11}{10}(2x)^{10} + (2x)^{11}$

  b $(3x)^{15} + \binom{15}{1}(3x)^{14}\left(\frac{2}{x}\right) + \binom{15}{2}(3x)^{13}\left(\frac{2}{x}\right)^2 + \ldots$

    $\ldots + \binom{15}{14}(3x)\left(\frac{2}{x}\right)^{14} + \left(\frac{2}{x}\right)^{15}$

  c $(2x)^{20} + \binom{20}{1}(2x)^{19}\left(-\frac{3}{x}\right) + \binom{20}{2}(2x)^{18}\left(-\frac{3}{x}\right)^2 + \ldots$

    $\ldots + \binom{20}{19}(2x)\left(-\frac{3}{x}\right)^{19} + \left(-\frac{3}{x}\right)^{20}$

2 **a** $T_6 = \binom{15}{5}(2x)^{10}5^5$ **b** $T_4 = \binom{9}{3}(x^2)^6\left(\frac{5}{x}\right)^3$

  c $T_{10} = \binom{17}{9}x^8\left(-\frac{2}{x}\right)^9$ **d** $T_9 = \binom{21}{8}(2x^2)^{13}\left(-\frac{1}{x}\right)^8$

3 **a** $\binom{10}{5}3^5 2^5$ **b** $\binom{6}{3}2^3(-3)^3$ **c** $\binom{12}{4}2^8(-1)^4$

4 **a** $\binom{15}{5}2^5$ **b** $\binom{9}{3}(-3)^3$

5 **a**

	b sum
1 1	2
1 2 1	4
1 3 3 1	8
1 4 6 4 1	16
1 5 10 10 5 1	32

  c It seems that the sum of the numbers in row n of Pascal's triangle is 2^n.

  d After the first part let $x = 1$.

6 **a** $\binom{8}{6} = 28$ **b** $2\binom{9}{3}3^6 - \binom{9}{4}3^5 = 91\,854$

7 **b** $84x^3$ **c** $n = 6$ and $k = -2$ **8** $a = 2$

REVIEW SET 9A

1 **a** $26^2 \times 10^4 = 6\,760\,000$ **b** $5 \times 26 \times 10^4 = 1\,300\,000$

  c $26 \times 25 \times 10 \times 9 \times 8 \times 7 = 3\,276\,000$

2 **a** 45 **b** 120 **3** **a** $n(n-1)$ **b** $n+2$

4 3003 **a** 980 **b** 2982 **5** 28 **6** **a** 252 **b** 246

7 **a** 24 **b** 6 **8** **a** $x^3 - 6x^2y + 12xy^2 - 8y^3$

        b $81x^4 + 216x^3 + 216x^2 + 96x + 16$

9 $20\,000$ **10** 4320 **11** **a** 900 **b** 180

EXERCISE 10A

1 **a** $4n - 1$ **b** all $n \in Z^+$, $n \geqslant 2$ **c** 10 for all $n \in Z^+$

  d $n(n+1)$, $n \in Z^+$ **e** $(n+1)! - 1$ for all $n \in Z^+$

  f $\dfrac{(n+1)! - 1}{(n+1)!}$ for all $n \in Z^+$ **g** 3 for all $n \in Z^+$

  h $\dfrac{1}{n+1}$ for all $n \in Z^+$ **i** $\dfrac{n}{6n+4}$, $n \in Z^+$

2 *Proposition:* The number of triangles for n points within the original triangle is given by $T_n = 2n + 1$, $n \in Z^+$.

EXERCISE 10B

2 **a** $\frac{11}{210}$ **3** **b** $\frac{3\,628\,799}{3\,628\,800}$

EXERCISE 11A

1 **a** 0 **b** 0.26 **c** 0.42 **d** 0.5 **e** 0.71 **f** 0.87

  g 0.97 **h** 1

3 **a** 1 **b** 0.97 **c** 0.91 **d** 0.87 **e** 0.71 **f** 0.5

  g 0.26 **h** 0

5 $(0.57, 0.82)$ **6**

7 **a** $\sin \theta = 0.6$

  b $\cos \theta \doteq 0.714$

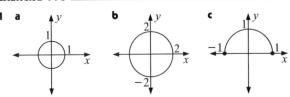

EXERCISE 11B

1 **a** 0.98 **b** 0.98 **c** 0.87 **d** 0.87 **e** 0.5 **f** 0.5

  g 0 **h** 0 **2** **a** $\sin(180 - \theta)^\circ = \sin \theta^\circ$

3 **a** -0.34 **b** 0.34 **c** -0.64 **d** 0.64 **e** -0.77

  f 0.77 **g** -1 **h** 1

4 **a** $\cos(180 - \theta)^\circ = -\cos \theta^\circ$

5 **a** 135° **b** 129° **c** 106° **d** 98°

6 **a** 50° **b** 34° **c** 18° **d** 9°

7 **a** 0.6820 **b** 0.8572 **c** -0.7986 **d** 0.9135

  e 0.9063 **f** -0.6691

8 **a** $(180 - \theta)^\circ$

  b OQ is a reflection of OP in the y-axis and so Q has coordinates $(-\cos \theta, \sin \theta)$

  c $\cos(180 - \theta) = -\cos \theta$ and $\sin(180 - \theta) = \sin \theta$

EXERCISE 11C

1 **a**   **b**   **c**

2 **a** **i** A$(\cos 26^\circ, \sin 26^\circ)$ B$(\cos 146^\circ, \sin 146^\circ)$

    C$(\cos 199^\circ, \sin 199^\circ)$

  ii A$(0.899, 0.438)$ B$(-0.829, 0.559)$

    C$(-0.946, -0.326)$

  b **i** A$(\cos 123^\circ, \sin 123^\circ)$ B$(\cos 251^\circ, \sin 251^\circ)$

    C$(\cos(-35^\circ), \sin(-35^\circ))$

  ii A$(-0.545, 0.839)$ B$(-0.326, -0.946)$

    C$(0.819, -0.574)$

3 **a** $\cos 0^\circ = 1$, $\sin 0^\circ = 0$ **b** $\cos 90^\circ = 0$, $\sin 90^\circ = 1$

  c $\cos 180^\circ = -1$, $\sin 180^\circ = 0$

  d $\cos 270^\circ = 0$, $\sin 270^\circ = -1$

  e $\cos(-90^\circ) = 0$, $\sin(-90^\circ) = -1$

  f $\cos 450^\circ = 0$, $\sin 450^\circ = 1$

EXERCISE 11D.1

1 **a** 45° **b** 30° **c** 120° **d** 270° **e** 300°

2 **a** $\frac{\pi}{6}$ units **b** $\frac{\pi}{3}$ units **c** $\frac{\pi}{2}$ units **d** $\frac{2\pi}{3}$ units

  e $\frac{3\pi}{4}$ units **f** $\frac{5\pi}{6}$ units **g** $\frac{5\pi}{4}$ units **h** $\frac{3\pi}{2}$ units

3 **a** $\theta = 60$ **b** AP $= \frac{\pi}{3}$ **c** decrease **d** $\theta = 57.3$

EXERCISE 11D.2

1 **a** $\frac{\pi}{2}^c$ **b** $\frac{\pi}{3}^c$ **c** $\frac{\pi}{6}^c$ **d** $\frac{\pi}{10}^c$ **e** $\frac{\pi}{20}^c$ **f** $\frac{3\pi}{4}^c$ **g** $\frac{5\pi}{4}^c$

  h $\frac{3\pi}{2}^c$ **i** $2\pi^c$ **j** $4\pi^c$ **k** $\frac{7\pi}{4}^c$ **l** $3\pi^c$ **m** $\frac{\pi c}{5}$ **n** $\frac{4\pi}{9}^c$ **o** $\frac{23\pi}{18}^c$

2 **a** 0.641^c **b** 2.39^c **c** 5.55^c **d** 3.83^c **e** 6.92^c

3 **a** 36° **b** 108° **c** 135° **d** 10° **e** 20° **f** 140°

g 18° **h** 27° **i** 150° **j** 22.5°

4 a 114.59° **b** 87.66° **c** 49.68° **d** 182.14° **e** 301.78°

5 a

Degrees	0	45	90	135	180	225
Radians	0	$\frac{\pi}{4}$	$\frac{\pi}{2}$	$\frac{3\pi}{4}$	π	$\frac{5\pi}{4}$

Degrees	270	315	360
Radians	$\frac{3\pi}{2}$	$\frac{7\pi}{4}$	2π

b

Degrees	0	30	60	90	120	150	180
Radians	0	$\frac{\pi}{6}$	$\frac{\pi}{3}$	$\frac{\pi}{2}$	$\frac{2\pi}{3}$	$\frac{5\pi}{6}$	π

Degrees	210	240	270	300	330	360
Radians	$\frac{7\pi}{6}$	$\frac{4\pi}{3}$	$\frac{3\pi}{2}$	$\frac{5\pi}{3}$	$\frac{11\pi}{6}$	2π

EXERCISE 11E.1

1 a $0, 1$ **b** $1, 0$ **c** $0, -1$ **d** $0, -1$

2 a $\cos\theta = \pm\frac{\sqrt{3}}{2}$ **b** $\cos\theta = \pm\frac{2\sqrt{2}}{3}$ **c** $\cos\theta = \pm1$
d $\cos\theta = 0$

3 a $\sin\theta = \pm\frac{3}{5}$ **b** $\sin\theta = \pm\frac{\sqrt{7}}{4}$ **c** $\sin\theta = 0$ **d** $\sin\theta = \pm1$

4 a

Quad-rant	Degree measure	Radian measure	$\cos\theta$	$\sin\theta$
1	$0 < \theta < 90$	$0 < \theta < \frac{\pi}{2}$	+ve	+ve
2	$90 < \theta < 180$	$\frac{\pi}{2} < \theta < \pi$	−ve	+ve
3	$180 < \theta < 270$	$\pi < \theta < \frac{3\pi}{2}$	−ve	−ve
4	$270 < \theta < 360$	$\frac{3\pi}{2} < \theta < 2\pi$	+ve	−ve

b i 1 and 4 **ii** 2 and 3 **iii** 3 **iv** 2

5 a $\sin\theta = \frac{\sqrt{5}}{3}$ **b** $\cos\theta = -\frac{\sqrt{21}}{5}$ **c** $\cos\theta = \frac{4}{5}$
d $\sin\theta = -\frac{12}{13}$

EXERCISE 11E.2

1

	a	**b**	**c**	**d**	**e**
$\sin\theta$	$\frac{1}{\sqrt{2}}$	$-\frac{1}{\sqrt{2}}$	$-\frac{1}{\sqrt{2}}$	0	$-\frac{1}{\sqrt{2}}$
$\cos\theta$	$\frac{1}{\sqrt{2}}$	$-\frac{1}{\sqrt{2}}$	$\frac{1}{\sqrt{2}}$	-1	$-\frac{1}{\sqrt{2}}$

2

	a	**b**	**c**	**d**	**e**
$\sin\beta$	$\frac{1}{2}$	$\frac{\sqrt{3}}{2}$	$-\frac{1}{2}$	$-\frac{\sqrt{3}}{2}$	$-\frac{1}{2}$
$\cos\beta$	$\frac{\sqrt{3}}{2}$	$-\frac{1}{2}$	$-\frac{\sqrt{3}}{2}$	$\frac{1}{2}$	$\frac{\sqrt{3}}{2}$

3 a $\frac{3}{4}$ **b** $\frac{1}{4}$ **c** 3 **d** $\frac{1}{4}$ **e** $-\frac{1}{4}$ **f** 1 **g** $\sqrt{2}$ **h** $\frac{1}{2}$ **i** $\frac{1}{2}$

4 a $30^\circ, 150^\circ$ **b** $60^\circ, 120^\circ$ **c** $45^\circ, 315^\circ$ **d** $120^\circ, 240^\circ$
e $135^\circ, 225^\circ$ **f** $240^\circ, 300^\circ$

5 a $30^\circ, 330^\circ, 390^\circ, 690^\circ$ **b** $210^\circ, 330^\circ, 570^\circ, 690^\circ$
c $270^\circ, 630^\circ$

6 a $\theta = \frac{\pi}{3}, \frac{5\pi}{3}$ **b** $\theta = \frac{\pi}{3}, \frac{2\pi}{3}$ **c** $\theta = \pi$ **d** $\theta = \frac{\pi}{2}$
e $\theta = \frac{3\pi}{4}, \frac{5\pi}{4}$ **f** $\theta = \frac{\pi}{2}, \frac{3\pi}{2}$ **g** $\theta = 0, \pi, 2\pi$
h $\theta = \frac{\pi}{4}, \frac{3\pi}{4}, \frac{5\pi}{4}, \frac{7\pi}{4}$

EXERCISE 11F

1 a 28.9 cm^2 **b** 384 km^2 **c** 26.7 cm^2 **2** $x = 19.0$
3 18.9 cm^2 **4** 137 cm^2 **5** 374 cm^2 **6** 7.49 cm
7 11.9 m **8 a** 48.6° or 131.4° **b** 42.1° or 137.9°
9 $\frac{1}{4}$ is not covered
10 a i and **ii** 6 cm^2 **b i** $\doteqdot 21.3$ cm^2 **ii** 30.7 cm^2

EXERCISE 11G

1 a i 6.53 cm **ii** 29.4 cm^2 **b i** 10.5 cm **ii** 25.9 cm^2
2 a 3.14 m **b** 9.30 m^2
3 a 5.91 cm **b** 18.9 cm **4 a** 39.3° **b** 34.4°
5 a 0.75^c **b** 1.68^c **c** 2.32^c
6 a 8.75 cm^2 **b** 36.2 cm^2 **c** 62.8 cm^2
7 10 cm, 25 cm^2 **8** 65 cm^2
9 a 11.7 cm **b** 11.7 **c** 37.7 cm **d** 185°
10 a $\alpha = 18.43$ **b** $\theta = 143.1$ **c** 387.3 m^2
11 b 2 h 24 min **12** 227 m^2
13 a $\alpha = 5.739$ **b** $\theta = 168.5$ **c** $\phi = 191.5$ **d** 71.62 cm

REVIEW SET 11A

1 a $\sin 70^\circ \doteqdot 0.94$ **b** $\cos 35^\circ \doteqdot 0.82$
2 M$(\cos 73^\circ, \sin 73^\circ) \doteqdot (0.292, 0.956)$
N$(\cos 190^\circ, \sin 190^\circ) \doteqdot (-0.985, -0.174)$
P$(\cos 307^\circ, \sin 307^\circ) \doteqdot (0.602, -0.799)$
3 $\theta \doteqdot 102.8^\circ$ **4 a** 60° **b** 15° **c** 85°
5 a 133° **b** 172° **c** 94°
6 a 0.358 **b** -0.035 **c** 0.259 **d** -0.731
7 a $1, 0$ **b** $-1, 0$ **8 a** 79° **b** 53° **c** 12°
9 a 84° **c** 62° **c** 3°
10 a 0.961 **b** -0.961 **c** -0.961 **d** -0.961
11 a -0.743 **b** -0.743 **c** 0.743 **d** -0.743

REVIEW SET 11B

1 21.1 km^2 **2 a** 118 cm^2 **b** 44.9 cm^2
3 perimeter $= 34.1$ cm, area $= 66.5$ cm^2
4 $r = 8.79$ cm, area $= 81.0$ cm^2 **5** 67.4° or 112.6°
6 $x = 47.5$, AC $= 14.3$ cm **or** $x = 132.5$, AC $= 28.1$ cm
7 36.8 cm^2 **8 a** $10\,600$ m^2 **b** 1.06 ha
10 a $\frac{2\pi}{3}$ **b** $\frac{5\pi}{4}$ **c** $\frac{5\pi}{6}$ **d** 3π
11 a 1.239^c **b** 2.175^c **c** -2.478^c **d** -0.4416^c
12 a 72° **b** 225° **c** 140° **d** 330°
13 a 171.89° **b** 83.65° **c** 24.92° **d** -302.01°

REVIEW SET 11C

1 a $(0.766, -0.643)$ **b** $(-0.956, 0.292)$

2

3 a $\sin(\frac{2\pi}{3}) = \frac{\sqrt{3}}{2}$,
$\cos(\frac{2\pi}{3}) = -\frac{1}{2}$
b $\sin(\frac{8\pi}{3}) = \frac{\sqrt{3}}{2}$,
$\cos(\frac{8\pi}{3}) = -\frac{1}{2}$

4 Hint: $\tan\theta = -1$ when $\cos\theta = -\sin\theta$

5 a $0, -1$ **b** $0, -1$ **6** $\pm\frac{\sqrt{7}}{4}$ **7** $\frac{\sqrt{7}}{4}$ **8 a** $\frac{3}{4}$ **b** $-\sqrt{2}$
9 a $\frac{\sqrt{3}}{2}$ **b** $-\frac{1}{2}$ **c** $\frac{1}{2}$ **10 a** $150^\circ, 210^\circ$ **b** $45^\circ, 135^\circ$
11 a $\theta = \pi + k2\pi$ **b** $\theta = \left.\begin{matrix}\frac{\pi}{3}\\\frac{2\pi}{3}\end{matrix}\right\} + k\pi$

EXERCISE 12A

1 a 28.8 cm **b** 3.38 km **c** 14.2 m
2 $\angle$A $= 52.0^\circ$, $\angle$B $= 59.3^\circ$, $\angle$C $= 68.7^\circ$ **3** 112°
4 a 40.3° **b** 107° **5 a** $\cos\theta = 0.65$ **b** $x = 3.81$

EXERCISE 12B.1

1 a $x = 28.4$ **b** $x = 13.4$ **c** $x = 3.79$

2 a $a = 21.25$ cm **b** $b = 76.9$ cm **c** $c = 5.09$ cm

EXERCISE 12B.2

1 $\angle C = 62.1°$ or $\angle C = 117.9°$

2 a $\angle A = 49.5°$ **b** $\angle B = 72.05°$ or $107.95°$ **c** $\angle C = 44.3°$

3 No, $\dfrac{\sin 85°}{11.4} \neq \dfrac{\sin 27°}{9.8}$ **4** $\angle ABC = 66°$, $BD = 4.55$ cm

5 $x = 17.7$, $y = 33.1$

6 a $88.7°$ or $91.3°$ **b** $91.3°$

c .... *cosine rule* as it avoids the *ambiguous case*.

EXERCISE 12C

1 17.7 m **2** 207 m **3** 23.9° **4** 77.5 m **5** 13.2°

6 69.1 m **7 a** 38.0 m **b** 94.0 m **8** 55.1°

9 $AC = 11.7$ km $BC = 8.49$ km

10 a 74.9 km^2 **b** 7490 hectares **11** 9.12 km

12 $\doteq 85$ mm **13** 10.1 km **14** 29.2 m **15** 37.6 km

REVIEW SET 12

1 a $x = 34.1$ **b** $x = 18.9$ **2 a** $x = 41.5$ **b** $x = 15.4$

3 $AC = 12.55$ cm, $\angle A = 48.6°$, $\angle C = 57.4°$

4 113 cm^2 **5** 7.32 m **6** 204 m

7 530 m, bearing 077.2° **8** 179 km, bearing 352°

9 If the unknown is an angle, use the cosine rule to avoid the ambiguous case.

10 a $x = 3$ or 5 **b** Kady can draw 2 triangles:

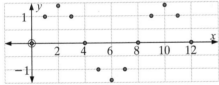

11 a The information given could give two triangles:

b $\doteq 2.23$ m^3

EXERCISE 13A

1 a

Data exhibits periodic behaviour.

b

Not enough information to say data is periodic. It may in fact be quadratic.

c

Not enough information to say data is periodic. It may in fact be quadratic.

d

Not enough information to say data is periodic.

2 a

b The data is periodic. **i** $y = 32$ (approx.)
ii $\doteq 64$ cm **iii** $\doteq 200$ cm **iv** $\doteq 32$ cm

c A curve can be fitted to the data.

3 a periodic **b** periodic **c** periodic **d** not periodic
e periodic **f** periodic

EXERCISE 13B.1

1 a

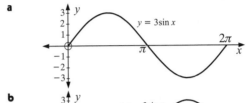

b

c

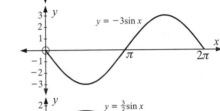

d

2 a

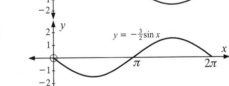

b

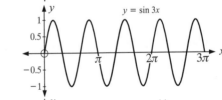

c

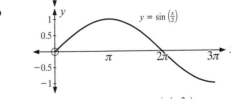

3 a $\dfrac{\pi}{2}$ **b** $\dfrac{\pi}{2}$ **c** 6π **d** $\dfrac{10\pi}{3}$

4 a $B = \dfrac{2}{5}$ **b** $B = 3$ **c** $B = \dfrac{1}{6}$ **d** $B = \dfrac{\pi}{2}$ **e** $B = \dfrac{\pi}{50}$

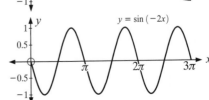

5 a

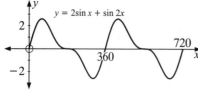

b

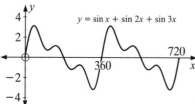

c

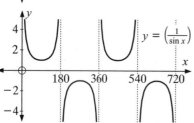

6 a

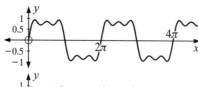

b

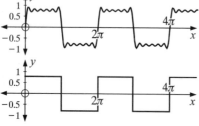

EXERCISE 13B.2

1 a

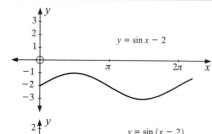

b

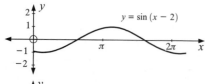

c

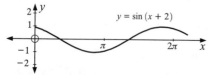

d

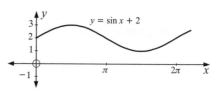

e

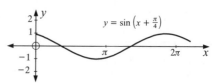

f

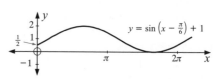

3 a $\frac{2\pi}{5}$ **b** 8π **c** π **4 a** $\frac{2}{3}$ **b** 20 **c** $\frac{1}{50}$ **d** $\frac{\pi}{25}$

5 a vert. translation -1 **b** horiz. translation $\frac{\pi}{4}$ right

  c vert. dilation, factor 2 **d** horiz. dilation, factor $\frac{1}{4}$

  e vert. dilation, factor $\frac{1}{2}$ **f** horiz. dilation, factor 4

  g reflection in the x-axis **h** translation $\begin{bmatrix} -2 \\ -3 \end{bmatrix}$

  i vert. dilation, factor 2, followed by a horiz. dilation, factor $\frac{1}{3}$ **j** translation $\begin{bmatrix} \frac{\pi}{3} \\ 2 \end{bmatrix}$

EXERCISE 13C

1 a $T \doteqdot 6.5 \sin \frac{\pi}{6}(t - 4.5) + 20.4$

2 a $T \doteqdot 4.5 \sin \frac{\pi}{6}(t - 4.5) + 11.5$

3 $T \doteqdot 13.1 \sin(0.345)(t + 6.87) - 5.43$

4 a $H \doteqdot 7 \sin 0.507(t - 6.2)$

  b

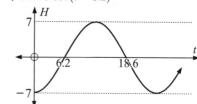

5 $H = 10 \sin \frac{\pi}{50}(t - 25) + 12$

EXERCISE 13D.1

1 a $x = 0.3, 2.8, 6.6, 9.1, 12.9$ **b** $x = 5.9, 9.8, 12.2$

2 a $x = \left.\begin{matrix} 0.4 \\ 1.2 \end{matrix}\right\} + k\pi$ **b** $x = \left.\begin{matrix} 1.7 \\ 3.0 \end{matrix}\right\} + k\pi$

EXERCISE 13D.2

1 a $x = 0.4268, 2.715, 6.710$ **b** $x = 3.880, 5.545$
  c no solutions
  d $x = 0.08136, 1.489, 3.223, 4.631, 6.365, 7.773$
  e $x = 7.585$ **f** $x = 1.076, 4.348, 7.360$
  g $x = 2.347, 3.394$ **h** $x = 1.831, 3.405$
  i $x = 6.532, 7.605$

EXERCISE 13D.3

1 a $x = \frac{\pi}{6}, \frac{13\pi}{6}, \frac{25\pi}{6}$ **b** $x = -\frac{\pi}{3}, \frac{5\pi}{3}$
  c $x = -\frac{7\pi}{2}, -\frac{5\pi}{2}, -\frac{3\pi}{2}, -\frac{\pi}{2}, \frac{\pi}{2}, \frac{3\pi}{2}, \frac{5\pi}{2}, \frac{7\pi}{2}$

d $x = \frac{\pi}{3}, \frac{5\pi}{6}, \frac{4\pi}{3}, \frac{11\pi}{6}, \frac{7\pi}{3}, \frac{17\pi}{6}, \frac{10\pi}{3}, \frac{23\pi}{6}$

2 a $x = \frac{\pi}{6}, \frac{5\pi}{6}, \frac{13\pi}{6}, \frac{17\pi}{6}, \frac{25\pi}{6}, \frac{29\pi}{6}$

b $x = \frac{\pi}{4}, \frac{3\pi}{4}, \frac{9\pi}{4}, \frac{11\pi}{4}$ **c** $x = -\frac{11\pi}{6}, -\frac{7\pi}{6}, \frac{\pi}{6}, \frac{5\pi}{6}$

d $x = -\frac{15\pi}{4}, -\frac{13\pi}{4}, -\frac{7\pi}{4}, -\frac{5\pi}{4}$ **e** $x = \frac{3\pi}{2}, \frac{7\pi}{2}, \frac{11\pi}{2}$

f $x = \frac{\pi}{2}, \frac{3\pi}{2}, \frac{5\pi}{2}, \frac{7\pi}{2}$ **g** $x = \frac{\pi}{12}, \frac{5\pi}{12}, \frac{13\pi}{12}, \frac{17\pi}{12}, \frac{25\pi}{12}, \frac{29\pi}{12}$

h $x = \frac{5\pi}{12}, \frac{7\pi}{12}, \frac{13\pi}{12}, \frac{5\pi}{4}, \frac{7\pi}{4}, \frac{23\pi}{12}$

i $x = \frac{\pi}{6}, \frac{\pi}{3}, \frac{7\pi}{6}, \frac{4\pi}{3}, \frac{13\pi}{6}, \frac{7\pi}{3}$

j $x = -\frac{\pi}{6}, \frac{\pi}{2}, \frac{11\pi}{6}, \frac{5\pi}{2}, \frac{-13\pi}{6}, \frac{-3\pi}{2}$

3 a $x = -\frac{3\pi}{2}, \frac{\pi}{2}$ **b** $x = \pm\frac{\pi}{3}, \pm\frac{2\pi}{3}, \pm\frac{4\pi}{3}, \pm\frac{5\pi}{3}$

c $x = -\frac{3\pi}{2}, -\frac{5\pi}{6}, -\frac{\pi}{6}, \frac{\pi}{2}, \frac{7\pi}{6}, \frac{11\pi}{6}$

d $x = -\frac{11\pi}{6}, -\frac{3\pi}{2}, -\frac{7\pi}{6}, \frac{\pi}{6}, \frac{\pi}{2}, \frac{5\pi}{6}$

4 a $x = 0, \frac{\pi}{2}, \pi$ **b** $x = \frac{\pi}{4}, \frac{5\pi}{4}, \frac{9\pi}{4}$

EXERCISE 13D.4

1 a i 7500 **ii** 10 300 **b** 10 500, when $t = 4$ weeks

c i at $t = 1\frac{1}{3}$ wks and $6\frac{2}{3}$ wks **ii** at $t = 9\frac{1}{3}$ wks

d $2.51 \leqslant t \leqslant 5.49$

2 a 20 m **b** at $t = \frac{3}{4}$ minute **c** 3 minutes

d

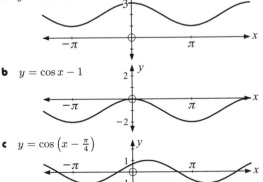

3 a 400 **b i** 577 **ii** 400

c 650 It is the maximum population.

d 150, after 3 years **e** $0.26 < t < 1.74$

4 a i true **ii** true **b** 116.8 cents/L

c on the 5th and 11th days

d 98.6 cents/L on the 15th day

EXERCISE 13E

1 a $y = \cos x + 2$

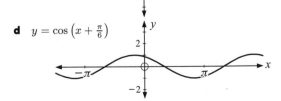

b $y = \cos x - 1$

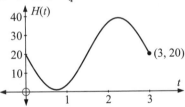

c $y = \cos\left(x - \frac{\pi}{4}\right)$

d $y = \cos\left(x + \frac{\pi}{6}\right)$

e $y = \frac{2}{3}\cos x$

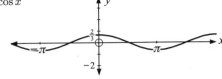

f $y = \frac{3}{2}\cos x$

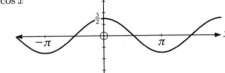

g $y = -\cos x$

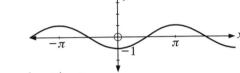

h $y = \cos\left(x - \frac{\pi}{6}\right) + 1$

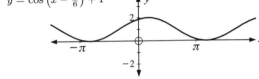

i $y = \cos\left(x + \frac{\pi}{4}\right) - 1$

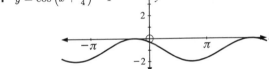

j $y = \cos 2x$

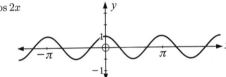

k $y = \cos\left(\frac{x}{2}\right)$

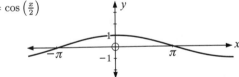

l $y = 3\cos 2x$

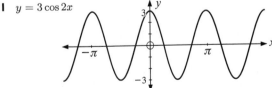

2 a $\frac{2\pi}{3}$ **c** 6π **c** 100

3 A: amplitude, B: $\dfrac{2\pi}{\text{period}}$, C: horizontal translation, D: vertical translation

4 a $y = 2\cos 2x$ **b** $y = \cos\left(\frac{x}{2}\right) + 2$ **c** $y = -5\cos\left(\frac{\pi}{3}x\right)$

EXERCISE 13F

1 a $x = 1.2, 5.1, 7.4$ **b** $x = 4.4, 8.2, 10.7$

2 a $x = 0.975, 5.308, 7.258$

b $x = 0.336, 2.805, 3.478, 5.947$

c $x = 3.526, 5.358, 9.809, 11.641$

d $x = 0.608, 1.487, 2.702, 3.581, 4.797$

3 **a** $x = \frac{\pi}{4}, \frac{7\pi}{4}, \frac{9\pi}{4}, \frac{15\pi}{4}$ **b** $x = \frac{2\pi}{3}, \frac{4\pi}{3}, \frac{8\pi}{3}, \frac{10\pi}{3}, \frac{14\pi}{3}$

   c $x = \frac{5\pi}{6}, \frac{7\pi}{6}, \frac{17\pi}{6}$ **d** $x = -\frac{5\pi}{3}, -\pi, \frac{\pi}{3}, \pi$

   e $x = \pi, \frac{3\pi}{2}, 3\pi$ **f** $x = \frac{\pi}{2}, \frac{3\pi}{2}$

4 **a** $H(t) = 3\cos(\frac{\pi t}{2}) + 4$ **b** $t \doteq 1.46$ sec

EXERCISE 13G.1

1 **a** $2\sin\theta$ **b** $3\cos\theta$ **c** $2\sin\theta$ **d** $\sin\theta$ **e** $-2\cos\theta$
   f $-3\cos\theta$

2 **a** 3 **b** -2 **c** -1 **d** $3\cos^2\theta$ **e** $4\sin^2\theta$ **f** $\sin\theta$
   g $-\sin^2\theta$ **h** $-\cos^2\theta$ **i** $-2\sin^2\theta$ **j** 1 **k** $\sin\theta$ **l** $\sin\theta$

3 **a** $1 + 2\sin\theta + \sin^2\theta$ **b** $\sin^2\alpha - 4\sin\alpha + 4$
   c $\cos^2\alpha - 2\cos\alpha + 1$ **d** $1 + 2\sin\alpha\cos\alpha$
   e $1 - 2\sin\beta\cos\beta$ **f** $-4 + 4\cos\alpha - \cos^2\alpha$

4 **a** $(1 - \sin\theta)(1 + \sin\theta)$ **b** $(\sin\alpha + \cos\alpha)(\sin\alpha - \cos\alpha)$
   c $(\cos\alpha + 1)(\cos\alpha - 1)$ **d** $\sin\beta(2\sin\beta - 1)$
   e $\cos\phi(2 + 3\cos\phi)$ **f** $3\sin\theta(\sin\theta - 2)$
   g $(\sin\theta + 3)(\sin\theta + 2)$ **h** $(2\cos\theta + 1)(\cos\theta + 3)$
   i $(3\cos\alpha + 1)(2\cos\alpha - 1)$

5 **a** $1 + \sin\alpha$ **b** $\cos\beta - 1$ **c** $\cos\phi - \sin\phi$

   d $\cos\phi + \sin\phi$ **e** $\dfrac{1}{\sin\alpha - \cos\alpha}$ **f** $\dfrac{\cos\theta}{2}$

EXERCISE 13G.2

1 **a** 0 **b** $-2\sin\theta$ **c** $3\cos\theta$ **d** $4\sin\theta$ **e** $\cos^2\alpha$
   f $\sin^2\alpha$ **g** 1

2 **a** $\sin\theta$ **b** $-2\sin\theta$ **c** 0 **d** $-\cos\theta$ **e** $4\cos\theta$
   f $5\sin\theta$ **3** $\phi - \theta = -(\theta - \phi)$

EXERCISE 13H

1 **a** $\sin M\cos N + \cos M\sin N$ **b** $\cos T\cos S + \sin T\sin S$
   c $\sin\alpha\cos\beta - \cos\alpha\sin\beta$ **d** $\sin\phi\cos\theta + \cos\phi\sin\theta$
   e $\cos\alpha\cos\beta - \sin\alpha\sin\beta$ **f** $\cos 2\theta\cos\alpha + \sin 2\theta\sin\alpha$
   g $\sin\alpha\cos 2\beta - \cos\alpha\sin 2\beta$ **h** $\cos 3A\cos B - \sin 3A\sin B$
   i $\cos B\cos 2C + \sin B\sin 2C$

2 **a** $\cos\theta$ **b** $-\sin\theta$ **c** $\sin\alpha$ **d** $-\cos\alpha$ **e** $-\sin A$ **f** $-\sin\theta$

3 **a** $\frac{1}{2}\sin\theta + \frac{\sqrt{3}}{2}\cos\theta$ **b** $\frac{\sqrt{3}}{2}\sin\theta - \frac{1}{2}\cos\theta$

   c $-\frac{1}{\sqrt{2}}\sin\theta + \frac{1}{\sqrt{2}}\cos\theta$ **d** $-\frac{\sqrt{3}}{2}\sin\theta + \frac{1}{2}\cos\theta$

4 **a** $\cos\theta$ **b** $\sin 3A$ **c** $\sin(B - A)$ **d** $\cos(\alpha - \beta)$
   e $-\cos(\theta + \phi)$ **f** $2\sin(\alpha - \beta)$

5 **a** $\cos 2\alpha$ **b** $-\sin 3\phi$ **c** $\cos\beta$

8 **b** **i** $\frac{1}{2}\sin 4\theta + \frac{1}{2}\sin 2\theta$ **ii** $\frac{1}{2}\sin 7\alpha + \frac{1}{2}\sin 5\alpha$
   iii $\sin 6\beta + \sin 4\beta$ **iv** $2\sin 5\theta + 2\sin 3\theta$
   v $3\sin 7\alpha - 3\sin\alpha$ **vi** $\frac{1}{6}\sin 8A - \frac{1}{6}\sin 2A$

9 **b** **i** $\frac{1}{2}\cos 5\theta + \frac{1}{2}\cos 3\theta$ **ii** $\frac{1}{2}\cos 8\alpha + \frac{1}{2}\cos 6\alpha$
   iii $\cos 4\beta + \cos 2\beta$ **iv** $3\cos 8x + 3\cos 6x$
   v $\frac{3}{2}\cos 5P + \frac{3}{2}\cos 3P$ **vi** $\frac{1}{8}\cos 6x + \frac{1}{8}\cos 2x$

10 **b** **i** $\frac{1}{2}\cos 2\theta - \frac{1}{2}\cos 4\theta$ **ii** $\frac{1}{2}\cos 5\alpha - \frac{1}{2}\cos 7\alpha$
   iii $\cos 4\beta - \cos 6\beta$ **iv** $2\cos 3\theta - 2\cos 5\theta$
   v $5\cos 6A - 5\cos 10A$ **vi** $\frac{1}{10}\cos 4M - \frac{1}{10}\cos 10M$

11 $\sin A\cos A = \frac{1}{2}\sin 2A$ $\cos^2 A = \frac{1}{2}\cos 2A + \frac{1}{2}$
   $\sin^2 A = \frac{1}{2} - \frac{1}{2}\cos 2A$

12 **d** $\cos\left(\frac{S+D}{2}\right)\cos\left(\frac{S-D}{2}\right) = \frac{1}{2}\cos S + \frac{1}{2}\cos D$

e $\sin\left(\frac{S+D}{2}\right)\sin\left(\frac{S-D}{2}\right) = \frac{1}{2}\cos D - \frac{1}{2}\cos S$

13 **a** $2\sin 3x\cos 2x$ **b** $2\cos 5A\cos 3A$ **c** $-2\sin 2\alpha\sin\alpha$
   d $2\cos 4\theta\sin\theta$ **e** $-2\sin 4\alpha\sin 3\alpha$ **f** $2\sin 5\alpha\cos 2\alpha$
   g $2\sin 3B\sin B$ **h** $2\cos\left(x + \frac{h}{2}\right)\sin\left(\frac{h}{2}\right)$
   i $-2\sin\left(x + \frac{h}{2}\right)\sin\left(\frac{h}{2}\right)$

EXERCISE 13I

1 **a** $\frac{24}{25}$ **b** $-\frac{7}{25}$ **2** $-\frac{7}{9}$ **3** $\frac{1}{9}$

4 **a** $\cos\alpha = \frac{-\sqrt{5}}{3}$, $\sin 2\alpha = \frac{4\sqrt{5}}{9}$

   b $\sin\beta = \frac{-\sqrt{21}}{5}$, $\sin 2\beta = \frac{-4\sqrt{21}}{25}$ **5** **a** $\frac{1}{3}$ **b** $\frac{2\sqrt{2}}{3}$

6 **a** $\sin 2\alpha$ **b** $2\sin 2\alpha$ **c** $\frac{1}{2}\sin 2\alpha$ **d** $\cos 2\beta$ **e** $-\cos 2\phi$
   f $\cos 2N$ **g** $-\cos 2M$ **h** $\cos 2\alpha$ **i** $-\cos 2\alpha$
   j $\sin 4A$ **k** $\sin 6\alpha$ **l** $\cos 8\theta$ **m** $-\cos 6\beta$ **n** $\cos 10\alpha$
   o $-\cos 6D$ **p** $\cos 4A$ **q** $\cos\alpha$ **r** $-2\cos 6P$

EXERCISE 13J.1

1 **a** 0 **b** 0.27 **c** 0.36 **2** triangle TON is
   d 0.47 **e** 0.70 **f** 1 isosceles, ON = TN
   g 1.19 **h** 1.43

EXERCISE 13J.2

1 **a** **i** $y = \tan(x - \frac{\pi}{2})$

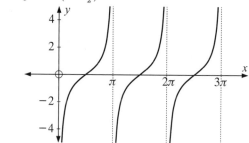

   ii $y = -\tan x$

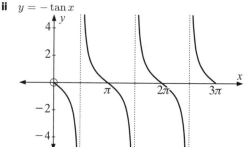

   iii $y = \tan 2x$

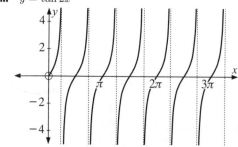

2 **a** translation through $\begin{bmatrix} 1 \\ 0 \end{bmatrix}$ **b** reflection in x-axis

   c horizontal dilation, factor $k = 2$

3 a i 1.6 **ii** −1.1 **b i** 1.557 **ii** −1.119
c i $x = 1.1, 4.2, 7.4$ **ii** $x = 2.2, 5.3$
4 a π **b** $\frac{\pi}{2}$ **c** $\frac{\pi}{n}$

EXERCISE 13K.1

1 $X \doteq 1.11 + k\pi$ **a** $x \doteq 0.554 + k\frac{\pi}{2}$
b $x \doteq 3.32 + k3\pi$ **c** $x \doteq -0.0929 + k\pi$
2 $X \doteq -1.25 + k\pi$ **a** $x \doteq 0.751 + k\pi$
b $x \doteq -0.416 + k\frac{\pi}{3}$ **c** $x \doteq -2.50 + k2\pi$
3 $X = \frac{\pi}{3} + k\pi$ **a** $x = \frac{\pi}{2} + k\pi$ **b** $x = \frac{\pi}{12} + k\frac{\pi}{4}$

c $x = \left.\begin{array}{c}\frac{\pi}{3} \\ -\frac{\pi}{3}\end{array}\right\} + k\pi$

EXERCISE 13K.2

1 a 0 **b** 1 **c** $\frac{1}{\sqrt{3}}$ **d** $\sqrt{3}$ **e** undefined **f** −1
g $-\sqrt{3}$ **h** undefined **i** $-\sqrt{3}$ **j** 1
2 a $\frac{\pi}{4}, \frac{5\pi}{4}$ **b** $\frac{3\pi}{4}, \frac{7\pi}{4}$ **c** $\frac{\pi}{3}, \frac{4\pi}{3}$ **d** $0, \pi, 2\pi$
e $\frac{\pi}{6}, \frac{7\pi}{6}$ **f** $\frac{2\pi}{3}, \frac{5\pi}{3}$
3 a $2\tan x$ **b** $-3\tan x$ **c** $\sin x$ **d** $\cos x$ **e** $5\sin x$ **f** $\frac{2}{\cos x}$
4 a $-\frac{1}{2\sqrt{2}}$ **b** $-2\sqrt{6}$ **c** $\frac{1}{\sqrt{2}}$ **d** $-\frac{\sqrt{7}}{3}$
5 a $\sin x = \frac{2}{\sqrt{13}}, \cos x = \frac{3}{\sqrt{13}}$ **b** $\sin x = \frac{4}{5}, \cos x = -\frac{3}{5}$
c $\sin x = -\sqrt{\frac{5}{14}}, \cos x = -\frac{3}{\sqrt{14}}$
d $\sin x = -\frac{12}{13}, \cos x = \frac{5}{13}$

EXERCISE 13L

1 a

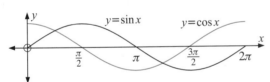

b $x = \frac{\pi}{4}$ or $\frac{5\pi}{4}$ **c** $x = \frac{\pi}{4}$ or $\frac{5\pi}{4}$
2 a $x = \frac{3\pi}{4}$ or $\frac{7\pi}{4}$ **b** $x = \frac{\pi}{12}, \frac{5\pi}{12}, \frac{3\pi}{4}, \frac{13\pi}{12}, \frac{17\pi}{12}, \frac{7\pi}{4}$
c $x = \frac{\pi}{6}, \frac{2\pi}{3}, \frac{7\pi}{6}, \frac{5\pi}{3}$
4 a $x \doteq 1.37, 4.51, 7.66$ **b** $x \doteq 2.50, 5.64, 8.78$

EXERCISE 13M

1 a $x = 0, \pi, \frac{7\pi}{6}, \frac{11\pi}{6}, 2\pi$ **b** $x = \frac{\pi}{3}, \frac{\pi}{2}, \frac{3\pi}{2}, \frac{5\pi}{3}$
c $x = \frac{\pi}{3}, \pi, \frac{5\pi}{3}$ **d** $x = \frac{7\pi}{6}, \frac{3\pi}{2}, \frac{11\pi}{6}$ **e** no solns.
f $x = 0.896$ or 2.246
2 a $x = 0, \frac{2\pi}{3}, \pi, \frac{4\pi}{3}, 2\pi$ **b** $x = \frac{\pi}{2}, \frac{3\pi}{2}$
c $x = 0, \frac{2\pi}{3}, \frac{4\pi}{3}, 2\pi$ **d** $x = \frac{\pi}{3}, \frac{5\pi}{3}$
e $x = 3.329, 6.096$ **f** $x = 0, \pi, 2\pi$

EXERCISE 13N

1 a $\csc x = \frac{5}{3}$, $\sec x = \frac{5}{4}$, $\cot x = \frac{4}{3}$
b $\csc x = -\frac{3}{\sqrt{5}}$, $\sec x = \frac{3}{2}$, $\cot x = -\frac{2}{\sqrt{5}}$
2 a $\frac{2}{\sqrt{3}}$ **b** $-\frac{1}{\sqrt{3}}$ **c** $-\frac{2}{\sqrt{3}}$ **d** undefined
3 a $\sin x = -\frac{\sqrt{7}}{4}$, $\tan x = -\frac{\sqrt{7}}{3}$, $\csc x = -\frac{4}{\sqrt{7}}$,
$\sec x = \frac{4}{3}$, $\cot x = -\frac{3}{\sqrt{7}}$
b $\cos x = -\frac{\sqrt{5}}{3}$, $\tan x = \frac{2}{\sqrt{5}}$, $\csc x = -\frac{3}{2}$,
$\sec x = -\frac{3}{\sqrt{5}}$, $\cot x = \frac{\sqrt{5}}{2}$

c $\sin x = \frac{\sqrt{21}}{5}$, $\cos x = \frac{2}{5}$, $\tan x = \frac{\sqrt{21}}{2}$,
$\csc x = \frac{5}{\sqrt{21}}$, $\cot x = \frac{2}{\sqrt{21}}$
d $\sin x = \frac{1}{2}$, $\cos x = -\frac{\sqrt{3}}{2}$, $\tan x = -\frac{1}{\sqrt{3}}$,
$\sec x = -\frac{2}{\sqrt{3}}$, $\cot x = -\sqrt{3}$
e $\sin x = -\frac{1}{\sqrt{5}}$, $\cos x = -\frac{2}{\sqrt{5}}$, $\csc x = -\sqrt{5}$,
$\sec x = -\frac{\sqrt{5}}{2}$, $\cot x = 2$
f $\sin x = -\frac{3}{5}$, $\cos x = -\frac{4}{5}$, $\tan x = \frac{3}{4}$,
$\csc x = -\frac{5}{3}$, $\sec x = -\frac{5}{4}$
4 a 1 **b** 1 **c** $\frac{\cos x}{\sin^2 x}$ **d** $\cos x$ **e** $\cos x$ **f** $5\sin x$
5 a

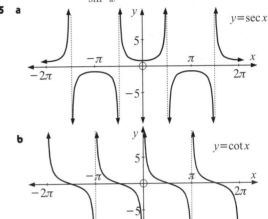

$y = \sec x$

b

$y = \cot x$

6 a $x = \frac{\pi}{3}, \frac{5\pi}{3}$ **b** $x = \frac{5\pi}{4}, \frac{7\pi}{4}$ **c** $x = 0.245, 3.387$
d no solutions **e** no solutions
f $x = 0.232, 1.803, 3.373, 4.944$

EXERCISE 13O

1 a $\frac{1 - \sin^n x}{1 - \sin x}$ **b** $\frac{1}{1 - \sin x}$ as $-1 \leqslant \sin x \leqslant 1$
c $\frac{7\pi}{6}$ or $\frac{11\pi}{6}$
2 b i $\sin 8x$ **ii** $\frac{\sin 20x}{2\sin x}$ **c** $\frac{\sin 2nx}{2\sin x}$
3 b i $\frac{\sin(2^4 x)}{2^4}$ **ii** $\frac{\sin(2^6 x)}{2^6}$
c $\sin x \cos x \cos 2x \ldots \ldots \cos 2^n x = \frac{\sin(2^{n+1}x)}{2^{n+1}}$
4 b $\frac{\sin 32\theta}{2\sin \theta}$ **5** 0

REVIEW SET 13A

1

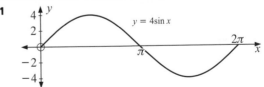

$y = 4\sin x$

2

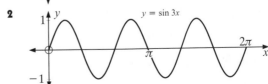

$y = \sin 3x$

3 a 6π **4**

b $\frac{\pi}{2}$

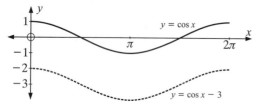

$y = \sin\left(x - \frac{\pi}{3}\right) + 2$

5 $T \doteq 7.05 \sin \frac{\pi}{6}(t - 4.5) + 24.75$

6 a $x \doteq 0.392, 2.75, 6.675$ **b** $x \doteq 7.235$

7 a $x \doteq 3.25, 4.69$ **b** $x \doteq 1.445, 5.89, 7.73$

8 a $x = \frac{7\pi}{6}, \frac{11\pi}{6}, \frac{19\pi}{6}, \frac{23\pi}{6}$ **b** $x = \frac{-7\pi}{4}, \frac{-5\pi}{4}, \frac{\pi}{4}, \frac{3\pi}{4}$

9 a $x = \frac{4\pi}{9}, \frac{5\pi}{9}, \frac{10\pi}{9}, \frac{11\pi}{9}, \frac{16\pi}{9}, \frac{17\pi}{9}$ **b** $x = \frac{3\pi}{4}, \frac{7\pi}{4}, \frac{11\pi}{4}$

10 a 5000 **b** 3000, 7000

c $0.5 < t < 2.5$ and $6.5 < t < 8$

REVIEW SET 13B

1 a $x = \frac{3\pi}{2} + k2\pi$ **b** $x = \left.\begin{array}{c}\frac{\pi}{6}\\\frac{5\pi}{6}\end{array}\right\} + k\pi$

2 a

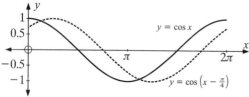

$y = \cos x$

$y = \cos x - 3$

b

$y = \cos x$

$y = \cos\left(x - \frac{\pi}{4}\right)$

c

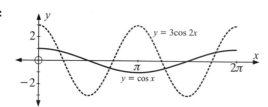

$y = 3\cos 2x$

$y = \cos x$

d

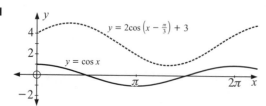

$y = 2\cos\left(x - \frac{\pi}{3}\right) + 3$

$y = \cos x$

3 a 28 milligrams per m³ **b** 8.00 am Monday

4 a $y = -4\cos 2x$ **b** $y = \cos \frac{\pi}{4}x + 2$

5 a $x \doteq 1.12, 5.17, 7.40$ **b** $x \doteq 0.184, 4.616$

6 a $x = \left.\begin{array}{c}0.317\\1.254\end{array}\right\} + k\frac{\pi}{2}$ **b** $x \doteq 0.912, 2.23, 4.05$

7 a $x = \frac{3\pi}{4}, \frac{5\pi}{4}, \frac{11\pi}{4}, \frac{13\pi}{4}$ **b** $x = -\pi, -\frac{\pi}{3}, \pi, \frac{5\pi}{3}$

8 a $x = 0, \frac{3\pi}{2}, 2\pi, \frac{7\pi}{2}, 4\pi$ **b** $x = \left.\begin{array}{c}\frac{\pi}{6}\\\frac{5\pi}{6}\end{array}\right\} + k\pi$

9 a $\cos\theta$ **b** $-\sin\theta$ **c** $2\cos\theta$ **d** $5\cos^2\theta$ **e** $-\cos\theta$

10 a $4\sin^2\alpha - 4\sin\alpha + 1$ **b** $1 - \sin 2\alpha$

EXERCISE 14A

1 a 1×4 **b** 2×1 **c** 2×2 **d** 3×3

2 a $\begin{bmatrix} 2 & 1 & 6 & 1 \end{bmatrix}$ **b** $\begin{bmatrix} 1.95 \\ 2.35 \\ 0.15 \\ 0.95 \end{bmatrix}$ **c** total cost of groceries

3 $\begin{bmatrix} 1000 & 1500 & 1250 \\ 1500 & 1000 & 1000 \\ 800 & 2300 & 1300 \\ 1200 & 1200 & 1200 \end{bmatrix}$ **4** $\begin{bmatrix} 40 & 50 & 55 & 40 \\ 25 & 65 & 44 & 30 \\ 35 & 40 & 40 & 35 \\ 35 & 40 & 35 & 50 \end{bmatrix}$

EXERCISE 14B

1 a $\begin{bmatrix} 9 & 1 \\ 3 & 3 \end{bmatrix}$ **b** $\begin{bmatrix} 6 & 8 \\ -1 & 1 \end{bmatrix}$ **c** $\begin{bmatrix} 3 & 4 \\ -6 & -1 \end{bmatrix}$ **d** $\begin{bmatrix} 0 & 0 \\ -11 & -3 \end{bmatrix}$

2 a $\begin{bmatrix} 20 & 1 & -8 \\ 8 & 10 & -2 \\ 1 & -5 & 18 \end{bmatrix}$ **b** $\begin{bmatrix} -14 & 9 & -14 \\ 12 & -6 & 14 \\ -5 & 3 & -4 \end{bmatrix}$ **c** $\begin{bmatrix} 14 & -9 & 14 \\ -12 & 6 & -14 \\ 5 & -3 & 4 \end{bmatrix}$

3 a Friday $\begin{bmatrix} 85 \\ 92 \\ 52 \end{bmatrix}$ Saturday $\begin{bmatrix} 102 \\ 137 \\ 49 \end{bmatrix}$ **b** $\begin{bmatrix} 187 \\ 229 \\ 101 \end{bmatrix}$

4 a i $\begin{bmatrix} 1.72 \\ 27.85 \\ 0.92 \\ 2.53 \\ 3.56 \end{bmatrix}$ **ii** $\begin{bmatrix} 1.79 \\ 28.75 \\ 1.33 \\ 2.25 \\ 3.51 \end{bmatrix}$ **b** subtract cost price from selling price **c** $\begin{bmatrix} 0.07 \\ 0.90 \\ 0.41 \\ -0.28 \\ -0.05 \end{bmatrix}$

5 a $\begin{array}{cc} \text{L} & \text{R} \end{array}$ $\begin{bmatrix} 23 & 19 \\ 17 & 29 \\ 31 & 24 \end{bmatrix} \begin{array}{l} \text{fr} \\ \text{st} \\ \text{mi} \end{array}$ **b** $\begin{array}{cc} \text{L} & \text{R} \end{array}$ $\begin{bmatrix} 18 & 25 \\ 7 & 13 \\ 36 & 19 \end{bmatrix} \begin{array}{l} \text{fr} \\ \text{st} \\ \text{mi} \end{array}$ **c** $\begin{array}{cc} \text{L} & \text{R} \end{array}$ $\begin{bmatrix} 41 & 44 \\ 24 & 42 \\ 67 & 43 \end{bmatrix} \begin{array}{l} \text{fr} \\ \text{st} \\ \text{mi} \end{array}$

6 a $x = -2, y = -2$ **b** $x = 0, y = 0$

7 a $\mathbf{A} + \mathbf{B} = \begin{bmatrix} 1 & 3 \\ 5 & 2 \end{bmatrix}$ $\mathbf{B} + \mathbf{A} = \begin{bmatrix} 1 & 3 \\ 5 & 2 \end{bmatrix}$

8 a $(\mathbf{A} + \mathbf{B}) + \mathbf{C} = \begin{bmatrix} 6 & 3 \\ -1 & 6 \end{bmatrix}$ $\mathbf{A} + (\mathbf{B} + \mathbf{C}) = \begin{bmatrix} 6 & 3 \\ -1 & 6 \end{bmatrix}$

EXERCISE 14C

1 a $\begin{bmatrix} 12 & 24 \\ 48 & 12 \end{bmatrix}$ **b** $\begin{bmatrix} 2 & 4 \\ 8 & 2 \end{bmatrix}$ **c** $\begin{bmatrix} \frac{1}{2} & 1 \\ 2 & \frac{1}{2} \end{bmatrix}$ **d** $\begin{bmatrix} -3 & -6 \\ -12 & -3 \end{bmatrix}$

2 a $\begin{bmatrix} 3 & 5 & 6 \\ 2 & 8 & 7 \end{bmatrix}$ **b** $\begin{bmatrix} 1 & 1 & 4 \\ 0 & 4 & 1 \end{bmatrix}$ **c** $\begin{bmatrix} 5 & 8 & 11 \\ 3 & 14 & 11 \end{bmatrix}$ **d** $\begin{bmatrix} 5 & 7 & 14 \\ 2 & 16 & 9 \end{bmatrix}$

3 a $\begin{array}{cccc} \text{A} & \text{B} & \text{C} & \text{D} \end{array}$ $\begin{bmatrix} 35 & 46 & 46 & 69 \\ 58 & 46 & 35 & 86 \\ 46 & 46 & 58 & 58 \\ 12 & 23 & 23 & 17 \end{bmatrix}$ **b** $\begin{array}{cccc} \text{A} & \text{B} & \text{C} & \text{D} \end{array}$ $\begin{bmatrix} 26 & 34 & 34 & 51 \\ 43 & 34 & 26 & 64 \\ 34 & 34 & 43 & 43 \\ 9 & 17 & 17 & 13 \end{bmatrix}$

4 a $\begin{bmatrix} 75 \\ 27 \\ 102 \end{bmatrix} \begin{array}{l} \leftarrow \text{VHS} \\ \leftarrow \text{DVD} \\ \leftarrow \text{gam.} \end{array}$ $\begin{bmatrix} 136 \\ 43 \\ 129 \end{bmatrix} \begin{array}{l} \leftarrow \text{VHS} \\ \leftarrow \text{DVD} \\ \leftarrow \text{gam.} \end{array}$ **b** $\begin{bmatrix} 211 \\ 70 \\ 231 \end{bmatrix} \begin{array}{l} \leftarrow \text{VHS} \\ \leftarrow \text{DVD} \\ \leftarrow \text{gam.} \end{array}$

c total weekly average hirings **5** 12F

EXERCISE 14D

1 a $3\mathbf{A}$ **b** $\mathbf{O}$ **c** $-\mathbf{C}$ **d** $\mathbf{O}$ **e** $2\mathbf{A} + 2\mathbf{B}$
f $-\mathbf{A} - \mathbf{B}$ **g** $-2\mathbf{A} + \mathbf{C}$ **h** $4\mathbf{A} - \mathbf{B}$ **i** $3\mathbf{B}$

2 a $\mathbf{X} = \mathbf{A} - \mathbf{B}$ **b** $\mathbf{X} = \mathbf{C} - \mathbf{B}$ **c** $\mathbf{X} = 2\mathbf{C} - 4\mathbf{B}$
d $\mathbf{X} = \frac{1}{2}\mathbf{A}$ **e** $\mathbf{X} = \frac{1}{3}\mathbf{B}$ **f** $\mathbf{X} = \mathbf{A} - \mathbf{B}$
g $\mathbf{X} = 2\mathbf{C}$ **h** $\mathbf{X} = \frac{1}{2}\mathbf{B} - \mathbf{A}$ **i** $\mathbf{X} = \frac{1}{4}(\mathbf{A} - \mathbf{C})$

3 a $\mathbf{X} = \begin{bmatrix} 3 & 6 \\ 9 & 18 \end{bmatrix}$ **b** $\mathbf{X} = \begin{bmatrix} \frac{1}{2} & -\frac{1}{4} \\ \frac{3}{4} & \frac{5}{4} \end{bmatrix}$ **c** $\mathbf{X} = \begin{bmatrix} -1 & -6 \\ 1 & -\frac{1}{2} \end{bmatrix}$

EXERCISE 14E.1

1 a $[11]$ **b** $[22]$ **c** $[16]$ **2** $\begin{bmatrix} w & x & y & z \end{bmatrix} \begin{bmatrix} \frac{1}{4} \\ \frac{1}{4} \\ \frac{1}{4} \\ \frac{1}{4} \end{bmatrix}$

3 a $\mathbf{P} = \begin{bmatrix} 27 & 35 & 39 \end{bmatrix}$ $\mathbf{Q} = \begin{bmatrix} 4 \\ 3 \\ 2 \end{bmatrix}$

b total cost $= \begin{bmatrix} 27 & 35 & 39 \end{bmatrix} \begin{bmatrix} 4 \\ 3 \\ 2 \end{bmatrix} = \$291$

4 a $\mathbf{P} = \begin{bmatrix} 10 & 6 & 3 & 1 \end{bmatrix}$ $\mathbf{N} = \begin{bmatrix} 3 \\ 2 \\ 4 \\ 2 \end{bmatrix}$

b total points $= \begin{bmatrix} 10 & 6 & 3 & 1 \end{bmatrix} \begin{bmatrix} 3 \\ 2 \\ 4 \\ 2 \end{bmatrix} = 56$ points

EXERCISE 14E.2

1 Number of cols. in A does not equal no. of rows in B.

2 a $m = n$ **b** 2×3 **c** B has 3 columns, A has 2 rows

3 a $\begin{bmatrix} 28 & 29 \end{bmatrix}$ **b i** $\begin{bmatrix} 8 \end{bmatrix}$ **ii** $\begin{bmatrix} 2 & 0 & 3 \\ 8 & 0 & 12 \\ 4 & 0 & 6 \end{bmatrix}$

4 a $\begin{bmatrix} 3 & 5 & 3 \end{bmatrix}$ **b** $\begin{bmatrix} -2 \\ 1 \\ 1 \end{bmatrix}$

5 a $\mathbf{C} = \begin{bmatrix} 12.5 \\ 9.5 \end{bmatrix}$ $\mathbf{N} = \begin{bmatrix} 2375 & 5156 \\ 2502 & 3612 \end{bmatrix}$

b $\begin{bmatrix} 78\,669.5 \\ 65\,589 \end{bmatrix}$ income from adult rides **c** $\$144\,258.50$ and children's rides

6 a $\mathbf{R} = \begin{bmatrix} 1 & 1 \\ 1 & 2 \\ 2 & 3 \end{bmatrix}$ **b** $\mathbf{P} = \begin{bmatrix} 7 & 3 & 19 \\ 6 & 2 & 22 \end{bmatrix}$ **c** $\begin{bmatrix} 48 & 70 \\ 52 & 76 \end{bmatrix}$

d My costs at store A are \$48, my friend's costs at store B are \$76. **e** store A

EXERCISE 14F

1 a $\begin{bmatrix} 16 & 18 & 15 \\ 13 & 21 & 16 \\ 10 & 22 & 24 \end{bmatrix}$ **b** $\begin{bmatrix} 10 & 6 & -7 \\ 9 & 3 & 0 \\ 4 & -4 & -10 \end{bmatrix}$

c $\begin{bmatrix} 22 & 0 & 132 & 176 & 198 \\ 44 & 154 & 88 & 110 & 0 \\ 176 & 44 & 88 & 88 & 132 \end{bmatrix}$ **d** $\begin{bmatrix} 115 \\ 136 \\ 46 \\ 106 \end{bmatrix}$

2 a $\begin{bmatrix} 3 & 3 & 2 \end{bmatrix}$ **b** $\begin{bmatrix} 125 & 150 & 140 \\ 44 & 40 & 40 \\ 75 & 80 & 65 \end{bmatrix}$ **c** $\begin{bmatrix} 657 & 730 & 670 \end{bmatrix}$

d $\begin{bmatrix} 369 & 420 & 385 \end{bmatrix}$ **e** $\begin{bmatrix} 657 & 730 & 670 \\ 369 & 420 & 385 \end{bmatrix}$

3 $\$224\,660$

4 a $\begin{bmatrix} 125 & 195 & 225 \end{bmatrix} \times \begin{bmatrix} 15 & 12 & 13 & 11 & 14 & 16 & 8 \\ 4 & 3 & 6 & 2 & 0 & 4 & 7 \\ 3 & 1 & 4 & 4 & 3 & 2 & 0 \end{bmatrix}$

$\qquad - \begin{bmatrix} 85 & 120 & 130 \end{bmatrix} \times \begin{bmatrix} 15 & 12 & 13 & 11 & 14 & 16 & 8 \\ 4 & 3 & 6 & 2 & 0 & 4 & 7 \\ 3 & 1 & 4 & 4 & 3 & 2 & 0 \end{bmatrix}$

$\qquad = \$7125$

b $\begin{bmatrix} 125 & 195 & 225 \end{bmatrix} \times \begin{bmatrix} 15 & 12 & 13 & 11 & 14 & 16 & 8 \\ 4 & 3 & 6 & 2 & 0 & 4 & 7 \\ 3 & 1 & 4 & 4 & 3 & 2 & 0 \end{bmatrix}$

$\qquad - \begin{bmatrix} 85 & 120 & 130 \end{bmatrix} \times \begin{bmatrix} 20 & 20 & 20 & 20 & 20 & 20 & 20 \\ 15 & 15 & 15 & 15 & 15 & 15 & 15 \\ 5 & 5 & 5 & 5 & 5 & 5 & 5 \end{bmatrix}$

$\qquad = -\$9030$, i.e., a loss of \$9030

c $(\begin{bmatrix} 125 & 195 & 225 \end{bmatrix} - \begin{bmatrix} 85 & 120 & 130 \end{bmatrix})$

$\qquad \times \begin{bmatrix} 15 & 12 & 13 & 11 & 14 & 16 & 8 \\ 4 & 3 & 6 & 2 & 0 & 4 & 7 \\ 3 & 1 & 4 & 4 & 3 & 2 & 0 \end{bmatrix}$

EXERCISE 14G

1 $\mathbf{AB} = \begin{bmatrix} -1 & 1 \\ -1 & 7 \end{bmatrix}$ $\mathbf{BA} = \begin{bmatrix} 0 & 2 \\ 3 & 6 \end{bmatrix}$ $\mathbf{AB} \neq \mathbf{BA}$

2 $\mathbf{AO} = \mathbf{OA} = \mathbf{O}$ **4 b** $\mathbf{I} = \begin{bmatrix} 1 & 0 \\ 0 & 1 \end{bmatrix}$

5 a $\begin{bmatrix} 7 & 0 \\ 0 & 7 \end{bmatrix}$ **b** $\begin{bmatrix} 97 & -59 \\ 118 & 38 \end{bmatrix}$

6 a $\mathbf{A}^2$ does not exist **b** when $\mathbf{A}$ is a square matrix

8 a $\mathbf{A}^2 + \mathbf{A}$ **b** $\mathbf{B}^2 + 2\mathbf{B}$ **c** $\mathbf{A}^3 - 2\mathbf{A}^2 + \mathbf{A}$
d $\mathbf{A}^3 + \mathbf{A}^2 - 2\mathbf{A}$ **e** $\mathbf{AC} + \mathbf{AD} + \mathbf{BC} + \mathbf{BD}$
f $\mathbf{A}^2 + \mathbf{AB} + \mathbf{BA} + \mathbf{B}^2$ **g** $\mathbf{A}^2 - \mathbf{AB} + \mathbf{BA} - \mathbf{B}^2$
h $\mathbf{A}^2 + 2\mathbf{A} + \mathbf{I}$ **i** $9\mathbf{I} - 6\mathbf{B} + \mathbf{B}^2$

9 a $\mathbf{A}^3 = 3\mathbf{A} - 2\mathbf{I}$ $\mathbf{A}^4 = 4\mathbf{A} - 3\mathbf{I}$
b $\mathbf{B}^3 = 3\mathbf{B} - 2\mathbf{I}$ $\mathbf{B}^4 = 6\mathbf{I} - 5\mathbf{B}$ $\mathbf{B}^5 = 11\mathbf{B} - 10\mathbf{I}$
c $\mathbf{C}^3 = 13\mathbf{C} - 12\mathbf{I}$ $\mathbf{C}^5 = 121\mathbf{C} - 120\mathbf{I}$

10 a i $\mathbf{I} + 2\mathbf{A}$ **ii** $2\mathbf{I} - 2\mathbf{A}$ **iii** $10\mathbf{A} + 6\mathbf{I}$
b $\mathbf{A}^2 + \mathbf{A} + 2\mathbf{I}$ **c i** $-3\mathbf{A}$ **ii** $-2\mathbf{A}$ **iii** $\mathbf{A}$

11 a $\mathbf{AB} = \begin{bmatrix} 0 & 0 \\ 0 & 0 \end{bmatrix}$ **b** $\mathbf{A}^2 = \begin{bmatrix} \frac{1}{2} & \frac{1}{2} \\ \frac{1}{2} & \frac{1}{2} \end{bmatrix}$

c false as $\mathbf{A}(\mathbf{A} - \mathbf{I}) = \mathbf{O}$ does not imply that $\mathbf{A} = \mathbf{O}$ or $\mathbf{A} - \mathbf{I} = \mathbf{O}$

d $\begin{bmatrix} 0 & 0 \\ 0 & 0 \end{bmatrix}, \begin{bmatrix} 1 & 0 \\ 0 & 1 \end{bmatrix}, \begin{bmatrix} a & b \\ \frac{a-a^2}{b} & 1-a \end{bmatrix}, b \neq 0$

12 For example, $\mathbf{A} = \begin{bmatrix} 0 & 1 \\ 0 & 0 \end{bmatrix}$, gives $\mathbf{A}^2 = \begin{bmatrix} 0 & 0 \\ 0 & 0 \end{bmatrix}$

13 a $a = 3, b = -4$ **b** $a = 1, b = 8$
14 $p = -2, q = 1$ **a** $\mathbf{A}^3 = 5\mathbf{A} - 2\mathbf{I}$ **b** $\mathbf{A}^4 = -12\mathbf{A} + 5\mathbf{I}$

EXERCISE 14H

1 a $\begin{bmatrix} 3 & 0 \\ 0 & 3 \end{bmatrix} = 3\mathbf{I}$, $\begin{bmatrix} 1 & -2 \\ -\frac{2}{3} & \frac{5}{3} \end{bmatrix}$

b $\begin{bmatrix} 10 & 0 \\ 0 & 10 \end{bmatrix} = 10\mathbf{I}$, $\begin{bmatrix} 0.2 & 0.4 \\ -0.1 & 0.3 \end{bmatrix}$

c $\begin{bmatrix} 2 & 0 & 0 \\ 0 & 2 & 0 \\ 0 & 0 & 2 \end{bmatrix} = 2\mathbf{I}$, $\begin{bmatrix} -\frac{11}{2} & \frac{9}{2} & \frac{15}{2} \\ -\frac{1}{2} & \frac{1}{2} & \frac{1}{2} \\ 4 & -3 & -5 \end{bmatrix}$

2 a -2 **b** -1 **c** 0 **d** 1

3 a 26 **b** 6 **c** -1 **d** $a^2 + a$

4 a -3 **b** 9 **c** -12 **5 Hint:** Let $A = \begin{bmatrix} a & b \\ c & d \end{bmatrix}$

6 a $|A| = ad - bc$ $|B| = wz - xy$

b $AB = \begin{bmatrix} aw + by & ax + bz \\ cw + dy & cx + dz \end{bmatrix}$ **c** $|AB| = (ad - bc)(wz - xy)$

7 a i -2 **ii** -8 **iii** -2 **iv** -9 **v** 2

8 a $\frac{1}{14}\begin{bmatrix} 5 & -4 \\ 1 & 2 \end{bmatrix}$ **b** $\begin{bmatrix} 1 & 0 \\ 1 & -1 \end{bmatrix}$ **c** does not exist **d** $\begin{bmatrix} 1 & 0 \\ 0 & 1 \end{bmatrix}$

e does not exist **f** $-\frac{1}{15}\begin{bmatrix} 7 & -2 \\ -4 & -1 \end{bmatrix}$ **g** $\frac{1}{10}\begin{bmatrix} 2 & -4 \\ 1 & 3 \end{bmatrix}$ **h** $\begin{bmatrix} -3 & -1 \\ 2 & 1 \end{bmatrix}$

EXERCISE 14I

1 a $\begin{bmatrix} 3 & -1 \\ 2 & 3 \end{bmatrix}\begin{bmatrix} x \\ y \end{bmatrix} = \begin{bmatrix} 8 \\ 6 \end{bmatrix}$ **b** $\begin{bmatrix} 4 & -3 \\ 3 & 2 \end{bmatrix}\begin{bmatrix} x \\ y \end{bmatrix} = \begin{bmatrix} 11 \\ -5 \end{bmatrix}$

c $\begin{bmatrix} 3 & -1 \\ 2 & 7 \end{bmatrix}\begin{bmatrix} a \\ b \end{bmatrix} = \begin{bmatrix} 6 \\ -4 \end{bmatrix}$

2 a $x = \frac{32}{7}, \ y = \frac{22}{7}$ **b** $x = -\frac{37}{23}, \ y = -\frac{75}{23}$

c $x = \frac{17}{13}, \ y = -\frac{37}{13}$ **d** $x = \frac{59}{13}, \ y = -\frac{25}{13}$

e $x = -40, \ y = -24$ **f** $x = \frac{1}{34}, \ y = \frac{55}{34}$

3 b i $X = \begin{bmatrix} -1 & 3 \\ 2 & 4 \end{bmatrix}$ **ii** $X = \begin{bmatrix} \frac{13}{7} & \frac{3}{7} \\ -\frac{2}{7} & -\frac{8}{7} \end{bmatrix}$

4 a i $k = -3$ **ii** $\frac{1}{2k+6}\begin{bmatrix} 2 & -1 \\ 6 & k \end{bmatrix}, \ k \neq -3$

b i $k = 0$ **ii** $\frac{1}{3k}\begin{bmatrix} k & 1 \\ 0 & 3 \end{bmatrix}, \ k \neq 0$

c i $k = -2$ or 1 **ii** $\frac{1}{(k+2)(k-1)}\begin{bmatrix} k & -2 \\ -1 & k+1 \end{bmatrix}, k \neq -2$ or 1

5 a $AB = \begin{bmatrix} 1 & 0 \\ 0 & 1 \end{bmatrix}$ **b** A and B are not inverses since they are not square matrices.

6 $X = \begin{bmatrix} \frac{1}{4} & \frac{3}{4} \\ 1 & 0 \end{bmatrix}$

7 a i $\begin{bmatrix} 2 & -3 \\ 4 & -1 \end{bmatrix}\begin{bmatrix} x \\ y \end{bmatrix} = \begin{bmatrix} 8 \\ 11 \end{bmatrix}, \ |A| = 10$

ii Yes, $x = 2.5, \ y = -1$

b i $\begin{bmatrix} 2 & k \\ 4 & -1 \end{bmatrix}\begin{bmatrix} x \\ y \end{bmatrix} = \begin{bmatrix} 8 \\ 11 \end{bmatrix}, \ |A| = -2 - 4k$

ii $k \neq -\frac{1}{2}, \ x = \frac{8 + 11k}{2 + 4k} \ \ y = \frac{5}{1 + 2k}$

iii $k = -\frac{1}{2}$, no solutions

8 b $\begin{bmatrix} 1 & 0 \\ 0 & 1 \end{bmatrix}, \begin{bmatrix} -1 & 0 \\ 0 & -1 \end{bmatrix}, \begin{bmatrix} 0 & 1 \\ 1 & 0 \end{bmatrix}, \begin{bmatrix} 0 & -1 \\ -1 & 0 \end{bmatrix}$

9 a $A^{-1} = \begin{bmatrix} 0 & -1 \\ \frac{1}{2} & \frac{1}{2} \end{bmatrix}, \ (A^{-1})^{-1} = \begin{bmatrix} 1 & 2 \\ -1 & 0 \end{bmatrix}$

b $(A^{-1})^{-1}(A^{-1}) = (A^{-1})(A^{-1})^{-1} = I$
c A^{-1} and $(A^{-1})^{-1}$ are inverses

10 a i $\begin{bmatrix} \frac{1}{3} & \frac{1}{3} \\ \frac{2}{3} & -\frac{1}{3} \end{bmatrix}$ **ii** $\begin{bmatrix} \frac{3}{2} & \frac{1}{2} \\ 1 & 0 \end{bmatrix}$ **iii** $\begin{bmatrix} \frac{5}{6} & \frac{1}{3} \\ \frac{1}{3} & \frac{1}{3} \end{bmatrix}$

iv $\begin{bmatrix} \frac{5}{6} & \frac{1}{6} \\ \frac{2}{3} & \frac{1}{3} \end{bmatrix}$ **v** $\begin{bmatrix} \frac{5}{6} & \frac{1}{6} \\ \frac{2}{3} & \frac{1}{3} \end{bmatrix}$ **vi** $\begin{bmatrix} \frac{5}{6} & \frac{1}{3} \\ \frac{1}{3} & \frac{1}{3} \end{bmatrix}$

c $(AB)^{-1} = B^{-1}A^{-1}$ and $(BA)^{-1} = A^{-1}B^{-1}$
d $(AB)(B^{-1}A^{-1}) = (B^{-1}A^{-1})(AB) = I$
    AB and $B^{-1}A^{-1}$ are inverses

11 $(kA)\left(\frac{1}{k}A^{-1}\right) = \left(\frac{1}{k}A^{-1}\right)(kA) = I$
    kA and $\frac{1}{k}A^{-1}$ are inverses

12 a $X = ABZ$ **b** $Z = B^{-1}A^{-1}X$

13 a $A^{-1} = 4I - A$ **b** $A^{-1} = 5I + A$ **c** $A^{-1} = \frac{3}{2}A - 2I$

14 $A^2 = 2A - I, \ A^{-1} = 2I - A$

16 If A^{-1} exists, i.e., $|A| \neq 0$.

EXERCISE 14J

1 a 41 **b** -8 **c** 0 **d** 6 **e** -6 **f** -12

2 a $x = 1$ or 5 **b** When $x = 1$ or 5, the matrix does not have an inverse.

3 a abc **b** 0 **c** $3abc - a^3 - b^3 - c^3$ **4** $k \neq -3$

5 for all values of k except $\frac{1}{2}$ or -9

6 a $k = \frac{5}{2}$ or 2 **b** $k = 1$ or $\dfrac{-1 \pm \sqrt{33}}{2}$

7 a $16,$

$\begin{bmatrix} -\frac{21}{16} & -\frac{17}{16} & \frac{5}{4} & \frac{11}{16} \\ -\frac{17}{16} & -\frac{29}{16} & \frac{5}{4} & \frac{15}{16} \\ \frac{5}{4} & \frac{5}{4} & -1 & -\frac{3}{4} \\ \frac{11}{16} & \frac{15}{16} & -\frac{3}{4} & -\frac{5}{16} \end{bmatrix}$

b $-34,$

$\begin{bmatrix} -\frac{1}{2} & \frac{1}{2} & -1 & \frac{3}{2} & -\frac{1}{2} \\ -\frac{15}{34} & \frac{1}{2} & -\frac{4}{17} & \frac{29}{34} & -\frac{23}{34} \\ -\frac{29}{34} & \frac{3}{2} & -\frac{61}{17} & \frac{149}{34} & -\frac{83}{34} \\ \frac{39}{34} & -\frac{3}{2} & \frac{58}{17} & -\frac{157}{34} & \frac{87}{34} \\ \frac{1}{17} & 0 & -\frac{4}{17} & \frac{6}{17} & -\frac{3}{17} \end{bmatrix}$

8 a $\begin{bmatrix} 1 & 2 & 1 & 1 & 1 \\ 2 & 1 & 2 & 1 & 1 \\ 1 & 2 & 3 & 1 & 1 \\ 2 & 2 & 1 & 1 & 3 \\ 3 & 3 & 5 & 2 & 2 \end{bmatrix}\begin{bmatrix} o \\ a \\ p \\ c \\ l \end{bmatrix} = \begin{bmatrix} 6.3 \\ 6.7 \\ 7.7 \\ 9.8 \\ 10.9 \end{bmatrix}$ **b** $|A| = 0$

c oranges 50 cents, apples 80 cents, pears 70 cents, cabbages \$2.00, lettuces \$1.50

EXERCISE 14K

1 a $\begin{bmatrix} \frac{5}{4} & \frac{3}{4} & -\frac{7}{4} \\ -\frac{1}{4} & -\frac{3}{4} & \frac{3}{4} \\ -\frac{3}{4} & -\frac{1}{4} & \frac{5}{4} \end{bmatrix}$ **b** $\begin{bmatrix} -5.5 & 4.5 & 7.5 \\ -0.5 & 0.5 & 0.5 \\ 4 & -3 & -5 \end{bmatrix}$

2 a $\begin{bmatrix} 0.050 & -0.011 & -0.066 \\ 0 & 000 & 0.014 & 0.028 \\ -0.030 & 0.039 & 0.030 \end{bmatrix}$ **b** $\begin{bmatrix} 1.596 & -0.996 & -0.169 \\ -3.224 & 1.925 & 0.629 \\ 2 & -1.086 & -0.396 \end{bmatrix}$

EXERCISE 14L

1 a $\begin{bmatrix} 1 & -1 & -1 \\ 1 & 1 & 3 \\ 9 & -1 & -3 \end{bmatrix}\begin{bmatrix} x \\ y \\ z \end{bmatrix} = \begin{bmatrix} 2 \\ 7 \\ -1 \end{bmatrix}$

b $\begin{bmatrix} 2 & 1 & -1 \\ 0 & 1 & 2 \\ 1 & -1 & 1 \end{bmatrix}\begin{bmatrix} x \\ y \\ z \end{bmatrix} = \begin{bmatrix} 3 \\ 6 \\ 13 \end{bmatrix}$

c $\begin{bmatrix} 1 & 1 & -1 \\ 1 & -1 & 1 \\ 2 & 1 & -3 \end{bmatrix}\begin{bmatrix} a \\ b \\ c \end{bmatrix} = \begin{bmatrix} 7 \\ 6 \\ -2 \end{bmatrix}$

2 $AB = I, \ a = 2, b = -1, c = 3$

3 $MN = 4I, \ u = -1, v = 3, w = 5$

4 a $x = 2.3, y = 1.3, z = -4.5$

b $x = -\frac{1}{3}, \ y = -\frac{95}{21}, \ z = \frac{2}{21}$

c $x = 2, \ y = 4, \ z = -1$

5 **a** $x = 2,\ y = -1,\ z = 5$ **b** $x = 4,\ y = -2,\ z = 1$
c $x = 4,\ y = -3,\ z = 2$ **d** $x = 4,\ y = 6,\ z = -7$
e $x = 3,\ y = 11,\ z = -7$
f $x \doteqdot 0.33,\ y \doteqdot 7.65,\ z \doteqdot 4.16$

6 **a** x represents the cost per football in dollars,
y represents the cost per baseball in dollars,
z represents the cost per basketball in dollars
b 12 basketballs

7 **a** $2x + 3y + 8z = 352$ **b** $x = 42,\ y = 28,\ z = 23$
$x + 5y + 4z = 274$ **c** \$1 201 000
$x + 2y + 11z = 351$

8 \$11.80 per kg

9 **a** $5p + 5q + 6r = 405$ **b** $p = 24,$
$15p + 20q + 6r = 1050$ $q = 27,$
$15p + 20q + 36r = 1800$ $r = 25$

10 **a** $a = 50\,000,\ b = 100\,000,\ c = 240\,000$ **b** yes
c $2003, \doteqdot \$284\,000,\ 2005, \doteqdot \$377\,000$

EXERCISE 14M.1

1 **a** $x = 2,\ y = -3$ **b** $x = -1,\ y = 5$ **c** $x = -2,\ y = -4$

2 **a** intersecting **b** parallel **c** intersecting
d coincident **e** intersecting **f** parallel

3 **a** The second equation is the same as the first when
divided throughout by 2. The lines are coincident.
b It gives no more information than the first. Gives the
same solutions for x and y.
c **i** when $x = t,\quad y = \dfrac{3 - t}{2},\quad t \in \mathcal{R}$
ii when $y = s,\quad x = 3 - 2s,\quad s \in \mathcal{R}$

4 **a** The system is inconsistent and so has no solutions.
The lines are parallel.
b The lines are coincident. Infinitely many solutions
exist of the form $x = t,\quad y = \dfrac{5 - 2t}{3},\quad t \in \mathcal{R}.$

5 **b** If $k \neq -4$, the system is inconsistent and so has no
solutions. If $k = 4$, the system has infinitely many
solutions of the form $x = t,\ y = 3t - 2,\ t \in R$.

6 **a** $\begin{bmatrix} 3 & -1 & | & 8 \\ 0 & 0 & | & k - 16 \end{bmatrix}$ **b** $k = 16$
c $x = t,\ y = 3t - 8,\ t \in \mathcal{R}$
d when $k \neq 16$

7 **a** $\begin{bmatrix} 4 & 8 & | & 1 \\ 0 & 2a + 8 & | & -21 \end{bmatrix}$ **b** $a \neq -4$
d When $a = -4$, last row is $0\ 0\ |\ -21$. So, the system
is inconsistent and $\therefore$ no solutions exist.

8 A unique solution for $m \neq 2$ or -2.
a $x = \dfrac{6}{m + 2},\quad y = \dfrac{6}{m + 2}$
b If $m = 2$, there are infinitely many solutions of the form
$x = t,\ y = 3 - t$ (t is real).
If $m = -2$, there are no solutions.

EXERCISE 14M.2

1 **a** $x = 2,\ y = -1,\ z = 5$ **b** $x = 4,\ y = -2,\ z = 1$
c $x = 4,\ y = -3,\ z = 2$

EXERCISE 14M.3

1 **a** $x = 1 + 2t,\ y = t,\ z = 0,\ t \in \mathcal{R}$
b no solution, system is inconsistent
c $x = \dfrac{1 - 5t}{3},\ y = t,\ z = \dfrac{1 - 2t}{3},\ t \in \mathcal{R}$
d no solution, system is inconsistent

2 **a** $\begin{bmatrix} 1 & 2 & 1 & | & 3 \\ 0 & -5 & 2 & | & -5 \\ 0 & 0 & 0 & | & k - 8 \end{bmatrix}$
b If $k \neq 8$, no solutions, if $k = 8$, infinitely many
solutions of the form $x = \dfrac{5 - 9t}{5},\ y = \dfrac{2t + 5}{5},$
$z = t$ (t is real).
c The last row does not enable us to solve for z.

3 **a** $\begin{bmatrix} 1 & 2 & -2 & | & 5 \\ 0 & -3 & 5 & | & -6 \\ 0 & 0 & k - 13 & | & -k + 13 \end{bmatrix}$
b If $k = 13$, infinitely many solutions of the form
$x = \dfrac{3 - 4t}{3},\ y = \dfrac{5t + 6}{3},\ z = t$ (t is real).
c If $k \neq 13$, $x = \dfrac{7}{3},\ y = \dfrac{1}{3},\ z = -1.$

4 **a** $\begin{bmatrix} 1 & 3 & 3 & | & a - 1 \\ 0 & -7 & -5 & | & 9 - 2a \\ 0 & 0 & a + 1 & | & a + 1 \end{bmatrix}$
b $x = \dfrac{19 - 6t}{7},\ y = \dfrac{-5t - 11}{7},\ z = t$ (t is real)
c $x = \frac{1}{7}a + 2,\quad y = \frac{2}{7}a - 2,\quad z = 1$

5 $\begin{bmatrix} 1 & 2 & m & | & -1 \\ 0 & -2(m+1) & 1 - m^2 & | & 1 + m \\ 0 & 0 & (m+1)(m+5) & | & -7(m+1) \end{bmatrix}$
a if $m = -5$, no solution
b if $m = -1$, infinitely many solutions
c if $m \neq -5$ or -1, unique solution

6 **a** $\begin{bmatrix} 1 & 3 & k & | & 2 \\ 0 & -(2+3k) & 3 - k^2 & | & -k \\ 0 & 0 & (3k+25)(k-1) & | & 6(k-1) \end{bmatrix}$
b $k = 1$, infinitely many solutions of the form
$x = \dfrac{7 - 11t}{5},\quad y = \dfrac{1 + 2t}{5},\quad z = t$ (t is real)
c $k = -\frac{25}{3}$ **d** $k \neq 1$ or $-\frac{25}{3}$

EXERCISE 14M.4

1 **a** $x = 2 - 2t,\ y = t,\ z = 3t + 1,\ t \in \mathcal{R}$
b $x = 18 - 5t,\ y = t,\ z = 7t - 22,\ t \in \mathcal{R}$ **c** no solution

2 $x = \dfrac{5t}{7},\ y = \dfrac{4t}{7},\ z = t,\ t \in \mathcal{R}$ $x = 5,\ y = 4,\ z = 7$

3 If $a \neq -\frac{2}{7}$, $x = y = z = 0$
If $a = -\frac{2}{7}$, $x = \dfrac{-7t}{5},\ y = \dfrac{3t}{5},\ z = t,\ t \in \mathcal{R}$

4 **c** $P(x) = -\dfrac{29}{9}x^2 + \dfrac{172}{9}x - \dfrac{71}{9}$ thousand \$
d Max. profit $= \$20\,448$ when producing 2966

EXERCISE 14N

1 **a** $\mathbf{M}^2 = \begin{bmatrix} 1 & 4 \\ 0 & 1 \end{bmatrix}$, $\mathbf{M}^3 = \begin{bmatrix} 1 & 6 \\ 0 & 1 \end{bmatrix}$, $\mathbf{M}^4 = \begin{bmatrix} 1 & 8 \\ 0 & 1 \end{bmatrix}$
b Conjecture is: $\mathbf{M}^n = \begin{bmatrix} 1 & 2n \\ 0 & 1 \end{bmatrix}$

2 **a** $\mathbf{A}^2 = \begin{bmatrix} 1 & 8 \\ 0 & 9 \end{bmatrix}$, $\mathbf{A}^3 = \begin{bmatrix} 1 & 26 \\ 0 & 27 \end{bmatrix}$, $\mathbf{A}^4 = \begin{bmatrix} 1 & 80 \\ 0 & 81 \end{bmatrix}$,
$\mathbf{A}^5 = \begin{bmatrix} 1 & 242 \\ 0 & 243 \end{bmatrix}$

b Conjecture is: $\mathbf{A}^n = \begin{bmatrix} 1 & 3^n - 1 \\ 0 & 3^n \end{bmatrix}$, $n \in Z^+$

d Yes as $\mathbf{A}^{-1} = \begin{bmatrix} 1 & -\frac{2}{3} \\ 0 & \frac{1}{3} \end{bmatrix}$.

3 a $\mathbf{P}^2 = \begin{bmatrix} 3 & 2 \\ -2 & -1 \end{bmatrix}$, $\mathbf{P}^3 = \begin{bmatrix} 4 & 3 \\ -3 & -2 \end{bmatrix}$, $\mathbf{P}^4 = \begin{bmatrix} 5 & 4 \\ -4 & -3 \end{bmatrix}$

b i $\mathbf{P}^n = \begin{bmatrix} n+1 & n \\ -n & 1-n \end{bmatrix}$ for all $n \in Z^+$

REVIEW SET 14A

1 a $\begin{bmatrix} 4 & 2 \\ -2 & 3 \end{bmatrix}$ **b** $\begin{bmatrix} 9 & 6 \\ 0 & -3 \end{bmatrix}$ **c** $\begin{bmatrix} -2 & 0 \\ 4 & -8 \end{bmatrix}$ **d** $\begin{bmatrix} 2 & 2 \\ 2 & -5 \end{bmatrix}$

e $\begin{bmatrix} -5 & -4 \\ -2 & 6 \end{bmatrix}$ **f** $\begin{bmatrix} 7 & 6 \\ 4 & -11 \end{bmatrix}$ **g** $\begin{bmatrix} -1 & 8 \\ 2 & -4 \end{bmatrix}$ **h** $\begin{bmatrix} 3 & 2 \\ -6 & -8 \end{bmatrix}$

i $\begin{bmatrix} \frac{1}{3} & \frac{2}{3} \\ 0 & -1 \end{bmatrix}$ **j** $\begin{bmatrix} 9 & 4 \\ 0 & 1 \end{bmatrix}$ **k** $\begin{bmatrix} -3 & -10 \\ 6 & 8 \end{bmatrix}$ **l** $\begin{bmatrix} \frac{1}{3} & \frac{2}{3} \\ \frac{1}{6} & \frac{1}{12} \end{bmatrix}$

2 a $a = 0$, $b = 5$, $c = 1$, $d = -4$
b $a = 2$, $b = -1$, $c = 3$, $d = 8$

3 a $\mathbf{Y} = \mathbf{B} - \mathbf{A}$ **b** $\mathbf{Y} = \frac{1}{2}(\mathbf{D} - \mathbf{C})$ **c** $\mathbf{Y} = \mathbf{A}^{-1}\mathbf{B}$
d $\mathbf{Y} = \mathbf{CB}^{-1}$ **e** $\mathbf{Y} = \mathbf{A}^{-1}(\mathbf{C} - \mathbf{B})$ **f** $\mathbf{Y} = \mathbf{B}^{-1}\mathbf{A}$

4 a $x = 0$, $y = -\frac{1}{2}$ **b** $x = \frac{12}{7}$, $y = \frac{13}{7}$ **c** $\mathbf{X} = \begin{bmatrix} -1 & 8 \\ -2 & 6 \end{bmatrix}$

d $\mathbf{X} = \begin{bmatrix} -\frac{1}{2} \\ \frac{3}{2} \end{bmatrix}$ **e** $\mathbf{X} = \begin{bmatrix} \frac{14}{3} \\ \frac{1}{3} \end{bmatrix}$ **f** $\mathbf{X} = \begin{bmatrix} \frac{1}{2} & \frac{3}{2} \\ \frac{3}{2} & -\frac{1}{2} \end{bmatrix}$

5 a $\begin{bmatrix} 4 & 8 \\ 0 & 2 \\ 6 & 4 \end{bmatrix}$ **b** $\begin{bmatrix} 1 & 2 \\ 0 & \frac{1}{2} \\ \frac{3}{2} & 1 \end{bmatrix}$ **c** $[\ 11 \ \ 12 \ ]$ **d** $\mathbf{BA}$ does not exist.

6 a $\begin{bmatrix} 4 & 2 \\ 2 & 4 \\ 3 & 4 \end{bmatrix}$ **b** $\begin{bmatrix} 2 & -2 \\ 0 & 4 \\ -1 & -2 \end{bmatrix}$ **c** $\begin{bmatrix} -\frac{3}{2} & 3 \\ \frac{1}{2} & -4 \\ 2 & \frac{7}{2} \end{bmatrix}$

7 unique solution if $k \neq \frac{3}{4}$, no solution if $k = \frac{3}{4}$

8 $x = 1$, $y = -2$, $z = -1$

9 a $-2a + 4b + c = -20$
$a + 3b + c = -10$
$\therefore\ a = 2 - t$, $b = -4 - 3t$, $c = 10t$ (t is real)
b There are three unknowns and only two pieces of information. **c** $x^2 + y^2 + 4x + 2y - 20 = 0$

10 When $k \neq 27$, there are no solutions.
When $k = 27$, there are infinite solutions of the form $x = 2 - t$, $y = 2t + 3$, $z = t$ (t is real).

11 $x = 3t$, $y = -7t$, $z = 2t$, t is real

REVIEW SET 14B

1 $\begin{bmatrix} 1 & 0 \\ 0 & 1 \end{bmatrix}$ **2 a** $[\ 10\ ]$ **b** $\begin{bmatrix} 4 & 3 & 2 \\ 8 & 6 & 4 \\ 0 & 0 & 0 \end{bmatrix}$ **c** $[\ 15 \ \ 18 \ \ 21\ ]$

d $\mathbf{CA}$ does not exist **e** $\begin{bmatrix} 5 \\ 7 \\ 5 \end{bmatrix}$

3 a $\begin{bmatrix} \frac{7}{2} & -4 \\ \frac{-5}{2} & 3 \end{bmatrix}$ **b** does not exist **c** $\begin{bmatrix} 1 & \frac{5}{3} \\ -2 & -\frac{11}{3} \end{bmatrix}$

4 b $2\mathbf{A} - \mathbf{I}$ **5** $\$56.30$ **6** $\mathbf{AB} = \mathbf{I}$, $\mathbf{BA} = \mathbf{I}$, $\mathbf{A}^{-1} = \mathbf{B}$

7 $x = 2$, $y = 1$, $z = 3$

8 $x = \dfrac{-13t - 1}{9}$, $y = \dfrac{20t + 14}{9}$, $z = t$, $t \in \mathcal{R}$

9 b when $m \neq \frac{14}{3}$

EXERCISE 15A.1

1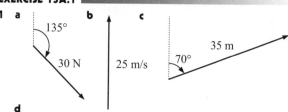

2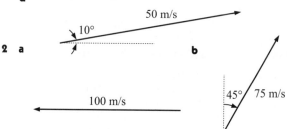

3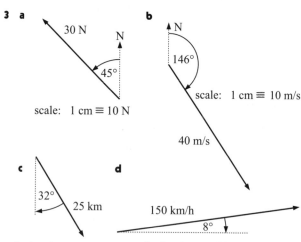

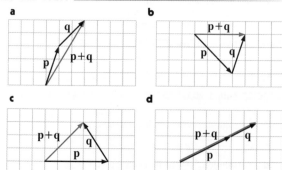

EXERCISE 15A.2

1 a p, q, s, t **b** p, q, r, t **c** p and r, q and t **d** q, t
e p and q, p and t

2 a true **b** true **c** false **d** false **e** true **f** false

EXERCISE 15B.1

1 a

![grid with vectors p, q, p+q]

b

![grid with vectors p, q, p+q]

c

![grid with vectors p, q, p+q]

d

![grid with vectors p, q, p+q]

e
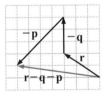

f
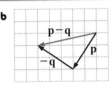

2 a $\overrightarrow{AC}$ **b** $\overrightarrow{BD}$ **c** $\overrightarrow{AD}$ **d** $\overrightarrow{AD}$

3 a i 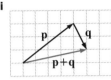 **ii**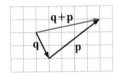

b yes

EXERCISE 15B.2

1 a **b**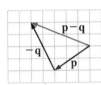

c 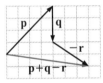 **d**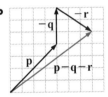

2 a **b**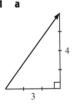

c

3 a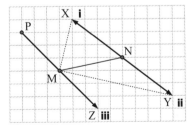

b a parallelogram

4 a $\overrightarrow{AB}$ **b** $\overrightarrow{AB}$ **c** 0 **d** $\overrightarrow{AD}$ **e** 0 **f** $\overrightarrow{AD}$

5 a $t = r + s$ **b** $r = -s - t$ **c** $r = -p - q - s$
d $r = q - p + s$ **e** $p = t + s + r - q$
f $p = -u + t + s - r - q$

6 a i $r + s$ **ii** $-t - s$ **iii** $r + s + t$
b i $p + q$ **ii** $q + r$ **iii** $p + q + r$

EXERCISE 15B.3

1 a **b**

c **d**

e 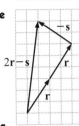 **f**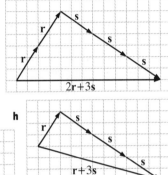

g **h**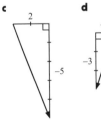

2 a 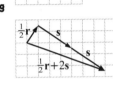 **b** **c** $p = 2q$
d $p = \frac{1}{3}q$ **e** $p = -3q$

EXERCISE 15C.1

1 a b c d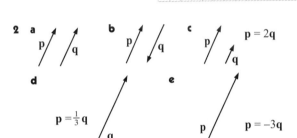

2 a $\begin{bmatrix} 7 \\ 3 \end{bmatrix}$ **b** $\begin{bmatrix} -6 \\ 0 \end{bmatrix}$ **c** $\begin{bmatrix} 2 \\ -5 \end{bmatrix}$ **d** $\begin{bmatrix} 0 \\ 6 \end{bmatrix}$ **e** $\begin{bmatrix} -6 \\ 3 \end{bmatrix}$ **f** $\begin{bmatrix} -5 \\ -5 \end{bmatrix}$

EXERCISE 15C.2

1 a $\begin{bmatrix} -2 \\ 6 \end{bmatrix}$ **b** $\begin{bmatrix} -2 \\ 6 \end{bmatrix}$ **c** $\begin{bmatrix} -1 \\ -1 \end{bmatrix}$ **d** $\begin{bmatrix} -1 \\ -1 \end{bmatrix}$ **e** $\begin{bmatrix} -5 \\ -3 \end{bmatrix}$
f $\begin{bmatrix} -5 \\ -3 \end{bmatrix}$ **g** $\begin{bmatrix} -6 \\ 4 \end{bmatrix}$ **h** $\begin{bmatrix} -4 \\ 1 \end{bmatrix}$

2 a $\begin{bmatrix} -3 \\ 7 \end{bmatrix}$ **b** $\begin{bmatrix} -4 \\ -3 \end{bmatrix}$ **c** $\begin{bmatrix} -8 \\ -1 \end{bmatrix}$ **d** $\begin{bmatrix} -6 \\ 9 \end{bmatrix}$ **e** $\begin{bmatrix} 0 \\ -5 \end{bmatrix}$
f $\begin{bmatrix} 6 \\ -9 \end{bmatrix}$ **3 a** $\begin{bmatrix} -5 \\ 4 \end{bmatrix}$ **b** $\begin{bmatrix} 1 \\ 2 \end{bmatrix}$ **c** $\begin{bmatrix} 6 \\ -5 \end{bmatrix}$

EXERCISE 15C.3

1 a $\begin{bmatrix} -3 \\ -15 \end{bmatrix}$ **b** $\begin{bmatrix} -1 \\ 2 \end{bmatrix}$ **c** $\begin{bmatrix} 0 \\ 14 \end{bmatrix}$ **d** $\begin{bmatrix} 5 \\ -3 \end{bmatrix}$ **e** $\begin{bmatrix} \frac{5}{2} \\ \frac{11}{2} \end{bmatrix}$ **f** $\begin{bmatrix} -7 \\ 7 \end{bmatrix}$

g $\begin{bmatrix} 5 \\ 11 \end{bmatrix}$ **h** $\begin{bmatrix} 3 \\ \frac{17}{3} \end{bmatrix}$ **2 a** $\begin{bmatrix} 8 \\ -1 \end{bmatrix}$ **b** $\begin{bmatrix} 8 \\ -1 \end{bmatrix}$ **c** $\begin{bmatrix} 8 \\ -1 \end{bmatrix}$

EXERCISE 15C.4

1 a $\sqrt{13}$ units **b** $\sqrt{17}$ units **c** $5\sqrt{2}$ units **d** $\sqrt{10}$ units
  e $\sqrt{29}$ units

2 a $\sqrt{10}$ units **b** $2\sqrt{10}$ units **c** $2\sqrt{10}$ units **d** $3\sqrt{10}$ units
  e $3\sqrt{10}$ units **f** $2\sqrt{5}$ units **g** $8\sqrt{5}$ units **h** $8\sqrt{5}$ units
  i $\sqrt{5}$ units **j** $\sqrt{5}$ units

EXERCISE 15D

1 a

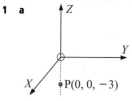

OP = 3 units

b P(0, −1, 2)

OP = $\sqrt{5}$ units

c

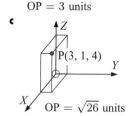

P(3, 1, 4)

OP = $\sqrt{26}$ units

d P(−1, −2, 3)

OP = $\sqrt{14}$ units

2 a i $\sqrt{14}$ units **ii** $(-\frac{1}{2}, \frac{1}{2}, 2)$ **b i** $\sqrt{14}$ units **ii** $(1, -\frac{1}{2}, \frac{3}{2})$
  c i $\sqrt{21}$ units **ii** $(1, -\frac{1}{2}, 0)$ **d i** $\sqrt{14}$ units **ii** $(1, \frac{1}{2}, -\frac{3}{2})$

4 a isosceles **b** right angled **c** right angled
  d straight line **5** (0, 3, 5), $r = \sqrt{3}$ units

6 a $(0, y, 0)$ **b** $(0, 2, 0)$ and $(0, -4, 0)$

EXERCISE 15E.1

1 a

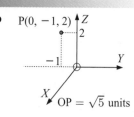

T(3, −1, 4)

b $\overrightarrow{OT} = \begin{bmatrix} 3 \\ -1 \\ 4 \end{bmatrix}$

c OT = $\sqrt{26}$ units

2 a $\overrightarrow{AB} = \begin{bmatrix} 4 \\ -1 \\ -3 \end{bmatrix}$, $\overrightarrow{BA} = \begin{bmatrix} -4 \\ 1 \\ 3 \end{bmatrix}$ **b** AB = $\sqrt{26}$ units
  BA = $\sqrt{26}$ units

3 $\overrightarrow{OA} = \begin{bmatrix} 3 \\ 1 \\ 0 \end{bmatrix}$, $\overrightarrow{OB} = \begin{bmatrix} -1 \\ 1 \\ 2 \end{bmatrix}$, $\overrightarrow{AB} = \begin{bmatrix} -4 \\ 0 \\ 2 \end{bmatrix}$

4 a $\overrightarrow{NM} = \begin{bmatrix} 5 \\ -4 \\ -1 \end{bmatrix}$ **b** $\overrightarrow{MN} = \begin{bmatrix} -5 \\ 4 \\ 1 \end{bmatrix}$ **c** MN = $\sqrt{42}$ units

5 a $\overrightarrow{OA} = \begin{bmatrix} -1 \\ 2 \\ 5 \end{bmatrix}$, OA = $\sqrt{30}$ units

b $\overrightarrow{AC} = \begin{bmatrix} -2 \\ -1 \\ -5 \end{bmatrix}$, AC = $\sqrt{30}$ units

c $\overrightarrow{CB} = \begin{bmatrix} 5 \\ -1 \\ 3 \end{bmatrix}$, CB = $\sqrt{35}$ units

6 a $\sqrt{13}$ units **b** $\sqrt{14}$ units **c** 3 units

EXERCISE 15E.2

1 a $a = 5$, $b = 6$, $c = -6$ **b** $a = 4$, $b = 2$, $c = 1$

2 a $a = \frac{1}{3}$, $b = 2$, $c = 1$ **b** $a = 1$, $b = 2$
  c $a = 1$, $b = -1$, $c = 2$

3 a $r = 2$, $s = 4$, $t = -7$ **b** $r = -4$, $s = 0$, $t = 3$

4 a $\overrightarrow{AB} = \begin{bmatrix} 2 \\ -5 \\ -1 \end{bmatrix}$, $\overrightarrow{DC} = \begin{bmatrix} 2 \\ -5 \\ -1 \end{bmatrix}$

  b ABCD is a parallelogram **5 a** S = $(-2, 8, -3)$

EXERCISE 15F

1 a $\mathbf{x} = \frac{1}{2}\mathbf{q}$ **b** $\mathbf{x} = 2\mathbf{n}$ **c** $\mathbf{x} = -\frac{1}{3}\mathbf{p}$ **d** $\mathbf{x} = \frac{1}{2}(\mathbf{r} - \mathbf{q})$
  e $\mathbf{x} = \frac{1}{5}(4\mathbf{s} - \mathbf{t})$ **f** $\mathbf{x} = 3(4\mathbf{m} - \mathbf{n})$

2 a $\mathbf{y} = \begin{bmatrix} -1 \\ \frac{3}{2} \end{bmatrix}$ **b** $\mathbf{y} = \begin{bmatrix} 2 \\ 4 \end{bmatrix}$ **c** $\mathbf{y} = \begin{bmatrix} \frac{3}{2} \\ -\frac{1}{2} \end{bmatrix}$ **d** $\mathbf{y} = \begin{bmatrix} \frac{5}{4} \\ \frac{3}{4} \end{bmatrix}$

4 a $\mathbf{x} = \begin{bmatrix} 4 \\ -6 \\ -5 \end{bmatrix}$ **b** $\mathbf{x} = \begin{bmatrix} 1 \\ -\frac{2}{3} \\ \frac{5}{3} \end{bmatrix}$ **c** $\mathbf{x} = \begin{bmatrix} \frac{3}{2} \\ -1 \\ \frac{5}{2} \end{bmatrix}$

5 $\overrightarrow{AB} = \begin{bmatrix} 3 \\ 4 \\ -2 \end{bmatrix}$, AB = $\sqrt{29}$ units

7 a $\overrightarrow{BD} = \frac{1}{2}\mathbf{a}$ **b** $\overrightarrow{AB} = \mathbf{b} - \mathbf{a}$ **c** $\overrightarrow{BA} = -\mathbf{b} + \mathbf{a}$
  d $\overrightarrow{OD} = \mathbf{b} + \frac{1}{2}\mathbf{a}$ **e** $\overrightarrow{AD} = \mathbf{b} - \frac{1}{2}\mathbf{a}$ **f** $\overrightarrow{DA} = \frac{1}{2}\mathbf{a} - \mathbf{b}$

8 a $\begin{bmatrix} -1 \\ 5 \\ -1 \end{bmatrix}$ **b** $\begin{bmatrix} -3 \\ 4 \\ -2 \end{bmatrix}$ **c** $\begin{bmatrix} -3 \\ 6 \\ -5 \end{bmatrix}$

9 a $\begin{bmatrix} 3 \\ 1 \\ -2 \end{bmatrix}$ **b** $\begin{bmatrix} 1 \\ -3 \\ 4 \end{bmatrix}$ **c** $\begin{bmatrix} 1 \\ 4 \\ -9 \end{bmatrix}$ **d** $\begin{bmatrix} 2 \\ -4 \\ 10 \end{bmatrix}$ **e** $\begin{bmatrix} 3 \\ 2 \\ -5 \end{bmatrix}$

  f $\begin{bmatrix} -1 \\ \frac{3}{2} \\ -\frac{7}{2} \end{bmatrix}$ **g** $\begin{bmatrix} 1 \\ -4 \\ 7 \end{bmatrix}$ **h** $\begin{bmatrix} 4 \\ 2 \\ -2 \end{bmatrix}$

10 a $\sqrt{11}$ units **b** $\sqrt{14}$ units **e** $\begin{bmatrix} \sqrt{11} \\ -3\sqrt{11} \\ 2\sqrt{11} \end{bmatrix}$ **f** $\begin{bmatrix} -\frac{1}{\sqrt{11}} \\ \frac{1}{\sqrt{11}} \\ \frac{3}{\sqrt{11}} \end{bmatrix}$
  c $\sqrt{38}$ units **d** $\sqrt{3}$ units

EXERCISE 15G

1 a M(1, 4) **b** $\overrightarrow{CA} = \begin{bmatrix} 7 \\ 5 \end{bmatrix}$, $\overrightarrow{CM} = \begin{bmatrix} 5 \\ 3 \end{bmatrix}$, $\overrightarrow{CB} = \begin{bmatrix} 3 \\ 1 \end{bmatrix}$

2 a B(−1, 10) **b** B(−2, −9) **c** B(7, 4)

3 C(5, 1, −8), D(8, −1, −13), E(11, −3, −18)

4 a parallelogram **b** parallelogram **c** not parallelogram

5 a D(9, −1) **b** R(3, 1, 6) **c** X(2, −1, 0)

6 a $r = 2$, $s = -5$ **b** $r = 4$, $s = -1$

7 a $-7 : 2$ **b** $-1 : 2$

8 a $a = 7$, $b = -1$ **b** $a = -\frac{7}{2}$, $b = -\frac{21}{2}$

EXERCISE 15H

1 $r = 3$, $s = -9$ **3 a** $\begin{bmatrix} \frac{2}{3} \\ -\frac{1}{3} \\ -\frac{2}{3} \end{bmatrix}$ **b** $\begin{bmatrix} -\frac{4}{3} \\ -\frac{2}{3} \\ \frac{4}{3} \end{bmatrix}$

2 $a = -6$, $b = -4$

4 a $\overrightarrow{AB} \parallel \overrightarrow{CD}$, AB = 3 CD
  b $\overrightarrow{RS} \parallel \overrightarrow{KL}$, RS = $\frac{1}{2}$KL   opposite direction

c A, B and C are collinear and $AB = 2BC$
d A, B and C are collinear and $AC = 3BC$

5 **a** $\overrightarrow{PR} = \begin{bmatrix} -1 \\ -3 \\ 3 \end{bmatrix}$, $\overrightarrow{QS} = \begin{bmatrix} -2 \\ -6 \\ 6 \end{bmatrix}$ **b** $PR = \frac{1}{2}QS$

EXERCISE 15I

1 **a** $\begin{bmatrix} 1 \\ -1 \\ 1 \end{bmatrix}$, $\sqrt{3}$ units **b** $\begin{bmatrix} 3 \\ -1 \\ 1 \end{bmatrix}$, $\sqrt{11}$ units

c $\begin{bmatrix} 1 \\ 0 \\ -5 \end{bmatrix}$, $\sqrt{26}$ units **d** $\begin{bmatrix} 0 \\ \frac{1}{2} \\ \frac{1}{2} \end{bmatrix}$, $\frac{1}{\sqrt{2}}$ units

2 **a** $k = \pm 1$ **b** $k = \pm 1$ **c** $k = 0$ **d** $k = \pm\frac{\sqrt{11}}{4}$ **e** $k = \pm\frac{2}{3}$

3 **a** 5 units **b** $\sqrt{6}$ units **c** 3 units **d** $\doteq 6.12$ units

4 **a** $\frac{1}{\sqrt{5}}(i + 2j)$ **b** $\frac{1}{\sqrt{13}}(2i - 3k)$ **c** $\frac{1}{\sqrt{33}}(-2i - 5j - 2k)$

5 **a** $\frac{3}{\sqrt{5}}\begin{bmatrix} 2 \\ -1 \end{bmatrix}$ **b** $-\frac{2}{\sqrt{17}}\begin{bmatrix} -1 \\ -4 \end{bmatrix}$ **c** $\frac{6}{\sqrt{18}}\begin{bmatrix} -1 \\ 4 \\ 1 \end{bmatrix}$ **d** $-\frac{5}{3}\begin{bmatrix} -1 \\ -2 \\ -2 \end{bmatrix}$

EXERCISE 15J.1

1 **a** 7 **b** 22 **c** 29 **d** 66 **e** 52 **f** 3 **g** 5 **h** 1

2 **a** 2 **b** 2 **c** 14 **d** 14 **e** 4 **f** 4

3 **a** 1 **b** 1 **c** 0

5 **a** $t = 6$ **b** $t = -8$ **c** $t = 0$ or 2 **d** $t = -\frac{3}{2}$

6 **a** $t = -\frac{3}{2}$ **b** $t = -\frac{6}{7}$ **c** $t = \frac{-1 \pm \sqrt{5}}{2}$ **d** impossible

7 Show $a \bullet b = b \bullet c = a \bullet c = 0$ **8** **b** $t = -\frac{5}{6}$

9 $\overrightarrow{AB} \bullet \overrightarrow{AC} = 0$, $\therefore$ $\angle BAC$ is a right angle

10 **b** $AB = \sqrt{14}$ units, $BC = \sqrt{14}$ units, ABCD is a rhombus
c 0, the diagonals of a rhombus are perpendicular.

11 **a** $101.3°$ or $78.7°$ **b** $116.6°$ or $63.4°$
c $63.4°$ or $116.6°$ **d** $71.6°$ or $108.4°$

12 **a** 5 **b** -9

13 **a** $k\begin{bmatrix} -2 \\ 5 \end{bmatrix}$, $k \neq 0$ **b** $k\begin{bmatrix} -2 \\ 1 \end{bmatrix}$, $k \neq 0$ **c** $k\begin{bmatrix} 1 \\ 3 \end{bmatrix}$, $k \neq 0$

d $k\begin{bmatrix} 3 \\ 4 \end{bmatrix}$, $k \neq 0$ **e** $k\begin{bmatrix} 0 \\ 1 \end{bmatrix}$, $k \neq 0$

EXERCISE 15J.2

1 **a** -1 **b** $109.5°$ (acute $70.5°$) **c** $\begin{bmatrix} -\frac{1}{3} \\ -\frac{1}{3} \\ -\frac{1}{3} \end{bmatrix}$ **d** $\frac{1}{\sqrt{3}}$

2 $\angle ABC \doteq 62.5°$, the exterior angle $117.5°$

3 **a** $54.7°$ **b** $60°$ **c** $35.3°$

4 **a** $30.3°$ **b** $54.2°$ **5** **a** $M(\frac{3}{2}, \frac{5}{2}, \frac{3}{2})$ **b** $51.5°$

6 **a** $t = 0$ or -3 **b** $r = -2$, $s = 5$, $t = -4$

7 **a** $74.5°$ **b** $72.45°$

8 $a = \begin{bmatrix} 1 \\ 0 \\ 0 \end{bmatrix}$, $b = \begin{bmatrix} 0 \\ 1 \\ 0 \end{bmatrix}$, $c = \begin{bmatrix} 0 \\ 0 \\ 1 \end{bmatrix}$ will do
$a \bullet b = a \bullet c$, but $b \neq c$

10 **a** **Hint:** Square both sides.
b Consider the parallelogram. Find $\overrightarrow{AB}$ and $\overrightarrow{OC}$, etc.

11 -7

12 $a \bullet b$ is a scalar and so $a \bullet b \bullet c$ is a scalar 'dotted' with a vector which is meaningless.

EXERCISE 15K.1

1 **a** $[2, 5, 11]$ **b** $[2, 4, 1]$ **c** $-i - j - k$ **d** $i - 6j + 2k$

2 **a** $a \times b = [-11, -2, 5]$,
$a \bullet (a \times b) = 0 = b \bullet (a \times b)$
$a \times b$ is a vector perpendicular to both a and b

3 **a** $i \times i = 0$ $j \times j = 0$ $k \times k = 0$
b $i \times j = k$ $j \times i = -k$ $j \times k = i$ $k \times j = -i$
$i \times k = -j$ $k \times i = j$
$a \times a = 0$ $a \times b = -b \times a$

5 **a** $\begin{bmatrix} 1 \\ 4 \\ 2 \end{bmatrix}$ **b** 17 **c** 17

7 **a** $\begin{bmatrix} 2 \\ -1 \\ -1 \end{bmatrix}$ **b** $\begin{bmatrix} 0 \\ 5 \\ 0 \end{bmatrix}$ **c** $\begin{bmatrix} 2 \\ 4 \\ -1 \end{bmatrix}$ **d** $\begin{bmatrix} 2 \\ 4 \\ -1 \end{bmatrix}$

8 $a \times (b + c) = (a \times b) + (a \times c)$

11 **a** $a \times b$ **b** 0 **c** 0

12 **a** $k\begin{bmatrix} -4 \\ 1 \\ 3 \end{bmatrix}$ **b** $k\begin{bmatrix} 6 \\ 22 \\ -15 \end{bmatrix}$ **c** $(-i + j - 2k)n$

d $(5i + j + 4k)n$ $n, k \in \mathcal{R}$, $n, k \neq 0$

13 $k\begin{bmatrix} 4 \\ -5 \\ -7 \end{bmatrix}$, $k \neq 0$, $\frac{\sqrt{10}}{6}\begin{bmatrix} 4 \\ -5 \\ -7 \end{bmatrix}$ or $-\frac{\sqrt{10}}{6}\begin{bmatrix} 4 \\ -5 \\ -7 \end{bmatrix}$

14 **a** $\begin{bmatrix} 2 \\ 5 \\ -1 \end{bmatrix}$ **b** $\begin{bmatrix} 2 \\ 0 \\ 1 \end{bmatrix}$

EXERCISE 15K.2

1 **a** $i \times k = -j$, $k \times i = j$

2 **a** $a \bullet b = -1$ $a \times b = [1, 5, 1]$
b $\cos\theta = -\frac{1}{\sqrt{28}}$ **c** $\sin\theta = \frac{\sqrt{27}}{\sqrt{28}}$ **d** $\sin\theta = \frac{\sqrt{27}}{\sqrt{28}}$

4 **a** $\overrightarrow{OA} = [2, 3, -1]$ $\overrightarrow{OB} = [-1, 1, 2]$
b $\overrightarrow{OA} \times \overrightarrow{OB} = [7, -3, 5]$ $|\overrightarrow{OA} \times \overrightarrow{OB}| = \sqrt{83}$
c Area $\triangle OAB = \frac{1}{2}|\overrightarrow{OA}||\overrightarrow{OB}|\sin\theta$
$= \frac{1}{2}|\overrightarrow{OA} \times \overrightarrow{OB}| = \frac{\sqrt{83}}{2}$ units^2

5 **a** $\overrightarrow{OC}$ is parallel to $\overrightarrow{AB}$ **b** $a \times b = b \times c$

EXERCISE 15K.3

1 **a** $\frac{\sqrt{101}}{2}$ units^2 **b** $\frac{\sqrt{133}}{2}$ units^2 **c** $\frac{\sqrt{69}}{2}$ units^2

2 $8\sqrt{2}$ units^2 **3** **a** $D(-4, 1, 3)$ **b** $\sqrt{307}$ units^2

4 **a** 4 units^3 **b** $(\sqrt{42} + 2\sqrt{3} + 3\sqrt{2} + 6)$ units^2

5 **a** $(3, 1, 0)$, $(1, 3, 3)$, $(4, 2, 3)$, $(4, 3, 3)$ **b** $\doteq 79.01°$
c 9 units^3 **6** $k = 2 \pm 2\sqrt{33}$

7 $S = \frac{1}{2}\{|a \times b| + |a \times c| + |b \times c| + |(b - a) \times (c - a)|\}$

9 **a** Yes **b** No **10** $k = \frac{23}{10}$

REVIEW SET 15A

1 **a**

60 m/s
8°

Scale: 1 cm ≡ 10 m/s

b

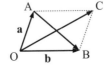

N
60°
45 m

Scale: 1 cm ≡ 10 m

2 a
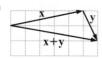
b
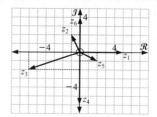

3 a $\overrightarrow{PQ}$ **b** $\overrightarrow{PR}$ **4** 4.845 km, $208°$ **5 a** $\overrightarrow{AC}$ **b** $\overrightarrow{AD}$

6 a $AB = \frac{1}{2}CD$, $AB \parallel CD$ **b** C is midpoint AB

7 a $p + r = q$ **b** $l + m = k - j + n$

8 a $r + q$ **b** $-p + r + q$ **c** $r + \frac{1}{2}q$ **d** $-\frac{1}{2}p + \frac{1}{2}r$

9 a
$\begin{bmatrix} 4 \\ 3 \end{bmatrix}$
b
$\begin{bmatrix} 3 \\ -5 \end{bmatrix}$
c
$\begin{bmatrix} 0 \\ -4 \end{bmatrix}$

10 a $\begin{bmatrix} -4 \\ -2 \end{bmatrix}$ **b** $\begin{bmatrix} -1 \\ -13 \end{bmatrix}$ **c** $\begin{bmatrix} -4 \\ 8 \end{bmatrix}$ **11** $\begin{bmatrix} 1 \\ 4 \end{bmatrix}$

12 a $\sqrt{17}$ units **b** $\sqrt{13}$ units **c** $\sqrt{10}$ units **d** $\sqrt{109}$ units

13 a $p + q$ **b** $\frac{3}{2}p + \frac{1}{2}q$

14 a $x = \begin{bmatrix} -1 \\ \frac{1}{3} \end{bmatrix}$ **b** $x = \begin{bmatrix} 1 \\ -10 \end{bmatrix}$ **16** $r = 4$, $s = 7$

17 a $q + r$ **b** $r + q$, $DB = AC$, $DB \parallel AC$

REVIEW SET 15B

1 a $\overrightarrow{PQ} = \begin{bmatrix} -3 \\ 12 \\ 3 \end{bmatrix}$ **b** $\sqrt{162}$ units **c** $\sqrt{61}$ units

2 a $\begin{bmatrix} 3 \\ -3 \\ 11 \end{bmatrix}$ **b** $\begin{bmatrix} 7 \\ -3 \\ -26 \end{bmatrix}$ **c** $\sqrt{74}$ units **3** $\begin{bmatrix} 8 \\ -8 \\ 7 \end{bmatrix}$

4 $m = 5$, $n = -\frac{1}{2}$ **5** $2 : 3$ **6** $t = 2 \pm \sqrt{2}$ **7** $80.3°$

8 $40.7°$ **9 a** $\begin{bmatrix} -6 \\ 1 \\ 3 \end{bmatrix}$ **b** $\sqrt{46}$ units **c** $(-1, 3\frac{1}{2}, \frac{1}{2})$

10 a -1 **b** $\begin{bmatrix} 4 \\ -1 \\ 7 \end{bmatrix}$ **c** $60°$

11 $\angle K \doteqdot 123.7°$, $\angle L \doteqdot 11.3°$, $\angle M \doteqdot 45.0°$

12 $63.95°$ **13** $c = \frac{50}{3}$

14 a $a \bullet b$ is a scalar, so $a \bullet b \bullet c$ is a scalar dotted with a vector, which is meaningless.

b $b \times c$ must be done first otherwise we have a scalar crossed with a vector which is meaningless.

15 a $k = \pm \frac{7}{\sqrt{33}}$ **b** $k = \pm \frac{1}{\sqrt{2}}$

REVIEW SET 15C

1 a -13 **b** -36 **3** $t = \frac{2}{3}$ or -3 **4** $k = 6$

5 $k\begin{bmatrix} 5 \\ 4 \end{bmatrix}$, $k \neq 0$ **6** $\angle K = 64.44°$, $\angle L = 56.89°$, $\angle M = 58.67°$

7 $72.35°$ or $107.65°$

8 a i (1) $p + q$ **(2)** $\frac{1}{2}p + \frac{1}{2}q$

b i $\overrightarrow{AC} = -p + r$, $\overrightarrow{BC} = -q + r$

9 a $\begin{bmatrix} 7 \\ -12 \\ -7 \end{bmatrix}$ **b** $\begin{bmatrix} 1 \\ -\frac{5}{3} \\ -\frac{2}{3} \end{bmatrix}$ **c** $\begin{bmatrix} \frac{5}{14} \\ -\frac{5}{7} \\ -\frac{15}{14} \end{bmatrix}$

10 a ± 7 **b** $\frac{\sqrt{14}}{2}$ units^2 **c** $\frac{7}{6}$ units^3

EXERCISE 16A.1

1

2 a $4 + i$
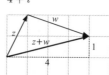
b $-2 + 3i$

c $-1 + 5i$
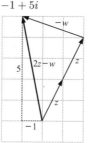
d $-7i$
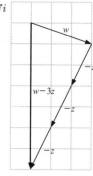

3 a $5 - i$

b $4 + i$
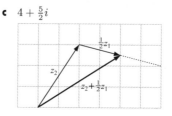

c $4 + \frac{5}{2}i$
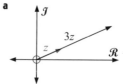

d $4 - \frac{1}{2}i$
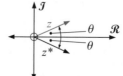

4 a
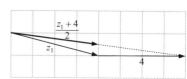
b

c
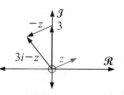
d
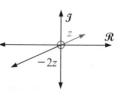

e 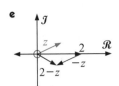   **f**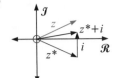

g 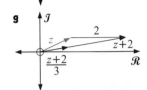   **h**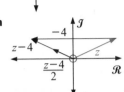

EXERCISE 16A.2

1 a   **b**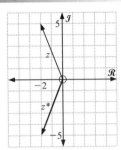

4 $z^* = z$

EXERCISE 16B.1

1 a 5 **b** 13 **c** $2\sqrt{17}$ **d** 3 **e** 4

2 a $\sqrt{5}$ **b** $\sqrt{5}$ **c** 5 **d** 5 **e** $5\sqrt{2}$ **f** $5\sqrt{2}$

   g $\frac{1}{\sqrt{2}}$ **h** $\frac{1}{\sqrt{2}}$ **i** 5 **j** 5 **k** $5\sqrt{5}$ **l** $5\sqrt{5}$

3 • $|z^*| = |z|$ • $zz^* = |z|^2$ • $|zw| = |z|\,|w|$

   • $\left|\frac{z}{w}\right| = \frac{|z|}{|w|}$ • $|z^n| = |z|^n$

6 $|z_1 z_2 z_3 .... z_n| = |z_1|\,|z_2|\, ... \,|z_n|$ and that $|z^n| = |z|^n$

8 a 6 **b** 9 **c** $3\sqrt{5}$ **d** 3 **e** $\frac{1}{3}$ **f** $\frac{2}{9}$ **9** 1

10 $2^{20} = 1\,048\,576$

11 a $\left[\frac{a^2+b^2-1}{(a-1)^2+b^2}\right] + \left[\frac{-2b}{(a-1)^2+b^2}\right]i$ **b** 0

EXERCISE 16B.2

1 a i $4\sqrt{2}$ units **ii** $(1, 4)$ **b i** $5\sqrt{5}$ units **ii** $\left(-\frac{3}{2}, 2\right)$

2 a i $w + z$ **ii** $w - z$

3 a reflection in the $\mathcal{R}$-axis **b** reflection in the $\mathcal{I}$-axis

   c anti-clockwise rotation of π about 0

   d clockwise rotation of $\frac{\pi}{2}$ about 0

EXERCISE 16B.3

1 a $4 \operatorname{cis} 0$ **b** $2 \operatorname{cis} \frac{\pi}{2}$ **c** $6 \operatorname{cis} \pi$ **d** $3 \operatorname{cis}\left(-\frac{\pi}{2}\right)$

   e $\sqrt{2} \operatorname{cis} \frac{\pi}{4}$ **f** $2\sqrt{2} \operatorname{cis}\left(-\frac{\pi}{4}\right)$ **g** $2 \operatorname{cis}\left(\frac{5\pi}{6}\right)$ **h** $4 \operatorname{cis} \frac{\pi}{6}$

2 0 **3** $k\sqrt{2} \operatorname{cis} \frac{\pi}{4}$ if $k > 0$, $-k\sqrt{2} \operatorname{cis}\left(-\frac{3\pi}{4}\right)$ if $k < 0$,

   not possible if $k = 0$

4 a $2i$ **b** $4\sqrt{2} + 4\sqrt{2}i$ **c** $2\sqrt{3} + 2i$ **d** $1 - i$

   e $-\frac{\sqrt{3}}{2} + \frac{3}{2}i$ **f** -5 **5 a** 1 **b** 1

EXERCISE 16B.4

1 a $\operatorname{cis} 3\theta$ **b** $\operatorname{cis} 2\theta$ **c** $\operatorname{cis} 3\theta$ **d** $\frac{\sqrt{3}}{2} + \frac{1}{2}i$

   e $\sqrt{2} + i\sqrt{2}$ **f** 8 **g** $-2i$ **h** -4 **i** $4i$

2 a -1 **b** -1 **c** $\frac{1}{2} + \frac{\sqrt{3}}{2}i$

3 a $|z| = 2$, $\arg(z) = \theta$ **b** $2 \operatorname{cis}(-\theta)$ **c** $2 \operatorname{cis}(\theta + \pi)$

   d $2 \operatorname{cis}(\pi - \theta)$

4 a $\operatorname{cis} \frac{\pi}{2}$ **b** $r \operatorname{cis}\left(\theta + \frac{\pi}{2}\right)$ **d** clock. rotn. of $\frac{\pi}{2}$ about 0

5 a $\operatorname{cis}(-\theta)$ **b** $\operatorname{cis}\left(\theta - \frac{\pi}{2}\right)$ ..... then $z^* = r \operatorname{cis}(-\theta)$

6 a $\cos\left(\frac{\pi}{12}\right) = \frac{\sqrt{2}+\sqrt{6}}{4}$, $\sin\left(\frac{\pi}{12}\right) = \frac{\sqrt{6}-\sqrt{2}}{4}$

   b $\cos\left(\frac{11\pi}{12}\right) = \frac{-\sqrt{2}-\sqrt{6}}{4}$, $\sin\left(\frac{11\pi}{12}\right) = \frac{\sqrt{6}-\sqrt{2}}{4}$

EXERCISE 16B.5

2 a $|-z| = 3$, $\arg(-z) = \theta - \pi$ **b** $|z^*| = 3$, $\arg(z^*) = -\theta$

   c $|iz| = 3$, $\arg(iz) = \theta + \frac{\pi}{2}$

   d $|(1+i)z| = 3\sqrt{2}$, $\arg((1+i)z) = \theta + \frac{\pi}{4}$

3 a $|z - 1| = 2\sin\frac{\phi}{2}$, $\arg(z - 1) = \frac{\phi}{2} + \frac{\pi}{2}$

   b $z - 1 = \left(2\sin(\frac{\phi}{2})\right)\operatorname{cis}\left(\frac{\phi}{2} + \frac{\pi}{2}\right)$

   c $(z - 1)^* = \left(2\sin(\frac{\phi}{2})\right)\operatorname{cis}\left(-\frac{\phi}{2} - \frac{\pi}{2}\right)$

4 b $\left|\frac{z_2-z_1}{z_3-z_2}\right| = 1$ **c** $\arg\left(\frac{z_2-z_1}{z_3-z_2}\right) = \frac{2\pi}{3}$ **d** 1

EXERCISE 16B.6

1 a $-1.41 + 1.01i$ **b** $1.27 - 3.06i$ **c** $-2.55 - 1.25i$

2 a $5 \operatorname{cis}(-0.927)$ **b** $13 \operatorname{cis}(-1.97)$ **c** $17.7 \operatorname{cis}(2.29)$

3 a $2 \operatorname{cis} \frac{\pi}{4}$ **b** $\sqrt{19} \operatorname{cis}(-2.50)$

4 a $a(x^2 + 2x + 4) = 0$, $a \neq 0$

   b $a(x^2 - 2x + 2) = 0$, $a \neq 0$

EXERCISE 16C

1 a 32 **b** -1 **c** $-64i$ **d** $\sqrt{5} \operatorname{cis}\left(\frac{\pi}{14}\right) \div (2.180 + 0.498i)$

   e $\sqrt{3} + i$ **f** $16 + 16\sqrt{3}i$

2 a $128 - 128i$ **b** $1024 + 1024\sqrt{3}i$ **c** $\frac{1}{524\,288}\left(\frac{-1}{\sqrt{2}} + \frac{1}{\sqrt{2}}i\right)$

   d $\frac{1}{64}(1 - i)$ **e** $\sqrt{2}\cos\left(-\frac{\pi}{12}\right) + i\sqrt{2}\sin\left(-\frac{\pi}{12}\right)$

   f $\frac{1}{64}(-\sqrt{3} - i)$

4 a $|z|^{\frac{1}{2}} \operatorname{cis} \frac{\theta}{2}$ **b** $-\frac{\pi}{2} < \theta \leqslant \frac{\pi}{2}$ **c** True **6** $\operatorname{cis} 3\theta$

7 $1 + i = \sqrt{2} \operatorname{cis}\left(\frac{\pi}{4}\right)$ $z^n = 2^{\frac{n}{2}} \operatorname{cis}\left(\frac{n\pi}{4}\right)$

   a $n = 4k$, k any integer **b** $n = 2 + 4k$, $k \in Z$

8 a $|z^3| = 8$, $\arg(z^3) = 3\theta$

   b $|iz^2| = 4$, $\arg(iz^2) = \frac{\pi}{2} + 2\theta$

   c $\left|\frac{1}{z}\right| = \frac{1}{2}$ $\arg\left(\frac{1}{z}\right) = -\theta$

   d $\left|\frac{-i}{z^2}\right| = \frac{1}{4}$ $\arg\left(\frac{-i}{z^2}\right) = -\frac{\pi}{2} - 2\theta$

11 c $\left(z + \frac{1}{z}\right)^3 = z^3 + 3z + \frac{3}{z} + \frac{1}{z^3}$

12 a $\overrightarrow{AB} \equiv z_2 - z_1$, $\overrightarrow{BC} \equiv z_3 - z_2$ **Hint:** Notice that

   $\overrightarrow{BC}$ is a 90° rotation of $\overrightarrow{BA}$ about B.

   b $\overrightarrow{OD} \equiv z_1 + z_3 - z_2$

13 a i $\cos 4\theta = 8\cos^4\theta - 8\cos^2\theta + 1$

     ii $\sin 4\theta = 4\cos^3\theta \sin\theta - 4\cos\theta \sin^3\theta$

   b **Hint:** When $n = 1$, $2i\sin\theta = z - \frac{1}{z}$.

     Now cube both sides.

EXERCISE 16D

1 $1, -\frac{1}{2} \pm i\frac{\sqrt{3}}{2}$ **2 a** $\sqrt{3} - i,\ 2i,\ -\sqrt{3} - i$

b $z = \frac{3\sqrt{3}}{2} - \frac{3}{2}i,\ 3i,\ -\frac{3\sqrt{3}}{2} - \frac{3}{2}i$

3 $-1,\ \frac{1}{2} \pm \frac{\sqrt{3}}{2}i$

4 a $z = \pm 2,\ \pm 2i$ **b** $z = \sqrt{2} \pm i\sqrt{2},\ -\sqrt{2} \pm i\sqrt{2}$

5 $\operatorname{cis}\left(\frac{3\pi}{8}\right),\ \operatorname{cis}\left(\frac{7\pi}{8}\right),$
$\operatorname{cis}\left(\frac{-\pi}{8}\right),\ \operatorname{cis}\left(\frac{-5\pi}{8}\right)$

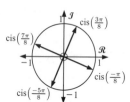

6 $z = \frac{1}{\sqrt{2}} - \frac{1}{\sqrt{2}}i,$
$\quad \frac{1}{\sqrt{2}} + \frac{1}{\sqrt{2}}i,$
$\quad -\frac{1}{\sqrt{2}} + \frac{1}{\sqrt{2}}i,$ or
$\quad -\frac{1}{\sqrt{2}} - \frac{1}{\sqrt{2}}i$

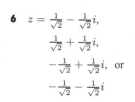

$z^4 + 1 = (z^2 - \sqrt{2}z + 1)(z^2 + \sqrt{2}z + 1)$

EXERCISE 16E

1 a i $z = w^n - 3$ ($n = 0, 1, 2$) and $w = \operatorname{cis} \frac{2\pi}{3}$
   ii $z = 2w^n + 1$ ($n = 0, 1, 2$) and $w = \operatorname{cis} \frac{2\pi}{3}$
   iii $z = \frac{1 - w^n}{2}$ ($n = 0, 1, 2$) and $w = \operatorname{cis} \frac{2\pi}{3}$

3 a Yes   **4 a** $z = \operatorname{cis} 0,$ **b**
$\operatorname{cis}\left(\frac{2\pi}{5}\right),$
$\operatorname{cis}\left(\frac{4\pi}{5}\right),$
$\operatorname{cis}\left(\frac{6\pi}{5}\right),$
$\operatorname{cis}\left(\frac{8\pi}{5}\right)$

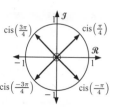

   c $1 - w^5$

5 b Hint: The LHS is a geometric series.

REVIEW SET 16A

1 Real part is $16\sqrt{3}$. Imaginary part is 16.

2 a $2x + 4y = -1$ **b** $y = x$ **3** $|z| = 4$

4 a $\frac{5\pi}{12}$ **b** $-\frac{11\pi}{12}$

5 a $5 \operatorname{cis}\left(-\frac{\pi}{2}\right)$ **b** $4 \operatorname{cis}\left(-\frac{\pi}{3}\right)$ **c** $-k\sqrt{2}\operatorname{cis}\left(\frac{3\pi}{4}\right)$

6 $b = \frac{1}{\sqrt{3}}$

7 b $(1 - i)z = 4 \operatorname{cis}\left(\alpha - \frac{\pi}{4}\right),\ \arg((1 - i)z) = \alpha - \frac{\pi}{4}$

8 a $\left|\frac{z_1^2}{z_2^2}\right| = 1,\ \arg\left(\frac{z_1^2}{z_2^2}\right) = \pi$

REVIEW SET 16B

1 $\frac{1}{\sqrt{2}} - \frac{1}{\sqrt{2}}i$ **2 a** $5 + 2i$ **b** $2\sqrt{2}$ **c** 17^5 **d** $\doteq -2.034$

3 $a = 0, b = -1$

4 a $x = 0,\ y > 1$ **b** $3x^2 + 3y^2 - 20x + 12 = 0$

5 $4 \operatorname{cis}\left(-\frac{\pi}{3}\right),\ n = 3k,\ k$ is an integer   **6** $\frac{3}{2} \pm \frac{i3\sqrt{3}}{2},\ -3$

7 a $|z^3| = 64,\ \arg(z^3) = 3\theta$ **b** $\left|\frac{1}{z}\right| = \frac{1}{4},\ \arg\left(\frac{1}{z}\right) = -\theta$
   c $|iz^*| = 4,\ \arg(iz^*) = \frac{\pi}{2} - \theta$

10 a $n = 3$ **b** $n = -2$ **c** $n = -1$

11 $\operatorname{cis} \frac{\pi}{10},\ i,\ \operatorname{cis} \frac{9\pi}{10},\ \operatorname{cis} \frac{13\pi}{10},\ \operatorname{cis} \frac{17\pi}{10}$

13 a $a(z^2 - 2\cos\left(\frac{2\pi}{5}\right)z + 1) = 0,\ a \neq 0$
   b $a(z^2 + z - 1) = 0,\ a \neq 0$

EXERCISE 17A.1

1 a i $\begin{bmatrix} x \\ y \end{bmatrix} = \begin{bmatrix} 3 \\ -4 \end{bmatrix} + t\begin{bmatrix} 1 \\ 4 \end{bmatrix}$ **ii** $x = 3 + t$
$\qquad\qquad y = -4 + 4t,\ t \in \mathcal{R}$

b i $\begin{bmatrix} x \\ y \end{bmatrix} = \begin{bmatrix} 5 \\ 2 \end{bmatrix} + t\begin{bmatrix} -8 \\ 2 \end{bmatrix}$ **ii** $x = 5 - 8t$
$\qquad\qquad y = 2 + 2t,\ t \in \mathcal{R}$

c i $\begin{bmatrix} x \\ y \end{bmatrix} = \begin{bmatrix} -6 \\ 0 \end{bmatrix} + t\begin{bmatrix} 3 \\ 7 \end{bmatrix}$ **ii** $x = -6 + 3t$
$\qquad\qquad y = 7t,\ t \in \mathcal{R}$

d i $\begin{bmatrix} x \\ y \end{bmatrix} = \begin{bmatrix} -1 \\ 11 \end{bmatrix} + t\begin{bmatrix} -2 \\ 1 \end{bmatrix}$ **ii** $x = -1 - 2t$
$\qquad\qquad y = 11 + t,\ t \in \mathcal{R}$

2 $x = -1 + 2\lambda,\ y = 4 - \lambda,\ \lambda \in \mathcal{R}$
Points are: $(-1, 4),\ (1, 3),\ (5, 1),\ (-3, 5),\ (-9, 8)$

3 a When $t = 1,\ x = 3,\ y = -2$ ∴ yes   **b** $k = -5$
When $t = -2,\ x = 0,\ y = 7$ ∴ no

4 a $(1, 2)$ **b**
   c $\sqrt{29}$ cm/s

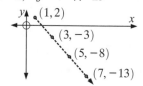

EXERCISE 17A.2

1 a $\begin{bmatrix} x \\ y \\ z \end{bmatrix} = \begin{bmatrix} 1 \\ 3 \\ -7 \end{bmatrix} + t\begin{bmatrix} 2 \\ 1 \\ 3 \end{bmatrix}\ \ t \in \mathcal{R}$

b $\begin{bmatrix} x \\ y \\ z \end{bmatrix} = \begin{bmatrix} 0 \\ 1 \\ 2 \end{bmatrix} + t\begin{bmatrix} 1 \\ 1 \\ -2 \end{bmatrix},\ \ t \in \mathcal{R}$

c $\begin{bmatrix} x \\ y \\ z \end{bmatrix} = \begin{bmatrix} -2 \\ 2 \\ 1 \end{bmatrix} + t\begin{bmatrix} 1 \\ 0 \\ 0 \end{bmatrix},\ \ t \in \mathcal{R}$

2 a $x = 5 - t,\ y = 2 + 2t,\ z = -1 + 6t,\ t \in \mathcal{R}$
   b $x = 2t,\ y = 2 - t,\ z = -1 + 3t,\ t \in \mathcal{R}$
   c $x = 3,\ y = 2,\ z = -1 + t,\ t \in \mathcal{R}$

3 a $x = 1 - 2t,\ y = 2 + t,\ z = 1 + t,\ t \in \mathcal{R}$
   b $x = 3t,\ y = 1,\ z = 3 - 4t,\ t \in \mathcal{R}$
   c $x = 1,\ y = 2 - 3t,\ z = 5,\ t \in \mathcal{R}$
   d $x = 5t,\ y = 1 - 2t,\ z = -1 + 4t,\ t \in \mathcal{R}$

4 a $(-\frac{1}{2}, \frac{9}{2}, 0)$ **b** $(0, 4, 1)$ **c** $(4, 0, 9)$

5 $(0, 7, 3)$ and $(\frac{20}{3}, -\frac{19}{3}, -\frac{11}{3})$

6 a $(1, 2, 3)$ **b** $(\frac{7}{3}, \frac{2}{3}, \frac{8}{3})$ **7 a** $3\sqrt{3}$ units   **b** $\sqrt{\frac{3}{2}}$ units

EXERCISE 17A.3

1 $75.5°$ **2** $75.7°$ **3** $\begin{bmatrix} 5 \\ -2 \end{bmatrix} \bullet \begin{bmatrix} 4 \\ 10 \end{bmatrix} = 0$ ∴ perpendicular

4 $28.6°$

EXERCISE 17B.1

1 a i $(-4, 3)$ **ii** $\begin{bmatrix} 12 \\ 5 \end{bmatrix}$ **iii** 13 m/s

b i $(0, -6)$ **ii** $\begin{bmatrix} 3 \\ -4 \end{bmatrix}$ **iii** 5 m/s

c i $(-2, -7)$ **ii** $\begin{bmatrix} -6 \\ -4 \end{bmatrix}$ **iii** $\sqrt{52}$ m/s

2 a i $\begin{bmatrix} 8 \\ 4 \end{bmatrix}$ **ii** $\sqrt{80}$ km/h **b i** $\begin{bmatrix} 6 \\ 2 \end{bmatrix}$ **ii** $\sqrt{40}$ km/h

c i $\begin{bmatrix} 7 \\ 24 \end{bmatrix}$ **ii** 25 km/h

3 a $\begin{bmatrix} 120 \\ -90 \end{bmatrix}$ **b** $\begin{bmatrix} 12 \\ 3.5 \end{bmatrix}$ **c** $\begin{bmatrix} 20\sqrt{5} \\ 10\sqrt{5} \end{bmatrix}$ **d** $\begin{bmatrix} -60 \\ 80 \end{bmatrix}$

EXERCISE 17B.2

1 a $\begin{bmatrix} -3 + 2t \\ -2 + 4t \end{bmatrix}$ **d**

$t = 0$

b $(2, 8)$

c i $t = 1.5$ sec
   ii $t = 0.5$ sec

2 a $\begin{bmatrix} x \\ y \end{bmatrix} = \begin{bmatrix} 8 \\ -10 \end{bmatrix} + t \begin{bmatrix} 4 \\ -3 \end{bmatrix}$, $t \in \mathcal{R}$

b $\begin{bmatrix} x \\ y \end{bmatrix} = \begin{bmatrix} -2 \\ 6 \end{bmatrix} + \dfrac{t}{2.5} \begin{bmatrix} 20 \\ 15 \end{bmatrix}$, $t \in \mathcal{R}$

c $\begin{bmatrix} x \\ y \end{bmatrix} = \begin{bmatrix} -5 \\ 0 \end{bmatrix} + t \begin{bmatrix} 2 \\ 1 \end{bmatrix}$, $t \in \mathcal{R}$

d $\begin{bmatrix} x \\ y \end{bmatrix} = \begin{bmatrix} -8 \\ -16 \end{bmatrix} + t \begin{bmatrix} 9 \\ 12 \end{bmatrix}$, $t \in \mathcal{R}$

3 a 37.7 km **b** 13 km/h **c** 7.40 am

4 a A is at $(4, 5)$, B is at $(1, -8)$

b For A it is $\begin{bmatrix} 1 \\ -2 \end{bmatrix}$. For B it is $\begin{bmatrix} 2 \\ 1 \end{bmatrix}$.

c For A, speed is $\sqrt{5}$ km/h. For B, speed is $\sqrt{5}$ km/h.

d $t = 10:12$ am

e $\begin{bmatrix} 1 \\ -2 \end{bmatrix} \bullet \begin{bmatrix} 2 \\ 1 \end{bmatrix} = 0$, $\therefore$ direction vectors are $\perp$

5 a $\begin{bmatrix} x_1 \\ y_1 \end{bmatrix} = \begin{bmatrix} -5 \\ 4 \end{bmatrix} + t \begin{bmatrix} 3 \\ -1 \end{bmatrix}$ $\therefore$ $x_1(t) = -5 + 3t$,
$y_1(t) = 4 - t$

b speed $= \sqrt{10}$ km/min

c a minutes later, $(t - a)$ min have elapsed.

$\therefore$ $\begin{bmatrix} x_2 \\ y_2 \end{bmatrix} = \begin{bmatrix} 15 \\ 7 \end{bmatrix} + (t - a) \begin{bmatrix} -4 \\ -3 \end{bmatrix}$

$\therefore$ $x_2(t) = 15 - 4(t - a)$, $y_2(t) = 7 - 3(t - a)$

d Torpedo is fired at 1:35:28 pm and the explosion occurs at 1:37:42 pm.

EXERCISE 17B.3

1 a $(-3 + 2t, -2 + 4t)$ **b i** $t = 0.5$ sec **ii** $t = 1.5$ sec
c $(0, 4)$ and $(-2, 0)$

2 a $(-2 - t, 1 - 3t)$ **b** $t = \frac{1}{3}$ sec **c** $(-2\frac{1}{3}, 0)$

3 a $-6i + 8j$ **b** $\begin{bmatrix} 6 - 6t \\ -6 + 8t \end{bmatrix}$ **c** when $t = \frac{3}{4}$ hour
d $t = 0.84$ and position is $(0.96, 0.72)$

4 a i $-8i - 5j$ **ii** $3i + 3j$ **iii** $(-8 + 3t)i + (-5 + 3t)j$
b $t = 2\frac{1}{6}$ hours, i.e., 2 h 10 min
c shortest distance is $\frac{3}{2}\sqrt{2} \doteqdot 2.12$ km $\therefore$ breaking the law

5 a $\begin{bmatrix} -120 \\ -40 \end{bmatrix}$ **b** $\begin{bmatrix} x \\ y \end{bmatrix} = \begin{bmatrix} 200 \\ 100 \end{bmatrix} + t \begin{bmatrix} -120 \\ -40 \end{bmatrix}$ **c** $\begin{bmatrix} 80 \\ 60 \end{bmatrix}$

d $\left| \begin{bmatrix} 80 \\ 60 \end{bmatrix} \right| = 100$ km **e** $t = 1\frac{3}{4}$ hours and $d_{min} \doteqdot 31.6$ km

f at 2:30 pm

6 a $A(18, 0)$ and $B(0, 12)$ **b** R is at $\left(x, \dfrac{36 - 2x}{3} \right)$

c $\overrightarrow{PR} = \begin{bmatrix} x - 4 \\ \frac{36 - 2x}{3} \end{bmatrix}$ and $\overrightarrow{AB} = \begin{bmatrix} -18 \\ 12 \end{bmatrix}$

d $\left(\dfrac{108}{13}, \dfrac{84}{13} \right)$ and distance $\doteqdot 7.766$ km

7 a $(10, 12)$ **b** $a = \pm 4\sqrt{10}$
c for $a = -4\sqrt{10}$, P is $(10 - 4\sqrt{10}t, 12 - 3t)$

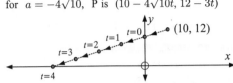

8 a $A(3, -4)$ and $B(4, 3)$ **b** For A $\begin{bmatrix} -1 \\ 2 \end{bmatrix}$, for B $\begin{bmatrix} -3 \\ -2 \end{bmatrix}$

c $97.1°$ **d** at $t = 1.5$ hours

EXERCISE 17B.4

1 a

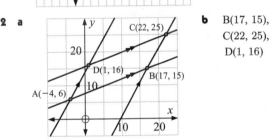

line 1 line 2 C A B line 3

b $A(2, 4)$,
$B(4, 6)$,
$C(8, 0)$

c $BC = CA$
$= \sqrt{52}$ units
$\therefore$ isosceles $\triangle$

2 a

C(22, 25) D(1, 16) B(17, 15) A(-4, 6)

b $B(17, 15)$,
$C(22, 25)$,
$D(1, 16)$

3 a A is at $(2, 3)$, $B(8, 6)$, $C(5, 0)$ **b** $AB = BC = \sqrt{45}$ units

4 a P is at $(10, 4)$, $Q(3, -1)$, $R(20, -10)$

b $\overrightarrow{PQ} = \begin{bmatrix} -7 \\ -5 \end{bmatrix}$, $\overrightarrow{PR} = \begin{bmatrix} 10 \\ -14 \end{bmatrix}$, $\overrightarrow{PQ} \bullet \overrightarrow{PR} = 0$

c $\angle QPR = 90°$ **d** 74 units^2

5 a B is at $(18, 9)$, $C(14, 25)$, $D(-2, 21)$

b $\overrightarrow{AC} = \begin{bmatrix} 12 \\ 20 \end{bmatrix}$ and $\overrightarrow{DB} = \begin{bmatrix} 20 \\ -12 \end{bmatrix}$

  i $\sqrt{544}$ units **ii** $\sqrt{544}$ units **iii** 0

c Diagonals are perpendicular and equal in length, and as their midpoints are the same, i.e., $(8, 15)$, ABCD is a square.

EXERCISE 17C

1 a They intersect at $(1, 2, 3)$, angle $\doteqdot 10.9°$.
b Lines are skew, angle $\doteqdot 62.7°$.
c They are parallel, $\therefore$ angle $= 0°$.
d They are skew, angle $\doteqdot 11.4°$.
e They intersect at $(-4, 7, -7)$, angle $\doteqdot 40.2°$.
f They are parallel, $\therefore$ angle $\doteqdot 0°$.

2 If $k \neq 16$, the lines are parallel and so there are no solutions. If $k = 16$, the lines are coincident. We $\therefore$ have infinitely many solutions of the form $x = t$, $y = 3t - 8$, $t \in \mathcal{R}$.

3 If $a \neq -4$, we have a unique solution. The lines meet at
$\left(\frac{a+88}{4a+16}, \frac{-21}{2a+8}\right)$. If $a = -4$, the lines are parallel and so do
not intersect (no solns). No case for infinite number of solns.

4 $\frac{5}{\sqrt{10}}$ units **5** $3\sqrt{3}$ units **6** $\sqrt{\frac{3}{2}}$ units

7 a $\frac{2}{\sqrt{26}}$ units **b** $2\sqrt{2}$ units

8 a 0 units **b** $\frac{111}{\sqrt{1498}} \doteq 2.87$ units **c** $\frac{\sqrt{2769}}{13} \doteq 4.05$ units

   d $\frac{3\sqrt{2}}{4}$ units **e** 0 units **f** $\frac{\sqrt{6180}}{10} \doteq 7.86$ units

EXERCISE 17D

1 a $2x - y + 3z = 8$ **b** $3x + 4y + z = 19$
   c $x - y - 2z = -1$ **d** $x + 3y + z = 10$

2 a $\begin{bmatrix} 2 \\ 3 \\ -1 \end{bmatrix}$ **b** $\begin{bmatrix} 3 \\ -1 \\ 0 \end{bmatrix}$ **c** $\begin{bmatrix} 0 \\ 0 \\ 1 \end{bmatrix}$ **d** $\begin{bmatrix} 1 \\ 0 \\ 0 \end{bmatrix}$

3 a $y = 0$ **b** $z = 4$

4 a ii $-2x + 6y + z = 18$ **b ii** $-5x + 3y + 12z = 12$
   c ii $-y + z = 3$

5 a $x = 1 + t, \ y = -2 - 3t, \ z = 4t, \ t \in \mathcal{R}$
   b $x = 3 + t, \ y = 4 - t, \ z = -1 - 2t, \ t \in \mathcal{R}$

6 $x = 2 - t, \ y = -1 + 3t, \ z = 3 - 3t, \ t \in \mathcal{R}$ $(1, 2, 0)$

7 $x = 1 + t, \ y = -2 + 2t, \ z = 4 - 5t, \ t \in \mathcal{R}$
   a $(0, -4, 9)$ **b** $(1, -2, 4)$ **c** $(-5, -14, 34)$

8 a $(-1, -1, 4)$; 3 units **b** $(0, 1, -3)$; $2\sqrt{11}$ units
   c $\left(-\frac{1}{7}, -\frac{26}{7}, -\frac{17}{7}\right)$; $2\sqrt{\frac{3}{7}}$ units

9 $(1, -3, 0)$ **10** X axis at $(2, 0, 0)$

11 a $y - 3z = -7$ **b** $x - z = -2$ **c** $3x - y = 1$

12 $y - 2z = 8$

13 a $k = -\frac{3}{2}$ **b** B$(3, 6, -\frac{11}{2})$ or $(-1, -2, \frac{5}{2})$

14 a N$(3.4, 1.2, 1), \ d = \frac{2}{\sqrt{5}}$ units

   b N$(\frac{1}{6}, \frac{5}{6}, -\frac{1}{3}), \ d = \frac{5}{\sqrt{6}}$ units

16 a $\frac{10}{\sqrt{6}}$ units **b** $2\sqrt{3}$ units

17 a $\frac{19}{2\sqrt{6}}$ units **b** $\frac{|d_2 - d_1|}{\sqrt{a^2 + b^2 + c^2}}$ units **18** $\frac{26}{\sqrt{138}}$ units

19 $2x - y + 2z = -1$ and $2x - y + 2z = 11$

EXERCISE 17E

1 a $\doteq 13.1°$ **b** the line and plane are parallel $\therefore$ $0°$
   c $\doteq 11.3°$ **d** $\doteq 30.7°$

2 a $\doteq 83.7°$ **b** $\doteq 84.8°$ **c** $\doteq 86.2°$ **d** $\doteq 73.2°$ **e** $\doteq 62.3°$

EXERCISE 17F

1 a Either no solutions or an infinite number of solutions.
   b i $a_1 = ka_2, \ b_1 = kb_2, \ c_1 = kc_2$ for some k
     ii $a_1 = ka_2, \ b_1 = kb_2, \ c_1 = kc_2, \ d_1 = kd_2$ for some k
   c i Planes meet in a line $x = -2 + 3t, \ y = t, \ z = 5,$
      $t \in \mathcal{R}$
    ii Planes meet in a line $x = 2 - 2t, \ y = t,$
      $z = 1 + 3t, \ t \in \mathcal{R}$
    iii Planes are coincident
      $\therefore$ $x = 6 - 2s + 3t, \ y = s, \ z = t, \ s, t \in \mathcal{R}$

2 a If $k = -2$, planes are coincident with infinitely many
   solutions. If $k \neq -2$, planes meet in a line with infinitely
   many solutions.

   b If $k = 16$, planes are coincident, with infinitely many
   solutions. If $k \neq 16$, planes are parallel with no solutions.

4 a Meet at a point $(1, -2, 4)$
   b Meet in a line $x = \frac{9 - t}{3}, \ y = \frac{6 + 5t}{3}, \ z = t, \ t \in \mathcal{R}$
   c Meet in a line $x = 3t - 3, \ y = t, \ z = 5t - 11, \ t \in \mathcal{R}$
   d No solutions as 2 planes are parallel and intersected by
   a third plane.
   e Two planes are coincident and the other cuts obliquely at
   the line $x = \frac{5}{2} + \frac{1}{2}t, \ y = -\frac{3}{2} + \frac{3}{2}t, \ z = t, \ t \in \mathcal{R}$
   f Meet at the point $(3, -2, 0)$

5 If $k = 5$ the planes meet in the line
   $x = -10t, \ y = -1 - 7t, \ z = t, \ t \in \mathcal{R}$. If $k \neq 5$,
   the line of intersection of any two planes is parallel to the
   third $\therefore$ no solutions.

6 A unique solution exists if $m \neq -1$ or $m \neq -5$.

   If $m = -1$, planes meet in a line $x = \frac{t + 7}{3}, \ y = \frac{t - 5}{3}$,

   $z = t, \ t \in \mathcal{R}$. If $m = -5$, the system is inconsistent,
   $\therefore$ no solutions.

7 They meet at the point $\left(\frac{94}{29}, \frac{-68}{29}, \frac{64}{29}\right)$

REVIEW SET 17A

1 a $\begin{bmatrix} x \\ y \end{bmatrix} = \begin{bmatrix} -6 \\ 3 \end{bmatrix} + t \begin{bmatrix} 4 \\ -3 \end{bmatrix}$ **b** $x = -6 + 4t, \ y = 3 - 3t, \ t \in \mathcal{R}$

2 $\begin{bmatrix} x \\ y \end{bmatrix} = \begin{bmatrix} 0 \\ 8 \end{bmatrix} + t \begin{bmatrix} 5 \\ 4 \end{bmatrix}, \ t \in \mathcal{R}$ **3** $m = 10$

4 a $(-4, 3)$ **b** $(28, 27)$ **c** 10 m/s **d** $\begin{bmatrix} 8 \\ 6 \end{bmatrix}$ **5** $2\sqrt{10}(3i - j)$

6 a i $-6i + 10j$ **ii** $-5i - 15j$ **iii** $(-6 - 5t)i + (10 - 15t)j$
   b $t = 0.48$ h **c** shortest dist. $\doteq 8.85$ km, so, will miss reef.

7 a X23, $x_1 = 2 + t, \ y_1 = 4 - 3t, \ t \geqslant 0$
   b Y18, $x_2 = 9 - t, \ y_2 = 3 + 2a + at, \ t \geqslant 0$
   c interception occurred at 2:20:30 pm
   d $\theta = 192°, \ \doteq 4.82$ km/min

8 a KL is parallel to MN as $\begin{bmatrix} 5 \\ -2 \end{bmatrix}$ is parallel to $\begin{bmatrix} -5 \\ 2 \end{bmatrix}$

   b KL is perpendicular to NK as $\begin{bmatrix} 5 \\ -2 \end{bmatrix} \bullet \begin{bmatrix} 4 \\ 10 \end{bmatrix} = 0$

   and NK is perpendicular to MN as $\begin{bmatrix} 4 \\ 10 \end{bmatrix} \bullet \begin{bmatrix} -5 \\ 2 \end{bmatrix} = 0$

   c K$(7, 17)$, M$(33, -5)$, N$(3, 7)$ **d** 261 units^2

REVIEW SET 17B

1 a $3x + 2y - z = -1$ **b** $(0, 1, 3)$

2 a $\begin{bmatrix} x \\ y \\ z \end{bmatrix} = \begin{bmatrix} 3 \\ 2 \\ -1 \end{bmatrix} + t \begin{bmatrix} -4 \\ 0 \\ 5 \end{bmatrix}, \ t \in \mathcal{R}$ **b** $-4x + 5z = 24$
   c $(-5, 2, 9)$ or $(11, 2, -11)$

3 a $\doteq 15.79°$ **b** $\doteq 65.91°$

4 a $\begin{bmatrix} x \\ y \\ z \end{bmatrix} = \begin{bmatrix} 3 \\ -1 \\ 1 \end{bmatrix} + t \begin{bmatrix} -3 \\ 3 \\ -2 \end{bmatrix}, \ t \in \mathcal{R}$ **b** P$(\frac{6}{7}, \frac{8}{7}, -\frac{3}{7})$

5 $(6, -1, -10)$ **6 b** $\doteq 28.61°$ **c** 14 units

7 a $\frac{17}{3}$ units **b** $(\frac{8}{3}, \frac{7}{3}, \frac{4}{3})$

8 a $\overrightarrow{PQ} = \begin{bmatrix} 1 \\ 4 \\ -3 \end{bmatrix}$ $|\overrightarrow{PQ}| = \sqrt{26}$ units, $\overrightarrow{QR} = \begin{bmatrix} -4 \\ -1 \\ 4 \end{bmatrix}$

   b $x = 2 + t, \ y = 4t, \ z = 1 - 3t, \ t \in \mathcal{R}$

   c $\begin{bmatrix} x \\ y \\ z \end{bmatrix} = \begin{bmatrix} 2 \\ 0 \\ 1 \end{bmatrix} + \lambda \begin{bmatrix} 1 \\ 4 \\ -3 \end{bmatrix} + \mu \begin{bmatrix} -4 \\ -1 \\ 4 \end{bmatrix}, \ \lambda, \mu \in \mathcal{R}$

9 **a** 3 units **b** (1, 2, 4) **c** $\sqrt{116}$ units

10 **a** $5x + y + 4z = 3$ **b** $x = 5t$, $y = t$, $z = 4t$, $t \in \mathcal{R}$
 c $(\frac{5}{14}, \frac{1}{14}, \frac{2}{7})$

11 If $k = -2$, the planes meet in the line
$x = \frac{4}{3}$, $y = -\frac{11}{3} + t$, $z = t$, $t \in \mathcal{R}$. If $k \neq -2$
the planes meet at the point $(\frac{4}{3}, -\frac{14}{3}, -1)$

EXERCISE 18A

1 **a** Heights can take any value from 170 cm to 205 cm,
 e.g., 181.37 cm

b

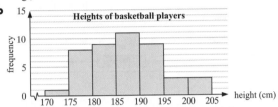

Heights of basketball players

c The modal class is (185-) cm, as this occurred the most
 frequently.

d slightly positively skewed

2 **a** Continuous numerical, but has been rounded to become
 discrete numerical data.

b

Stem	Leaf
0	3 6 8 8 8 8
1	0 0 0 0 2 2 2 4 4 4 4 5 5 5 5 6 6 6 6 7 8 8 8 8 9
2	0 0 0 1 2 4 5 5 5 6 7 7 8
3	1 2 2 2 3 4 5 7 8
4	0 2 5 5 5 6

1 | 2 means 12 minutes

c positively skewed

d The modal travelling time was between 10 and 20 minutes.

3 **a** column graph **b** histogram

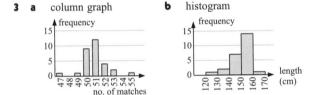

4 **a**

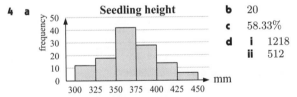

Seedling height

b 20
c 58.33%
d **i** 1218
 ii 512

EXERCISE 18B.1

1 **a** **i** 5.61 **ii** 6 **iii** 6 **b** **i** 16.3 **ii** 17 **iii** 18
 c **i** 24.8 **ii** 24.9 **iii** 23.5

2 **a** $A : 6.46$ $B : 6.85$ **b** $A : 7$ $B : 7$

 c The data sets are the same except for the last value, and
 the last value of A is less than the last value of B, so the
 mean of A is less than the mean of B.

 d The middle value of the data sets is the same, so the median is the same.

3 **a** mean: $29\,300, median: $23\,500, mode: $23\,000

 b The mode is the lowest value, so does not take the higher
 values into account.

 c No, since the data is positively skewed, the median is not
 in the centre.

4 **a** mean: 3.19, median: 0, mode: 0

b The data is very positively skewed so the median is not in
 the centre.

c The mode is the lowest value so does not take the higher
 values into account.

d yes, 21 and 42 **e** no

5 **a** 44 **b** 44 **c** 40.2 **d** increase mean to 40.3

6 116 **7** 3144 km **8** $185\,604 **9** $x = 15$

10 $a = 5$ **11** 37 **12** 14.77 **13** 9 and 7

EXERCISE 18B.2

1 **a** 1 **b** 1 **c** 1.43

2 **a** **i** 2.96 **ii** 2 **iii** 2

b

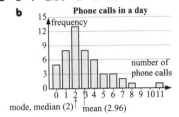

Phone calls in a day

mode, median (2) | mean (2.96)

c positively skewed
with data value
11 as an outlier

d The mean takes
into account the
larger numbers
of phone calls.

e the mean

3 **a** **i** 49 **ii** 49 **iii** 49.03 **b** no

 c The sample of only 30 is not large enough. The company
 could have won its case by arguing that a larger sample
 would have found an average of 50 matches per box.

4 **a** **i** 2.61 **ii** 2 **iii** 2 **b** This school has more children per
 family than the average Australian family. **c** positive

 d The mean is larger than the median and the mode.

5 **a** **i** 69.1 **ii** 67 **iii** 73 **b** **i** 5.86 **ii** 5.8 **iii** 6.7

6 **a** **i** 5.63 **ii** 6 **iii** 6 **b** **i** 6.79 **ii** 7 **iii** 7

 c the mean **d** yes

7 **a** mean = $163\,770, median = $147\,200 (differ by $16\,570)

 b **i** mean selling price **ii** median selling price

8 **a** $\doteqdot 70.9$ g **b** $\doteqdot 210$ g **c** 139 g **9** 10.1 cm

10 **a** mean for A $\doteqdot 50.8$, mean for B $\doteqdot 49.9$

 b No, as to the nearest match, A is 51 and B is 50.

11 17.25 goals per game **12** 6 and 12

13 **a** **i** $31\,500 **ii** $28\,000 **iii** $33\,300

 b The mean as it is the highest measure.

EXERCISE 18B.3

1 31.7

2 **a** 70 **b** $\doteqdot 411\,000$ litres, i.e., $\doteqdot 411$ kL **c** $\doteqdot 5870$ L

3 **a** 125 people **b** $\doteqdot 119$ marks **c** $\frac{3}{25}$ **d** 137 marks

EXERCISE 18C

1 **a** 8 **b** **i** 40 **ii** 40

2 **a**

Length (x cm)	Frequency	C. frequency
$24 \leqslant x < 27$	1	1
$27 \leqslant x < 30$	2	3
$30 \leqslant x < 33$	5	8
$33 \leqslant x < 36$	10	18
$36 \leqslant x < 39$	9	27
$39 \leqslant x < 42$	2	29
$42 \leqslant x < 45$	1	30

b
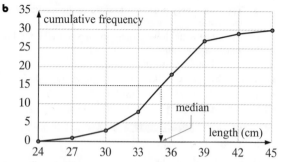

c median ≑ 35 cm

d actual median = 34.5, i.e., a good approximation

3
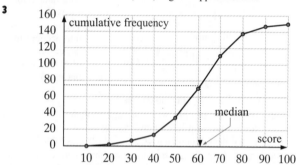

a ≑ 61   **b** ≑ 91 students   **c** ≑ 76 students
d 24 (or 25) students   **e** 76 marks

4 a 26 years   **b** 36%   **c i** 0.527   **ii** 0.030

5 a 2270 h   **b** 69.3%   **c** 62 or 63

EXERCISE 18D.1

1 a i 6   **ii** $Q_1 = 4$, $Q_3 = 7$ **iii** 7   **iv** 3
  b i 17.5   **ii** $Q_1 = 15$, $Q_3 = 19$ **iii** 14   **iv** 4
  c i 24.9   **ii** $Q_1 = 23.5$, $Q_3 = 26.1$ **iii** 7.7   **iv** 2.6

2 a median = 2.45, $Q_1 = 1.45$, $Q_3 = 3.8$
  b range = 5.2, IQR = 2.35
  c i ...... greater than 2.45 min   **ii** ...... less than 3.8 min
    iii The minimum waiting time was 0 minutes and the max-
       imum waiting time was 5.2 minutes. The waiting times
       were spread over 5.2 minutes.

3 a 3   **b** 42   **c** 20   **d** 13   **e** 29   **f** 39   **g** 16

4 a i 124 cm   **ii** $Q_1 = 116$ cm, $Q_3 = 130$ cm
  b i ...... 124 cm   **ii** ...... 130 cm tall
  c i 29 cm   **ii** 14 cm   **d** .... over 14 cm

5 a i 7   **ii** 6   **iii** 5   **iv** 7   **v** 2
  b i 10   **ii** 7   **iii** 6   **iv** 8   **v** 2

EXERCISE 18D.2

1 a i 35   **ii** 78   **iii** 13   **iv** 53   **v** 26   **b i** 65   **ii** 27

2 a ...... was 98, ... was 25
  b .... greater than or equal to 70   **c** .... at least 85 marks
  d ...... between 55 and 85 ......   **e** 73   **f** 30

3 a i min = 3, $Q_1 = 5$, median = 6, $Q_3 = 8$, max = 10
    ii
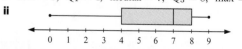
    iii range = 7   **iv** IQR = 3
  b i min = 0, $Q_1 = 4$, median = 7, $Q_3 = 8$, max = 9
    ii
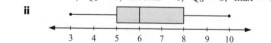

iii range = 9   **iv** IQR = 4

c i min = 117, $Q_1 = 127$, median = 132, $Q_3 = 145.5$,
    max = 151
  ii
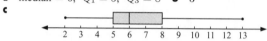

iii range = 34   **iv** IQR = 18.5

4 a

Statistic	Year 9	Year 12
min value	1	6
Q_1	5	10
median	7.5	14
Q_3	10	16
max value	12	17.5

b i Year 9: 11,
    Year 12: 11.5
  ii Year 9: 5,
    Year 12: 6
c i true
  ii true

5 a median = 6, $Q_1 = 5$, $Q_3 = 8$ **b** 3
  c
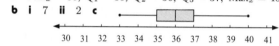

6 a $Min_x = 33$, $Q_1 = 35$, $Q_2 = 36$, $Q_3 = 37$, $Max_x = 40$
  b i 7   **ii** 2   **c**
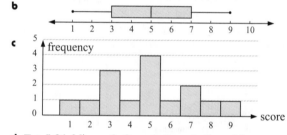

7 a 10   **b** ≑ 28.3%   **c** 7 cm   **d** IQR ≑ 2.6 cm
  e 10 cm, which means that 90% of the seedlings have a
    height of 10 cm or less.

8 a 27 min   **b** 29 min   **c** $31\frac{1}{2}$ min   **d** IQR ≑ $4\frac{1}{2}$ min
  e 28 min 10 sec

EXERCISE 18E.1

1 a $\overline{x} ≑ 4.87$, $Min_x = 1$, $Q_1 = 3$, $Q_2 = 5$, $Q_3 = 7$, $Max_x = 9$
  b

  c
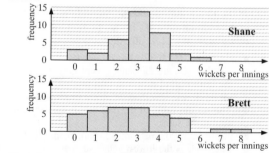

d $\overline{x} ≑ 5.24$, $Min_x = 2$, $Q_1 = 4$, $Q_2 = 5$, $Q_3 = 6.5$,
    $Max_x = 9$

EXERCISE 18E.2

1 a discrete
  c

d There are no outliers for Shane. Brett has outliers of 7 and
    8 which must not be removed.
  e Shane's distribution is reasonably symmetrical.
    Brett's distribution is positively skewed.

f Shane has a higher mean ($\doteqdot 2.89$ wickets) compared with Brett ($\doteqdot 2.67$ wickets). Shane has a higher median (3 wickets) compared with Brett (2.5 wickets). Shane's modal number of wickets is 3 (14 times) compared with Brett, who has a bi-modal distribution of 2 and 3 (7 times each).

g Shane's range is 6 wickets, compared with Brett's range of 8 wickets. Shane's IQR is 2 wickets, compared with Brett's IQR of 3 wickets. Brett's wicket taking shows greater spread or variability.

h

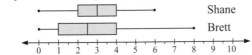

Shane

Brett

i Generally, Shane takes more wickets than Brett and is a more consistent bowler.

2 a continuous

c For the 'New type' globes, 191 hours could be considered an outlier. However, it could be a genuine piece of data, so we will include it in the analysis.

d

	Old type	New type
Mean	107	134
Median	110.5	132
Range	56	84
IQR	19	18.5

The mean and median are $\doteqdot 25\%$ and $\doteqdot 19\%$ higher for the 'new type' of globe compared with the 'old type'.
The range is higher for the 'new type' of globe (but has been affected by the 191 hours).
The IQR for each type of globe is almost the same.

e

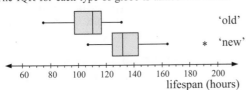

'old'

* 'new'

lifespan (hours)

f For the 'old type' of globe, the data is bunched to the right of the median, hence the distribution is negatively skewed. For the 'new type' of globe, the data is bunched to the left of the median, hence the distribution is positively skewed.

g The manufacturer's claim, that the 'new type' of globe has a 20% longer life than the 'old type' seems to be backed up by the 25% higher mean life and 19.5% higher median life.

EXERCISE 18F

1 a Sally: $\overline{x} = 25$, $s = 4.97$; Joanne: $\overline{x} = 30.5$, $s = 12.56$

b The standard deviation is an indicator of consistency; lower s means better consistency.

2 a Glen: range $= 11$, $\overline{x} = 5.7$;
Shane: range $= 11$, $\overline{x} = 5.7$

b We suspect Glen's, he has two zeros.

c Glen: $s = 3.9$ $\leftarrow$ greater variability
Shane: $s = 3.29$

d standard deviation

3 a We suspect variability in standard deviation since the factors may change every day.

b i sample mean **ii** sample standard deviation

c less variability

4 a $\overline{x} = 69$, $s = 6.05$ **b** $\overline{x} = 79$, $s = 6.05$

c The distribution has simply shifted by 10 kg. The mean increases by 10 kg and the standard deviation remains the same.

5 a $\overline{x} = 1.01$ kg; $s = 0.17$ **b** $\overline{x} = 2.02$ kg; $s = 0.34$

c Doubling the values doubles the mean and the standard deviation.

6 a $s_n \doteqdot 6.77$ kg **b** $\mu \doteqdot 93.8$ kg, $\sigma \doteqdot 6.81$ kg

7 a $\overline{x} \doteqdot 77.5$ g, $s_n \doteqdot 7.45$ g **b** $\mu = 77.5$ g, $\sigma \doteqdot 7.68$ g

8 $p = 6$, $q = 9$ **9** $a = 8$, $b = 6$

10 a $\displaystyle\sum_{i=1}^{n}(x_i - \overline{x})^2 = \sum_{i=1}^{n} x_i{}^2 - n\overline{x}^2$

b i 32.4 min **ii** 9.86 min

11 a $\overline{x} \doteqdot 1.72$ children, $s \doteqdot 1.67$ children

b $\mu \doteqdot 1.72$ children, $\sigma \doteqdot 1.68$ children

12 a $\overline{x} = 14.5$ years, $s \doteqdot 1.75$ years

b $\mu \doteqdot 14.5$ years, $\sigma \doteqdot 1.78$ years

13 a $\overline{x} \doteqdot 37.3$ toothpicks, $s \doteqdot 1.45$ toothpicks

b $\mu \doteqdot 37.3$ toothpicks, $\sigma \doteqdot 1.47$ toothpicks

14 a $\overline{x} \doteqdot 47.8$ cm, $s \doteqdot 2.66$ cm

b $\mu \doteqdot 47.8$ cm, $\sigma \doteqdot 2.70$ cm

15 a $\overline{x} = \$390.30$, $s \doteqdot \$15.87$ **b** $\mu \doteqdot \$390.30$, $\sigma \doteqdot \$15.91$

EXERCISE 18G

1 a 16% **b** 84% **c** 97.4% **d** 0.15%

2 3 times **3 a** 5 **b** 32 **c** 136

4 a 458 babies **b** 444 babies

REVIEW SET 18A

1 a Diameter of bacteria colonies **b i** 3.15 cm
ii 4.5 cm

0	4 8 9
1	3 5 5 7
2	1 1 5 6 8 8
3	0 1 2 3 4 5 5 6 6 7 7 9
4	0 1 2 7 9

leaf unit: 0.1 cm

c The distribution is slightly negatively skewed.

2 a highest $= 97.5$ m, lowest $= 64.6$ m

b use groups 60 -, 65 -, 70 -, etc.

c

A frequency distribution table for distances thrown by Thabiso		
distance (m)	tally	freq. (f)
60 -	I	1
65 -	III	3
70 -	HHT	5
75 -	II	2
80 -	HHT III	8
85 -	HHT I	6
90 -	III	3
$95 < 100$	II	2
	Total	30

d

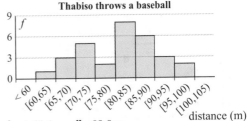

Frequency histogram displaying the distance Thabiso throws a baseball

distance (m)

e i $\doteqdot 81.1$ m **ii** 83.0 m

3 $a = 8$ and $b = 6$ or $a = 6$ and $b = 8$

4 a

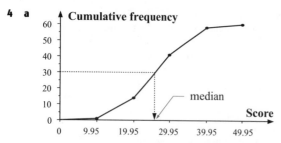

b $\div 25.9$ **c** $\div 12.0$ **d** $\overline{x} \div 26.0$, $s \div 8.31$

5 a

	Girls	*Boys*
shape	pos. skewed	approx. symm.
centre (median)	36.3 sec	34.9 sec
spread (range)	7.7 sec	4.9 sec

b The girls' distribution is positively skewed and boys' distribution is approximately symmetrical. The median swim times for boys is 1.4 seconds lower than for girls but the range of the girls' swim times is 2.8 seconds higher than for boys. The analysis supports the conjecture that boys generally swim faster than girls with less spread of times.

6 a

	A	*B*
Min	11	11.2
Q_1	11.6	12
Median	12	12.6
Q_3	12.6	13.2
Max	13	13.8

b i
ii

	A	*B*
Range	2	2.6
IQR	1	1.2

c i The members of squad *A* generally ran faster times.
ii The times in squad *B* were more varied.

7 a i 101.5 **ii** 98 **iii** 105.5 **b** 7.5 **c** $\overline{x} = 100.2$, $s \div 7.59$
8 a $\overline{x} \div 33.1$ L, $s \div 7.63$ L   **b** $\mu \div 33.1$ L, $\sigma \div 7.66$ L
9 a $2\frac{1}{2}\%$ **b** 95% **c** 68%

EXERCISE 19A

1 a 0.78 **b** 0.22 **2 a** 0.487 **b** 0.051 **c** 0.731
3 a 43 days **b i** $\div 0.047$ **ii** $\div 0.186$ **iii** 0.465
4 a $\div 0.089$ **b** $\div 0.126$

EXERCISE 19B

1 a {A, B, C, D}   **b** {BB, BG, GB, GG}
c {ABCD, ABDC, ACBD, ACDB, ADBC, ADCB, BACD,
BADC, BCAD, BCDA, BDAC, BDCA, CABD, CADB,
CBDA, CBDA, CDAB, CDBA, DABC, DACB, DBAC,
DBCA, DCAB, DCBA}
d {GGG, GGB, GBG, BGG, GBB, BGB, BBG, BBB}
2 a

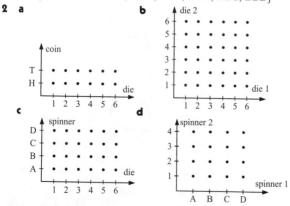

3 a

b

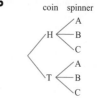

c

d

EXERCISE 19C

1 a $\frac{1}{5}$ **b** $\frac{1}{3}$ **c** $\frac{7}{15}$ **d** $\frac{4}{5}$ **e** $\frac{1}{5}$ **f** $\frac{8}{15}$
2 a 4 **b i** $\frac{2}{3}$ **ii** $\frac{1}{3}$
3 a $\frac{1}{4}$ **b** $\frac{1}{9}$ **c** $\frac{4}{9}$ **d** $\frac{1}{36}$ **e** $\frac{1}{18}$ **f** $\frac{1}{6}$
4 a $\frac{1}{7}$ **b** $\frac{2}{7}$ **c** $\frac{124}{1461}$ **d** $\frac{237}{1461}$ {remember leap years}
5 {AKN, ANK, KAN, KNA, NAK, NKA} **a** $\frac{1}{3}$ **b** $\frac{1}{3}$ **c** $\frac{1}{3}$ **d** $\frac{2}{3}$
6 a {GGG, GGB, GBG, BGG, GBB, BGB, BBG, BBB}
b i $\frac{1}{8}$ **ii** $\frac{1}{8}$ **iii** $\frac{1}{8}$ **iv** $\frac{3}{8}$ **v** $\frac{1}{2}$ **vi** $\frac{7}{8}$
7 a {ABCD, ABDC, ACBD, ACDB, ADBC, ADCB,
BACD, BADC, BCAD, BCDA, BDAC, BDCA,
CABD, CADB, CBAD, CBDA, CDAB, CDBA,
DABC, DACB, DBAC, DBCA, DCAB, DCBA}
b i $\frac{1}{2}$ **ii** $\frac{1}{2}$ **iii** $\frac{1}{2}$ **iv** $\frac{1}{2}$ **8** $\frac{4}{9}$

EXERCISE 19D

1

a $\frac{1}{4}$ **b** $\frac{1}{4}$ **c** $\frac{1}{2}$ **d** $\frac{3}{4}$

2 a

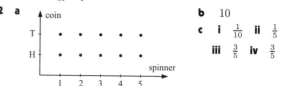

b 10
c i $\frac{1}{10}$ **ii** $\frac{1}{5}$
iii $\frac{3}{5}$ **iv** $\frac{3}{5}$

3 a $\frac{1}{36}$ **b** $\frac{1}{18}$ **c** $\frac{5}{9}$ **d** $\frac{11}{36}$ **e** $\frac{5}{18}$ **f** $\frac{25}{36}$ **g** $\frac{1}{6}$
h $\frac{5}{18}$ **i** $\frac{2}{9}$ **j** $\frac{13}{18}$

EXERCISE 19E.1

1 a $\frac{6}{7}$ **b** $\frac{36}{49}$ **c** $\frac{216}{343}$ **2 a** $\frac{1}{8}$ **b** $\frac{1}{8}$
3 a 0.0096 **b** 0.8096 **4 a** $\frac{1}{16}$ **b** $\frac{15}{16}$
5 a 0.56 **b** 0.06 **c** 0.14 **d** 0.24 **6 a** $\frac{8}{125}$ **b** $\frac{12}{125}$ **c** $\frac{27}{125}$

EXERCISE 19E.2

1 a $\frac{7}{15}$ **b** $\frac{7}{30}$ **c** $\frac{7}{15}$ **2 a** $\frac{14}{55}$ **b** $\frac{1}{55}$
3 a $\frac{3}{100}$ **b** $\frac{3}{100} \times \frac{2}{99} \div 0.0006$
c $\frac{3}{100} \times \frac{2}{99} \times \frac{1}{98} \div 0.000\,006$ **d** $\frac{97}{100} \times \frac{96}{99} \times \frac{95}{98} \div 0.912$
4 a $\frac{3}{7}$ **b** $\frac{1}{7}$

EXERCISE 19F

1 a

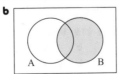

1st spin   2nd spin

$\frac{1}{2}$ — B
$\frac{1}{2}$ B $\frac{1}{4}$ — R
$\frac{1}{4}$ — Y

$\frac{1}{4}$ R $\frac{1}{2}$ — B
$\frac{1}{4}$ — R
$\frac{1}{4}$ — Y

$\frac{1}{4}$ Y $\frac{1}{2}$ — B
$\frac{1}{4}$ — R
$\frac{1}{4}$ — Y

b $\frac{1}{4}$ **c** $\frac{1}{16}$

d $\frac{5}{8}$ **e** $\frac{3}{4}$

2

$\frac{1}{5}$ rain $\frac{1}{2}$ — win
$\frac{1}{2}$ — lose

$\frac{4}{5}$ no rain $\frac{1}{20}$ — win
$\frac{19}{20}$ — lose

$\Pr(\text{win}) = \frac{7}{50}$

3 0.032 **4** $\frac{17}{40}$ **5 a** $\frac{11}{30}$ **b** $\frac{19}{30}$

EXERCISE 19G

1 a $\frac{20}{49}$ **b** $\frac{10}{21}$ **2 a** $\frac{3}{10}$ **b** $\frac{1}{10}$ **c** $\frac{3}{5}$

3 a $\frac{2}{9}$ **b** $\frac{5}{9}$ **4 a** $\frac{1}{3}$ **b** $\frac{2}{15}$ **c** $\frac{4}{15}$ **d** $\frac{4}{15}$

These cases cover all possibilities, so their probabilities must sum to 1.

5 a $\frac{1}{5}$ **b** $\frac{3}{5}$ **c** $\frac{4}{5}$ **6** $\frac{19}{45}$ **7 a** $\frac{2}{100} \times \frac{1}{99} \doteqdot 0.0002$

b $\frac{98}{100} \times \frac{97}{99} \doteqdot 0.9602$ **c** $1 - \frac{98}{100} \times \frac{97}{99} \doteqdot 0.0398$

EXERCISE 19H

1 a $(p+q)^4 = p^4 + 4p^3q + 6p^2q^2 + 4pq^3 + q^4$

b $4(\frac{1}{2})^3(\frac{1}{2}) = \frac{1}{4}$

2 a $(p+q)^5 = p^5 + 5p^4q + 10p^3q^2 + 10p^2q^3 + 5pq^4 + q^5$

b i $5(\frac{1}{2})^4(\frac{1}{2}) = \frac{5}{32}$ **ii** $10(\frac{1}{2})^2(\frac{1}{2})^3 = \frac{5}{16}$

3 a $\left(\frac{2}{3} + \frac{1}{3}\right)^4 = \left(\frac{2}{3}\right)^4 + 4\left(\frac{2}{3}\right)^3\left(\frac{1}{3}\right) + 6\left(\frac{2}{3}\right)^2\left(\frac{1}{3}\right)^2 + 4\left(\frac{2}{3}\right)\left(\frac{1}{3}\right)^3 + \left(\frac{1}{3}\right)^4$ **b i** $\left(\frac{2}{3}\right)^4 = \frac{16}{81}$ **ii** $6\left(\frac{2}{3}\right)^2\left(\frac{1}{3}\right)^2 = \frac{8}{27}$ **iii** $\frac{8}{9}$

4 a $\left(\frac{3}{4} + \frac{1}{4}\right)^5 = \left(\frac{3}{4}\right)^5 + 5\left(\frac{3}{4}\right)^4\left(\frac{1}{4}\right)^1 + 10\left(\frac{3}{4}\right)^3\left(\frac{1}{4}\right)^2 + 10\left(\frac{3}{4}\right)^2\left(\frac{1}{4}\right)^3 + 5\left(\frac{3}{4}\right)\left(\frac{1}{4}\right)^4 + \left(\frac{1}{4}\right)^5$

b i $10\left(\frac{3}{4}\right)^3\left(\frac{1}{4}\right)^2 = \frac{135}{512}$ **ii** $\frac{53}{512}$

5 a $\doteqdot 0.154$ **b** $\doteqdot 0.973$ **6 a** $\doteqdot 0.0305$ **b** $\doteqdot 0.265$

7 $\doteqdot 0.000864$ **8** $\doteqdot 0.0341$

EXERCISE 19I

1 a

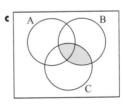

b

c

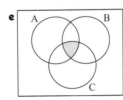

d

e

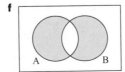

f

---

2 a 29 **b** 17 **c** 26 **d** 5 **3 a** 65 **b** 9 **c** 4 **d** 52

4 a $\frac{19}{40}$ **b** $\frac{1}{2}$ **c** $\frac{4}{5}$ **d** $\frac{5}{8}$ **e** $\frac{13}{40}$ **f** $\frac{7}{20}$

5 a $\frac{19}{25}$ **b** $\frac{13}{25}$ **c** $\frac{6}{25}$ **d** $\frac{7}{19}$

6 a $\frac{7}{15}$ **b** $\frac{1}{15}$ **c** $\frac{2}{15}$ **d** $\frac{6}{7}$

7 a

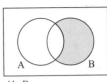

A'

b

A'∩B

c

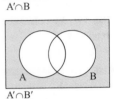

A ∪ B'

d

A'∩B'

8 a

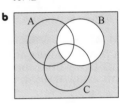

b

c

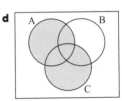

d

e

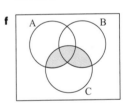

f

9 For each of these draw **two** diagrams, shade the first with the LHS set and the second with the RHS set.

10 a A = {7, 14, 21, 28, 35, ..., 98}
B = {5, 10, 15, 20, 25, ..., 95}
  i $n(A) = 14$ **ii** $n(B) = 19$ **iii** 2 **iv** 31

11 a i $\frac{b+c}{a+b+c+d}$ **ii** $\frac{b}{a+b+c+d}$ **iii** $\frac{a+b+c}{a+b+c+d}$ **iv** $\frac{a+b+c}{a+b+c+d}$

b P(A or B) = P(A) + P(B) − P(A and B)

EXERCISE 19J

1 a

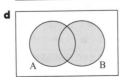

22 study both

b i $\frac{9}{25}$ **ii** $\frac{11}{20}$

2 a $\frac{3}{8}$ **b** $\frac{7}{20}$ **c** $\frac{1}{5}$ **d** $\frac{15}{23}$

3 a $\frac{14}{25}$ **b** $\frac{4}{5}$ **c** $\frac{1}{5}$ **d** $\frac{5}{23}$ **e** $\frac{9}{14}$ **4** $\frac{5}{6}$

5 a $\frac{13}{20}$ **b** $\frac{7}{20}$ **c** $\frac{11}{50}$ **d** $\frac{7}{25}$ **e** $\frac{4}{7}$ **f** $\frac{1}{4}$

6 a $\frac{3}{5}$ **b** $\frac{2}{3}$ **7 a** 0.46 **b** $\frac{14}{23}$ **8** $\frac{70}{163}$

9 a 0.45 **b** 0.75 **c** 0.65 **10 a** 0.0484 **b** 0.3926
11 $\frac{2}{3}$

EXERCISE 19K

1 $P(R \cap S) = 0.2$ and $P(R) \times P(S) = 0.2$
$\therefore$ are independent events

2 a $\frac{7}{30}$ **b** $\frac{7}{12}$ **c** $\frac{7}{10}$ No, as $P(A \cap B) \neq P(A) \times P(B)$

3 a 0.35 **b** 0.85 **c** 0.15 **d** 0.15 **e** 0.5

4 $\frac{14}{15}$ **5 a** $\frac{91}{216}$ **b** 26

6 Hint: Show $P(A \cap B') = P(A)\, P(B')$
using a Venn diagram and $P(A \cap B)$

EXERCISE 19L

1 $\div 0.655$ **2** $\frac{1}{12}$ **3** $\div 0.318$ **4** $\div 0.530$

5 a $\frac{2}{5}$ **b** $\frac{2}{5}$ **6 a** $\div 0.0288$ **b** $\div 0.635$ **c** $\div 0.966$ **7** $\frac{1}{5}$

EXERCISE 19M

1 a 0.0435 **b** $\div 0.598$ **2 a** $\div 0.773$ **b** $\div 0.556$

3 $\frac{10}{13}$ **4** $\div 0.424$ **5 b i** 0.95 **ii** $\div 0.306$ **iii** 0.6

6 a 0.104 **b** $\div 0.267$ **c** $\div 0.0168$

REVIEW SET 19A

1 ABCD, ABDC, ACBD, ACDB, ADBC, ADCB, BACD, BADC,
BCAD, BCDA, BDAC, BDCA, CABD, CADB, CBAD, CBDA,
CDAB, CDBA, DABC, DACB, DBAC, DBCA, DCAB, DCBA
a $\frac{1}{2}$ **b** $\frac{1}{3}$

2 a $\frac{3}{8}$ **b** $\frac{1}{8}$ **c** $\frac{5}{8}$ **3 a** $\frac{3}{25}$ **b** $\frac{24}{25}$ **c** $\frac{11}{12}$

4 P(N wins)
$= \frac{44}{125}$
$= 0.352$

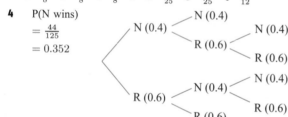

5 a $\frac{2}{5}$ **b** $\frac{13}{15}$ **c** $\frac{4}{15}$

6 a $10(\frac{4}{5})^3(\frac{1}{5})^2 \div 0.205$ **b** $5(\frac{4}{5})^4(\frac{1}{5}) + (\frac{4}{5})^5 \div 0.737$

7 a $\frac{4}{500} \times \frac{3}{499} \times \frac{2}{498} \div 0.000\,000\,193$

b $1 - \frac{496}{500} \times \frac{495}{499} \times \frac{494}{498} \div 0.023\,86$

8

W (0.95) — W (0.95)
           W' (0.05)
                    0.9975
W' (0.05) — W (0.95)
           W' (0.05)

9 a $\div 0.0238$ **b** $\div 0.976$ **10 a** $\frac{1}{10}$ **b** $\frac{1}{5}$

11 a $\div 0.259$ **b** $\div 0.703$

EXERCISE 20A.1

1 a 96.2 km/h **b** 65.5 km/h

2 a 800 m **b** 125 **c** 125 m/min **d** average walking speed
e 8 minutes **f** 66.7 m/min **g** 1.6 km **3** 509 000 kL/day

4 a 1.187 kL/day **b** 1.029 kL/day **c** 1.052 kL/day

EXERCISE 20A.2

1 a 0.1 m/s **b** 0.9 m/s **c** 0.5 m/s

2 a i 3.2 beetles/gram **ii** 4.5 beetles/gram
b No effect 0 to 1 gram, rapid decrease 1 to 8 grams,
rate of decrease decreases for 8 to 14 grams.

EXERCISE 20B.1

1 a 1 m/s **b** 3 km/h **c** $\frac{1}{20}$ \$1000/item **d** -5 bats/week
2 a 8000 L **b** 3000 L **c** 7500 L/hour **d** 3000 L/hour

EXERCISE 20B.2

1 3 **2 b** $1 + 3h + 3h^2 + h^3$ **c** M$\left(1 + h, (1+h)^3\right)$
d $3 + 3h + h^2$ **e** 3

3 b $8 + 12h + 6h^2 + h^3$ **c** M$\left(2 + h, (2+h)^3\right)$
d $12 + 6h + h^2$ **e** 12

4 a $\dfrac{-h}{x(x+h)}$ **b** M$\left(2 + h, \dfrac{1}{2+h}\right)$ slope MF $= \dfrac{-1}{2(2+h)}$

c $-\frac{1}{4}$ **d** $-\frac{1}{9}$

5 b $\dfrac{1}{(2+h)^2} - \frac{1}{4}$ **c** **d** $-\frac{1}{4}$
$= \dfrac{-4h - h^2}{4(2+h)^2}$

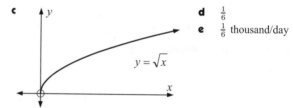

$y = \dfrac{1}{x^2}$

6 a $\dfrac{1}{\sqrt{x+h} + \sqrt{x}}$ **b** $\dfrac{\sqrt{9+h} - 3}{h} = \dfrac{1}{\sqrt{9+h} + 3}$

c **d** $\frac{1}{6}$
e $\frac{1}{6}$ thousand/day

$y = \sqrt{x}$

REVIEW SET 20

1 a 10 m/s **b** 4.6 m/s **2 b** $\div 5.9$ **3** 8

4 a $4x^2 + 8xh + 4h^2 + 12x + 12h + 9$ **b** $8x + 12 + 4h$
c It is the slope of chord AB. **d i** $8x + 12$ **ii** 20
e i $8x + 12$ gives us the slope of the tangent at any point
with x-coordinate x.
ii 20 is the slope of the tangent at $x = 1$.

5 a 11 m/s **b** $(8 + h)$ m/s
c 8 m/s, the instantaneous velocity at $t = 2$ sec

EXERCISE 21A

1 a 6 **b** $-\frac{1}{4}$ **2 b** 12

3 a Hint: $x - a = \left(\sqrt{x} + \sqrt{a}\right)\left(\sqrt{x} - \sqrt{a}\right)$ **b** $\frac{1}{6}$

EXERCISE 21B

1 a -4 **b** 1 **c** -12 **d** 3

2 a -1 **b** $\frac{3}{4}$ **c** $-\frac{1}{32}$ **d** -12 **e** -1 **f** $-\frac{45}{289}$

3 a $\frac{1}{4}$ **b** 1 **c** $-\frac{1}{27}$ **d** $\frac{1}{4}$

4 a 9 **b** 10 **c** $-\frac{2}{25}$ **d** $-\frac{2}{27}$ **e** $\frac{1}{4}$ **f** $-\frac{1}{2}$

5 a 12 **b** 108

EXERCISE 21C

1 a 1 **b** 0 **c** $3x^2$ **d** $4x^3$

2 a 2 **b** $2x - 3$ **c** $3x^2 - 4x$

3 a $\dfrac{-1}{(x+2)^2}$ **b** $\dfrac{-2}{(2x-1)^2}$ **c** $-\dfrac{2}{x^3}$ **d** $-\dfrac{3}{x^4}$

4 a $\dfrac{1}{2\sqrt{x+2}}$ **b** $-\dfrac{1}{2x\sqrt{x}}$ **c** $\dfrac{1}{\sqrt{2x+1}}$

5

Function	Derivative	Function	Derivative
x	1	x^{-2}	$-2x^{-3}$
x^2	$2x^1$	x^{-3}	$-3x^{-4}$
x^3	$3x^2$	$x^{\frac{1}{2}}$	$\frac{1}{2}x^{-\frac{1}{2}}$
x^4	$4x^3$	$x^{-\frac{1}{2}}$	$-\frac{1}{2}x^{-\frac{3}{2}}$
x^{-1}	$-x^{-2}$	x^n	nx^{n-1}

EXERCISE 21D

1 a $3x^2$ **b** $6x^2$ **c** $14x$ **d** $2x+1$ **e** $-4x$
f $2x+3$ **g** $3x^2+6x+4$ **h** $20x^3-12x$ **i** $\dfrac{6}{x^2}$
j $-\dfrac{2}{x^2}+\dfrac{6}{x^3}$ **k** $2x-\dfrac{5}{x^2}$ **l** $2x+\dfrac{3}{x^2}$ **m** $-\dfrac{1}{2x\sqrt{x}}$
n $8x-4$ **o** $3x^2+12x+12$

2 a $6x^2-14x$ **b** $2\pi x$ **c** $-\dfrac{2}{5x^3}$ **d** 100 **e** 10 **f** $12\pi x^2$

3 a 6 **b** $\dfrac{3\sqrt{x}}{2}$ **c** $2x-10$ **d** $2-9x^2$ **e** $4+\dfrac{1}{4x^2}$
f $6x^2-6x-5$

4 a 4 **b** $-\dfrac{16}{729}$ **c** -7 **d** $\dfrac{13}{4}$ **e** $\dfrac{1}{8}$ **f** -11

5 a $\dfrac{2}{\sqrt{x}}+1$ **b** $\dfrac{1}{3\sqrt[3]{x^2}}$ **c** $\dfrac{1}{x\sqrt{x}}$ **d** $2-\dfrac{1}{2\sqrt{x}}$
e $-\dfrac{2}{x\sqrt{x}}$ **f** $6x-\dfrac{3}{2}\sqrt{x}$ **g** $\dfrac{-25}{2x^3\sqrt{x}}$ **h** $2+\dfrac{9}{2x^2\sqrt{x}}$

6 a $\dfrac{dy}{dx}=4+\dfrac{3}{x^2}$, $\dfrac{dy}{dx}$ is the slope function of $y=4x-\dfrac{3}{x}$
from which the slope at any point can be found.
b $\dfrac{dS}{dt}=4t+4$ metres per second, $\dfrac{dS}{dt}$ is the
instantaneous rate of change in position at the time t,
i.e., it is the velocity function.
c $\dfrac{dC}{dx}=3+0.004x$ dollars per toaster, $\dfrac{dC}{dx}$ is the
instantaneous rate of change in cost as the number of
toasters changes.

EXERCISE 21E.1

1 a $f(g(x))=(2x+7)^2$ **b** $f(g(x))=2x^2+7$
c $f(g(x))=\sqrt{3-4x}$ **d** $f(g(x))=3-4\sqrt{x}$
e $f(g(x))=\dfrac{2}{x^2+3}$ **f** $f(g(x))=\dfrac{4}{x^2}+3$

2 a $f(x)=x^3$, $g(x)=3x+10$
b $f(x)=\dfrac{1}{x}$, $g(x)=2x+4$
c $f(x)=\sqrt{x}$, $g(x)=x^2-3x$
d $f(x)=\dfrac{10}{x^3}$, $g(x)=3x-x^2$

EXERCISE 21E.2

1 a u^{-2}, $u=2x-1$ **b** $u^{\frac{1}{2}}$, $u=x^2-3x$
c $2u^{-\frac{1}{2}}$, $u=2-x^2$ **d** $u^{\frac{1}{3}}$, $u=x^3-x^2$
e $4u^{-3}$, $u=3-x$ **f** $10u^{-1}$, $u=x^2-3$

2 a $8(4x-5)$ **b** $2(5-2x)^{-2}$ **c** $\frac{1}{2}(3x-x^2)^{-\frac{1}{2}}\times(3-2x)$
d $-12(1-3x)^3$ **e** $-18(5-x)^2$
f $\frac{1}{3}(2x^3-x^2)^{-\frac{2}{3}}\times(6x^2-2x)$ **g** $-60(5x-4)^{-3}$

h $-4(3x-x^2)^{-2}\times(3-2x)$ **i** $6(x^2-\dfrac{2}{x})^2\times(2x+\dfrac{2}{x^2})$

3 a $-\dfrac{1}{\sqrt{3}}$ **b** -18 **c** -8 **d** -4 **e** $-\dfrac{3}{32}$ **f** 0

4 a $\dfrac{dy}{dx}=3x^2$, $\dfrac{dx}{dy}=\frac{1}{3}y^{-\frac{2}{3}}$ **Hint:** Substitute $y=x^3$
b $\dfrac{dy}{dx}\times\dfrac{dx}{dy}=\dfrac{dy}{dy}=1$

EXERCISE 21F.1

1 a $2x(2x-1)+2x^2$ **b** $4(2x+1)^3+24x(2x+1)^2$
c $2x(3-x)^{\frac{1}{2}}-\frac{1}{2}x^2(3-x)^{-\frac{1}{2}}$
d $\frac{1}{2}x^{-\frac{1}{2}}(x-3)^2+2\sqrt{x}(x-3)$
e $10x(3x^2-1)^2+60x^3(3x^2-1)$
f $\frac{1}{2}x^{-\frac{1}{2}}(x-x^2)^3+3\sqrt{x}(x-x^2)^2(1-2x)$

2 a -48 **b** $406\frac{1}{4}$ **c** $\dfrac{13}{3}$ **d** $\dfrac{11}{2}$ **3** $x=3$ or $\dfrac{3}{5}$

EXERCISE 21F.2

1 a $\dfrac{3(2-x)+(1+3x)}{(2-x)^2}$ **b** $\dfrac{2x(2x+1)-2x^2}{(2x+1)^2}$
c $\dfrac{(x^2-3)-2x^2}{(x^2-3)^2}$ **d** $\dfrac{\frac{1}{2}x^{-\frac{1}{2}}(1-2x)+2\sqrt{x}}{(1-2x)^2}$
e $\dfrac{2x(3x-x^2)-(x^2-3)(3-2x)}{(3x-x^2)^2}$
f $\dfrac{(1-3x)^{\frac{1}{2}}+\frac{3}{2}x(1-3x)^{-\frac{1}{2}}}{1-3x}$

2 a 1 **b** 1 **c** $-\dfrac{7}{324}$ **d** $-\dfrac{28}{27}$

3 a i never (note: $\dfrac{dy}{dx}$ is undefined at $x=-1$)
ii $x\leqslant 0$ and $x=1$ **b i** $x=-2\pm\sqrt{11}$ **ii** $x=-2$

EXERCISE 21G

1 a $y=-7x+11$ **b** $4y=x+8$ **c** $y=-2x-2$
d $y=-2x+6$
2 a $6y=-x+57$ **b** $7y=-x+26$ **c** $3y=x+11$
d $x+6y=43$
3 a $y=21$ and $y=-6$ **b** $(\frac{1}{2}, 2\sqrt{2})$ **c** $k=-5$
d $y=-3x+1$
4 a $a=-4$, $b=7$ **b** $a=2$, $b=4$
5 a $3y=x+5$ **b** $9y=x+4$ **c** $16y=x-3$
d $y=-4$
6 a $y=2x-\dfrac{7}{4}$ **b** $y=-27x-\dfrac{242}{3}$
c $57y=-4x+1042$ **d** $2y=x+1$
7 $a=4$, $b=3$ **8 a** $(-4,-64)$ **b** $(4,-31)$
c does not meet the curve again
9 a $y=(2a-1)x-a^2+9$; $y=5x$, contact at $(3, 15)$
$y=-7x$, contact at $(-3, 21)$
b $y=0$, $y=27x+54$ **c** $y=0$, $y=-\sqrt{14}x+4\sqrt{14}$

EXERCISE 21H

1 a 6 **b** $12x-6$ **c** $\dfrac{3}{2x^{\frac{5}{2}}}$ **d** $\dfrac{12-6x}{x^4}$ **e** $24-48x$
f $\dfrac{20}{(2x-1)^3}$ **2 a** $-6x$ **b** $2-\dfrac{30}{x^4}$ **c** $-\dfrac{9}{4}x^{-\frac{5}{2}}$ **d** $\dfrac{8}{x^3}$
e $6(x^2-3x)(5x^2-15x+9)$ **f** $2+\dfrac{2}{(1-x)^3}$

3 a $x=1$ **b** $x=0$, $\pm\sqrt{6}$

REVIEW SET 21A

1 $y = 4x + 2$ **2 a** $6x - 4x^3$ **b** $1 + \dfrac{1}{x^2}$ **3** $2x + 2$

4 $x = 1$ **5** $(-2, -25)$ **6** $a = \frac{5}{2}$, $b = -\frac{3}{2}$ **7** $a = \frac{1}{2}$

8 $y = 16x - \dfrac{127}{2}$

9 a $\dfrac{dM}{dt} = 8t(t^2+3)^3$ **b** $\dfrac{dA}{dt} = \dfrac{\frac{1}{2}t(t+5)^{-\frac{1}{2}} - 2(t+5)^{\frac{1}{2}}}{t^3}$

10 a $-\dfrac{2}{x\sqrt{x}} - 3$ **b** $4\left(x - \dfrac{1}{x}\right)^3\left(1 + \dfrac{1}{x^2}\right)$

   c $\frac{1}{2}(x^2 - 3x)^{-\frac{1}{2}}(2x - 3)$

EXERCISE 22A

1 a $118\,000$ **b** $\dfrac{dP}{dt} = 4t - 12$ $1000 per year

   c $\dfrac{dP}{dt}$ is the rate of change in profit with time

   d i $0 \leqslant t \leqslant 3$ years **ii** $t \geqslant 3$ years

   e minimum profit is $100\,000 when $t = 3$

   f $\left.\dfrac{dP}{dt}\right]_{t=4} = 4$ Profit is increasing at $4000 per year after 4 years.

   $\left.\dfrac{dP}{dt}\right]_{t=10} = 28$ Profit is increasing at $28\,000 per year after 10 years.

   $\left.\dfrac{dP}{dt}\right]_{t=25} = 88$ Profit is increasing at $88\,000 per year after 25 years.

2 a $19\,000$ m^3 per minute **b** $18\,000$ m^3 per minute

3 a 1.2 m **b** $\dfrac{ds}{dt} = 28.1 - 9.8t$ represents the instantaneous velocity of the ball

   c $t = 2.867$ secs. The ball has stopped and reached its maximum height. **d** 41.49 m

   e i 28.1 m/s **ii** 8.5 m/s **iii** -20.9 m/s

   $s'(t) \geqslant 0$ ball travelling upwards
   $s'(t) \leqslant 0$ ball travelling downwards

   f 5.777 sec **g** $\dfrac{d^2s}{dt^2}$ is the rate of change of $\dfrac{ds}{dt}$, i.e., the instantaneous acceleration. **4 b** 69.58 m/s

EXERCISE 22B

1 a i $Q = 100$ **ii** $Q = 50$ **iii** $Q = 0$

   b i decr. 1 unit per year **ii** decr. $\frac{1}{\sqrt{2}}$ units per year

   c Hint: Consider the graph of $\dfrac{dQ}{dt}$ against t.

   $\dfrac{dQ}{dt} = \dfrac{-5}{\sqrt{t}} < 0$ for all $t > 0$

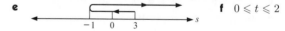

2 a 18.2 m **b** $t = 4$; 19 m, $t = 8$; 19.3 m, $t = 12$; 19.5 m

   c $t = 0$: 0.36 m/year $t = 5$: 0.09 m/year
   $t = 10$: 0.04 m/year

   d as $\dfrac{dH}{dt} = \dfrac{9}{(t+5)^2} > 0$, for all $t \geqslant 0$, the tree is always growing, and $\dfrac{dH}{dt} \to 0$ as t increases

3 a i $4500 **ii** $8250

   b i incr. of $100 per km/h **ii** incr. of $188.89 per km/h

   c $\dfrac{dC}{dt} = 0$ at $v = \sqrt{50}$ i.e., 7.1 km/h

4 a The near part of the lake is 2 km from the sea, the furthest part is 3 km.

   b $\dfrac{dy}{dx} = \frac{3}{10}x^2 - x + \frac{3}{5}$ $x = \frac{1}{2}$; $\dfrac{dy}{dx} = 0.175$, height of hill is increasing as slope is positive

   $x = 1\frac{1}{2}$; $\dfrac{dy}{dx} = -0.225$, height of hill is decreasing as slope is negative

   $\therefore$ top of the hill is between $x = \frac{1}{2}$ and $x = 1\frac{1}{2}$

   c 2.55 km from the sea, 63.1 m deep

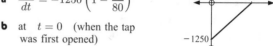

5 a $\dfrac{dV}{dt} = -1250\left(1 - \dfrac{t}{80}\right)$

   b at $t = 0$ (when the tap was first opened)

   c $\dfrac{d^2V}{dt^2} = \dfrac{125}{8}$ This shows that the rate of change of V is constantly increasing, i.e., the outflow is decreasing at a constant rate.

6 a When $\dfrac{dP}{dt} = 0$, the population is not changing over time, i.e., it is stable. **b** 4000 fish **c** 8000 fish

7 a $C'(x) = 0.0009x^2 + 0.04x + 4$ dollars per pair

   b $C'(220) = \$56.36$ per pair. This estimates the additional cost of making one more pair of jeans if 220 pairs are currently being made.

   c $56.58 This is the actual increase in cost to make an extra pair of jeans (221 rather than 220).

   d $C''(x) = 0.0018x + 0.04$, $C''(x) = 0$ when $x = -22.2$ This is where the rate of change is a minimum, however it is out of the bounds of the model (you cannot make < 0 jeans!)

EXERCISE 22C.1

1 a 7 m/s **b** $(h + 5)$ m/s **c** 5 m/s $= s'(1)$

   d av. velocity $= (2t + h + 3)$ m/s,
   $\displaystyle\lim_{h \to 0}(2t + h + 3) = s'(t) \to 2t + 3$ as $h \to 0$

2 a -14 cm/s **b** $(-8 - 2h)$ cm/s

   c -8 cm/s $= s'(2)$ i.e., velocity $= -8$ cm/s at $t = 2$

   d $-4t = s'(t) = v(t)$

3 a $\frac{2}{3}$ cm/s^2 **b** $\left(\dfrac{2}{\sqrt{1+h}+1}\right)$ cm/s^2 **c** 1 cm/s$^2 = v'(1)$

   d $\dfrac{1}{\sqrt{t}}$ cm/s$^2 = v'(t)$ i.e., the instantaneous accn. at time t

4 a velocity at $t = 4$ **b** acceleration at $t = 4$

EXERCISE 22C.2

1 a $v(t) = 2t - 4$, $a(t) = 2$

   $s(t)$: $\begin{array}{c}+\ -\ +\\ 1\ \ 3\end{array}$ $v(t)$: $\begin{array}{c}-\ +\\ 2\end{array}$ $a(t)$: $\begin{array}{c}+\end{array}$

   b The object is initially 3 cm to the right of the origin and is moving to the left at 4 cm/s. It is accelerating at 2 m/s^2 to the right.

   c The object is instantaneously stationary, 1 cm to the left of the origin and is accelerating to the right at 2 m/s^2.

   d At $t = 2$, $s(2) = 1$ cm to the left of the origin.

   e (number line from -1, 0, 3 on s) **f** $0 \leqslant t \leqslant 2$

2 a $v(t) = 98 - 9.8t$, $a(t) = -9.8$

   $s(t)$: $\begin{array}{c}+\\ 0\end{array}$ $v(t)$: $\begin{array}{c}+\ -\\ 10\end{array}$ $a(t)$: $\begin{array}{c}-\end{array}$
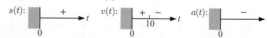

b $s(0) = 0$ m above the ground, $v(0) = 98$ m/s skyward

c $t = 5$ Stone is 367.5 m above the ground and moving skyward at 49 m/s. Its speed is decreasing. $t = 12$ Stone is 470.4 m above the ground and moving groundward at 19.6 m/s. Its speed is increasing.

d 490 m **e** 20 seconds

3 **a** $v(t) = 12 - 6t^2$, $a(t) = -12t$

b $s(0) = -1$, $v(0) = 12$, $a(0) = 0$
Particle started 1 cm to the left of the origin and was travelling to the right at a constant speed of 12 cm/s.

c $t = \sqrt{2}$, $s(\sqrt{2}) = 8\sqrt{2} - 1$ **d** **i** $t \geqslant \sqrt{2}$ **ii** never

4 **a** $v(t) = 3t^2 - 18t + 24$ $\quad a(t) = 6t - 18$

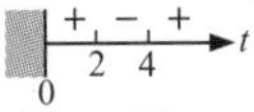

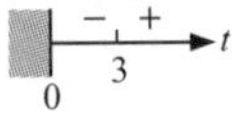

b $x(2) = 20$, $x(4) = 16$

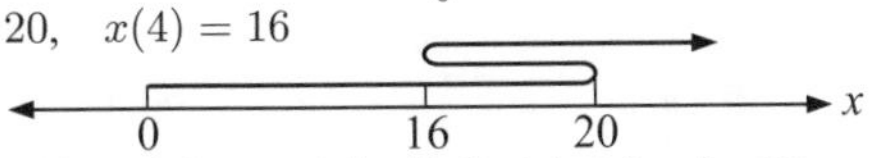

c **i** $0 \leqslant t \leqslant 2$ and $3 \leqslant t \leqslant 4$ **ii** $0 \leqslant t \leqslant 3$ **d** 28 m

5 **Hint**: $s'(t) = v(t)$ and $s''(t) = a(t) = g$
Show that $a = \frac{1}{2}g$ $b = v(0)$ $c = 0$

EXERCISE 22D.1

1 **a** **i** $x \geqslant 0$ **ii** never **b** **i** never **ii** $-2 < x \leqslant 3$
c **i** $x \leqslant 2$ **ii** $x \geqslant 2$ **d** **i** all real x **ii** never
e **i** $1 \leqslant x \leqslant 5$ **ii** $x \leqslant 1, x \geqslant 5$
f **i** $2 \leqslant x < 4$, $x > 4$ **ii** $x < 0$, $0 < x \leqslant 2$

EXERCISE 22D.2

1 **a** increasing for $x \geqslant 0$, decreasing for $x \leqslant 0$
b decreasing for all x
c increasing for $x \geqslant -\frac{3}{4}$, decreasing for $x \leqslant -\frac{3}{4}$
d increasing for $x \geqslant 0$, never decreasing
e decreasing for $x > 0$, never increasing
f incr. for $x \leqslant 0$ and $x \geqslant 4$, decr. for $0 \leqslant x \leqslant 4$
g increasing for $-\sqrt{\frac{2}{3}} \leqslant x \leqslant \sqrt{\frac{2}{3}}$,
decreasing for $x \leqslant -\sqrt{\frac{2}{3}}$, $x \geqslant \sqrt{\frac{2}{3}}$
h decr. for $x \leqslant -\frac{1}{2}$, $x \geqslant 3$, incr. for $-\frac{1}{2} \leqslant x \leqslant 3$
i increasing for $x \geqslant 0$, decreasing for $x \leqslant 0$
j increasing for $x \geqslant -\frac{3}{2} + \frac{\sqrt{5}}{2}$ and $x \leqslant -\frac{3}{2} - \frac{\sqrt{5}}{2}$
decreasing for $-\frac{3}{2} - \frac{\sqrt{5}}{2} \leqslant x \leqslant -\frac{3}{2} + \frac{\sqrt{5}}{2}$
k increasing for $x \leqslant 2 - \sqrt{3}$, $x \geqslant 2 + \sqrt{3}$
decreasing for $2 - \sqrt{3} \leqslant x \leqslant 2 + \sqrt{3}$
l increasing for $x \geqslant 1$, decreasing for $0 \leqslant x \leqslant 1$
m increasing for $-1 \leqslant x \leqslant 1$, $x \geqslant 2$
decreasing for $x \leqslant -1$, $1 \leqslant x \leqslant 2$
n increasing for $1 - \sqrt{2} \leqslant x \leqslant 1$, $x \geqslant 1 + \sqrt{2}$
decreasing for $x \leqslant 1 - \sqrt{2}$, $1 \leqslant x \leqslant 1 + \sqrt{2}$

2 **a** **i**

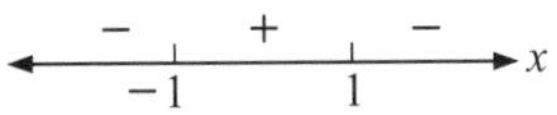

ii increasing for $-1 \leqslant x \leqslant 1$
decreasing for $x \leqslant -1$, $x \geqslant 1$

b **i**

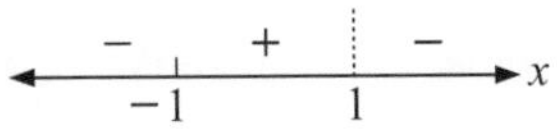

ii increasing for $-1 \leqslant x < 1$
decreasing for $x \leqslant -1$, $x > 1$

c **i**

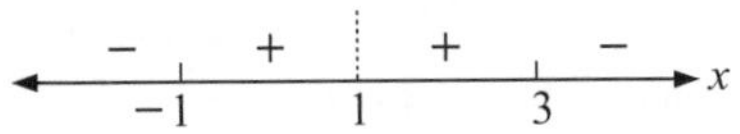

ii increasing for $-1 \leqslant x < 1$, $1 < x \leqslant 3$
decreasing for $x \leqslant -1$, $x \geqslant 3$

3 **a** increasing for $x \geqslant \sqrt{3}$ and $x \leqslant -\sqrt{3}$
decreasing for $-\sqrt{3} \leqslant x < -1$, $-1 < x \leqslant 0$,
$0 \leqslant x < 1$, $1 < x \leqslant \sqrt{3}$

b increasing for $x \geqslant 2$ decreasing for $x < 1$, $1 < x \leqslant 2$

EXERCISE 22D.3

1 **a** A - local min B - local max C - horiz. inflection

b

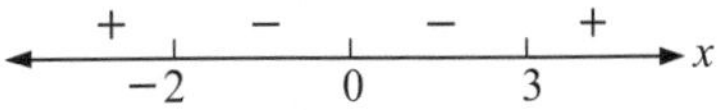

c **i** $x \leqslant -2, x \geqslant 3$ **ii** $-2 \leqslant x \leqslant 3$

2 **a**

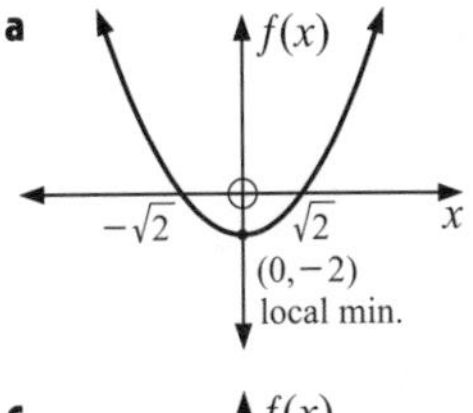

b

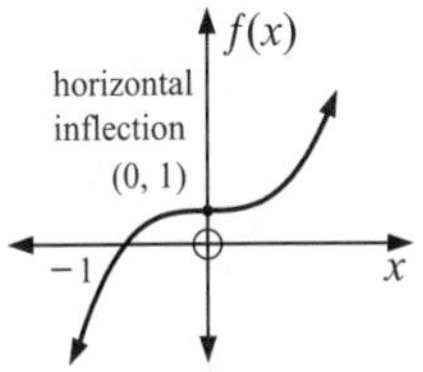

c

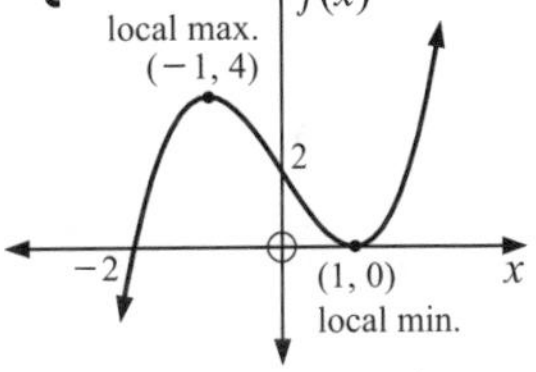

d

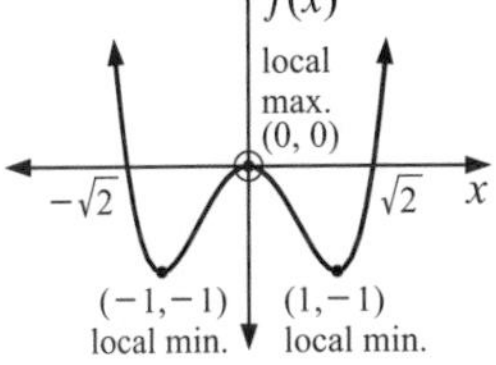

e

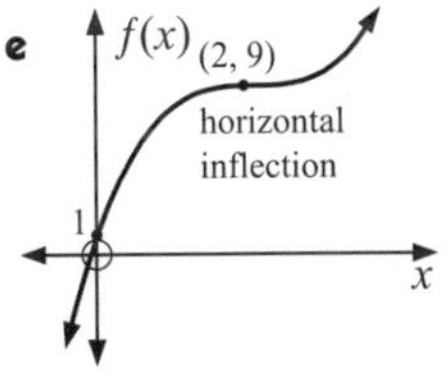

f

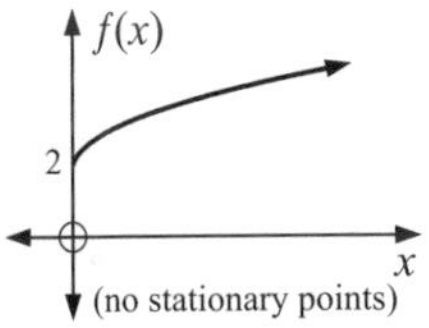

g

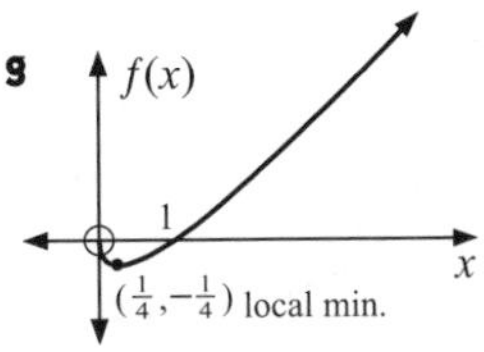

h

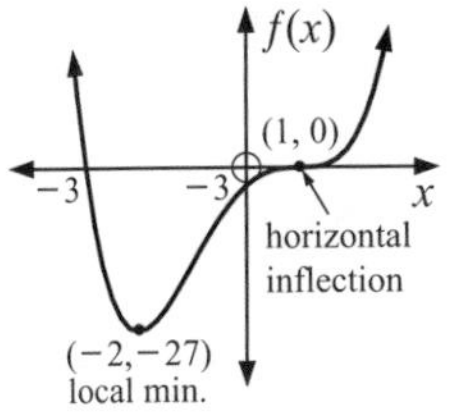

i

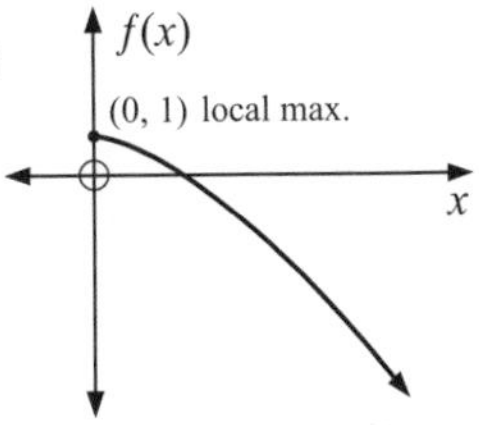

j

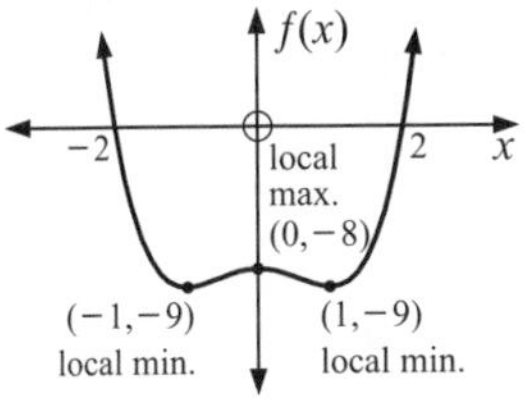

3 $x = -\dfrac{b}{2a}$, local min if $a > 0$, local max if $a < 0$ **4** $a = 9$

5 **a** $a = -12$, $b = -13$
b $(-2, 3)$ local max. $(2, -29)$ local min

6 $P(x) = -9x^3 - 9x^2 + 9x + 2$

7 **a** greatest value 63 (at $x = 5$) least value -18 (at $x = 2$)
b greatest value $= 4$ (at $x = 3$ and $x = 0$)
least value $= -16$ (at $x = -2$)

8 Maximum hourly cost $=$ \$680.95 when 150 hinges are made per hour. Minimum hourly cost $=$ \$529.80 when 104 hinges are made per hour.

EXERCISE 22E.1

1 a H.A. $y = 0$, V.A. $x = 2$ and $x = -2$

  b H.A. $y = 0$, V.A. $x = -2$ **c** H.A. $y = 0$, no V.A

2 a i H.A. $y = 0$

  ii $(1, 2)$ is a local max.

  $(-1, -2)$ is a local min. $\left[f'(x) = \dfrac{-4(x+1)(x-1)}{(x^2+1)^2} \right]$

  iii x-intercept is 0, y-intercept is 0

  iv

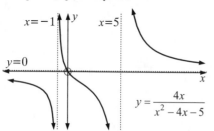

local max $(1, 2)$

$y = 0$

local min $(-1, -2)$

$y = \dfrac{4x}{x^2+1}$

b i H.A. $y = 0$, V.A.s $x = 5$ and $x = -1$

  ii no stationary points $\left[f'(x) = \dfrac{-4(x^2+5)}{(x-5)^2(x+1)^2} \right]$

  iii x-intercept is 0, y-intercept is 0

  iv

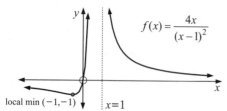

$x = -1$ $x = 5$

$y = 0$

$y = \dfrac{4x}{x^2-4x-5}$

c i H.A. $y = 0$, V.A. $x = 1$

  ii $(-1, -1)$ is a local minimum $\left[f'(x) = \dfrac{-4(x+1)}{(x-1)^3} \right]$

  iii x-intercept is 0, y-intercept is 0

  iv

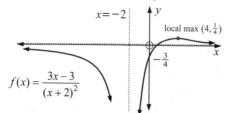

$f(x) = \dfrac{4x}{(x-1)^2}$

local min $(-1, -1)$ $x = 1$

d i H.A. $y = 0$, V.A. $x = -2$

  ii $(4, \frac{1}{4})$ is a local maximum $\left[f'(x) = \dfrac{-3(x-4)}{(x+2)^3} \right]$

  iii x-intercept is 1, y-intercept is $-\frac{3}{4}$

  iv

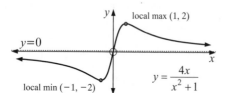

$x = -2$

local max $(4, \frac{1}{4})$

$-\frac{3}{4}$

$f(x) = \dfrac{3x-3}{(x+2)^2}$

EXERCISE 22E.2

1 a H.A. $y = 2$, V.A.s $x = 1$ and $x = -1$

  b H.A. $y = -1$, no V.A. **c** H.A. $y = 3$, V.A. $x = -2$

2 a i H.A. $y = 1$, V.A.s $x = 3$ and $x = -2$

  ii $(\frac{1}{2}, \frac{1}{25})$ is a local maximum

  iii x-intercepts are 0 and 1, y-intercept is 0

  iv

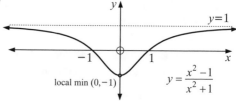

local max $(\frac{1}{2}, \frac{1}{25})$

$y = 1$

$x = -2$ $x = 3$

$y = \dfrac{x^2 - x}{x^2 - x - 6}$

b i H.A. $y = 1$, no V.A.

  ii $(0, -1)$ is a local minimum

  iii x-intercepts are 1 and -1, y-intercept is -1

  iv

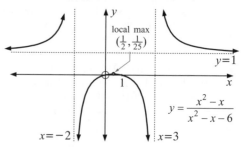

$y = 1$

local min $(0, -1)$

$y = \dfrac{x^2 - 1}{x^2 + 1}$

c i H.A. $y = 1$, V.A.s $x = -4$ and $x = -1$

  ii $(2, -\frac{1}{9})$ is a local min., $(-2, -9)$ is a local max.

  iii x-intercepts are 4 and 1, y-intercept is 1

  iv

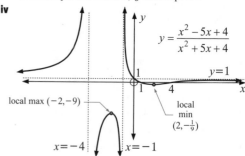

$y = \dfrac{x^2 - 5x + 4}{x^2 + 5x + 4}$

$y = 1$

local max $(-2, -9)$

local min $(2, -\frac{1}{9})$

$x = -4$ $x = -1$

d i H.A. $y = 1$, V.A. $x = -1$

  ii $(2, -\frac{1}{3})$ is a local minimum

  iii x-intercepts are 5 and 1, y-intercept is 5

  iv

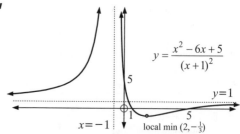

$y = \dfrac{x^2 - 6x + 5}{(x+1)^2}$

$y = 1$

$x = -1$ local min $(2, -\frac{1}{3})$

EXERCISE 22E.3

1 a VA $x = -2$, oblique asymptote $y = x + 2$

  ii $f'(x) = \dfrac{(x+1)(x+3)}{(x+2)^2}$, local min. at $(-1, 2)$,

  local max. at $(-3, -2)$

  iii no x-intercept, y-intercept is $2\frac{1}{2}$

iv

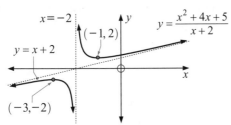

$x = -2$

$y = \dfrac{x^2 + 4x + 5}{x+2}$

$(-1, 2)$

$y = x + 2$

$(-3, -2)$

b i VA $x = -1$, oblique asymptote $y = x + 2$

ii $f'(x) = \dfrac{x^2 + 2x + 3}{(x+1)^2}$, no turning points

iii x-intercepts 0 and -3, y-intercept 0

iv

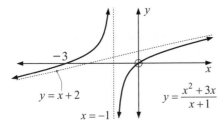

-3

$y = x + 2$

$y = \dfrac{x^2 + 3x}{x+1}$

$x = -1$

c i VA $x = 2$, oblique asymptote $y = -2x + 1$

ii $f'(x) = \dfrac{-2(x-3)(x-1)}{(x-2)^2}$, local min. at $(1, 1)$, local max. at $(3, -7)$

iii no x-intercept, y-intercept is 2

iv

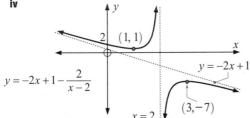

2 $(1, 1)$

$y = -2x + 1$

$y = -2x + 1 - \dfrac{2}{x-2}$

$x = 2$ $(3, -7)$

EXERCISE 22F

1 a no inflection **b** horizontal inflection at $(0, 2)$
  c non-horizontal inflection at $(2, 3)$
  d horizontal inflection at $(-2, -3)$
  e horizontal inflection at $(0, 2)$
    non-horizontal inflection at $(-\frac{4}{3}, \frac{310}{27})$ **f** no inflection

2 a i local minimum at $(0, 0)$
  ii no points of inflection
  iii decreasing for $x \leqslant 0$, increasing for $x \geqslant 0$
  iv function is concave up for all x

  v

  $f(x)$

  $(0,0)$
  local min.

b i horizontal inflection at $(0, 0)$
  ii horizontal inflection at $(0, 0)$
  iii increasing for all real x
  iv concave down for $x \leqslant 0$, concave up for $x \geqslant 0$

  v

  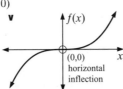

  $f(x)$

  $(0,0)$
  horizontal inflection

c i $f'(x) \neq 0$, no stationary points
  ii no points of inflection

iii incr. for $x \geqslant 0$, never decr.
iv concave down for $x \geqslant 0$, never concave up

v

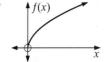

$f(x)$

d i local max. at $(-2, 29)$ local min at $(4, -79)$
  ii non-horizontal inflection at $(1, -25)$
  iii increasing for $x \leqslant -2$, $x \geqslant 4$
    decreasing for $-2 \leqslant x \leqslant 4$
  iv concave down for $x \leqslant 1$, concave up for $x \geqslant 1$

  v

  local max. $f(x)$
  $(-2, 29)$ non-horizontal inflection
  -4 4 x
  $(1, -25)$
  -80 $(4, -79)$ local min

e i horiz. inflection at $(0, -2)$ local min. at $(-1, -3)$
  ii horizontal inflection at $(0, -2)$
    non-horizontal inflection at $(-\frac{2}{3}, -\frac{70}{27})$
  iii increasing for $x \geqslant -1$, decreasing for $x \leqslant -1$
  iv concave down for $-\frac{2}{3} \leqslant x \leqslant 0$
    concave up for $x \leqslant -\frac{2}{3}$, $x \geqslant 0$

  v

  non-horizontal inflection $f(x)$
  $(-\frac{2}{3}, -\frac{70}{27})$
  -2 -1 1 x
  local min. $(-1, -3)$ $(0, -2)$ horizontal inflection

f i local min. at $(1, 0)$
  ii no points of inflection
  iii increasing for $x \geqslant 1$, decreasing for $x \leqslant 1$
  iv concave up for all x

  v

  y

  $y = (x-1)^4$

  1
  1 x
  local min $(1, 0)$

g i local minimum at $(-\sqrt{2}, -1)$ and $(\sqrt{2}, -1)$, local maximum at $(0, 3)$,
  ii non-horizontal inflection at $(\sqrt{\frac{2}{3}}, \frac{7}{9})$
    non-horizontal inflection at $(-\sqrt{\frac{2}{3}}, \frac{7}{9})$
  iii increasing for $-\sqrt{2} \leqslant x \leqslant 0$, $x \geqslant \sqrt{2}$
    decreasing for $x \leqslant -\sqrt{2}$, $0 \leqslant x \leqslant \sqrt{2}$
  iv concave down for $-\sqrt{\frac{2}{3}} \leqslant x \leqslant \sqrt{\frac{2}{3}}$
    concave up for $x \leqslant -\sqrt{\frac{2}{3}}$, $x \geqslant \sqrt{\frac{2}{3}}$

  v

  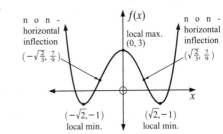

  non-horizontal inflection $f(x)$ non-horizontal inflection
  $(-\sqrt{\frac{2}{3}}, \frac{7}{9})$ local max. $(0, 3)$ $(\sqrt{\frac{2}{3}}, \frac{7}{9})$
  x
  $(-\sqrt{2}, -1)$ $(\sqrt{2}, -1)$
  local min.   local min.

h i no stationary points
ii no inflections
iii increasing for $x > 0$, never decreasing
iv concave down for $x > 0$, never concave up

v

EXERCISE 22G

1 b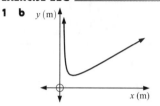

c $L_{\min} = 28.28$ m, $x = 7.07$ m

d 14.14 m   7.07 m

2 a $2x$ cm   **b** $V = 200 = 2x \times x \times h$

c Hint: Show $h = \dfrac{100}{x^2}$ and substitute into the surface area equation.

d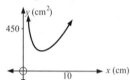

e $SA_{\min} = 213.4$ cm^2, $x = 4.22$ cm

f 5.62 cm   8.43 cm   4.22 cm

3 a recall that $V_{\text{cylinder}} = \pi r^2 h$ and that 1 L $= 1000$ cm^3
b recall that $SA_{\text{cylinder}} = 2\pi r^2 + 2\pi rh$

c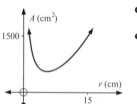

d $A = 554$ cm^2, $r = 5.42$ cm

e 5.42 cm   10.84 cm

4 b 6 cm $\times$ 6 cm

5 a $0 \leqslant x \leqslant 63.66$ **c** $x = 63.66$ m, $l = 0$ m (i.e., circular)

6 a Hint: Show that $AC = \frac{\theta}{360} \times 2\pi \times 10$
b Hint: Show that $2\pi r = AC$
c Hint: Use the result from **b** and Pythagoras' theorem.

d $V(\theta) = \frac{1}{3}\pi \left(\frac{\theta}{36}\right)^2 \sqrt{100 - \left(\frac{\theta}{36}\right)^2}$

e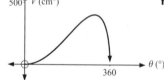

f $\theta = 293.9°$

7 a For $x < 0$ or $x > 6$, X is not on AC.
c $x = 2.67$ km   This is the distance from A to X which minimises the time taken to get from B to C. (Proof: Use sign diagram or second derivative test. Be sure to check the end points.)

8 3.33 km   **9** $r = 31.7$ cm, $h = 31.7$ cm
10 4 m from the 40 cp globe

11 a $D(x) = \sqrt{x^2 + (24-x)^2}$ **b** $\dfrac{d[D(x)]^2}{dx} = 4x - 48$

c Smallest $D(x) = 17.0$ Largest $D(x) = 24$, which is not an acceptable solution as can be seen in the diagram.

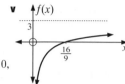

12 a Hint: Use the cosine rule.
b 3553 km^2 **c** 5:36 pm

13 a QR $= \left(\dfrac{2+x}{x}\right)$ m   **c** Hint: All solutions < 0 can be discarded as $x \geqslant 0$.
d 416 cm

14 between A and N, 2.578 m from N
15 at grid reference $(3.544, 8)$ **16** $\sqrt{\frac{3}{2}} : 1$ **17 e** 63.7%

EXERCISE 22H

1 a cost $= \$878\,000$, AC $= \$1097.50$, MC $= \$1850$
b 195 items, $\$639.87$

2 a $A(x) = \frac{295}{x} + 24 - 0.08x + 0.0008x^2$
$C'(x) = 24 - 0.16x + 0.0024x^2$
b min. average cost $= \$26.41$ (when 79 items are made)
c min. marginal cost $= \$21.33$ (when 33 items are made)
3 50 fittings   **4** 250 items   **5** 10 blankets   **6** 25 km/h

EXERCISE 22I

1 a $2\dfrac{dy}{dx}$ **b** $-3\dfrac{dy}{dx}$ **c** $3y^2\dfrac{dy}{dx}$ **d** $-y^{-2}\dfrac{dy}{dx}$ **e** $4y^3\dfrac{dy}{dx}$

f $\frac{1}{2}y^{-\frac{1}{2}}\dfrac{dy}{dx}$ **g** $-2y^{-3}\dfrac{dy}{dx}$ **h** $y + x\dfrac{dy}{dx}$ **i** $2xy + x^2\dfrac{dy}{dx}$

j $y^2 + 2xy\dfrac{dy}{dx}$

2 a $\dfrac{dy}{dx} = -\dfrac{x}{y}$ **b** $\dfrac{dy}{dx} = -\dfrac{x}{3y}$ **c** $\dfrac{dy}{dx} = \dfrac{x}{y}$

d $\dfrac{dy}{dx} = \dfrac{2x}{3y^2}$ **e** $\dfrac{dy}{dx} = \dfrac{-2x-y}{x}$ **f** $\dfrac{dy}{dx} = \dfrac{3x^2 - 2y}{2x}$

3 a 1   **b** $-\frac{1}{9}$

REVIEW SET 22A

1 a $v(t) = (6t^2 - 18t + 12)$ cm/s
$a(t) = (12t - 18)$ cm/s^2
$v(t)$: $+ \quad - \quad +$ over $0, 1, 2$ t
$a(t)$: $- \quad +$ over $0, 1\frac{1}{2}$ t

b $s(0) = 5$ cm to left of origin
$v(0) = 12$ cm/s towards origin
$a(0) = -18$ cm/s^2 (reducing speed)

c At $t = 2$, particle is 1 cm to the left of the origin, is stationary and is accelerating towards the origin.

d $t = 1$, $s = 0$ and $t = 2$, $s = -1$

e number line from -5 to -1, 0 s

f Speed is increasing for $1 \leqslant t \leqslant 1\frac{1}{2}$ and $t \geqslant 2$.

2 a i $\$312$ **ii** $\$1218.75$
b i $\$9.10$ per km/h   **ii** $\$7.50$ per km/h   **c** 3 km/h

3 a local maximum at $(-2, 51)$, local minimum at $(3, -74)$
non-horizontal inflection at $(\frac{1}{2}, -11.5)$

b increasing for
$x \leqslant -2, \ x \geqslant 3$
decreasing for
$-2 \leqslant x \leqslant 3$

c concave down for $x \leqslant \frac{1}{2}$,
concave up for $x \geqslant \frac{1}{2}$

d local max $(-2, 51)$

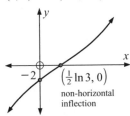

local min $(3, -74)$

4 b $k = 9$

5 a $y = \dfrac{1}{x^2}, \ x > 0$ **c** base is 1.26 m square, height 0.630 m

6 a $\dfrac{dy}{dx} = \dfrac{-2y(x + y^2)}{x(x + 6y^2)}$ **b** $4x - 5y = 14$

EXERCISE 23A

1 a $4e^{4x}$ **b** e^x **c** $-2e^{-2x}$ **d** $\frac{1}{2}e^{\frac{x}{2}}$ **e** $-e^{-\frac{x}{2}}$ **f** $2e^{-x}$

g $2e^{\frac{x}{2}} + 3e^{-x}$ **h** $\dfrac{e^x - e^{-x}}{2}$ **i** $-2xe^{-x^2}$ **j** $e^{\frac{1}{x}} \times \dfrac{-1}{x^2}$

k $20e^{2x}$ **l** $40e^{-2x}$ **m** $2e^{2x+1}$ **n** $\frac{1}{4}e^{\frac{x}{4}}$ **o** $-4xe^{1-2x^2}$

p $-0.02e^{-0.02x}$

2 a $e^x + xe^x$ **b** $3x^2e^{-x} - x^3e^{-x}$ **c** $\dfrac{xe^x - e^x}{x^2}$

d $\dfrac{1 - x}{e^x}$ **e** $2xe^{3x} + 3x^2e^{3x}$ **f** $\dfrac{xe^x - \frac{1}{2}e^x}{x\sqrt{x}}$

g $\frac{1}{2}x^{-\frac{1}{2}}e^{-x} - x^{\frac{1}{2}}e^{-x}$ **h** $\dfrac{e^x + 2 + 2e^{-x}}{(e^{-x} + 1)^2}$

3 a $4e^x(e^x + 2)^3$ **b** $\dfrac{-e^{-x}}{(1 - e^{-x})^2}$ **c** $\dfrac{e^{2x}}{\sqrt{e^{2x} + 10}}$

d $\dfrac{6e^{3x}}{(1 - e^{3x})^3}$ **e** $-\dfrac{e^{-x}}{2}(1 - e^{-x})^{-\frac{3}{2}}$ **f** $\dfrac{1 - 2e^{-x} + xe^{-x}}{\sqrt{1 - 2e^{-x}}}$

4 b $\dfrac{d^n y}{dx^n} = k^n y$

5 Hint: Find $\dfrac{dy}{dx}$ and $\dfrac{d^2 y}{dx^2}$ and substitute into the equation.

6 a local maximum at $(1, e^{-1})$
b local max. at $(-2, 4e^{-2})$, local min. at $(0, 0)$
c local minimum at $(1, e)$ **d** local maximum at $(-1, e)$

EXERCISE 23B

1 a $\ln N = \ln 50 + 2t$ **b** $\ln P = \ln 8.69 - 0.0541t$
c $\ln S = 2\ln a - kt$

2 a 2 **b** $\frac{1}{2}$ **c** -1 **d** $-\frac{1}{2}$ **e** 3 **f** 9 **g** $\frac{1}{5}$ **h** $\frac{1}{4}$

3 a $e^{\ln 2}$ **b** $e^{\ln 10}$ **c** $e^{\ln a}$ **d** $e^{x \ln a}$

4 a $x = \ln 2$ **b** no real solutions **c** no real solutions
d $x = \ln 2$ **e** $x = 0$ **f** $x = \ln 2$ or $\ln 3$ **g** $x = 0$

h $x = \ln 4$ **i** $x = \ln\left(\dfrac{3 + \sqrt{5}}{2}\right)$ or $\ln\left(\dfrac{3 - \sqrt{5}}{2}\right)$

5 a $2^x \ln 2$ **b** $5^x \ln 5$ **c** $2^x + x2^x \ln 2$

d $\dfrac{3x^2 - x^3 \ln 6}{6^x}$ **e** $\dfrac{x2^x \ln 2 - 2^x}{x^2}$ **f** $\dfrac{1 - x \ln 3}{3^x}$

6 a $(\ln 3, 3)$ **b** $(\ln 2, 5)$ **c** $(0, 2)$ and $(\ln 5, -2)$

7 a $P = (\frac{1}{2}\ln 3, 0)$
$Q = (0, -2)$

b $f'(x) = e^x + 3e^{-x} > 0$
for all x

c $f(x)$ is concave down
below the x-axis and
concave up above the
x-axis

d

non-horizontal
inflection

$(\frac{1}{2}\ln 3, 0)$

8 a $f(x)$: x-intercept is at $x = \ln 3$,
y-intercept is at $y = -2$

$g(x)$: x-intercept is at $x = \ln\left(\frac{5}{3}\right)$
y-intercept is at $y = -2$

b $f(x)$: as $x \to \infty$, $f(x) \to \infty$
as $x \to -\infty$, $f(x) \to -3$ (above)

$g(x)$: as $x \to \infty$, $g(x) \to 3$ (below)
as $x \to -\infty$, $g(x) \to -\infty$

c intersect at $(0, -2)$ and $(\ln 5, 2)$

d

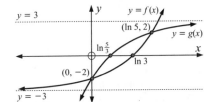

EXERCISE 23C

1 a $\dfrac{1}{x}$ **b** $\dfrac{2}{2x + 1}$ **c** $\dfrac{1 - 2x}{x - x^2}$ **d** $-\dfrac{2}{x}$ **e** $2x \ln x + x$

f $\dfrac{1 - \ln x}{2x^2}$ **g** $e^x \ln x + \dfrac{e^x}{x}$ **h** $\dfrac{2\ln x}{x}$ **i** $\dfrac{1}{2x\sqrt{\ln x}}$

j $\dfrac{e^{-x}}{x} - e^{-x}\ln x$ **k** $\dfrac{\ln(2x)}{2\sqrt{x}} + \dfrac{1}{\sqrt{x}}$ **l** $\dfrac{\ln x - 2}{\sqrt{x}(\ln x)^2}$

2 a $\ln 5$ **b** $\dfrac{3}{x}$ **c** $\dfrac{4x^3 + 1}{x^4 + x}$ **d** $\dfrac{1}{x - 2}$ **e** $\dfrac{6}{2x + 1}[\ln(2x + 1)]^2$

f $\dfrac{1 - \ln(4x)}{x^2}$ **g** $-\dfrac{1}{x}$ **h** $\dfrac{1}{x \ln(\ln x)}$ **i** $\dfrac{-1}{x[\ln x]^2}$

3 a $\dfrac{-1}{1 - 2x}$ **b** $\dfrac{-2}{2x + 3}$ **c** $1 + \dfrac{1}{2x}$ **d** $\dfrac{1}{x} - \dfrac{1}{2(2 - x)}$

e $\dfrac{1}{x + 3} - \dfrac{1}{x - 1}$ **f** $\dfrac{2}{x} + \dfrac{1}{3 - x}$ **g** $\dfrac{9}{3x - 4}$

h $\dfrac{1}{x} + \dfrac{2x}{x^2 + 1}$ **i** $\dfrac{2x + 2}{x^2 + 2x} - \dfrac{1}{x - 5}$

4 a i $\dfrac{1}{x \ln 2}$ **ii** $\dfrac{1}{x \ln 10}$ **iii** $\log_3 x + \dfrac{1}{\ln 3}$ **b** $\dfrac{dy}{dx} = 2^x \ln 2$

5 a $x = \dfrac{e^3 + 1}{2}$ $(\doteqdot 10.54)$ **b** no, $\therefore$ there is no y-int.
c slope $= 2$ **d** $x > \frac{1}{2}$ **e** $f''(x) = \dfrac{-4}{(2x - 1)^2} < 0$ for
all $x > \frac{1}{2}$, so $f(x)$ is concave down

f

$f(x)$ $x = \frac{1}{2}$

$\dfrac{e^3 + 1}{2}$

6 Hint: Show that as $x \to 0$, $f(x) \to -\infty$,
and as $x \to \infty$, $f(x) \to 0$.

7 Hint: Show that $f(x) \geqslant 1$ for all $x > 0$.

EXERCISE 23D

1 $y = -\dfrac{1}{e}x + \dfrac{2}{e}$ **2** $3y = -x + 3\ln 3 - 1$

3 A is $\left(\frac{2}{3}, 0\right)$, B is $(0, -2e)$ **4** $y = -\dfrac{2}{e^2}x + \dfrac{2}{e^4} - 1$

5 $y = e^a x + e^a(1 - a)$ so $y = ex$ is the tangent to $y = e^x$
from the origin

6 a $x > 0$

b $f'(x) > 0$ for all $x > 0$, so $f(x)$ is always increasing. Its slope is always positive.
$f''(x) < 0$ for all $x > 0$, so $f(x)$ is concave down for all $x > 0$.

c

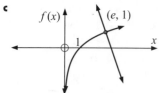

normal has equation $f(x) = -ex + 1 + e^2$

7 $\doteq 63.4°$

8 a $k = \frac{1}{50} \ln 2$ $(\doteq 0.0139)$

b i 20 grams **ii** 14.3 grams **iii** 1.95 grams

c 9 days and 6 minutes (216 hours)

d i -0.0693 g/h **ii** -2.64×10^{-7} g/h

e **Hint:** You should find
$$\frac{dW}{dt} = -\frac{1}{50} \ln 2 \times 20 e^{-\frac{1}{50} \ln 2t}$$

9 a $k = \frac{-1}{15} \ln \left(\frac{95}{15}\right)$ $(\doteq 0.123)$ **b** $100°C$

d i decreasing by $11.7°C$ per minute
ii decreasing by $3.42°C$ per minute
iii decreasing by $0.998°C$ per minute

10 a 43.9 cm **b** 10.4 years
c i growing by 5.45 cm per year
ii growing by 1.88 cm per year

11 a $A = 0$ **b** $k = \frac{\ln 2}{3}$ $(\doteq 0.231)$

c 0.728 units of alcohol produced per hour

12 a $f(x)$ does not have any x or y-intercepts

b as $x \to \infty$, $f(x) \to \infty$, as $x \to -\infty$, $f(x) \to 0$ (negative)

c local minimum at $(1, e)$

d

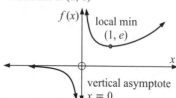

e $ey = -2x - 3$

13 a $v(t) = 100 - 40e^{-\frac{t}{5}}$ cm/s, $a(t) = 8e^{-\frac{t}{5}}$ cm/s^2

b $s(0) = 200$ cm on positive side of origin
$v(0) = 60$ cm/s $a(0) = 8$ cm/s^2

c as $t \to \infty$, $v(t) \to 100$ cm/s (below)

d

$v(t)$ (cm/s) $y=100$

60

t (sec)

e after 3.47 seconds

14 a at 4.41 months old **b**

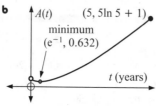

$A(t)$ $(5, 5\ln 5 + 1)$
minimum
$(e^{-1}, 0.632)$
t (years)

15 a There is a local maximum at $\left(0, \frac{1}{\pi\sqrt{2}}\right)$.
$f(x)$ is incr. for all $x \leqslant 0$ and decr. for all $x \geqslant 0$.

b Inflections at $\left(-1, \frac{1}{\pi\sqrt{2e}}\right)$ and $\left(1, \frac{1}{\pi\sqrt{2e}}\right)$

c as $x \to \infty$, $f(x) \to 0$ (positive)
as $x \to -\infty$, $f(x) \to 0$ (positive)

d

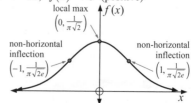

local max $f(x)$
$\left(0, \frac{1}{\pi\sqrt{2}}\right)$
non-horizontal inflection $\left(-1, \frac{1}{\pi\sqrt{2e}}\right)$
non-horizontal inflection $\left(1, \frac{1}{\pi\sqrt{2e}}\right)$
x

16 20 kettles **17** $C = \left(\frac{1}{\sqrt{2}}, e^{\left(-\frac{1}{2}\right)}\right)$ **18** 267 torches

19 a **Hint:** They must have the same y-coordinate at $x = b$ and the same slope. **c** $a = \frac{1}{2e}$ **d** $y = e^{-\frac{1}{2}}x - \frac{1}{2}$

20 after 13.8 weeks **21** $a = \frac{\sqrt{e}}{2}$, $b = -\frac{1}{8}$

REVIEW SET 23A

1 a $3x^2 e^{x^3 + 2}$ **b** $\dfrac{xe^x - 2e^x}{x^3}$

c $3x^2 + y^4 + 4xy^3 \dfrac{dy}{dx} = e^y + xe^y \dfrac{dy}{dx}$ **2** $y = \dfrac{e}{2}x + \dfrac{1}{e} - \dfrac{e}{2}$

3

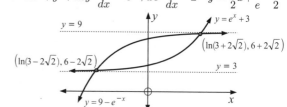

$y = 9$
$y = e^x + 3$
$(\ln(3 + 2\sqrt{2}), 6 + 2\sqrt{2})$
$(\ln(3 - 2\sqrt{2}), 6 - 2\sqrt{2})$
$y = 3$
$y = 9 - e^{-x}$
x

4 a y-intercept at $y = -1$, no x-intercept

b $f(x)$ is defined for all $x \neq 1$

c $f'(x) < 0$ for $x < 1$ and $1 < x \leqslant 2$ and $f'(x) > 0$ for $x \geqslant 2$. $f''(x) > 0$ for $x > 1$, $f''(x) < 0$ for $x < 1$.
So, the slope of the curve is negative for all defined values of $x \leqslant 2$ and positive for all $x \geqslant 2$. The curve is concave down for $x \leqslant 1$ and concave up for $x \geqslant 1$.

d tangent is $y = e^2$

y
$y = \dfrac{e^x}{x-1}$
$y = e^2$
x
$x = 1$

5 a 60 cm **b i** 4.244 years **ii** 201.2 years
c i 16 cm per year **ii** 1.95 cm per year

6 a $v(t) = -8e^{-\frac{t}{10}} - 40$ m/s $t \geqslant 0$
$a(t) = \frac{4}{5}e^{-\frac{t}{10}}$ m/s^2 $t \geqslant 0$

b $s(0) = 80$ m,
$v(0) = -48$ m/s,
$a(0) = 0.8$ m/s^2

c as $t \to \infty$,
$v(t) \to -40$ m/s (below)

d

$v(t)$ m/s
t
$v(t) = -40$
-48

e $t = 6.93$ seconds

7 $A(1, e^{-1})$ **8** 100 or 101 shirts, $938.63 profit

EXERCISE 24A

1 a $2\cos(2x)$ **b** $\cos x - \sin x$ **c** $-3\sin(3x) - \cos x$

d $\cos(x+1)$ **e** $2\sin(3-2x)$ **f** $\dfrac{5}{\cos^2(5x)}$

g $\frac{1}{2}\cos(\frac{x}{2}) + 3\sin x$ **h** $\dfrac{3\pi}{\cos^2(\pi x)}$ **i** $4\cos x + 2\sin(2x)$

2 a $2x - \sin x$ **b** $\dfrac{1}{\cos^2 x} - 3\cos x$ **c** $e^x\cos x - e^x\sin x$

d $-e^{-x}\sin x + e^{-x}\cos x$ **e** $\cot x$ **f** $2e^{2x}\tan x + \dfrac{e^{2x}}{\cos^2 x}$

g $3\cos(3x)$ **h** $-\frac{1}{2}\sin\left(\frac{x}{2}\right)$ **i** $\dfrac{6}{\cos^2(2x)}$

j $\cos x - x\sin x$ **k** $\dfrac{x\cos x - \sin x}{x^2}$ **l** $\tan x + \dfrac{x}{\cos^2 x}$

3 a $2x\cos(x^2)$ **b** $-\dfrac{1}{2\sqrt{x}}\sin(\sqrt{x})$ **c** $-\dfrac{\sin x}{2\sqrt{\cos x}}$

d $2\sin x\cos x$ **e** $-3\sin x\cos^2 x$

f $-\sin x\sin(2x) + 2\cos x\cos(2x)$ **g** $\sin x\sin(\cos x)$

h $-12\sin(4x)\cos^2(4x)$ **i** $-\dfrac{\cos x}{\sin^2 x}$ **j** $\dfrac{2\sin(2x)}{\cos^2(2x)}$

k $-\dfrac{8\cos(2x)}{\sin^3(2x)}$ **l** $\dfrac{-12}{\cos^2(\frac{x}{2})\tan^4(\frac{x}{2})}$

4 a $\dfrac{dy}{dx} = \cos x$, $\dfrac{d^2y}{dx^2} = -\sin x$, $\dfrac{d^3y}{dx^3} = -\cos x$, $\dfrac{d^4y}{dx^4} = \sin x$

b The answers of **a** are cycled over and over.

6 a $y = x$ **b** $y = x$ **c** $2x - y = \frac{\pi}{3} - \frac{\sqrt{3}}{2}$ **d** $x = \frac{\pi}{4}$

7 a rising **b** rising at 2.731 m per hour

8 a $-34\,000\pi$ units per second **b** $V'(t) = 0$

9 b i 0 **ii** 1 **iii** $\doteqdot 1.106$

10 a

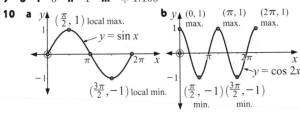

$\left(\frac{\pi}{2}, 1\right)$ local max. $y = \sin x$ $\left(\frac{3\pi}{2}, -1\right)$ local min.

b $(0, 1)$ max. $(\pi, 1)$ max. $(2\pi, 1)$ max. $y = \cos 2x$ $\left(\frac{\pi}{2}, -1\right)\left(\frac{3\pi}{2}, -1\right)$ min. min.

c $\left(\frac{\pi}{2}, 1\right)$ max. $\left(\frac{3\pi}{2}, 1\right)$ max. $y = \sin^2 x$ $(0, 0)$ min. $(\pi, 0)$ min. $(2\pi, 0)$ min.

11 a $x = \frac{\pi}{2}, \frac{3\pi}{2}$

b $(0, 1)$ is a local minimum, $(\pi, -1)$ is a local maximum $(2\pi, 1)$ is a local minimum

c $f(x)$ has a period 2π

d

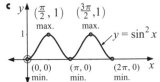

$y = \dfrac{1}{\cos x}$ $[0, 2\pi]$

local min $(0, 1)$ local max $(\pi, -1)$ local min $(2\pi, 1)$ $x = \frac{\pi}{2}$ $x = \frac{3\pi}{2}$ $x = \frac{5\pi}{2}$

12 $y = \sin(2x) + 2\cos x$ $[0, 2\pi]$

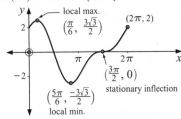

local max. $\left(\frac{\pi}{6}, \frac{3\sqrt{3}}{2}\right)$ $(2\pi, 2)$
$\left(\frac{3\pi}{2}, 0\right)$ stationary inflection
$\left(\frac{5\pi}{6}, \frac{-3\sqrt{3}}{2}\right)$ local min.

13 a $x(0) = -1$ cm $v(0) = 0$ cm/s $a(0) = 2$ cm/s^2

b At $t = \frac{\pi}{4}$ seconds, the particle is $(\sqrt{2} - 1)$ cm, left of the origin moving right at $\sqrt{2}$ cm/s, with increasing speed.

c At $t = 0$, $x(0) = -1$ cm, at $t = \pi$, $x(\pi) = 3$ cm, at $t = 2\pi$, $x(2\pi) = -1$ cm

d for $0 \leqslant t \leqslant \frac{\pi}{2}$ and $\pi \leqslant t \leqslant \frac{3\pi}{2}$

EXERCISE 24B

2 a $\sec x + x\sec x\tan x$ **b** $e^x(\cot x - \csc^2 x)$

c $8\sec(2x)\tan(2x)$ **d** $-e^{-x}\left[\cot\left(\frac{x}{2}\right) + \frac{1}{2}\csc^2\left(\frac{x}{2}\right)\right]$

e $x\csc x[2 - x\cot x]$ **f** $\sqrt{\csc x}\left[1 - \frac{x}{2}\cot x\right]$

g $\tan x$ **h** $\csc(x^2)\left[1 - 2x^2\cot(x^2)\right]$

i $\dfrac{-\sqrt{x}\csc^2 x - \frac{1}{2}x^{-\frac{1}{2}}\cot x}{x} \equiv -\dfrac{\cos x\sin x + 2x}{2x\sqrt{x}\sin^2 x}$

3 a $\sqrt{2}x - y = \sqrt{2}\left(\frac{\pi}{4} - 1\right)$ **b** $2x + y = \frac{2\pi}{3} + \sqrt{3}$

4 a $x - 2\sqrt{3}y = \frac{\pi}{6} - 4\sqrt{3}$ **b** $\sqrt{6}x + y = \pi\sqrt{6} + \sqrt{2}$

EXERCISE 24C.1

2 a 0 **b** $-\frac{\pi}{2}$ **c** $\frac{\pi}{4}$ **d** $-\frac{\pi}{4}$ **e** $\frac{\pi}{6}$ **f** $\frac{5\pi}{6}$ **g** $\frac{\pi}{3}$

h $\frac{3\pi}{4}$ **i** $-\frac{\pi}{6}$ **j** $\doteqdot -0.874$ **k** $\doteqdot 1.238$ **l** $\doteqdot -1.551$

3 a $x = \frac{\sqrt{3}}{2}$ **b** $x = -\frac{1}{3}$

4 Hint: Let $\theta = \arctan(5)$ $\therefore$ $\tan\theta = 5$, etc.

EXERCISE 24C.2

2 a $\dfrac{2}{1 + 4x^2}$ **b** $\dfrac{-3}{\sqrt{1 - 9x^2}}$ **c** $\dfrac{1}{\sqrt{16 - x^2}}$ **d** $\dfrac{-1}{\sqrt{25 - x^2}}$

e $\dfrac{2x}{1 + x^4}$ **f** -1

3 a $\dfrac{dy}{dx} = \arcsin x + \dfrac{x}{\sqrt{1 - x^2}}$ **b** $\dfrac{dy}{dx} = e^x\arccos x - \dfrac{e^x}{\sqrt{1 - x^2}}$

c $\dfrac{dy}{dx} = -e^{-x}\arctan x + \dfrac{e^{-x}}{1 + x^2}$

4 c $\dfrac{dy}{dx} = -\dfrac{1}{\sqrt{a^2 - x^2}}$, $x \in [-a, a]$

5 a $\tan\alpha = \dfrac{2}{x}$ and $\tan(\alpha + \theta) = \dfrac{3}{x}$

b $\theta = \arctan\left(\dfrac{3}{x}\right) - \arctan\left(\dfrac{2}{x}\right)$ **c** $x = \sqrt{6}$

d The maximum angle of view (θ) occurs when Sonia's eye is $\sqrt{6}$ m from the wall.

EXERCISE 24D

1 $\doteqdot 109.5°$ **2 c** $\theta = 30°$

3 1 hour 34 min 53 sec when $\theta = 36.9°$

4 c $4\sqrt{2}$ m **5** 9.866 m **6** 1.340 m from A

7 e AP + PB is a minimum when $\theta = \phi$

EXERCISE 24E

1 a is decreasing at 7.5 units per second

2 increasing at 1 cm per minute

3 a 4π m^2 per second   **b** 8π m^2 per second

4 increasing at 6π m^2 per minute

5 decreasing at 0.16 m^3 per minute   **6** $\frac{20}{3}$ cm per minute

7 $\frac{25\sqrt{3}}{6}$ cm per minute   **8** decreasing at $\frac{250}{13}$ m/s

9 a 0.2 m/s **b** $\frac{8}{90}$ m/s

10 decreasing at $\frac{\sqrt{2}}{100}$ radians per second

11 a decreasing at $\frac{3}{100}$ radians per second

 b decreasing at $\frac{1}{100}$ radians per second

12 increasing at 0.128 radians per second

13 0.12 radians per minute   **14** $4\sqrt{37}$ m/s

15 a $\frac{\sqrt{3}}{2}\pi$ cm/s **b** 0 cm/s

16 a $\frac{200}{\sqrt{13}}\pi$ radians per second **b** 100π radians per second

17 b $\frac{\sqrt{3}}{120}$ m per minute

REVIEW SET 24A

1 a $5\cos(5x)\ln(x) + \dfrac{\sin(5x)}{x}$

 b $\cos(x)\cos(2x) - 2\sin(x)\sin(2x)$

 c $-2e^{-2x}\tan x + e^{-2x}\sec^2 x$

3 a $f'(x) = 3\cos x + 8\sin(2x)$, $f''(x) = -3\sin x + 16\cos(2x)$

 b $f'(x) = \frac{1}{2}x^{-\frac{1}{2}}\cos(4x) - 4x^{\frac{1}{2}}\sin(4x)$,
  $f''(x) = -\frac{1}{4}x^{-\frac{3}{2}}\cos(4x) - 4x^{-\frac{1}{2}}\sin(4x) - 16x^{\frac{1}{2}}\cos(4x)$

4 a $x(0) = 3$ cm, $x'(0) = 2$ cm/s, $x''(0) = 0$ cm/s^2

 b $t = \frac{\pi}{4}$ sec and $\frac{3\pi}{4}$ sec **c** 4 cm

5 a for $0 \leqslant x \leqslant \frac{\pi}{2}$ and $\frac{3\pi}{2} \leqslant x \leqslant 2\pi$

 b increasing for $\frac{3\pi}{2} < x < 2\pi$, decreasing for $0 < x < \frac{\pi}{2}$

 c

6 a $v(0) = 0$ cm/s, $v(\frac{1}{2}) = -\pi$ cm/s, $v(1) = 0$ cm/s,
  $v(\frac{3}{2}) = \pi$ cm/s $v(2) = 0$ cm/s

 b $0 \leqslant t \leqslant 1$, $2 \leqslant t \leqslant 3$, $4 \leqslant t \leqslant 5$, etc.
  i.e., for $2n \leqslant t \leqslant 2n+1$, $n \in \{0, 1, 2, 3, ...\}$

7 a $a^2 + b^2 - 2ab\cos\theta = c^2 + d^2 - 2cd\cos\phi$

8 b $\frac{1}{\sqrt{2}}$ m above the floor

EXERCISE 25A

1 a i $\dfrac{x^2}{2}$ **ii** $\dfrac{x^3}{3}$ **iii** $\dfrac{x^6}{6}$ **iv** $-\dfrac{1}{x}$ **v** $-\dfrac{1}{3x^3}$ **vi** $\frac{3}{4}x^{\frac{4}{3}}$ **vii** $2\sqrt{x}$

 b the antiderivative of x^n is $\dfrac{x^{n+1}}{n+1}$.

2 a i $\frac{1}{2}e^{2x}$ **ii** $\frac{1}{5}e^{5x}$ **iii** $2e^{\frac{1}{2}x}$ **iv** $100e^{0.01x}$ **v** $\frac{1}{\pi}e^{\pi x}$

 vi $3e^{\frac{x}{3}}$ **b** the antiderivative of e^{kx} is $\dfrac{1}{k}e^{kx}$.

3 a $\dfrac{d}{dx}(x^3 + x^2) = 3x^2 + 2x$

 $\therefore$ antiderivative of $6x^2 + 4x = 2x^3 + 2x^2$

 b $\dfrac{d}{dx}(e^{3x+1}) = 3e^{3x+1}$

 $\therefore$ antiderivative of $e^{3x+1} = \frac{1}{3}e^{3x+1}$

 c $\dfrac{d}{dx}(x\sqrt{x}) = \frac{3}{2}\sqrt{x}$

 $\therefore$ antiderivative of $\sqrt{x} = \frac{2}{3}x\sqrt{x}$

 d $\dfrac{d}{dx}(2x+1)^4 = 8(2x+1)^3$

 $\therefore$ antiderivative of $(2x+1)^3 = \frac{1}{8}(2x+1)^4$

EXERCISE 25B.1

1 $\dfrac{dy}{dx} = 7x^6$; $\displaystyle\int x^6\,dx = \frac{1}{7}x^7 + c$

2 $\dfrac{dy}{dx} = 3x^2 + 2x$; $\displaystyle\int(3x^2 + 2x)\,dx = x^3 + x^2 + c$

3 $\dfrac{dy}{dx} = 2e^{2x+1}$; $\displaystyle\int e^{2x+1}\,dx = \frac{1}{2}e^{2x+1} + c$

4 $\dfrac{dy}{dx} = 8(2x+1)^3$; $\displaystyle\int(2x+1)^3\,dx = \frac{1}{8}(2x+1)^4 + c$

5 $\dfrac{dy}{dx} = \frac{3}{2}\sqrt{x}$; $\displaystyle\int\sqrt{x}\,dx = \frac{2}{3}x\sqrt{x} + c$

6 $\dfrac{dy}{dx} = -\dfrac{1}{2x\sqrt{x}}$; $\displaystyle\int\dfrac{1}{x\sqrt{x}}\,dx = -\dfrac{2}{\sqrt{x}} + c$

8 $\dfrac{dy}{dx} = \dfrac{-2}{\sqrt{1-4x}}$; $\displaystyle\int\dfrac{1}{\sqrt{1-4x}}\,dx = -\frac{1}{2}\sqrt{1-4x} + c$

9 $2\ln(5 - 3x + x^2) + c$ $(5 - 3x + x^2$ is $> 0)$ **10** $\dfrac{1}{\ln 2}2^x + c$

11 $x\ln x - x + c$

EXERCISE 25B.2

1 a $\dfrac{x^5}{5} - \dfrac{x^3}{3} - \dfrac{x^2}{2} + 2x + c$ **b** $\frac{2}{3}x^{\frac{3}{2}} + e^x + c$

 c $3e^x - \ln|x| + c$ **d** $\frac{2}{5}x^{\frac{5}{2}} - 2\ln|x| + c$

 e $-2x^{-\frac{1}{2}} + 4\ln|x| + c$ **f** $\frac{1}{8}x^4 - \frac{1}{5}x^5 + \frac{3}{4}x^{\frac{4}{3}} + c$

 g $\frac{1}{3}x^3 + 3\ln|x| + c$ **h** $\frac{1}{2}\ln|x| + \frac{1}{3}x^3 - e^x + c$

 i $5e^x + \frac{1}{12}x^4 - 4\ln|x| + c$

2 a $\frac{1}{3}x^3 + \frac{3}{2}x^2 - 2x + c$ **b** $\frac{2}{3}x^{\frac{3}{2}} - 2x^{\frac{1}{2}} + c$ **c** $2e^x + \dfrac{1}{x} + c$

 d $-2x^{-\frac{1}{2}} - 8x^{\frac{1}{2}} + c$ **e** $\frac{4}{3}x^3 + 2x^2 + x + c$

 f $\frac{1}{2}x^2 + x - 3\ln|x| + c$ **g** $\frac{4}{3}x^{\frac{3}{2}} - 2x^{\frac{1}{2}} + c$

 h $2x^{\frac{1}{2}} + 8x^{-\frac{1}{2}} - \frac{20}{3}x^{-\frac{3}{2}} + c$ **i** $\frac{1}{4}x^4 + x^3 + \frac{3}{2}x^2 + x + c$

3 a $y = 6x + c$ **b** $y = \frac{4}{3}x^3 + c$ **c** $y = \frac{5}{2}x^2 - \frac{1}{3}x^3 + c$

 d $y = -\dfrac{1}{x} + c$ **e** $y = 2e^x - 5x + c$ **f** $y = x^4 + x^3 + c$

4 a $y = x - 2x^2 + \frac{4}{3}x^3 + c$ **b** $y = \frac{2}{3}x^{\frac{3}{2}} - 4\sqrt{x} + c$

 c $y = x + 2\ln|x| + \dfrac{5}{x} + c$

5 a $f(x) = \frac{1}{4}x^4 - \frac{5}{2}x^2 + 3x + c$ **b** $f(x) = \frac{4}{3}x^{\frac{3}{2}} - \frac{12}{5}x^{\frac{5}{2}} + c$

 c $f(x) = 3e^x - 4\ln|x| + c$

6 a $f(x) = x^2 - x + 3$ **b** $f(x) = x^3 + x^2 - 7$

 c $f(x) = e^x + 2\sqrt{x} - 1 - e$ **d** $f(x) = \frac{1}{2}x^2 - 4\sqrt{x} + \frac{11}{2}$

7 a $f(x) = \frac{1}{3}x^3 + \frac{1}{2}x^2 + x + \frac{1}{3}$ **b** $f(x) = 4x^{\frac{5}{2}} + 4x^{\frac{3}{2}} - 4x + 5$

 c $f(x) = \frac{1}{3}x^3 - \frac{16}{3}x + 5$

EXERCISE 25C

1 **a** $\frac{1}{8}(2x+5)^4+c$ **b** $\frac{1}{2(3-2x)}+c$ **c** $\frac{-2}{3(2x-1)^3}+c$

 d $\frac{1}{32}(4x-3)^8+c$ **e** $\frac{2}{9}(3x-4)^{\frac{3}{2}}+c$ **f** $-4\sqrt{1-5x}+c$

 g $-\frac{3}{5}(1-x)^5+c$ **h** $-2\sqrt{3-4x}+c$

2 **a** $y=\frac{1}{3}(2x-7)^{\frac{3}{2}}+2$ **b** $(-8,-19)$

3 **a** $\frac{1}{2}(2x-1)^3+c$ **b** $\frac{1}{5}x^5-\frac{1}{2}x^4+\frac{1}{3}x^3+c$

 c $-\frac{1}{12}(1-3x)^4+c$ **d** $x-\frac{2}{3}x^3+\frac{1}{5}x^5+c$

 e $-\frac{8}{3}(5-x)^{\frac{3}{2}}+c$ **f** $\frac{1}{7}x^7+\frac{3}{5}x^5+x^3+x+c$

4 **a** $2e^x+\frac{5}{2}e^{2x}+c$ **b** $\frac{1}{3}x^3+\frac{2}{3}e^{-3x}+c$

 c $\frac{2}{3}x^{\frac{3}{2}}+2e^{2x}+e^{-x}+c$ **d** $\frac{1}{2}\ln|2x-1|+c$

 e $-\frac{5}{3}\ln|1-3x|+c$ **f** $-e^{-x}-2\ln|2x+1|+c$

 g $\frac{1}{2}e^{2x}+2x-\frac{1}{2}e^{-2x}+c$ **h** $-\frac{1}{2}e^{-2x}-4e^{-x}+4x+c$

 i $\frac{1}{2}x^2+5\ln|1-x|+c$

5 **a** $y=x-2e^x+\frac{1}{2}e^{2x}+c$ **b** $y=x-x^2+3\ln|x+2|+c$

 c $y=-\frac{1}{2}e^{-2x}+2\ln|2x-1|+c$

6 Both are correct. Recall that: $\frac{d}{dx}(\ln|Ax|)=\frac{d}{dx}(\ln|A|+\ln|x|)=\frac{1}{x}$

7 **a** $f(x)=-e^{-2x}+4$ **b** $f(x)=x^2+2\ln|1-x|+2-2\ln 2$

 c $f(x)=\frac{2}{3}x^{\frac{3}{2}}-\frac{1}{8}e^{-4x}+\frac{1}{8}e^{-4}-\frac{2}{3}$

8 $\int \frac{2x-8}{x^2-4}\,dx=3\ln|x+2|-\ln|x-2|+c$

9 $\int \frac{2}{4x^2-1}\,dx=\frac{1}{2}\ln|2x-1|-\frac{1}{2}\ln|2x+1|+c$

EXERCISE 25D

1 **a** $\frac{1}{5}(x^3+1)^5+c$ **b** $2\sqrt{x^2+3}+c$ **c** $\frac{2}{3}(x^3+x)^{\frac{3}{2}}+c$

 d $\frac{1}{4}(2+x^4)^4+c$ **e** $\frac{1}{5}(x^3+2x+1)^5+c$

 f $-\frac{1}{27(3x^3-1)^3}+c$ **g** $\frac{1}{8(1-x^2)^4}+c$

 h $-\frac{1}{2(x^2+4x-3)}+c$ **i** $\frac{1}{5}(x^2+x)^5+c$

2 **a** $e^{1-2x}+c$ **b** $e^{x^2}+c$ **c** $\frac{1}{3}e^{x^3+1}+c$

 d $2e^{\sqrt{x}}+c$ **e** $-e^{x-x^2}+c$ **f** $e^{1-\frac{1}{x}}+c$

3 **a** $\ln|x^2+1|+c$ **b** $-\frac{1}{2}\ln|2-x^2|+c$

 c $\ln|x^2-3x|+c$ **d** $2\ln|x^3-x|+c$

 e $-2\ln|5x-x^2|+c$ **f** $-\frac{1}{3}\ln|x^3-3x|+c$

4 **a** $f(x)=-\frac{1}{9}(3-x^3)^3+c$ **b** $f(x)=4\ln|\ln x|+c$

 c $f(x)=-\frac{1}{3}(1-x^2)^{\frac{3}{2}}+c$ **d** $f(x)=-\frac{1}{2}e^{1-x^2}+c$

 e $f(x)=-\ln|x^3-x|+c$ **f** $f(x)=\frac{1}{4}(\ln x)^4+c$

EXERCISE 25E.1

1 **a** $\frac{1}{4}$ **b** $\frac{2}{3}$ **c** $e-1\ (\doteqdot 1.718)$ **d** $1\frac{1}{2}$ **e** $6\frac{2}{3}$

 f $\ln 3\ (\doteqdot 1.099)$ **g** 1.524 **h** 2 **i** $e-1\ (\doteqdot 1.718)$

2 **a** $\frac{1}{12}$ **b** 1.557 **c** $20\frac{1}{3}$ **d** 0.0337

 e $\frac{1}{2}\ln(\frac{2}{7})\ (\doteqdot -0.6264)$ **f** $\frac{1}{2}(\ln 2)^2\ (\doteqdot 0.2402)$

 g 0 **h** $2\ln 7\ (\doteqdot 3.892)$ **i** $\frac{3^{n+1}}{2n+2}$, $n\neq -1$

EXERCISE 25E.2

1 **a** $\int_1^4 \sqrt{x}\,dx=4.667$ $\int_1^4 (-\sqrt{x})\,dx=-4.667$

 b $\int_0^1 x^7\,dx=\frac{1}{8}$ $\int_0^1 (-x^7)\,dx=-\frac{1}{8}$

2 **a** $\frac{1}{3}$ **b** $\frac{7}{3}$ **c** $\frac{8}{3}$ **d** 1 **3 a** -4 **b** 6.25 **c** 2.25

4 **a** $\int_a^b [-f(x)]\,dx=-\int_a^b f(x)\,dx$

 b $\int_a^b f(x)\,dx+\int_b^c f(x)\,dx=\int_a^c f(x)\,dx$

 $\int_a^b k\,f(x)\,dx=k\int_a^b f(x)\,dx$

5 **a** $\frac{1}{3}$ **b** $\frac{2}{3}$ **c** 1

 i.e., $\int_0^1 x^2\,dx+\int_0^1 \sqrt{x}\,dx=\int_0^1 (x^2+\sqrt{x})\,dx$

EXERCISE 25E.3

1 **a** 6.5 **b** -9 **c** 0 **d** -2.5

2 **a** 2π **b** -4 **c** $\frac{\pi}{2}$ **d** $\frac{5\pi}{2}-4$

3 **a** $\int_2^7 f(x)\,dx$ **b** $\int_1^9 g(x)\,dx$ **4** **a** -5 **b** 4

REVIEW SET 25A

1 **a** $8\sqrt{x}+c$ **b** $-\frac{3}{2}\ln|1-2x|+c$ **c** $-\frac{1}{2}e^{1-x^2}+c$

2 **a** $12\frac{4}{9}$ **b** $\frac{5}{54}$ **3** $\frac{dy}{dx}=\frac{x}{\sqrt{x^2-4}}$;

 $\int \frac{x}{\sqrt{x^2-4}}\,dx=\sqrt{x^2-4}+c$

4 $f(x)=3x^3+5x^2+6x-1$

5 **a** $A=2,\ B=-5$ **b** $\int_0^2 \frac{4x-3}{2x+1}\,dx=4-\frac{5}{2}\ln 5\ (\doteqdot -0.0236)$

6 **a** $3-\sqrt{7}$ **b** $\frac{1}{3}(e^2-e)$ **7** $a=\ln\sqrt{2}$

REVIEW SET 25B

1 **a** $-2e^{-x}-\ln|x|+3x+c$ **b** $\frac{1}{2}x^2-2x+\ln|x|+c$

2 **a** $2\frac{8}{15}$ **b** $4\frac{1}{2}$

3 $\frac{d}{dx}(3x^2+x)^3=3(3x^2+x)^2(6x+1)$

 $\int(3x^2+x)^2(6x+1)\,dx=\frac{1}{3}(3x^2+x)^3+c$

4 $f(x)=\frac{1}{3}x^3-\frac{3}{2}x^2+2x+2\frac{1}{6}$ **5** $\frac{2}{3}(\sqrt{5}-\sqrt{2})$

6 **a** $f(x)=\frac{1}{4}x^4+\frac{1}{3}x^3-\frac{10}{3}x+3$ **b** $3x+26y=84$

7 $A=1,\ B=2,\ C=1,\ D=4,\ \frac{(x-1)^3}{3}+4\ln|x-2|+c$

8 **a** $\ln\left(\frac{|x+2|}{(x-1)^2}\right)+c$ **b** $\ln\left(\frac{(x-1)^2}{|x+2|}\right)+c$

REVIEW SET 25C

1 **a** $y=\frac{1}{5}x^5-\frac{2}{3}x^3+x+c$ **b** $y=400x+40e^{-\frac{x}{2}}+c$

2 **a** $-2\ln 5$ **b** $3\frac{1}{3}$ **3** $\frac{2(\ln x)}{x}$, $\frac{1}{2}(\ln x)^2+c$ **4** $23\frac{1}{6}$

5 if $n\neq -1$, $\frac{1}{2(n+1)}(2x+3)^{n+1}+c$

 if $n=-1$, $\frac{1}{2}\ln|2x+3|+c$

6 **a** $e^{3x}+6e^{2x}+12e^x+8$ **b** $\frac{1}{3}e^3+3e^2+12e-7\frac{1}{3}$

7 $a=\frac{1}{3}$, $f'(x)=2\sqrt{x}+\frac{1}{3\sqrt{x}}$ is never 0

 as $\sqrt{x}\geqslant 0$ for all x, $\therefore f'(x)>0$ for all x

8 $a=0$ or ± 3

EXERCISE 26A.1

1 a 0.34 u^2 **b** 0.70 u^2 **2 a** 0.335 u^2 **b** 0.6938 u^2

EXERCISE 26A.2

1 a lower $= 2.693$,
upper $= 3$

b lower $= 2.69$,
upper $= 3.09$

c

n	Lower	Upper
10	2.79	2.99
50	2.87	2.91
100	2.88	2.90
500	2.883	2.887
5000	2.8852	2.8856

2 a lower $= 2.55$,
upper $= 2.90$

b

n	Lower	Upper
100	2.709 70	2.726 89
1000	2.717 42	2.719 14
10 000	2.718 20	2.718 37
100 000	2.718 27	2.718 29

c Upper and lower sums converge.

3 a

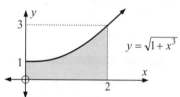

$y = \sqrt{1 + x^3}$

b

n	Lower	Upper
100	3.22	3.26
10 000	3.2411	3.2415

c 3.2413 units^2

4 a

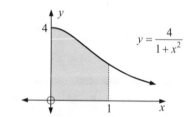

$y = \dfrac{4}{1 + x^2}$

b

n	Lower	Upper
100	3.13	3.15
1000	3.141	3.143
10 000	3.1415	3.1417

c 3.1416 units^2

5 $10.203\,22$ **6 a** 18 **b** 4.5 **c** 1 **d** 1 **e** 2π **f** $2 + \pi$

EXERCISE 26B

2 a $\frac{1}{4}$ units^2 **b** $45\frac{3}{4}$ units^2 **c** $24\frac{2}{3}$ units^2 **d** $\frac{4\sqrt{2}}{3}$ units^2
e 3.482 units^2 **f** 2 units^2 **g** 3.965 units^2

EXERCISE 26C

1 a $\frac{1}{3}$ units^2 **b** $3\frac{3}{4}$ units^2 **c** $e - 1$ ($\doteqdot 1.718$) units^2
d $20\frac{5}{6}$ units^2 **e** $3\frac{1}{3}$ units^2 **f** $12\frac{2}{3}$ units^2

2 a 18 units^2 **b** $\ln 4$ ($\doteqdot 1.386$) units^2 **c** $\ln 3$ ($\doteqdot 1.099$) u^2
d $4\frac{1}{2}$ u^2 **e** $2e - \dfrac{2}{e}$ ($\doteqdot 4.701$) u^2 **f** $\ln\left(\frac{27}{4}\right) - 1$ u^2

3 a $4\frac{1}{2}$ u^2 **b** $1 + e^{-2}$ ($\doteqdot 1.135$) u^2 **c** $1\frac{5}{27}$ u^2 **d** $2\frac{1}{4}$ u^2

4 a $10\frac{2}{3}$ units^2
b i, ii

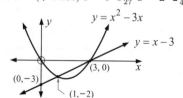

$y = x^2 - 3x$
$y = x - 3$
$(3, 0)$
$(0, -3)$
$(1, -2)$

iii $1\frac{1}{3}$ units^2

c $\frac{1}{3}$ units^2

d

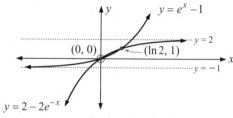

$y = e^x - 1$
$y = 2$
$(0, 0)$
$(\ln 2, 1)$
$y = -1$
$y = 2 - 2e^{-x}$

enclosed area $= 3\ln 2 - 2$ ($\doteqdot 0.0794$) units^2

e $\frac{1}{2}$ units^2

5

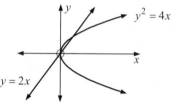

$y^2 = 4x$
$y = 2x$

enclosed area $= \frac{1}{3}$ units^2

6 a

$x^2 + y^2 = 9$
3
-3 3
-3

b $\frac{9\pi}{4}$ units^2 ($\doteqdot 7.07$ units^2)

7 a $40\frac{1}{2}$ units^2 **b** 8 units^2 **c** 8 units^2

8 a i $A = \int_{-2}^{-1} (x^3 - 7x - 6)\,dx + \int_{-1}^{3} (7x + 6 - x^3)\,dx$
ii $A = \int_{-2}^{3} \left| x^3 - 7x - 6 \right|\,dx$
b Area $= 32\frac{3}{4}$ units^2

9 a $21\frac{1}{12}$ units^2 **b** 8 units^2 **c** $101\frac{3}{4}$ units^2

10 a $\int_{3}^{5} f(x)\,dx = -$ (area between $x = 3$ and $x = 5$)
b $\int_{1}^{3} f(x)\,dx - \int_{3}^{5} f(x)\,dx + \int_{5}^{7} f(x)\,dx$

11 $k \doteqdot 1.7377$ **12** $b \doteqdot 1.3104$ **13** $k \doteqdot 2.3489$
14 $a = \sqrt{3}$

EXERCISE 26D.1

1 110 m

2 a i travelling forwards
ii travelling backwards (or in the opposite direction)
b 8 km from starting point (on positive side)

3 9.75 km

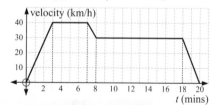

velocity (km/h)
t (mins)

EXERCISE 26D.2

1 a $\frac{1}{2}$ cm **b** 0 cm **2 a** $5\frac{1}{6}$ cm **b** $1\frac{1}{2}$ cm left
3 a 41 units **b** 34 units
4 a 40 m/s **b** 47.77 m/s **c** 1.386 seconds

d as $t \to \infty$, $v(t) \to 50$ **f**

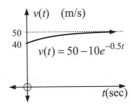

e $a(t) = 5e^{-0.5t}$ and as
$e^x > 0$ for all x,
$a(t) > 0$ for all t.

g 134.5 m

5 900 m

6 a Show that $v(t) = 100 - 80e^{-\frac{1}{20}t}$ m/s and
as $t \to \infty$, $v(t) \to 100$ m/s **b** 370.4 m

EXERCISE 26E

1 \$4250 **2 a** $P(x) = 15x - 0.015x^2 - 650$ dollars
b maximum profit is \$3100, when 500 plates are made
c $46 \leqslant x \leqslant 954$ plates (you can't produce part of a plate)

3 14 400 calories **4** 76.3° C

5 a $y = -\frac{1}{120}(1-x)^4 - \frac{x}{30} + \frac{1}{120}$ **b** 2.5 cm (at $x = 1$ m)

6 a $y = \left(\frac{0.01}{3}x^3 - \frac{0.005}{12}x^4 - \frac{0.08}{3}x\right)$ metres **b** 3.33 cm
c 2.375 cm **d** 1.05°

7 Extra hint: $\dfrac{dC}{dV} = \frac{1}{2}x^2 + 4$ and $\dfrac{dV}{dx} = \pi r^2$

8 e 0.974 km × 2.05 km

REVIEW SET 26A

1 a

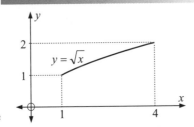

b 4.41 units^2

2 a $2 + \pi$ **b** -2 **c** π

3 a $A = \displaystyle\int_a^b [f(x) - g(x)]dx + \int_b^c [g(x) - f(x)]\,dx$
$+ \displaystyle\int_c^d [f(x) - g(x)]\,dx$

b $\displaystyle\int_a^d |f(x) - g(x)|\,dx$ or $\int_a^d |g(x) - f(x)|\,dx$

4 269 cm

5

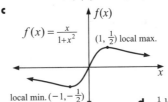

a $(2, -1)$ and $(5, 2)$ **b** 4.5 units^2

6 $k = \sqrt[3]{16}$

7 **Hint:** Show that the areas represented by the integrals
can be arranged to form a $1 \times e$ unit rectangle.

8 a $v(0) = 25$ m/s, $v(3) = 4$ m/s
b as $t \to \infty$, $v(t) \to 0$

c

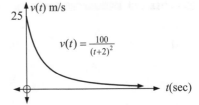

d 3 seconds

e $a(t) = \dfrac{-200}{(t+2)^3}$, $t \geqslant 0$ **f** $k = \frac{1}{5}$

9 $21\frac{1}{12}$ units^2 **10** $a = \ln 3$, $b = \ln 5$

REVIEW SET 26B

1 29.6 cm **2** 4.5 units^2

3 $I(t) = \dfrac{100}{t} + 100$ **a** 105 amps **b** as $t \to \infty$, $I \to 100$

4 π units^2 **5** no, $\int_1^3 f(x)\,dx = -$ (area from $x = 1$ to $x = 3$)

6 a local maximum at $(1, \frac{1}{2})$, local minimum at $(-1, -\frac{1}{2})$
b as $x \to \infty$, $f(x) \to 0$ (right) as
$x \to -\infty$, $f(x) \to 0$ (left)

c

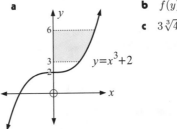

d $\frac{1}{2} \ln 5$ ($\doteqdot 0.805$) units^2

7 $k = 1\frac{1}{3}$

8 a

b $f(y) = \sqrt[3]{y - 2}$
c $3\sqrt[3]{4} - \frac{3}{4} \doteqdot 4.01$ units^2

9 31.2 units^2

EXERCISE 27A

1 a $-3 \cos x - 2x + c$ **b** $2x^2 - 2\sin x + c$
c $\frac{4}{3}x^{\frac{3}{2}} + 4 \tan x + c$ **d** $\tan x - 2 \cos x + c$
e $\dfrac{x^2}{4} - \tan x + c$ **f** $-\cos x - 2 \sin x + e^x + c$

2 a $\frac{2}{3}x^{\frac{3}{2}} + \frac{1}{2} \sin x + c$ **b** $\dfrac{\theta^2}{2} + \cos \theta + c$ **c** $\frac{2}{5}t^{\frac{5}{2}} + 2 \tan t + c$
d $2e^t + 4 \cos t + c$ **e** $3 \sin t - \ln|t| + c$
f $3\theta - 2 \ln|\theta| + \tan \theta + c$

3 a $e^x \sin x + e^x \cos x$, $e^x \sin x + c$
b $-e^{-x} \sin x + e^{-x} \cos x$, $e^{-x} \sin x + c$
c $\cos x - x \sin x$, $\sin x - x \cos x + c$ **d** $\dfrac{1}{\cos x} + c$

4 a $f(x) = \dfrac{x^3}{3} - 4 \sin x + 3$
b $f(x) = 2 \sin x + 3 \cos x - 2\sqrt{2}$
c $f(x) = \frac{2}{3}x^{\frac{3}{2}} - 2 \tan x - \frac{2}{3}\pi^{\frac{3}{2}}$

EXERCISE 27B

1 **a** $-\frac{1}{3}\cos(3x)+c$ **b** $\frac{1}{2}\sin(4x)+c$ **c** $\frac{1}{2}\tan(2x)+c$

   d $6\sin\left(\frac{x}{2}\right)+c$ **e** $-\frac{3}{2}\cos(2x)+e^{-x}+c$

   f $\frac{1}{2}e^{2x}-4\tan\left(\frac{x}{2}\right)+c$ **g** $-\cos\left(2x+\frac{\pi}{6}\right)+c$

   h $3\sin\left(\frac{\pi}{4}-x\right)+c$ **i** $-2\tan\left(\frac{\pi}{3}-2x\right)+c$

   j $\frac{1}{2}\sin(2x)-\frac{1}{2}\cos(2x)+c$ **k** $-\frac{2}{3}\cos(3x)+\frac{5}{4}\sin(4x)+c$

   l $\frac{1}{16}\sin(8x)+3\cos x+c$

2 **a** $\frac{1}{2}x+\frac{1}{4}\sin(2x)+c$ **b** $\frac{1}{2}x-\frac{1}{4}\sin(2x)+c$

   c $\frac{3}{2}x+\frac{1}{8}\sin(4x)+c$ **d** $\frac{5}{2}x+\frac{1}{12}\sin(6x)+c$

   e $\frac{1}{4}x+\frac{1}{32}\sin(8x)+c$ **f** $\frac{3}{2}x+2\sin x+\frac{1}{4}\sin(2x)+c$

3 $\frac{1}{32}\sin(4x)+\frac{1}{4}\sin(2x)+\frac{3}{8}x+c$

4 **a** $\frac{1}{5}\sin^5 x+c$ **b** $-2(\cos x)^{\frac{1}{2}}+c$ **c** $-\ln|\cos x|+c$

   d $\frac{2}{3}(\sin x)^{\frac{3}{2}}+c$ **e** $-(2+\sin x)^{-1}+c$ **f** $\frac{1}{2}(\cos x)^{-2}+c$

   g $\ln|1-\cos x|+c$ **h** $\frac{1}{2}\ln|\sin(2x)-3|+c$

5 **a** $\sin x-\frac{1}{3}\sin^3 x+c$ **b** $-\cos x+\frac{2}{3}\cos^3 x-\frac{1}{5}\cos^5 x+c$

   c $\frac{1}{5}\sin^5 x-\frac{1}{7}\sin^7 x+c$

6 **a** $-e^{\cos x}+c$ **b** $\frac{1}{8}\sin^4(2x)+c$ **c** $\ln|\sin x-\cos x|+c$

   d $e^{\tan x}+c$

7 **a** $\ln|\sin x|+c$ **b** $\frac{1}{3}\ln|\sin(3x)|+c$ **c** $-\cot x+c$

   d $\sec x+c$ **e** $-\csc x+c$ **f** $\frac{1}{3}\sec(3x)+c$

   g $-2\csc\left(\frac{x}{2}\right)+c$ **h** $\frac{1}{2}\sec^2 x+c$ **i** $-2\sqrt{\cot x}+c$

EXERCISE 27C

1 **a** $\frac{1}{2}$ **b** $\frac{1}{2}$ **c** $\sqrt{3}-1$ **d** $\frac{1}{3}$ **e** $\frac{\pi}{8}+\frac{1}{4}$ **f** $\frac{\pi}{4}$

2 **a** $2-\sqrt{2}$ **b** $\frac{1}{24}$ **c** $\frac{1}{2}\ln 2$ **d** $\ln 2$ **e** $\ln 2$

EXERCISE 27D

1 **b** $\frac{\pi}{2}$ u^2 **2** $(\sqrt{2}-1)$ u^2 **3** **a** $(\frac{\pi}{4}, 1)$ **b** $\ln\sqrt{2}$ u^2

4 **a** C_1 is $y=\sin 2x$, C_2 is $y=\sin x$ **b** $A(\frac{\pi}{3}, \frac{\sqrt{3}}{2})$ **c** $2\frac{1}{2}$ u^2

5 **a** C_1 is $y=\cos^2 x$, C_2 is $y=\cos(2x)$

   b $A(0, 1)$ $B(\frac{\pi}{4}, 0)$ $C(\frac{\pi}{2}, 0)$ $D(\frac{3\pi}{4}, 0)$ $E(\pi, 1)$

REVIEW SET 27A

1 **a** $\frac{1}{8}\sin^8 x+c$ **b** $-\frac{1}{2}\ln|\cos(2x)|+c$ **c** $e^{\sin x}+c$

2 $x\tan x+\ln|\cos x|+c$ **3** $\left(1-\frac{\pi}{4}\right)$ units^2

4 **a** $\frac{\pi}{6}+\frac{\sqrt{3}}{4}$ **b** $\frac{1}{2}\ln 2$

5 $\tan x$, $\int\tan x\, dx=\ln(\sec x)+c$ **6** $\ln 2$ **7** $\left(\frac{\pi^2}{2}-2\right)$ u^2

EXERCISE 28A.1

1 **a** 36π units^3 **b** 8π units^3 **c** $\frac{127\pi}{7}$ units^3

   d $\frac{255\pi}{4}$ units^3 **e** $\frac{992\pi}{5}$ units^3 **f** $\frac{250\pi}{3}$ units^3

2 **a** 186π units^3 **b** $\frac{146\pi}{5}$ units^3 **c** $\frac{\pi}{2}(e^8-1)$ units^3

3 **a** 63π units^3 **b** $\doteqdot 198$ cm^3

4 **a** a cone of base radius r and height h

   b $y=-\left(\frac{r}{h}\right)x+r$ **c** $V=\frac{1}{3}\pi r^2 h$

5 **a** a sphere of radius r

6 **a** 8π units^3 **b** $\frac{1024\pi}{5}$ units^3 **c** $\frac{\pi}{2}(e^4-1)$ units^3

EXERCISE 28A.2

1 **a** $\frac{\pi^2}{4}$ units^3 **b** $\frac{\pi^2}{8}$ units^3 **c** 2π units^3 **d** $\pi\sqrt{3}$ units^3

2 **a**

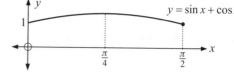

   b $\pi\left(\frac{\pi}{4}+\frac{1}{2}\right)$ units^3

3 **a**

(graph: $y=4\sin(2x)$)

   b $2\pi^2$ units^3

EXERCISE 28B

1 **a** A is at $(-1, 3)$, B$(1, 3)$ **b** $\frac{136\pi}{15}$ units^3

2 **a** A is at $(2, e)$ **b** $\pi(e^2+1)$ units^3

3 **a** A is at $(1, 1)$ **b** $\frac{11\pi}{6}$ u^3 **4** **a** A is at $(5, 1)$ **b** $\frac{9\pi}{2}$ u^3

5 **b**

(figure: circle with $y=3+\sqrt{4-x^2}$ and $y=3-\sqrt{4-x^2}$)

   c $\doteqdot 237$ units^3

REVIEW SET 28

1 **a** 312π units^3 **b** 402π units^3 **c** $\frac{\pi^2}{2}$ units^3 **d** 18π units^3

2 **a** $\pi\left(\frac{3\pi}{32}-\frac{1}{8\sqrt{2}}\right)$ units^3 **b** $\doteqdot 123.8$ units^3 **3** 2π units^3

4 $\frac{128\pi}{5}$ units^3 **5** $\frac{\pi}{2}$ units^3 **6** **a** $\frac{128\pi}{3}$ units^3 **b** $\frac{128\pi}{3}$ units^3

7 $\frac{96\pi}{5}$ units^3

EXERCISE 29A

1 **a** $4\arcsin x+c$ **b** $3\arcsin\left(\frac{x}{2}\right)+c$

   c $\frac{1}{4}\arctan\left(\frac{x}{4}\right)+c$ **d** $\frac{1}{2}\arctan(2x)+c$

   e $\frac{1}{2}\arcsin(2x)+c$ **f** $\frac{2}{3}\arcsin\left(\frac{3x}{2}\right)+c$

   g $\frac{1}{2\sqrt{2}}\arctan\left(\frac{x}{\sqrt{2}}\right)+c$ **h** $\frac{5}{6}\arctan\left(\frac{2x}{3}\right)+c$

2 **a**

(graph)

   b **i** $f(-x)=\dfrac{1}{\sqrt{1-(-x)^2}}=\dfrac{1}{\sqrt{1-x^2}}=f(x)$ for all x

      ii For y to have meaning $1-x^2>0$ which has solution $x\in\,]-1,\,1[$

   c Area $=\frac{\pi}{6}$ units^2

EXERCISE 29B

1 a $\frac{2}{5}(x-3)^{\frac{5}{2}} + 2(x-3)^{\frac{3}{2}} + c$

  b $\frac{2}{7}(x+1)^{\frac{7}{2}} - \frac{4}{5}(x+1)^{\frac{5}{2}} + \frac{2}{3}(x+1)^{\frac{3}{2}} + c$

  c $-(3-x^2)^{\frac{3}{2}} + \frac{1}{5}(3-x^2)^{\frac{5}{2}} + c$

  d $\frac{1}{5}(t^2+2)^{\frac{5}{2}} - \frac{2}{3}(t^2+2)^{\frac{3}{2}} + c$

  e $2\sqrt{x-1} - 2\arccos\left(\frac{1}{\sqrt{x}}\right) + c$

2 a $\frac{28\sqrt{3}}{5} - \frac{44\sqrt{2}}{15}$ **b** $\frac{48\sqrt{6}-54}{5}$ **c** $\frac{1054\sqrt{3}}{35}$

3 a $x - 3\arctan\left(\frac{x}{3}\right) + c$ **b** $\frac{1}{2}\arcsin x - \frac{1}{2}x\sqrt{1-x^2} + c$

  c $\ln(x^2+9) + c$ **d** $2\ln(1 + [\ln x]^2) + c$

  e $\sqrt{x^2-4} - 2\arccos\left(\frac{2}{x}\right) + c$ **f** $\cos x - \frac{2}{3}\cos^3 x + c$

  g $\frac{1}{2}\arcsin\left(\frac{2x}{3}\right) + c$ **h** $\frac{1}{2}x^2 - \frac{1}{2}\ln(1+x^2) + c$

  i $\frac{1}{6}\arctan\left(\frac{2}{3}\ln x\right) + c$ **j** $\frac{1}{16}\ln\left(\frac{|x|}{\sqrt{x^2+16}}\right) + c$

  k $\frac{-1}{16x}\sqrt{16-x^2} + c$ **l** $2\arcsin\left(\frac{x}{2}\right) - \frac{1}{4}x(2-x^2)\sqrt{4-x^2} + c$

EXERCISE 29C

1 a $xe^x - e^x + c$ **b** $-x\cos x + \sin x + c$

  c $\frac{1}{3}x^3\ln x - \frac{1}{9}x^3 + c$ **d** $-\frac{1}{3}x\cos 3x + \frac{1}{9}\sin 3x + c$

  e $\frac{1}{2}x\sin 2x + \frac{1}{4}\cos 2x + c$ **f** $x\tan x + \ln|\cos x| + c$

  g $x\ln x - x + c$ **h** $x(\ln x)^2 - 2x\ln x + 2x + c$

  i $x\arctan x - \frac{1}{2}\ln(x^2+1) + c$

2 a $-x^2 e^{-x} - 2xe^{-x} - 2e^{-x} + c$ **b** $\frac{1}{2}e^x(\sin x + \cos x) + c$

  c $-\frac{1}{2}e^{-x}(\cos x + \sin x) + c$

  d $-x^2\cos x + 2x\sin x + 2\cos x + c$

3 a $u^2 e^u - 2ue^u + 2e^u + c$ **b** $x(\ln x)^2 - 2x\ln x + 2x + c$

4 a $-u\cos u + \sin u + c$ **b** $-\sqrt{2x}\cos\sqrt{2x} + \sin\sqrt{2x} + c$

5 $\frac{2}{3}\sqrt{3x}\sin\sqrt{3x} + \frac{2}{3}\cos\sqrt{3x} + c$

EXERCISE 29D.1

1 a $y = Ae^{5x}$ **b** $M = Ae^{-2t}$ **c** $y^2 = 4x + c$

  d $P^{\frac{1}{2}} = \frac{3}{2}t + c$ **e** $Q = Ae^{2t} - \frac{3}{2}$ **f** $t = Q^2 + 3Q + c$

2 a $y = 10e^{4x}$ **b** $M = 20e^{-3t}$ **c** $\sqrt{y} = \frac{1}{6}t - 1$

  d $P = \frac{7}{2}e^{2n} - \frac{3}{2}$ **e** $y = (x-3)^2$

3 $y = Ae^{2x}$ **4 a** $p = \frac{10}{e}$ **b** $r = \ln 2$

EXERCISE 29D.2

1 a $y = Ax^3$ **b** $y = Ae^{\frac{x^2}{8}}$ **c** $y = Ae^{e^x}$

  d $y = -\ln\left(-\frac{x^2}{2} + c\right)$

2 $z = e^{\frac{1}{3}r^3 + r}$ **3** $y = e^{-x^2}$ **4** $y = 2e^{-\frac{1}{3}x}$

5 $y^2 = x^2 - 9, \ a = \pm 3\sqrt{2}$

6 a $y = \frac{-2}{x^2 + 2x - 4}$ **b** Horizontal asymptote $y = 0$, vertical asymptotes $x = -1 \pm \sqrt{5}$

7 b $x^2 + y^2 = c$ circle centre $(0, 0)$, radius $= \sqrt{c}$ $y = dx$ line passing through $(0, 0)$, slope d "diameter meets the tangent to the circle at right angles".

8 $v = 4(1.5)^{\frac{t}{4}}$ m/s, $v \doteq 6.64$ m/s **9** 0.8% **10** $t = 3$ sec

11 a $v \to \frac{g}{4}$ m/s **b** $t = \frac{1}{4}\ln\left(\frac{5}{3}\right) \doteq 0.128$ sec

12 a V_0 is the original volume of water, V is the volume of water that has evaporated. $\therefore$ $V_0 - V$ is the volume remaining.

  b $\doteq 17.7\%$

13 4 hours **14 a** $\frac{dh}{dt} = \frac{r^2}{\pi h^2 - 2\pi rh}$ **b** $\doteq 14.4$ hours

15 $\doteq 12.5$ minutes **16** 12 midnight **17 c** $\operatorname{cis}\theta = e^{i\theta}$

EXERCISE 29D.3

1 $y = e^x(x^2 + c)$ **2** $y = e^x(x + c)$ or $y = Ae^{-x} - \frac{1}{2}e^x$

3 $x(x^2 + 5y^2)^2 = k$ **4** $y = Axe^{2x^2}$

REVIEW SET 29A

1 $-\frac{32}{3}(4-x)^{\frac{3}{2}} + \frac{16}{5}(4-x)^{\frac{5}{2}} - \frac{2}{7}(4-x)^{\frac{7}{2}} + c$

2 $x\arctan x - \frac{1}{2}\ln(x^2+1) + c$

3 a $\frac{1}{2}e^{-x}(\sin x - \cos x) + c$ **b** $e^x(x^2 - 2x + 2) + c$

  c $\frac{1}{3}(9-x^2)^{\frac{3}{2}} - 9\sqrt{9-x^2} + c$

4 $y^2 = 20 - 4e^x$ **5** $\doteq 0.00527$ sec **6** $y = 3e^{\frac{1}{3}x}$

7 $y^2 = x^2 + Ax$

REVIEW SET 29B

1 a $5\arcsin\left(\frac{x}{3}\right) + c$ **b** $\frac{1}{6}\arctan\left(\frac{2x}{3}\right) + c$ **c** $\frac{80}{3}\sqrt{5} - \frac{124}{15}\sqrt{2}$

2 a $\cos x + x\sin x + c$ **b** $\sqrt{x^2-4} + 2\arccos\left(\frac{2}{x}\right) + c$

5 b 0.0248 units **c** $m_H = -2, \ m_L \doteq -0.00496$

6 a $\frac{dN}{dt} = kN$ (k a constant) **b** $\doteq 8.97 \times 10^6$ bacteria

7 a $y = 1 - \frac{2}{x^2 + 4x + 1}$

  b HA $y = 1$, VA $x = -2 + \sqrt{3}, \ x = -2 - \sqrt{3}$

8 $\frac{1}{8}$ remains

EXERCISE 30A

1 a continuous **b** discrete **c** continuous **d** continuous

  e discrete **f** discrete **g** continuous **h** continuous

2 a i height of water in the rain gauge

    ii $0 \leqslant x \leqslant 200$ mm **iii** continuous

  b i stopping distance **ii** $0 \leqslant x \leqslant 50$ m **iii** continuous

  c i time for the switch to fail

    ii $0 \leqslant x \leqslant 10\,000$ hours **iii** continuous

3 a $0 \leqslant x \leqslant 4$

  b

YYYY	YYYN	YYNN	NNNY	NNNN
	YYNY	YNYN	NNYN	
	YNYY	YNNY	NYNN	
	NYYY	NNYY	YNNN	
		NYNY		
		NYYN		
$(x=4)$	$(x=3)$	$(x=2)$	$(x=1)$	$(x=0)$

  c i $x = 2$ **ii** $x = 2, 3$ or 4

4 a $x = 0, 1, 2, 3$

  b

HHH	HHT	TTH	TTT
	HTH	THT	
	THH	HTT	
$(x=3)$	$(x=2)$	$(x=1)$	$(x=0)$

  c $\Pr(x=3) = \frac{1}{8}$,

    $\Pr(x=2) = \frac{3}{8}$,

    $\Pr(x=1) = \frac{3}{8}$,

    $\Pr(x=0) = \frac{1}{8}$

  d

EXERCISE 30B

1 a $k = 0.2$ **b** $k = \frac{1}{7}$

2 a $a = 0.5488$, the probability that Jason does not hit a home run in a game.

b $P(2) = 0.1088$

c $P(1) + P(2) + P(3) + P(4) + P(5) = 0.4512$ and is the probability that Jason will hit one or more home runs in a game.

d

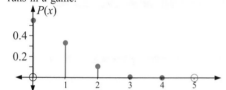

3 a $\sum P(x_i) > 1$ **b** $P(5) < 0$ which is not possible

4 a The random variable represents the number of hits that Sally has in each game.

b $k = 0.23$ **c i** $P(x \geqslant 2) = 0.79$ **ii** $P(1 \leqslant x \leqslant 3) = 0.83$

5 a

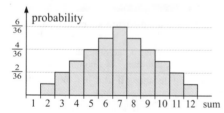

roll 1						
6	(6, 1)	(6, 2)	(6, 3)	(6, 4)	(6, 5)	(6, 6)
5	(5, 1)	(5, 2)	(5, 3)	(5, 4)	(5, 5)	(5, 6)
4	(4, 1)	(4, 2)	(4, 3)	(4, 4)	(4, 5)	(4, 6)
3	(3, 1)	(3, 2)	(3, 3)	(3, 4)	(3, 5)	(3, 6)
2	(2, 1)	(2, 2)	(2, 3)	(2, 4)	(2, 5)	(2, 6)
1	(1, 1)	(1, 2)	(1, 3)	(1, 4)	(1, 5)	(1, 6)
	1	2	3	4	5	6

roll 2

b $P(0) = 0$; $P(1) = 0$; $P(2) = \frac{1}{36}$; $P(3) = \frac{2}{36}$;
$P(4) = \frac{3}{36}$; $P(5) = \frac{4}{36}$; $P(6) = \frac{5}{36}$;
$P(7) = \frac{6}{36}$; $P(8) = \frac{5}{36}$; $P(9) = \frac{4}{36}$;
$P(10) = \frac{3}{36}$; $P(11) = \frac{2}{36}$; $P(12) = \frac{1}{36}$

c

probability histogram for sum from 1 to 12

6 a $k = \frac{1}{12}$ **b** $k = \frac{12}{25}$

7 a $P(0) = 0.1975k$; $P(1) = 0.0988k$; $P(2) = 0.0494k$;
$P(3) = 0.0247k$; $P(4) = 0.0123k$

b $k = 2.6130$ $P(x \geqslant 2) = 0.2258$

8 a $P(0) = 0.6648$ **b** $P(x \geqslant 1) = 0.3352$

9 a

X	0	1	2
P(X = x)	$\frac{3}{28}$	$\frac{15}{28}$	$\frac{10}{28}$

b

X	0	1	2	3
P(X = x)	$\frac{1}{56}$	$\frac{15}{56}$	$\frac{30}{56}$	$\frac{10}{56}$

10 a

Die 2

Die 1	1	2	3	4	5	6
1	2	3	4	5	6	7
2	3	4	5	6	7	8
3	4	5	6	7	8	9
4	5	6	7	8	9	10
5	6	7	8	9	10	11
6	7	8	9	10	11	12

b $\frac{1}{6}$

d $\frac{15}{26}$

c

D	2	3	4	5	6	7
$P(D = d)$	$\frac{1}{36}$	$\frac{2}{36}$	$\frac{3}{36}$	$\frac{4}{36}$	$\frac{5}{36}$	$\frac{6}{36}$

D	8	9	10	11	12
$P(D = d)$	$\frac{5}{36}$	$\frac{4}{36}$	$\frac{3}{36}$	$\frac{2}{36}$	$\frac{1}{36}$

11 a i $\doteqdot 0.8187$ **ii** 0.1637 **iii** $\doteqdot 0.0164$ **b** 0.00115

EXERCISE 30C

1 102 days **2 a** $\frac{1}{8}$ **b** 25 **3** 30 times

4 a i $\frac{1}{6}$ **ii** $\frac{1}{3}$ **iii** $\frac{1}{2}$ **b i** \$1.33 **ii** \$0.50 **iii** \$3.50

c lose 50 cents **d** lose \$50

5 15 days

6 a i 0.55 **ii** 0.29 **iii** 0.16 **b i** 4125 **ii** 2175 **iii** 1200

7 a \$3.50 **b** No **8** \$1.50 **9 a** \$2.75 **b** \$3.75

EXERCISE 30D

1 a $k = 0.03$ **b** $\mu = 0.74$ **c** $\sigma = 0.9962$

2 $P(1) = \frac{1}{10}$, $P(2) = \frac{3}{10}$, $P(3) = \frac{6}{10}$, $\mu = 2.5$, $\sigma = 0.6708$

3 a $P(0) = 0.216$, $P(1) = 0.432$, $P(2) = 0.288$, $P(3) = 0.064$

x_i	0	1	2	3
$P(x_i)$	0.216	0.432	0.288	0.064

b $\mu = 1.2$, $\sigma = 0.8485$

5 a

x_i	1	2	3	4	5
$P(x_i)$	0.1	0.2	0.4	0.2	0.1

b $\mu = 3.0$, **c i** $P(\mu - \sigma < x < \mu + \sigma) \doteqdot 0.8$
$\sigma = 1.0954$ **ii** $P(\mu - 2\sigma < x < \mu + 2\sigma) \doteqdot 1$

6 \$390 **7 a**

x_i	1	2	3	4	5	6
$P(m_i)$	$\frac{1}{36}$	$\frac{3}{36}$	$\frac{5}{36}$	$\frac{7}{36}$	$\frac{9}{36}$	$\frac{11}{36}$

b $\mu = 4.472$, $\sigma = 1.404$

8 Tossing a coin $P(\text{head}) = P(\text{tail}) = \frac{1}{2}$ or rolling a die
$P(1) = P(2) = P(3) = ... = P(6) = \frac{1}{6}$

EXERCISE 30E.1

1 a 3.4 **b** 1.64 **c** $\doteqdot 1.28$

2 a $k = 0.3$ **b** 6.4 **c** 0.84

3 a 2 **b** 5 **c** 1 **d** 1 **e** 3 **f** 1 **g** 9

4 $a = 0.15$, $b = 0.35$

5 a $a = -\frac{1}{84}$ **b** 4 **c** $\sqrt{3} \doteqdot 1.73$

6 a

x	0	1	2	3	4
p_x	$\frac{1}{16}$	$\frac{4}{16}$	$\frac{6}{16}$	$\frac{4}{16}$	$\frac{1}{16}$

b i 2 **ii** 1

7

x	0	1	2
p_x	$\frac{7}{15}$	$\frac{7}{15}$	$\frac{1}{15}$

a 0.6 **b** $\doteqdot 0.611$

EXERCISE 30E.2

1 17 and 4 respectively

2 a $E(aX + b) = E(aX) + E(b) = aE(X) + b$

b i 13 **ii** -5 **iii** $3\frac{1}{3}$

3 a i 13 **ii** 16 **b i** -7 **ii** 16 **c i** 0 **ii** 1

4 a $2E(X) + 3$ **b** $4E(X^2) + 12E(X) + 9$

c $4E(X^2) - 4\{E(X)\}^2$

EXERCISE 30F

1 a The binomial distribution applies, as tossing a coin has one of two possible outcomes (H or T) and each toss is independent of every other toss.

b The binomial distribution applies, as this is equivalent to tossing one coin 100 times.

c The binomial distribution applies as we can draw out a red or a blue marble with the same chances each time.

d The binomial distribution does not apply as the result of each draw is dependent upon the results of previous draws.

e The binomial distribution does not apply, assuming that ten bolts are drawn without replacement. We do not have a repetition of independent trials.

2 a $\doteqdot 0.268$ **b** $\doteqdot 0.800$ **c** $\doteqdot 0.200$

3 a $\doteqdot 0.476$ **b** $\doteqdot 0.840$ **c** $\doteqdot 0.160$ **d** $\doteqdot 0.996$

4 a $\doteqdot 0.0280$ **b** $\doteqdot 0.00246$ **c** $\doteqdot 0.131$ **d** $\doteqdot 0.710$

5 a $\doteqdot 0.998$ **b** $\doteqdot 0.807$

EXERCISE 30G

1 a i $\mu = 3$, $\sigma = 1.2247$

x_i	0 or 6	1 or 5	2 or 4	3
$P(x_i)$	0.0156	0.0938	0.2344	0.3125

ii

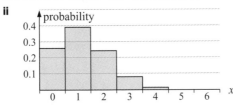

iii The distribution is bell-shaped.

b i $\mu = 1.2$, $\sigma = 0.980$

x_i	0	1	2	3	4	5	6
$P(x_i)$	0.262	0.393	0.246	0.082	0.015	0.002	0.000

ii

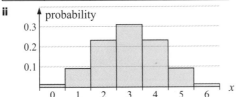

iii The distribution is positively skewed.

c i $\mu = 4.8$, $\sigma = 0.980$

ii

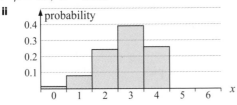

iii This distribution is negatively skewed and is the exact reflection of **b**.

2 $\mu = 5$, $\sigma = 1.58$ **4** $\mu = 1.2$, $\sigma = 1.07$

5 $\mu = 0.65$, $\sigma = 0.752$

EXERCISE 30H

1 a 1.5 **b** $p_x = \dfrac{(1.5)^x e^{-1.5}}{x!}$ for $x = 0, 1, 2, 3, 4, 5, 6, ...$

X	0	1	2	3	4	5	6
f	12	18	12	6	3	0	1
$52p_x$	11.6	17.4	13.0	6.5	2.4	0.7	0.2

The fit is excellent.

2 a i $\doteqdot 7.13$ **ii** $p_x = \dfrac{(7.13)^x e^{-7.13}}{x!}$, $x = 0, 1, 2, 3, ...$

b i $\doteqdot 0.0204$ **ii** $\doteqdot 0.0752$ **iii** $\doteqdot 0.839$ **iv** $\doteqdot 0.974$

3 a 1.694, so $p_x = \dfrac{(1.694)^x e^{-1.694}}{x!}$, $x = 0, 1, 2, 3, ...$

b

X	0	1	2	3	4	5	6	7
f	91	156	132	75	33	9	3	1
$500p_x$	92	156	132	74	32	11	3	1

The fit is excellent.

c $s \doteqdot 1.292$ and $\sqrt{m} \doteqdot 1.302$ so, s is very close to $\sqrt{m}$ in value.

4 a $\doteqdot 0.0498$ **b** $\doteqdot 0.392$ **c** $\doteqdot 0.185$ **d** $\doteqdot 0.210$

5 a $m = \dfrac{3+\sqrt{33}}{2}$ **b i** $\doteqdot 0.506$ **ii** $\doteqdot 0.818$

EXERCISE 30I

1 a $a = -\dfrac{3}{32}$

b

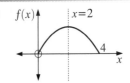

c i 2 **ii** 2 **iii** 2 **iv** 0.8

2 a $b = \sqrt[3]{30}$ **b i** mean $\doteqdot 1.55$ **ii** $\doteqdot 0.483$

3 a $k \doteqdot 1.0524$ **b** median $\doteqdot 0.645$

4 a $k = -\dfrac{4}{375}$ **b** mode $= 4$ **c** median $\doteqdot 3.46$
  d mean $= 3\frac{1}{3}$ **e** $1\frac{1}{9}$

EXERCISE 30J.1

1

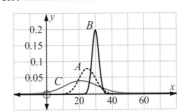

2 a, b The mean volume (or diameter) is likely to occur most often with variations around the mean occurring symmetrically as a result of random variations in the production process.

3 a 84.1% **b** 2.3% **c** 2.15%, 95.4% **d** 97.7%, 2.3%

4 a i 34.1% **ii** 47.7%
  b i 0.136 **ii** 0.159 **iii** 0.0228 **iv** 0.841

5 a $\doteqdot 41$ days **b** $\doteqdot 254$ days **c** $\doteqdot 213$ days

EXERCISE 30J.2

1 a 0.341 **b** 0.383 **c** 0.106

2 a 0.341 **b** 0.264 **c** 0.212 **d** 0.945 **e** 0.579
  f 0.383

EXERCISE 30K.1

1 a $E\left(\dfrac{X-\mu}{\sigma}\right) = E\left(\dfrac{1}{\sigma}X - \dfrac{\mu}{\sigma}\right)$, etc.

$$\text{Var}\left(\frac{X-\mu}{\sigma}\right) = \text{Var}\left(\tfrac{1}{\sigma}X - \tfrac{\mu}{\sigma}\right), \quad \text{etc.}$$

2 a 0.885 **b** 0.195 **c** 0.3015 **d** 0.947 **e** 0.431
3 a 0.201 **b** 0.524 **c** 0.809 **d** 0.249 **e** 0.249
4 a 0.383 **b** 0.950
5 a $a = 1.645$ **b** $a = -1.282$
6 a Physics 0.463, Chemistry 0.431, Maths 0.990, German 0.521, Biology 0.820
b Maths, Biology, German, Physics, Chemistry
7 65.6%

EXERCISE 30K.2

1 a 0.159 **b** 0.3085 **c** 0.335
2 a 0.348 **b** 0.324 **c** 0.685
3 a 0.585 **b** 0.805 **c** 0.528

EXERCISE 30K.3

1 a $k \doteq 0.878$ **b** $k \doteq 0.202$ **c** $k \doteq -0.954$
2 a $k \doteq -0.295$ **b** $k \doteq 1.165$ **c** $k \doteq -1.089$
3 b i $k \doteq 0.303$ **ii** $k \doteq 1.037$
4 a $k \doteq 61.4$ **b** $k \doteq 36.2$

EXERCISE 30L

1 0.378 **2 a** 90.4% **b** 4.78% **3** 83
4 a 0.003 33 **b** 61.5% **c** 23 eels

5 $\mu \doteq 23.6$, $\sigma \doteq 24.3$
6 a $\mu = 52.4$, $\sigma = 21.6$ **b** 54.4%
7 a $\mu = 2.00$, $\sigma = 0.0305$ **b** 0.736

REVIEW SET 30A

1 a $a = \frac{5}{9}$ **b** $\frac{4}{9}$

2 a

x_i	0	1	2	3	4
$P(x_i)$	0.0625	0.25	0.375	0.25	0.0625

b $\mu = 2$, $\sigma = 1$
3 $p = 0.18$, **a** 0.302 **b** 0.298 **c** 0.561
4 $p = 0.04$, $n = 120$ **a** $\mu = 4.8$ **b** $\sigma = 2.15$
5 a $4 **b** $75
6 $\mu = 64$, $\sigma = 4$ **a i** 81.85% **ii** 84.1% **b** 81.85%
7 $\mu = 31.2$
8 a $a = -\frac{3}{10}$ **b**
c i 1.2 **ii** 1.5
iii $\doteq 1.24$
iv 0.24
d $\frac{13}{20}$

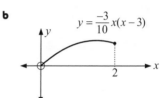

$$y = \frac{-3}{10}x(x-3)$$

INDEX